MW00398291

Timber Design and Construction Sourcebook

Timber Design and Construction Sourcebook

A Comprehensive Guide to Methods and Practice

Karl-Heinz Götz

Dieter Hoor

Karl Möhler

Julius Natterer

McGraw-Hill Publishing Company

New York St. Louis San Francisco Auckland Bogotá
Caracas Hamburg Lisbon London Madrid Mexico
Milan Montreal New Delhi Oklahoma City
Paris San Juan São Paulo Singapore
Sydney Tokyo Toronto

Library of Congress Cataloging-in-Publication Data

Holzbau Atlas. English.
Timber design & construction sourcebook.

Translation of Holzbau Atlas.
Bibliography: p.
Includes index.
1. Building, Wooden. 2. Structural design.
I. Goetz, Karl-Heinz. II. Title. III. Title:
Timber design and construction sourcebook.
TA666.H6413 1989 694 89-8201
ISBN 0-07-023851-0

Authors
Dr.-Ing. Karl Möhler, Professor at the Technical University of Karlsruhe
in collaboration with Dipl.-Ing. Gerhard Meickl
Dipl.-Ing. Julius Natterer, Consulting Engineer, Munich
in collaboration with Johannes Goehl and Dr.-Ing. Gunter Henn
Dipl.-Ing. Karl-Heinz Götz, Professor at the School of Arts, Berlin
in collaboration with Dr.-Ing. Gunter Henn, Johannes Goehl, Dipl.-Ing. Hermann Rotermund,
Dipl.-Ing. Hans-Jürgen Spehr, and Dipl.-Ing. Peter Stürzebecher
Dipl.-Ing. Dieter Hoor, Professor at the School of Arts, Hamburg
in collaboration with Dipl.-Ing. Wolfgang Haux

The original German language version was prepared by the Institut für internationale Architektur-Dokumentation with the collaboration of Hans-Jürgen Meier-Menzel, Dr. Margret Wanetschek-Gatz, Horst Wanetschek, and Klaus Halmburger. Drawings by Hans-Jürgen and Eva-Maria Meier-Menzel with Ursula Fiedler and Marina Kinzel.

English translation by Dr. Eng. Peter F. Martecchini, P.E., L.S., New York, N.Y. Technical review of manuscript by Andre P. Martecchini, M.C.E., P.E., New York, N.Y. Project coordination, preparation and correction of manuscript by Goetz G. Drescher, Principal, Technoport International, Holicong, Pa.

234567890 KPKP 943210

ISBN 0-07-023851-0

The editors for this book were Joel Stein and Ingeborg M. Stochmal, and the production supervisor was Richard A. Ausburn. It was set in Avant Garde by Progressive Typographers, Inc. Printed and bound by Arcata Graphics/Halliday.

CONTENTS

TRANSLATOR'S REMARKS

This book is a veritable encyclopedia of timber construction. Its comprehensive treatment of wood as an engineering material focuses on its great architectural and structural potential.

A thorough review of the numerous timber buildings of outstanding quality presented in this book is in itself a monument to the state of the art in timber construction, but informative texts that precede and follow the review give a key to the conception of such remarkable works of architecture. The key lies in an in-depth knowledge of materials, design methods, and past experiences. This knowledge enables a designer to fuse engineering and architecture together into an integral whole. It is in such a fusion that we lose the view of architects and engineers behind a structure and see only a work of art.

Above all, this is a book of ideas. Timber buildings of great daring and architectural significance are presented here in a most practical and detailed manner. Some of these buildings were erected several years ago. They are outstanding structures and represent seminal ideas in their type of construction.

Of even greater importance to the readers is a profusion of alternate details for every key element of construction. Pages after pages offer alternate engineering solutions to connections, structural systems, and architectural layouts. Readers can be sure to discover in them an idea that will solve their problem.

The book is an essential reference to an engineer engaged in the design of timber structures. However, the engineering fundamentals presented in the first part of the book do not pretend to be substitutes for a thorough knowledge of structural engineering and a complete familiarity with local design conditions.

The book is equally valuable to all who wish to work with timber. To a designer, the book represents a very creative partner in the process of design development. To a student, the book is a comprehensive textbook. To a builder, the book is a handbook of alternate solutions to construction problems and a source of economic and practical answers to questions of field assembly and erection.

It must be recognized that wood is a parochial material. Every region of the world has its own timber species best suited for construction and its own building codes. In the United States, timber design is governed by several standards, such as the Grading Rules for western timber or southern pine, and is subject to various building codes, most of them local. Such a variety of rules and regulations is often difficult to master. It is therefore extremely useful to a practicing professional to have an insight into the practice of other professionals, especially those who work under a different set of standards.

The standards used in the design of most structures illustrated in this book is the West German building code (DIN) which regulates in the most detailed manner the applications of wood and its products. This code, an internationally used standard, provides authoritative answers even in the fields of design not covered by the American codes, such as the design of flexibly connected timber beams. Chapters on theory and practice presented here are related to this code, but are universally valid.

Similarly, various products and building components shown here are sometimes identified by their local names, as they were applied in the buildings illustrated in the book. It would have been fruitless to find a locally manufactured equivalent for each such product or component, particularly in a book that has an international appeal. The reader should therefore take advantage of the consistent presentation of the text in order to understand the basic concepts and the enormous potential of timber design and construction.

The metric system used in the book should be familiar to American readers because metrication is advancing in all trades. However, for easy reference, rapid conversion tables and factors are given at the end of the book. It would have been confusing to transpose metric timber dimensions into feet and inches because metric dimensions are net, while lumber dimensions in inches are nominal and their roundings depend not only on the sizes of lumber, but also on the year of production.

In the interest of accuracy, the numerical information in tables and figures was reproduced photographically from the original German text. Therefore the decimal comma, used in European notation in lieu of the decimal point, appears in such reproduced material. The reader will easily recognize this special notation.

It was a challenging task to translate a reference book on a material that is so familiar to all but so difficult to use in design. As a practicing engineer, I endeavored to convey the often complex structural concepts in a concise and direct manner aimed at practical use. The readers will find this book to be a constant source of ideas and an authoritative and practical reference.

PETER F. MARTECCHINI

INTRODUCTION

Timber is becoming increasingly competitive with other building materials because of the development of new techniques in timber construction. Among these are new types of connections and combinations of lumber with derivative wood products. As a result, designers are turning to timber construction in order to replace masonry, reinforced concrete, steel, or their combinations.

The design decision to build a timber structure is often based solely on a desire to bring out the intimate and warm qualities of wood. As Frank Lloyd Wright said: "There is a need to bring forth the beauty of wood, the beauty being its intrinsic property."

However, the present wide range of timber construction is due mostly to advanced engineering techniques which rest on principles proven and refined over a period of a thousand years.

The following are the advantages of timber construction:

- Wood is a comparatively lightweight material.
- Wood is simple and clean to work with, both during construction and in the finishing stages.
- Structural components made of wood can be assembled in many ways.
- Timber construction allows many spacial configurations which cannot be achieved easily with other materials.
- Timber shells, especially, are often more economical than those of reinforced concrete or other materials.
- Wood has a good insulating value, a physical property essential in buildings.

Wood construction was traditionally handled by architects and carpenters, but new techniques call for specialists in timber engineering, particularly in the planning and design phases of larger projects. Engineering, starting from the very conception of a building, is indispensable today, especially if there are difficult design and erection problems. In fact, engineers and contractors have developed many types of buildings without the help of architects.

Ultimately, good architecture depends on intuition regarding the structural shapes under stress; this is valid in spite of scientific design and a rational approach to construction, regardless of the complexity of a structure.

The classic frame buildings of Europe, America, and Japan are proof of the unique achievements in timber construction. Together with the ancient beam-on-post or pole structures of Nordic countries, they attest to the validity of the basic principles of building with timber.

Timber construction was dominant in many lands through past ages. However, some structural systems used in the past cannot be applied today without modification.

In this respect all designers try something new, although their technique may be an old routine. Only when architectural and structural components come to complement each other at their maximum potential do we reach a natural unity that we call "architecture."

Everything has to work together in harmony: the rationality of the calculations and the designer's form giving should not be superimposed formalistically and superficially. A structure should not be forced into a shape contrary to its nature.

The main purpose of the *Timber Design and Construction Sourcebook* is to serve the architects and their working associates in the field of building design. It answers their specific questions on special conditions, potential uses, and requirements of design and construction. It also serves the purpose of advancing timber as a design or construction bid alternative.

This book provides a general basis of understanding between architects, engineers, technicians, and those artisans or contractors who are going to erect a building. Until now there was no appropriate comprehensive literature focusing on this basic and unifying aspect of building design. A much richer, varied, and purely technical literature is available to engineers, technicians, or artisans on the subject of structural design, detailing, and construction. In such literature there may be works that are important and relevant to architects interested in timber design, but those books are generally not written specifically for architects and do not serve their needs.

This book concentrates on the general principles of timber design, the presentation of large halls and roofed structures, frame and panel construction, and other basic prototypes of construction. These basic elements are examined critically and are analyzed with regard to their broad potential uses.

Many buildings described and discussed here could be considered trendsetters in their overall context, some of them only in their detail. It would be interesting to follow up on these trends and thus increase the use of timber in contemporary buildings.

The first part of the book covers the fundamentals of timber design, but does not pretend to teach structural engineering. Architects should consult with structural engineers right from the conception of their design and remain in continuous collaboration throughout the project. Consequently, this book does not describe details of structural theory or technical problems with solutions that are primarily the domain of the engineers and only secondarily that of the architects. The partnership of architects and engineers is therefore desirable from the very beginning.

The general concept and parts of this book are as follows:

Part I: Fundamentals of timber construction. General properties and application potentials of wood and wood products are treated here. Connections are emphasized, because they are particularly important for the development, detailing, and practical erection of timber buildings.

Part II: Review of a multifaceted group of large halls and roof structures built in wood. The uses of these structures vary from sports or exhibition halls to nursery schools, churches, industrial buildings, storage sheds, and others. The presentation is arranged systematically according to the types of structure, focusing on critical details. Presented are 166 buildings, each with a short analysis. They were selected on the basis of their functionality, basic architectural concept, and structural system. Various alternatives to a problem are shown whenever this provides a useful and stimulating insight into specific problems of form, space, or assembly.

Part III: An overview of present timber framing techniques, divided into eight categories. Essential and characteristic elements of these types of construction are described and illustrated. This section concludes with the plans and descriptions of prototype buildings in each category. Specific items are discussed if they are of interest from the point of view of construction or finishes. A checklist is provided at the end in order to compare joints, bases, roof connections, and finishes in each category.

Part IV: Wood panel construction, beginning from the origins of this type of construction. A presentation of the main principles and potential applications of this type of structure follows a description of commonly fabricated panel and room units. This information is also useful for the application of timber panels in other types of structures.

Part V: A systematic review of the most important elements of timber construction, such as roofs, floors, walls, and partitions. At the end of this section there is a description of buildings constructed using logs.

KONRAD GATZ

Fundamentals of Timber Building Construction

KARL MÖHLER

In collaboration with:
Gerhard Meickl

WOOD AS A CONSTRUCTION MATERIAL FOR BUILDINGS

Types of Wood and Wood Products Suitable for Building

Physical and Mechanical Properties of Wood and Wood Products

Protective Treatments

FUNDAMENTALS OF TIMBER BUILDING CONSTRUCTION

Materials, Connections, and Building Components

Structural Systems and Design

Technical Codes, Standards, and Quality Requirements

Wood as a Construction Material for Buildings

TYPES OF WOOD AND WOOD PRODUCTS SUITABLE FOR BUILDING

Wood as a Construction Material

Structure of Wood

Structural timber is derived from the wood of tree trunks. The live trunks perform three functions: they support the crown of the tree, carry nutrients from the roots to the crown, and store these nutrients. In hardwoods, these functions are performed by three different types of wood cells. Of the three, those which form tubular fibers are primarily arranged in the longitudinal direction of the trunk. On the other hand, in conifers, which have a simple and regular structure, a single cell type performs all three functions: conducting and storing fluids and providing strength. Wood cells have lengths varying from 1 to 8 mm and rectangular or hexagonal tubular cross sections with diameters of less than 0.1 mm. They constitute more than 90% of the wood mass and are arranged in a longitudinal direction. Numerous, barely visible transverse cells, called wood rays, penetrate through longitudinal cells from the bark to the pith. Wood thus resembles a bundle of parallel tubes whose directional structures impart to the wood an anisotropic character. As a result, most physical and mechanical properties of wood in the direction parallel to the trunk axis (direction of the grain) differ greatly from those in the direction normal to this axis. The naked eye can readily discern the structure of conifer woods in the three main sections of a trunk cut perpendicularly to each other (Fig. 1):

- Transverse section
- Radial section
- Tangential section

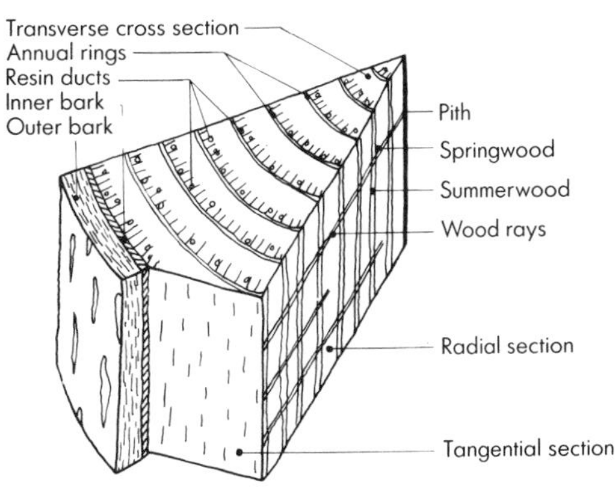

Fig. 1. Wood wedge from a 9-year-old stem.

Transverse Section

In this section, which is cut perpendicularly to the axis of the trunk, the following layers can be seen:

a. *Bark.* Composed of outer and inner bark.

b. *Wood.* Composed of yearly cell growth. The naked eye can easily see the yearly limits of growth in the form of annual rings. Within an annual ring, the early growth, known as springwood, distinguishes itself by lighter color and thinner cell walls, while the later growth, the summerwood, has a darker color and thicker cell walls.

c. *Pith.* Dead core tissue surrounded by annual rings.

Between bark and wood there is a layer of growth cells, called the cambium layer, which is visible only by microscope. These cells multiply by division and thus cause the tree to grow.

Radial Section

In this section, which is cut along the axis of the tree (Fig. 2), the annual rings appear as stripes parallel to the axis, while the wood rays appear as radial lines. The wood rays serve as horizontal conduits and storage for nutrients. Initially formed at the pith, they radiate to the bark, and they shine when cut longitudinally in a radial section.

Fig. 2. Radial section.

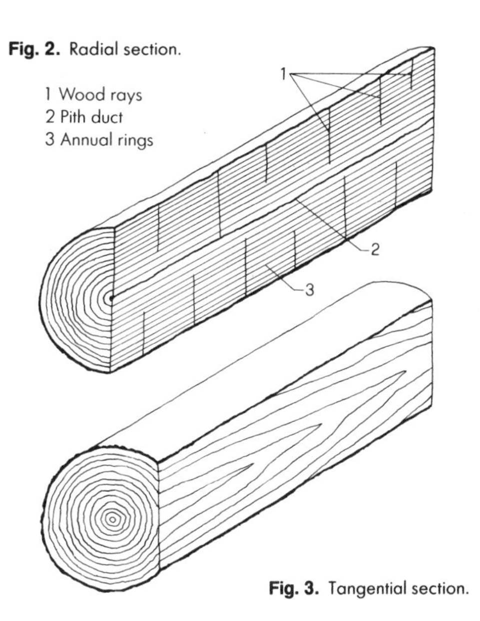

Fig. 3. Tangential section.

Tangential Section

The annual rings appear in this section as curved or wavy lines (Fig. 3). Major wood rays cut at right angles may appear as spindle-shaped dark stripes (mainly in oak and beech woods).

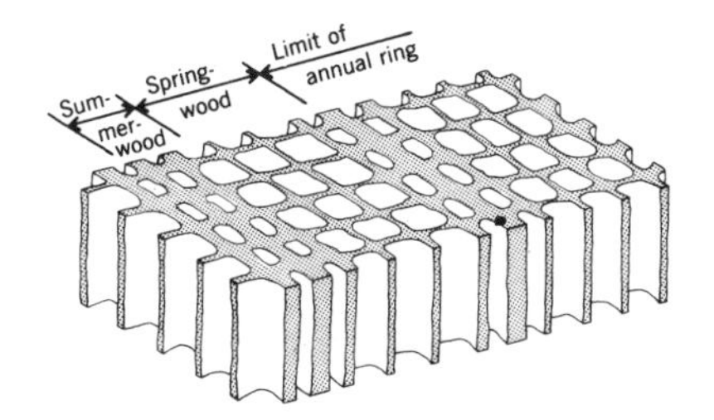

Fig. 4. Growth of springwood and summerwood (conifers).

Growth and Annual Rings

The growth of a tree occurs when cells divide within the cambium layer that envelops the wood core. During this process more new wood cells are produced on the inside of the layer than bark cells on the outside. In a moderate climate, the growth period begins in April or May and ends in August or September. During this period a clearly distinguished cell layer of variable thickness surrounds the existing wood core with a cylindrical or conical shell. Early cells are thin-walled tubes with large diameters; in conifers they have a lighter color than the thicker cells of later growth, which are of smaller diameter (Fig. 4). The early cells, called springwood, quickly lead the nutrient liquids from the roots to the leaves, while the later growth, called summerwood, mainly strengthens the trunk.

In tropical areas the growth of rings is related to alternating dry and rainy periods, but not necessarily on a yearly basis. Evergreen tropical plants, whose development is not interrupted by periods of rest, do not form growth rings.

The width of the annual rings and the proportion of springwood and summerwood depend on the soil characteristics, the climate, the tree's age, forestry practice, and possible parasite infestation. The width of the annual rings varies from 1 to more than 10 mm. Considerable variation may occur even within the same tree, but as a rule slow growing trees have thin rings and fast growing trees have thick rings. In most commercial timber the ring width varies from 1 to 4 mm when trees are 20 years old. Conifers with thin rings provide timber with higher strength and density than conifers with thick rings; however, the determining factor is the amount of summerwood in each ring and its proportion within the entire cross section. A section with more summerwood is stronger.

Heartwood and Sapwood

If transverse cross sections of different woods are compared with each other, some exhibit a uniform color for the entire section, while in others, the darker inner area of the section is surrounded by a lighter area of variable width. The wood cells in this lighter area, called sapwood, are living and physiologically active, while those in the inner core, called heartwood, are largely dead.

The formation of heartwood begins when a tree is 20 to 40 years old, the age at which the sapwood's thickness is of sufficient size to conduct all the required fluids. The core is then relieved of the necessity to serve as a conduit, its cavities become clogged through chemical and structural changes in the wood cells, and its humidity content decreases.

The dead cells of the heartwood become a repository for substances such as tannin, dyes, resin, fats, and rubberlike materials, and thus the heartwood is darker; it becomes denser, harder, and more resistant to infestation. The partial clogging of cell voids reduces the cell's hygroscopic potential, and therefore the heartwood has less of a tendency to swell or shrink.

The border between heartwood and sapwood is generally not contained within one annual ring. In older trees the sapwood is often wider near the base than near the top. Trees can generally be grouped by the difference in color between sapwood and heartwood, and according to the manner of formation of heartwood, as follows:

1. Heartwood trees in which the heartwood is distinguishable from sapwood by color, such as pine, larch, and oak
2. Aged trees in which the heartwood has a lesser humidity content than the sapwood, but without exhibiting any difference in color, such as fir, spruce, and beech
3. Sapwood trees, such as birch, which contain no heartwood

A colored core appearing sometimes in a cloud-like and irregular shape in aged or sapwood trees is known as a false core.

Growth Characteristics and Grading Features

Wood is a material grown naturally, and therefore its properties vary. Such variations determine its practical usefulness as a building material. First of all, there are natural and unavoidable growth characteristics which can make the wood acceptable within certain limits only by sorting it according to its intended use. Such growth characteristics include the presence of knots, the average width of the annual rings, the direction of the grain, and the number of resin pockets. Other departures from normal characteristics stem from events that occurred before or after felling of the trees or sawing of the wood. These include splitting and attacks by fungi or insects.

Quality grading features which are established as criteria for classifying the grades of wood according to DIN 4074, parts 1 and 2, are explained here in detail. DIN 4074 establishes three grades of lumber or round timber:

Grade I: Lumber with especially high structural strength
Grade II: Lumber with ordinary structural strength
Grade III: Lumber with lesser structural strength

The grades according to DIN 4074 are to be used for lumber whose cross sections are designed for their structural strength. Such lumber has to correspond to its grading class only in that part of its length in which the design stresses occur, provided the cross-sectional area used is equal to 1.5 times the maximum area required by structural computations. Structural components or their parts which require grade I lumber have to be specially marked on the drawings. On the other hand, the portions that correspond to grade I requirements must also be marked on the lumber. Otherwise, with the exception of planking, timber of grade II quality is generally used in design and construction. Such lumber does not have to carry any identification.

DIN 68365, "Lumber for Carpentry Work," establishes general properties, especially the visual ones, of all lumber used on construction sites. It distinguishes for all lumber between a common grade and a special grade, but it lists also the grades and grading properties for boards and planks as well as for strips and slats.

Lumber for construction must be cut from tree stems or parts of stems which are as straight as possible and whose departure from true cylindrical form ought not to exceed a certain given dimension. Such departures from true cylindrical form are often associated with reduced density and lesser strength of the wood.

Curvature

Minor curvature of live trees is unavoidable because uneven growth causes changes in moisture content and consequently different configurations of wood cells. For lumber used in compression members, the ratio of allowable chord deformation to column height equals 1/400 for grade I and 1/250 for grade II. For members subject to bending, these ratios shall not be exceeded when measured along a chord of 2 m at the point of largest curvature. Larger curvatures are allowed for round timbers.

Grain Slope

Parallel sawing of curved or markedly noncylindrical tree stems creates a departure of otherwise straight grain from the longitudinal surfaces of lumber because annual rings are cut on a skew. Such a slope is expressed in mm on a length of 1 m (Fig. 5).

Spiral Grain

Spiral grain denotes a wood in which the grain takes a spiral course around the axis of the tree stem. Wood with spiral grain can be recognized outwardly by the direction of drying and shrinkage cracks, which in a round timber run spirally and in cut lumber on a skew. Spiral grain barely affects the strength of round timber because the grain is continuous, but in rectangular lumber many fibers are cut on a skew and therefore the strength of such lumber is lower than that of wood with straight fibers. Spirally grained wood undergoing changes in moisture content warps in the direction of the spiral.

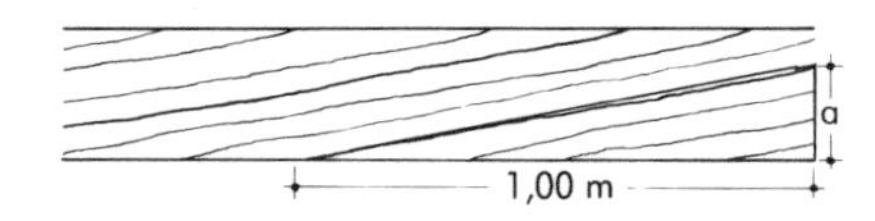

Fig. 5. Slope of grain. Allowable grain slope *a* on a length of 1 m.

Grade I $a = 70$ mm
Grade II $a = 120$ mm

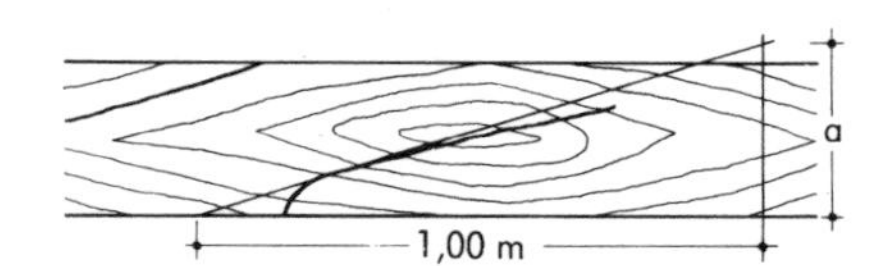

Fig. 6. Spiral grain. Allowable grain slope *a*, measured along shrinkage cracks, on a length of 1 m.

Grade I $a = 100$ mm
Grade II $a = 200$ mm
Grade III $a = 330$ mm

The maximum slope *a* of grain on a length of 1 m, when measured on tangentially extended shrinkage cracks, is established for all three grades of lumber as shown in Fig. 6.

Knots

In most cases knots reduce the strength of wood considerably. Tension and bending strength are much more affected than compression strength. On the other hand, the resistance to deformation from shear normal to the grain may be even higher in the

Arrangements of Knots (The smallest actually visible diameter of each knot governs)	Grade I (Lumber of especially high strength)	Grade II (Lumber of common strength)	Grade III (Lumber of lesser strength)
Single knots	$\frac{d_1}{b}$ or $\frac{d_2}{h} \leqq 0{,}20$ d_1 or $d_2 \leqq 50$ mm	$\frac{d_1}{b}$ or $\frac{d_2}{h} \leqq 0{,}33$ d_1 or $d_2 \leqq 70$ mm	$\frac{d_1}{b}$ or $\frac{d_2}{h} \leqq 0{,}50$ –
Multiple knots within a length of 150 mm	$\frac{d_1 + d_2}{b} \leqq 0{,}40$ or $\frac{d_3 + d_4 + d_5}{h} \leqq 0{,}40$	$\frac{d_1 + d_2}{b} \leqq 0{,}66$ or $\frac{d_3 + d_4 + d_5}{h} \leqq 0{,}66$	$\frac{d_1 + d_2}{b} \leqq 0{,}75$ or $\frac{d_3 + d_4 + d_5}{h} \leqq 0{,}75$

Fig. 7. Limits of knottiness for rectangular lumber and beams.

region of knots than in clear wood. Knots are a critical factor when determining the safe design strength of lumber. The most important criteria for assigning wood to a particular grade are the diameter of single knots and the sum of the diameters of all knots within a certain length, as seen on the surface of a piece of lumber (see Figs. 7 and 8).

For round timber the ratios are related to the timber diameter. For exposed surfaces of boards, planks, and strips, the sum of all knot diameters should be related to twice the width of the exposed surfaces. For lumber weakened by a reduction in cross section, the dimensions of the remainder of the reduced section govern.

Pitch Pockets

Resin bubbles or pitch pockets are created in a living tree by large swaying movements produced by wind. These movements sporadically separate the cambium from the sapwood and cause resin to flow into cavities. Because of this, it is to be expected that woods containing resin will be interspersed with pitch pockets. Depending on their size and number, such pockets can degrade the wood to varying degrees.

The rules for allowable pitch pockets in boards and beams are given in DIN 68365; pitch pockets less than 2 mm wide and 2 cm long are considered unavoidable and are ignored.

After the surfaces of wood are finished, resin must be removed and holes have to be filled with putty. Most coatings do not adhere on resin; dried and hardened resin becomes liquid when exposed to heat and penetrates through every coating. Because of this, installations which are exposed to a considerable amount of heat, such as saunas, should be built with wood that does not contain pitch pockets (fir, for example).

Fig. 8. Limit of knottiness for boards, planks, and strips.

Arrangement of Knots	Grade I	Grade II	Grade III
Single knots	$\frac{a_1 + a_2 + a_3}{2b} \leqq 0{,}20$ $\frac{a_4 + a_5}{2b} \leqq 0{,}20$	$\frac{a_1 + a_2 + a_3}{2b} \leqq 0{,}33$ $\frac{a_4 + a_5}{2b} \leqq 0{,}33$	$\frac{a_1 + a_2 + a_3}{2b} \leqq 0{,}50$ $\frac{a_4 + a_5}{2b} \leqq 0{,}50$
Multiple knots within a length of 150 mm	$\frac{a_1 + a_2 + a_3 + a_4 +}{2b}$ $\frac{+ a_5 + a_6 + a_7}{2b} \leqq 0{,}33$	$\frac{a_1 + a_2 + a_3 + a_4 +}{2b}$ $\frac{+ a_5 + a_6 + a_7}{2b} \leqq 0{,}50$	$\frac{a_1 + a_2 + a_3 + a_4 +}{2b}$ $\frac{+ a_5 + a_6 + a_7}{2b} \leqq 0{,}66$

Splits

Splits develop in a standing tree in different ways. Circular or otherwise partial peeling of wood layers along an annual ring are called shakes; they are often associated with a sudden change in thickness of the annual rings (Fig. 9). Boards with shakes are likely to fail. Shakes in dimension timber severely reduce the load capacity because individual cross sections cannot resist shear stresses. Therefore, shakes should not be present in lumber of grades I and II.

Frost shakes occur along a limited length of stem and penetrate from the bark radially into the interior of the stem (Fig. 10). The subsequent annual rings try to span the split, but in the winter the split opens up again. This process often creates frost ledges.

Lightning damage varies from a narrow loosening of bark along the length of the stem (lightning grooves, Fig. 11) to splitting of entire timber stems. Often, though, small outer splits are connected by fine hairline cracks that run through most of a tree section.

Fig. 9. Shakes, often with radial splits.

Fig. 10. Frost split (frost ledge), more frequent in hardwoods than in conifers.

Fig. 11. Lightning damage (lightning groove).

Under extreme conditions drying can cause major cracks, such as frost shakes, to run radially in a standing tree. In a radial crack the protective bark is damaged and it is from here that secondary damage from fungal infections may start. Such cracks are not allowed in lumber of grades I and II.

On the other hand, the unavoidable drying of shrinkage cracks which occur on the face of felled or sawn trees do not affect the grading of lumber because in most cases they are not deep and are short in length.

Damage by Insects or Fungi

Insects, depending on their type, may attack a standing tree or one already used in construction.

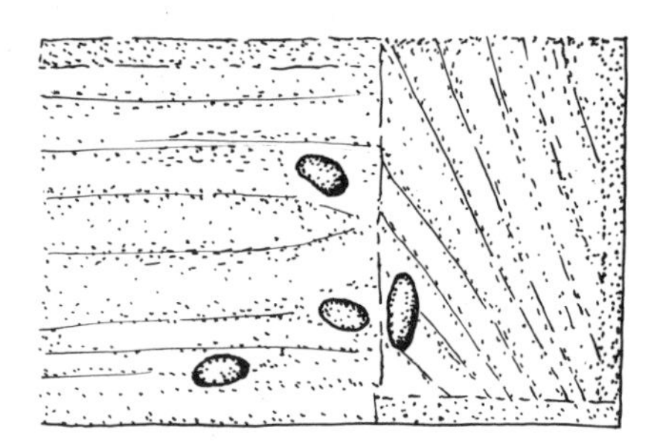

Fig. 12. Escape holes of house borer.

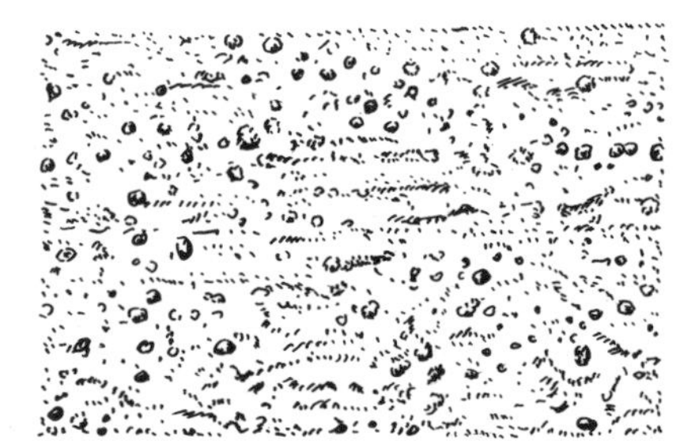

Fig. 13. Burrows and escape holes of the ordinary gnawing beetle.

Different insect species prefer either hardwoods or conifers, but some appear in both. Beetles that damage timber lay their eggs in the surface cracks, but the larvae that slip out after a few weeks are the real pests. They live in the timber for many years and they feed on it until they develop into pupae. The timber structure is destroyed to a greater or lesser degree by their tunneling. The presence of insects can be recognized from the outside only by their escape tunnels through which the adult beetle leaves the wood after it emerged from the pupa (Figs. 12 and 13). The type of pest can be recognized by different tunneling patterns and the residue left in the tunnels. Infestation of timber in a building can only be arrested through appropriate extermination measures.

The most common vermin are the house borer whose larvae often cause extensive damage under the surface in roof framing, the ordinary gnawing beetle, and the wood wasp which attacks only recently felled timber or still standing but sick trees. Insect damage is not allowed in grade I timber. In grade II and common grades under DIN 68365 some surface damage by insects is allowed. Living larvae or insect eggs are not permitted in construction timber. In certain climates, termites represent the most serious danger to the wood.

Damage by fungi can take many forms. In extreme cases the wood can be completely destroyed by rot, but sometimes there is only a light change of color. The most dangerous are the fungi which destroy wood by disintegrating either its lignin or its cellulose, or both. These fungi can destroy the wood completely if left to act for an extended duration. The growth of fungi can occur in wood only at certain moisture levels, varying between 20 and 35 percent, and at temperatures varying between +3 and +38°C. Nevertheless, many types of fungi can survive dry periods and low temperatures, only to continue their destructive work after the return of more favorable conditions.

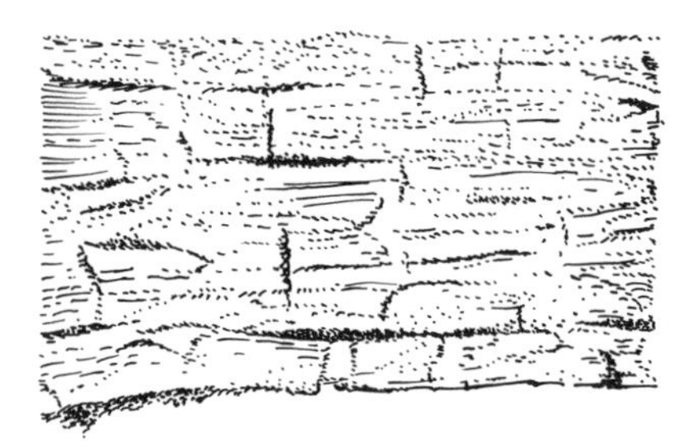

Fig. 14. Brown rot creates disintegration into rectangular chunks.

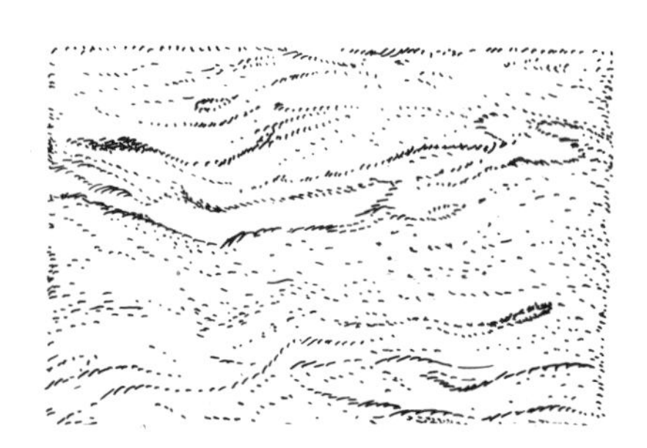

Fig. 15. White rot leaves a weak and fibrous mass.

Without attacking the cell walls, staining fungi can stain the sapwood of conifers, especially pine, into a blue-gray or blackish color. This does not affect the strength of the wood so that the blue stain is permitted even in grade I; it is not permitted in the special grade, which requires clear wood. Red and brown streaks are often a sign of incipient fungal action; yet they do not affect the structural or chemical properties of the wood. Such wood can be used in grade II and common grades of timber.

Red and brown rot slowly disintegrate the cellulose of cell walls. The wood increasingly acquires a reddish-brown color and becomes brittle and frayed; it disintegrates in rectangular chunks and assumes a charcoallike appearance (Fig. 14). Most building fungi, such as true building dry rot, pores rot, and cellar dry rot, result in red rotting material.

White rot fungi feed first on lignin, but may also attack cellulose, which finally results in a complete disintegration of the wood. The staining is initially gray and later becomes white. The wood in the affected area often disintegrates in a spotty manner with the formation of small grooves and holes filled with white residue of cellulose (Fig. 15). Red and white rot are not permitted in building lumber.

Timber Species Used in Buildings

In Germany lumber used for construction is generally obtained from European conifers, which are listed below. Domestic hardwoods (beech, oak) are used only for special construction needs, such as bearing plates, dowels, or wedges. Properties of non-European timbers vary greatly, even within the same species, depending on the location of origin. Prior to their use in construction, reliable data as to their properties must be obtained.

Conifers

Conifers (abbreviated NH, according to DIN 4076) have good strength properties, are lightweight, and exhibit moderate shrinkage and swelling characteristics. They can be easily worked with tools or machinery.

- *Spruce (FI), red fir, pitch fir.* This is the main timber species of central and northern Europe. The mature wood has a yellowish white color. The transverse cross section clearly exhibits annual rings and fine resin ducts. Planed faces shine and there may be resin pockets. Spruce and fir should be lightly treated with ordinary coatings (surface protection) for they do not easily absorb the impregnating substances under pressure treatment (deep protection). Spruce is not weatherproof in open construction without protection. *Application:* Building material for interior or exterior use, boards, laminates, sidings, floors, etc.
- *Fir (TA), noble fir, white fir.* The wood of the fir is generally of paler color than that of the spruce; however, it resembles it in structure and properties, but contains no resin. *Application:* Fir is used in construction in the same manner as spruce, and is often delivered with it in a mixed assortment.
- *Pines (KI), white pine.* Pines are spread widely over all of Europe, Siberia, and Asia. Heartwood has a reddish core; sapwood is wide and yellowish. Pine wood has clear annual rings, is rich in resin, and both heartwood and sapwood become darker. Surface treatments have to take into account knots and resin content. Sapwood can be impregnated well, but the heartwood, which is already well protected by itself, resists deeper penetration by protective treatment. Pine is more weather-resistant than spruce, but for exterior use it must be treated for protection. Pine is also easily attacked by staining fungi which can affect the appearance of the wood considerably in case of transparent finishes. *Application:* Structural lumber for interior and exterior use, windows, doors, planking, siding, floors, wood patches, fillers, plywood, and fences.
- *Larch (LA).* Widely spread in central Europe, prevalent in the Alps. Heartwood has a dark red core; sapwood is narrow and of yellowish brown color. The annual rings are distinctly visible and often wavy. The summerwood portion of the rings is prominent. The wood is very rich in resin and is, therefore, suitable for exterior siding. Only the sapwood can be easily pressure-treated, but the heartwood can be protected adequately by painting and is durable even without pressure treatment. Larch can be split easily into shingles, but has to be predrilled for nailing. *Application:* Lumber for exte-

rior construction, windows, doors, siding, porches, and lumber for agricultural buildings.

Hardwoods

Hardwoods (LH) are not as workable as softwoods because of their increased density. They are stronger and have better swelling and shrinkage properties.

- *Beech (BU), common beech.* Widely spread over all of Europe. Mature wood has yellowish red color. In a tangential cut the wood rays appear in spindle form, about 6 mm long. Annual rings are less distinct. Beech is often worked wet. It then acquires a reddish shimmer and can be bent more easily. Beech can be pressure- or surface-treated easily and such treatments assure its durability. *Application:* Bearing plates, dowels, wedges, veneers, stair treads, floors, and sleepers.
- *Oak (EI).* Well spread all over Europe; related species in Japan, Iran, and North America. Heartwood has a core of light to dark brown color. The sapwood layer is narrow and grayish white. Annual rings in oak are distinct and wood rays are large. The heartwood is very durable, but the sapwood is not. Oak swells and shrinks less than beech, and its planed surfaces can be made very smooth. Oak is very suitable for painting or lacquering and can be pressure-treated well. *Application:* Very versatile. Oak can also be used in structures that are exposed to weathering (hydraulic structures and bridges).

Commercial Sizes

Round Timbers

Round timbers are tree trunks cleared of bark and branches. They can be used without other reworking, especially for scaffoldings, agricultural buildings, piles, posts, and beams for temporary bridges. Half-round timbers are used for stiffening and bracing of scaffoldings, and for steps of scaffolding ladders. The quality grades for round timbers are established in DIN 4074, part 2. As for lumber, part 1 lists three quality grades and quality requirements. They refer to general use, knottiness, and curvature.

Lumber

Debarked tree stems (rough timbers) are sawn into rectangular lumber shapes of various sizes. Lumber is cut as narrow as possible in order to fit a maximum number of shapes into the smallest cross section of the irregularly shaped stem. The remaining irregular wood is generally used for a combination of boards and strips.

Lumber can be divided into the following types:

Strips	Lumber having a cross section of up to 32 cm² and a width of less than 8 cm.
Boards	Lumber having a thickness of 8 mm minimum and 40 mm maximum, and a minimum width of 8 cm.
Planks	Lumber having a minimum thickness of 40 mm. The larger side of the cross section is at least twice as large as the smaller side.
Dimension lumber	Lumber with a square or rectangular cross section having a relation of side widths of up to 1:3. Minimum side width is 6 cm.
Timbers	Lumber where the width of its larger side is greater than or equal to 20 cm.

Sawing lumber in standard sizes results in a better utilization of raw timbers and therefore a lower cost. Special cross sections are called dimension or specification lumber (DIN 4070, part 2) and are available by ordering in accordance with special specifications. Cross sections over 26 cm should be avoided, those over 30 cm cannot be furnished.

Lumber dimensions are given for dry wood. DIN 4074 allows a basic reduction in dimension of 1.5%. For quality grades II and III, the tolerance for a single piece may be as large as 3%, provided this does not apply to more than 10% of the total number of pieces. Additional shrinkage may be expected because the wood is mostly fresh or half-dry at the time of sawing. (See also Swelling and Shrinkage, p. 26.)

Saw mills add a price surcharge for lumber lengths greater than 8 m. Lengths over 10 m are difficult to transport, and they are generally not available because of the limited lengths of trees.

Shapes and Dimensions

Strips, dimension lumber, and timbers are available in the following standard sizes, which should be used in preference to other sizes:

Type	Width and Height b/h, cm	Cross-Sectional Area F, cm²	W_x, cm³	I_x, cm⁴	W_y, cm³	I_y, cm⁴	i_x, cm	i_y, cm
Dimension lumber	6/6	36	36	108	36	108	1,73	1,73
	6/8	48	64	256	48	144	2,31	1,73
	6/12	72	144	864	72	216	3,46	1,73
	8/8	64	85	341	85	341	2,31	2,31
	8/10	80	133	667	107	427	2,89	2,31
	8/12	96	192	1 152	128	512	3,46	2,31
	8/16	128	341	2 731	171	683	4,62	2,31
	10/10	100	167	833	167	833	2,89	2,89
	10/12	120	240	1 440	200	1 000	3,46	2,89
	12/12	144	288	1 728	288	1 728	3,46	3,46
	12/14	168	392	2 744	336	2 016	4,04	3,46
	12/16	192	512	4 096	384	2 304	4,62	3,46
	14/14	196	457	3 201	457	3 201	4,04	4,04
	14/16	224	597	4 779	523	3 659	4,62	4,04
	16/16	256	683	5 461	683	5 461	4,62	4,62
	16/18	288	864	7 776	768	6 144	5,20	4,62
Timbers	10/20	200	667	6 667	333	1 667	5,77	2,89
	10/22	220	807	8 873	367	1 833	6,35	2,89
	12/20	240	800	8 000	480	2 880	5,77	3,46
	12/24	288	1152	13 824	576	3 456	6,93	3,46
	16/20	320	1067	10 667	853	6 827	5,77	4,62
	18/22	396	1452	15 972	1188	10 692	6,35	5,20
	20/20	400	1333	13 333	1333	13 333	5,77	5,77
	20/24	480	1920	23 040	1600	16 000	6,93	5,77
Strips	mm							
	24/48	11,5	9,2	22,1	4,6	5,5	1,39	0,69
	30/50	15,0	12,5	31,3	7,5	11,3	1,44	0,87
	40/60	24,0	24,0	72,0	16,0	32,0	1,73	1,15

Sawing Specifications

Criteria for allowable rough edges or wanes can be found in the specifications for sawing of DIN 4074 and DIN 68365 (Fig. 16).

Sharp-edged lumber is generally not required; lumber for carpentry has to conform at least to class B quality, unless specifications indicate otherwise. Rough edges must be free of outer and inner bark and should not cause any reduction in the carrying capacity of the member. Wanes are not permitted within the area of connections because a full section is required for connecting hardware.

Cutting Class	Full Timbers	Half Timbers	Quarter Timbers	Permitted in Grades
S, sharp edges				I, II, III
A, eased edges				
B, wanes				II, III
C, sawn off edges				III

Fig. 16. Allowable edges according to cutting class and quality grade.

Boards and Planks in Softwood

Dimensions in mm are established for wood having a 14 to 20% moisture content, expressed as a percentage of the weight of oven-dried wood. Allowable tolerances refer only to unavoidable imprecision of workmanship and to dimensional changes due to the moisture content varying between 14 and 20%.

ROUGH BOARDS AND PLANKS (DIN 4071)

Thickness	Allowable Tolerance	Thickness	Allowable Tolerance
16		44	
18		48	±1,5
22	±1	50	
24		63	
28		70	±2
38		75	

Width	Allowable Tolerance	Width	Allowable Tolerance
75	±2	180	
80		200	
100		220	
115		225	
120		240	
125	±3	250	±3
140		260	
150		275	
160		280	
175		300	

Length	Increments	Allowable Tolerance
1500 to 6000	250 300	+50 −25

PLANED BOARDS AND PLANKS (DIN 4073)

Planed boards are smooth on one side; on the other side, they are cut to uniform thickness. The narrow surfaces have sawn finish. Two-sided planed boards are 1 mm thinner than the nominal thicknesses given below.

Thickness	Allowable Tolerance
13,5	
15,5	±0,5
19,5	
25,5	
35,5	±1
41,5	
45,5	

The widths and lengths are governed by the nominal dimensions of unplaned boards and planks.

TONGUE AND GROOVE BOARDS (DIN 4072)

These are planed boards with grooves and planed tongues. The width *b* of this shape is the width of the board, including the tongue. The covering width is the width without the tongue. These dimensions are also valid for rough sheeting.

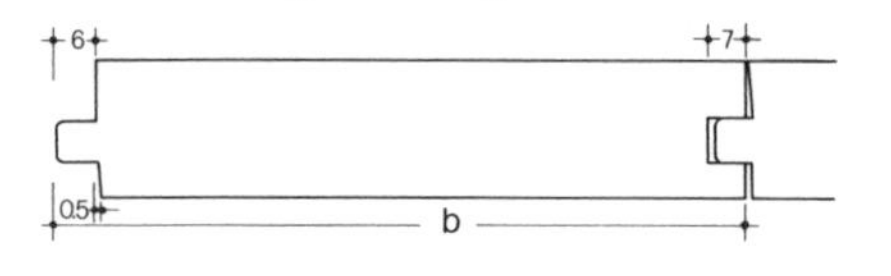

Thickness	Allowable Tolerance
15,5	±0,5
19,5	
25,5	±1
35,5	

Width *b* (Board Width)	Allowable Tolerance
95	±1,5
115	
135	±2
155	

Length	Increments	Allowable Tolerance
From 1500 to 4500	250	+50
Over 4500 to 6000	500	−25

PLANED TONGUE AND GROOVE DECKING (DIN 68122)

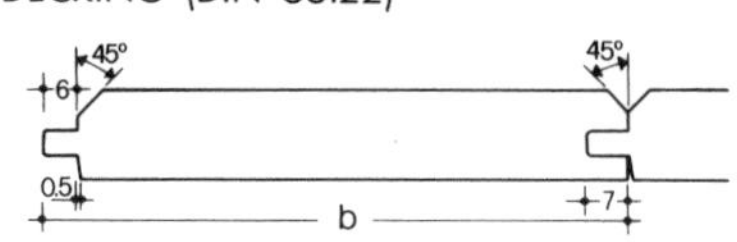

Thickness	Allowable Tolerance
15,5	±0,5
19,5	

Width *b* (Board Width)	Allowable Tolerance
95	±1,5
115	

The lengths are the same as for tongue and groove boards.

PLANED DROP SIDING (DIN 68123)

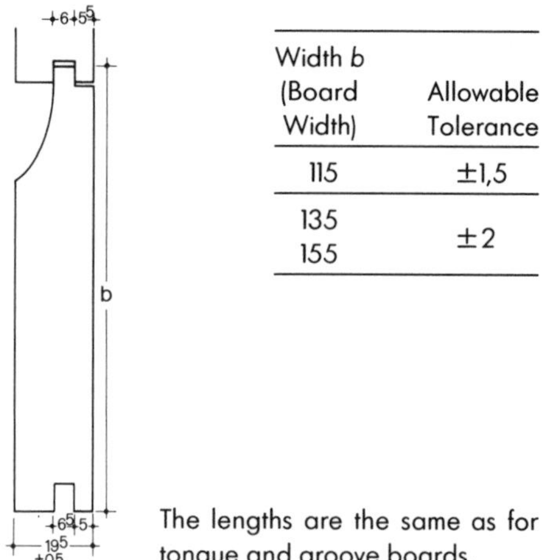

Width *b* (Board Width)	Allowable Tolerance
115	±1,5
135	±2
155	

The lengths are the same as for tongue and groove boards.

SIDING WITH A SHADOW GROOVE (DIN 68126)

These are used mostly for decking or siding.

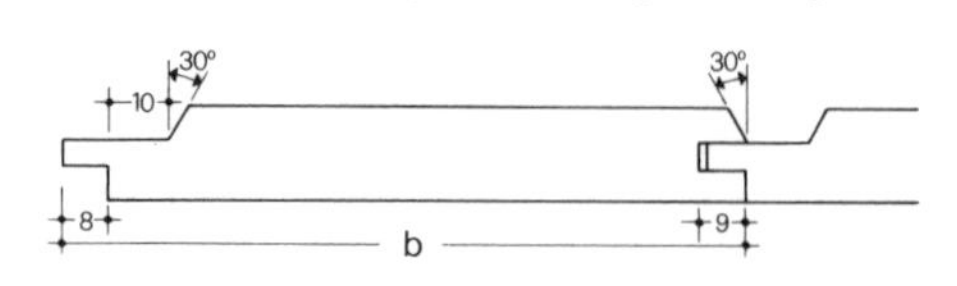

Thickness	Allowable Tolerances
12,5	
15,5	±0,5
19,5	

Width *b* (Board Width)	Allowable Tolerances
95	±1,5
115	

SHELVING BOARDS (DIN 68128)
These are boards surfaced on four sides. They are sharply rectangular (A), eased (B), or skewed (C).

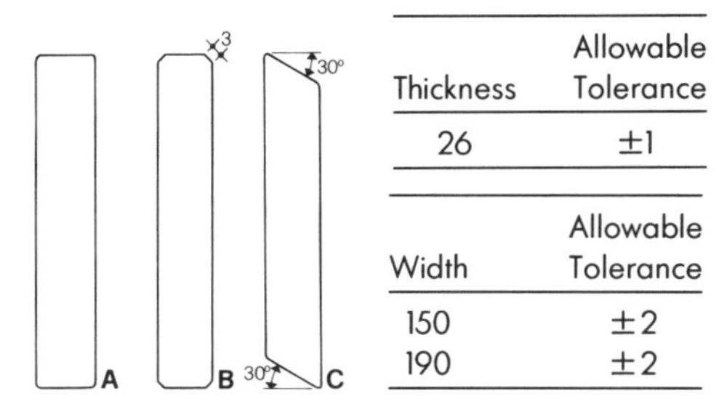

Thickness	Allowable Tolerance
26	±1

Width	Allowable Tolerance
150	±2
190	±2

Boards and planks can be stacked together for measuring and handling, either in compact or in spaced stacks. Compact stacks are generally used for expensive softwoods and for hardwoods (Fig. 17).

Surfacing of Lumber
Lumber is generally delivered rough-sawn. If planed lumber surfaces are used in construction, this has to be expressly indicated in the specifications. Boards and planks conforming to DIN 4073 have to be planed smooth on one side; on the other side, they are worked to a uniform thickness. Edge treatments have to be specified. Unless the specifications require the use of standard board profiles as described above or some other special treatment (such as rough-sawn, sandblasted, or flame-treated timber), exposed siding and sheathing has to conform to grade II lumber, surfaced on the exposed side, uniformly edged, notched or tongue and grooved. Roofing planks, unless otherwise specified, are to be furnished as rough-sawn boards conforming to grade III lumber.

If rejected end-cut planks are used for secondary purposes, such as excavation sheeting, they have to be cleaned of outer and inner bark.

Fig. 17. Lumber.

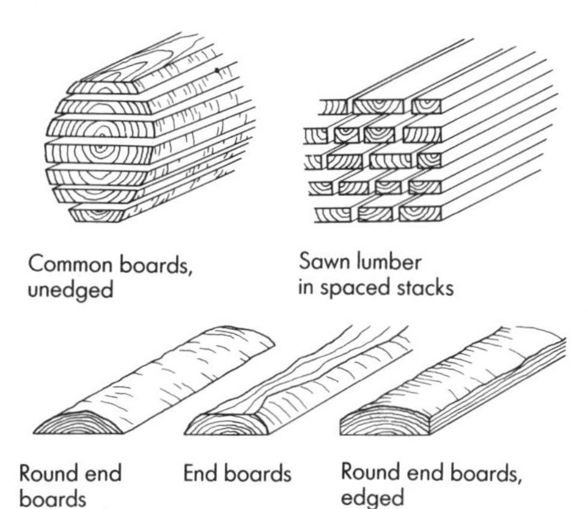

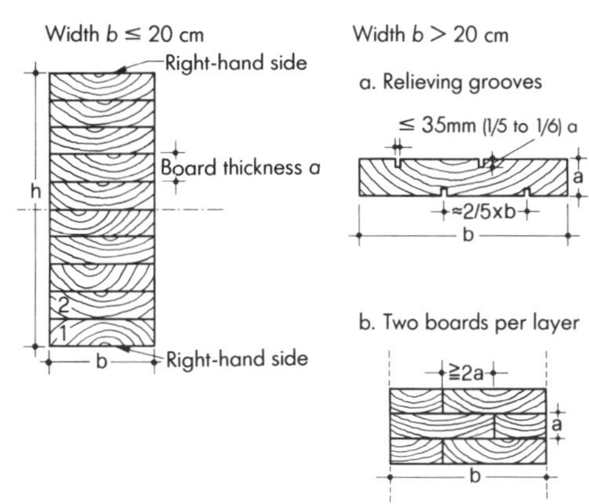

Fig. 18. Assembly of laminated beams.

Laminated Wood Beams

Composition and Assembly

Laminated beams consist of two or more boards glued together along their wider sides. By rule, the boards should not exceed a thickness of 30 mm, but this thickness may be increased to 40 mm for straight members if the wood is carefully selected and dried, and if members are not exposed to extreme variations in climate. As a rule, the boards less than 20 cm wide are arranged in such a way that "left" and "right" sides of the boards are glued together, with only the "right" sides facing the exterior. This arrangement is necessary in order to minimize transverse tension stresses induced in the wood and in the joints due to variations in the climate. For members wider than 20 cm it is necessary to use at least two boards for each laminated layer and no less than two laminated layers. Butt joints in each layer must be offset. Boards wider than 20 cm must contain two longitudinal relieving grooves on each face (Fig. 18).

Laminated beams can be furnished in practically any length and depth. The length is limited only by the length of the shop, the length of the gluing bed, and transportation facilities. The depth is limited only by the available width of the assembly machines, which now ranges from 2.0 to 2.30 m. Even the limitations of these machines can be bypassed by gluing together two members which have been previously fabricated on the assembly machine. Lengths from 30 to 35 m and depths of up to 2.20 m are commonly available. Single boards are brought to the desired length by finger-jointing the abutting ends in conformance to DIN 68140. Instead of finger joints, scarf joints with slopes flatter than 1:10 can also be used. All such sloped interior joints lying within the areas of compression and tension stresses must be offset by at least 50 cm.

In modern laminating plants nearly all preparation of the boards is automated and practically all butt joints are finger joints. Since the quality grade requirements for laminated wood contained in DIN 4074 refer to entire members and not to their single components, some single boards within a member may be of lesser quality.

The compensating properties of wood laminations allow the use of the quality grades required by design to be limited to only the outer 15% of depth in the tension zone of the members subject to bending, but to no less than two outer boards.

The fabrication of laminated members, which in Europe is practically limited to spruce, requires special equipment and experienced personnel who have to be specially licensed. The installation requires drying facilities, a heated shop in which temperature and air humidity can be monitored continuously, a finger-jointing machine, and a pressing bed for the assembly of straight or curved members. The gluing process must be supervised by a timber expert or a gluing master-craftsperson. Depending on the climatic exposure of the finished member, the adhesives used consist of thickened artificial resins derived from urea or resorcinol. These are applied, by means of a spreading machine, to both sides of planed or finger-jointed boards which have a predetermined moisture content. Spreading may be done by rollers, simultaneously on both sides, or by a pouring machine, on each side separately. The boards are glued together into rectangular cross sections and are pressed and held together on an assembly bed for a prescribed period of time. The pressure must act uniformly and must be applied by a spindle mechanism or hydraulic presses. After the adhesives have dried sufficiently, the rough sides are planed or further finished, and bolt or dowel holes are drilled. In order to assure stability and integrity of the laminated construction, special attention is given to the moisture content of the wood at the time of applying the adhesives. Special precautions are taken not to expose finished laminated products to significant variations in humidity during transportation and storage or during prolonged intervals of storage in heated sheds.

Cross Sections and Shapes

Laminated wood members for columns, beams, or frames are generally fabricated with rectangular cross sections. For bending members the ratio of height to width of a section varies mostly between 3

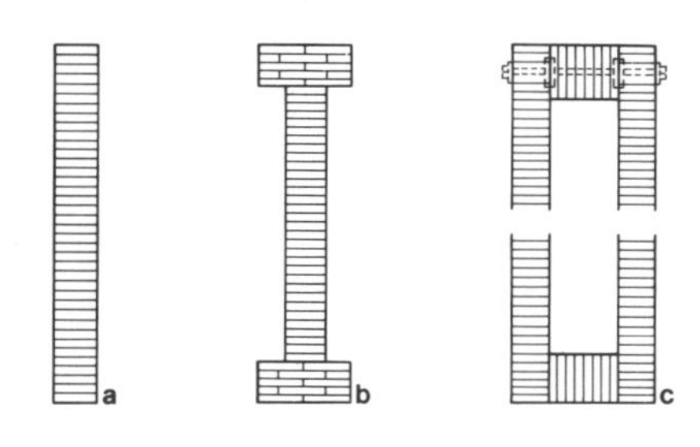

Fig. 19. Cross sections. (a) Rectangular. (b) I beam, laminated. (c) Box section, doweled or glued.

and 8, but should not exceed 10. The use of I-beam and box sections can also be considered in exceptional cases, although savings of material are offset by the need for more extensive workmanship; the advantages of better buckling and bracing stability may make such sections competitive (Fig. 19).

The excellent workability of timber allows the use of many beam forms having rectangular cross sections. Variable depths of cross sections can be fabricated easily by letting the laminations run out, but the sloped beam areas must be built up in a relatively flat arrangement because of vertical and horizontal shear at the beam ends.

Curved laminated beams for frames and arches can be fabricated by curving the boards lightly before gluing. In such cases, the radius R_1 of 30-mm-thick laminated boards should not exceed 200 times the thickness of the board. Even smaller radii, up to 150 times the thickness, are possible, provided the board thickness a is chosen according to the formula $a = \sqrt{625 + 0.4R_1} - 25$, expressed in mm. In such instances the curvature of the member (ratio $R_m/h = \beta$) must be considered in the design. Curvatures having $\beta < 2$ must be avoided.

Wood Products

There are three limitations to the use of solid timber: the relatively small sizes of beams that can be obtained from tree stems, the anisotropic properties of wood, and different shrinkage or swelling properties of wood, both longitudinally and transversely. These limitations have led to the development of wood panels which are made in widths varying from 2 to 3 m. They have more uniform strength and deformation properties, and a better dimensional stability than solid wood under conditions of variable humidity. The panels are prepared by pressing together many smaller wood particles after adding adhesives. Three types of panels can be identified, depending on the size of the particles:

1. Plywood
2. Chipboard
3. Particle board

Panels can be used as load-carrying members, as stiffeners, or as non-load-bearing covering of walls and floors intended for insulation or sound proofing.

The allowable applications of wood products with regard to weathering and humidity are specified for each type of panel and for each wood product in DIN 68800, part 2, "Wood Preservation in Buildings, Preventive Detailing Measures" (see page 34).

Plywood Conforming to DIN 68705

The plywood category encompasses all panels having at least three layers of wood glued together, the grain of each layer being at a right angle to that of the adjacent layers.

Fabrication

Plywood is fabricated from thin layers of wood, called veneers, which are obtained by sawing, cutting, or stripping timber and vary from 0.05 to 8 mm. Thinly sawn or stripped veneers of valuable wood are used mostly for decorative surfaces of furniture.

Plywood plies are generally stripped on a lathe in continuous operation and are kept rolled until needed. Most woods can be used for this purpose. Boiling or wetting makes the wood softer and easier to cut. Cut plies are coated with adhesives in a gluing machine and are pressed together for 5 to 25 min in presses heated from 90 to 150°C. In general, the number of plies are odd. The exterior plies, called surfacing, have grain parallel to each other. The various thicknesses are layered symmetrically about the centerline of the panel.

Types of Plywood Adhesives

Plywoods used in construction are prepared with adhesives having different degrees of resistance to humidity. The type of adhesive is chosen on the basis of the climatic conditions and the degree of humidity to which the plywood will be exposed in use.

The following types of adhesives are available:

IF 20	Interior plywood, adhesives not weatherproof
AW 100	Exterior plywood, weatherproof adhesives
AW 100G	Exterior plywood, weatherproof adhesives containing ingredients for protection of the wood against destructive fungi.

Quality Grades

Plywood is sorted into quality grades I, II, and III, in which the properties of plywoods are described in relation to the type of wood used in surface veneers. Mixed types of plywood, such as I/III or II/II, are obtained through a combination of quality grades of surface veneers.

Construction Plywood (BFU) Conforming to DIN 68705, Part 3

Construction plywood is plywood in which all layers are made from veneers which are glued transverse to each other. The elastic and mechanical properties of plywood depend on the grain directions. They are different for each main direction and for each direction at an angle to the surface veneer. Generally, the direction of the surface veneer is considered as the main direction (Fig. 20).

Construction plywoods are especially suited for load-carrying members in timber construction, for roofing decks, and for reinforced concrete forms, because in comparison with other wood product panels, plywood has the highest modulus of elasticity and strength and therefore the highest allowable span loads. Plywoods are generally more expensive than chipboards or particle boards, but their use is especially justified when their higher strength and larger load capacity are combined with their superior weather resistance.

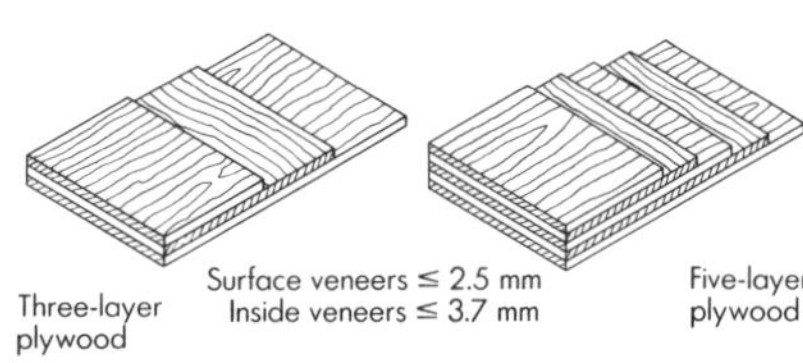

Fig. 20. Composition of construction plywood.

• *Quality requirements.* Quality requirements for plywoods apply to the type of wood used, to the properties and maximum thickness, to the bending strength, to the minimum moisture content, and to the adhesive strength of the glues.

Besides the plywood sheets that conform to standards, some plywood types conforming to partially modified standards are also allowed in construction. When using such types in load-carrying members, the allowable design parameters must be observed.

• *Sizes.* Following are the standard sizes for finished panels according to DIN 4078, "Plywood Sizes":

Thickness (mm)	4, 5, 6, 8, 10, 12, 13, 16, 19, 22, 25, 30, 38
Length (mm)	1250, 1530, 1730, 2050, 2200, 2500, 3050
Width (mm)	1250, 1530, 1730, 1830

The length is measured in the direction of the grain of the surface veneer.

Building and Furniture Panels (BTI) Conforming to DIN 68705, Part 4

Furniture panels consist of at least two surface veneers and a core made from wood strips placed adjacent to each other. The direction of the grain of each layer is normal to that of adjacent layers, the same as for plywood panels.

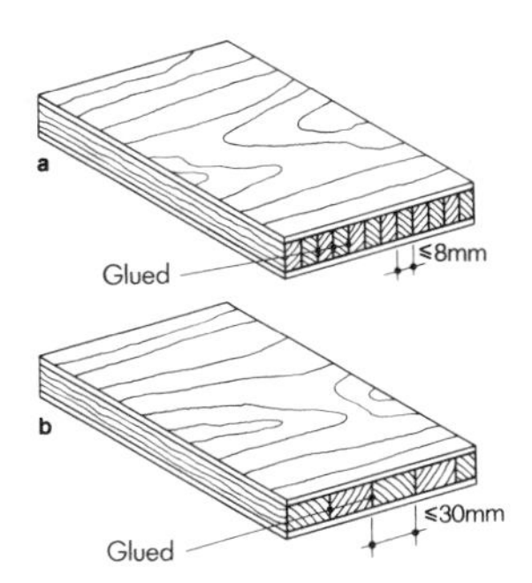

Fig. 21. Composition of furniture panels. (a) Small strips, placed transversely. (b) Large strips, placed flat.

Furniture panels are differentiated according to the following types:

1. Core made from small wood strips glued together and placed normal to the panel surface. The strips are made from circularly stripped veneers having a thickness of up to 8 mm (Fig. 21a).
2. Core made from larger wood strips varying in width from 24 to 30 mm and glued together parallel to the panel surface (Fig. 21b).
3. Core made from the same type of wood strips as above, varying in width from 24 to 30 mm, but not glued together.

Only types 1 and 2 qualify for building or furniture panels. The grain direction of the core strips is the main direction of the furniture panels. Therefore, a three-layered panel subject to bending must span in the direction normal to the grain of the surface veneer.

Building or furniture panels are used in load-carrying members of panel-type construction as webs or decking.

• *Quality requirements.* Similar to plywood. The quality of panels that are identified by DIN number is guaranteed.

• *Sizes.* Standard sizes of finished panels according to DIN 4078 are:

Thickness (mm)	13, 16, 19, 22, 25, 30, 38
Length (mm)	1530, 1730, 1830
Width (mm)	4600, 5100

The lengths are shorter than the widths because they are measured along the grain of the surface veneers.

Chipboards

Chipboards are fabricated from wood chips and similar fiber materials, such as bagasse, flax, or hemp, which are customarily mixed and pressed together with hardening resins. Chipboards with mineral binders have recently gained in importance. When chips are made exclusively from wood, the boards are called wood-chip boards.

Fabrication

After tree stems have been debarked, they are splintered in large tearing machines, which splinter the wood into chips of various sizes. The product quality depends on the quality of the equipment. Chips are dried and sorted. Two practical fabrication procedures are available; they produce chipboards which differ by the layout of the chips in the board.

In the flat-pressing procedure, the resin-coated chips are spread on form liners and thus they tend to be parallel to the panel surface. A multilayered buildup is achieved by successively spreading various types of chips. The forms are then pressed together and panels are formed under heat and pressure.

On the other hand, extruded pressboards are made by pressing the resin-coated chips into forms by means of an extruding device which moves inside the forms within the cross section of the panel. Deposited in this way, the chips are placed normal to the plane of the panel. The heat in the forms and the speed of deposition are adjusted such that, combined with the applied pressure, the core is produced in continuous formation. Cross sections that have tubular voids may also be made by this procedure. This process can produce various thicknesses, but the core still consists of a single layer. Extruded pressboards have lower bending strengths than multilayered flat-pressed panels. The relatively large longitudinal swelling properties and lesser durability of extruded boards can be reduced significantly by laminating the core with veneers, veneered boards, or wood-chip boards. Laminated, hollow-core extruded boards with thicknesses of up to 12.5 cm can be used as wall elements because of their great insulating value (Fig. 22).

Multilayered pressboards are the most valuable as load-bearing members. In the simplest case they consist of a surface layer having a larger adhesive content, with a core of lesser density and sometimes lesser chips quality. The better strength of denser surface layers increases the bending resistance of such boards in comparison with single-layered boards. Five-layer boards have an even better durability. Their greater thickness makes them preferable for building construction.

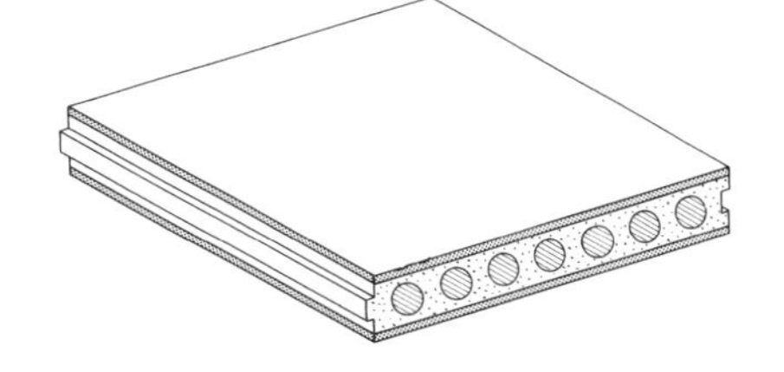

Fig. 22. Three-layer chipboard with tubular voids.

Quality Requirements

All chipboards have to have uniform thickness, sharp corners, and a rectangular shape, all within established tolerances. The bending capacity must exceed certain minimum values. In addition, the flat-pressed chipboards must fulfill certain shear strength requirements, while extruded chipboards must satisfy certain tension requirements. The average moisture content of all boards may vary between 5 and 13%. The swelling of flat-pressed boards during a 24-hour submersion in water, depending on the type of adhesives, must not exceed certain values.

Panels which are impregnated against decay and those that have a higher fire rating (materials class B1, fire-retardant materials) must be certified for these properties in order to obtain the seal of approval (see Protective Treatments, page 34).

Sizes, Nominal Thicknesses

Only preferred chipboard thicknesses are standardized (DIN 68760): 6, 8, 10, 13, 16, 19, 22, 25, 28, 32, 36, 40, 45, 50, 60, and 70 mm. Widths from 1250 to 2000 mm and lengths from 2250 to 8400 mm can be delivered, where lengths of 3800 to 5110 mm are produced more frequently. Although the lengths or widths are not standardized, it is recommended that the manufacturer be contacted for larger orders and the design of the product possibly be adjusted to available sizes; otherwise the cost of special cutting may increase the cost of construction by 20 to 30%.

Flat-Pressed Chipboard Panels Conforming to DIN 68763

Flat-pressed panels have approximately the same strength properties in all directions of the panel plane. If the chip-spreading technique has a preferred direction within the panel plane, this cannot be considered in design. The allowable strengths must apply to the weaker direction, namely the one normal to the preferred direction.

Flat-pressed panels are often used as load-bearing members acting together with roof and floor planking subject to bending, with wall elements subject to compression, and with stiffeners subject to shear. They are also used as roof decking, in which case they transmit the vertical forces of roofing, snow, and live load to the underlying structure. In special cases they could be used as stiffening diaphragms.

• *Standard types, adhesives.* The types of adhesives and wood protection additives govern the moisture and weather resistance of the panels. Panel types are:

V20 Non-weather-resistant adhesives. Binder: Aminoplast.

V100 Limited weather-resistant adhesives. Binder: Phenolresorcinol resins.
V100G Limited weather-resistant adhesives with protection against wood decaying fungi. Binder: Phenoresorcinol resins with wood protective additives.

Laminated Extrusion-Pressed Panels for Panel Construction Conforming to DIN 68764, Part 2

Extrusion-pressed panels are fabricated solid or with a hollow core, either as plain panels without laminates, or as laminated panels. The latter have higher elastic and mechanical properties. The load-carrying direction of a panel laminated with a veneer is the direction of the veneer, and for the panel with tubular voids it is the direction of the voids. If a panel is laminated with chipboards, all directions are equally strong. Because of the many possible combinations of panel construction, it is not possible to standardize the allowable stresses for extrusion-pressed panels. The above listed standard applies only to full panels having thicknesses of 12 to 16 mm whose laminates consist of beech veneers 1.0- to 1.5-mm thickness, or hard chipboards of 2-mm thickness. Such panels may be used as plank elements of composite timber load-carrying members, provided they are stiffened with ribs. Other types of laminated extrusion-pressed panels may be used in accordance with pertinent sections of the building codes which apply to panel construction.

• *Standard types, glues.* The panels are differentiated as follows according to the type of glue used between core and laminations (SV = full core, SR = hollow core):

SV1, SR1 Glues not weatherproof
SV2, SR2 Glues not weatherproof but resistant against high humidity

Standard panels SV2 and SR2 must have a full wood strip glued along all the outside edges or a moisture sealer of equivalent value.

Extrusion-pressed panels that qualify under DIN 68764, part 2, are designated as TSV1 and TSV2 (panel construction).

Non-Load-Bearing Chipboard Panels

Chipboard panels for special building uses conforming to DIN 68764 are mostly applied for acoustical purposes or in wall and floor linings. Depending on the type of installations, the following standard types can be distinguished:

LF Light flat-pressed panels with high sound-absorption quality, with or without layering or lamination
LRD Extrusion-pressed panels with tubular voids, layered or laminated on both sides, with perforated surfaces and high sound-absorption qualities
LMD Extrusion-pressed solid panels, layered or laminated on both sides with perforated surfaces and high sound-absorption qualities
LR Extrusion-pressed panels with tubular voids, layered or laminated on both sides with non-perforated surfaces.

In addition, wood-chip panels can be used for interior work as plastic-laminated, decorative, flat-pressed, layered boards of up to 32-mm thickness (see DIN 68765), as underflooring in rooms intended for constant human occupancy, or in special buildings such as sports halls or storage rooms. Special considerations needed in such applications are treated in DIN 68771. They center mostly on protection from and on the fabrication of these panels, including their impact on substructures.

Chipboards with Mineral Binders

The use of a mineral binder for wood chips started long ago, mainly in the fabrication of light shredded-wood building panels. Cement or magnesium-impregnated wood-chip panels were developed in an effort to improve their weathering and fire-rating characteristics. Chemically treated mineral-filled panels of spruce and fir chips, varying in thickness from 8 to 25 mm, are much heavier than panels with artificial resins, but they are better from the points of view of weathering and fire resistance, and are equally easy to work with. Their use is regulated by licensing.

Particle Boards

In the fabrication of particle boards, the wood is reduced to fibers or bundles of fibers. Randomly placed, they are formed into a new material with or without the help of binders and fillers. In this product the wood structure can no longer be recognized. However, since there are wood chipboards fabricated from very finely ground chips, there is an area of transition between chipboards and particle boards.

Fabrication

The raw material for particle boards can consist of softwood and bark of the lowest quality. Hardwoods are suitable only as additives because of their short fibers. Other plant fibers, such as straw, wood shavings, jute, or coconut, can also be added. The raw materials are ground to splinters, humidified, and mechanically reduced to fibers in a defibrator. In order to homogenize the composition, ground fibers are then mixed with water and thoroughly stirred in large vats. The strength and the water-repellent properties of the end product are regulated by admixtures of chemicals and binders. The pulp is dried on long sieves, partially by gravity and partially by vacuum and rolling cylinders. The final handling depends on the type of panel to be produced. Porous panels are dried lightly, while those of greater density are simultaneously dried and hardened in heated presses. In most cases, one side is confined by a sieve, which allows the removal of water and humidity, while the other side is hardened by heated steel plates.

In the newest drying procedure, in which air is replacing water for mixing and gluing, several layers of panels may be prepared, and the panels may be smooth on both sides. Wood-particle boards are differentiated mostly by hardness (strength) or surface treatment.

Hard and Medium-Hard Wood-Particle Panels Conforming to DIN 68754

Wood-particle panels are a homogeneous material and possess the same elastic and mechanical properties in all directions of the panel surface. Panels which conform to listed standards can be used as composite load-bearing members of flooring or as stiffeners.

In Sweden, Australia, the United States, and other countries, the hard and medium-hard particle boards were used for many years as load-bearing structural elements, such as webs of girders or shells of various types.

In many instances hardboard panels can be used for roof decking provided they carry only the light loads of roofing or insulation. Live load has to be carried by furring strips. In such instances, oil-tempered panels can be used without an impermeable sheet or bituminous roofing paper for the purpose of shedding water that might pass through the roofing.

Hard and medium-hard particle boards having different surface treatments may also be used for partitions, floor coverings, interior finishes, or exterior sheathing.

• *Standard types, binders*

HFH Hard wood-particle panels with a density greater than 800 kg/m^3
HFM Medium-hard wood-particle panels with a density of between 350 and 800 kg/m^3

The standard for hard and medium-hard wood-particle panels encompasses only the wood materials of class 20 (designation HFH 20, or HFM 20). It is expected that the standard will be extended to classes 100 and 100G by adding humidity-resistant binders and other additives to the materials. For the time being only a Swedish manufacturer has a construction license for HFM panels of all classes.

• *Quality requirements.* Quality requirements refer to straight and sharp edges, rectangularity of panels, parallelism of edges, dimensional tolerances, moisture content, swelling in water, bending strength, and shear strength.

• *Sizes.* There are no standard sizes for wood-particle panels. Current sizes according to manufacturers are:

Thickness	HFH: 2, 2.5, 3.2, 4, 5, 6, 7, 8, 10, 12, 15 mm; thicknesses of over 8 mm may be obtained by gluing two panels together
	HFM: 5 to 16 mm, but mostly 9 to 12 mm
Width	1220 to 2030 mm
Length	2500 to 5200 mm

Non-Load-Bearing Wood-Particle Panels

HFD Porous wood-particle panels conforming to DIN 68750 (also called insulating or sound-proofing panels) are panels with a density varying from 230 to 350 kg/m³. Thicknesses from 10 to 20 mm are available.

KH Wood-particle panels laminated with decorative artificial materials conforming to DIN 68751 are hard panels rimmed with frames, impregnated with artificial resins, and laminated under heat and pressure. Panels can be laminated on one or both sides.

BPH1 Bituminous wood-particle panels conforming to DIN 68752 are porous and are made from wood fibers with the addition of 10 to 15% of bitumen, by weight.

BPH2 Same as BPH1, but with more than 15% bitumen, by weight.

Quality Guarantees, Identification, and Markings

The rating of timber materials which are to have a load-bearing function in a building is established by the appropriate standards. Such materials must be subject to continuous inspection by recognized laboratories or by officially approved testing institutes.

Wood-product panels which have been fabricated according to standards or licenses, and have been inspected, are to be marked at appropriate locations with the following data:

• Manufacturer's name and type of fabrication (may be coded)
• Thickness in millimeters
• Standard of conformance
• DIN or license number
• Inspection identification

If standard or licensed panels are considered for construction, the following specific information must be shown in the specifications, plans, and orders:

• Type of wood-fiber panel (veneer, furniture, flat-pressed, extrusion-pressed, hard or medium hard)
• Thickness, length, and width in millimeters
• Standard of conformance or licensing description
• DIN number or licensing number
• Special requirements (for example, low flammability, class B1)

PHYSICAL AND MECHANICAL PROPERTIES OF WOOD AND WOOD PRODUCTS

Physical Properties

Unit Weight

The unit weight ρ of wood is a ratio of its mass m and gross volume V, including voids. For a moisture content u the unit weight is given by

$$\rho_u = \frac{M_u}{V_u} \quad [\text{g/cm}^3]$$

Certain physical and technological properties essential for the proper use of wood depend on the unit weight. It is often possible to determine the suitability of wood for certain uses on the basis of its unit weight alone.

The unit weight of wood depends on its macroscopic structure and its porosity. It varies widely with the species of trees and their location. It also varies within the same tree and the location of a sample. However, the specific weight of the wood substance itself, equal to 1.55 g/cm³, remains practically constant. The unit weight of wood also depends on the moisture content and, therefore, the moisture content u must be given when stating the unit weight. The normal values of unit weight ρ_N are given for storage in a normal climate (+20°C, 65% relative air humidity); ρ_o is the unit weight for oven-dry conditions (Fig. 23).

Fig. 23. Oven-dry unit weights ρ_o for the most important woods (g/cm³).

European Conifers	Minimum	Average	Maximum
Spruce and fir	0,30	0,43	0,64
Pine	0,30	0,49	0,86
Larch	0,40	0,65	0,82
Hardwoods			
Beech	0,49	0,68	0,88
Oak	0,39	0,65	0,93

For design computations of structural members according to DIN 1055, part 1, upper and lower limits of unit weights should be established in order to account for the most unfavorable future moisture contents.

Moisture Content

The moisture content influences not only the unit weight but also most mechanical, physical, and technological properties of wood and its by-products. Limited variations in humidity cause dimensional changes both in wood and in its by-products. Strength and deformation properties are similarly affected.

As in other materials, the moisture content u of wood is given as a percentage of the oven-dry weight G_o (weight after drying to a constant weight at a temperature of +103°C ± 2°C),

$$u = \frac{G_u - G_o}{G_o} \times 100 \quad [\%]$$

where G_u is the weight of the wood at a moisture content of u%.

Hygroscopic and porous wood cell walls absorb water from the humidity in the surrounding air, while cell voids absorb it by capillary action. Therefore, two ranges of moisture content can be distinguished:

1. *Hygroscopic range.* The moisture content lies below the saturation point of fibers u_F, which is about 28%. In this range the moisture content of wood depends on the relative humidity and the temperature of the surrounding air (Fig. 24).
2. *Capillary range.* The moisture content is above the saturation point of the fibers. After the cell walls have reached saturation, the cell voids fill up with water to some degree. This condition exists in freshly cut wood, where u is mostly over 40%, and in structural members which are wholly or partly in contact with water.

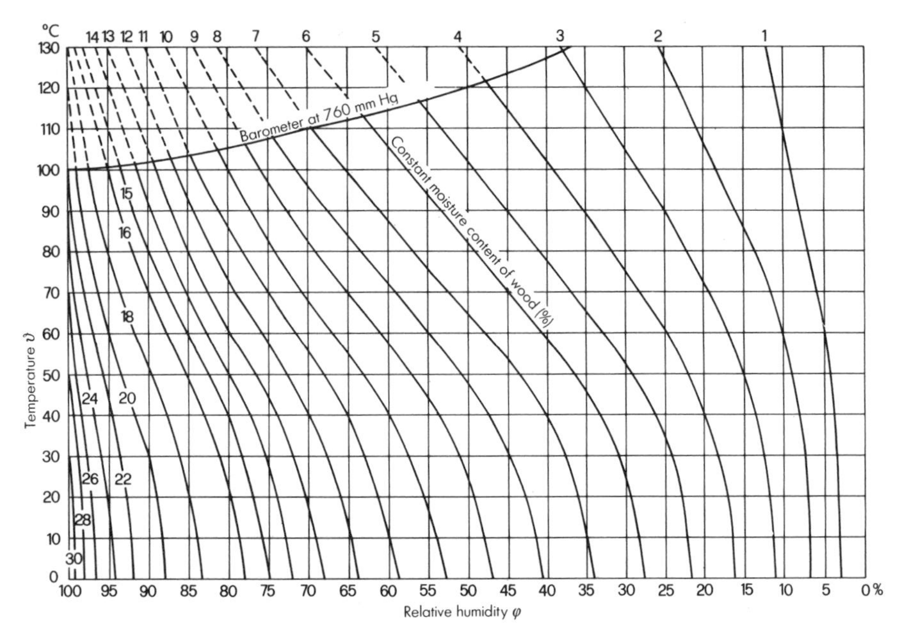

Fig. 24. Hygroscopic isothermal curves for spruce (according to Loughborough/Keylwerth).

Measurement of the moisture content can be performed either by the oven-drying process (DIN 52183, "Testing of Wood, Measurements of Moisture Content") or, in case of solid wood, by means of electrical measuring devices based on the principles that electric resistance varies with the moisture content. The latter method has the advantage of immediate readings, while the oven-drying process requires a long drying time.

The use of penetrating or drilled electrodes permits measuring the moisture content to some depth. This is of importance in woodworking and in the quality control of beams and timbers.

Quality requirements for round or sawn timber recognize three moisture content ranges:

Dry wood $u \leq 20\%$
Half-dry wood $u \leq 30\%$
$u \leq 35\%$ for cross sections over $200\ cm^2$
Fresh wood u is not limited

The hygroscopic moisture content influences the strength of wood, in particular its compression strength, so that the allowable stresses for wood and its by-products must be limited when structural members are exposed to moisture and the weather. The reduction in allowable stresses equals 1/6 for structural members treated with preservative compounds during fabrication or before installation, as per DIN 68800. This reduction equals 1/3 for untreated wood or wood continuously submerged. A reduction of 5/6 applies to E and G moduli, which govern deformation, when the moisture content is above 20%. In order to prevent undesirable or damaging deformations, it is recommended that wood be dry before use, or that it be dried as soon as possible after it has been used in construction.

Wood also dries naturally in air. If properly stacked, smaller sizes, such as boards and beams, can dry in a few weeks to a point below the saturation of fibers. Because of the long drying time and the dependence of the ultimate moisture content on the weather, the prevalent practice today is to use artificially dried wood. Such wood is exposed in a drying kiln to streams of air having a certain humidity and temperature. Any desirable moisture content between 6 and 25% can be reached by this method.

Artificial drying is performed on all wood used in glue-laminated members where, as a rule, a moisture content of 8 to 12% is required before gluing. After this, a normal moisture content in the environment of the finished building can be reached without damage. DIN 1052, part 1, gives the following normal moisture content values:

Building enclosed on all sides, heated: $9 \pm 3\%$
Building enclosed on all sides, unheated: $12 \pm 3\%$
Open, but roofed building: $15 \pm 3\%$
Structure open to weather on all sides: $\geq 18\%$

Lumber used for interior building work, such as floor or wall linings, flooring, and stairs, should reach these moisture contents before construction, as this will prevent future splitting, cracking, breakage, and surface deterioration.

Wood products are generally furnished with slightly lower moisture contents because of their fabrication process. A minimum moisture content of 6% is prescribed for veneers and furniture panels, while wood-chip panels may have a moisture content of $9 \pm 4\%$ and wood-particle panels $5 \pm 3\%$. In order to prevent damaging deformations at a later time, these materials should be acclimatized to their future environment before use.

Swelling and Shrinkage

Swelling and shrinkage represent dimensional changes due to variations in moisture content. An increase in moisture causes swelling, a decrease causes shrinkage. Within the hygroscopic range, each moisture content corresponds to a certain cell-wall thickness. An increase in moisture content increases the wall thickness and causes swelling, while a decrease in moisture content reduces the wall thickness and causes shrinkage. In the hygroscopic range there is almost a linear correspondence between the moisture content and dimensional changes, and therefore, the corresponding swelling curves can be determined, as shown in Fig. 25. After saturation of the fibers there are no more dimensional changes.

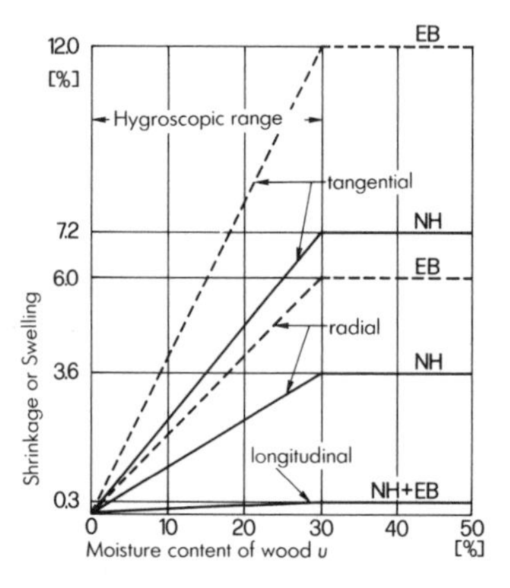

Fig. 25. Swelling curves for European conifers (NH) and for Beech and Oak (EB).

Swelling and shrinkage are reversible and vary considerably according to various directions of the yearly growth rings and the grain of wood. Dimensional changes are largest tangentially to the yearly rings, they are half as large radially, and they are negligible in the direction of the grain (longitudinally).

According to DIN 1052, part 1, the following shrinkage and swelling rates α_t, α_r, and α_l, expressed as percentages of a 1% change in moisture content, are to be expected:

	α_t	α_r	α_l
European conifers ($\rho_o = 0.40\ g/cm^3$)	0.24	0.12	0.01
Oak, beech ($\rho_o = 0.65\ g/cm^3$)	0.40	0.20	0.01

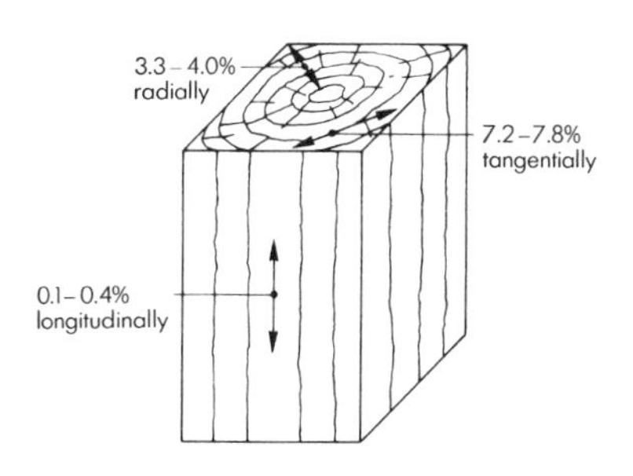

Fig. 26. Maximum shrinkage and swelling rates of spruce for three main directions.

Shrinkage and swelling rates depend on the unit weight of the wood. The higher the ρ values are, the more material there is in the cell walls. As a rule, lighter woods are less prone to dimensional changes caused by changes in moisture.

During the drying process, the differences in shrinkage properties and moisture contents between heartwood and sapwood cause the splitting and cracking of lumber that was produced by sawing across the section of an entire tree. Round timbers as well as all rectangular lumber and timber develop shrinkage cracks during the drying process, but these do not affect their load-bearing capacity.

If dimensional changes due to changes in humidity can propagate themselves to other structural components and connections without interruption, the expected dimensional changes can be calculated knowing the shrinkage and swelling rates of the wood and by anticipating the changes in moisture contents. To be safe, a tangential yearly ring layout should be assumed for boards and planks, while an average value of $0.5(\alpha_t + \alpha_r)$ should be assumed for dimension lumber and beams. If dimensional changes are restrained, major forces can be created. These can be computed by assuming half-values of the dimensional changes due to shrinkage and swelling. Larger dimensional changes caused by shrinkage or swelling must be resolved through appropriate construction details if damage to timber is to be prevented.

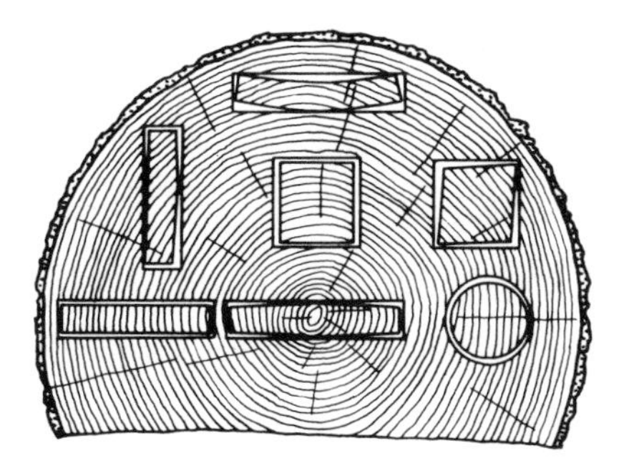

Fig. 27. Tearing of timber section due to shrinkage.

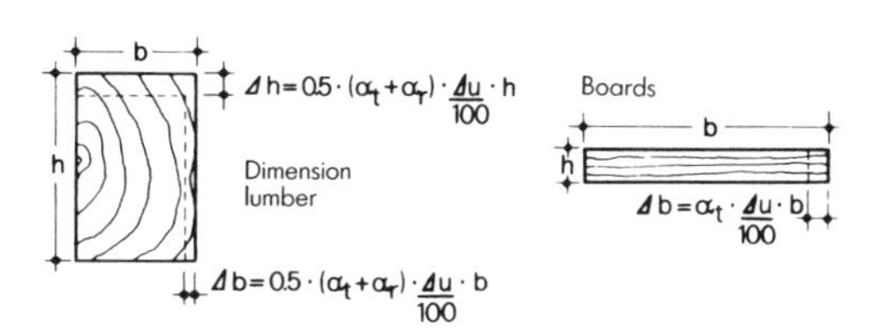

Fig. 28. Computation of shrinkage deformations in dimension lumber and boards.

In wood-product materials there is a difference between the dimensional changes in the plane of the panel and those normal to that plane. Changes in thickness normal to the plane correspond closely to the values for solid wood. Within the plane of the panel, however, dimensional changes are restricted through gluing of veneers and the layout of chips or fibers in various directions. As a result, only dimensional changes corresponding to the longitudinal direction of solid wood may apply here. At this time the following values can be used for all directions within the panel plane.

Shrinkage and swelling percentages for wood-product materials, expressed as a percentage of moisture change:

Veneer panels	0.020
Flat-pressed panels V20	0.035
Flat-pressed panels V100, V100G	0.025
Hard wood-fiber panels	0.040

Thermal Properties

The thermal properties of wood, within the normal temperature range of between −25 and +60°C encountered in buildings, generally determine its suitability as a structural material or as a material for interior finishes and insulation. The following thermal properties of wood and wood products are important.

Thermal Expansion Coefficient α_T

Wood and wood products change their dimensions with changes of temperature, as do all other materials. Within the normal temperature range, the dimensional changes are almost proportional to the temperature changes. Dimensional changes can be computed by using the thermal expansion coefficient α_T:

$$\Delta l_T = \alpha_T l \, \Delta T$$

where α_T is the dimensional rate of change for a temperature change of 1°C and l is length.

Three different values of α_T apply to wood, depending on the direction: longitudinal, tangential, or radial. Only the longitudinal direction parallel to the grain has any practical significance for timber, for which a value of $\alpha_T = 3$ to 6×10^{-6} applies. These values are small in comparison to steel, light metals, or concrete. In normal structures thermal expansion is not significant, but concurrent changes in humidity cause corresponding shrinkage or swelling movements. The essentially higher values of the thermal coefficient in the transverse direction have no practical significance for normal construction. The negligible lengthening of wood in its longitudinal direction is of great advantage at high temperatures, such as those caused by fire, because even overheated timbers barely move against their bearings. This increases the durability of a building.

There are no appreciable differences between thermal expansion coefficients of panels of various wood products having different textures. In wood-chip or particle board panels a larger thermal coefficient normal to the fibers is noticeable. Expansion coefficients vary from 10×10^{-6} to 15×10^{-6} and have to be taken into account.

Thermal Conductivity λ

The thermal coefficient λ [W/m·K] is critical for an evaluation of the insulating value of wood or wood products. The coefficient is obtained by measuring the amount of heat W that can pass in 1 hour through 1 m^2 of a material having a thickness of 1 m when the temperature differential is 1°C. Since for the air in the pores this coefficient is very small ($\lambda_{air} = 0.26$ W/m·K) and for the water it is high ($\lambda_{water} = 0.58$ W/m·K), λ is less for lower unit weights, but increases with the moisture content. The coefficient λ is significantly less normal to the grain than in the direction of the grain.

DIN 4108, "Insulation in Buildings," gives the following values in W/m·K for computing insulating values of wood and wood products:

Wood	λ	Wood Products	λ
Spruce	0.14	Plywood	0.14
Pine	0.14	Hard fiber panels	0.17
Fir	0.14	Porous fiber panels	0.058
Oak	0.21	Wood-chip panels	0.14–0.17
Beech	0.17		

These values are valid for air-dried materials. They are also valid up to a moisture content of 20% for solid timber conforming to DIN 4074, and up to a moisture content of 12% for wood products. However, the latter values rarely occur in building elements that are permanently protected from wetness.

Considering the degrees of moisture generally existing in buildings, the heat conductivity values of wood or wood products are considerably lower than those of most inorganic materials.

Specific Heat c

Specific heat c is the amount of heat W that has to be brought to 1 kg of material in order to raise its temperature by 1°C. This value is used to compute the heat storage capacity of the material. The value of c depends greatly on the moisture content

u of the wood, as shown in the following formula:

$$c = 1.16 \frac{0.324 + u}{1 + u} \quad [\text{W/kg} \cdot \text{K}]$$

This gives a thermal capacity c equal to 5.07 W/kg·K for a moisture content of 20%.

Vapor Diffusion Resistance Factor μ

It is necessary to know the factor of resistance of vapor diffusion in a building element in order to evaluate the danger of a dew point within that element, that is, the point at which condensation occurs. The value of μ is obtained by measuring how much more a material resists vapor diffusion than an equal thickness of air ($\mu_{air} = 1$). Vapor in a material travels in the direction of lower vapor pressure, generally from a warm to a cold side. A dew point may occur in a cross section in which the existing vapor reaches saturation. The μ value of a material is needed for the computation of the vapor content in a particular cross section and for an evaluation of the risk of a dew point. For wood and wood products values μ are as follows:

	μ
Solid wood (European conifers, oak, beech)	50
Interior plywood	50
Exterior plywood	200
Hard wood-particle boards	70
Porous wood-particle boards	5
Interior wood-chip boards	50
Exterior wood-chip boards	100

The values of μ vary widely; they also depend on the unit weight and the moisture content of the material. In special cases the appropriate values can be obtained by testing.

Mechanical Properties (Deformation and Strength)

Solid Wood

Elastic Values

Wood behaves practically as a fully elastic body for tensile loads of short duration applied in the direction of the grain, up to a certain stress. This means that the induced dimensional changes disappear after removal of the load. After exceeding the elastic limit, large plastic deformations occur and increase progressively until the breaking limit is reached. The relationship between tension and elongation is shown by a line that is straight almost to the breaking point. A similar line for compression shows that there is an elastic limit β_{DP} at about 65 to 85% of the ultimate compressive stress. Beyond this limit the deformations increase much more rapidly

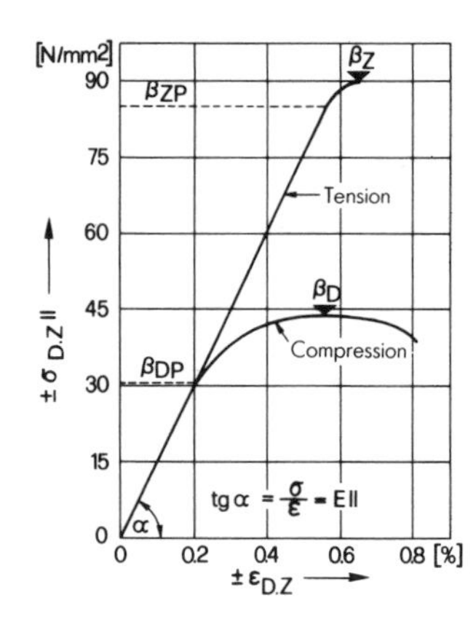

Fig. 29. Stress versus strain diagram σ/ϵ for conifers under tension or compression in the direction of the grain.

than the stresses. Hooke's law is valid for the straight portion of the line, which defines the elastic properties of wood:

$$\sigma_{D,Z} = E_{D,Z} \, \epsilon_{D,Z}$$

where E is the modulus of elasticity. E has the value of that hypothetical unit stress, N/mm², for which a test sample after loading returns to its original shape. The modulus of elasticity E can vary widely even within the same species of wood and is also influenced by the moisture content. Within the hygroscopic range, the E modulus decreases with increasing moisture content of the wood. The tensile and compressive moduli are practically equal, and so is the modulus for bending, as long as the compressive stress does not exceed the value β_{DP}.

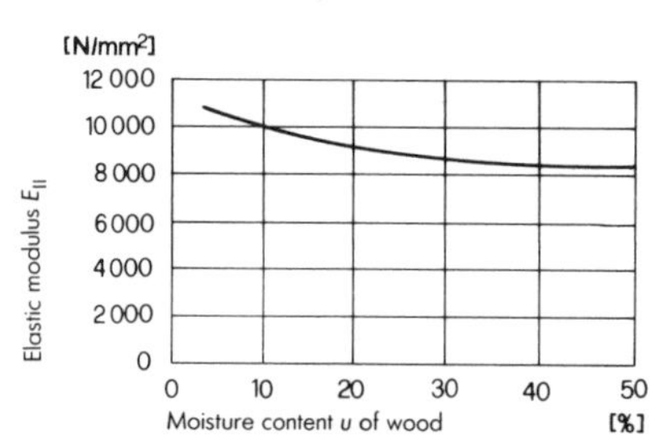

Fig. 30. Modulus of elasticity E in relation to moisture content u of wood.

These rules are also valid for construction lumber which, because of its random growth, has a much greater scatter of values than selected wood samples.

	Range of E values parallel to grain	Design E value parallel to grain
European conifers	6000 – 16 000 N/mm²	10 000 N/mm²
Oak, beech	8000 – 22 000 N/mm²	12 500 N/mm²

When a load is applied at an angle α to the direction of the grain, the modulus of elasticity E decreases with increasing angle α. The following rule can be assumed with sufficient accuracy:

$$E_\alpha = \frac{E_{||} E_\perp}{E_\perp \cos^3\alpha + E_{||} \sin^3\alpha}$$

Deformations under loads applied normal to the grain are much greater than those for loads applied parallel to the grain. This is due to the tubular structure of the cells. There is also a difference between loads applied tangentially and those applied radially to yearly rings. The smallest deformation values are obtained for loads applied in the tangential direction. For design purposes an aver-

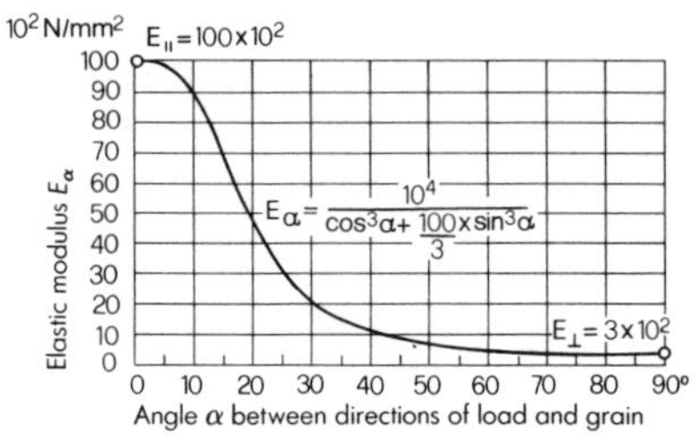

Fig. 31. Modulus of elasticity E in relation to angle α in conifers.

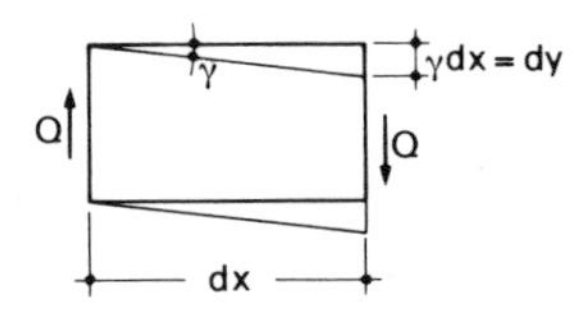

Fig. 32. Shear deformation of a wood prism under shear stresses induced by shear forces.

age E value can be used. According to DIN 1052, part 1, values of $E_\perp = 300$ N/mm² for conifers and 600 N/mm² for hardwoods can be used.

In regard to E_α, which depends on the angle between the load and the direction of the grain, values of $E_{||} = 10{,}000$ N/mm² and $E_\perp = 300$ N/mm² can be assumed for European conifers, as shown in Fig. 31.

Rectangular cross sections subject to shear forces deform in a way that can be expressed by the slippage angle $\gamma = dy/dx$. The following relationship exists between γ and the shear stress τ_Q:

$$\tau_Q = G_S \gamma \quad \text{or} \quad \gamma = \frac{\tau_Q}{G_S}$$

where G_S is the shear modulus, that is, an imaginary shear stress that produces a slippage angle equal to 1.

Under tensile stresses there is a relationship between the rotation of the member length l and the torsional moment M_T:

$$\phi = \frac{M_T l}{G_T J_T}$$

Here G_T is the torsional modulus, which for wood depends on the shear modulus in each of three

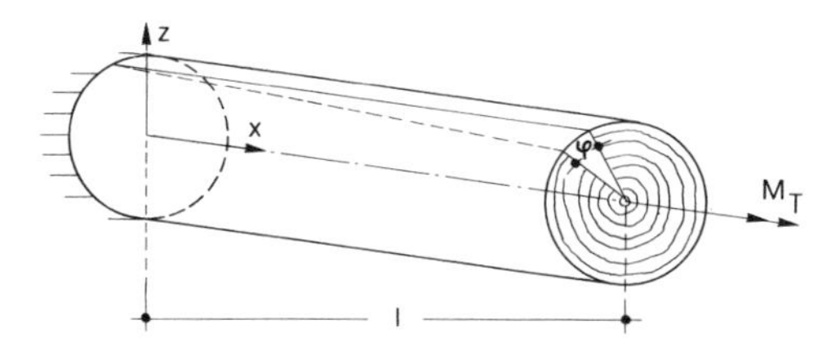

Fig. 33. Rotation of a beam under torsional load.

planes. For normal beam cross sections of solid or laminated wood it can be assumed that $G_T \approx G_S = G$. There is no firm relationship between E and G. The relationship E/G obtained by testing varies between 12 and 35. The design values for G are given in DIN 1052, part 1:

	G	E/G
European conifers	500 N/mm²	20
Oak and beech	1000 N/mm²	12.5

The G modulus is used for the computation of shear and torsional deformations, and to check for buckling in members subject to bending.

Longitudinal and Transverse Compressive Strength, Buckling Strength

Longitudinal and transverse compressive strengths (ultimate stresses) depend on the angle of incidence between the load and the direction of the grain. In connections, especially at notches, the angular compressive strength also plays a role, generally for angles between 20 and 70°.

The ultimate longitudinal compressive stress of conifers varies between 30 and 90 N/mm², depending on growth characteristics. The resistance of tubular cells to compression is much lower in the transverse than in the longitudinal direction. The wood's strength is lowest for conditions of one-

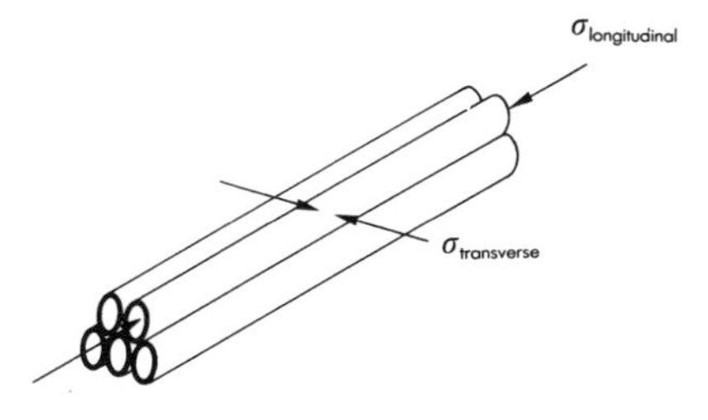

Fig. 34. Tubular cells loaded longitudinally and transversely.

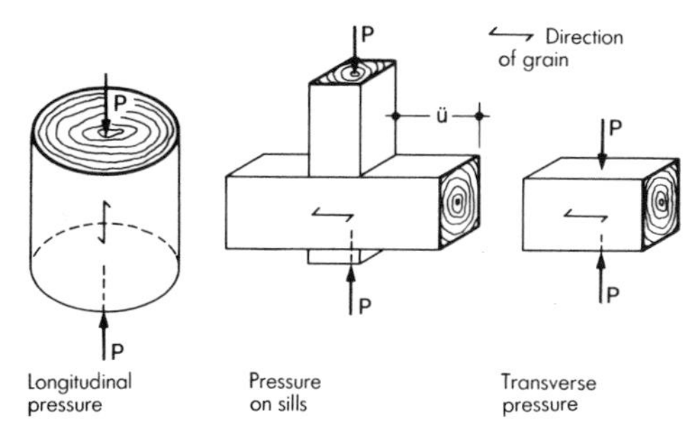

Fig. 35. Loading parallel and transverse to grain.

sided transverse loads. Greater strengths are obtained for a two-sided application of loads, where each of the opposite loaded surfaces offers a certain resistance. The design rules indicate that one-sided loading requires a 20% reduction of the allowable compressive stress $\sigma_{D\perp}$ compared to two-sided loading.

When the incidence of compressive load is on a skew, the allowable skew compressive stress $\sigma_{D\alpha}$ can be computed according to DIN 1052, part 1, for the allowable longitudinal and transverse stresses $\sigma_{D\|}$ and $\sigma_{D\perp}$ as follows:

$$\sigma_{D\alpha\,allow} = \sigma_{D\|\,allow} - (\sigma_{D\|\,allow} - \sigma_{D\perp allow})\sin\alpha$$

Sound knots do not reduce compressive strength because the wood in knots is stronger than ordinary wood, but the grain pattern around knots may lead to earlier splitting. Generally, under normal conditions a failure occurs because of the buckling of cell walls or shear deformations in the shear planes.

The moisture content has a significant effect on the strength of wood. Below the saturation point, there is a great reduction in β_D corresponding to an increase in moisture content.

The failure of longer structural members under longitudinal (axial) load occurs through lateral buckling when the length of the member exceeds

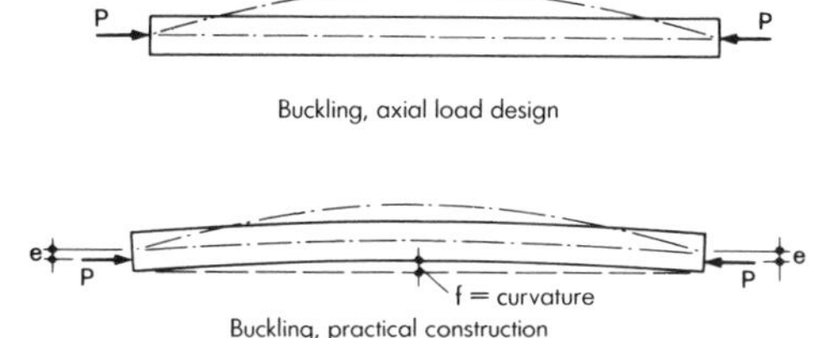

Fig. 36. Buckling under axial design load.

six times the smallest lateral side. The buckling strength β_k (maximum load-carrying stress) of members designed for axial load must take into account an eccentric load because of unavoidable construction imperfections, such as nonhomogeneous cross sections, curvature of members, and eccentric loading. It can be computed by

$$\beta_k = \frac{\pi^2 E}{\lambda^2}\left(1 - \frac{\epsilon\beta_k}{\beta_{D\|} - \beta_k}\right)$$

Critical, in addition to values depending on material, such as E and β_u, are the values of slenderness $\lambda = S_k/\min\ I$, where S_k is the length and I is the moment of inertia of the cross section; and eccentricity $\epsilon = e/K$, where K is the width of the kern and e the eccentricity of the load. The usual β_k versus λ graphs can be plotted for construction lumber of all three classes following the requirements of DIN 4074, parts 1 and 2, which give the allowable curvature $e = f = s_k/a$ and the load eccentricity $e = 0.1k$ independently of the length of the member. The allowable stresses for slender members can be calculated from those graphs after the buckling factor of safety ν_k and the slenderness ratio λ have been determined.

$$\sigma_{k\,allow} = \frac{\beta_k}{\nu_k}$$

The graphs of $\sigma_{k\,allow}$ versus λ obtained in this manner are the basis for the design of buckling members with the so-called omega ω procedure, in which $\omega = \sigma_{D\|allow}/\sigma_{k\,allow}$.

Tensile Strength

The tensile strength of knot-free and straight-grained wood is 2 to 2.5 times that of the wood's

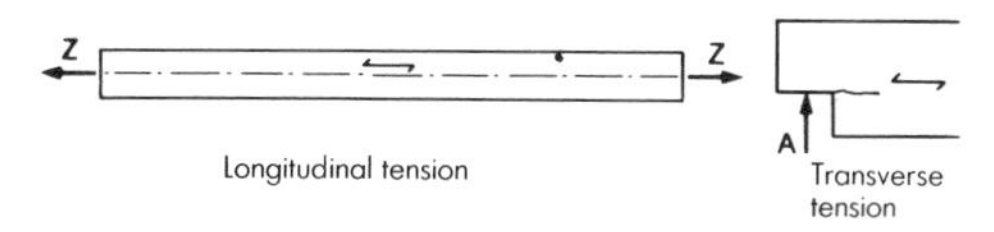

Fig. 37. Tensile stress applied longitudinally and transversely to grain.

compressive strength. It equals 60 to 150 N/mm² for conifers. The tensile strength of normal timber is reduced by imperfections of growth, so that the practical values of both the tensile and the compressive strengths are assumed to be equal. Tensile strength is influenced by moisture content to a lesser degree than compressive strength.

The tensile strength normal to the grain for perfect small test samples can vary from 1.5 to 4.0 N/mm², but for larger cross sections the unavoidable cracks and splits may reduce such tensile stress to zero. The skewed tensile strength is also not always reliable. Because of this, structures of solid or laminated wood must often adopt special construction details intended to resist transverse loads.

Bending Strength

Members subject to bending can maintain a linear stress distribution within a cross section only as long as the elastic limit β_{DP} is not exceeded at the extreme fiber. Since the E modulus is practically the same for compression and for tension, it is possible to count on a linear relationship of stresses even beyond the allowable stresses, and thus the extreme fiber stresses in a section conform to the relationship

$$\sigma_{D,z} = \pm\frac{M}{W}$$

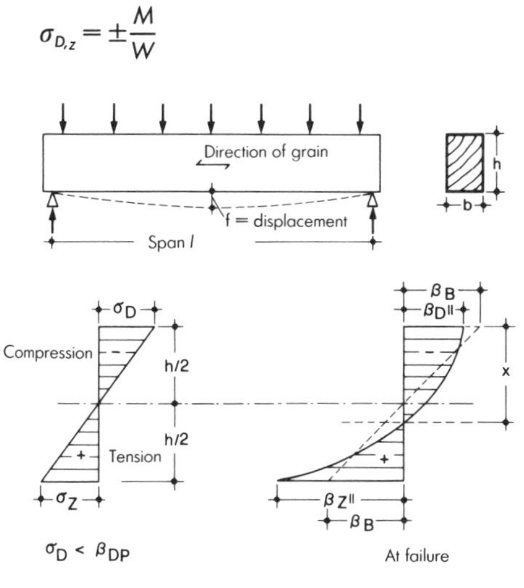

Fig. 38. Solid wood beams under bending load.

For higher bending moments, the stress distribution over the cross section becomes uneven. At extreme fiber compression the stress rises to its maximum compressive value of $\beta_{D||}$, while at extreme fiber tension it increases to $\beta_{Z||}$. In clear wood the extreme tensile stress is substantially greater than the maximum compressive stress, but in ordinary wood with knots and other imperfections in the tension zone, the failure of the entire member occurs before reaching this maximum. As a result, in ordinary lumber the stress distribution at failure is still generally a straight line. Thus the maximum fiber stresses at failure can be computed with good approximation by

$$\beta_B = \pm \frac{M_{max}}{W}$$

where β_B indicates the bending strength (ultimate stress) of wood and W is the section modulus.

The bending strength, like the compressive strength, is influenced by the unit weight and the moisture of the wood. Above all, it is affected by the direction of the grain and the knottiness, similar to the tensile strength.

Longitudinal and Transverse Shear Strengths and Torsional Resistance

In laterally loaded beams, transverse forces cause, in addition to bending stresses, longitudinal shear stresses parallel to the grain. The longitudinal

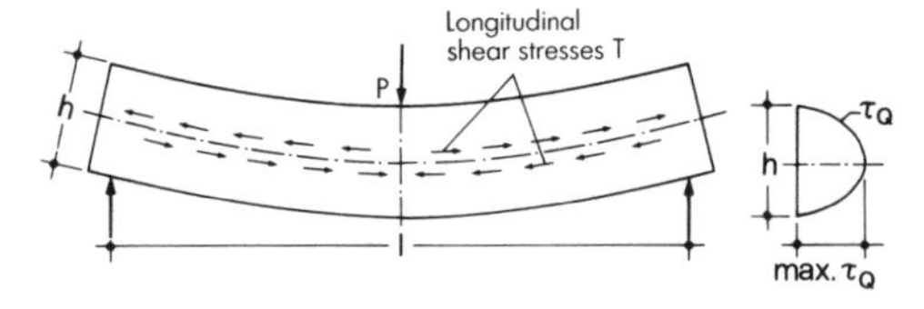

Fig. 39. Longitudinal shear and its distribution in beams subject to bending.

shear stresses reach their maximum values at the central axis of the cross section at locations of maximum shear.

The maximum shear stresses are computed by

$$\tau_{Qmax} = \frac{Q_{max}\, S_x}{b I_x}$$

and for rectangular cross sections this amounts to

$$\tau_{Qmax} = 1.5\, \frac{Q_{max}}{F}$$

where Q is the shear, S is the static moment, b is the beam width, I is the moment of inertia, and F is the area of the section.

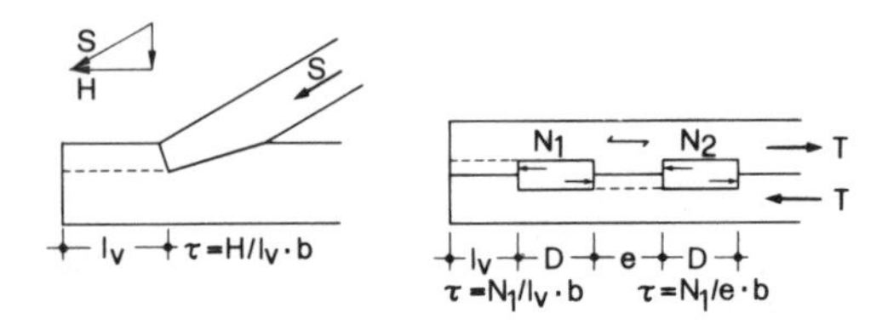

Fig. 40. Shear in connections.

Shear forces are mostly generated at connections or between two adjacent connectors. Shear parallel to the grain also develops. Wood without cracks in the plane of shear parallel to the grain may have a considerably larger shear strength,

$$\tau_S = \frac{N}{F_S}$$

For example, at a notch (Fig. 40),

$$\tau_S = \frac{H}{b l_v}$$

Longitudinal shear strength parallel to the grain is only 1/8 to 1/10 of the compressive strength. Shear normal to the grain is considerably higher and has practically no meaning because the normal compressive strength is so small.

Torsional stresses are induced when structural members are subject to torque. For the anisotropic properties of wood, the torsional stresses can be approximated by the formula for isotropic materials:

$$\tau_T = \frac{M_T}{W_T}$$

where M_T is the torsional moment and W_T the section modulus for torsion.

For wood or laminated wood members of quality classes I and II, the torsional strength can be assumed to be at least equal to the shear strength. For conifers of classes I and II this strength varies between 3.0 and 5.0 N/mm^2 and for laminated wood from 4.0 to 7.0 N/mm^2.

Deflection

The deflection of singly supported solid wood members subject to bending results from the changes in length of compressive and tensile fibers, and from shear deformations that are mostly negligible:

$$f = f_M + f_Q = \frac{C M_{max} l^2}{EJ} + \frac{M_{max}}{GF'}$$

The deflection f_M due to bending moments depends on the stiffness EJ of the solid cross section, the load distribution, and on the span length l. Since E can vary widely, the actual deflection may vary from that computed by normal E values. The contribution f_Q due to shear deformations is significant only for certain beam shapes, such as webbed girders.

The deflection of trusses is due to elastic elongations of members and slippage of connections. In special cases, such as at contact points of members, shrinkage may also be significant.

In members subject mostly to bending, deflection must be limited in order not to impair a member's usefulness (for example, in floors and flat roofs). It must also be limited to reduce the effects not normally calculated, such as creep and additional secondary forces. These might lead to localized overstresses. The allowable total deflection in building members varies between 1/200 and 1/300 of the span length. Allowances must be made for construction with or without camber.

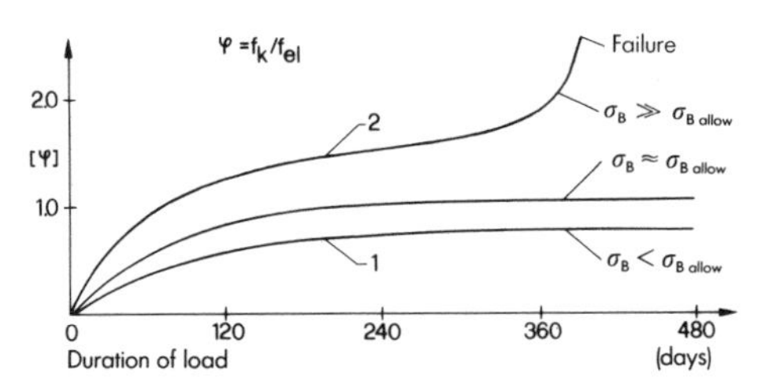

Fig. 41. Creep curves of beams subject to bending.

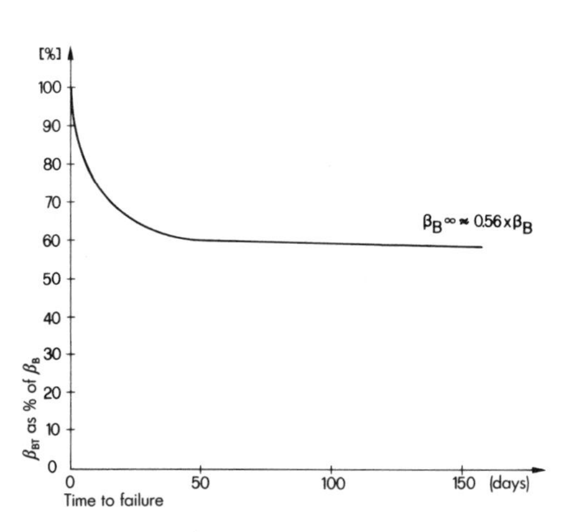

Fig. 42. Curve of strength versus time for conifer wood (clear).

Creep and Long-Range Strength of Wood

For loads of long duration, plastic deformations dependent on time have to be added to elastic deformations. In the case of trusses, there are additional displacements of connections and joints due to plastic deformations which occur with time. Deformations caused by loads of long duration are called creep. Curves showing deformations related to the duration of applied load are given in Fig. 41. The diagrams show that creep deformations depend on time and that after a while they reach a limit, which is approximately 1.6 to 2.0 times that of elastic deformations (curve 1) for the usual range of stresses. For higher stresses, exceeding the so-called creep limit, the deformations increase rapidly after a certain time, until the beam fails (curve 2). The stress that can be sustained without failure for an indefinite period of time is called long-range stress. In most woods creep limit and long-range stress coincide; in sound wood without blemishes this limit varies between 50 and 60% of the ultimate stress (Fig. 42). The rules for creep in wood are not well known, so that in design creep can only be approximated. Particularly uncertain is the influence of moisture changes, intermittent loading, and cyclic loading and unloading.

The total elongation ϵ_{ges} is the sum of elastic elongation ϵ_{el} and creep elongation ϵ_k as determined experimentally,

$$\epsilon_{ges} = \epsilon_{el} + \epsilon_k = \epsilon_{el} + \phi\epsilon_{el} = \epsilon_{el}(1 + \phi)$$

where ϕ is the ratio between creep and elastic deformations.

Since $\epsilon_{el} = \sigma/E$, it follows that

$$\epsilon_{ges} = \frac{\sigma}{E}(1 + \phi)$$

from which we can derive the long-range modulus E_ϕ:

$$E_\phi = \frac{E}{1+\phi} = \eta E$$

Experimental results to date indicate that the values of ϕ range from 0.6 to 1.0 for stresses below the allowable design stresses. The long-range stress is generally based on a safety factor of 3 compared with the ultimate stress, but in the design of deflections, the creep deformations could be approximated by using a reduced modulus of elasticity. The reduction factor η can be assumed as

$$\eta = 1.5 - \frac{\sigma_g}{\sigma_{allow}} \leq 1.0$$

where σ_g is the stress due to long-range load.

Fig. 43. Mechanical properties of European lumber for moisture content $u = 12\%$.

Type of Wood		Modulus of Elasticity E, N/mm²	Compressive Strength β_D, N/mm²	Tensile Strength β_Z, N/mm²	Bending Strength β_B, N/mm²	Shear Strength τ_S, N/mm²
Spruce	∥	6000–**11 000**–21 000	30–**43**–79	21–**90**–245	49–**66**–136	4,0–**6,7**–12
	⊥	150–**300**–500	2,0–**5,8**–9,5	1,5–2,7–4,0	–	–
Pine	∥	7000–**12 000**–20 000	30–**47**–94	35–**104**–196	35–**87**–206	6,0–**10,0**–15
	⊥	–	3,7–**7,7**–14	1,0–**3,0**–4,4	–	–
Larch	∥	6300–**13 800**–20 000	35–**55**–81	–**107**–	52–**99**–132	4,5–**9,0**–10
	⊥	–	–**7,5**–	–**2,3**–	–	–
Beech	∥	10 000–**16 000**–22 000	41–**62**–99	57–**135**–180	63–**105**–180	6,5–**10,0**–19
	⊥	–	–**9,0**–	–**7,0**–	–	–
Oak	∥	9200–**13 000**–13 500	42–**54**–87	50–**90**–180	46–**91**–154	6,0–**11,0**–13
	⊥	–	8–**11**–19	2,0–**4,0**–9,6	–	–

∥ = parallel to grain; ⊥ = normal to grain; bold type = most common values.

Laminated Wood

Laminated wood beams generally have the physical properties of solid wood. In Europe they are fabricated mostly from spruce boards of quality grades I to III. Laminated beams, however, have better mechanical properties than the component materials. The improvement is obtained by the so-called laminating effect, which is due to the drying required by the gluing process, to an absence of cracks, and to the generally larger dimensions of laminated beams.

Solid wood is affected by unavoidable knots, knot areas, and skewed grain, all of which reduce tension and bending strengths. The formation of cracks after the application of loads further reduces resistance to longitudinal and transverse shear.

The improvement of laminated wood compared to its component boards increases with the number of layers and with their degree of knottiness. The lower moisture content also improves the strength and the E modulus of the wood product. Because of this, higher stresses are allowed for laminated wood of quality grades I and II than for comparable solid wood. This increase equals about 10% for bending stresses and 33% for longitudinal shear stresses on the order of 1.2 N/mm². The E modulus parallel to the grain can be taken as 11,000 N/mm² versus 10,000 N/mm² used for solid wood. Finally, transverse tensile stresses of 0.25 N/mm² are considered allowable in the curved regions of curved laminated beams.

Summary of the Most Important Mechanical Properties of European Lumber

Figure 43 shows the modulus of elasticity and the mechanical properties of lumber normally used for load-bearing members.

Because of wide variations in natural wood, higher and lower limits are given in Fig. 43 in addition to the most common values. This facilitates an evaluation of the scatter values of each property. The values are valid for a moisture content of 12%, which is attained under normal climatic conditions. It must be noted, however, that strength values have been obtained on sample material without defects; for construction lumber considerably lower values must be used for tension, bending, and shear stresses because of imperfections inherent in the natural growth of wood. In practice, if quality specifications are observed for each quality grade of wood, the allowable stresses under static loads should be 2.5 to 3.5 times smaller than the breaking strength of the wood.

Wood Products

Plywoods for Construction and Furniture

The strength and the elasticity of plywood depend greatly on its thickness, the number and the arrangement of plies, and on the properties of the wood itself. If cross-sectional properties are measured on the basis of plywood thickness, the values of the E modulus, the bending strength, and the tensile strength in the direction of surface grain are less than those for solid wood. These values are higher, however, for loads applied at an angle to the surface grain (Fig. 44) and for longitudinal and transverse shears normal to the panels.

The orthotropic character of plywood makes it possible to calculate deflection and stresses for anticipated loadings. A distinction must be made between bending normal to the panel plane, and bending within the panel plane parallel or normal to the direction of span and grain (Fig. 45). Finally, for longitudinal and normal shear a distinction must be made between stresses in the panel plane and those normal to it.

The relationship of stress to strain proceeds generally in a straight line, as in solid wood, so that within the range of allowable stresses we can count on the validity of Hooke's law.

Even for the same type of wood, the strength of plywood varies widely according to the type of fabrication.

Bending and axial strengths in plywood can be calculated on the basis of the strength of wood plies oriented in the same direction, if cross layers and glued joints are neglected. For construction plywood conforming to DIN 68705, part 3, this

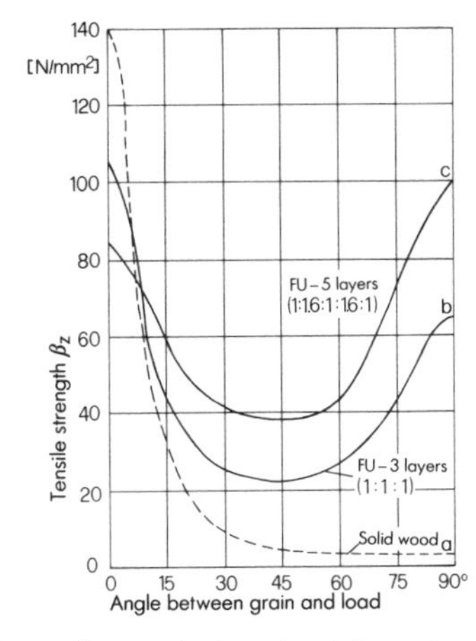

Fig. 44. Tensile strength of wood and plywood in relation to angle of load incidence.

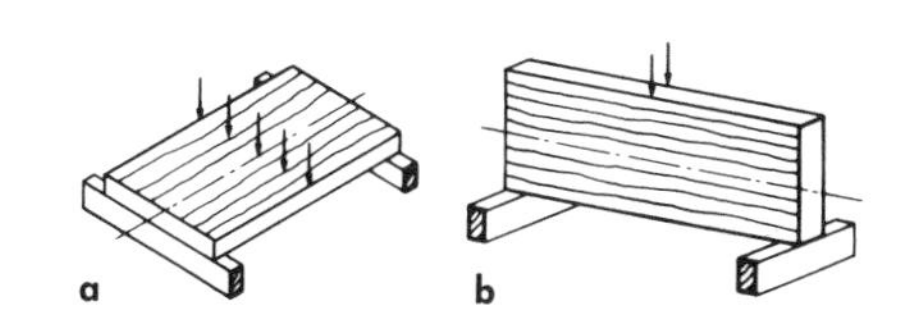

Fig. 45. Load arrangement for plywood subject to bending, grain parallel to span. (a) Normal to panel plane. (b) Within panel plane.

Fig. 46. Mechanical properties of solid sections of construction and furniture plywoods in N/mm² (moisture content ≤ 12%).

Type of Panel		Construction Plywood			Furniture Plywood
Number of Layers		3	5	≧ 7	≧ 3
Panel Thickness, mm		≦ 8	> 8–15	> 15–29	13–45
Bending normal to panel plane					
Moduli	$E_{\parallel}$	7000–14000	6000–12000	5000–10000	3000–8500
	$E_{\perp}$	300– 1500	2000– 7000	2500– 7000	3500–6500
	G	≧ 600	≧ 600	≧ 600	–
Bending strength	$\beta_{B\parallel}$	65–130	58–110	50–75	20–55
	$\beta_{B\perp}$	7,5–19	25–70	30–60	30–45
Bending in panel plane					
Moduli	$E_{\parallel}$	5000–10000	4500–8500	4000–7000	
	$E_{\perp}$	2500– 5000	3000–5500	3500–6000	
	G	500– 1000	500–1000	500–1000	
Bending strength	$\beta_{B\parallel}$	≧ 27	≧ 27	≧ 27	
	$\beta_{B\perp}$	≧ 18	≧ 18	≧ 18	
Compressive strength in panel plane	$\beta_{D\parallel}$	25–50	22,5–45	20–40	
	$\beta_{D\perp}$	10–25	14–30	17–35	
Tensile strength in panel plane	$\beta_{Z\parallel}$	45–80	40–75	35–70	
	$\beta_{Z\perp}$	20–45	25–53	30–60	
Shear strength					
In panel plane	$\tau_{\parallel}$	3– 5	3– 5	3– 5	
Normal to panel plane	$\tau_{\perp}$	10–18	10–18	10–18	

closely corresponds to actual conditions. Since the buildup of plies and the types of wood to be used in plywood are not established by code, minimum allowable stresses have been established on the basis of thickness. The stresses are equal to 40 N/mm² for longitudinal and transverse bending, and 15 N/mm² for bending normal to the panel plane. The most important mechanical and elastic properties are shown in Fig. 46.

The allowable stresses for each loading type have a factor of safety of 3 compared with the lower limits of ultimate stresses. Further testing may change these values, some of which are quite low (transverse shear, for example). However, if testing is performed according to the applicable standards, higher deformation moduli and higher allowable stresses can be used in design, provided they are approved by the appropriate authorities. This applies to panel construction, plywood thickness, and type of wood.

Plywood is also subject to plastic deformation under loads of long duration. These deformations can cause substantial deflections in the course of time. The allowable stresses under loads of long duration must be assumed to produce deflections equal to two or three times those of the initial deflections. This is equivalent to reducing the E modulus to values varying between 0.5 and 0.3 times its original value. The difference between long-range and short-range bending strengths of some construction plywoods is shown in Fig. 47.

The long-range strength of plywood can be assumed to be 50 to 60% of its ultimate strength, the same as for solid wood. Generally when allowable stresses are established, this reduction is further influenced by appropriate safety factors. If the wood has a moisture content over 18%, the E and G moduli and the allowable stresses are reduced by 1/6 of their original values.

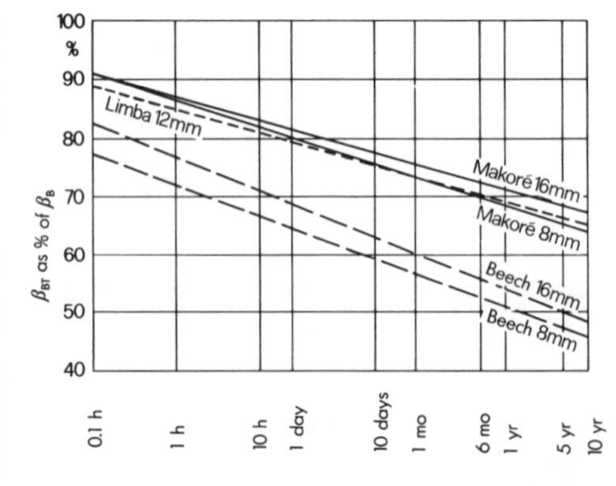

Fig. 47. Relationship between long-range bending strength β_{BT} and short-range static bending strength β_B for plywood.

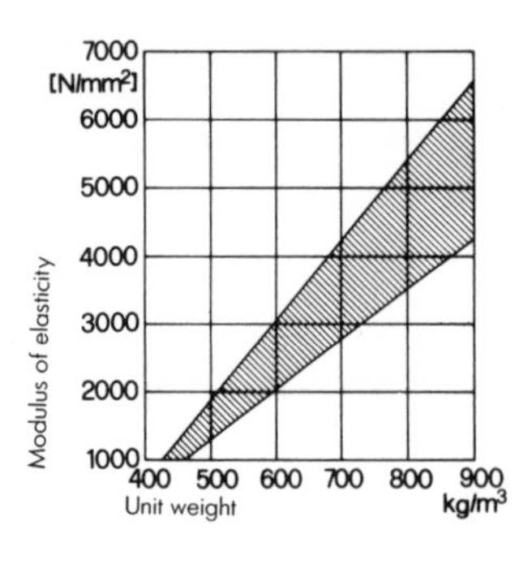

Fig. 48. Modulus of elasticity E of single-layer wood-chip boards in relation to unit weight (according to Kollmann).

Wood-Chip Boards (Flat-Pressed Panels)

Wood-chip boards used as individual building elements (such as for roof decking or flooring) are generally loaded normal to the panel plane. If they are used as flat elements in panel construction, they are subject to tensile and compressive stresses; if used as webs in girders, they are stressed in bending and shear within the panel plane. Deformation and strength in flat-pressed panels depend mostly on unit weight and panel thickness (Fig. 48). Multilayered panels which have denser surface layers can achieve higher strengths than single-layer panels. For example, three-layered panels have a higher E modulus than single-layered panels for loads normal to the panel plane.

Flat-pressed panels conforming to DIN 68763 and having thicknesses of 6 to 50 mm are subject to a reduction in their modulus of elasticity and bending strength for loads normal to the panel plane with increasing panel thickness. Even within each thickness range the deformation and strength values differ for different types of loading because of the layered structure and the anisotropic character of the wood chips. The mechanical and elastic values of flat-pressed panels, as established by current standards and special testing in recent years, are shown in Fig. 49.

The lower limits shown in bold type indicate the minimum strengths of each thickness range. The allowable strengths have been established on the basis of a factor of safety of 4. Long-range loads may cause significant deflections in flat-pressed panels because of creep. Tests in a room open on all sides show that within a year deflections increase to 1.65 to 4.25 times the initial deflection (Fig. 50). This indicates a need to consider a reduction both in the E modulus and in the allowable bending stresses for long-range loads.

Wood-Particle Boards

Wood-particle boards for construction are available according to DIN 68754, part 1, either as hard boards (HFH) with a unit weight in excess of 800 kg/m³ or as medium-hard boards (HFM) with a unit weight of between 350 and 800 kg/m³. Porous insulating and acoustic boards having unit weights of between 200 and 350 kg/m³ should not be used for load-bearing purposes.

Like the chipboards, particle boards have nearly equal deformation and strength characteristics in

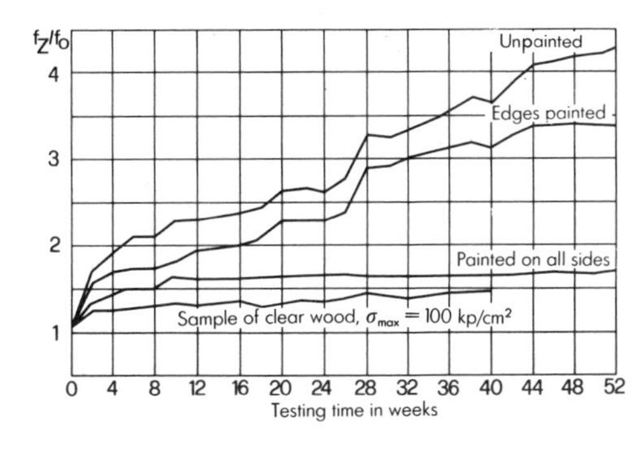

Fig. 50. Diagram of deflection ratios f_Z/f_0 for 25-mm thick chipboards with phenolic glues at 7-day loading cycles under stresses of $\sigma_{B\,allow}$ and $\sigma_{B\,allow}/2$.

Fig. 49. Mechanical properties in N/mm² of flat-pressed wood-chip boards conforming to DIN 68763 (moisture content ≤ 12%).

Thickness, mm	6–13	> 13–20	> 20–25	> 25–32	> 32–40	> 40–50
Bending normal to panel plane						
Moduli E	**3200**–4500	**2800**–4000	**2400**–3500	**2000**–3000	**1600**–2500	**1200**–2000
G	150– 250	150– 250	150– 250	100– 200	100– 200	100– 200
Bend. strength β_B	**20**– 28	**18**– 25	**15**– 22	**12**– 18	**10**– 16	**8**– 13
Bending in panel plane						
Moduli E	2200–3200	1900–2800	1600–2400	1300–2000	1000–1600	800–1200
G	1100–1200	1000–1200	850–1200	700–1000	550–1000	450–1000
Bend. strength β_B	13– 18	12– 15	10– 12	8– 10	6,5– 8,5	5– 7
Compressive strength in panel plane β_D	12–16	11–15	10–14	9–13	8–12	7–11
Tensile strength in panel plane β_Z	10–14	9–12,5	8–11	7–10	6–9	5–8
Shear strength						
In panel plane $\tau_{\parallel}$	1,5–2,0	1,5–2,0	1,5–2,0	1,0–2,0	1,0–2,0	1,0–2,0
Normal to panel plane $\tau_{\perp}$	7,5–11	7,5–11	7,5–11	5,0–8,5	5,0–8,5	5,0–8,5

Bold values are minimum values according to DIN 68763.

Fig. 51. Mechanical properties in N/mm² of wood-particle boards conforming to DIN 68754 (moisture content ≤ 12%).

Panel Type		Hard Boards (HFH)		Medium Hard Boards (HFM)
Thickness, mm		≤4	>4	6–16
Bending normal to panel plane				
Moduli	E	4000–7000	3500–6000	1500–4500
	G	≥200	≥200	≥100
Bending strength	β_B	**40**–60	**35**–50	**12**–22
Bending in panel plane				
Moduli	E	2500–6500	2000–5000	1000–2500
	G	≥1250	≥1000	≥500
Bending strength	β_B	≥28	≥20	≥10
Compressive strength	β_D	20–40	18–35	≈10
Tensile strength	β_Z	25–50	20–40	10–15
Shear strength in panel plane	$\tau_{\parallel}$	3–6	3–6	1,5–2,0
Normal to panel plane	$\tau_{\perp}$	≥20	≥20	≥4

Bold values are minimum values according to DIN 68754.

all directions of the panel plane. The most important properties are shown in Fig. 51. Few well-established values for long-term mechanical and elastic properties of particle boards are available, especially for medium-hard panels. It is therefore required that lower limit values be used for allowable deformations, and that a factor of safety of 5 be applied to the lower values of stresses determined experimentally for loads of short duration.

Hardness and Wear Resistance

The surface hardness of solid wood and wood products plays an important role in numerous applications. It not only gives an indication of the strength of the material, in particular its compressive strength, but also of its workability and its abrasive properties. In the case of floors, it is necessary for the material not to allow visible impression marks and that it have sufficiently high wear resistance.

Hardness is the resistance to penetration of a harder material. Naturally, the shape of the harder material is decisive. The Brinell procedure of applying pressure to metals by means of a ball also seems to be best suited for wood. Brinell hardness is the stress computed by dividing the load by the surface of the impression. Depending on the expected hardness, the load applied to a ball of 10 mm diameter may be 1000 N or it may vary from 100 to 500 N. The hardness of solid wood depends on its unit weight and moisture content. The hardness longitudinally along the grain is about twice that normal to the grain.

According to Kollmann, the Brinell hardness of wood at 12% moisture content is as follows:

	$H_{\parallel}$	$H_{\perp}$		$H_{\parallel}$	$H_{\perp}$
Spruce	32	12	Oak	66	34
Pine	40	19	Beech	72	34
Larch	53	19			

The higher normal-to-grain hardness of hardwoods makes them more suitable than soft woods to sustain direct concentrated loads such as floor loads. The hardness of wood products varies between 20 and 120 N/mm², depending on thickness and fabrication processes. For certain applications, hardness may be one of the criteria in the choice of a wood product panel.

It is difficult to express wear resistance in numerical terms. In many instances, such as for floors or parts of machines, resistance to wear represents a significant mechanical property. A satisfactory testing process could never be established because of the variables of loading, humidity, and temperature. Since the results depend on the method of testing, it is best to rely on comparative testing and practical observations. We can say, however, that wear resistance increases with the unit weight and surface hardness of the material.

PROTECTIVE TREATMENTS

Protective treatments are intended to protect the quality of the wood for an extended length of time. Although it is well known that wood is susceptible to decay, many wood structures which are hundreds of years old testify to the durability of the wood, including those parts that were never specially protected. This can be explained by the fact that wood whose moisture content is permanently below 20% or wood that is permanently immersed in water does not get attacked by rot.

The resistance and durability of structural wood members can be jeopardized by new methods of construction and by the ever-expanding new uses of wood. Special construction methods and chemical treatments of wood for the purpose of protection may then become indispensable.

Meaningful measures of protecting wood are responsible for the wider general use of wood as a construction material and also for newly developed or rediscovered methods of construction (which are described later in this book). In fact, many structurally and aesthetically excellent buildings testify to correct applications of this material. The standards for the protection of wood in buildings, DIN 68800, parts 1 to 5, give ample information on the type, extent, and execution of measures for protecting wood. These rules and regulations must be observed in all instances.

Design of Protective Measures

Structural and chemical protective measures must be carefully planned in advance if long-range protection is to be achieved. Above all, wood and wood products must be protected from fungi and insects through appropriate actions. But even measures needed to solve a particular case must be undertaken within the general context of various structural requirements and protective needs. Planning has to include not only the actual protective measures, but also the timing of their application during the progress of construction. The following individual points have to be considered:

- Type and degree of risk, such as humidity or fire
- Choice of wood according to scope of work, including appropriate storage and preparation, removal of bark and bast (inner bark), and drying of fresh wood
- Type and condition of preparatory handling, such as initial protective treatments or painting
- Possible side effects of applications of chemicals, such as health hazards and incompatibility with lime, glues, or paints
- Timing of protective treatments within construction schedules, uninterrupted flow of work, timely finishing and handling of drying cracks
- Location of protective treatments, such as treatment plant, finishing yard, covered construction site
- Opportunity for later protection through access to all built-in members
- Demands on the workers, their sufficient experience in working with wood, potential exposure of wood to various hazards, and necessary means and procedures for protective applications
- Checking of required protective measures

Protection against Weathering

Wood exposed to weather is affected by the simultaneous impact of moisture and physical, mechanical, and biological influences. They vary, depending on the environment and the orientation of the structure. The type and extent of protection measures depend on the type of wood and the kind of surface treatment. Protection against weathering begins with the choice of wood or wood product. It extends to structural details which provide a positive shedding of water or ventilation in locations of higher humidity and ends with appropriate surface treatments.

Preventive Construction Details

Preventive construction details (which are often neglected) aim at reducing the influence of moisture on wood and wood products. Even when wood is chemically treated, the basic rules of correct detailing must be observed. Moisture can be present as a by-product of the construction process. For example, a considerable amount of water from concrete, masonry, or plaster is released in a new building under construction. The water can also be introduced later, either directly:

- From precipitation
- As a result of use, such as spray or plumbing damage
- From adjacent wet materials through capillary action

or indirectly through the condensation of vapor on outer surfaces or on the inside of buildings.

Large changes in moisture cause swelling, shrinkage, and cracking. They affect the mechanical properties of wood, its surface protection, and the appearance of the wood surfaces. For sustained periods of higher moisture (20% is the limit of danger), favorable conditions for growth of destructive fungi develop.

Since most destructive insects prefer wood attacked by fungi, the neglect of appropriate construction details may bring additional damages. A preventive construction detail against insects is the installation of screens in attics and other places. Rarely used basements should be well ventilated and secured against the penetration of insects, at least during the insects' flying period from June to August.

The following points should be especially considered in protecting wood from moisture.

Transportation and Storage

The moisture content of wood or wood products should not basically change during their transportation and storage. Storage in the open should not be allowed because of the damaging effects of ground humidity, rainfall, and rapid drying through usual stacking and covering. On the other hand, wood that is packaged in plastics without admission of air for as long as 8 to 12 days becomes endangered by mildew and bacteria. Today, special surface treatments are being proposed and tried mainly to protect wood during transportation and construction.

Erection of Structural Members

Whenever possible, structural members of wood, laminated wood, and wood products should be built into the structure with the moisture content that is to be expected to prevail during use (see DIN 1052, "Timber Construction"). Structural components of buildings enclosed on all sides, with or without heating, should have a moisture content of 12 to 15%, and both during and after erection they should be protected from the rain. Even with that precaution, extended periods of excessive humidity have to be avoided inside newly constructed buildings because the buildings release moisture during construction. The VOB regulations, part C, section on carpentry, determine that timber in buildings has to be dry when erected. However, lumber, beams, strips, and round timbers may be used in construction even if they are at least half-dry.

If in spite of all precautionary measures the moisture content of individual pieces of wood is substantially increased during transportation or storage, or if the wood is used in a half-dry condition, it becomes necessary to remove excess moisture promptly, regardless of how this affects the progress of the remainder of the construction. This can be achieved most easily by providing sufficient ventilation and by preventing exposure to additional moisture. The moisture content can be checked by electrical metering or by oven-dry testing.

Outdoor Applications of Wood

As a rule, wood should be protected from rain. If this is not possible, water should be drained away quickly. If neither is possible for reasons of layout or design, chemical treatments become necessary. The moisture content can be minimized in exposed timber by using the following methods:
• Provide sufficiently large eaves
• Recess construction behind the facade
• Provide unobstructed roof drainage
• Avoid splash by starting wood construction at least 30 cm above the ground (see Fig. 63)

Parts exposed to rain, including their connections, should be built in such a way that runoff is drained without reaching adjacent structural elements. In particular, the following protection requirements should be observed for exposed building elements:
• Choose the correct shapes for the structure and its sheathing.
• Arrange down spouts, gutters, etc., appropriately.
• Avoid covering corners, depressions, and joints which accumulate water or snow and absorb water.
• Ensure rapid drying of wet wood.

In addition, the following precautions should be taken:
• All connective material should be noncorrosive or galvanized, even for enclosed buildings.
• Horizontal or sloped timber surfaces must be covered.
• End grain surfaces must always be sealed.
• Joints in timber or wood-product materials should be designed to allow free movement without undesirable consequences.

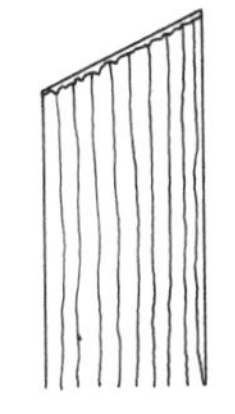

The end grain surfaces of simpler wood members, such as posts, porch supports, and garden furniture, should be protected by a primer and several layers of paint. Horizontal end grain surfaces that could absorb water should be avoided. Railings, preferably made from oak or larch heartwood, should have drip grooves to shed water.

Exposed end grain surfaces should be protected with a sealer.

A free-standing cantilevered laminated beam should have a copper roofing in order to prevent water from seeping into shrinkage cracks. The beam end should be covered with a board or a piece of weatherproof plywood, either screwed on directly or allowing for a breathing space. The lower end of the end board should protrude below the bottom of the beam to serve as a drip.

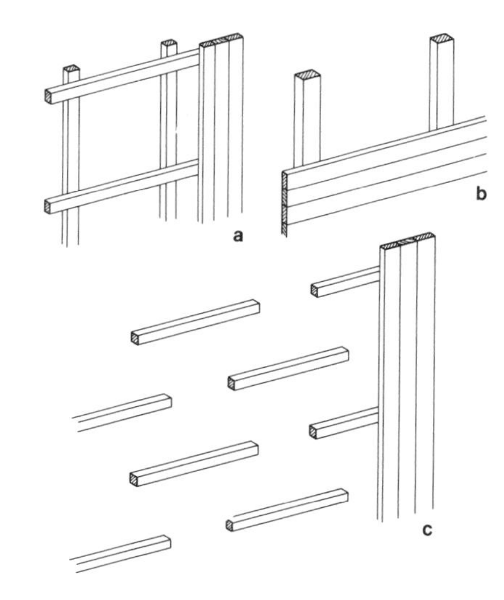

Fig. 52. Sheathing. (a) Vertical sheathing with wood nailers. (b) Horizontal boards. (c) Vertical boards with offset nailers.

Exterior wood sheathing should always be fully ventilated, because even perfect construction allows penetration of moisture during storms. The openings for the circulation of air should have a cross section equal to at least 1/500 of the surface to be ventilated. Upward ventilation due to the heating of air on the inside of exterior siding must always be available. Vertical siding also allows for horizontal ventilation by wind pressure or suction, because the layout of nailers is horizontal. The wood under the siding must have an appropriate protective treatment.

• Vertical siding allows quicker removal of water and is, therefore, preferred for untreated facades without eaves.
• For horizontal (clapboard) siding of plain planed

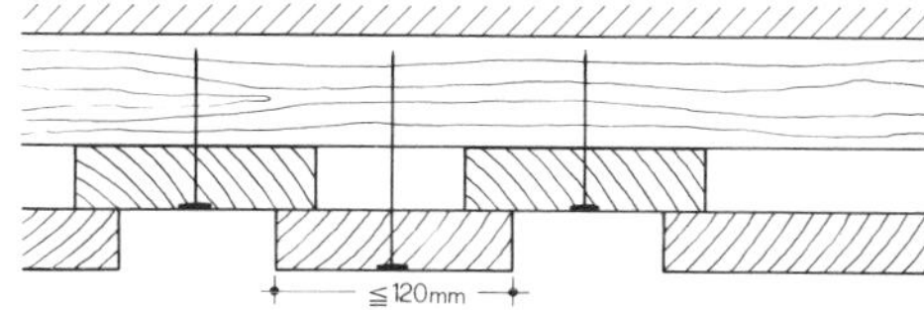

Fig. 53. Single boards, planed or unfinished. Fastenings should not hinder free movement of boards.

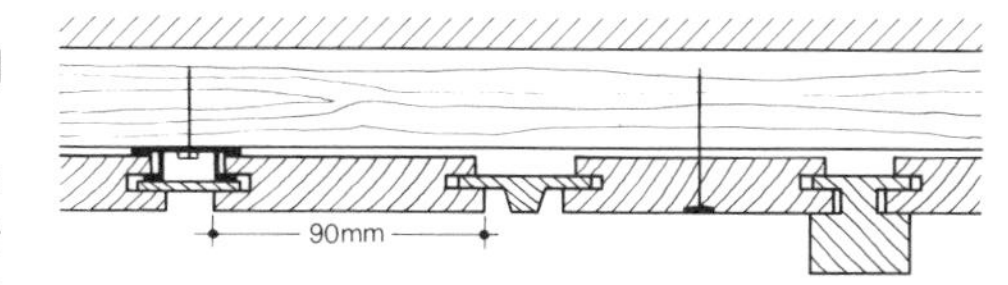

Fig. 54. Acoustic boards conforming to DIN 68127 and having simple tongue and groove or profiled strips. Fastenings: visible, if screwed or nailed; covered, if anchored with special clips. Other possibilities: planed tongue and groove decking, siding with a shadow groove (see page 20).

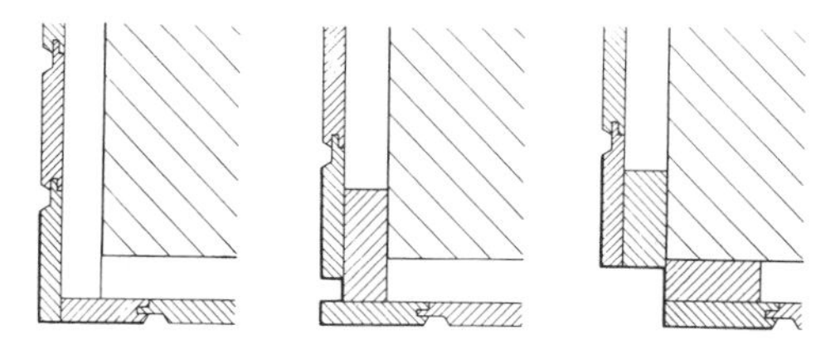

Fig. 55. Corner details for vertical siding.

boards the overlap must be equal to at least 12% of the board width, but not less than 10 mm.

Other possibilities include clapboards and tongue and groove or profiled boards with shadow grooves (see page 20). The latter should be used only in protected conditions because the joint has no drip.

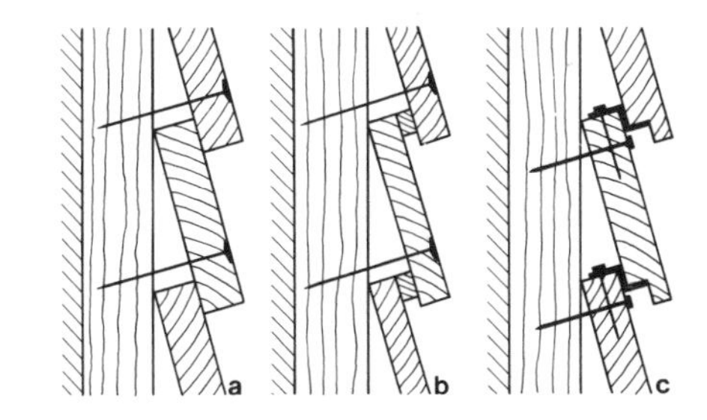

Fig. 56. Clapboards. Details (b) and (c) are preferable to (a) because they result in better shedding of stormwater and should be used for exposed facades. Fastenings in (a) and (b) are visible, in (c) they are covered.

Splices in horizontal siding should not be plain butt joints. Notched but free-moving joints which allow inspection and maintenance of the end grain work well.

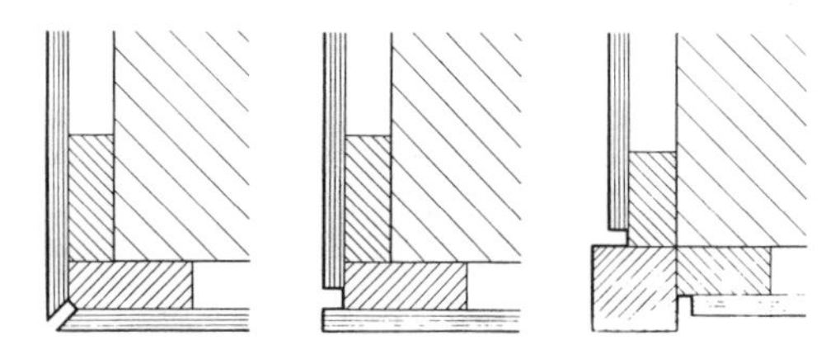

Fig. 57. Corner details for horizontal wood siding.

When wood products are used as exterior siding, a tolerance of 3 mm per meter is necessary in vertical joints. Corner protection is especially important for construction details (a) and (d) in Fig. 58.

Fig. 58. Types of vertical joints. (a) Recessed splint (plywood, for example). (b) Neoprene extrusion (pressed fit). (c) Special profile, metal or plastic. (d) Joint with permanently elastic sealant.

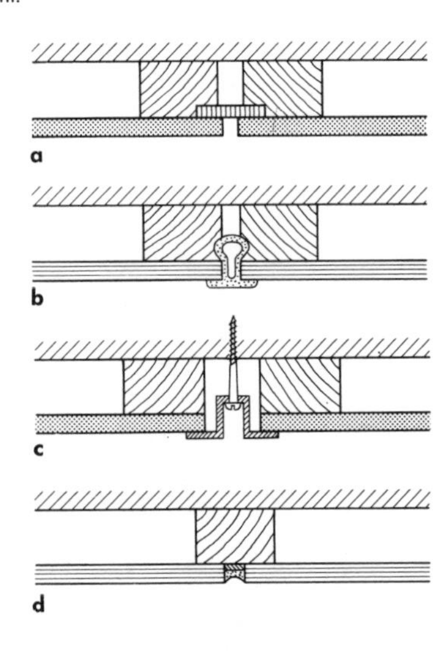

Humid and Wet Environments

Humid environments, such as kitchens and bathrooms, and wet environments, in which surfaces are in direct contact with water, such as baths, showers, or stables, must have ample ventilation so that the average relative humidity is minimized.

Timber framing and sheathing is feasible even in humid and wet environments provided there is appropriate execution of work and additional protection through painting. Timber that cannot be reached for servicing should be treated. Substructures for timber paneling in wet rooms should be pressure-treated or saturation methods may be used.

Timber in structures subjected to extreme humidity require special chemical protection against dry rot. Such impregnated frames can achieve a minimum durability of 20 years even with continuous wetting.

Timber paneling in wet rooms requires that only wood of excellent durability (spruce, larch, or oak) or wood products of class 100G be used. Peripheral edges of wood product panels should be spe-

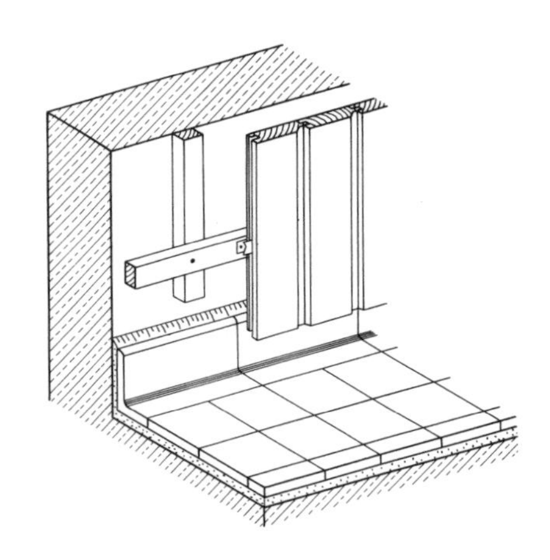

cially protected. Paneling which may allow the passage of humidity must be well ventilated. Surface treatments must be adequate for customary usage; protective coatings that subsequently can be reapplied regularly are appropriate. The rear side of paneling must be chemically impregnated before installation.

Crawl spaces between the ground and the structure must be well ventilated. The ground should be covered with an impermeable layer, such as a polyethylene vapor barrier, to prevent a rise in humidity. The cross section of the vents has to equal at least 1/500 of the surface to be ventilated; larger

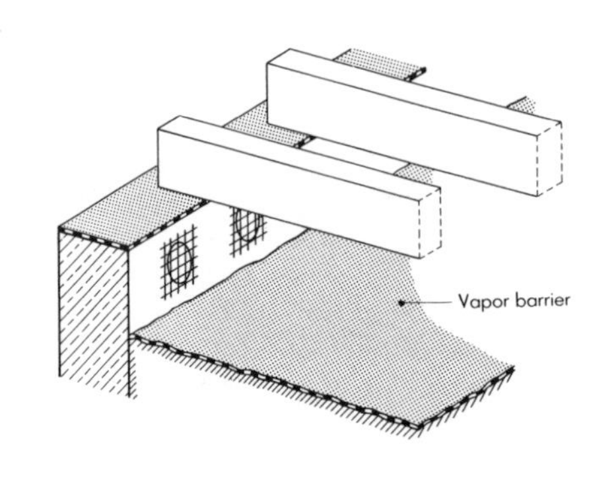

vents are preferable. Beams should be protected chemically.

Transfer of Humidity from Adjacent Materials

The penetration of humidity into the wood from adjacent structural members or materials must be prevented by appropriate jointless membranes. They should be provided:

• Under the bearing of beams, thresholds, and posts in masonry or concrete
• Between a floor slab and flooring of timber or wood products

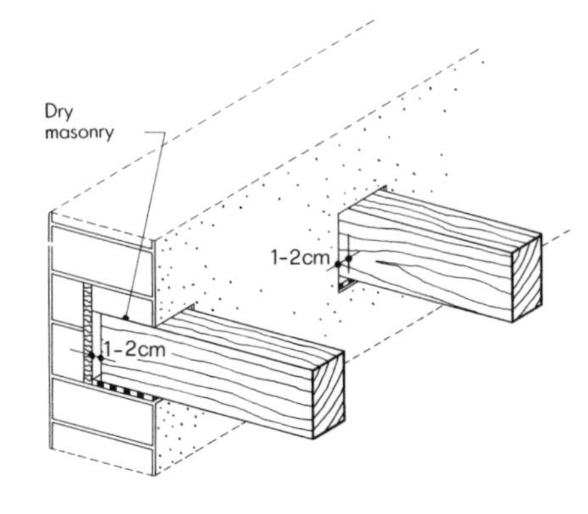

Fig. 59. Anchorage of beams into masonry. Below beams there is a moisture barrier; on the sides and in the rear, 1 to 2 cm of air space; insulation on the outside, and dry masonry above. Beam ends are to be chemically treated according to special procedures.

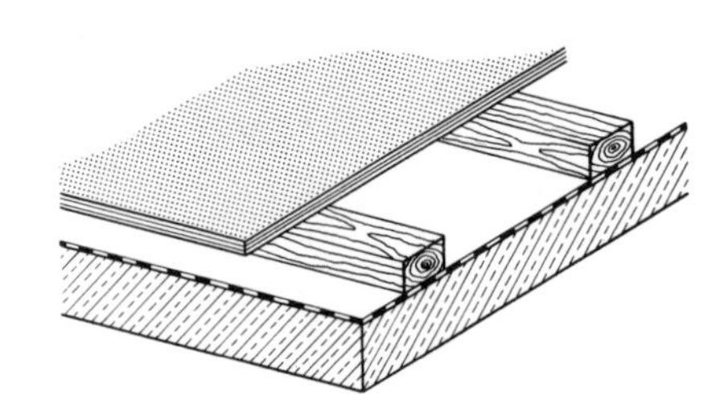

Fig. 60. Flooring of timber or other wood materials. Sleepers are protected by chemical means; moisture barrier between slab and timber deck.

Bearing members made of wood must be protected against humidity rising from the ground. When timber is embedded in masonry on all sides, an allowance must be made for free air circulation around the timber.

Condensation Buildup

In outer walls, as in walls that divide rooms having different climates, the types of structures and finishes should be chosen in such a way that there is no damage from condensation that forms inside the building. The dew point and the quantity of condensation to be expected from the given climatic conditions should be estimated.

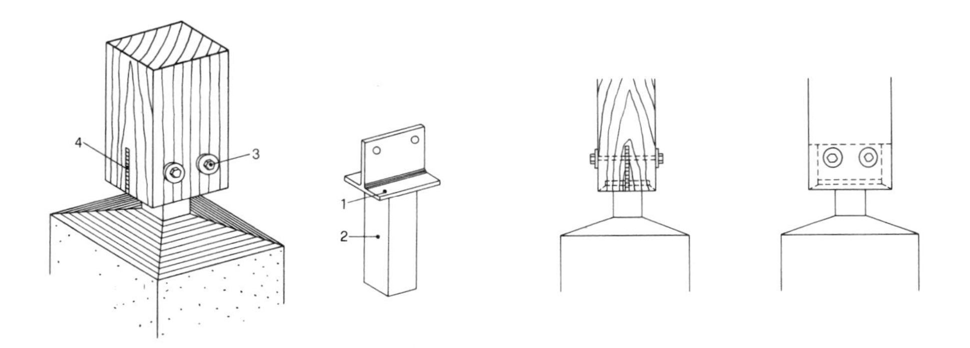

Fig. 61. Post base on concrete. 1—welded steel section, T or 1/2 I profile, fastened into post end; 2—square tube; 3—bolts; 4—slit either sealed with elastic sealant or not cut to outside face.

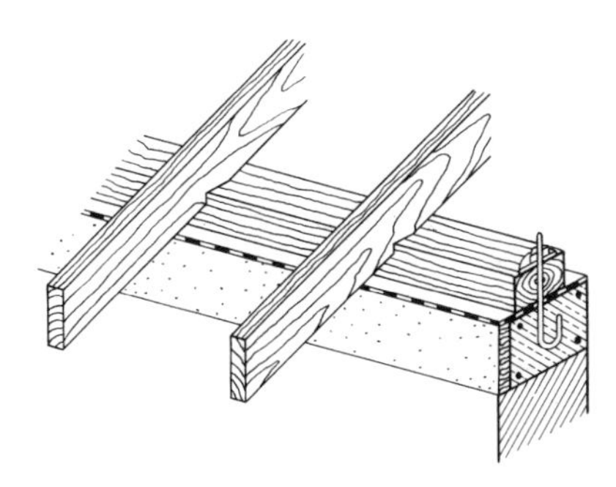

Fig. 62. Wood sills on masonry or concrete. Anchored against uplift, resting on moisture barrier; continuous, sealed with bitumen at penetrations.

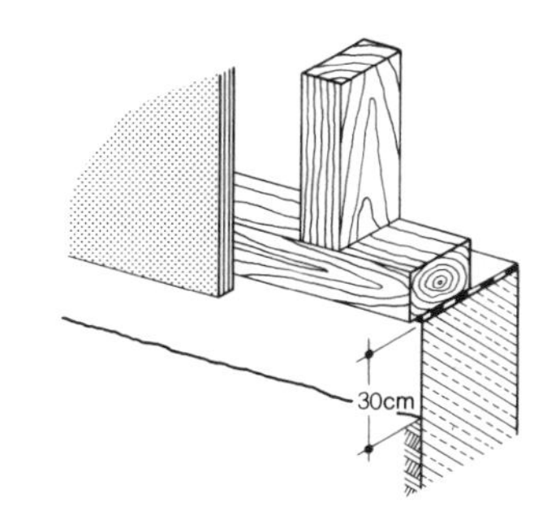

Fig. 63. Timber wall on low masonry. Sill overhanging, at least 30 cm above ground, resting on moisture barrier to avoid splash. Outer sheathing (timber siding, wood-product panels, asbestos-cement tiles, metal siding, etc.) forms a drip.

Buildings endangered by interior condensation may be improved by:

• Introducing a vapor barrier close to the inside of the building.

• Creating a vented interstice. A generally impermeable outer barrier (tar paper, plastic sheet, sheet metal) should be thoroughly vented from behind.

The surface temperature on the inside of the insulation can drop below the dew point of the adjoining air. Additional insulation should be provided at such locations to prevent condensation (see Fig. 59).

Application of Wood Products

Plywood, wood-chip boards, and wood-particle boards can be fabricated with glues having different resistance against humidity. The glues of various types of panels are identified by three classes of wood products: 20, 100, and 100G.

The numbers refer to the temperatures (20°C or 100°C) that correspond to the moisture content at which the testing of the glue strength is performed. Identification G refers to the application of an approved wood treatment against fungi that is added to the glue. (Standard panel types are described in the section Wood Products; see page 22.)

Application of the various kinds of wood products depends on the degree of humidity expected in use and the potential exposure to damages by fungi. The applications listed below refer to load-bearing panels. Revetments made from wood products and having no load-bearing or stiffening roles should be used as recommended by experts in these materials.

WOOD-PRODUCT MATERIALS, GRADE 20

Wood products of this grade may be used only at locations where there is no direct or indirect wetting of panels. An occasional increase in moisture content up to a maximum of 15% of weight is allowable. Reduction of absorbed moisture must be uninhibited. Conditions for an occasional increase in moisture content exist in rooms with generally poor ventilation, such as living rooms, bedrooms, kitchens, bathrooms, and toilets. When exterior sheathing, especially that of vented elements, consists of panels of grade 20, it must be protected from precipitation during construction. Otherwise, grade 100 has to be used.

WOOD-PRODUCT MATERIALS, GRADE 100

Wood products of this type are more resistant to humidity. They permit a temporary increase in moisture content up to 18% of weight if the additional moisture can be dried out again. Examples of such building elements are:

• Outer wall sheathing if there is an amply vented space between sheathing and siding

• Upper planking of an unventilated deck over a crawl space

WOOD-PRODUCT MATERIALS, GRADE 100G

Wood products of this grade are protected against destructive fungi by a protective chemical added during fabrication. The quality and quantity of protective chemicals are prescribed. Grade 100G wood products are specified when panels are to be subjected to high humidity for an extended period of time and the penetrated moisture will not be able to escape rapidly. Despite its better resist-

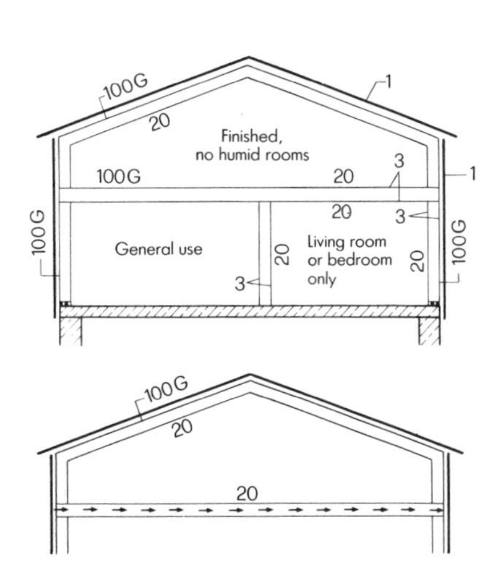

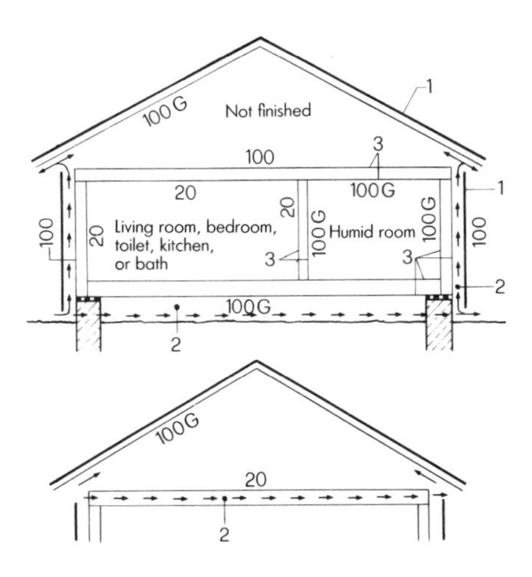

Fig. 64. Examples of the use of wood products for lining framed and panel type timber structures, roofs, and exterior walls. 20, 100, 100G—grades of wood products; 1—roofing that does not allow penetration of water; 2—ventilated dead space; 3—wood product finishes.

ance to humidity, all requirements for wood protection are applicable to wood products of grade 100G, in particular those intended to reduce the buildup of condensation. This is necessary if mechanical and elastic properties are to be preserved and creep deflections avoided.

Conditions requiring the use of grade 100G include:

• Ventilated dead spaces above ground (see Fig. 64)
• Outer sheathing in walls that are unventilated or insufficiently ventilated (and no additional permanent weathering protection is provided)
• Flooring of unventilated decks and in finished attic rooms. (exception: floors above living rooms and bedrooms)
• Walls or floors of wet rooms or in new buildings that are humid due to construction
• Roof decking or roof tiles

These are minimum rules to be applied when the use of rooms is known. When buildings are threatened by moisture, the amount of condensation buildup must be calculated.

Sufficient ventilation of floors and walls requires vents equal in area to at least 1/500 of the surface to be vented. It is recommended that the openings be increased by up to 50%. Wood products are not allowed in insufficiently ventilated crawl spaces. Exposed wood-product panels must be protected by a waterproof outer envelope. The latter can be:

• Usual roof coverings which are also applied to larger buildings
• Overlapping shingles
• Stucco on an appropriate stucco support system
• Sheathing of asbestos cement
• Water- or vaporproof protective coatings applied to appropriate wall construction

Underflooring made from wood products, in both timber and other types of structures, should be of grade 100. Grade 20 wood products should be used only if the contractor fully guarantees that because of appropriate construction methods, there will be no penetration of moisture during later use, even from such sources as cleaning water. In special cases, panels of grade 100G may become necessary, depending on the degree of humidity.

Decorative and Preservative Coatings

In addition to chemical treatments of wood, which will be described later, there are coatings that serve architectural purposes by limiting aesthetically undesirable effects of weathering while at the same time enhancing the natural durability of wood. Although such surface coatings often contain an antifungal additive, they are not included in the chemical treatments described in DIN 68800.

Weathering of Wood and Its Coatings

Wood exposed to weathering without any coatings becomes gray within a short time due to mildew. This color change in the thin surface layer generally does not depend on the type of wood; it affects equally the weather-resistant and durable woods and the less resistant ones. The heartwood of larch, the most weather-resistant conifer, loses its reddish color within a few months, becoming silver gray. While such a gray color may be desirable, it is most often found disturbing and can be prevented by the application of various coatings. The strength of wood is not affected by graying. Since certain molds are able to attack even thin coatings mechanically, it is best to add to coatings an antifungal agent.

Intensive exposure to the sun's rays influences timber surfaces in two ways:

• Wood is destroyed to a minor degree by ultraviolet rays and the surface is bleached in a weathering process.
• Heating and related drying causes deformations. The adherence of coatings is therefore subject to larger stresses.

Protection of Wood by Painting

The most important function of paint is to protect wood from moisture. Here the porosity of paints is of great importance. Two limiting conditions affect the various degrees of paint protection:

• Paints having little waterproofing capability let the moisture in the wood evaporate slowly. Exterior building elements, particularly windows, absorb water through end grain surfaces and joints, where sooner or later the paint begins to deteriorate. Moisture which is retained in the wood for a long time may cause the development of rot.
• Paints having considerable waterproofing capability may affect the performance of wood by their excessive thickness (jamming of windows, opening of connections, distortion of boards).

Taking all factors into account, the recommended choice is a surface treatment that has sufficient porosity. It is assumed, however, that the chosen paint system will correspond to the degree of exposure of the wood and that there will be no additional exposure to moisture because of local failures of the paint.

The danger of moisture retained within the wood is critical in most cases. Because of this, paints with greater porosity should be recommended in order to secure better protection against rot.

Special requirements are set for painting woodchip boards exposed to weather. The paint must be nearly impermeable, highly water-repellent, and sufficiently elastic so that the swelling of the surface chips will not destroy the painted surface. Few paints meet all these criteria.

Wood surfaces that have a beautiful natural color and texture may present an attractive finish. The use of clear coatings, however, will cause faster deterioration of the wood than opaque coatings because of the passage of ultraviolet rays. A more durable protection against light can be achieved only through the homogeneous distribution of pigment in paints. Transparent lacquers permit a photochemical reaction on the wood's surface, causing the lacquer to pull off at certain points and eventually to peel off.

On the other hand, dark or black paints expose the wood to a high degree of heat through radiation. Good ventilation is therefore necessary. Interior wood surfaces, clear or tinted, generally do not require any penetrating treatment. There are a great variety of other types of surface treatments available.

Appropriate Coatings

The choice of coatings, in addition to economic considerations and the degree of protection needed, depends on the following criteria:

• Workability and demands on the workers
• Compatibility with other materials, such as joint materials and glues
• Susceptibility to damage and quality control
• Time interval between recoatings and cost of recoating; important criteria, always to be considered together in order to obtain a true picture of the maintenance effort
• Durability of the entire coating system on wood or wood products

Figure 65, prepared by the Institute for Window Technology, offers a practical reference for the choice of coatings.

VARNISHES (ADDITIONAL TERMS: WOOD PROTECTIVE VARNISHES, IMPREGNATING COATINGS, LACQUERS)

Varnishes are transparent. Depending on the amount of color, they allow the character of the wood and its natural color to appear unhindered.

These coatings are obtained from artificial resins with pigments added. Depending on the amount of solids, the coatings may be thin and more penetrating, or they may be thick and produce a heavier coating. The former are known as sealants, but they provide only limited protection against penetration of water; the latter are known as lacquers.

• Properties

1. High porosity and therefore no danger of moisture formation under the coating, but more severe deformation of building members.
2. Heavier pigmenting and darker colors increase the durability of coatings because of better protection against ultraviolet rays. (From this point of view clear coatings are undesirable.)
3. Coatings are more or less durable.
4. Coatings remain elastic but are not recommended for heavily used surfaces, such as banisters.

• Workmanship. Simple manual application on all types of wood that may be considered for exterior work. The owner's specifications for workmanship require among other things the application of an antibleaching coating for wood subject to discoloration. Generally the coatings are applied by brush. Immersion or spraying are also possible, but it is recommended that the finishing be done by brush. Two or three coats are necessary. In order to prevent spotting, it is recommended that the first coat be a clear varnish.

Wood should not contain more than 15% moisture because retained moisture evaporates slowly, even through a porous coating, and thus there is danger of the wood being attacked by destructive molds. Fine hairline cracks in finished surfaces are due to the type of coating. They develop through the deterioration of wood surfaces caused by ultraviolet rays. Successive coatings, which become necessary after 1 to 3 years, may be applied over the old coating after loose layers have been removed. Varnishes are very suitable for exposed locations and solid wood.

Large dimensional changes in windows caused by changing moisture contents must be compensated for by appropriate structural details, such as expansion joints.

Fig. 65. Coatings for wood in exterior use.[1]

Exposure		Color	Critical Building Elements						Noncritical Building Elements					
			Transparent Coatings			Opaque Coatings			Transparent Coatings			Opaque Coatings		
			Type of Wood[2]						Type of Wood					
			I	II	III	I	II	III	I	II	III	I	II	III
Exterior environment DIN 50010 (indirect weathering)[3]	1	Without limitations[4]	A	A	B	E	E	F	J	J	K	N	N	O
Exposed environment I (direct weathering)[5]	2	Light				G	G	H				P	P	R
	3	Medium	Ⓒ	C	D	G	G	H	L	L	M	P	P	R
	4	Dark	Ⓒ	C	D	Ⓖ	G	H	L	L	M	P	P	R
Exposed environment II (severe direct weathering)[6]	5	Light				G	G	H				P	P	R
	6	Medium		Ⓒ	D	Ⓖ	G	H	Ⓛ	L	M	Ⓟ	P	R
	7	Dark		Ⓒ	D		G	H	Ⓛ	L	M	Ⓟ	P	R

[1] This table gives architects the opportunity to choose and specify the appropriate coatings corresponding to the type of wood and the degree of exposure. The suppliers are responsible for ordering coatings and protective treatment according to groups A to R, depending on the type of wood (I to III) and color (1 to 7). They have to certify that ample care will be taken and that the coatings comply with DIN 18355, "Technical Guidelines for Window Coatings" and DIN 18363, "Recommendations for Treatment of Windows." Groups indicated with a circle mean that there may be damage to surfaces and coatings because of resin pockets and cracking of wood or movement of connections.

[2] Types of wood: I—resin-rich conifers, such as pine, Oregon pine, pitch pine, larch; II—conifers lean in resin, such as spruce, redwood, red cedar; III—Hardwoods, such as sipo, dark red meranti, teak, afzelia, cedrela, oak.

[3] Building elements are protected against rain and direct sunlight, but otherwise exposed to the exterior environment. For example: windows facing covered balconies.

[4] Clear lacquers can be used in exterior environment.

[5] All normal environmental forces can act on building elements. Example: buildings up to three stories high.

[6] All normal environmental forces can act on building elements. Examples: buildings over three stories high or buildings up to three stories high in particularly exposed locations.

SUSPENSION PAINTS

Water-based suspensions, using an acrylic resin base, are presently being tested for the protection of wood from weathering.

• *Properties.* Suspension paints are thick, cover well, and are available in many colors. These paints are markedly porous, allowing free breathing of wood. Deterioration from exposure to light is prevented by opaque pigments. Finishes are either glossy or satin.

• *Workmanship.* The work should be done according to specifications and does not require any special skills. Suspension paints are mostly applied by brushing and they dry fast. Painted wood must be painted again when aging requires it.

OPAQUE ENAMELS

Today white or colored enamels with an alkyde resin base have replaced the earlier oil-based paints.

Opaque enamels provide protection by a dense surface film of at least 0.1-mm thickness when dry. Accelerated drying times reduce penetration of the paint into the wood, but may be less durable as a consequence.

• *Properties.* Opaque enamals have low to average porosity. Because of this, enameled parts are subject to only limited variations in moisture content; they exhibit good dimensional stability. The danger of moisture accumulation under the paint must be prevented by good construction methods. The so-called "ventilating" base coats have to be considered with care; such coatings should be used only on dry wood (10 to 12% moisture content).

White paints remain cooler under sunlight. The danger of cracking of wood, enamel, or joints caused by uneven heating under dark paints is often underestimated. Opaque enamels offer protection against the sunlight's ultraviolet rays.

• *Workmanship.* A professional application of opaque enamels requires good workmanship. Failures may occur by applying paint to fresh wood, neglecting appropriate preparation procedures, or applying too thin a coat of paint. In order to obtain proper workmanship, it is best to entrust the work to a professional painter. The manufacturer's instructions have to be followed carefully.

Rounding the edges with about a 2-mm radius will allow for a uniform thickness of the paint. On sharp edges the paint pulls back, or the brush makes a thinner coat.

Opaque paints are most durable. Repainting, however, requires better preparation than the varnishes. A repainting job requires the removal of old paint where it has been damaged by cracks and peeling, and the application of several new coats of paint. The entire surface should be repainted within 6 to 10 years. In the meantime, damaged areas should be repainted periodically in order to lengthen the period between total renovations. Opaque enamels are used more for windows than for siding. Paints with ample porosity have been used satisfactorily on windows.

A recommended coating for wood-chip boards consists of exterior nonporous polyurethane varnishes, or two-coat systems consisting of a base coat of DD-varnish and a coat of paint or plastic.

CLEAR COATINGS (ADDITIONAL TERMS: CLEAR VARNISHES, TRANSPARENT VARNISHES)

In spite of many tests with clear components intended to absorb ultraviolet radiation, transparent varnishes have to date proved unsuitable for wood exposed to rain and direct sunlight. Experience unmistakably shows that clear varnishes deteriorate within a few years by peeling, and spotty graying of wood appears. Since the restoration of such damage may require extensive work, the application of clear varnishes is not recommended.

Protection against Insects and Fungi

Chemical Protection—General Considerations

In addition to protective measures through appropriate detailing, critical building members of wood or wood products may be protected by appropriate chemical treatments. Such treatments are in most cases also specified for non-load-bearing members. Chemical protection has to correspond to the degree of the wood's exposure. Its success and durability depend on the type of treatment, the quality of the chemicals applied, and their distribution within the wood. These treatments should only be entrusted to those workers and firms that have a thorough understanding and experience in this field, and who have the tools and the machinery necessary to apply the chemicals. The firms should display a visible sign on the construction site indicating the name of the firm, the type of treatment used, and the quantities and dates of treatment.

Chemical treatments are generally applied prior to installation. Occasionally some foaming fire protection treatments and preventive treatments against insects may be applied to wood-product panels after they have been installed.

Wood Preservative Treatments

All preservative treatments used in building construction must have an approval by the appropriate authorities. In the Federal Republic of Germany, a list is published annually by E. Schmidt Publishers.

Approved preservative treatments carry test results and instructions for use on the package so that the type of protection and methods of application can be evaluated. The properties tested are coded as follows:

P	Effective against fungi
Iv	Preventive protection against insects
(Iv)	Preventive protection against insects only through deep impregnation (penetration depth at least 10 mm)
Ib	Actively effective against insects
S	Suitable for spraying, brushing, or immersion
W	Suitable also for wood exposed to weathering since it cannot be leached out
F	Suitable for reducing flammability of wood (fire protection)

Water-Soluble Protective Compounds

Most of these protective compounds are based on salt and can be used only when dissolved in water. They are mainly suitable for dry or semidry wood. Solutions become gradually diffused in the wood and penetrate deeply into it. If the substance is insufficient in quantity, it can be diluted to the point of being ineffective. The solvent may become absorbed in the dry wood so that the diffusion movement comes to a standstill. Preparations are more or less odorless. The intensity of added pigments cannot, however, be an indication of the degree of protection offered by the treatment. The flammability of wood is not increased by such treatment. Opaque and clear pigments may also be added. In particular, the following salts are applied:

• *CF salts.* Alkali fluoride and bichromate. Slow to leach out, but not suitable for wood that could be washed out easily or is in permanent contact with the soil. Coatings can pass through. *Properties:* P, Iv, W, S.

• *CFA salts.* Alkali fluoride, alkali arsenate, alkali bichromate. These substances cannot be used in closed rooms intended for human or animal occupancy or for food storage. Very slow to leach out, but not suitable for wood in permanent contact with the soil. *Properties:* P, Iv, W.

• *sF salts.* Silicofluorides. Will leach out, may corrode nonferrous metals and glass. *Properties:* P, Iv, S.

• *hF salts.* Hydrogen fluorides. Will leach out, may corrode nonferrous metals and glass. *Properties:* P, Iv, S, often Ib.

• *B salts.* Inorganic boric compounds. Will leach out. *Properties:* P, Iv, S.

• *CK salts.* Copper salts, bichromate, arsenic, boric, or fluoric compound additives. Preparations containing arsenic are not to be used in closed rooms, similar to CFA salts. Suitable for conditions of considerable wash-out and for continuous contact with the soil. *Properties:* P, Iv, W, partially only (Iv), partially S.

Substances of different chemical compositions and variable toxicity must be evaluated with regard to their properties and areas of applicability as indicated on their certification. *Properties:* P, Iv, partially S, W, F.

Oil-Based Protective Compounds

Oil-based compounds are suitable for dry and semidry wood, but not for fresh wood because the protective solutions penetrate by capillary action. Wood that has become wet through storage, in transport, or during installation must be dried before such protective compounds are applied. The compounds are liquid; they are used undiluted and may have a strong smell. They cannot be leached out and, therefore, are also recommended for construction elements exposed to the weather. Deep penetration is required for long-term contact with water or soil.

TAR-OIL COMPOUNDS

• Pure distillates of mineral coal tar oils (carbols). *Properties:* P, (Iv), S, W.

• Distillates of mineral coal tar oils with the addition of special substances, partly also other oils. *Properties:* P, Iv, partially Ib, S, W.

COMPOUNDS CONTAINING SOLVENTS

• Without binding agents, sometimes with natural pigments. *Properties:* P, Iv, often Ib, S, W.

• With binding agents, no pigments. *Properties:* P, Iv, S, W.
• With binding agents and pigments. *Properties:* P, Iv, S, W.
• Special compounds for application in stationary settings. *Properties:* P, Iv, partially S, W.

COMPOUNDS FOR SPECIAL APPLICATIONS
• Oil and salt mixes in the form of a paste are used for the protection of masts or piles and may be applied for protection of wood after installation. *Properties:* P, Iv, W.
• Compounds for reducing efflorescence in masonry: phenol chlorides.
• Protective compounds for wood-product materials. These compounds protect only against fungi and are added to the adhesives. *Property:* P.

Compounds Active against Destructive Insects in Timber Structures already Built
Water-soluble salts and oil compounds, applicable by brush or spraying and mostly having only a faint odor, may be used in the fight against the larvae of the common house beetle *(Hylotrupes bajulus)* and various species of anobiids. In tightly closed rooms pest control can be achieved by means of hot air or gas. Such work is done by specially licensed firms.

Treatment Methods and Quantities of Preservatives
Protective treatment is essentially applied to wood after all other fabrication work has been completed. If later work, such as drilling, is necessary, exposed surfaces have to be treated again. Because treatments do not penetrate the inner or outer bark, these must be completely removed. Cracks that develop at a later stage must be treated. Such treatments must not damage earlier treatments.

If the treatment is applied after assembly, the contact surfaces and inaccessible locations must be treated beforehand. A permanent protection is achieved with those processes that distribute a sufficient amount of treatment compounds evenly, possibly with deep penetration.

Treatments are distinguished according to their depth of penetration:
• *Surface treatments.* The depth of penetration is on the order of a few millimeters.
• *Deep penetration.* The depth of penetration is at least 10 mm. When heartwood has a sapwood of less than 10-mm thickness, the sapwood should be penetrated fully.

Immersion, Spraying, and Brushing
These methods are the least expensive, and they are sufficient for most woods. Methods other than brushing or spraying are generally not applicable for the treatment of already assembled timber.

Immersion may last from several seconds to several minutes. The quantity of compounds absorbed in this way depends on the wood surface and, in the case of salt and oil solutions, results in the following penetration quantities:
• About 200 mL/m^2 for rough-sawn timber
• About 80 to 120 mL/m^2 for planed timber

Larger penetration quantities are not obtained by longer immersion, but rather by repeated immersions after sufficient drying times. When a water-soluble compound is applied repeatedly, the concentration of the solution in the immersion bath has to be checked regularly and strengthened by the addition of salts. Spraying and brushing require two applications in order to achieve an even distribution. The second application can be omitted only when spraying in an automatically advancing device, a spraying tunnel, which provides sufficiently concentrated treatment.

DIN 68800, part 3, details the minimum penetration quantities for immersion, spraying, and brushing methods.

In water-soluble compounds the quantity of protective substance is determined by the weight of the salts and not by the weight of the applied solution. In oil-based compounds, which are mostly delivered in liquid form, the quantity is measured by the volume of undiluted liquid. The required quantity of treatment compounds can be obtained by a single immersion only in rough-sawn timbers. When timbers are planed, the quantity of absorption can be increased by perforations made with sawteeth. Since this procedure is often not allowed for aesthetic reasons, the wood protection industry is now using oil-based compounds with a greater concentration of active materials. When protective materials are applied by immersion or spray equipment with a regulated automatic advance, smaller quantities are needed to achieve the required results.

The amount of protective materials needed is determined by considering the usual losses of about 10 to 30%.

A more exact verification of the penetrated substances with vat treatment or by immersion, spray, or brushing methods can only be undertaken in appropriately equipped laboratories, where the depths of penetration can be established by reactivity.

Vat Immersion
Wood is immersed in treating compounds contained in open vats for a period of time varying from several hours to several days. Sometimes only the endangered ends of timber are immersed. The necessary duration of the bath depends on the type of wood and the quantity of protective material in kg/m^3. Pine wood requires a shorter immersion time because of its higher absorption capacity. In addition, the dimensions of the wood and the concentration of the water-soluble compounds also play a role.

The so-called hot – cold immersion, achieved by alternating the temperature of immersion between cold and hot (60 to 80°C), requires shorter immersion times and achieves better penetration in less absorbent woods. In water-soluble compounds, the concentration of the solution must be checked regularly.

Wood preservatives applied through vat immersion or by pressure treatment are recommended for:
a. Wood that will be used in an enclosed building and will have a humidity of more than 18%, and where a later treatment is not anticipated or is not possible.
b. Wood that will be exposed to fungi because of humidity or condensation.
c. Wood of over 4-cm thickness that will be exposed to rain without any surface coating protection. After a certain time the treatment will have to be repeated.

Pressure Treatment
In this treatment process, the wood is impregnated with preservative compounds in a steel tank while subjected to various pressure levels. The expense and the degree of protection achieved depend on the sequence of applications of vacuum and pressure.
• *Full saturation procedure.* In a steel tank, the wood is first subjected to a vacuum for 30 min. The preservative liquid is then pumped in, followed by actual impregnation under pressure, which has to last at least 60 min. Near the end, a vacuum can be applied again to prevent dripping. The full saturation procedure is used mainly for water-soluble preservatives.
• *Economic method of saturation.* Before impregnation, the wood is exposed to compressed air (Rüping method) or only to atmospheric air pressure (Lowry method). The tank is then pressurized and flooded and the pressure is maintained for up to 12 hours. After the pressure is released, the compressed air in the cells expands and expels the excess preservative liquid from the cells so that only the cell walls remain impregnated. The expulsion of liquid can be increased by applying a vacuum, as long as the prescribed weight of the preservative remains within the wood. This procedure may be applied to both water-soluble and oil-based compounds.

• *Vacuum method.* This procedure begins with a vacuum of at least 10-min duration. The compounds are then introduced under vacuum. As the vacuum is released, impregnation occurs at atmospheric pressure. A vacuum can be introduced at the end to expel some of the excess preservative liquid.
• *Variable-pressure impregnation.* In this procedure, cleaned fresh logs are subjected to pressures and vacuums rapidly following each other. Only water-soluble preservatives can be used in this procedure because only they can be exchanged against the fresh sap.

The amount of preservative applied by pressure treatment is measured by weighing the wood both before and after impregnation. Except for variable-pressure impregnation, the wood must be half-dry (moisture content 30% maximum) for both oil-based and water-soluble treatments.

The tank pressure method achieves the highest absorption and generally results in deep penetration.

Timber which is in permanent contact with the soil must be pressure-treated. When water-soluble compounds are used, the wood cannot be exposed to any moisture before treatment.

Special Procedures

Special procedures add a number of protective compounds as a second protection, either to ward off a new infestation or to reinforce an existing protection in specially endangered locations.

The special compounds are applied either by brush or by spatula, with or without covering, by applying impregnated bandages, or by saturation through drilled holes. In the latter procedure holes of about 10-mm diameter are drilled at intervals of 10 to 25 cm and are arranged in such a way that the reduced cross section results in a minimal loss of strength. The impregnation occurs through multiple applications of preservatives, by application of preservative pastes, or by pressure injection of preservatives using special injection tools. The strength of the wood is least affected when the preservative is forced into the wood by means of injection needles. When using drilled-hole or injection-needle methods, the wood surface should also be treated.

Side Effects of Chemical Preservatives

Wood preservatives can cause undesirable effects on wood, on connections, and on other materials. Before treatment, in addition to checking specifications and test results, the following should also be verified:

• Compatibility with glues.
• Corrosion of metals. Connections and wood fittings may be affected, as well as containers and tools for application of the preservatives.
• Etching of glass by fluorides, particularly the HF salts.
• Compatibility with rubber, plastics, or insulation materials.
• Penetration through stucco or masonry (efflorescence).
• Compatibility with previously applied coatings, wood treatments, and caulking or cement mortar.
• Compatibility with future coatings.

The strength and flammability of wood are generally not affected but the rate of moisture absorption may be.

Precautionary Measures for Working with Wood Preservatives

Precautionary measures during storage, fabrication, and application of treated wood are indispensable because of varying degrees of toxicity of the preservatives. Manufacturers' directives and safety recommendations are to be followed carefully.

Fire Protection

All materials, combustible or noncombustible, are damaged by fire and can become useless quickly. The fire resistance of massive timbers of large dimensions is particularly favorable because charring increases the insulation value of the wood, thus protecting its inner core for a longer time. The fire resistance of structural members made from wood or wood products can be increased by protective measures in such a way that members can have a fire rating of more than 90 min.

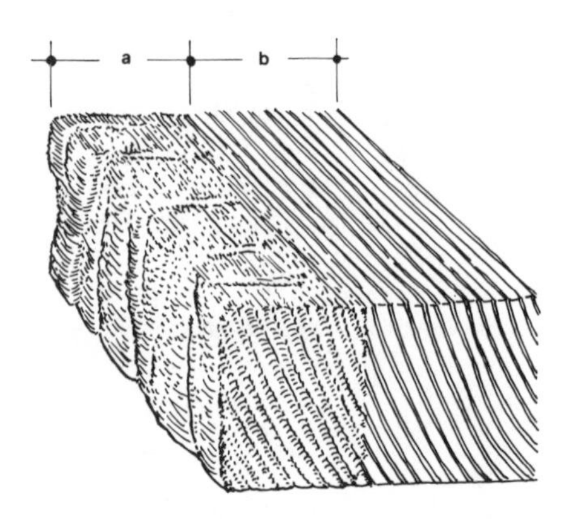

Fig. 66. Timber cross section after fire. *a* — charred zone; *b* — load-carrying portion of wood.

Technical Criteria for Fire Protection

DIN 4102 describes the concepts, requirements, and procedures for testing the fire resistance of materials. This standard classifies the materials according to their behavior in fire and the building components according to their fire resistance.

Classes of Building Materials

Building materials are grouped into the following classes according to their behavior in fire:

Class of Building Material	Description
A Noncombustible Materials	
A1	
A2	
B Combustible Materials	
B1	Materials of low combustibility
B2	Normally combustible materials
B3	Highly combustible materials

Building regulations require the approval of building materials of class A if they enclose combustible components, and all of those of class B1. All materials must be accompanied on delivery by a certificate indicating their combustibility. Excepted from that requirement are noncombustible materials such as brick, metals, and sand, and also wood boards, planks, strips, and beams which are described as normally combustible.

Solid and laminated wood obtain classification B1 after they have been chemically treated for fire protection. Wood products can be classified, depending on binders and later treatment, as being normally combustible, of low combustibility, or even noncombustible if fabricated with mineral binders (class A1).

Fire Resistance Classification

Fire resistance classes correspond to the duration of the functional capability of a structural member under fire:

F30 Fire-retardant
F60 Fire-resistant
F90 Fire-resistant
F120
F180

The number indicates the time in minutes during which a structural member fulfills its requirements for structural capacity and room-enclosing function under temperature stress, according to prescribed fire tests.

DIN 4102 lists building components that may be applied within their appropriate fire resistance classes without further certification. Many timber buildings achieve fire resistance classes F30 to F60 without any additional measures. This is mostly due to a favorable fire rating of timbers of large dimensions and to sufficiently thick panels of wood-product materials.

Fig. 67. Smallest dimensions of bare beams of solid wood.

Fire Resistance Class	F30				F60			
Fire exposure	Three-Sided		Four-Sided		Three-Sided		Four-Sided	
Bending stress, N/mm²	min b (mm)	min h (mm)	min b (mm)	min h (mm)	min b (mm)	min h (mm)	min b (mm)	min h (mm)
13	150	260	160	300	300	520	320	600
10	120	200	130	240	240	400	260	480
7	90	160	100	200	200	320	220	400
3	80	140	90	180	180	240	200	320

Interpolate for intermediate bending values.

Fig. 68. Smallest dimensions of bare laminated wood beams.

Fire Resistance Class	F30				F60			
Fire exposure	Three-Sided		Four-Sided		Three-Sided		Four-Sided	
Bending stress, N/mm²	min b (mm)	min h (mm)	min b (mm)	min h (mm)	min b (mm)	min h (mm)	min b (mm)	min h (mm)
14	140	260	150	310	280	520	300	620
11	110	200	120	250	220	400	240	500
7	80	150	90	190	160	300	180	380
3	80	120	80	160	140	220	160	300

Interpolate for intermediate bending values.

Behavior of Wood and Wood Products under Fire

Wood is chemically destroyed by direct or indirect fire (high-degree temperature), which transforms wood into charcoal and gases. The period of time until the liberated gases begin to burn depends on many circumstances, such as availability of oxygen, moisture content, unit weight, and thermal gradient. If the fire is generated by a flame, wood can last 15 to 40 min at temperatures of 180°C, but small wood samples ignite spontaneously at temperatures of 340 to 430°C. On the other hand, ignition does not depend on the presence of a flame. The wood that is exposed to hot air at a temperature of 330°C ignites within an hour without a flame. Ignition can also result from longer exposure to temperatures over 120°C when the heat generated by exothermal reactions within the wood cannot be removed.

When the fire starts, its intensity increases because of a higher heating value of the liberated gases, provided there is sufficient oxygen. The thickness of charred wood increases with the advancement of the flame, but the burning of charred wood progresses more slowly than that of the inner core, which burns at about 300°C. After a few minutes of fire, its progress slows down because of the lower heat conductivity of charred wood (Fig. 66).

In the full fire phase the temperatures range from 500 to 1100°C. The temperature penetrates slowly into the interior of massive timber cross sections because of the insulating quality of charred wood. The burning speed, that is, the speed with which the formation of charred wood progresses, is reduced by a higher moisture content of wood and is less for heavier wood. Except at joints and cracks, the speed normal to grain is about 0.6 to 0.8 mm/min for conifers and about 0.4 mm/min for oak. In the direction parallel to the grain it is twice as much.

Generally the fire resistance of wood depends on its surface shape. The larger the surface in relation to its volume, the less the fire resistance. In this sense larger cracks are detrimental, but they are often present in large timbers. Because of this, the fire resistance of boards which are free of cracks is relatively higher and can be determined with more accuracy than that of larger timbers.

Most wood-product panels count as combustible because binding materials generally do not fulfill the requirements for noncombustible materials. Untreated wood-product plates are counted as having normal combustibility (class B2). The fire resistance of members with linings or sheathing made with wood products depends mostly on their thickness. In case of fire, wood-chip panels behave better than plywood panels because individual plywood layers can separate and expose a larger surface to the fire.

In wood-product panels of low combustibility the fire protection compounds have been added to the glues during fabrication, or by later application of foam layers. These improved characteristics with regard to fire resistance have to be proven by appropriate testing and certification.

The construction of panel joints and splices that must resist the propagation of fire considerably influences the fire resistance of wood-product panels.

Chemical Fire Protection Compounds

Chemical fire protection compounds may slow down the ignition and the propagation of fire, but the fire rating time is increased very little. From the point of view of effectiveness, there are two compounds:

- Fire protection compounds, which form a foam layer protecting the surface.
- Salts, which are introduced by pressure treatment.

Foam fire protection compounds retard the thermal destruction of wood by insulating it. The foam is created when the surface coating is heated. The effectiveness of the foam layer should not be jeopardized by previous applications. The adherence of foam may be affected by the adhesive properties of previous coatings.

Foaming compounds are mostly pigmented, but may also be transparent. They are not suitable for exterior surfaces exposed to weathering. Their chemical compatibility with previous coatings, such as those protecting against fungi or insects, and also with subsequent coatings must be checked.

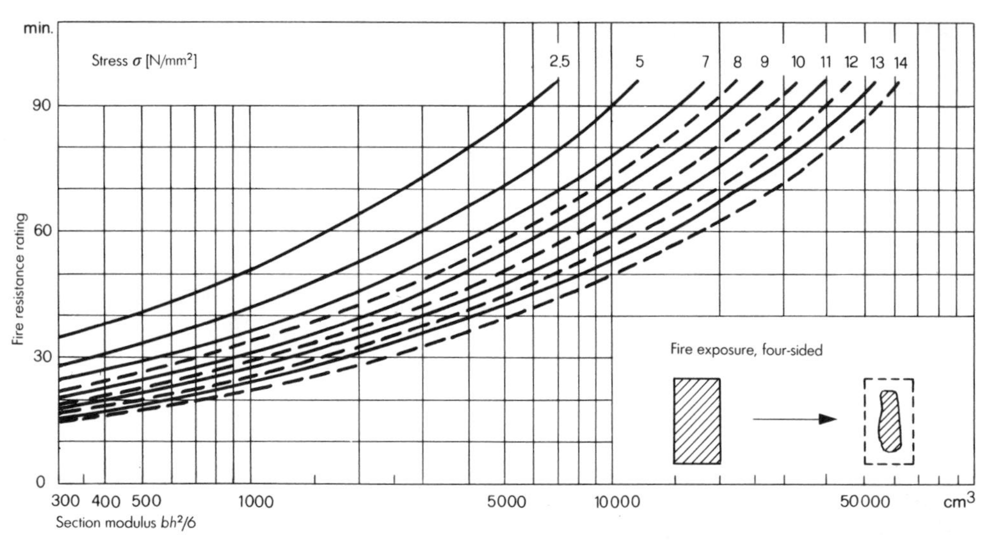

Fig. 69. Fire resistance rating of timber beams with four-sided exposure to fire.

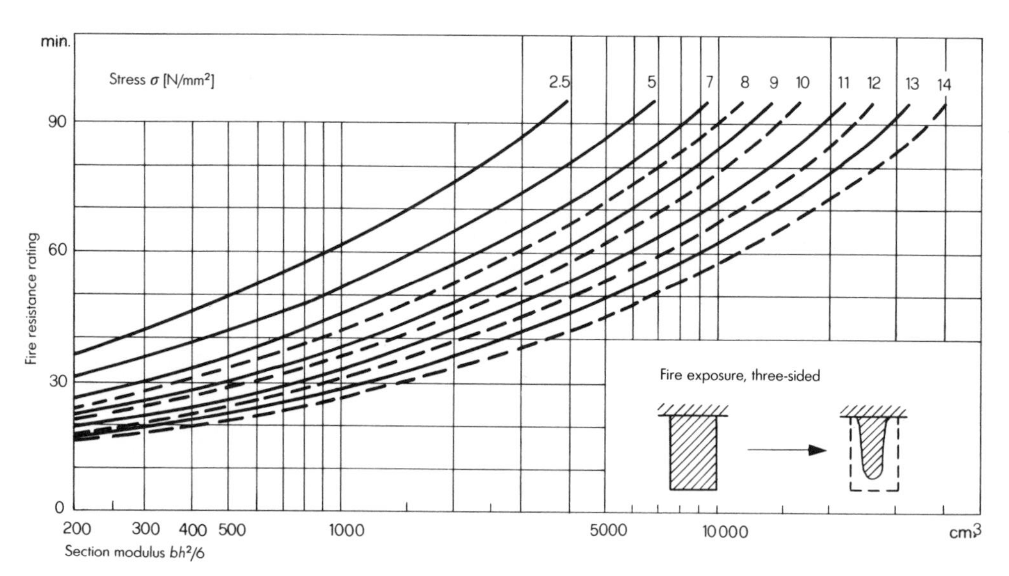

Fig. 70. Fire resistance rating of timber beams with three-sided exposure to fire.

The importance of salts has diminished with the development of foams. Phosphate salts accelerate the formation of charred wood under heat and they increase the wood's natural protection against fire. Fire protective salts combined with antifungal and antiinsect components are known as triple compounds.

In order to obtain low combustibility, such large quantities of salts are required that only pressure treatment can be considered. Wood-chip boards have higher fire resistance if their chips have been impregnated with a fire protection compound before fabrication.

Fire Resistance of Building Components

It is possible to anticipate the fire resistance of timber members on the basis of tests establishing the speed of fire advancement. Boards can be rated more reliably than solid wood because knots and cracks can cause different speeds of fire advancement. Since the strength of the unburned part of the cross section of a beam determines its margin of structural safety, it follows that members with an initially oversized cross section are able to keep stresses within the allowable limits even after some loss of cross section. DIN 4102, part 4, "Assembly and Application of Graded Materials, Building Components, and Special Construction Members," gives, on the basis of tests and related computations, the smallest dimensions of beams and posts required for their respective fire resistance ratings.

Timber Beams

Statically determinate or indeterminate beams may be exposed to fire on three or four sides. The depth of their bearing surfaces must be equal to or more than 40 mm for the fire rating class F30, and 80 mm for the fire rating class F60. The lateral bracing of beams with a side relationship $h/b > 4$ must have the same fire rating as the beams. The bare timber beams with rectangular cross sections fulfill the requirements for fire rating class F30 or F60, according to DIN 4102, part 4, when their minimum dimensions conform to those given in Figs. 67 and 68. If the minimum dimensions are observed, the fire rating may be estimated by means of Figs. 69 and 70.

DIN 4102, part 4, also contains the requirements for structural details and minimum cross sections of covered solid or laminated beams (for example, covered with gypsum boards).

Timber Posts

Minimum dimensions are similarly established for solid-wood or laminated posts having rectangular cross sections when they are axially loaded. Eccentrically loaded posts in which the axial load is small in comparison with the bending load should be designed as timber beams.

Solid-wood posts should be designed using Euler's condition 2, pinned at both ends, regardless of the actual loading conditions. They can be considered as having a fire rating F30 when their length does not exceed 4 m and when their minimum dimensions conform to Fig. 71. Posts of longer lengths and those having a fire rating of F60 may be used only if covered with fire protective linings conforming to DIN 4102, part 4.

Laminated wood posts which are pinned at both ends (Euler condition 2) must have minimum cross sections for fire rating purposes, as shown in Fig. 72.

Somewhat smaller dimensions are allowed for laminated columns fixed at one or both ends. DIN 4102, part 4, contains the applicable values for these conditions and also the requirements for columns that do not have a rectangular cross section.

Fig. 71. Minimum thickness d, in mm, of axially loaded bare solid-wood rectangular posts having a length $s \leq 4.0$ m.

Structural Conditions	Minimum Thickness d for Fire Rating, mm	
	F30-B	F60-B
Posts with compressive stress $\sigma \geq 11.0$ N/mm²	240	—
Posts with compressive stress $\sigma = 8.5$ N/mm²	220	—
Posts with compressive stress $\sigma \leq 5.0$ N/mm²	200	—

Fig. 72. Minimum dimensions of bare laminated wood posts with a rectangular cross section and axial loads when end supports correspond either to Euler's buckling condition 2 ($s_k = 1.0$ s) or to Euler's buckling condition 3 ($s_k = 0.7$ s).

Structural Conditions	Minimum Thickness *d* for Fire Rating, mm			
	F30-B		F60-B	
Posts with a side ratio $b/d = 1$	Euler's Case 2	Euler's Case 3	Euler's Case 2	Euler's Case 3
For compressive stress $\sigma \geq 11.0$ N/mm², length of post				
$s \leq 2.0$ m	160	150	240	230
$s = 7.0$ m	200	170	340	280
For $\sigma = 8.5$ N/mm²,				
$s \leq 2.0$ m	145	140	215	210
$s = 7.0$ m	175	155	295	250
For $\sigma \leq 5.0$ N/mm²,				
$s \leq 2.0$ m	120	120	180	180
$s = 7.0$ m	140	130	230	210
Posts with a side ratio $b/d \geq 2$	Euler's Case 2	Euler's Case 3	Euler's Case 2	Euler's Case 3
For $\sigma \geq 11.0$ N/mm²,				
$s \leq$ 2.0 m	140	140	220	210
$s =$ 7.0 m	180	160	310	260
For $\sigma = 8.5$ N/mm²,				
$s \leq 2.0$ m	130	130	200	195
$s = 7.0$ m	160	145	270	230
For $\sigma \leq 5.0$ N/mm²,				
$s \leq 2.0$ m	120	115	170	170
$s = 7.0$ m	130	120	210	190

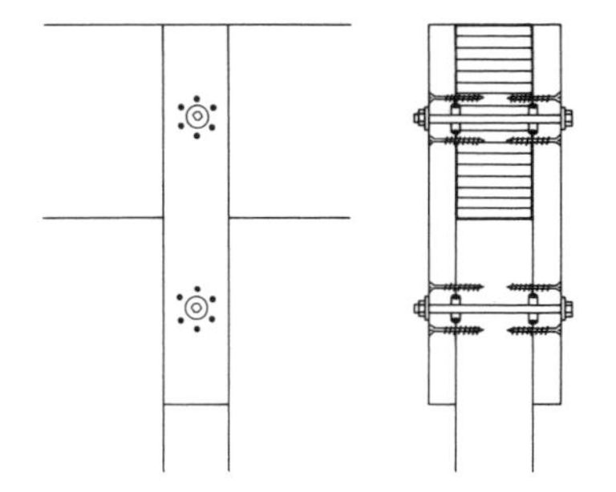

Fig. 73. Special shear connectors with bolts and six additional screws.

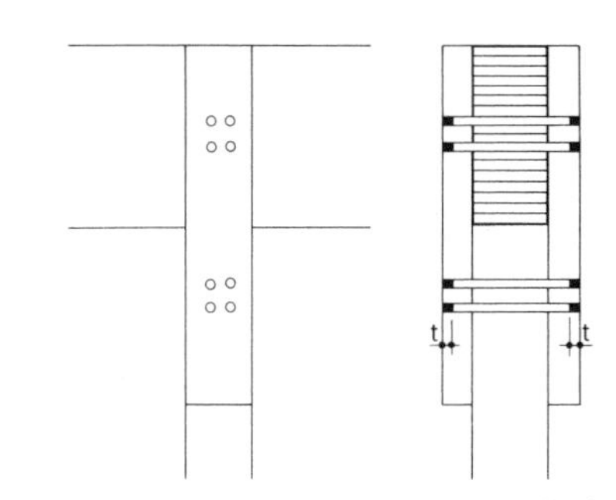

Fig. 74. Steel dowels recessed, covered with glued wood plugs, $t = 2$ cm thick or larger.

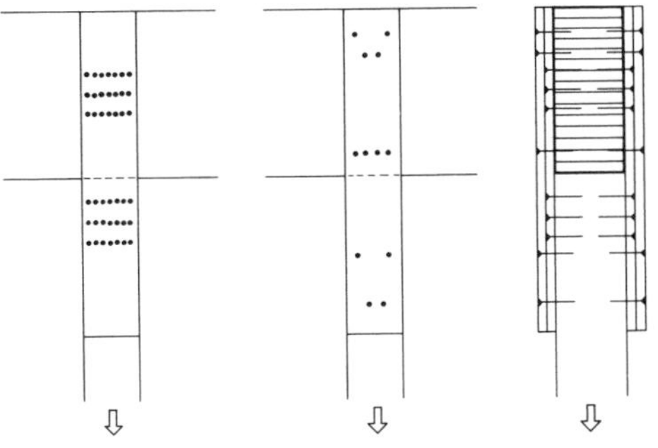

Fig. 75. Nail plates protected by additional wood cover plates.

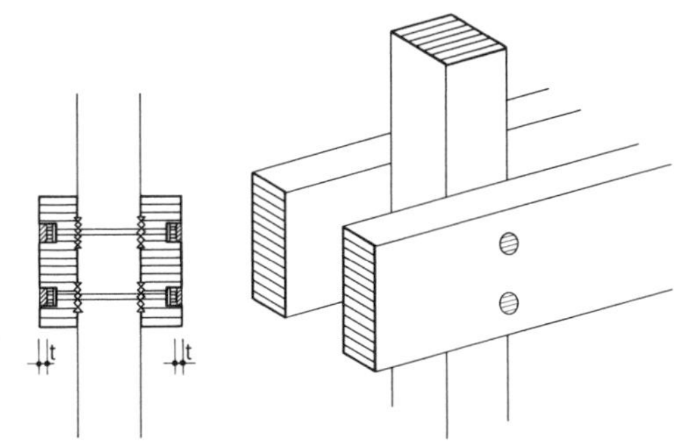

Fig. 76. Twin beam to column connection with toothed sheer rings. Bolts and washers covered with glued wood plugs, $t = 2$ cm thick or larger.

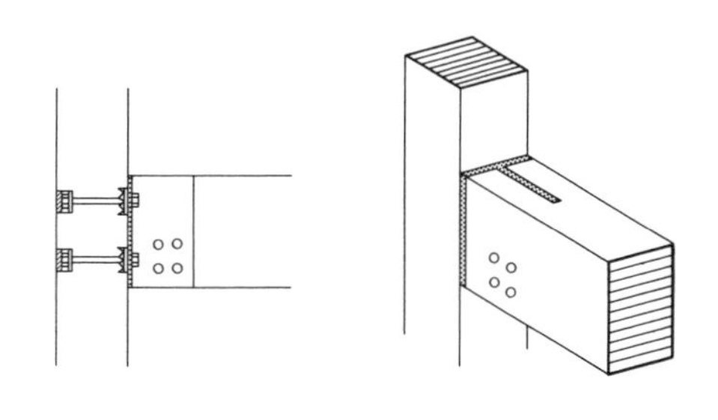

Fig. 77. Beam to column connection made with a steel T section, steel dowels, and shear connectors. The latter are covered with glued wood plugs.

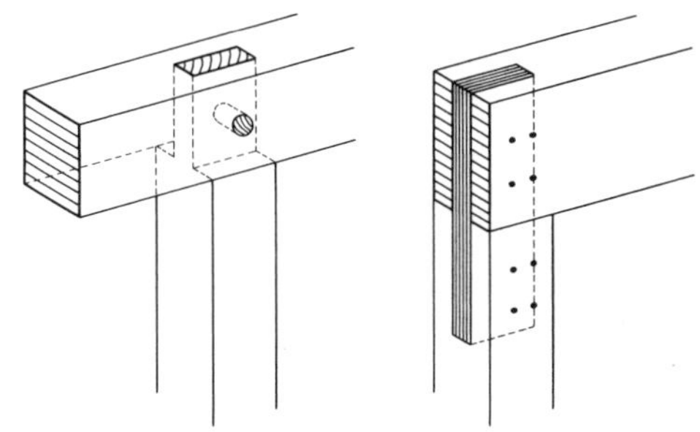

Fig. 78. Left: Mortise and tenon with hardwood dowel. Right: Plywood or solid wood strap secured by nails.

Stiffeners and Shear Walls

If a building is to be protected against fire, the fire rating of stiffening members (wall panels, shear walls) must be equal to or exceed the requirements for the entire building. Steel members, such as tension bars or tension diagonals, must be protected by a coating, otherwise their fire rating would be less than that of massive timbers.

Fire Rating of Timber Connections

In most timber structures the choice and arrangement of metal connections has a substantial influence on structural safety and fire rating. Nevertheless, only recently have tests been made on the fire resistance of connections. From the point of view of fire protection, those nodes and connections which are of primary importance for the stability of the structural system should be designed with special care. For example:

- Frame elbows with mechanical connectors
- Pinned joints: ridge pin, bottom chord pin, Gerber pin
- Bearings
- Joints, especially of tension and bending members
- Truss nodes
- Connections of multicomponent columns

Normal construction methods may not result in a sufficient fire rating for many connections. These should be improved by adding fire protective coatings. It is often sufficient to cover standard metal connectors by a sufficiently thick wood cover. Simple fire protective measures for connections that remain exposed:

- Add additional screws to bolted connections (Fig. 73).
- Recess the bolts or dowels and cover them with sufficiently thick, glued wood plugs (Figs. 74 and 76).
- Protect nailed connectors by nailing over them non-load-carrying wood or wood-product plates (Fig. 75).
- Do not leave metal shoe plates or joint connectors exposed, but place them in slits within structural members (Figs. 77 and 78).

Many special nailed, doweled, or bolted connections have been tested for their fire ratings. After improvements by the means mentioned above, they could be qualified as having fire ratings of F30 and sometimes even F60.

Fundamentals of Timber Building Construction

MATERIALS, CONNECTIONS, AND BUILDING COMPONENTS

Criteria for the Choice of Materials

Materials for timber buildings consist of solid lumber, laminated wood beams, and wood products. Solid lumber has an economic advantage over other materials when it can be used as round timber, beams, dimension lumber, and boards, provided its limited cross sections are sufficient, there are no special aesthetic requirements regarding cracking, and normal timber connections are applicable. Laminated wood is to be used when larger cross sections are required, and when the appearance of planed or smooth surfaces is necessary. Also, tapered columns or beams can only be made from laminated wood. Weathering glues are necessary if laminated wood is exposed to weather or variations in humidity.

The choice of wood products (plywood, chipboard, particle board) is made on the basis of their technical properties, price, and availability. Because of its relatively high price, plywood is used only where its higher strength and insulation properties are necessary. For interior use the chipboards are often sufficient because they can also be considered as load-carrying components of walls, decks, and roofs. Particle boards are generally limited to interior use. The thicker medium-hard panels also find application in buildings. All panels may be secured to solid lumber by gluing or stapling.

Connections and Connecting Hardware

Traditional Connections

This category includes a multitude of hand-cut connections which have been developed by carpenters through centuries of experience. They are most aptly adapted to the intrinsic characteristics of wood. Because of their drawbacks, namely, the weakening of timbers, the high degree of workmanship required, and the difficult assembly, they are less frequently used today. Therefore, only the most important ones will be discussed.

Notched Joints

A notched joint is one of few traditional carpentry connections whose load capacity in a skewed connection can be correctly computed to a certain degree.

Among the variations of this joint, the head notch, back notch and double notch are the most significant (Fig. 1). The head notch is preferred, because the back notch and the double notch require more precision in their execution. If the joint does not fit well, a longitudinal failure of the tie beam is often the result. The load-carrying capacity of a notched joint depends on the skew angle α, the notch depth t_v, and the end length l_v. End lengths of 10 to 50 cm are necessary, depending on the type of construction and the size of the load, and should be established by computation. Generally, every notched joint should be secured by a bolt or by laterally affixed connection plates (Fig. 2). Examples of application are compression struts, knee braces, compression diagonals in trusses, tie beams in tied roof frames, and eaves of triangular frames.

Lap Joints

Lap joints are structural connections of timbers within the same plane (Fig. 3). Compression stresses are transferred by contact or through additional connection devices. The transfer of even small tensile stresses requires additional fasteners such as nails. Longitudinal or corner joints at wall headers or sills are built today mostly as plain butt joints fastened with toe nails or nailed metal plates.

Mortise and Tenon Joints

Mortise and tenon joints serve to secure the adjacent faces of two timbers (for example, to secure compression members against lateral movement) such as posts, struts, diagonals, or knee struts (Fig. 4). The bearing surface is reduced by the mortise hole, because the bottom of the hole may not be effective in bearing. Therefore, in highly stressed compression members, the mortise and tenon joint should not be used and members have to be secured against lateral movement by other means

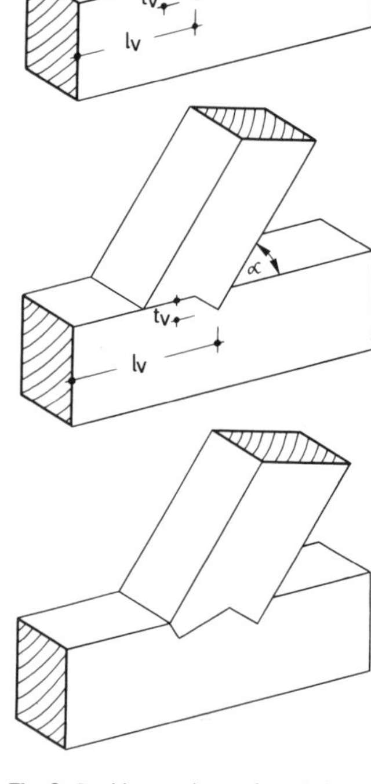

Fig. 1. (a) Head notch. Simplest notch joint when end length is ample.

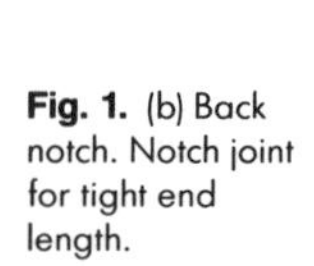

Fig. 1. (b) Back notch. Notch joint for tight end length.

Fig. 1. (c) Double notch. Detail for very high strut compressive forces.

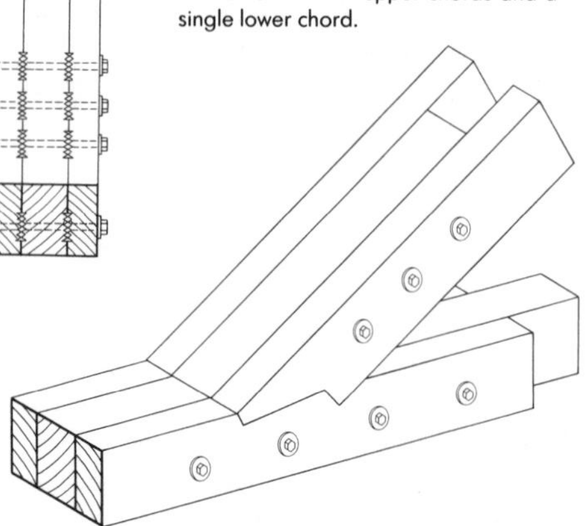

Fig. 2. Double notch reinforced by bolts. Example: eave point of a triangular frame with twin upper chords and a single lower chord.

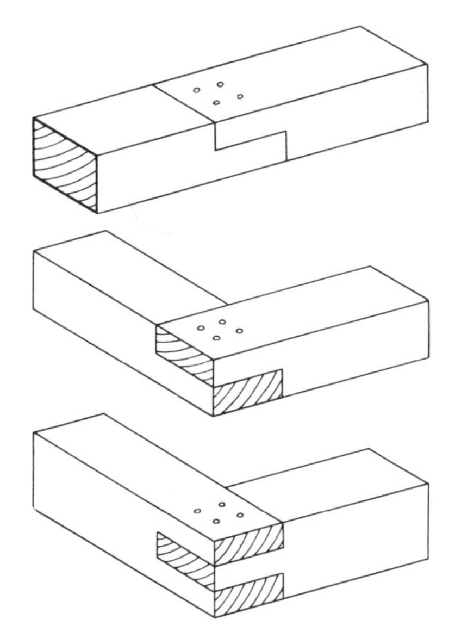

Fig. 3. Top: Straight lap joint for wall headers, sills, supported beams. Center: Corner lap joint for wall headers or sills. Bottom: Forked lap joint for corner joints of heavier timbers.

(side plates of wood or steel, sheet metal angles, etc.).

Mortise and tenon joints which transfer tensile stresses through nails are not in use today.

Shear Connectors

Shear connectors are devices that are mostly stressed in compression and shear. They can be tightly fitted in depressions (square or round connectors, plates, dish shapes, rings), or they can be pressed into the wood with their toothlike protrusions. Mixed type connectors are also available.

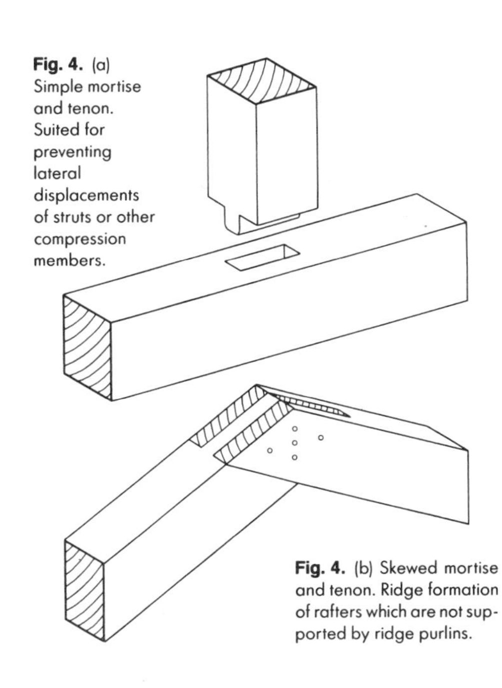

Fig. 4. (a) Simple mortise and tenon. Suited for preventing lateral displacements of struts or other compression members.

Fig. 4. (b) Skewed mortise and tenon. Ridge formation of rafters which are not supported by ridge purlins.

Rectangular Shear Connectors

These connectors consist mostly of rectangular pieces of hardwood (Fig. 5) and their load resistance can therefore be computed. They are set in matching grooves within the timbers to be connected. Their load capacity depends on the groove depth t_d, the connection length l_d, and the distance between connectors e. The ratio l_d/t_d is of special importance. A similar function is performed by T-shaped steel extrusions (Fig. 6). The additional transverse forces generated by the rotational tendency of shear connectors have to be absorbed by tightening bolts. Hardwood and T-shaped shear connectors are seldom used today because of the need to prepare the necessary grooves.

Fig. 5. Rectangular shear connectors. Hardwood connectors and bolts in grooved beams. Connectors and beams have the same direction of grain.

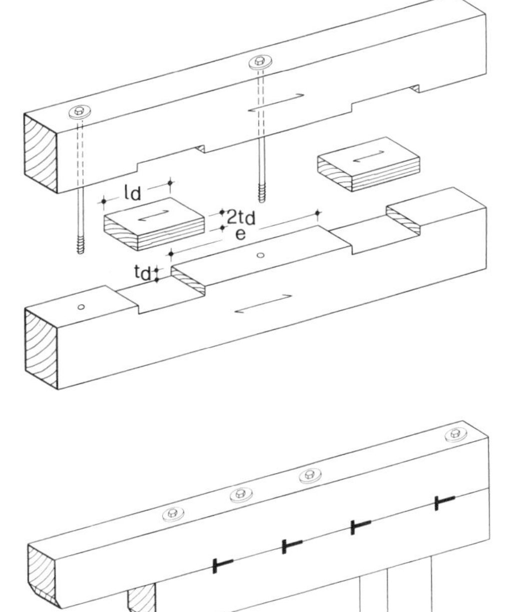

Fig. 6. T-shaped steel sections with tightening bolts. Example: cantilevered beam connected to a saddle beam.

Flat-Steel Shear Connectors

These rectangular steel plates of 10- to 30-mm thickness, depending on the load size, are cut into the wood. Their length is equal to the width of the wood member (Fig. 7). They are welded to steel plates or steel extrusions, which are fastened to the wood by bolts or retaining screws. The smallest width of the connectors is obtained by the necessary length of the welds. After welding, all steel parts should be well protected against corrosion. The number of flat-steel or rectangular connectors in joints or connections is limited to a maximum of four in a row because it is not possible to assure an even distribution of stress on all connectors.

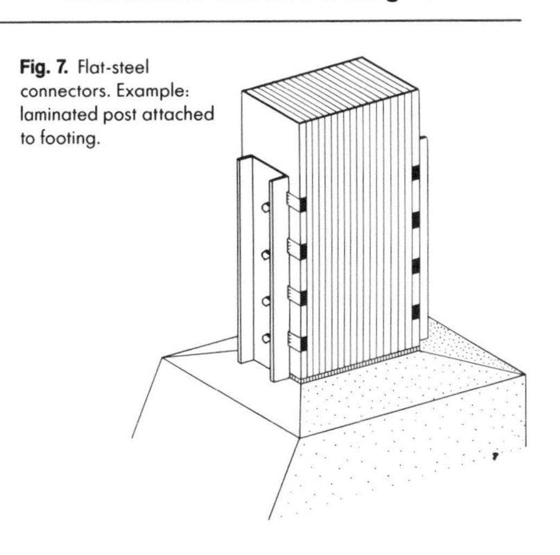

Fig. 7. Flat-steel connectors. Example: laminated post attached to footing.

Special Shear Connectors

These can be made from hardwood, steel, cast iron, or light metals. DIN 1052, part 2, lists several types, but of these only a few are used at present. The most common are the shear rings of the Appel system and the toothed Geka and Bulldog connectors (Fig. 8). The one-sided connectors, such as the one shown in Fig. 8(c), allow a positive load transfer between timbers, nowadays an arrangement of special importance.

The load capacity of connectors is given in the above referenced standard on the basis of load tests because it is generally not possible to deter-

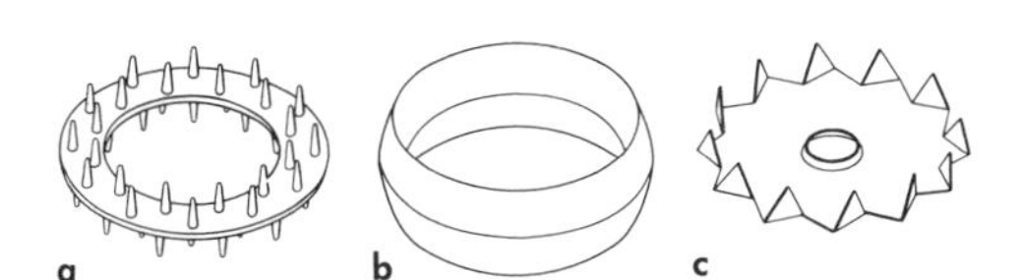

Fig. 8. (a) Two-sided shear connector (Geka system). (b) Two-sided shear ring connector (Appel system). (c) One-sided toothed shear connector (Bulldog system).

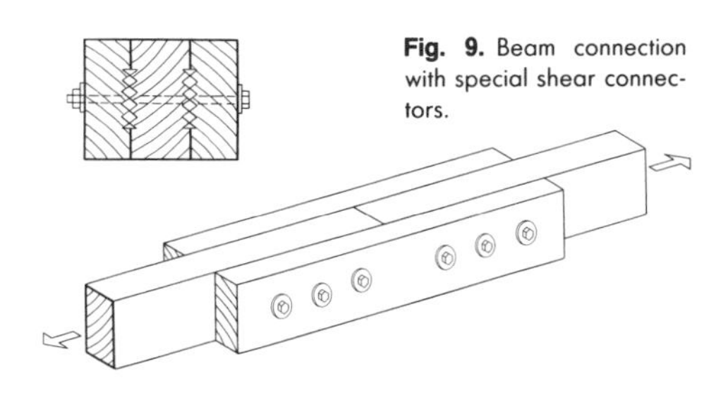

Fig. 9. Beam connection with special shear connectors.

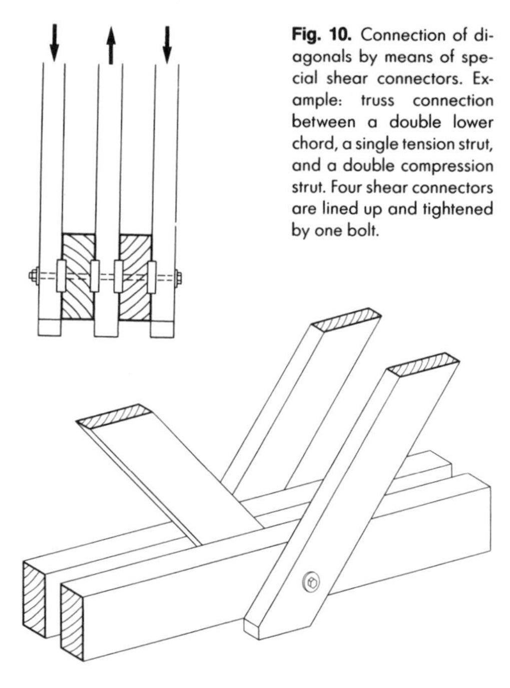

Fig. 10. Connection of diagonals by means of special shear connectors. Example: truss connection between a double lower chord, a single tension strut, and a double compression strut. Four shear connectors are lined up and tightened by one bolt.

mine it through computations. The standard also gives the minimum spacing of connectors, the corresponding bolt diameters, and the minimum thickness of timbers for each type of connector.

Bolts are required for clamping and to resist overturning moments. The properties of the connector materials must correspond to the requirements listed in the standards. Because of this, the connectors may have to be ordered from specific manufacturers.

One-sided shear connectors have been developed for connections between steel and timber (Fig. 11). In such cases the shear is transferred either by the shear connector bearing on the wood (Appel system) or through the bolts (Geka and Bulldog systems), but the hole in the connector should not be larger than the nominal diameter of the bolt plus 0.2 mm. A weld between the connector and the bolt is not permitted and in most cases cannot be satisfactorily made because of the nature of the materials used.

For building elements exposed to exceptional humidity and corrosion (such as underwater structures, cooling towers, and salt storage buildings) there are fiberglass or ceramic shear connectors, as well as bolts made from corrosion-resistant metals.

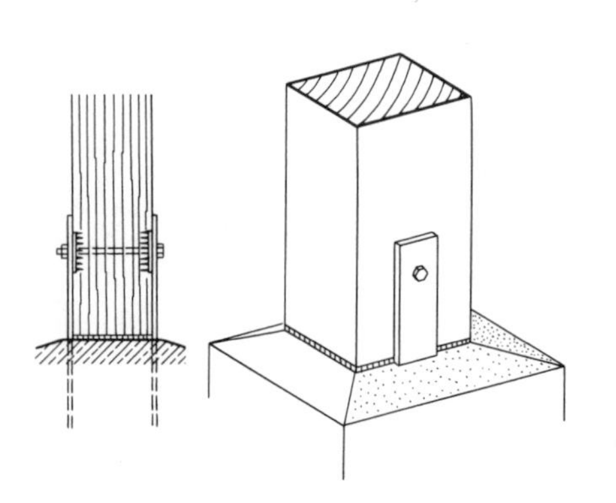

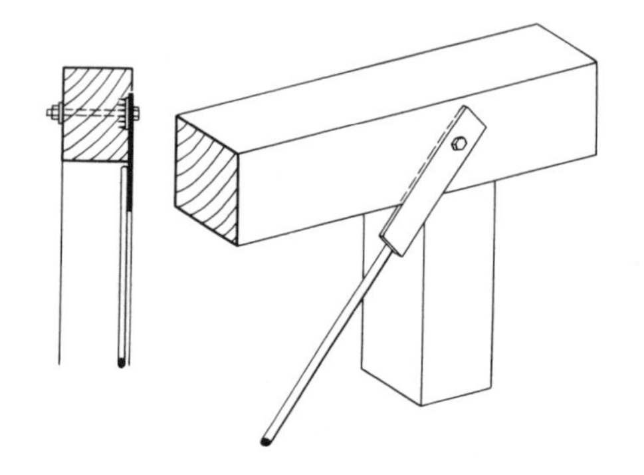

Fig. 11. Connection of steel parts to timber by means of special shear connectors. Examples: post base and connection of a tension rod by metal plates.

Doweled Connections

Bolts

Bolts are primarily threaded bolts placed normal to shearing surfaces and subject to bending and shear; the wood is subject to both shear and bearing stresses in the holes. Bolts have about a 1-mm clearance in the bolt holes. Clamping bolts must have washers conforming to DIN 436 and DIN 440 inserted under the head and the nut (Fig. 12a).

Load-carrying bolted connections should have at least two bolts, each having at least a 12-mm diameter. Diameters of 24 mm should not be exceeded. Large and thick washers are required on both sides. The minimum distance between bolts as well as their minimum distance from the edge are determined by the allowable shear stresses in the wood. Because of clearance in the bolt holes, considerable slippage occurs in a connection where the clamping friction of a bolt is overcome. The clamping force of bolts is reduced and finally eliminated through shrinkage and drying of the wood and through creep under shear stress. Because of this, bolts can be used in load transfer connections within buildings that depend on stiffness and permanent configuration only if special precautions are taken to prevent slippage. This can only be achieved by drilling holes having diameters equal to those of the bolts, or by filling the gap between bolt and hole. In laminated members which are assembled dry, there is generally little shrinkage. In this case, pure bolt connections can be used provided the bolts can be tightened several times prior to the application of a full load. Bolted connections are primarily used for temporary buildings, scaffoldings, secondary buildings (sheds, agricultural buildings, etc.), hung members subject to tension (Fig. 13), or for non-load-carrying stitch or clamping connections.

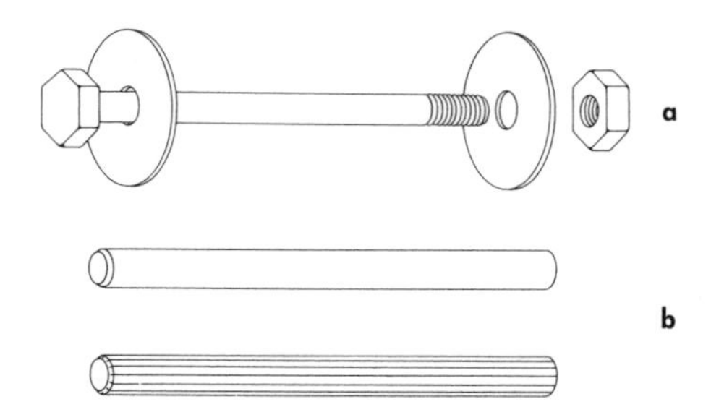

Fig. 12. (a) Bolts. Hexagonal-head bolt conforming to DIN 601 (machine bolts). Designation: thread (metric), diameter X length in mm. Example: M12 X 260. (b) Dowel. The shaft can be either smooth or grooved. The dowels may have eased edges on one end in order to facilitate driving and reduce damage to wood (not standardized).

Fig. 13. (a) Hung beam. Bolts may only be subject to tension. In this case the clearance of bolts in holes does not call for any limitations of use.

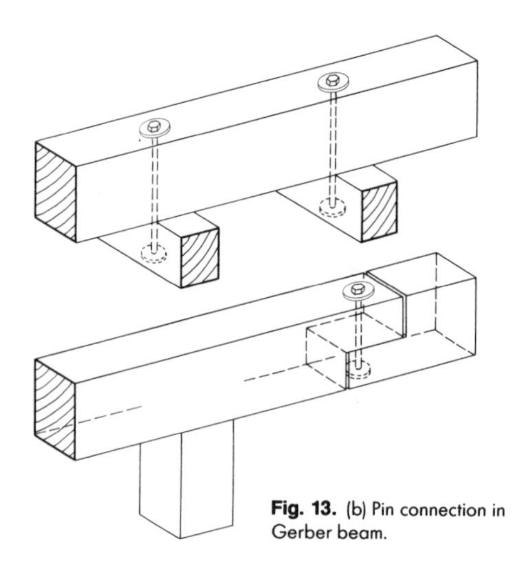

Fig. 13. (b) Pin connection in Gerber beam.

The load capacity of the connection is mostly determined by the bolt diameter and the allowable bearing stress on the bolt hole.

Dowels

Dowels are cylindrical steel bars, generally without nut or thread, which are driven into predrilled holes having a diameter 0.2 to 0.5 mm smaller than that of the dowel (Fig. 12b). Such dowels are of greater importance in connections because they are not subject to subsequent slippage due to clearance in the holes. They are also not subject to the effects of shrinkage.

High connection load capacities can be achieved using dowels because higher forces can be transferred through smaller dowel diameters. This is the preferred type of connection for laminated wood and it can be used together with inset steel plates (Fig. 14). There should be at least four dowels per connection, and dowels must have a

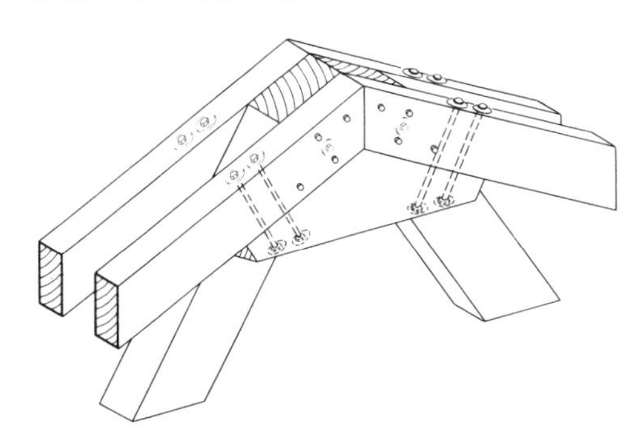

Fig. 14. (a) Ridge connection of a truss. Diagonals are connected to the upper chord by four steel dowels; clamping bolts are in the middle; the upper chords are tied together by bolts through a filler wood.

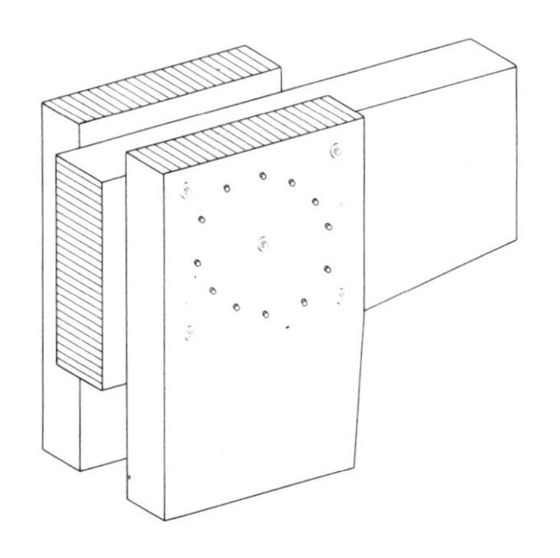

Fig. 14. (b) Frame elbow. Practical connection between a double post and a single beam by means of a ring of steel dowels. Clamping bolts secure the connection and are used also for assembly.

minimum diameter of 8 mm. Although dowels in wood provide sufficient resistance to lateral movement due to their tight fit, at major connections it is necessary to add clamping bolts or load-carrying dowels with a head and nut, which are not taken into consideration in the design.

Steel dowels are generally not kept in stock, but are custom-fabricated from steel bars (St37, plain steel). The loading capacity of the dowels is limited by their diameter and the resulting bearing stress on the wood.

Nails

Systematic tests made in the 1930s proved that normal wire nails can be used in load-carrying timber connections if they are stressed in shear (Fig. 15a). Today this is even more significant because of the simplicity of workmanship. Automatic impact nailers which can drive nails up to 120 mm in length have been developed. Larger nails can be driven pneumatically after setting.

Normally, round wire nails with flush driven heads conforming to DIN 1151 can be driven directly without predrilling. By this method wood grain is displaced laterally and is cut only under the nail's point. Because of the danger of splitting the wood, DIN 1052 gives detailed requirements for the minimum thickness of wood, nail spacing, and depth of nailing in relation to nail diameters. To avoid wasting wood, a maximum distance of nails is also given. Nails parallel to the grain cannot be considered as load-bearing.

Corrosion-proof nails should be used for building elements exposed to the weather.

Nails may also be subjected to pullout forces, but their resistance to pullout is sharply reduced after the wood dries out. Because of this, they may only be relied upon to resist pullout for wind forces of short duration, such as they occur in roof shingles, purlins, and rafters. Smooth wire nails are not permitted to resist permanent tension forces at locations such as hung ceilings. Serious failures have resulted from nails that have lost their grip in wood, even after many years of satisfactory performance.

Woods prone to splitting require predrilling. This is recommended for woods such as larch, large nail diameters, difficult access locations, and especially when larger forces act on small surfaces. Oak and beech woods should always be predrilled. In order to obtain good grip after predrilling, the holes should be predrilled to a diameter equal to 85% of the nail diameter.

Fig. 15. (a) Round wire nails with flush head conforming to DIN 1151. Designation: diameter in 1/10 mm × length in mm. Example 38 × 100.

Fig. 15. (b) Half-round wood screw with head groove conforming to DIN 96. Designation: diameter × length in mm. Example: 6 × 100.

Fig. 15. (c) Flathead wood screw with head groove conforming to DIN 97.

Fig. 15. (d) Hexagonal-head wood screw conforming to DIN 571.

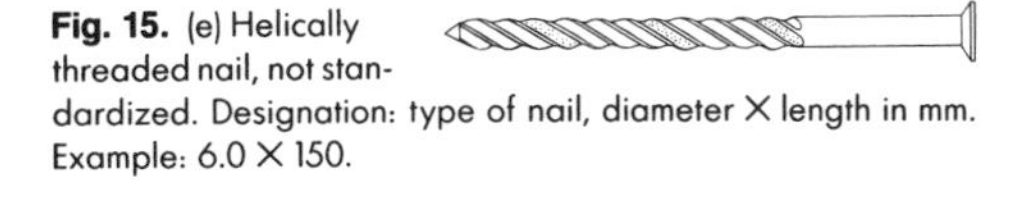

Fig. 15. (e) Helically threaded nail, not standardized. Designation: type of nail, diameter × length in mm. Example: 6.0 × 150.

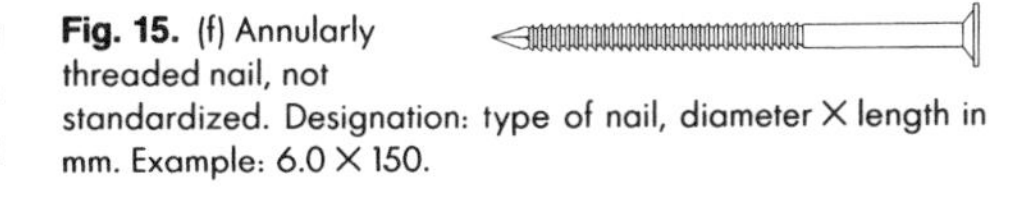

Fig. 15. (f) Annularly threaded nail, not standardized. Designation: type of nail, diameter × length in mm. Example: 6.0 × 150.

Fig. 15. (g) Staple, wire diameter 1 to 2 mm, ends generally resin-coated.

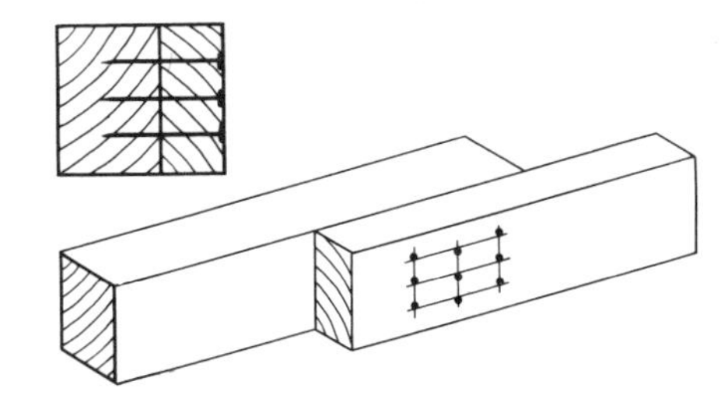

Fig. 16. (a) Single-shear nailing.

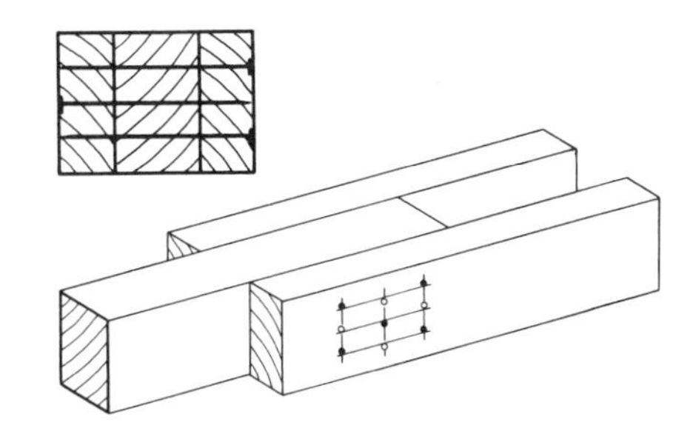

Fig. 16. (b) Double-shear nailing.

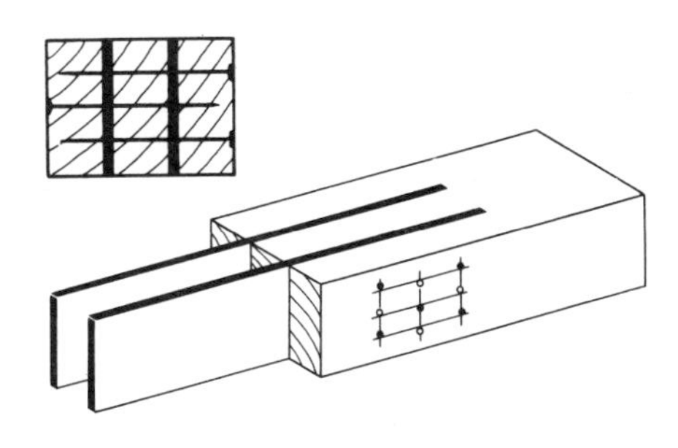

Fig. 16. (c) Fourfold-shear steel-to-wood nailing.

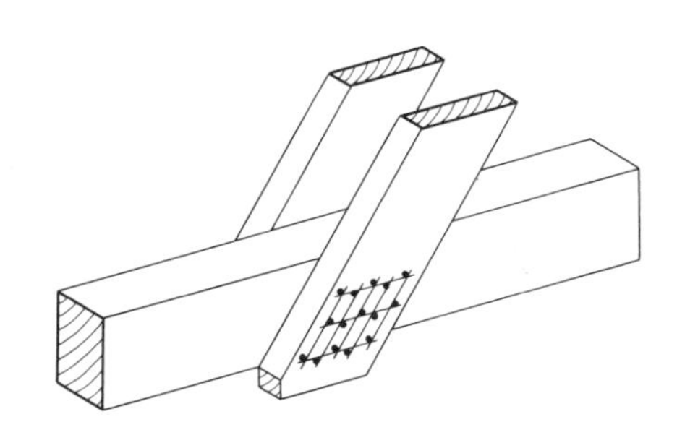

Fig. 16. (d) Offset nail arrangement. Nails are offset in the direction of the grain in order to reduce the danger of splitting.

The danger of splitting may dictate the use of thin nails, and therefore a closer spacing than for thick nails (minimum distances depend on the nail diameters). It can be seen that in such a case smaller nails can transfer a proportionally larger force per unit of surface. Also, predrilled nails allow proportionally larger forces per unit of surface because they can be spaced more closely. The allowable loads are shown in Fig. 58, page 71; they depend on nail diameters and their shear capacity (Fig. 16).

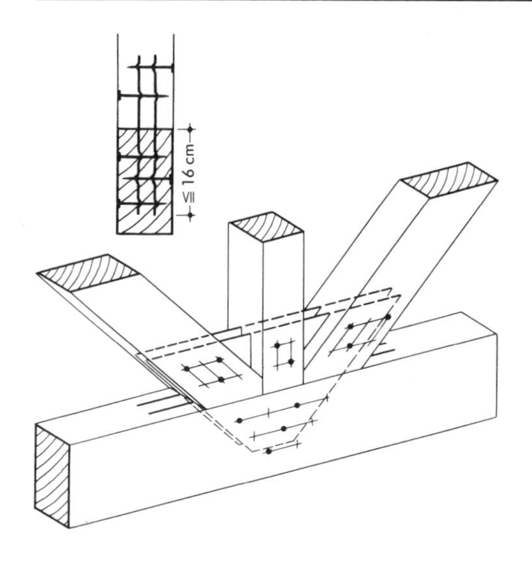

Fig. 17. (a) Greim system. Connection plates of 1.0- to 1.75-mm thickness are placed in 2.0-mm-wide sawn slits; load is transferred to plates by nails. Several struts can be joined, but no more than six parallel plates are allowed.

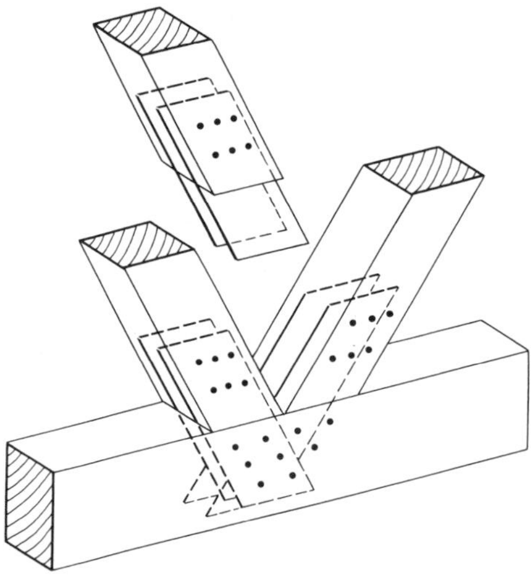

Fig. 17. (b) VB-Construction system. Each strut has its own nailed connection plate of 1-mm thickness, and compression struts are secured against buckling by 1-mm-thick metal inserts (stabilizing plates) placed beyond the connection.

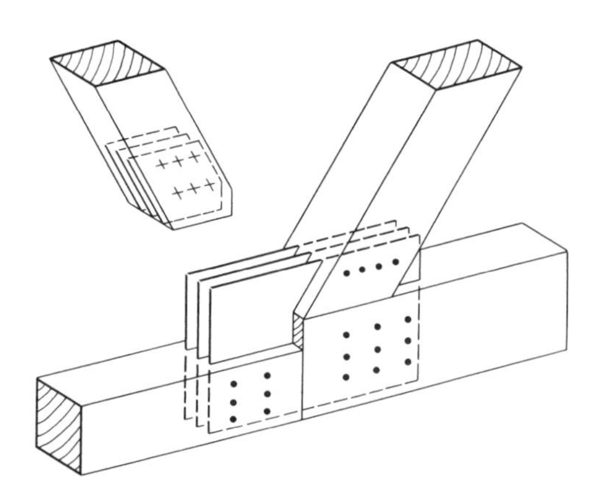

Fig. 17. (c) Greim system for truss nodes. Node connection plates are used simultaneously for splicing of members.

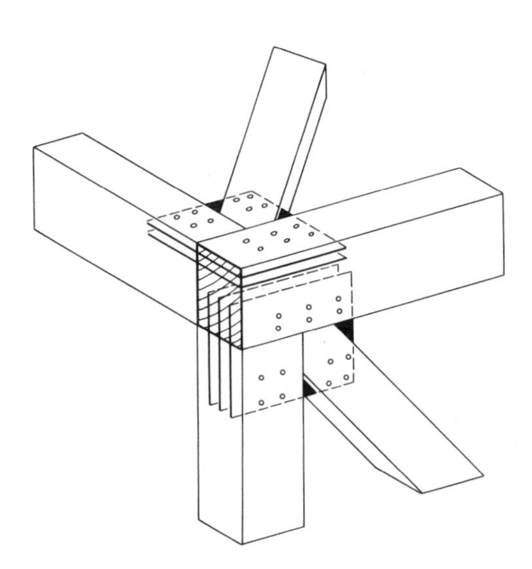

Fig. 17. (d) Steel-metal plate connection for three-dimensional nodes. If member sections are of sufficient size, struts can be connected in different directions, such as several stiffening diagonals.

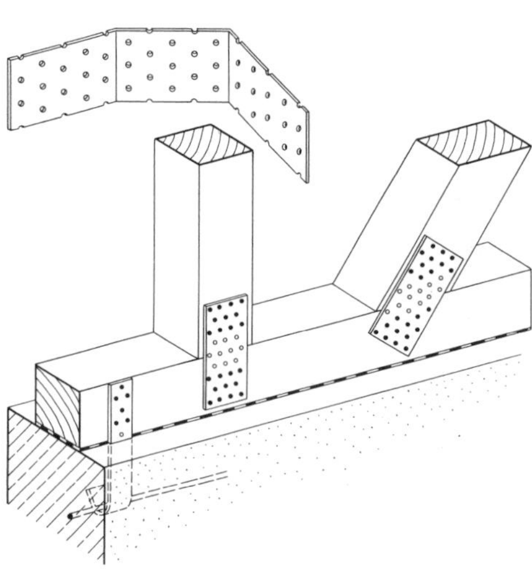

Fig. 17. (e) Perforated plates. Examples: connection plates, flat steel anchors.

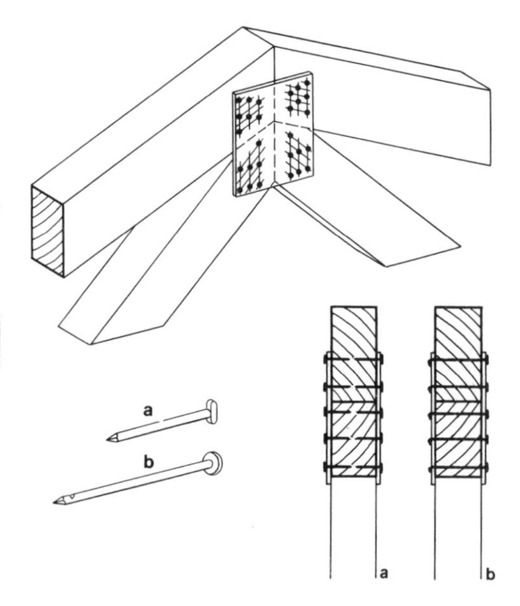

Fig. 17. (f) Bostitch system. External nonperforated steel plates 1 mm thick are nailed to timber either in single shear (a), or in double shear (b) by special Bostitch clinch nails.

Arrangement of Nailed Connections

In nailed connections, the member sizes are often governed by the requirement to provide sufficient connection surface for nailing purposes.

In order to obtain a correct nail arrangement in connections, those connections that occur only once should have their patterns drawn on their outer surfaces. Those that are used repeatedly should have a template of hard fiberboard or cardboard to mark nail locations on the surface. For load-carrying members, particularly for nailed trusses and cross sections nailed together, the design arrangement of nailed connections should be shown on the drawings. The arrangement of nails should only be left to the contractor if there is ample nailing surface or when staples are used. Even for a linear arrangement of nails, such as along the edge of a wood member, the nail spacing should be shown on the drawings in order to prevent splitting and to observe the usually small edge distances. Nail connections deform greatly in moist wood and their load capacity diminishes in comparison with similar connections in dry wood. Even if allowable stresses are reduced to take this into account, greater slippages should be anticipated. In such cases it is often advisable to use another type of connection.

Connections with Sheet-Metal Plates

Wood members subject to higher loads can be connected by means of sheet-metal nail plates. Generally the plates are prepunched and are at least 2 mm thick. They can be placed between the timbers or on the exterior faces. The nail holes must be equal to the diameter of the nails in order to allow for free nailing. If the plates work in compression, there is a danger of buckling unless they are supported laterally by wood. In such cases there should be a tight fit between the plates and timber surfaces, particularly at joints, in order to prevent buckling.

Connections can also be made with thin steel sheet-metal plates which can be penetrated by nails without predrilling. These plates are subject to building regulations because their thinness makes them susceptible to buckling. By arranging them in slits or on the exterior of the connections, and by nailing through them, very satisfactory and acceptable work can be achieved. Accepted systems such as Greim and VB-Construction can be used for compression and tension connections of several converging struts (Figs. 17a and b). Lateral wood members and wood fillers are not permitted because forces in struts are transmitted through plates. The nails connect the plates to the wood; they are loaded in multiple shear. The allowable nail load increases with the number of shear planes through each nail. For example, a nail subject to quadruple shear has a shear load capacity four times greater than a nail subject to single shear (Fig. 16).

Multishear nail connections are able to transfer relatively large forces with a small connection surface because the nail spacing requirements are the same as for double-shear connections (Fig. 17c). Oversizing of timbers to allow for nail connections is rarely necessary, and therefore normal nailed connections result in economical construction. Metal plates are generally galvanized. Under more corrosive conditions they may in addition be coated with a well-adhering plastic coating. Building components such as trusses and lateral bracing are generally fabricated in the shop, but single connection points such as truss field splices and lateral bracing field connections can be nailed together without any difficulty (Fig. 17d).

Perforated Plates

Connections for timbers that lie in one plane may be made with perforated or stamped galvanized steel plates, generally 2 mm thick (Fig. 17e). Wire nails and helically or annularly threaded nails may be hammered manually or by air hammers through predrilled holes. Connections with perforated plates may be assembled either in the shop, on site, or at the time when the various components are joined together.

Connection Plates, Bostitch System

This system uses nonperforated galvanized steel plates of 1-mm thickness which are nailed to the wood (Fig. 17f). Special T-shaped nails are driven pneumatically through the plates from both sides of the connection. Recently a new procedure has been approved. It consists of driving long Bostitch clinch nails with notched tips through plates on both sides of the connection. The nail tip automatically bends at the end and clamps both plates together. This procedure is most suitable for industrial fabrication of triangular or parallel chord trusses, but on-site assembly or individual connections are also possible.

Wood Screws

Wood screws of at least 4-mm diameter may be used for connections (Fig. 15b and c). In such cases, the length of the smooth shank has to be predrilled with a diameter d equal to the diameter of the screw, while the threaded part is to be predrilled to $0.7d$. Longer and larger screws generally have hexagonal heads so that they can be screwed with a wrench (Fig. 15d).

Load-bearing screws can be applied to all kinds of plates, panels, panel elements, and solid wood roof elements. Screws can be loaded both in shear normal to the screw axis and in axial tension. A screw can develop more than double the capacity of a nail, provided the screw holes are predrilled and the screws are properly screwed in. A hammered-in screw does not develop full gripping strength because the thread tears the wood so much that the screw is practically equal to a nail.

Flathead screws should not be subject to tension. The round-headed ones can be, but only if the fastened member has a shear and punching shear strength equal to that of conifers. For material of lesser strength sufficiently large washers should be used.

Properly screwed-in screws are suitable for resisting pullout forces of both short and long duration. Connections with screws parallel to the grain should not be considered in design.

Special Nails (Threaded Helically or Annularly)

Special nails are those that differ from the standard round wire nails (Fig. 15e and f). Because predrilling and screwing in screws is very labor-intensive, grooved driven nails were developed to obtain greater pullout strengths. However, their general application to date has been hampered by the absence of standardized allowable values for their shear and pullout loads in relation to nail size, type, and material. Load-carrying connections should therefore rely only on those products which are permitted by building codes.

The gripping value of special nails is not affected by the drying of wood. They are therefore suitable to resist pullout forces of long duration. Special nails are equivalent to wire nails in shear. In addition, better materials allow the use of more slender nails, as long as they do not buckle while being driven. Machine driving is particularly advantageous here.

Staples

Staples have long been used successfully in the packing industry. In timber construction they have been used to date only for fastening non-load-carrying wood linings (Fig. 15g). Many test results have recently become available showing that staples can be loaded both in shear and in tension. Because of this, they can now also be used in load-carrying members. In addition to fastening linings and sheathing to wood elements (Fig. 18), staples are now being used for connections of simple timber trusses spanning up to 8 m, but not exceeding 12 m in total length.

Standard staples are made from 1.5- to 2.0-mm steel wire whose originally round cross section has been shaped into a slightly barrel-shaped form. They are bent into a U shape; both shafts are thus connected by the staple's back. Staples are galvanized and generally resin-coated up to a certain distance from the tip. This coating results in easier staple penetration and assures a better grip. Staples are driven by a stapling machine and the staple's back can be either driven flush or left exposed, depending on the setting of the machine. Staples may be driven at right angles, but not more than at 45°, to the grain of the wood, because otherwise the danger of splitting requires that the

Fig. 18. Staples as wood connectors. Left: when wood products are connected to solid wood (a panel is shown here), the direction of staple backs is important. The angle between the grain of wood ribs and the staple backs should not exceed 45°. Right: when solid wood members are stapled together at right angles, only angles of less than 45° to the grain are acceptable without loss of load capacity.

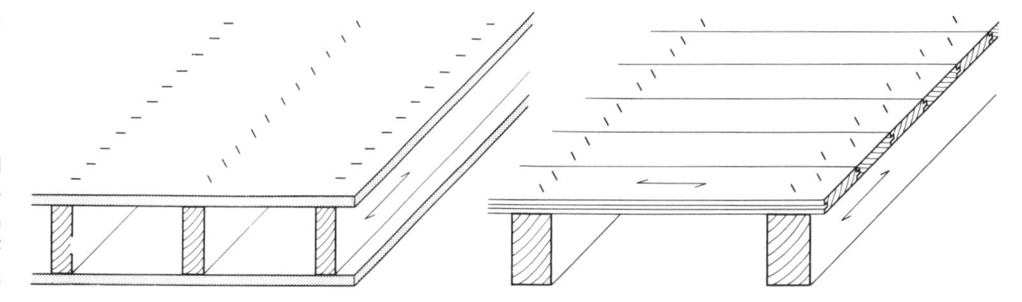

connection be considered as having a lesser load capacity and stiffness. Wood products connected with protruding staple backs must have the following minimum thickness:

Wood-chip boards	8 mm
Plywood	6 mm
Hardwood fiberboards	4 mm

These thicknesses have to be increased by 2 mm if staples are driven flush.

Additional details and possible limitations in the use of staples are given in building codes for each staple type, because this type of connector is also not standardized. Staples could also be considered as double nails by assuming the staple back to be a head. It has proved appropriate to apply the same design rules to staples as to round wire nails.

Nail Plates and Plate Components

Nail Plates

Nail plates consist of stamped steel plates 1 to 2 mm thick with one-sided nail- or claw-type stampings which are pressed into the wood (Fig. 19). They are used as truss node or connection plates. The stamped-out protrusions run in one direction, the main direction of a plate, which generally allows for a maximum loading. The remainder of the plate keeps the entire nailing group together and resists the tearing of wood when the plate is pressed in, or when the wood swells or shrinks. The plate carries the load transferred to it by the protrusions.

Wood members of equal thickness to be connected by nail plates are brought together tightly and presses simultaneously on both sides between the nail plates. Only single-piece member connections are possible. A certain economy of wood is achieved by this method, as compared to ordinary nail connections, because there is no overlap of members at joints and connections, and the allowable load transferred by nail plates is larger than that in ordinary nail connections (Fig. 20).

Nail plates must be driven by special machines in appropriate workshops; driving with a hammer is not permitted. Single presses can grip only one pair of plates, but larger flat presses can press several node connections at the same time. Machine assembly is especially suited for the fabrication of large numbers of wood members. Manual labor in such cases is minimal. A daily assembly of 100 standard roof trusses can be achieved easily.

Allowable loads of nail plates are regulated by special codes. The standard types can be loaded up to 1.2 N/mm² of the connection surface. The size of the surfaces to be considered in design is limited by the allowable loads permitted on the gross cross section of the plate. Standard nail plates made from fireproof galvanized steel having a minimum galvanizing thickness of 138 g/m² can be used for enclosed rooms and roof spaces subject to normal corrosion conditions. If nail plates are used without waterproofing in rooms of consistently high humidity or in the open, they have to be protected by additional corrosion-proof materials, such as plastics.

Fig. 19. (a) Nail plate, Twinaplate system. The round penetrations serve for load transfer, the straight ones anchor the plate.

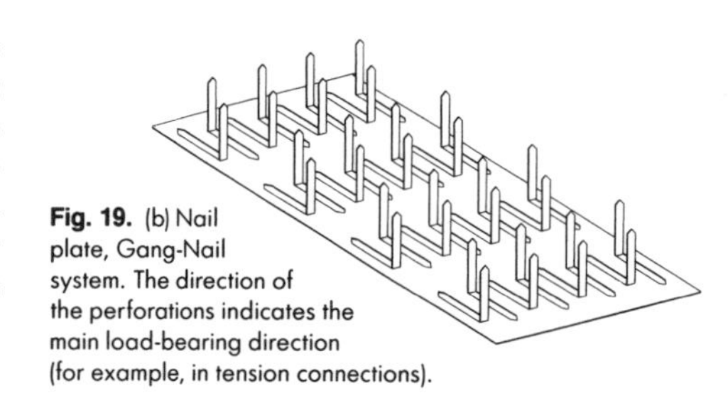

Fig. 19. (b) Nail plate, Gang-Nail system. The direction of the perforations indicates the main load-bearing direction (for example, in tension connections).

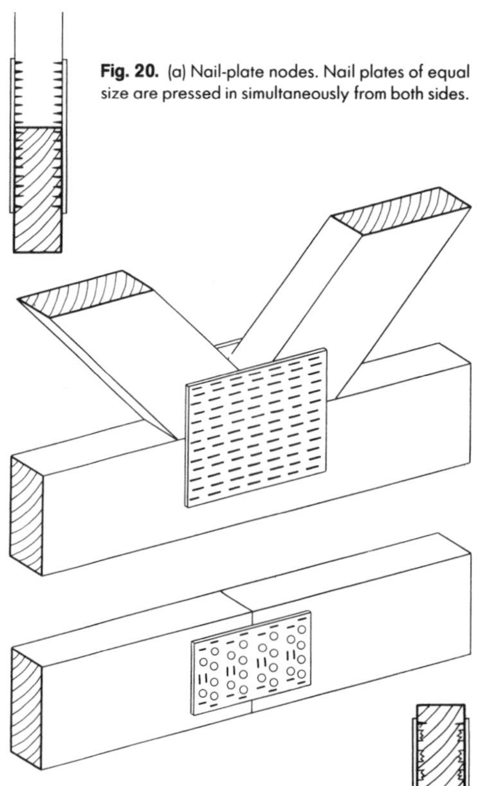

Fig. 20. (a) Nail-plate nodes. Nail plates of equal size are pressed in simultaneously from both sides.

Fig. 20. (b) Nail-plate joint.

Timbers connected by nail plates must be at least of grade II quality. In the connection areas they cannot be chamfered. Timbers must have equal thickness up to a tolerance of 1 mm, and the moisture content at the time of pressing must be at most 20 to 25%. The minimum thickness of wood, depending on the type of nail plates, should be 30 to 50 mm. Nail plates of each type are available in several sizes, so that they can be selected on the basis of loads to be transferred, cross sections of wood members, and the angle between members.

The Menig nail plate is basically different in construction and has a different load capacity (Fig. 21). It is placed between the wood members that are to be connected. Because of its double nail capacity, the Menig plate can be compared to two-sided shear connectors. It is generally used for connections of single or double members or for connections with two wood splices. Wood members can be up to 8 cm thick. Menig nail plates consist of steel wire dowels sharpened at both ends and embedded in a two-layered plastic holding plate. Dowels have a diameter of about 1.6 mm and a length of 25 mm. The holding plates consist of a 3-mm-thick foam layer and a fiberglass layer of 2-mm thickness. The fiberglass provides for a uniform penetration of nails, while the foam layer keeps the nails together during the fabrication of the plate and is completely compressed in the finished assembly. The plates necessary for node connections or splices can be cut from standard plates of 50- by 75-cm size, so that the plate can be well fitted to the connecting surface. Menig plates can carry a load of 0.75 to 1.0 N/mm² of the con-

Fig. 21. (a) Nail plate, Menig system. Two-sided sharpened wire dowels embedded in plastic plate. Only the dowels are load-carrying; therefore, the load can be transferred only through contact surfaces.

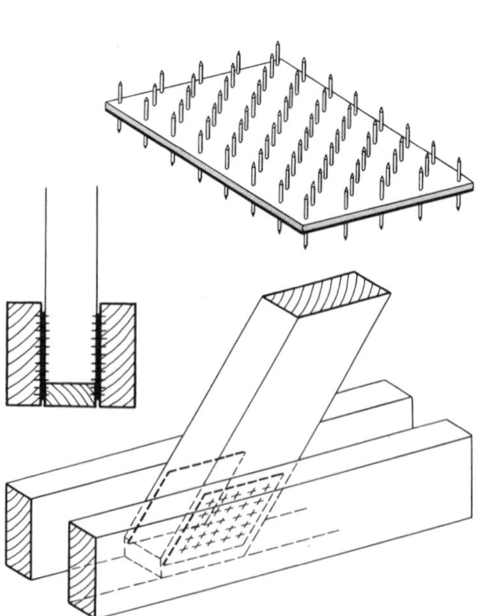

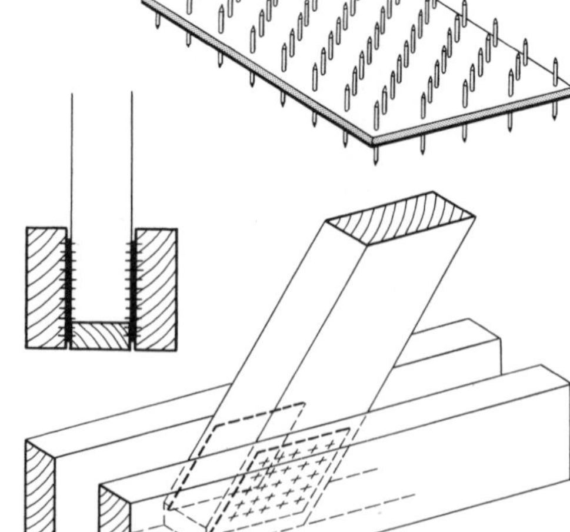

Fig. 21. (b) Strut connection with Menig plates.

nection surface. Care should be taken in assembly, choice of wood, and arrangement of wood surfaces according to the layout of yearly rings. In the shop, plates are pressed into the wood by means of hydraulic presses and stiff pressure plates parallel to the wood surface, but this can also be done on the construction site. There is no limitation on the span of assembled members. As a rule, Menig plates are used in heavy truss construction. In West Germany this plate system can be used only after a building permit has been obtained that controls the application, design, and quality of the system.

Formed Plate Connectors

Formed corrosion-resistant plates are used more and more frequently in beam connections which until recently were assembled by means of mortise and tenon joints, bridle joints, or bracket fillers. The advantage lies in more economical workmanship which does not require highly skilled labor. There is no weakening of cross sections. Connections which formerly were assembled in an approximate way can now be designed or their behavior can be proven by tests. Since there are no general building regulations giving their allowable loads, their design must be done on the basis of the allowable stresses for nails and plates.

Formed plates are factory made in practically all required sizes and are generally put together by special helically or annularly threaded nails which fit the holes. The arrangements of single plates are manyfold. The most important products today are HVV, BMF, and BIRA.

Angle plates, for example, are suitable for anchoring posts, supporting beams, or anchoring timber members to steel or concrete (Fig. 22).

Beam seats serve as connections of secondary beams to main girders. Anchoring of rafters between trusses, connection of wall head beams between posts, or connecting beams lying in one plane are all typical examples (Fig. 23).

Rafter anchors are generally used for anchoring roof or wall components against uplift. Purlins on rafters or trusses and wall head beams on posts are typical examples (Fig. 24). In addition, there are rafter seats for embedding the ends of rafters or roof beams, metal plate brackets, links for Gerber beams, universal connectors, ridge connections for lighter construction, and other special fittings. Special shapes for particular problem locations can also be produced on request.

These metal plates are suitable for connections of solid wood beams or smaller laminated wood sections, depending on the plate dimensions and thicknesses. The use of ready-made connection hardware is not suitable for larger laminated wood building elements. For large sections it is necessary to prepare individually the necessary hardware for joints, bearings, and pins so that each connection will be designed properly (Fig. 25).

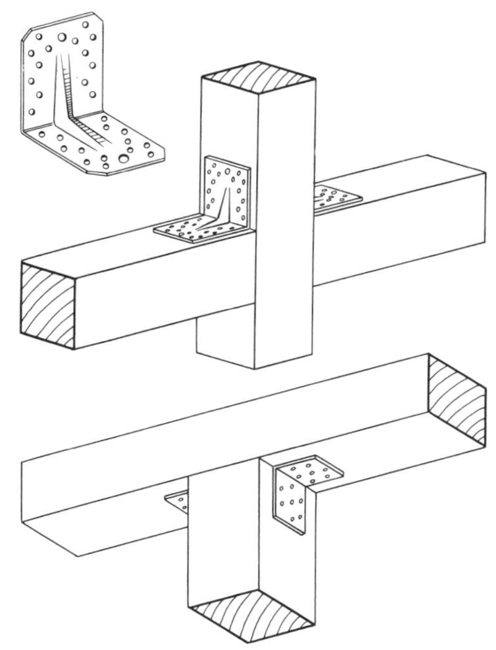

Fig. 22. Angle plates.

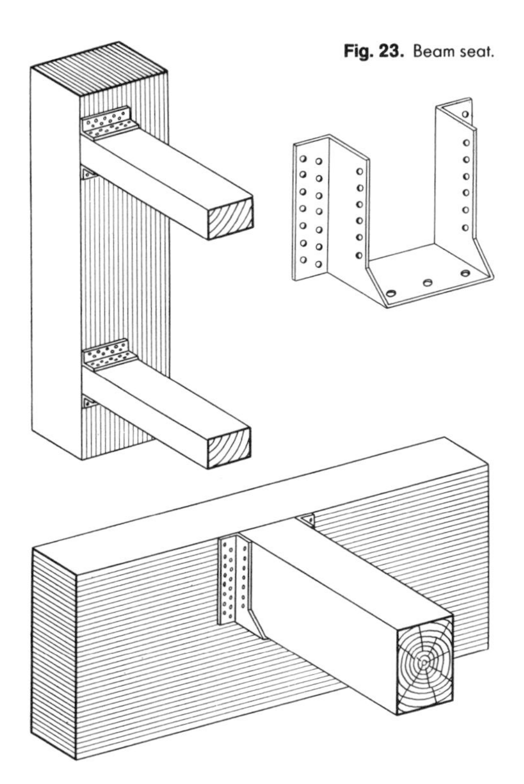

Fig. 23. Beam seat.

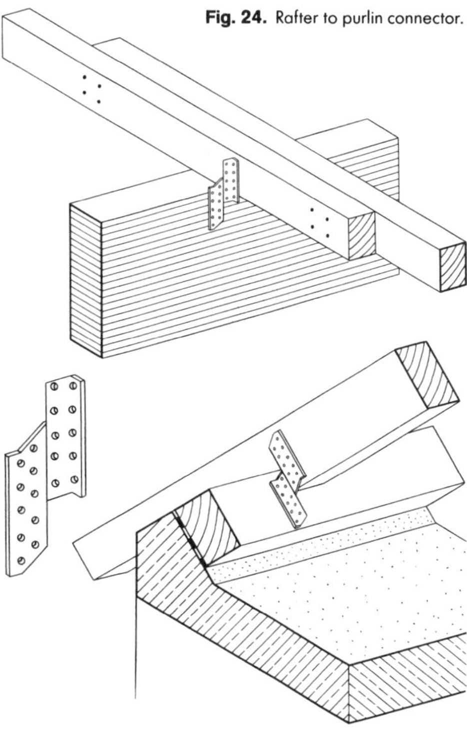

Fig. 24. Rafter to purlin connector.

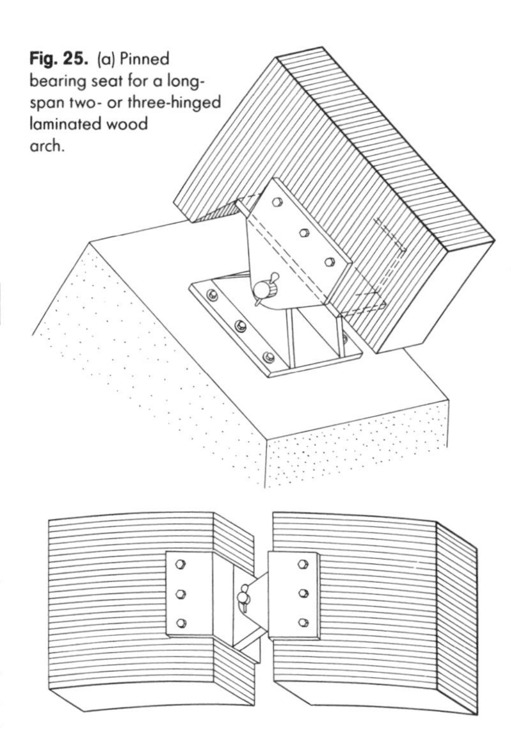

Fig. 25. (a) Pinned bearing seat for a long-span two- or three-hinged laminated wood arch.

Fig. 25. (b) Crown pin connection for a three-hinged arch.

Glued Connections

Building timbers can also be glued together along their surfaces, a type of connection completely different from those described previously. Glued joints primarily transfer shear forces.

Glued connections differentiate themselves from other connections in that they are stiff, namely, that under load there is no relative movement within the joint. Special structural configurations are needed in such cases if maximum strength is to be achieved.

The strength of a properly built glued connection parallel to the grain is limited by the shear strength of the connected timbers and the strength of the glue. The full strength of individual members can therefore be developed through the proper use of glued connections.

Load-carrying glued connections must be constructed with dry wood and planed surfaces using appropriate pressures and drying times, both of which depend on the type of glue and wood. Therefore, the furnishing of glued load-carrying members should be limited to those firms having qualified personnel and equipment to perform the work.

Glued connections in engineered timber buildings should employ weather- and moisture-proof artificial resin adhesives such as resorcinol or urea-based resin glues, which must be specially certified for such use.

Should the glued members be treated with a wood preservative, the compatibility of the adhesives with the preservative should be verified. Generally, however, preservation treatments are applied after the adhesives have hardened. There is practically no reaction between adhesives and fire-protective or oil-based compounds. Similarly, the compatibility between salt preservatives and resorcinol adhesives is assured. Other combinations of adhesives and preservatives may call for shorter preservative immersion times or longer adhesive drying times. If building elements have to be treated before gluing because of the need for longer immersion times or because the elements will be inaccessible after construction, only those oil-based treatment compounds for which there is verification of compatibility with the adhesives should be used.

Fabrication of Glued Connections

Gluing of wood having a moisture content greater than 20% is generally not possible. The wood should be dried to a moisture content varying between 7 and 15%, which is practical only in controlled drying rooms. Immediately before gluing, the moisture content should be checked by means of appropriate instruments, such as an electric moisture-measuring device.

In order to assure a very tight fit, wood surfaces should be readied immediately before gluing. After this, the surfaces are cleaned of sawdust using vacuum cleaning machines. The adhesive is applied in a uniform layer, preferably on both surfaces. In small sections, the adhesives are applied by brush, trowel, or hand roller, while for larger sections, such as the assembly of glue-laminated beams, they are applied by machines.

Glued and joined members have to be held together under pressure for about 6 to 20 hours until the adhesives have hardened. Various types of presses are used, for example, hydraulic flat presses for the assembly of panels, heavy threaded presses for laminated members, and even bolt clamps for the assembly of flanges of lighter members. Applying pressure by nailing is allowed only with I beams for joining laminated wood flanges with a previously prepared web (Fig. 26b). The room temperature at pressing should be at least 20°C for the usual cold gluing process; shorter drying times can be achieved by higher temperatures, particularly for hot gluing. In such cases, however, the setting time of glues is noticeably shortened, so that pressing times can be shorter, but the application of adhesives should be controlled tightly.

Glued connections are generally used for continuous longitudinal splices, such as in laminated wood beams, glued webs or girders, or panel construction. They are also used for joining single timbers, mostly boards and dimension lumber, by means of finger joints or, more rarely, scarf joints. In such cases, standard finger joint shapes and joint slopes should be used to achieve the necessary safety. Glued load-bearing finger joints with parallel surfaces are allowed only for special buildings and in joints with small contact surfaces (Fig. 28).

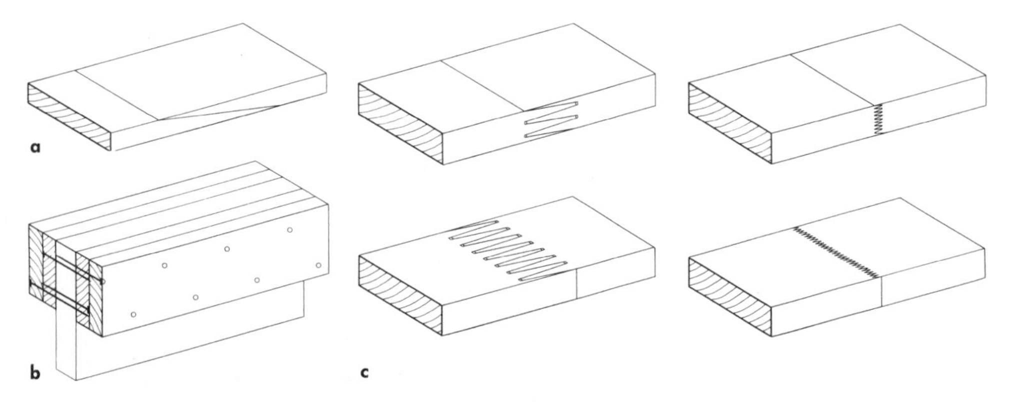

Fig. 26. (a) Joinery. Load-carrying, longitudinal splices can be fabricated as scarf joints with the slope of glued surfaces not exceeding 1:10. (b) Nail-pressed gluing. The application of pressure by means of nails is allowed only in special cases of I beams. (c) Finger joints are fabricated with fingers having a length of 7.5 to 60 mm. The new development of shorter fingers results in a saving of wood and adhesives without sacrificing the load-bearing capacity of the connection.

Building Components

Laminated Wood Components

Rectangular laminated wood cross sections can now be fabricated in one operation for widths of up to 50 cm, depths of 3 m, and lengths of over 30 m. Customary cross sections have a width of 12 to 18 cm and a depth of up to 2 m. Beams are fabricated as uniform or tapered girders, or as doubly tapered girders having maximum depth at the centerline, with both straight and curved lower chords (Fig. 27). In addition to single members, there are also twin members joined by intermediate timbers or fillers. The latter types are most suitable for the fabrication of solid-web girders or trusses. Laminated wood frames can be fabricated with curved elbows, with or without a protruding corner. Finger jointing of the entire elbow is also possible in lieu of the customary single beam and double post which are joined in the field by dowels (Fig. 14b).

It is also possible to assemble the entire elbow by means of finger jointing, provided the design takes into account a considerable reduction in allowable stresses, and members are fabricated with special precautions regarding weather protection, temperature, and gluing pressures. Finally, laminated wood is especially suited for arches, which have been executed in the form of two- or three-hinged arches spanning up to 100 m.

Glued Girders

In the 1950s special girder forms were developed using glued assemblies: "light" shapes for roofing rafters and purlins and "heavy" shapes for girders, beams, and frames. Laminated wood beams later replaced the heavy shapes, but today light shapes have even wider applications, particularly for roof structures such as triangular strut trusses, Trigonit, and undulated web girders.

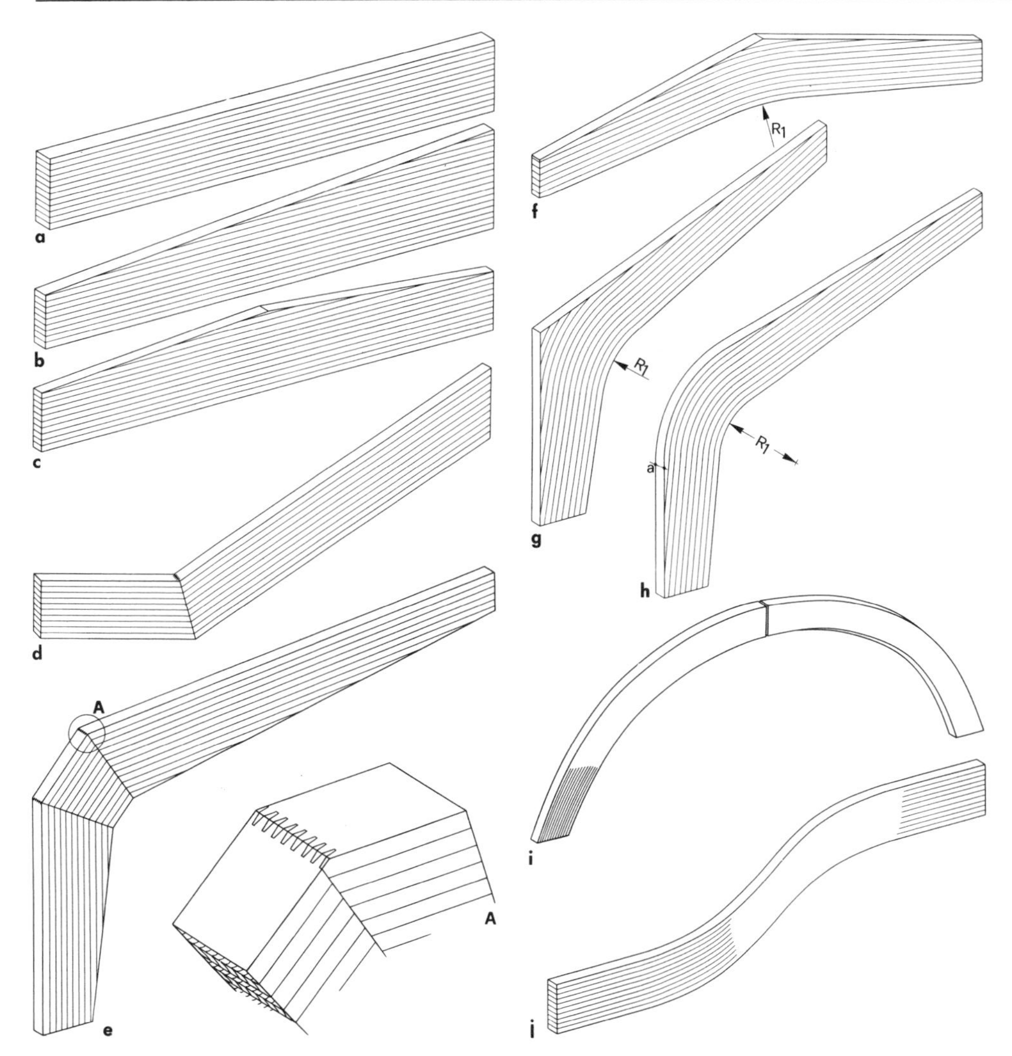

Fig. 27. Laminated wood girders and frames with straight edges. (a) Uniform-depth girder. (b) Tapered girder with variable depth. (c) Saddle roof girder with straight lower edge. (d) Bent girder; transverse tension forces in elbow must be investigated (for example, stadium bleacher girder). (e) Half-frame. Curved girders or frames. (f) Saddle roof girder with curved intrados. (g) Frames with protruding elbow. (h) Frames with curved elbow. (i) Arch. (j) Girder with longitudinally variable curvature. The elbows of (d) and (e) are built as finger joints over the entire cross section of the girder.

Diagonal connections consist of small-surface connections between timbers of different grain directions. Because of this, the allowable shear stresses in the joint are less than for parallel grain. Shear stresses are established in building codes in relation to the size of the glued surfaces.

The largest allowable span for such systems is 10 m for parallel or trapezoidal trusses, and 30 m for triangular type trusses. The truss depth for parallel chords should not exceed 100 cm; for trapezoidal trusses this is the average depth. Triangular trusses may be up to 300 cm deep. The depths of standard parallel chord trusses vary from 30 to 80 cm.

Triangular trusses shorter than 15 m may be fabricated in two sections, but those over 15 m must be made in two sections and have a nonglued field splice.

Flange timbers should not be thicker than 8 cm in order to achieve uniform drying. Flange cross sections should not exceed 120 cm^2, with the side ratio b/h not to exceed the ratio of 2.5 to 1. The angle between struts and the lower chord should not exceed 75°. Bearings must be placed on a node. Web plates may be added at bearings in order to transfer shear forces.

Trigonit-Glued Truss

Trigonit is a trade name for a glued truss in which the diagonals are joined together into a web by means of finger joints and then nailed to the flanges (Fig. 29).

The girder may be a single- or multiple-member truss and may have flanges that are parallel, tapered, or form a triangle. Glued connections of

Triangular Strut Truss (DSB)

A triangular strut system consists of a truss glued together (Fig. 28). Upper and lower chords can be either parallel or converging, and they can be fabricated in any length by means of finger joint splices. At their ends, web diagonals are provided with parallel or skewed tenons, which are glued into corresponding mortises in the chords. In the vicinity of truss nodes, the wood of chords and struts must correspond to grade I because of possible knots.

Adhesives consist only of resorcinol glues. Accurate fit of the joint fingers is extremely important.

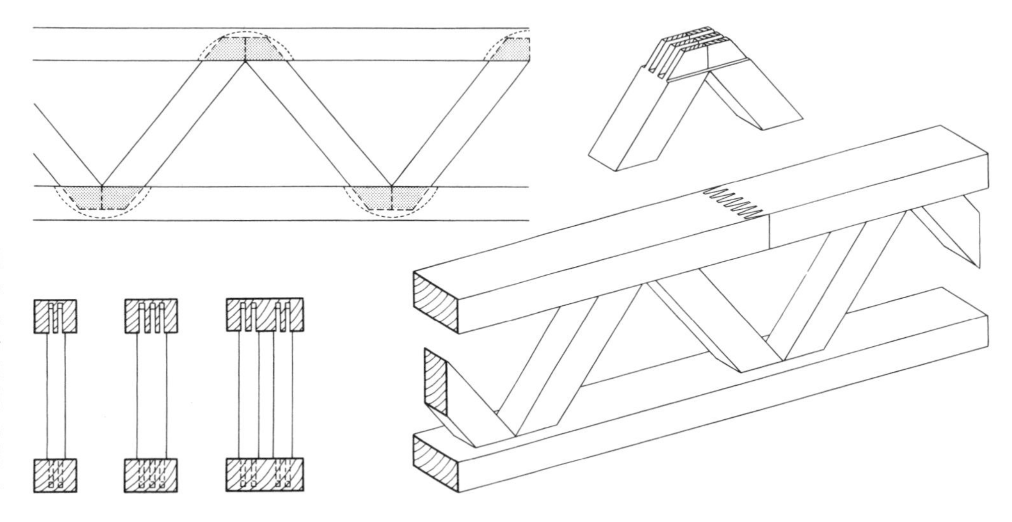

Fig. 28. Triangular strut construction, DSB girder. Diagonal struts are glued by means of finger joints. Depending on the intensity of stress, joints may have two or three fingers or there may be two adjacent diagonals.

diagonals are connections between woods of different grain directions, and their allowable stresses are regulated by building codes that govern Trigonit construction. The trusses glued in one machine setting should not exceed a length of 15 m. The depths of the standard parallel trusses vary from 30 to 80 cm. Single-flange timbers are generally at least 30 mm thick and 60 mm high, with the web thickness at least 19 mm. The width of struts is generally at least 60 mm, with the angle between struts and flanges not less than 30° and not more than 60°.

Only good straight grown timber conforming to at least grade II quality should be used for Trigonit construction. The truss can be reinforced at bearings by web plates nailed on both sides.

Undulating Web Girder

The undulating web girder is a solid-web girder with an I-shaped cross section (Fig. 30). One or more plywood webs are glued to the solid wood flanges. The web runs longitudinally in a sinusoidal wave, which stiffens it against buckling. It consists of a three-layered beech or birch plywood sheet made with an adhesive of quality grade AW 100 (weather and moisture resistant) and is spliced into a continuous sheet. The web is anchored in slightly tapered grooves within the upper and lower flanges. Since the flanges can also be spliced by finger joints, the undulating web girder can be fabricated in any length. The girder can be lengthened at any point because at all locations it has full moment and shear capacity.

The assembly of undulating web girders is subject to special criteria and requires considerable investment. At this time there are only four factories in West Germany that assemble undulating web girders.

Permitted uses for undulating web girders are limited to roof and floor construction. The maximum permissible depth of a girder is 800 mm; girders deeper than 600 mm must be built as box girders. Available standard shapes are:

- Girders with single web of 240- to 500-mm depth
- Girders with double webs of 430- and 440-mm depth
- Box girders having depths of 460 to 600 mm

In box girders, two or more plywood webs run sinusoidally parallel to each other at a distance of at least 5 cm.

The ratios of wave height to wave length range from 1:8 to 1:14 in all girders. Flanges thicker than 65 mm and wider than 160 mm must be constructed of at least three layers of boards glued together with parallel grain. Girder bearings can be strengthened by plywood sheets glued on the sides or, in case of box girders, by filler wood. The web is not taken into account in the computations of bending moments or deflections.

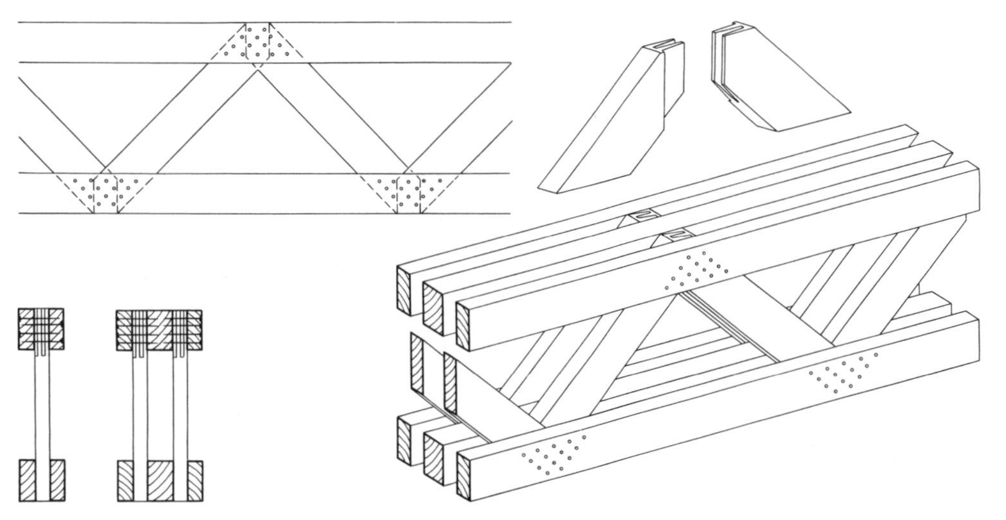

Fig. 29. Trigonit girder. Diagonals are joined together by finger joints; double or triple flanges are nailed together with each nail loaded in double shear.

Field Application of DSB, Trigonit, and Undulating Web Girders

These types of girders can be used only to support static loads or live loads smaller than 5 kN/m². Main applications are:

- As primary girders for rafters, floor beams, flat roof beams, support girders, and frames
- As secondary girders for rafters or purlins, associated with main girders of timber, steel, reinforced concrete, or prestressed concrete

Other applications of these types of girders have to be considered on a case by case basis. They also can be used for bracing or bracing struts, as supports at convergence points of several girders, or as ribs in panel elements.

Building codes do not permit these girders to be used under libraries, archives, filing rooms, factories, vehicular decks, and shops with either light or heavy manufacturing.

When these girders are used as floor beams, the floors may not contain any fillers that absorb humidity. When used as roof beams in cold roofs, there must be ample ventilation. Truss constructions

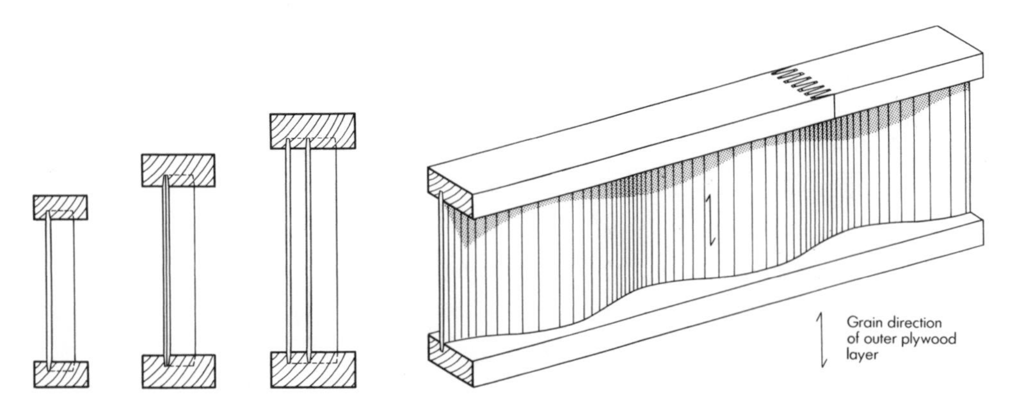

Fig. 30. Undulating web girder. The I-shaped girder cross section with an undulating plywood web glued into the flanges may be fabricated as a double web girder or as a box girder.

using DSB and Trigonit systems facilitate ample longitudinal and transverse ventilation.

The load capacity of girders must be computed for each case. If load tables are used, they should be checked for errors by a structural design office. The construction of standard truss nodes and connections, such as the eaves and ridge points of roof trusses, bearings, and interconnections, is shown in the building codes or in the brochures for each system.

These publications also contain the standard cross sections and design rules for each system. Treatment with wood preservatives can begin only after gluing is complete and ample time for drying has passed. Use only those preservatives that are certified.

Each DSB, Trigonit, or undulating web girder leaving the shop must be marked with a durable waterproof sign carrying the date of assembly and the name of the shop. The shop should have a permit approving its ability to perform gluing and should be supervised continuously by either internal or external personnel.

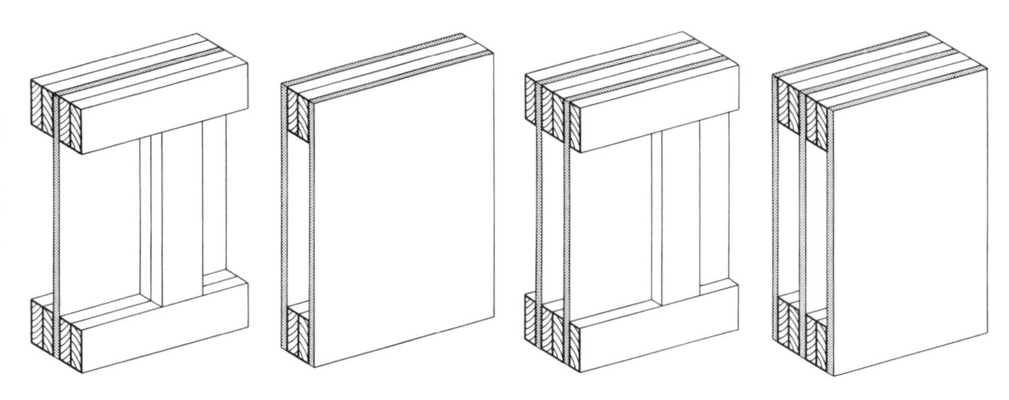

Fig. 31. Girder with panel webs. Girders subject to bending may have an I or box shape. Thin web panels must be stiffened by bearing stiffeners and generally also by intermediate stiffeners.

Girders with Plank Webs

The advantages of I shapes, compared to solid sections, is that higher bending moments and stiffnesses can be achieved with a minimum use of material. I shapes and box cross sections which are common in steel construction can also be assembled in engineered wood structures composed of glued or nailed members (Fig. 31).

Glued girders with webs made from plywood can be designed and fabricated according to the guidelines of DIN 1052, "Timber Construction," as long as the manufacturer has a permit for gluing load-carrying members. Web joints may consist of glued splice plates, scarf joints, or finger joints. Flanges may be spliced by finger jointing, and they are generally joined by glued nail-pressed joints (Fig. 26b).

There are also several types of webbed girders. One consists of webs composed of several layers of boards glued together with their grains crossed. This type of heavy web girder, known as the Kämpf, Wolff, or Poppensieker system, is licensed with regard to its construction and design. In spite of their economy of materials, heavy-web girders cannot compete with laminated wood girders which are economical in terms of workmanship. However, the Kämpf web girder is still used for some structures. Its web consists of two or three layers of boards inclined toward each other by 5 or 10° (Fig. 32). Web boards are spliced by means of finger joints to the required length, and individual flange boards are affixed to the web by glued nail pressings. The web can be stressed to twice the solid wood stress, up to 1.8 N/mm² in horizontal shear. The full web section can be used fully in computations of bending moment and deflections.

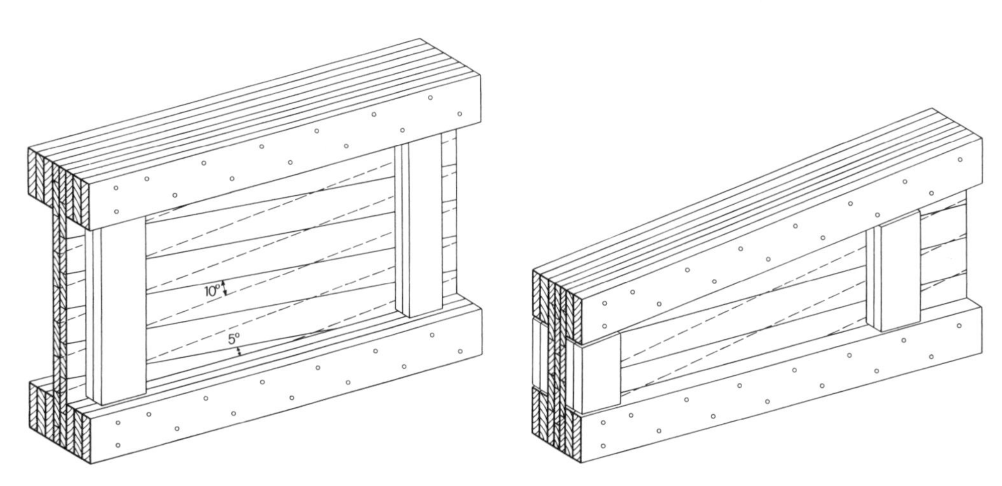

Fig. 32. Kämpf web girder. Girder web consists of two or three crossed layers of boards which are glued together. Layered flanges are attached by adhesives and nail pressing.

Special Trusses

The types of girders described here as Greim, Menig, and nail plate generally replaced earlier nailed girders made of planks and beams and girders with full web planks. They are outstanding because of their efficient shop assembly and their economy of materials. The construction of their node points is also efficient. All three types of girders can be fabricated as a saddle roof, a parallel girder, or a tapered girder, as shown in Figs. 33 to 35.

In addition, special structures can also be constructed in this manner, such as two- or three-hinged frames, all types of horizontal bracing, walls, and scaffoldings. For common construction, such as triangular or parallel roof trusses with spans of 7.5 to 20 m, each system has standard designs.

Erection of lighter trusses is simple because they can be erected by hand. Heavier ones need a light-capacity crane.

Exacting industrial production makes time-consuming finishing unnecessary. Required protective treatments can be applied right before fabrication.

Nail-Plate Truss

Nail plates of galvanized steel are permitted in the fabrication of timber trusses subject mostly to static loads (Fig. 33). Generally, the distance between trusses is 1.25 m, but depending on the load, it may vary from 0.625 m to 2.50 m.

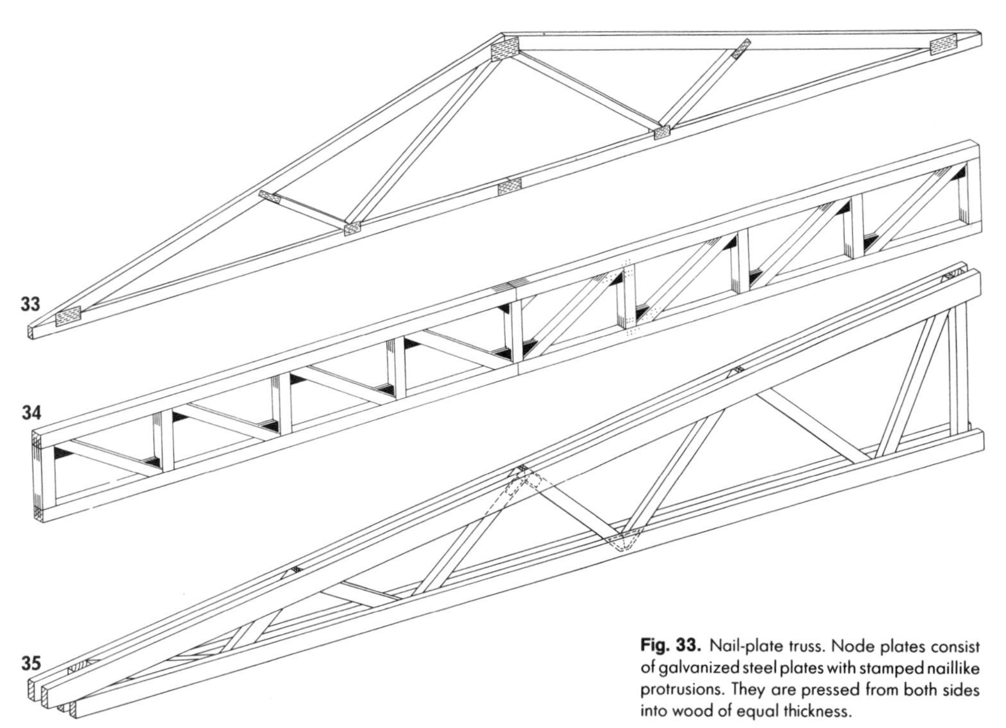

Fig. 33. Nail-plate truss. Node plates consist of galvanized steel plates with stamped naillike protrusions. They are pressed from both sides into wood of equal thickness.

Fig. 34. Greim truss. Steel plates are placed in sawn mortises and are nailed from the outside without predrilling.

Fig. 35. Menig truss. Node plates are placed between struts and are not visible in the finished truss.

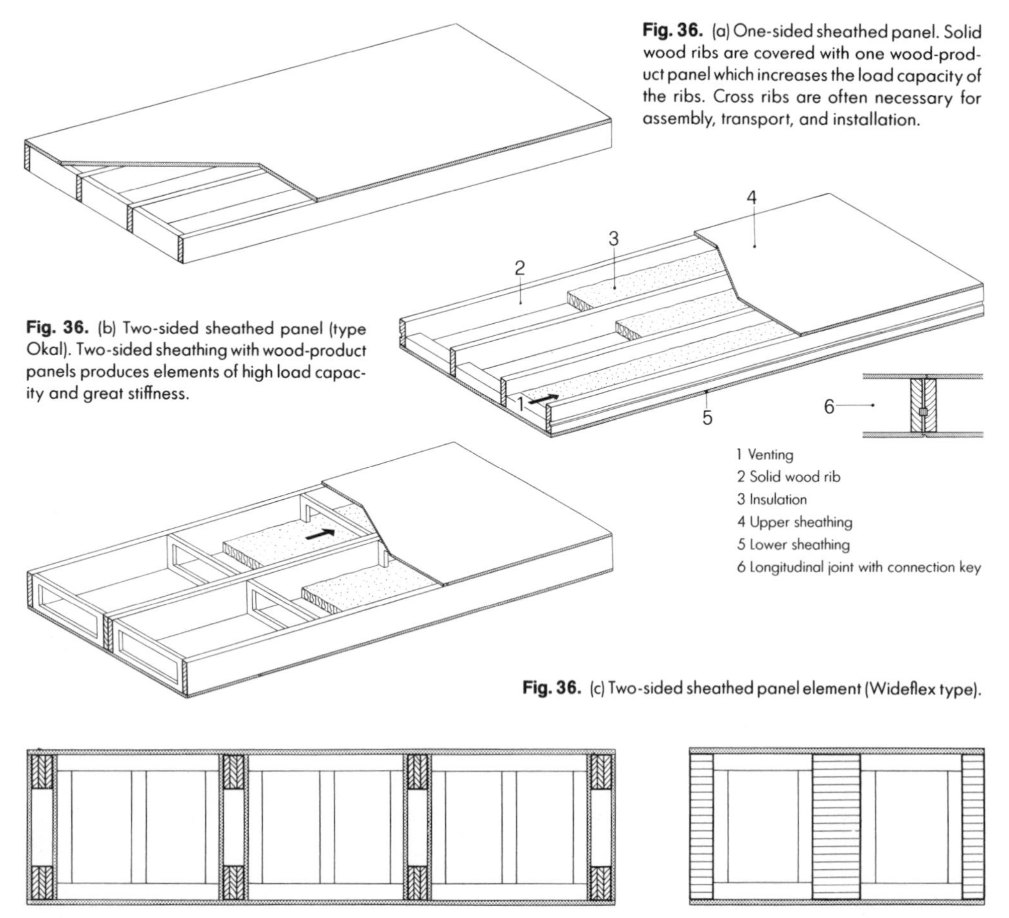

Fig. 36. (a) One-sided sheathed panel. Solid wood ribs are covered with one wood-product panel which increases the load capacity of the ribs. Cross ribs are often necessary for assembly, transport, and installation.

Fig. 36. (b) Two-sided sheathed panel (type Okal). Two-sided sheathing with wood-product panels produces elements of high load capacity and great stiffness.

Fig. 36. (c) Two-sided sheathed panel element (Wideflex type).

Fig. 36. (d) Cross section of long-span panel elements with glued ribs. Ribs can be built with thin web girders or glue-laminated beams, as shown here (Wideflex type), but they can also be built with DSB girders.

When there are additional loads or there is a need for wider spacing, several adjacent trusses could be bunched to carry the load. If the distance between trusses is small, small purlins, timber decking, wood-chip boards, or plywood can be placed directly on top of the trusses. The span of nail-plate trusses should not exceed 20 m. (For nail plates see Fig. 19.)

Greim Truss

Truss construction of the Greim type (Fig. 34) or of the similar VB type (described earlier) is available for:

1. Saddle roof trusses spanning 10 to 20 m and having a ridge height of about 1/10 of the span
2. Flat roof trusses spanning 7 to 35 m with a depth of about 0.08 of the span

Trusses are spaced at 2.50 m since this is a handy distance for supporting roof, wall, or suspended deck elements of the construction. A normal range of truss spacings varies between 1 and 4 m, depending on decking, snow loads, and lengths of span. For Greim type construction, see also prior illustrations (page 50).

Menig Truss

In comparison with the nail-plate trusses, Menig trusses are suited for heavier loads because in this type of construction several flange or diagonal cross sections can be assembled together (Fig. 35). Greater truss spacing, up to 5 m, can be achieved with normal roof loads. Optimum spans for this type of construction vary from 16 to 25 m.

If the loads are greater, smaller spans are recommended, starting from about 10 m. On the other hand, spans of up to 45 m have been constructed with Menig nail plates, particularly saddle roof trusses, with the depth of the truss at the centerline equal to 1/10 of the span. (See also Menig system nail plates, Fig. 21, page 52.)

Panel Elements

Panel-type load-bearing elements can be assembled by joining wood-product panels and solid wood ribs through gluing, nailing, or stapling. Such panels can resist compression and bending in floor or roof elements. They are especially suited for prefabricated buildings. Panels can be built with one- or two-sided planking (Fig. 36). Panels with double planking are preferred, because planking significantly increases the bending capacity and the stiffness of slender ribs and prevents their buckling.

This is especially true for glued two-sided sheathed panels for which the contribution of sheathing to the total load capacity under conditions of normal fabrication amounts to 30 to 60% of the total. If the sheathing is fixed to the ribs by nails or staples, the slippage of these connectors causes a decrease in stiffness as compared to the full section. In this case the contribution of sheathing reaches only 10 to 30%. Still, nailed or stapled two-sided sheathed panels can be very economical because the cross sections of ribs can be much smaller than for single-sheathed panels. Prefabrication of the panel elements results in significant savings at installation. The fabrication of nailed or stapled panels can be more economical than that of glued panels because the latter require the use of large flat presses.

Cross ribs may be necessary for securing panels against buckling or for reasons of construction. In roof and floor elements, they may be useful for hanging other building components. When panels are vented, the venting must not be interrupted by cross ribs. Because of this, cross ribs are built thinner than the ribs, or are built as cross frames with openings. The hollow space between the ribs is filled with the required insulation, generally a fiber product. If higher sound protection is required, additional construction elements can be introduced, such as acoustical sheathing on walls, additional hung ceilings, or elastically supported floor coverings in floors.

Panels are generally fabricated in widths of 1.25 to 2.50 m, with the length of the panels reaching 12 m or more. Joints in sheathing or ribs must be professionally executed. Plywood sheathing is generally jointed with scarf joints, wood-chip boards are strap-spliced, and rib splices are finger-jointed.

STRUCTURAL SYSTEMS AND DESIGN

Loading Assumptions

The loads acting on a structure are divided as follows:

1. Primary loads H
   a. Dead load g: sum of permanent loads. Example: dead load of structure itself, finishes, etc.
   b. Live load p: variable or moving loads on structure, especially live loads on floors
   c. Snow load s
   d. Other loads, such as soil pressure, liquid pressure, loads in silos, stabilizing loads from bracing members, etc.
2. Secondary loads Z
   a. Wind load w
   b. Braking loads
   c. Horizontal loads, from cranes, bells, etc.
   d. Earthquake loads

If a structural component is loaded only by secondary loads, in addition to its own dead load, the largest secondary load is used as primary load (for example, in wind bracing).

For the structural design of timber structures, two loading conditions are used:

- Loading case H: sum of primary loads
- Loading case HZ: sum of primary and secondary loads

Dead Load

Permanent loads are derived by adding the dead loads of all material and structural components. For timber roof construction, permanent loads consist essentially of the following:

a. Roofing
b. Insulation and decking
c. Dead load of structural components:
   - Planking or furring
   - Rafters or purlins
   - Beams or trusses
   - Wind and stiffener bracing
d. Finishes (suspended ceilings, linings)

The unit weights of materials, building components, and storage materials are given in DIN 1055, part 1.

Common Loads

	kN/m²
a. *Roof consisting of roofing tiles and concrete planking* Weights are given without mortar, but include furring. Mortar adds 0.1 kN/m².	
• Concrete planking with multiple ribs	
Up to 10 ribs/m²	0.50–0.60
More than 10 ribs/m²	0.55–0.65
• Plain roof tile according to DIN 456 and plain concrete decking according to DIN 1116	
For simple roofs (including slats)	0.60
For double or crowned roofs	0.75
• Interlocking roof tiles, interlocking pans, or flat roof pans according to DIN 456	0.55
b. *Metal roofing*	
• Aluminum roof (0.7 mm), including sheathing	0.25
• Double interlocking metal decking	0.30
• Steel decking, trapezoidal, U or W section	0.11–0.24
c. *Bituminous or other man-made roofing materials*	
• Roofing, 2-ply roofing membrane, including asphalt	0.15
• Surfacing, 5-cm gravel protection, including adhesive	1.0
Additional load for each 1 cm	0.19
d. *Asbestos-cement sheathing*	
• German sheathing on 22-mm decking, including roofing paper and planking	0.40
• Horizontal decking on furring strips, including furring	0.25
• Asbestos-cement corrugated roofing according to DIN 274	0.20
• Asbestos-cement sheets, small corrugation (residential sheets), unit weight 1.6 kg/dm³	0.24
e. *Insulation per cm of thickness*	
• Fiber materials as per DIN 18165 in rolls, mats, felts, or planks	0.01
• Foam material planks per DIN 18164	0.0015–0.004
f. *Wood sheathing, wood-product panels per cm of thickness*	
• Sheathing of conifer wood	0.06
• Wood-chip boards per DIN 68763	0.075
• Construction plywood per DIN 68705	0.08
• Hard particle boards HFH per DIN 68754	0.11
• Medium-hard particle boards per DIN 68754	0.085
• Porous particle boards (insulation) per DIN 68750	0.04
• Gypsum boards	0.10
• Plaster on lath in usual thickness	0.40

The weight of solid wood for design purposes is 6 kN/m³, that of laminated wood is 5 kN/m³. Purlins, rafters, and bracing for flat roofs can be considered as weighing 0.15 kN/m² of plan projection, and 0.25 to 0.45 kN/m² for sloping roofs with tiles. The dead load of trusses can be derived approximately by the formula:

$$g = 0.150 + \frac{l - 15}{200} \text{ kN/m}^2$$

where l equals the span in meters. In the design of sloped roof elements it is often useful to reduce the sloped weight g to its horizontal projection on the roof,

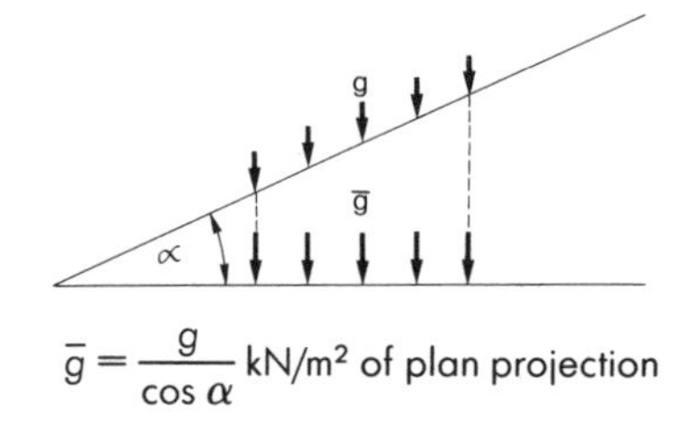

$\bar{g} = \dfrac{g}{\cos \alpha}$ kN/m² of plan projection

Live Loads

Live loads p are shown in DIN 1055, part 3. They are to be applied in such a way as to produce the most unfavorable shears and deformations. Therefore, in many instances a partial live load may govern.

Example. Beam with a cantilever. The maximum moment M_F and the maximum deflection f_F in the span are caused by a maximum span load $(g + p)$ and a minimum cantilever load consisting of only the dead load g.

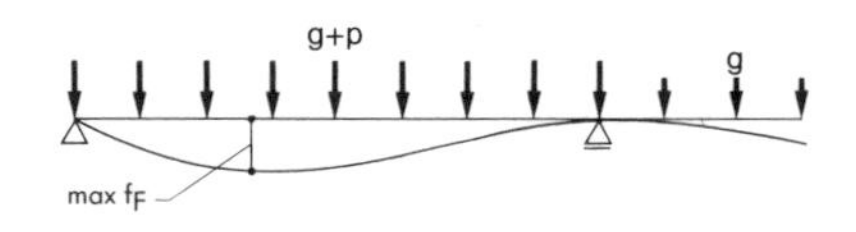

On the other hand, the maximum cantilever deflection f_K occurs for a minimum span loading and maximum cantilever load.

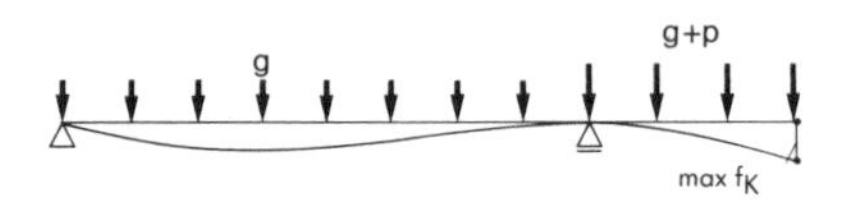

The following live loads are generally present in timber structures.

Vertical Loads

1. Roofs. Valid for horizontal roofs or those sloped up to 1:20, when temporary access by people is foreseen, such as for play, observation, or recreation. Wind and snow loads do not have to be added simultaneously. A single concentrated load of 1 kN (one person) is to be assumed at the centerline of each purlin, rafter, or upper chord of trusses which carries the roof directly. This load is not to be superimposed on snow and wind loads, and does not have to be considered when the snow and wind load on these members is larger than 2 kN. — 2 kN/m²
2. Floors
   - Attic floors — 1 kN/m²
   - Floors without sufficient lateral distribution of loads (planking floors) — 2 kN/m²
   - Floors with sufficient lateral distribution of loads (panel elements as long as they are keyed at joints) — 1.5 kN/m²
3. Balconies
   - Area ≥ 10 m² — 3.5 kN/m²
   - Area < 10 m² — 5 kN/m²
4. Stairs, access to stairs — 3.5 kN/m²
5. Bleachers with fixed seats — 5 kN/m²
6. Bleachers without fixed seats — 7.5 kN/m²

Horizontal Loads

Side loads on parapets and railings at rail height

- For stairs and balconies — 0.5 kN/m
- In assembly rooms, churches, schools, sports buildings, and grandstands — 1 kN/m

Snow Load

The standard snow load s_0 is established by DIN 1055, part 5, for various snow zones and the altitude of the site. Four snow zones and altitudes above sea level are given there for West Germany. The critical snow loads for zones 1 to 3 are 0.75 kN/m² for altitudes up to 200 m. They increase with altitude:

- Zone 1 up to 1.25 kN/m² at 800 m
- Zone 2 up to 2.30 kN/m² at 900 m
- Zone 3 up to 3.80 kN/m² at 1000 m

Only limited areas in the Harz and the Alps count as zone 4, the area with the most snow load. For altitudes above 1000 m, the snow load is determined individually by local authorities in coordination with the central German Weather Bureau in Offenbach.

For horizontal roofs the snow load s is equal to the standard snow load s_0. For roofs sloped at an angle α with the horizontal, and shedding snow freely, the snow load is

$$s = ks_0 \qquad \text{for } 0 \le k \le 1$$

where $k = 1 - (\alpha - 30°)/40$. The snow load is distributed uniformly on the plan projection of the roof surface. In addition, it is necessary to consider possible snow accumulations. In such cases the unit weight of snow should be considered as 5 kN/m³ as long as no melting can occur.

For roofs up to 45° of slope, the snow and wind loads overlap and the design is made for loading case HZ. It is also permitted to consider the snow load s and the wind load w simultaneously using the following formulas, where the most unfavorable load governs:

$$s + \frac{w}{2}$$

or

$$w + \frac{s}{2}$$

In these cases it is not possible to take advantage of stress increases allowed for loading case HZ. For steeper roofs the simultaneous loads of wind and snow should be considered only where accumulations of snow are possible, such as at the confluence of several roofs. The computation of snow load s' in the plane of the roof can be transposed from the horizontal snow load s by means of

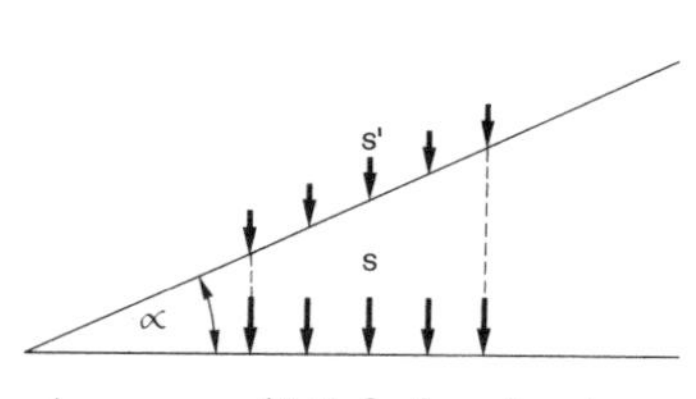

$s' = s \cos \alpha$ kN/m² of roof surface

Wind Load

DIN 1055, part 4, is the basic code for wind loads on structures not subject to oscillation.

Structures can be considered as nonoscillating without any special analysis if their slenderness ratio $h/b_1 \le 5$, where b_1 is the smallest width of the laterally stiffened structure and h is its height.

For more slender structures it can be determined by the code whether or not the structure is oscillating after its natural frequency has been established.

Structures are generally designed for wind loads acting in the direction of their main axes, with the wind acting horizontally. The applied wind load depends on the form of the building. It acts as pressure, suction, and friction simultaneously. The magnitude of the resulting wind load on a building is

$$W = c_f q A \quad [\text{kN}]$$

where c_f = aerodynamic load coefficient
q = wind pressure, in kN/m²
A = exposed surface, in m²

Fig. 37. Wind speed and wind pressure in relation to height.

1 Height above Land, m	2 Wind Speed v, m/s	3 Wind Pressure q, kN/m²
From 0 to 8	28.3	0.5
Above 8 to 20	35.8	0.8
Above 20 to 100	42.0	1.1
Over 100	45.6	1.3

The aerodynamic coefficient for prismatic buildings enclosed on all sides with usual building surfaces equals 1.2.

DIN 1055, part 4, also contains c_f coefficients for buildings with curved surfaces, for trusses, single beams, building elements lying behind each other, and flexible objects (flags). If the wind-resisting object is composed of several bodies, their wind resistance is seldom an addition of single wind resistances. In important cases the values should be derived by wind tunnel tests.

The exposed surface *A* is defined in tables of coefficients and can coincide with the main projection of a building.

The wind pressure *q* depends on the wind speed and is shown in Fig. 37 according to the elevation above ground. Higher wind speeds can be caused by local conditions.

While the design of a building is based on the total wind load *W*, individual building components have to be designed for higher wind pressures that depend on the shape of the building surfaces as defined for various building shapes and wind directions.

Wind pressures act normal to exposed surfaces of objects. Their magnitude equals

$$W = c_p q \quad [\text{kN/m}^2]$$

where c_p is the aerodynamic pressure coefficient.

The c_p coefficients for pressure or suction are average values for single surfaces of components. Therefore, the pressure for single members, such as purlins, rafters, wall posts, or facade elements, should be set 25% higher. The list of c_p coefficients includes values for building elements enclosed from all sides or partially open, for free-standing roofs, and for cylindrical shapes.

Because of repeated major storm damages that occurred primarily on flat roofs through suction, and as a result of new research, more exact requirements have been established for suction at the intersection of roofs and walls. Correspondingly higher values of c_p are to be used for anchoring roofs and walls at edges and corners. A structural analysis may be omitted for ordinary buildings having a maximum height of 20 m and widths of less than 12 m, provided the following construction rules are used:

- Sheathing boards are to be fastened onto each rafter, truss, or wall post by at least two wire nails or equivalent fasteners, such as screws or staples.
- Roof sheathing consisting of wood-chip or plywood panels mut be secured by at least six wire nails per square meter. At edges and corners there must be at least 12 to 18 wire nails per square meter. Generally, screws are preferable.
- In addition to the customary fastening by rafter nails, every third rafter must be secured at its support to beams by lashings, ties, bolts, or metal plates.
- The roof structure must be fastened to its understructure by steel anchors (flat-steel anchors no less than 4 mm thick) spaced at least every 1 m in corners and 2 m at edges. Each building component to which an anchor is secured must weigh at least 4.5 kN.

Structural Systems

The design of load-carrying members requires the knowledge of the bending moments *M*, axial forces *N*, and shear *Q* at every cross section for each load case. Structural computations give the necessary values. For this purpose the structure is idealized to a certain degree and the static system is represented by lines which denote the axes of actual members and indicate the end bearing conditions or continuity of members. Internal forces can later be computed by the rules of statics, and deflections by the analysis of deformations.

Of special importance are the assumptions of support on which the static analysis is based. They must correspond to the actual field conditions. In wood construction, fixed supports and fully fixed longitudinal movements are rarely assumed because of the compressibility of wood and the flexibility of connections. Most bearings are assumed to allow free rotation, pin support, and free longitudinal movement.

Single-Span Beams

A single-span beam supported at both ends is representative of floor beams, rafters, girders, roof beams, or struts. One bearing can be fixed, but free to rotate, the other is free to rotate and move longitudinally. The dimensioning of single-span timber beams is often governed by a limitation on allowable deflection rather than by their load capacity. Because of this, beams with a uniform cross section are generally not the most economical ones, but in many instances are the only feasible solutions for members such as floor beams and suspended roof beams.

Single-Span Beams with Cantilever

A better deflection relationship occurs in single-span beams with one or two cantilever ends. The end moments reduce moment and deflection at the centerline of the span. As the cantilever length increases, the end moment or cantilever deflection finally governs the design. For a uniform load and one cantilever, the moments at the support and at the centerline are approximately equal when the ratio of span *l* to cantilever *a* equals:

$$\frac{l}{a} = \frac{7}{3}$$

In this case, the beam with uniform cross section is utilized to its greatest advantage.

Multispan Beams

Continuous Beam

A continuous beam over two or three supports allows the use of smaller cross sections than those needed for single-span beams of equal span. In most cases deflection does not govern the design. In addition, the allowable stresses for moments at interior supports, which govern in most cases, are 10% higher. For continuous beams over more than two equal spans the maximum moments at an interior support are smaller than the maximum moments at the centerline of simple beams.

It must be remembered, however, that each beam's cross section must be spliced by means of appropriately stiff connections because solid wood cannot be furnished in lengths required for multispan beams, and the length of laminated beams is limited by restrictions on transportation.

Moment splices can be built with solid wood lashes, steel gusset plates, or extruded steel sections, connected by nails, dowels, or shear connectors. Splices can also be made by finger jointing the entire cross section.

Special designs are necessary if the multispan beam has different span lengths and moving loads or when there is settlement of supports due to shrinkage of the substructure or subsidence of foundations. Not only internal forces, but also deflections are affected by such settlement.

Coupled Beams

Coupled beams are a special kind of continuous beam. They are generally used for purlins, that is, horizontal dimension lumber resting on rafters and carrying roof sheathing. In this type of construction the purlins overlap each other at interior supports, so that moments at the supports, which are higher than those at the centerline of the span, are resisted by double sections. In order to achieve the maximum load-carrying capacity, the ends of the overlap are attached to the adjacent sections by means of ordinary connection devices, such as nails, steel dowels, or sheer connectors. When roof sheathing is nailed, it must be kept in mind that the purlins are offset by one width in every bay. If the underside of the roof is exposed to view, it may be necessary in some cases to avoid this system because of its appearance.

Gerber Beam

By introducing pin connections within a beam, the bending moments in a continuous beam can be arranged in such a way that moments at the supports and at the centerlines are approximately equal for a uniform load. Zero moments are present in pin connections. The number of pins must be equal to the number of interior supports. Generally, spans with pins alternate with those without them. Gerber beams with only one span without pins may be used for larger spans in order to reduce the length of each beam.

SINGLE-SPAN BEAM

Uniform load

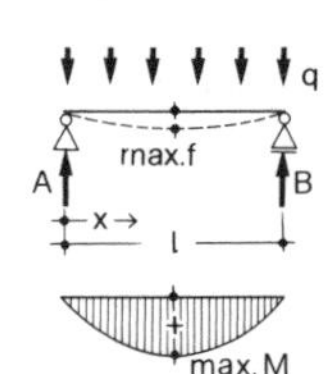

$A = B = \frac{q \cdot l}{2} = \max Q$

$M = \frac{q \cdot x \cdot (l-x)}{2}$;

$\max M = \frac{q \cdot l^2}{8}$

Moment diagram M

Deflection at centerline

$\max f = \frac{5 \cdot q \cdot l^4}{384 \cdot E \cdot J}$

for $f = \frac{l}{300}$ we have

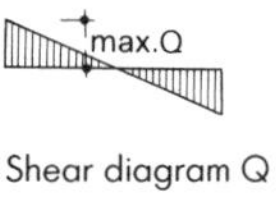

Shear diagram Q

req'd $J = 0{,}313 \cdot \max M \cdot l$

(J in cm⁴, M in Nm, l in m)

Concentrated load at centerline

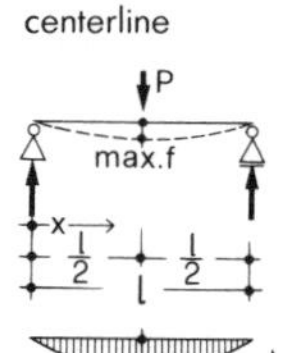

$A = B = \frac{P}{2} = \max Q$

$M = \frac{P \cdot x}{2}$; $\max M = \frac{P \cdot l}{4}$

$\max f = \frac{P \cdot l^3}{48 \cdot E \cdot J}$

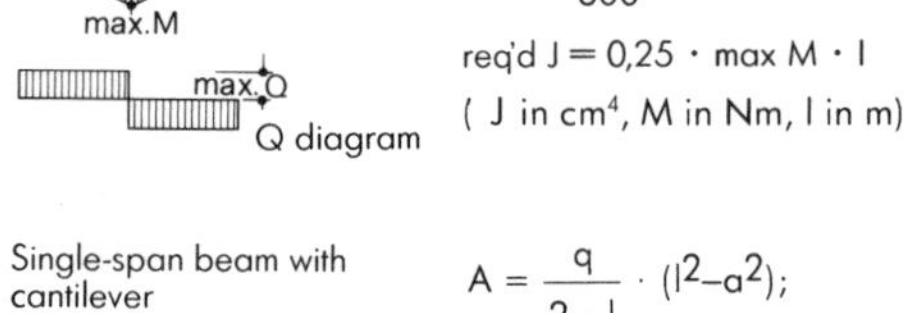

M diagram

for $f = \frac{l}{300}$ we have

Q diagram

req'd $J = 0{,}25 \cdot \max M \cdot l$

(J in cm⁴, M in Nm, l in m)

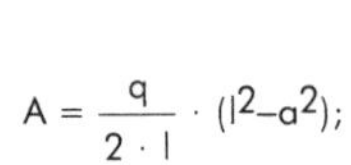

Single-span beam with cantilever

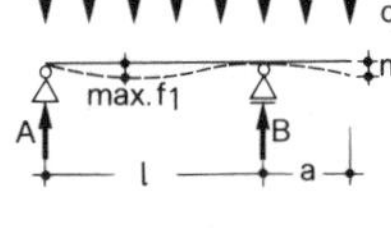

$A = \frac{q}{2 \cdot l} \cdot (l^2 - a^2)$;

$B = \frac{q}{2l} \cdot (l + a)^2$

$M_B = \frac{q \cdot a^2}{2}$;

$\max M = \frac{A^2}{2 \cdot q}$

M diagram

$\max f_1 = \frac{q \cdot l^2}{384 \cdot E \cdot J} \cdot (5l^2 - 12a^2)$ for $a \leq \frac{l}{2}$

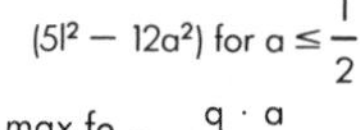

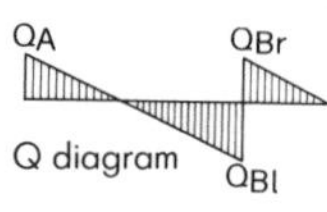

Q diagram

$\max f_2 = \frac{q \cdot a}{24 \cdot E \cdot J} \cdot (3a^3 + 4a^2 \cdot l - l^3)$

CONTINUOUS BEAM

Two-span beam

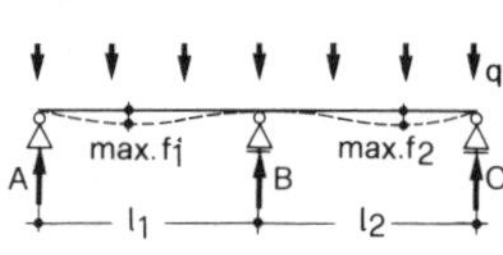

for $l_1 = l_2 = l$ we have

$A = C = \frac{3}{8} \cdot q \cdot l$;

$B = \frac{5}{4} q \cdot l$

$M_B = -\frac{q \cdot l^2}{8}$;

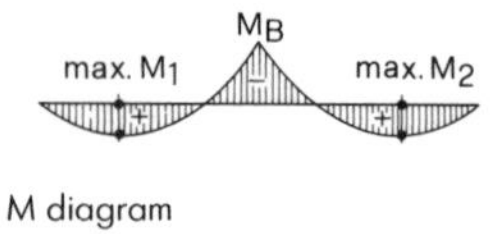

M diagram

$\max M_1 = \max M_2 = \frac{9 \cdot q \cdot l^2}{128}$

Q diagram

$\max f_1 = \max f_2 = 0{,}0054 \frac{q \cdot l^4}{E \cdot J}$

Three-span beam

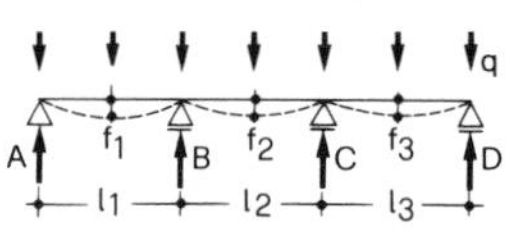

M diagram

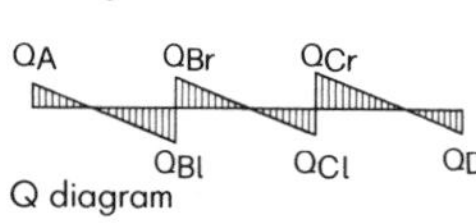

Q diagram

for $l_1 = l_2 = l_3 = l$ we have

$A = D = 0{,}4 \cdot q \cdot l$

$B = C = 1{,}1 \cdot q \cdot l$

$M_B = M_2 = -\frac{q \cdot l^2}{10}$

$M_1 = M_3 = \frac{q \cdot l^2}{12{,}5}$

$M_2 = \frac{q \cdot l^2}{40}$

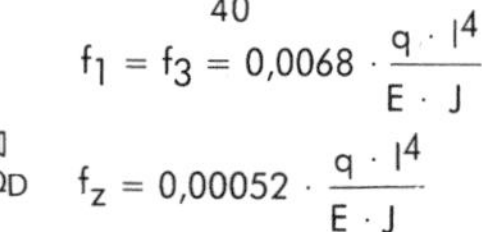

$f_1 = f_3 = 0{,}0068 \cdot \frac{q \cdot l^4}{E \cdot J}$

$f_z = 0{,}00052 \cdot \frac{q \cdot l^4}{E \cdot J}$

Coupled beam

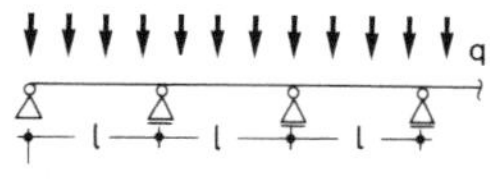

Plan view

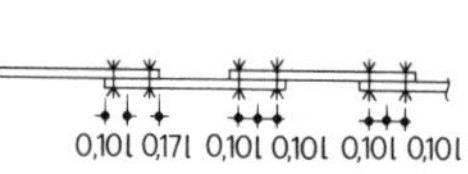

M diagram

Moments/
End span:
$M \approx 0{,}080 \cdot q \cdot l^2$
Inner span:
$M \approx 0{,}046 \cdot q \cdot l^2$
Moments at support don't govern!
Couple force:
$P \approx 0{,}42 \cdot q \cdot l$

Distance of couple force from inner support (center of connection)

Gerber beam
for regular span length l

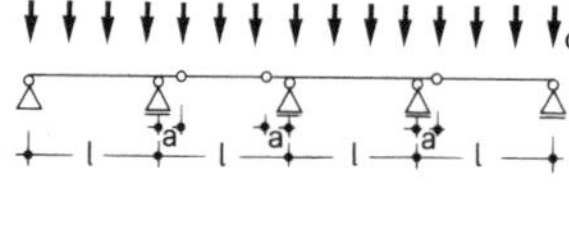

Beam moments ≈ support moments
End span:
$M_E \approx 0{,}96 \cdot q \cdot l^2$
Inner span:
$M_l \approx 0{,}63 \cdot q \cdot l^2$

M diagram

Gerber beam
for long span length l

Beam lengths
Interior:
$L_l = l$
Exterior:
$L_A = l + a = 1{,}1465 \cdot l$
$L_E = l - e = 0{,}875 \cdot l$

M diagram

KNEE-BRACED BEAMS, STRUT-SUPPORTED BEAMS

Knee-braced beam

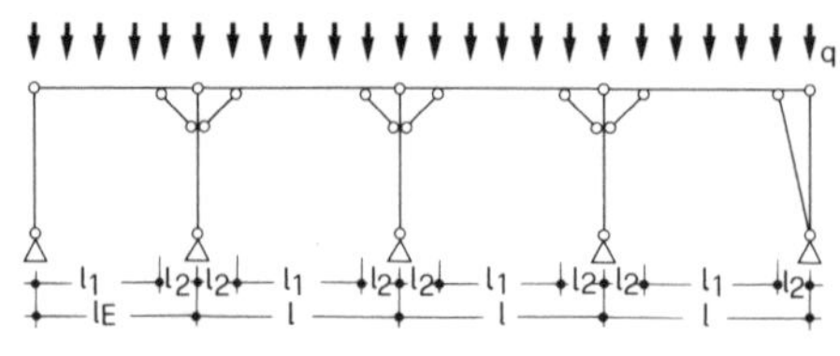

Strut-supported beam

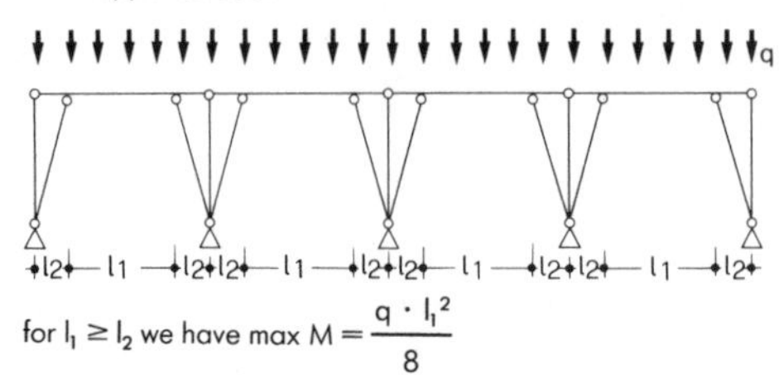

for $l_1 \geq l_2$ we have $\max M = \frac{q \cdot l_1^2}{8}$

Numerical tables are available for establishing the distance between pins. Pin connections must be built with care. Connections may consist of bolts (Fig. 13b), preassembled hardware, or special shear connectors.

Since they are statically determinate, Gerber beams are not sensitive to settlement of supports.

Note: In diagrams at left, J = moment of inertia of cross section; E = modulus of elasticity.

Knee-Braced and Strut-Supported Beams

The knee-braced beam has been known in timber construction since ancient times. It was mostly used for purlins and cross beams subject to a uniform load. If the knees are extended to a footing, the beam is known as strut-supported. This type of construction reduces the beam span, and at the same time a horizontal stiffening is obtained through frame action. The system is generally used for supporting purlins, beams, or columns in large halls and timber buildings.

For equal span l, the beam can be computed as simply supported over a reduced length l_1. Span variations of up to 20% are allowed under this assumption.

The one-sided knee brace or end post produces a considerable bending moment and deflection. It would be best to introduce a strut for support at that point, or select for that side a shorter span l_E, which will produce equal centerline bending moments in the beam.

Trusses

A single-span truss may be used in timber construction either as a roof girder in large halls, as a long-span rafter, or as a cross beam. For sloping roofs, the upper chord of the truss is sloped accordingly. The truss is made of straight members, connected into undeformable triangles. It is assumed for design purposes that the members are pinned at the nodal points and that concentrated loads are applied at such points. As a result of these assumptions, all members are only axially loaded (tension or compression). For simple, statically determinate trusses (number of members = 2 × number of nodes − 3) member forces can be computed graphically (Cremona method) or numerically (Ritter's method of sections). For customary trusses, the truss member loads are tabulated. Trusses with numerous or redundant members and special trusses may be designed using computers.

If the loads on the upper and lower flanges are not applied at nodal points, the flanges are subject to bending moments in addition to the axial loads derived from a truss analysis. Eccentric connections are also not always avoidable, and they require

Parallel chord truss, req'd $h \geq \frac{l}{10}$

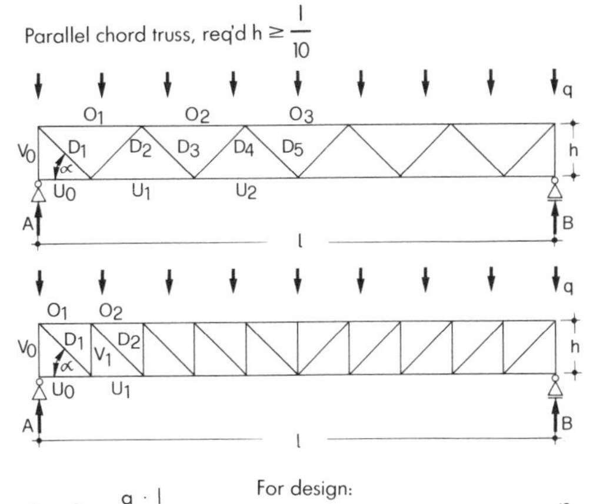

$A = B = \frac{q \cdot l}{2}$

For design:

Chords: $\max U \simeq -\max O \simeq \frac{q \cdot l^2}{8 \cdot h}$

Diagonals: $\max D = D_1 \simeq \frac{A}{\sin \alpha}$

Triangular truss, req'd $h \geq \frac{l}{8}$

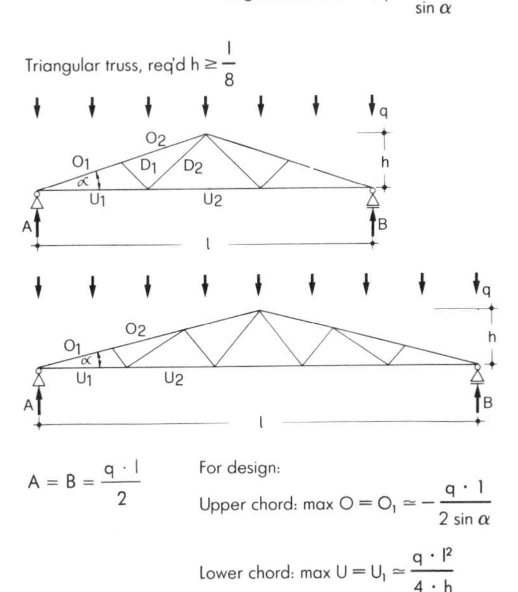

$A = B = \frac{q \cdot l}{2}$

For design:

Upper chord: $\max O = O_1 \simeq -\frac{q \cdot l}{2 \sin \alpha}$

Lower chord: $\max U = U_1 \simeq \frac{q \cdot l^2}{4 \cdot h}$

special attention. The partial fixity of members due to their imperfectly pinned connections is generally neglected for flexible connections.

Wind and buckling bracing are preferably built with crossed diagonals made from wood, or with flat or round steel bars. In this arrangement, the trusses act as flanges and the purlins as the perpendiculars of a horizontal bracing truss (Fig. 38).

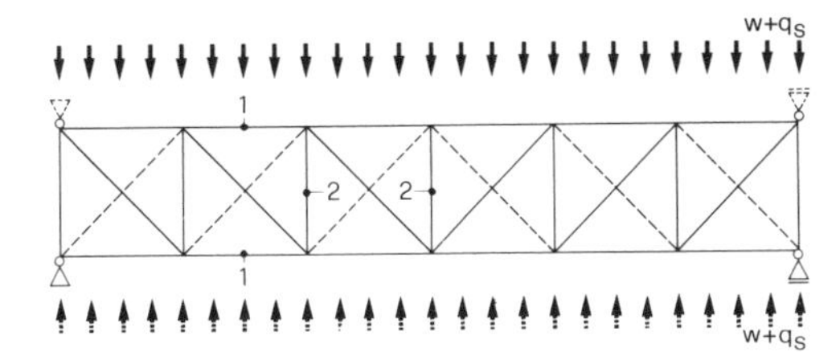

Fig. 38. Lateral bracing in roof plane for wind and stiffening forces $(w + q_s)$ acting from alternate directions. 1—trusses; 2—purlins.

In the design of such bracing only tension diagonals are considered as loaded. Diagonals subject to compression have such a negligible stiffness that they buckle, or in the case of steel wires, fall slack. However, it is necessary to provide diagonals in both directions because of changing load directions. If there are no purlins to serve as perpendicular members, additional stiff members have to be introduced.

Continuous, externally statically indeterminate trusses are rarely used because of their sensitivity to deformations caused by settlement of supports, slippage of connections, and shrinkage of wood. Otherwise their design does not present any difficulties once the bearing reactions are known.

Three-Hinged Girder Systems as Frames and Arches

Three-hinged girder systems as frames and arches are statically determinate and their moments, shears, and axial forces can be derived from the externally applied loads. They are not very sensitive to movements of supports, either vertically or horizontally, and to deformations caused by slippage of connections. This makes them especially suitable for timber construction.

Three-hinged laminated wood arches have been built up to a 100-m clear span. Computations of bearing reactions and forces at every cross section can be made quickly and exactly by methods of simple statics, considering that $M_c = 0$ (equilibrium condition). In practice, the crown and spring pins must be built as friction-free as possible (Fig. 25, page 53). For short spans it is necessary to check the flexibility of these points, but it is not always required to provide true pins.

Three-Hinged Trusses

Three-hinged trusses are often used in timber construction. Today nail-plate, Greim, or Menig trusses are economical for medium and short spans. Laminated wood or Kämpf systems with shallower depth are preferred for longer spans. As in three-hinged girder systems, the structural design begins with the determination of vertical and horizontal bearing reactions. Once these reactions are known, the forces in each truss member are determined by numerical or graphic methods.

Two-Hinged Frames or Arches

Two-hinged frames or arches are seldom chosen as structural members because they are statically indeterminate to the first degree and as such are sensitive to the movement of bearings or to deformations of connections. They are also often subject to difficulties during transportation so that only two-hinged frames with horizontal or sloped portal beams have any significance. Laminated two-hinged arches of longer span lengths (80 to 90 m), with or without a tie, may be built if the difficulty of assembling load-bearing glued splices in the field is kept in mind.

The equilibrium conditions are not sufficient for the design of two-hinged frames; an additional deformation condition is necessary. This indeterminacy of the first degree is already a little more expensive to compute. However, the design of most commercial frames is already available in formulas and tables.

Multiple-Span Frames

In most cases it is necessary to have field joints in the portal beams of multiple span frames for reasons of assembly, transportation, and erection. In practice, they are built as pins and are placed in the vicinity of zero-moment points. The introduction of pins reduces the degree of indeterminacy and greatly simplifies computations. Frames of higher statical indeterminacy are designed today mostly by computer. Loading conditions due to movement of supports or flexibility of connections must also be taken into consideration.

Collar-Beam Rafter Roof

If the two sides of a triangular frame are tied by means of a horizontal beam (collar beam), we obtain the simple tied-rafter roof which is typically used as the roof structural system in timber houses. Two types have to be distinguished:

- Laterally fixed tied-rafter roof, in which the collar-beam deck acts as a lateral shear plate and transfers the load to gable or end walls
- Tied-rafter roof not fixed laterally; horizontal movement of the collar beams is possible

The advantages of a collar beam lie in the lesser bending moments and deflections of rafters, because rafters consist of single pieces of solid wood, even in houses of larger width.

For symmetrical loads the stresses are the same in laterally fixed and in free tied-rafter roofs. This makes the fixed system economically advantageous only when there is a floor on the level of the collar beams which acts as a shear plate.

Ready-made formulas for the computation of tied-rafter roofs have been published. For standard dimensions in residential housing there are design tables available.

THREE-HINGED GIRDER SYSTEMS

Three-hinged beam

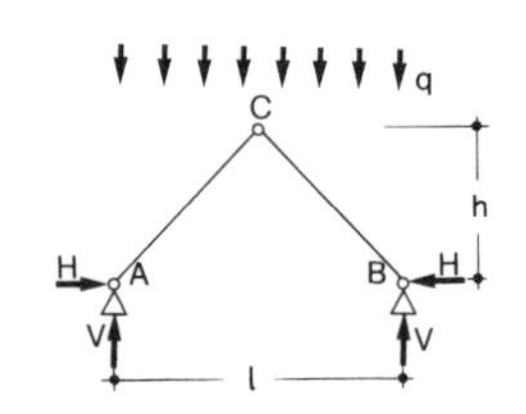

For symmetrical systems:

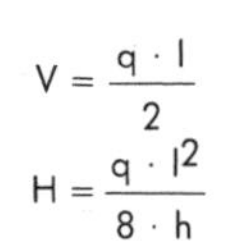

$$V = \frac{q \cdot l}{2}$$

$$H = \frac{q \cdot l^2}{8 \cdot h}$$

Three-hinged frames

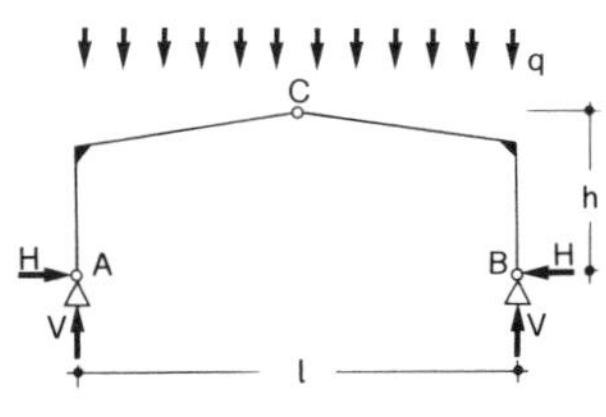

Bearing loads same as for three-hinged beam

Alternates

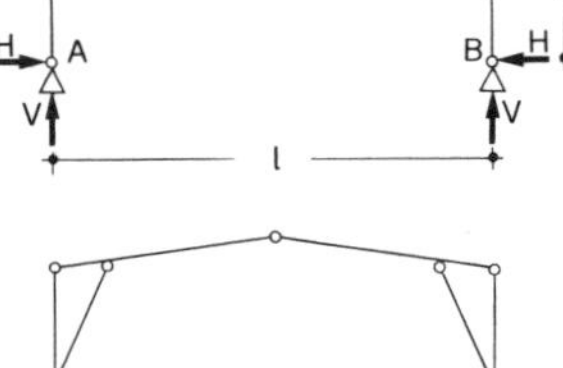

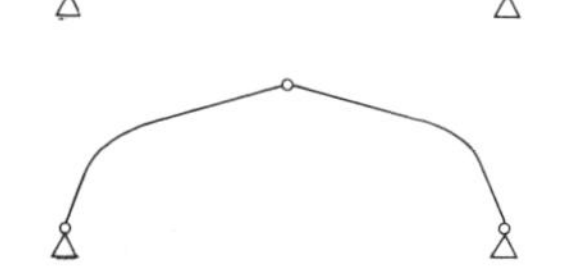

Three-hinged arch

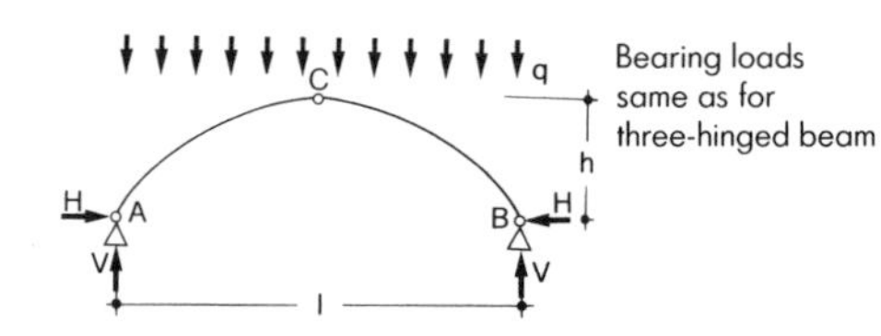

Bearing loads same as for three-hinged beam

THREE-HINGED TRUSS SYSTEMS

As beams, frames, or arches

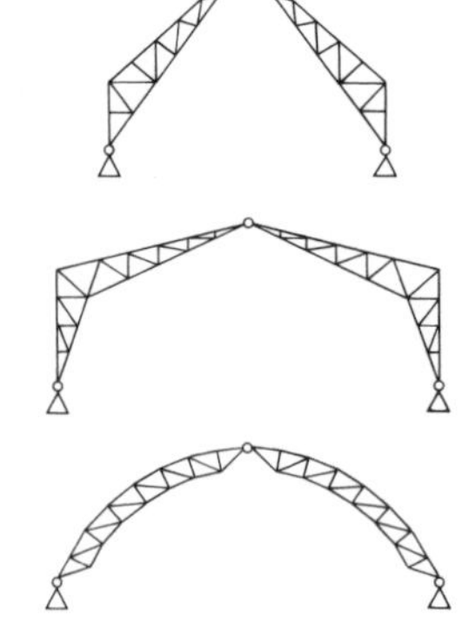

Bearing loads same as for three-hinged girder system

TWO-HINGED GIRDER SYSTEMS

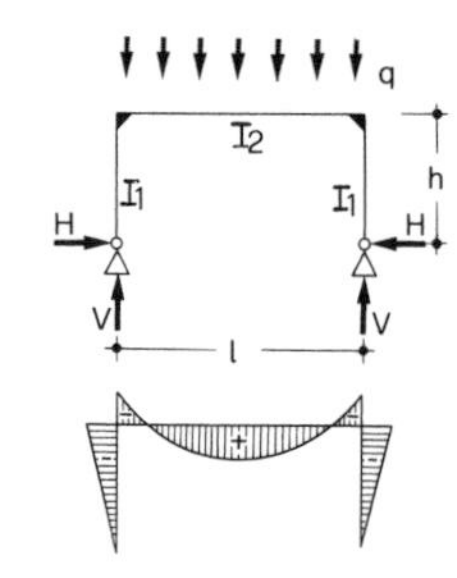

$$V = \frac{q \cdot l}{2}$$

$$H = \frac{q \cdot l^2}{4\,h\,(2\,k + 3)}$$

$$k = \frac{J_2 \cdot h}{J_1 \cdot l}$$

M diagram

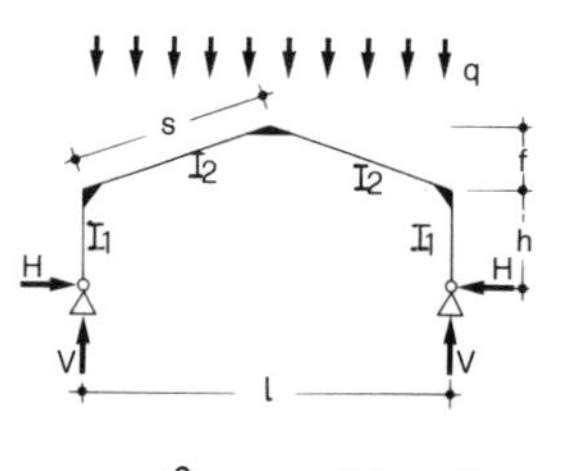

$$V = \frac{q \cdot l}{2}$$

$$H = \frac{q \cdot l^2}{32} \cdot \frac{8\,h + 5\,f}{h^2\,(k + 3) + f\,(3\,h + f)}; \quad k = \frac{J_2 \cdot h}{J_1 \cdot s}$$

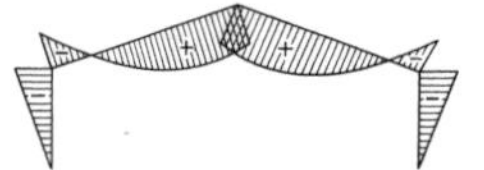

M diagram

TWO-HINGED TRUSS SYSTEM

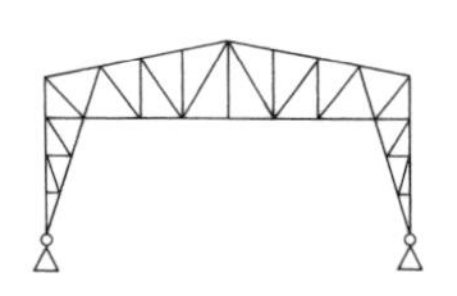

TWO-HINGED PARABOLIC GIRDER

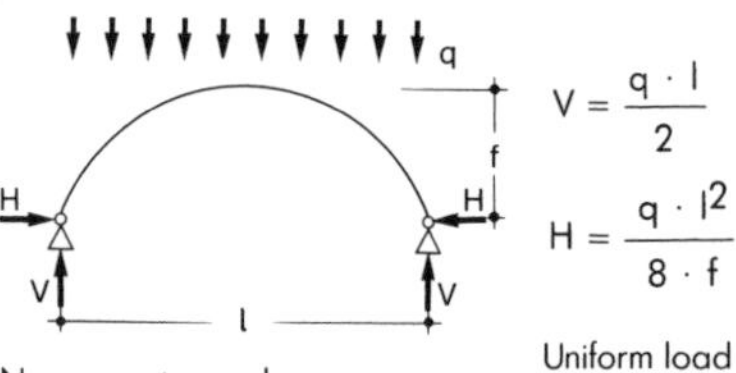

$$V = \frac{q \cdot l}{2}$$

$$H = \frac{q \cdot l^2}{8 \cdot f}$$

No moments, no shears

Uniform load

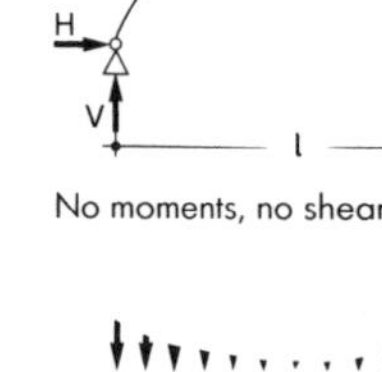

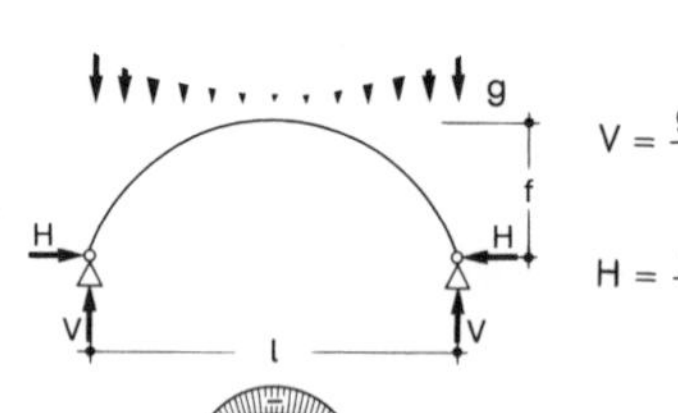

$$V = \frac{g \cdot l}{6}$$

$$H = \frac{g \cdot l^2}{52\,f}$$

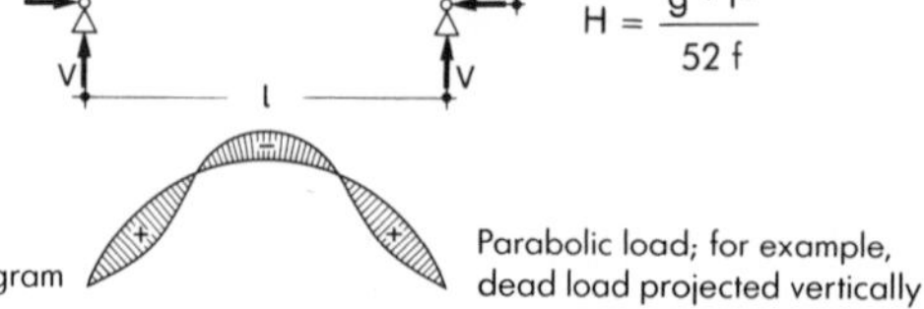

M diagram

Parabolic load; for example, dead load projected vertically

FRAMES IN LARGE-HALL CONSTRUCTION

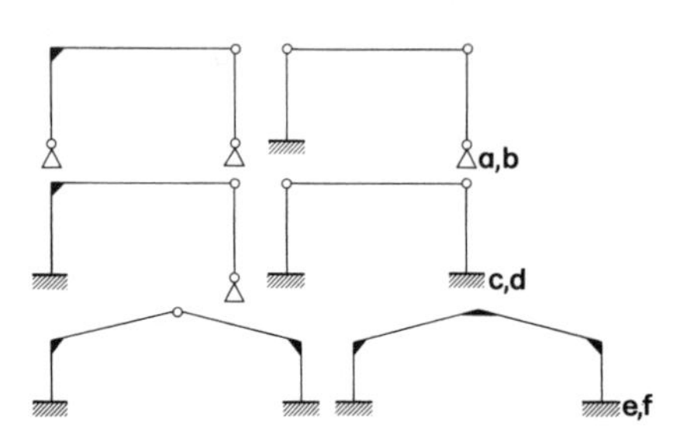

(a) Special case of three-hinged beams. Examples: laminated wood posts and beams, stiffened elbow, steel dowel ring or finger joint.
(b) Statically determinate system. Example: fixed post in steel or reinforced concrete, laminated wood beam and free post.
(c),(d) Indeterminate systems, first degree. System (c) is advisable for uneven support settlement.
(e),(f) Sensitive, multidegree indeterminate systems. Seldom applied in timber construction because of difficulties of transportation and erection.

MULTIPLE-SPAN FRAMES

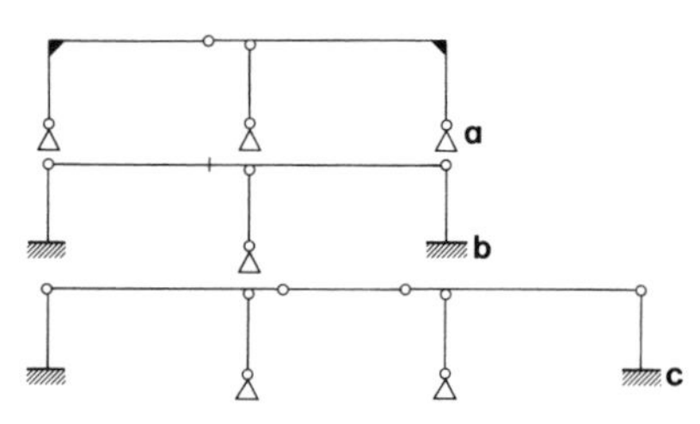

(a) Frame over two spans. First-degree statically indeterminate. Pin in deck beam because of assembly, transportation, and erection.
(b) Frame deck beams as a continuous beam. For spans over 12 m a fixed joint in beam is necessary.
(c) Frame deck beam as Gerber beam. Outer posts fixed because of wind or earthquake loads.

COLLAR-BEAM RAFTER ROOF

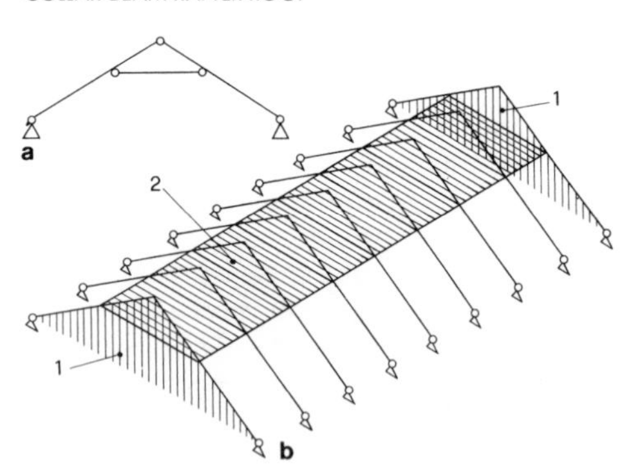

(a) Movable collar-beam rafter roof. First-degree statically indeterminate.
(b) Fixed collar-beam roof. Collar beam fixed horizontally by means of stiffening floor which transfers load from gable wall to gable wall. 1—gable wall; 2—collar-beam stiffening floor.

Dimensioning of Building Components

After the critical internal forces have been determined, there are two ways of designing each structural component:
a. Cross sections of members are determined in such a way that the resulting general stresses and deformations are less than the allowable ones.
b. Allowable stresses and deformations are established and minimum computed cross-sectional areas are compared to those proposed.

Certain choices, such as quality of material, width of section, or thickness of member, must be made beforehand because they are not given by structural requirements. The minimum dimensions for solid wood are 4 cm thickness and 40 cm² cross-sectional area. For nailed, screwed, or glued members they are 2.4 cm and 14 cm², respectively, and for load-bearing plywoods the minimum thickness is 10 mm.

The structural design must be made for the loading case that requires the largest cross section and the most connectors. In loading case HZ there is an allowance for 15% overstress in materials and connectors.

Tension Members

Tension members may only be stressed parallel to the grain. Stress computation is made by taking into account all reductions within one cross section or all reductions of cross sections within a length of 15 cm. Assuming a uniform distribution of stress:

$$\sigma_{Z\|act} = \frac{Z}{F_n}$$

where $\sigma_{Z\|act}$ = actual tensile stress parallel to the grain
Z = tensile force
F_n = net cross section, taking into account the reductions

A stress check is made with

$$\frac{\sigma_{Z\|act}}{\sigma_{Z\|allow}} \leq 1$$

where $\sigma_{Z\|allow}$ is the allowable stress parallel to the grain as given in Fig. 50 (page 68).

The reductions that have to be taken into account are all structural changes in cross sections such as mortises, anchor holes, or grooves, including reductions caused by connections. Nail diameters larger than 4.2 mm are to be subtracted, as well as predrilled holes for nails, bolts, and steel dowels. At shear connectors, both the bolt and the shear connector depression weaken the section.

Wood edges eased according to their grade classification do not have to be subtracted from the cross section. The tensile capacity is reduced significantly by knots and growth defects; therefore only choice wood is allowed for highly stressed members.

Joints and Connections

Joints in tension members should preferably be symmetrical. Timber splices, which are engaged on one side (normally the outer splices) must be computed for a 1.5 times greater tensile force because of their additional bending loads.

The allowable stresses in nailed tension splices or connections must be reduced by 20% in consideration of their weakened cross section, unless the 1.5 times increased tensile force governs.

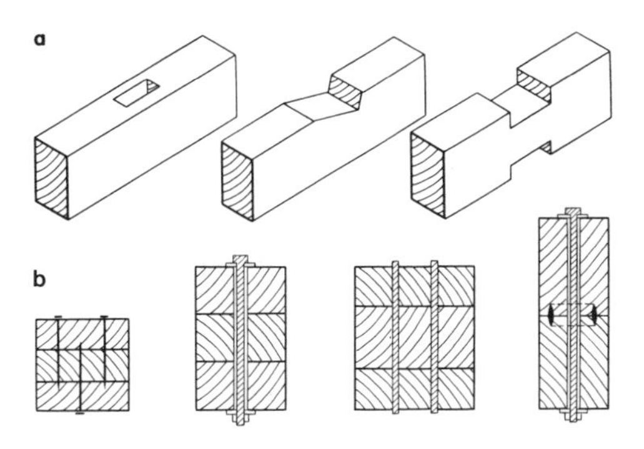

Fig. 39. Reductions of cross sections. (a) Mortises. (b) Connections: nails $d_n \geq 4.2$ mm, bolts, steel dowels, shear connectors.

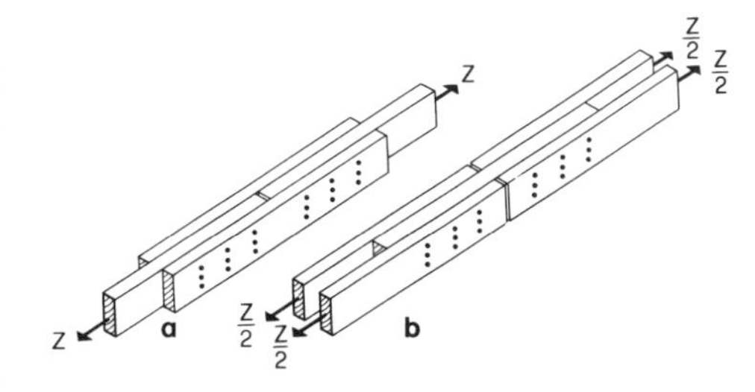

Fig. 40. Tension member splices. (a) Normal case, splice timbers are to be designed for 1.5 times tensile load (here 1.5Z/2). (b) Axially loaded splices. Double tension member must be designed for 1.5Z/2 load each.

Compression Members

The load capacity of compression members is limited by either the buckling of the entire section or the maximum allowable compressive stress of the weakest cross section. Buckling effects are accounted for in design by multiplying the actual load with a factor ω. A fictitious load $D' = \omega D$ is used in computing the member as if there were no danger of buckling:

$$\sigma_\omega = \frac{\omega D}{F}$$

where σ_ω = compressive stress at point of buckling
ω = buckling factor
D = compressive load
F = cross-sectional area (not reduced)

The check against buckling is obtained by setting

$$\frac{\sigma_\omega}{\sigma_{D\|allow}} \leq 1$$

where $\sigma_{D\|allow}$ is the allowable compressive stress parallel to the grain as given in Fig. 50.

Buckling factors ω for solid wood and laminated wood of all grades depend on the slenderness ratio λ and can be taken from Fig. 41. The table is also valid for grouped members.

Fig. 41. Buckling factors ω.

λ	0	1	2	3	4	5	6	7	8	9
0	1,00	1,00	1,01	1,01	1,02	1,02	1,02	1,03	1,03	1,04
10	1,04	1,04	1,05	1,05	1,06	1,06	1,06	1,07	1,07	1,08
20	1,08	1,09	1,09	1,10	1,11	1,11	1,12	1,13	1,13	1,14
30	1,15	1,16	1,17	1,18	1,19	1,20	1,21	1,22	1,24	1,25
40	1,26	1,27	1,29	1,30	1,32	1,33	1,35	1,36	1,38	1,40
50	1,42	1,44	1,46	1,48	1,50	1,52	1,54	1,56	1,58	1,60
60	1,62	1,64	1,67	1,69	1,72	1,74	1,77	1,80	1,82	1,85
70	1,88	1,91	1,94	1,97	2,00	2,03	2,06	2,10	2,13	2,16
80	2,20	2,23	2,27	2,31	2,35	2,38	2,42	2,46	2,50	2,54
90	2,58	2,62	2,66	2,70	2,74	2,78	2,82	2,87	2,91	2,95
100	3,00	3,06	3,12	3,18	3,24	3,31	3,37	3,44	3,50	3,57
110	3,63	3,70	3,76	3,83	3,90	3,97	4,04	4,11	4,18	4,25
120	4,32	4,39	4,46	4,54	4,61	4,68	4,76	4,84	4,92	4,99
130	5,07	5,15	5,23	5,31	5,39	5,47	5,55	5,63	5,71	5,80
140	5,88	5,96	6,05	6,13	6,22	6,31	6,39	6,48	6,57	6,66
150	6,75	6,84	6,93	7,02	7,11	7,21	7,30	7,39	7,49	7,58
160	7,68	7,78	7,87	7,97	8,07	8,17	8,27	8,37	8,47	8,57
170	8,67	8,77	8,88	8,98	9,08	9,19	9,29	9,40	9,51	9,61
180	9,72	9,83	9,94	10,05	10,16	10,27	10,38	10,49	10,60	10,72
190	10,83	10,94	11,06	11,17	11,29	11,41	11,52	11,64	11,76	11,88
200	12,00	12,12	12,24	12,36	12,48	12,61	12,73	12,85	12,98	13,10

The slenderness ratio λ is defined as

$$\lambda = \frac{s_k}{i}$$

where s_k is the buckling length and i the radius of gyration obtained from the table on page 19. For rectangular sections, $i = 0.289d$, where d is the width in the direction of buckling.

For solid or continuously glued cross sections of compression members the maximum permissible slenderness ratio is $\lambda = 150$. For built-up nonglued sections of compression members slenderness ratios may reach $\lambda = 175$ for primary members and $\lambda = 200$ for secondary members.

As long as a compression member is not supported within its length, buckling about the weakest axis must be considered.

Buckling Lengths

If a compression member is not secured against buckling at both ends by means of stiffeners or shear walls, both ends are considered pinned and the buckling length s_k is equal to span l. If the compression member is supported at intermediate points against other points, the buckling length becomes the length between intermediate supports. The buckling length for web members of trusses within the plane of the truss may be taken as 80% of the theoretical length if a certain fixity is provided by their end connections. When connections are made only by notching or by shear connectors with one bolt, no fixity can be assumed for buckling outside of the plane of the truss.

Special regulations govern the slenderness of collar-beam rafters, frames, and arches.

In addition, compressive stresses (without buckling) must be checked at points of weakness of the compression member, such as at the point of load application, and compared against the allowable stress:

$$\sigma_{D\|act} = \frac{D}{F_n}$$

where $\sigma_{D\|act}$ is the actual compressive stress parallel to the grain and F_n is the net cross-sectional area.

Weakened sections of compression members must be checked only when the holes are not fully filled, or when the filler has a smaller E modulus (for example, when filler wood grain is normal to member grain).

A stress check is made by

$$\frac{\sigma_{D\|act}}{\sigma_{D\|allow}} \leq 1$$

Built-up Compression Members

There is a difference between solid and expanded members. Members which are continuously glued together and are not expanded may be handled as solid members in both directions. This is valid for glue-laminated wood members.

When flexible connections are used to form a compression member (such as with nails or shear connectors), the effective moment of inertia J_w is to be determined as for bending members (see page 68). The radius of gyration i_w is computed from J_w:

$$i_w = \sqrt{\frac{J_w}{F}}$$

and the buckling ratio λ_w and the buckling factor ω_w are derived as for solid members. The member can then be designed as a solid member.

For built-up expanded members, such as frames or laced members, the slenderness of individual members is limited to $\lambda_1 \leq 60$. The buckling load of the entire member is computed with an effective slenderness ratio of λ_w, computed according to formulas in DIN 1052.

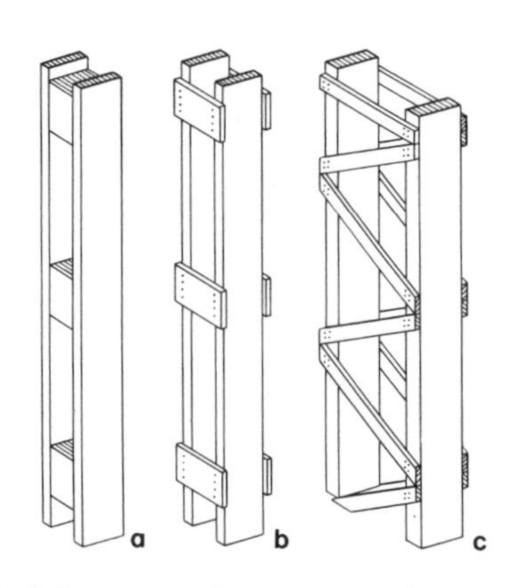

Fig. 42. Built-up expanded compression members. (a) Framed member with filler wood (glued, nailed, or shear connected). (b) Framed member with tie timbers (may also be plywood, glued, or nailed). (c) Laced members (diagonals nailed).

Members Subject to Bending

Span Lengths

For a simply supported or a continuous beam, the span length equals the distance between supports. If beams are resting directly on masonry, the effective span length is equal to 1.05 times the clear span. In such cases appropriate protection against humidity should be provided.

Bearings

Bearing loads exerted by the beam on its support are generally transferred by contact, namely, by stresses normal to the grain. The required bearing length l_A is derived from the net width b of the beam resting on the bearing:

$$l_A = \frac{A}{\sigma_{D\perp allow} b}$$

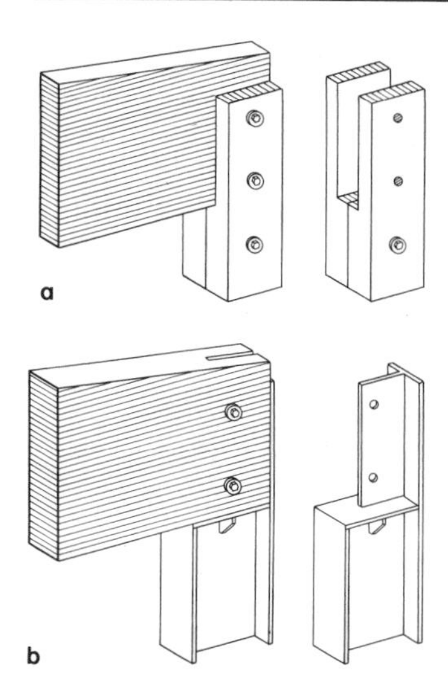

Fig. 43. Bearing of a laminated wood beam (forked bearing). (a) Timber column. (b) Steel column. The bolts must not hinder free horizontal movement, or vertical movement due to swelling and shrinkage of the beam (bolt holes should have a play of about 1% of bolt spacing).

where A is the bearing load and $\sigma_{D\perp allow}$ is the allowable stress normal to the grain (1.6 N/mm² for conifers, 2.0 N/mm² for laminated wood).

Deep laminated beams are secured against side movements by so-called forked bearings (Fig. 43) or by stiffening diagonals in the plane of the outer wall.

Bending Stresses

Maximum bending stresses for solid wood or laminated uniform depth girders are obtained at the points of maximum bending moments or at the points of minimum cross section as

$$\sigma_{B\,act} = \frac{M_{max}}{W} \quad \text{or} \quad \frac{M_{max}}{W_n} \quad \text{or} \quad \frac{M}{W_n}$$

where $\sigma_{B\,act}$ = bending stress
M = bending moment
W = section modulus (see table on page 19)
W_n = section modulus of reduced cross section

A check of stresses is done by comparing the actual stresses with the allowable stresses (see Fig. 50):

$$\frac{\sigma_{B\,act}}{\sigma_{B\,allow}} \leq 1$$

Horizontal Shear Stresses

In timber construction, horizontal shear stresses often govern at the point of maximum vertical shear. This is especially true for beams on shorter spans with high loading.

The horizontal shear at any section equals

$$\tau_{act} = \frac{QS}{Jb}$$

where Q = vertical shear, at bearing, for simple spans
S = section modulus for area above neutral axis, at section considered
J = moment of inertia (see table on page 19)
b = width of cross section

For a rectangular cross section,

$$\tau_{act} = \frac{1.5Q}{F}$$

where F is the cross-sectional area bh.

A check of horizontal shears is made by

$$\frac{\tau_{act}}{\tau_{\parallel allow}} \leq 1$$

Combined Axial Force (Compression or Tension) and Bending

A beam subject to bending is often loaded axially: for example, parts of frames, trusses with loads applied outside of nodes, or struts that have to take wind loads in addition to axial loads.

Because of different allowable loads, a composite stress check is required:

$$\frac{\sigma_{D,Z\parallel act}}{\sigma_{D,Z\parallel allow}} + \frac{\sigma_{B\,act}}{\sigma_{B\,allow}} \leq 1$$

where $\sigma_{D,Z\parallel allow}$ are the compressive or tensile stresses parallel to the grain shown in Fig. 50.

If compression and bending are superimposed, buckling must be checked. The largest ω value is to be considered regardless of the bending direction.

Eccentricity of compression or tension members caused by asymmetrical weakening of a member or application of load must be taken into account in the design.

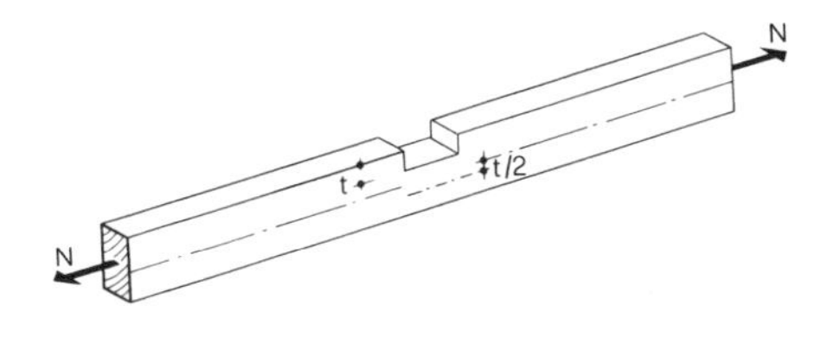

Fig. 44. Additional bending moments caused by asymmetrical weakening of cross section: $M = Nt/2$.

Variable-Depth Laminated Girders

Laminated wood girders can be built with a variable depth that follows the moment diagram. This results in the economical form of a saddle roof girder, but a check of horizontal shears must be made.

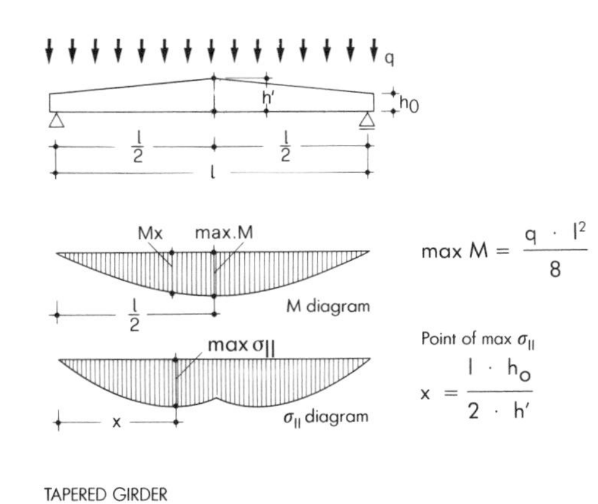

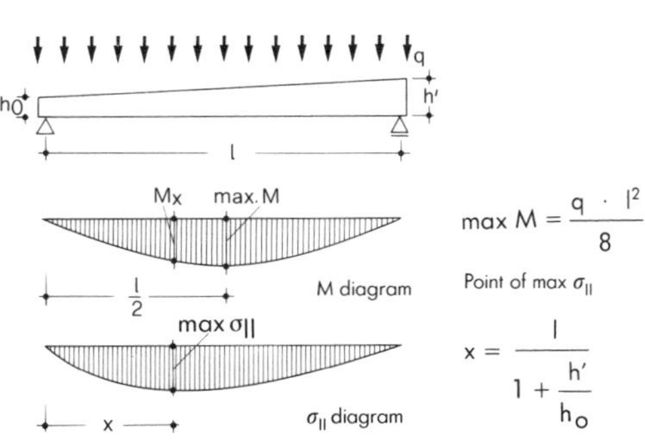

A tapered girder does not correspond to a moment diagram under uniform load; it is used, however, for aesthetic reasons or for roof drainage purposes.

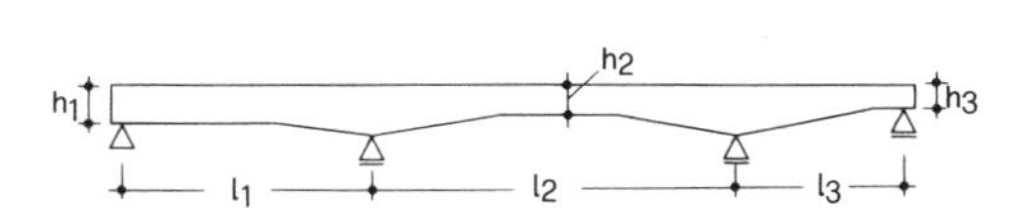

Fig. 45. Haunched girder. Maximum haunch slope ≃ 1:12 for efficient use of allowable stresses.

For girders of variable depth, the maximum stresses do not necessarily occur at the point of maximum moment. A stress analysis is made at point x, for a moment M_x using the section modulus at that point. For saddle back girders with a steep slope, stresses must be checked at all points. Fitting the moment diagram by haunching the girder is recommended only for flat haunches. Steeper haunches may cause higher horizontal shears (Fig. 45).

Curved Laminated Beams

In curved beams the bending stresses $\sigma_{\parallel}$ (longitudinal stresses) and shear $\sigma_{\perp}$ are not uniformly distributed over a cross section.

For rectangular girders of uniform depth the stresses depend on curvature:

$$\beta = \frac{R}{h} \geq 2$$

where R is the radius of the axis of curvature and h is the section depth.

The maximum bending stress $\sigma_{\parallel max}$ occurs at the intrados,

$$\sigma_{\parallel max} = \frac{M}{W}\left(1 + \frac{1}{2\beta}\right) \leq \sigma_{B\,allow}$$

For values $\beta \geq 10$, the bending stress can be computed as for straight girders. In addition the maximum vertical shear $\sigma_{\perp max}$ is

$$\sigma_{\perp max} = \frac{M}{W}\frac{1}{4\beta} \leq \sigma_{\perp allow}$$

When the longitudinal stress $\sigma_{\parallel}$ at the intrados is tensile, the vertical shear results in vertical cross-grain tension. Only small cross-grain tensile stresses can be resisted by laminated wood. They should not exceed 0.25 N/mm². These values should not be exceeded even in load cases HZ. Special precautions should be taken in choosing wood for curved laminated beams because only wood without splits can resist cross-grain tension.

Horizontal shears can be computed as for straight girders. The equations shown above are not valid for curved girders of variable depth. For an analysis of stresses in these girder shapes see *Building with Wood* (July 1979).

Fig. 46. Curved girder with constant section depth.

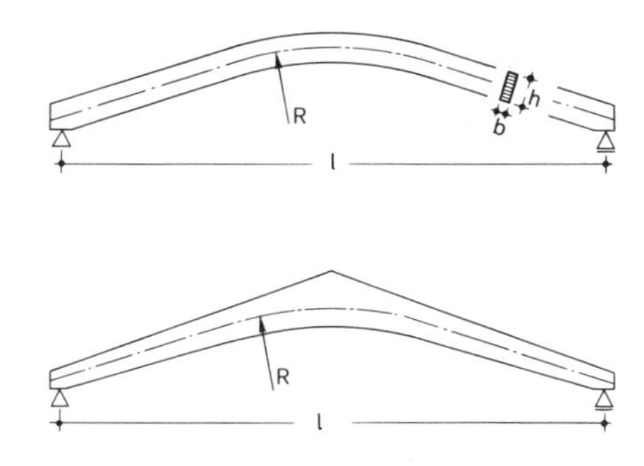

Fig. 47. Curved girder with variable section depth.

Composite Girders with Flexible Connections

A girder composed of individual solid-wood components is usually connected by shear connectors, dowels, or nails.

Flexible connections cause a movement of parts relative to each other, and this significantly influences the load-carrying capacity and deflection behavior of the girder. The full cross section of the girder is not fully effective to resist loads. Therefore, in the design of cross-sectional properties, a reduction factor takes into account the slippage between adjacent surfaces.

The effective moment of inertia of a composite cross section is given by

$$J_w = \sum_{i=1}^{n} J_i + \gamma \sum_{i=1}^{n} F_i a_i^2$$

where J_w = effective moment of inertia of cross section without reductions

$\sum_{i=1}^{n} J_i$ = sum of moments of inertia of single components

γ = reduction factor; $\gamma < 1$

F_i = cross-sectional area of individual components

a_i = distance of each unreduced cross section from the neutral axis

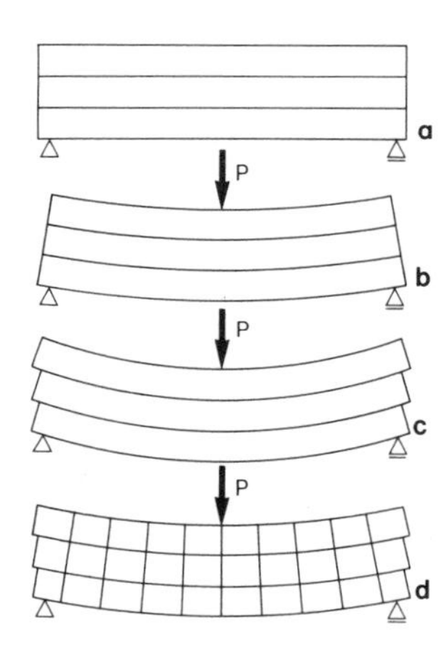

Fig. 48. Composite girder. (a) Girder without load (shown cambered for dead load). (b) Girder with stiff connectors (achievable in timber only through gluing). (c) Loose superimposed components; maximum slippage of end sections, minimum bending strength. (d) Girder with flexible connectors; little slippage in end sections, bending strength between that of (b) and (c).

The effective moment of inertia is computed using the principles of statics, in which the contribution of the static moments $F_i a^2$ is reduced by a reduction factor γ. DIN 1052 gives formulas for the determination of γ factors for the symmetrical three-element and two-element cross sections shown in Fig. 49.

Fig. 49. (a) Three-component symmetrical cross sections.

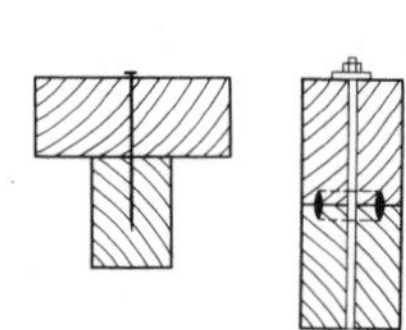

Fig. 49. (b) Two-component cross sections.

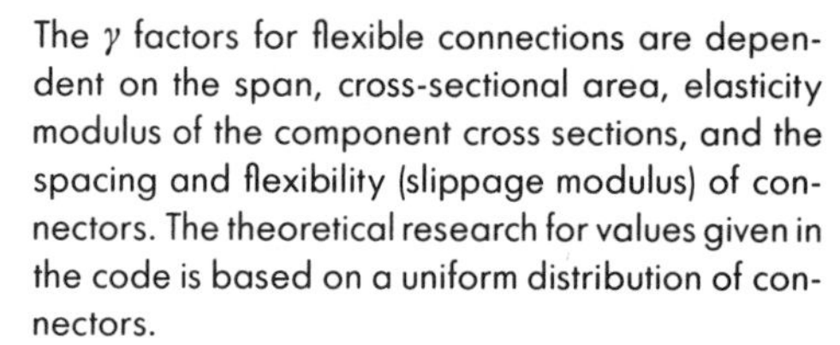

The γ factors for flexible connections are dependent on the span, cross-sectional area, elasticity modulus of the component cross sections, and the spacing and flexibility (slippage modulus) of connectors. The theoretical research for values given in the code is based on a uniform distribution of connectors.

If the spacing of connectors is proportioned to the shear diagram, an effective spacing e' can be assumed in computing γ, thus reducing the number of connectors required without significantly reducing the stiffness or the load capacity of the beam.

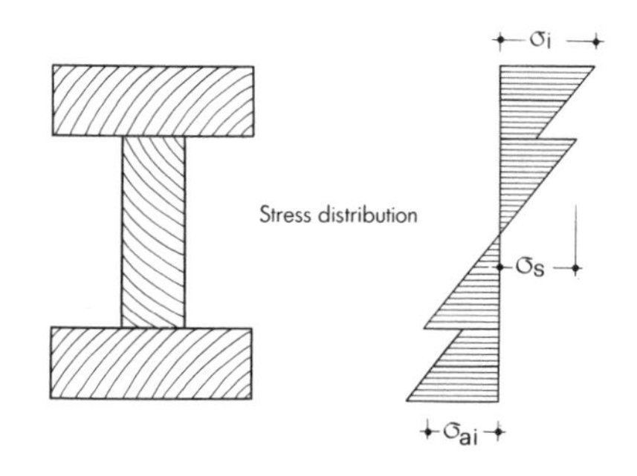

For a girder with flexible connections, the following stresses can be derived from bending moments:

σ_s Extreme fiber stress in web

σ_i Extreme fiber stress in attached flange component i ($i = 1, 2, 3, \ldots$)

σ_{ai} Neutral axis stress in component i

σ_s and σ_i must not exceed the allowable bending stress and σ_{ai} the allowable axial stress.

Shear connectors should be computed for the largest horizontal shear due to the effective moment of inertia J_w. The effective moment of inertia is also to be used for determining deflections.

Girders with Panel Webs, Panel Elements

Composite sections made with wood-product boards, solid wood, or laminated wood have different moduli of elasticity for each component. In the computation of cross-sectional properties (areas, section moduli, moments of inertia), each component cross section must be taken with its corresponding E value. The lining of panel elements, such as those shown on page 58, can be taken into account in the computation of strength only partially because horizontal shear deformations between stiffeners cause a reduction in stress. Wood-product panels subject to compression, compression and bending, or shear must be amply stiffened against buckling. This can be achieved by maintaining certain minimum thicknesses.

Allowable Stresses for Solid-Wood and Laminated Beams

The allowable stresses for solid-wood or laminated beams for building members are given in Fig. 50 for the loading case H. For members made from European conifers, the values are given for grades I to III. For oak and beech, for which there are no grades, only averages are given. If in special cases the wood originates in other countries and is used for load-bearing members, the allowable stresses must be determined on the basis of special investigations in which the type of wood, its area of growth, and general characteristics of delivery are all taken into account. In larger buildings, engaging an expert timber research institute is a necessity.

When tables are applied, the following should be observed:

• In loading cases H and HZ the values can be increased by 15%.

• For continuous girders without pin connections, the allowable σ_B values can be increased by 10% at interior supports (not for free-moving collar-beam rafters).

• For round timbers the allowable σ_B and σ_D values can be increased by 20% in extreme fibers which have not been weakened.

• The allowable $\tau_{||}$ values (horizontal shear due to vertical shear) may be increased to allowable $\tau_{||}$ = 1.2 N/mm² for continuous or cantilevered solid timber beams in the areas within 1.50 m from a beam end.

• Stress adjustments for various degrees of moisture must be made as discussed on page 26.

Fig. 50. Allowable stresses in N/mm² for lumber in loading case H.[1]

Type of Allowable Stress		European Conifers					Oak and Beech
		Solid Timber			Laminated Wood		
		Grade			Grade		Average Grade
		III	II	I	II	I	
Bending	$\sigma_{B\ allow}$	7	10	13	11	14	11
Tension	$\sigma_{Z\|\|\ allow}$	0	8,5	10,5	8,5	10,5	10
Compression	$\sigma_{D\|\|\ allow}$	6	8,5	11	8,5	11	10
Compression	$\sigma_{D\perp\ allow}$	2 (2,5)	2 (2,5)	2 (2,5)	2 (2,5)	2 (2,5)	3 (4)
Shear	$\tau_{\|\|\ allow}$	0,9	0,9	0,9	0,9	0,9	1
Horizontal shear	$\tau_{\|\|\ allow}$	0,9	0,9	0,9	1,2	1,2	1

[1] For values in parentheses, larger deflections must be expected.

Fig. 51. Load–deformation relationships of connectors.

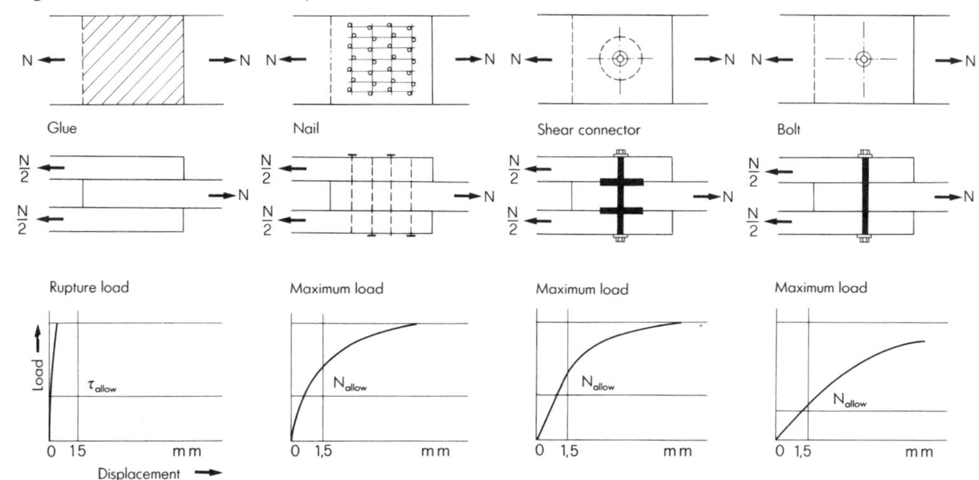

Design of Connections

The theory behind each type of connection (Fig. 51) reveals that tension, compression, or shear forces are transmitted through shear and bending stresses in connectors to bearing loads on the connected members. This means that deformations in wood connector holes and in the connectors themselves increase with load, resulting in a slippage of the connection proportionate to the applied load. Forces normal to wood surfaces can be transmitted as pressure only if there is immediate contact. For a right angle post connection (Fig. 52a), the size of the contact surface is determined by the allowable stress, but additional securing of this connection by means of stitch nails is also necessary. Splices of posts butted directly, or with metal or plywood inserts between them, require only side timbers to keep them in line. However, this is allowed only in the immediate vicinity of side supports which are ensured against lateral movement. In all other cases the bending moment capacity of the post in both directions is to be fully developed by the connecting timbers. If tightly fitting posts themselves carry the compression load, the connecting timbers may be designed to carry half the total compression load (Fig. 52b).

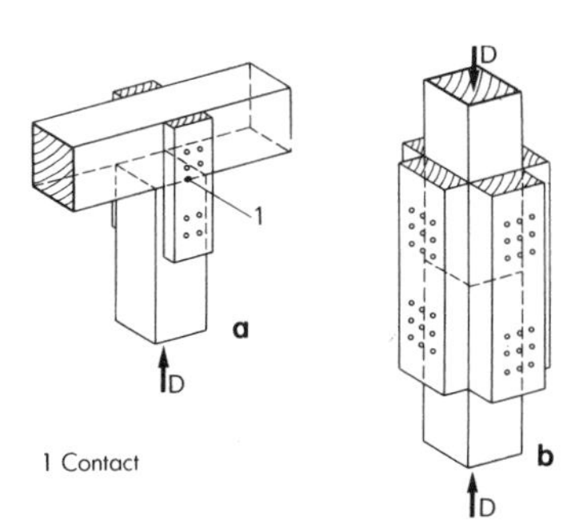

Fig. 52. Compression connections. (a) Contact connection secured by splice timbers and nails. (b) Compression splice; splice timber thickness equals half of post thickness.

Notched Joint

Skewed connections of compression members are often made with notched joints, such as a head notch, rear notch, or double notch. The design in these cases is based on determining the load transfer surfaces and the end lengths of the timber.

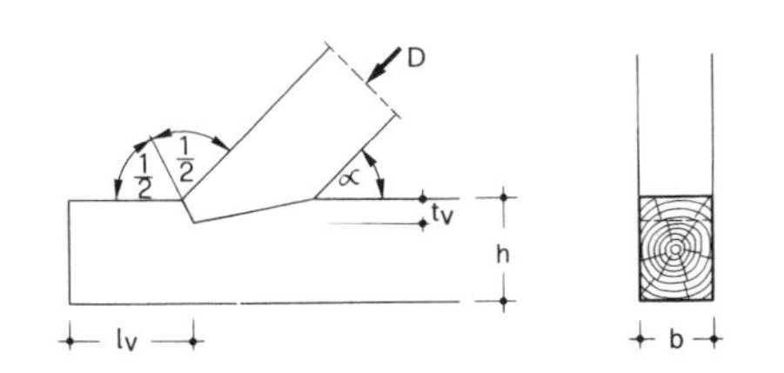

For a simple head notch joint the following is to be checked:

$$t_{v\,req'd} = \frac{D \cos^2 (\alpha/2)}{b\, \sigma_{D\,allow} \alpha/2} \simeq \frac{D}{7b} \quad \text{[mm]}$$

$$l_{v\,req'd} = \frac{D \cos \alpha}{b\, \tau_{a\,allow}} \quad \text{[mm]}$$

where D is measured in newtons and b in mm, t_v is the depth of the head notch required to receive the horizontal load component, and l_v is the end timber length required to resist the horizontal load component. $\sigma_{D\,allow}\alpha/2$ is the allowable compression stress for an angle $\alpha/2$ to the grain (see page 29), and $\tau_{e\,allow}$ is the allowable shear stress as shown in Fig. 50.

It must be noted that the notch depth t_v for $\alpha \leq 50°$ should not exceed $h/4$ and for $\alpha > 60°$ it should not exceed $h/6$. Between 50 and 60°, maximum depths can be interpolated. If notches are on both sides of a member (connections to knee beams), the notch depth should not exceed $h/6$, regardless of the angle.

For various types of notched joints there are also tables from which to obtain the allowable compressive force D and the required end length l_v in relation to the notch depth t_v and the angle α.

Mechanical Connections

In shear connector or dowel connections the design has to consider not only the allowable loads and stresses, but also an arrangement of connectors that provides for minimum spacing and edge distances. Connections should not be left to the contractor, but rather, the arrangement of connectors should be shown on construction drawings.

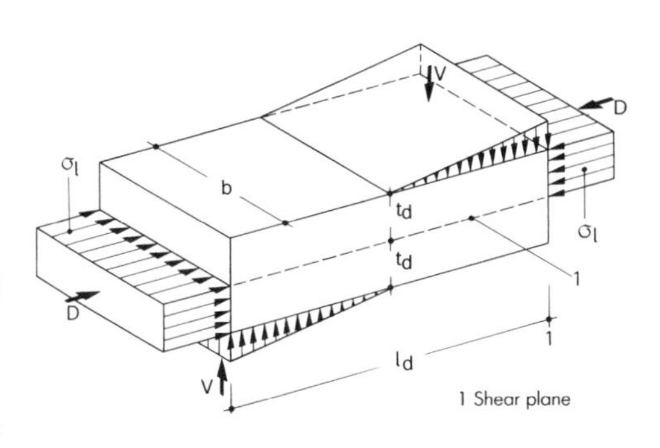

Fig. 53. Stress distribution for rectangular shear connector.

Rectangular Shear Connectors

The bearing stresses in loaded surfaces of block shear connectors will be assumed to be distributed uniformly and are computed as

$$\sigma_l = \frac{D}{b t_d} \leq \sigma_{l\,allow}$$

Allowable bearing loads σ_l, in N/mm², parallel to the grain are as follows:

Ratio of Shear Connector Length l_d to Notch Depth t_d	Number of Shear Connectors in Line of Load: 1 or 2 and in Doweled Beams	3 or 4
$l_d/t_d \geq 5$	8.5	7.5
$l_d/t_d < 5$	4.0	3.5

For shear connector length l_d, the allowable shear stress $\tau_{a\,allow}$ of the material governs:

$$l_{d\,req'd} = \frac{D}{\tau_{a\,allow} b}$$

where $\tau_{a\,allow} = 1.0$ N/mm² for oak and beech. For metal connectors no design is necessary.

Similarly the minimum shear connector spacing is to be determined by the allowable shear in the connected material ($\tau_{a\,allow} = 0.9$ N/mm²). The vertical component V is taken up by clamping bolts on both sides (to secure against rotation of shear connectors).

Special Shear Connectors

DIN 1052, part 2, shows the allowable loads on various shear connectors and minimum connector spacings for conifer wood of at least grade II. These values have been established on the basis of tests. Figure 54 lists the values for those connector types that are available and generally used.

Bolts and Steel Dowels

The allowable load on a bolt or steel dowel is related to its bearing area in the direction of the grain, regardless of the quality grade of the wood, and is given by

$$N_{b,st\,allow} = \sigma_{l\,allow} a d_{b,st}$$

not to exceed

$$N_{b,st\,allow} = A d_{b,st}^2 \quad [N]$$

where $\sigma_{l\,allow}$ = allowable average bearing on holes in wood, in N/mm², as per Fig. 55

a = minimum wood thickness, in mm

$d_{b,st}$ = diameter of bolt or steel dowel, in mm

A = strength, in N/mm², as per Fig. 55

For skewed load incidence, $N_{b,st\,allow}$ is to be reduced by $(1 - \alpha/360)$, where α is the angle between load and grain.

For wood-to-steel gusset plate connections the allowable load on bolts and steel dowels can be increased by 25% provided that the bearing load of the bolts or steel dowels on steel is not exceeded.

Figures 56 and 57 show minimum edge distances for the arrangement of bolts and steel dowels in connections.

Fig. 55. Design values for computing allowable loads of bolts and steel dowels for European conifers, oak, and beech.

	Bolts $\sigma_{l\,allow}$	Bolts A	Steel Dowels $\sigma_{l\,allow}$	Steel Dowels A
Single shear (a_1, a_2, d_b)	4	17	4	23
	5	20	5	27
	Interior Timber			
Double shear (a_{s1}, a_m, a_{s2}, d_b)	8,5	38	8,5	51
	10,0	45	10,0	60
	Exterior Timber			
	5,5	26	5,5	33
	6,5	30	6,5	39

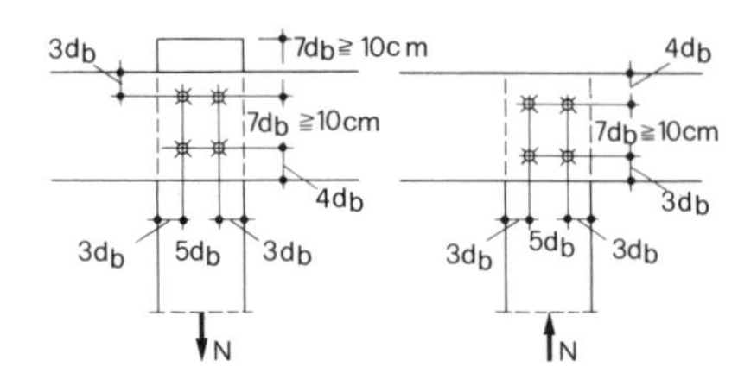

Fig. 56. Minimum edge distances for bolts.

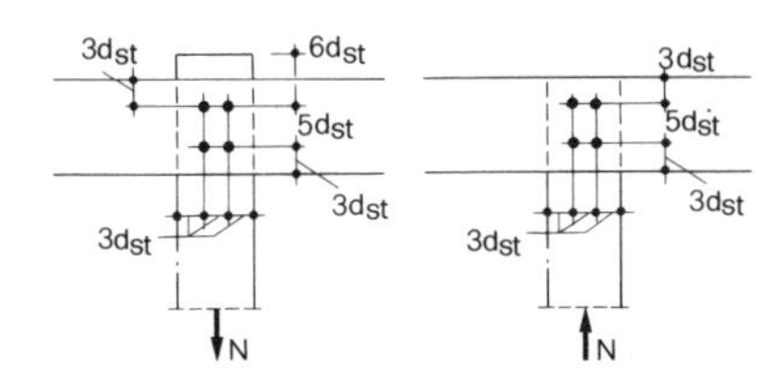

Fig. 57. Minimum edge distances for steel dowels.

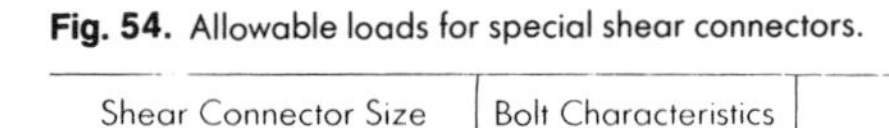

Fig. 54. Allowable loads for special shear connectors.

Outer Diameter d_d	Height h_d	Thickness s	Number of Teeth	Critical Area of Shear Connector ΔF	Hexagonal Head Screws per DIN 601, Part I d_b	Round Washers, Diameter/Thickness d_s	Rectangular Washers, Side Length/Thickness	Minimum Dimensions of Wood for One Connector Row and Angle of Inclination of Load to Grain: 0° to 30° b/a	Over 30 to 90° b/a	Minimum Connector Spacing and End Length for One Connector Row e_{dll}	Allowable Load for One Connector in Loading Case H for a Load to Grain Angle 0 to 30°; Number of Shear Connectors in One Row in the Direction of Load: 1 or 2	0 to 30°: 3 or 4	0 to 30°: 5 or 6	Over 30 to 60°: 1 or 2	Over 60 to 90°: 1 or 2
mm	mm	mm		cm²	mm	mm	mm	cm	cm	cm	kN	kN	kN	kN	kN
Double- or Single-Sided Shear Ring Connector, Appel System															
65	30	5	–	7,8	M 12	58/6	50/6	10/4	11/4	14	11,5	10,5	9	10	9
80	30	6	–	10,1	M 12	58/6	50/6	11/5	13/5	18	14	12,5	11	12,5	11
95	30	6	–	12,3	M 12	58/6	50/6	12/6	15/6	22	17	15,5	13,5	14,5	12,5
126	30	6	–	17,0	M 12	58/6	50/6	16/6	20/6	25	20	18	16	17	14
128	45	8	–	25,9	M 12	58/6	50/6	16/6	20/6	30	28	25	22,5	23,5	19
160	45	10	–	32,2	M 16	68/6	60/6	20/10	24/10	34	34	30,5	27	27,5	21,5
190	45	10	–	39,0	M 16	68/6	60/6	23/10	28/10	43	48	43	38,5	38,5	29
Double- or Single-Sided Shear Connector, Geka System															
50	27	3	8	2,8	M 12	58/6	50/6	10/4 od 8/6	10/4 od 9/6	12	8	7	6,5	7,5	7
65	27	3	12	3,6	M 16	68/6	60/6	10/4 od 9/6	11/4 od 10/6	14	11,5	10	9	11	10
80	27	3	18	4,6	M 20	80/8	70/8	11/5	13/5	17	17	15	13,5	16	14,5
95	27	3	24	5,6	M 22	92/8	80/8	12/6	14/6	20	21	19	17	19,5	17,5
115	27	3	32	7,0	M 24	105/8	95/8	14/6	17/6	23	27	24	21,5	24,5	21,5
Double- or Single-Sided Shear Connector, Bulldog System															
50	10	1,3	12	0,9	M 12	58/6	50/6	10/4 od 8/6	10/4	12	5	4,5	4	4,5	4,5
62	17	1,3	12	2,0	M 12	58/6	50/6	10/4 od 9/6	11/4	12	7	6,5	5,5	6,5	6
75	19	1,3	12	2,6	M 16	68/6	60/6	10/5	12/5	14	9	8	7	8,5	8
95	25	1,3	12	4,7	M 16	68/6	60/6	12/5	14/5	14	12	11	9,5	11	10,5
117	30	1,5	12 bzw. 13	6,9	M 20	80/8	70/8	15/8	18/8	17	16	14,5	13	15	14
140	31	1,5	16	8,7	M 22	92/8	80/8	17/8	20/10	20	22	20	17,5	20	18,5
165	33	1,8	24	11,0	M 24	105/8	95/8	19/8	23/10	23	30	27	24	27	24
Square Shear Connector, Bulldog System															
100/100	15	1,4	28	2,7	M 20	80/8	70/8	13/6	16/6	17	17	15	13,5	15,5	14,5
130/130	18	1,5	28	4,5	M 22	92/8	80/8	16/6	19/8	20	23	20,5	18,5	21	19

Nails

The allowable nail load for a load normal to the shank is given for a conifer wood surface, regardless of grain direction, by

$$N_{l\,allow} = \frac{500 d_n^2}{10 + d_n} \quad [N]$$

where d_n is the nail diameter in mm.

Figure 58 contains only nails conforming to DIN 1151. The allowable loads were computed by the above formula. The same formula can be used for an approximate computation of allowable loads for special helically or annularly threaded nails, and for staples, for which the capacity is equal to two nails, unless higher allowable loads are permitted on the basis of tests.

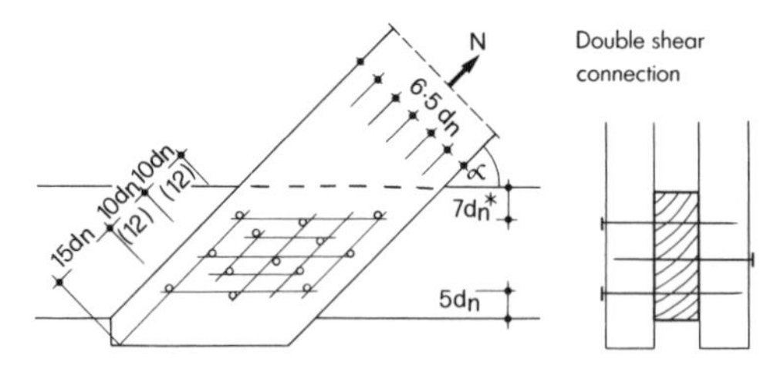

Fig. 59. Minimum distances between nails without predrilling. Values in parentheses are for $d_n > 4.2$ mm.
*For $\alpha < 30°$, $5d_n$ $(7d_n)$.

DIN 1052 gives further data for predrilled holes (smaller distances), for excess-length nails, and also for nails that are subjected to uplift forces for brief periods.

While the values for sheathing nails are given as 31/70 and 34/90, the allowable nail loads for purlins and rafters are given per centimeter of length and for each nail diameter from 4.6 to 8.0 mm.

Fig. 58. Timber thicknesses, driving depths, and allowable nail loads.

For Nail Size $d_n \times l_n$	Minimum Timber Thickness a at Nails		Minimum Driven Nail Depth s		Allowable Nail Load N_l for One Shear Surface		
					For Conifers		For Oak and Beech, always Predrilled
	Not Pre-drilled mm	Pre-drilled mm	Single Shear $12d_n$ mm	Multi-Shear $8d_n$ mm	Not Pre-drilled N	Pre-drilled N	N
22 x 45 22 x 50	24	24	27	18	200	250	300
25 x 55 25 x 60	24	24	30	20	250	310	375
28 x 65	24	24	34	23	300	375	450
31 x 65 31 x 70 31 x 80	24	24	38	25	375	460	560
34 x 90	24	24	41	27	430	540	650
38 x 100	24	24	46	30	525	650	780
42 x 110	26	26	51	34	625	775	930
46 x 130	30	28	56	37	725	905	1090
55 x 140 55 x 160	40	35	66	44	975	1220	1460
60 x 180	50	35	72	48	1120	1400	1680
70 x 210	60	45	84	56	1450	1800	2170
76 x 230	70	46	91	61	1640	2050	2460
88 x 260	88	53	106	70	2060	2575	3090

Wood Screws

Connections with wood screws are generally built in single shear and are loaded normal to the screw axis as follows:

$$N_{allow} = 4a_1 d_s$$

not to exceed

$$N_{allow} = 17d_s^2 \quad [N]$$

where a_1 is the timber or sheet thickness and d_s the diameter of the screw shank, both in mm.

If the screw diameter is less than 10 mm, the load does not depend on the direction of the grain, as for nails.

If $d_s \geq 10$ mm, the allowable load is reduced by

$$\left(1 - \frac{\alpha}{360}\right)$$

where α is the angle between load and grain.

Pullout loads can be taken as

$$N_{Z\,allow} = 3d_s s_g \quad [N]$$

not to exceed

$$N_{Z\,allow} = 21d_s^2 \quad [N]$$

where $N_{Z\,allow}$ is the allowable axial load and s_g the depth of the threaded shank in mm, minimum depth $4d_s$.

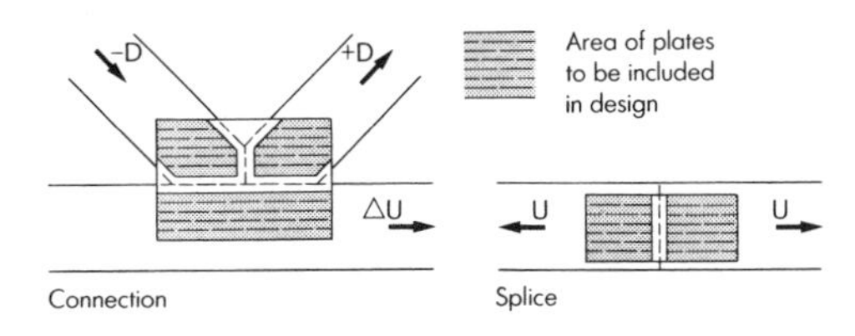

Nail Plates

Nail plates are designed either by the number of load-carrying teeth or punch-outs within the area to be included in the design, or by the allowable bearing stress on the wood in this area. In addition, the plate loads should not exceed the allowable unit stresses on the gross plate cross sections within the effective areas. For most types of plates, the allowable stresses depend on the angle α between the load and the direction of the plate, and on the angle β between the load and the grain of the wood. Individual nail plate designs should be approved after determining allowable loads, edge distances, and size of plates.

Glued Connections

The gluing of surfaces cannot be applied to splices and joints as illustrated in Fig. 51 because the stiffness of the glued surfaces and the low allowable transverse tensile stress of adhesives do not make such joints durable. This type of connection is therefore limited to joining single pieces to composite sections, such as in laminated wood beams, I beams, and panels, in which the joint is subject to shear only. In such cases, the allowable shear in a glued joint parallel to the grain is equal to the allowable shear of the wood because generally adhesives have a greater shear strength than do wood or wood products.

The equation for the allowable shear stress of a glued joint is

$$\tau_{l\,avail} = \frac{QS}{bJ} \leq \tau_{a\,allow}$$

is therefore applied using the allowable shear stress in wood.

Today, longitudinal timber splices in glued members are made exclusively by means of finger joints conforming to DIN 68140. Shear and tension failure of glued finger joints is prevented by their flat slope, so that the design is limited to the determination of stress in the reduced section,

$$F_{red} = (1 - v)F$$

where $v = \frac{b}{t}$

F_{red} = reduced cross section
v = degree of reduction
t = finger joint spacing
b = width of finger joint base

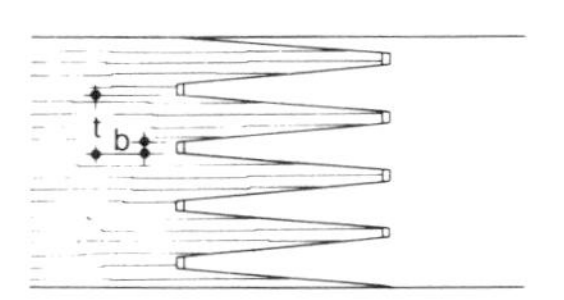

The stress in the reduced section must not exceed the allowable stress in the wood.

For the design of finger joints in laminated wood the degree of reduction can be ignored.

Limitations on Deformations and Deflections

Every material is subject to deformation under external forces and temperature changes. In wood and wood products there are, in addition, deformations due to creep and moisture changes, the latter in the form of swelling or shrinkage. When structural members are assembled by mechanical connections, deformations also occur because of the flexibility of connections.

In members subject to bending, deflections are very evident and are limited by design codes. These limitations are based on either functional or purely aesthetic reasons and assume that a deflection equal to 1/300 of span is still acceptable from a visual point of view. For roofs or floors of sheds or agricultural buildings, this limit can be increased to 1/200. Solid beams cannot be built with a camber and, therefore, must not exceed the maximum deflections under full load. This limitation on deflection often governs the design.

It must be remembered that the E modulus of a single wood member may fall substantially below the averages given by DIN, and therefore it is recommended that the E value in deflection calculations for single beams be reduced by 25%. Deflection due to permanent loads may be computed with $\eta E_{||}$ (see pages 28 and 30).

Deflections of assembled members can be influenced significantly by the flexibility of connections, less so for trusses than for beams. Exact numerical calculations should be prepared for beams, but in continuously connected beams an effective moment of inertia is used to replace the gross moment of inertia. For trusses, consideration must be given to the slippage of connections and the foreshortening of members due to compression. Relatively shallow trusses with flatly sloped diagonals are particularly subject to large deflections.

Simple beams composed of several elements should preferably be fabricated with a camber. In order to make the beam appear horizontal to the eye, it is advisable to give it a parabolic camber slightly larger than required, so that the beam retains a camber even under full load. Camber for glue-laminated members may be computed exactly for dead and live loads because the beams have no connections subject to slippage. For all other types of construction the camber should be at least 1/300 to 1/200 of the span. If such a camber cannot be achieved, the beam should not be subjected to full bending.

Flat roofs are especially endangered by ponding, and should therefore be sufficiently superelevated and drained. Perfectly horizontal roofs should be avoided because even a few centimeters of ponding adds a substantial weight to light timber construction, and both deflection and ponding increase as a result.

Special efforts to limit deflections and introduce camber are necessary if any detrimental effects due to deflections are expected on floors, planking, or walls, or if no deviations from the horizontal can be tolerated for aesthetic reasons. For cantilevers or beams with cantilevers, rotation of the cantilevered end often governs and not its deflection. In order to obtain acceptable deflections and provide the necessary cambers due to inevitable changes in the configuration of loaded beams, especially those subject to bending, careful planning is necessary in all but the most simple cases. Few engineering criteria govern allowable deflections and the appearance of a structure. In many instances it is the architect who must give the appropriate criteria for design and construction.

Lateral Stability and Spatial Stiffening

Lateral displacements of the ends of single-compression members or members of a truss are generally prevented, and these members are considered pinned at both ends in all directions. On the other hand, compression flanges of girders or trusses may buckle laterally in one direction unless prevented from doing so. They must, therefore, be supported laterally, either continuously or at certain intervals. Lateral support may be achieved through flooring or roofing panels, but it is generally provided by lateral bracing in the plane of the upper flanges. Such bracing can also be used for wind bracing.

The compression flange of a simple beam is usually on the top. Since in most cases the floor beams or similar members also lie on top, the stiffening of the upper flange is easy to achieve if such members are formed into horizontal trusses, attached to the beams at their node points, and designed to transmit lateral forces. Thus the buckling length of a beam's upper flange is determined by the spacing of the stiffeners. Trusses over open sheds or sheds that have at least one third of one side open may be subject to uplifting forces. If the roof dead load is small, the lower truss flange may also become stressed in compression and must be secured against lateral buckling. If the stiffening is not provided by lateral trussing, knee braces or half-frames should be provided (Fig. 63).

In addition to designing structural elements and their components for vertical loads and buckling, a check must be made of the stability of the entire structure. This means that besides vertical loads, lateral loads such as wind and earthquake must also be accounted for. The latter must be carried by special structural members and must be conveyed to the foundation. In timber structures this is achieved by lateral trussing or by walls or floors that act as stiffening panels.

Lateral trussing is placed mostly in roof surfaces, as shown in Figs. 60 and 61. Vertical trussing serves to absorb the lateral loads of roof trussing; it is generally placed in the building corners.

If walls or floors consist of panel elements, these can be used to take and carry the horizontal loads (Fig. 62).

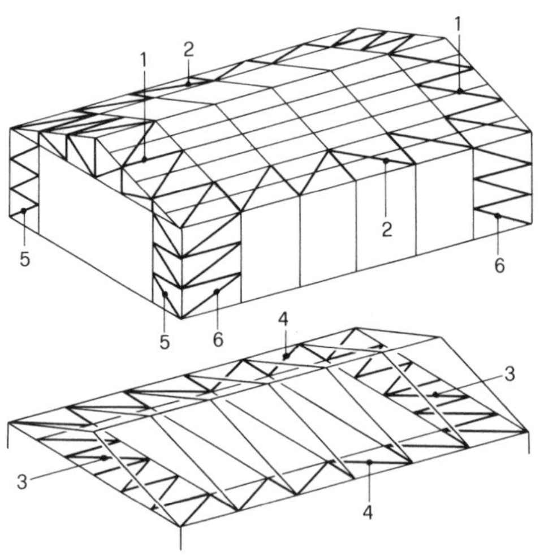

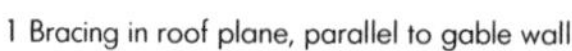

1 Bracing in roof plane, parallel to gable wall
2 Bracing along gutter, in roof plane
3 Bracing of lower chord, parallel to gable wall
4 Bracing of lower chord, parallel to gutter
5 Vertical bracing in gable wall
6 Vertical bracing in gutter wall

Fig. 60. Arrangement of lateral stiffening.

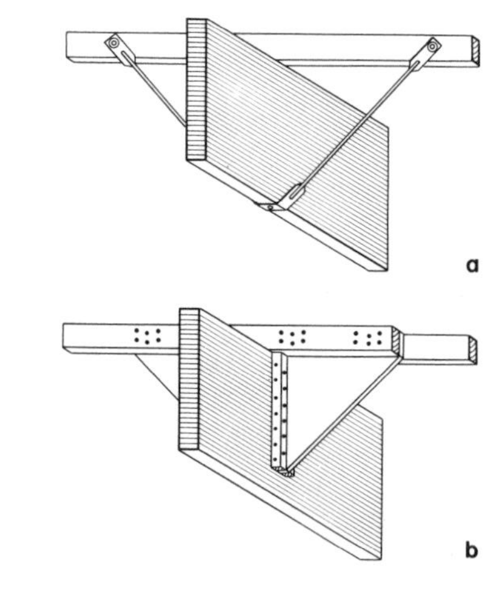

Fig. 63. Stiffening of lower compression flange (continuous beams at support, frame elbows, arches). (a) Tension diagonal bars, connected with one-sided shear connector. (b) Stiffener plates, such as plywood.

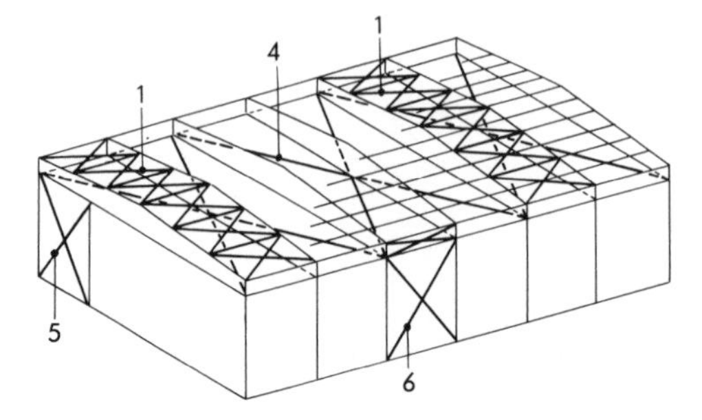

Fig. 61. Stiffening by means of crossed diagonals; stressed only in tension (boards, tension bars, flat steel bars).

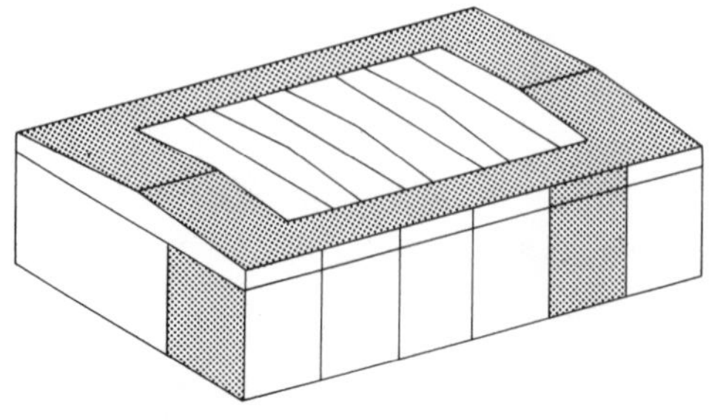

Fig. 62. Stiffening by panels in wall and roof surfaces.

Technical Codes, Standards, and Quality Requirements

The design and construction of timber structures and their critical structural components should conform to the technical rules of the codes that regulate the structural and deformational performance during the life of a structure. These rules are given in DIN 1052, parts 1 and 2, and in their supplements. The quality requirements of timber and wood products are contained in special codes. It is understood that allowable stresses and deformation values of materials used in design should conform to those requirements. The newly established regulations for wood products are an essential part of the codes because they result in additional safety when these products are used for structural members. In addition to the requirements of DIN 1052, special building permits are required for unusual timber structures and special types of connections. The need for such permits is due to special qualifications of technical personnel and shops needed for such work. In some cases even special design methods are called for.

Following is a list of the most important regulations and codes, together with their contents. It should be noted that new editions are expected for some of their parts, a few resulting in substantial changes. This is particularly valid for regulations regarding wood-product panels, because of their continuing development in building construction. The following standards and regulations are officially valid in the Federal Republic of Germany.

Design Regulations

DIN 1052, Part 1, October 1969, "Timber Structures, Design and Construction"

This basic standard is valid for all load-carrying members of wood and plywood. It contains rules regarding the structural design and drawings, material properties (*E* and *G* moduli and shrinkage), allowable stresses and deflections, design of members subject to bending, tension, and compression, bracing and lateral support, and ordinary connections. Rules for construction procedures are also given.

DIN 1052, Part 2, October 1969, "Timber Structures, Rules for Special Connections"

This standard is valid, together with part 1, for the design and construction of those doweled connections which have been recognized as useful and allowable in timber structures. It contains the shapes and the allowable stresses and arrangements of shear connectors (Fig. 54).

Supplement to DIN 1052, August 1963 Edition, "Timber Panel Buildings, Design and Construction"

These regulations are valid for one- and two-story buildings consisting generally of full-story-high wood or wood-product panels (to about 3 m). They contain *E* values and allowable stresses for wood-chip or wood-particle boards, and for stiffening panel members such as furniture panels, light chip-boards, etc.

Important data include load distribution widths for compression or bending of panel elements, the allowable loads for connections of wood or wood products, and rules for construction methods of wall elements used for horizontal stiffening. The rules will be newly presented as part 3 of DIN 1052 and will give necessary data for the design and construction of load-carrying and stiffening wood boards.

"Roof Sheathing Made from Wood-Chip Boards or Plywood," Temporary Regulations for Design and Construction, May 1967 Edition

These regulations complement DIN 1052 and are valid for roof sheathing composed of wood-chip boards or plywood. Given for wood-chip boards are *E* values, allowable stresses in relation to thickness, critical loading cases for determining stress and deflection, distribution of load, and allowable deflections. Tables give the required panel thicknesses for single spans, depending on panel width and span length. The section "Construction Procedures" contains rules on the arrangement and anchorage of panels to their foundations, and on protection against moisture, weather, decay, and fire. A new part 4 of DIN 1052 is being prepared for these rules.

Detailed explanations of DIN 1052, parts 1 and 2, and of the additional rules and regulations are published in *Holzbautaschenbuch*, 7th edition, 1984.

Material Standards (Quality Requirements)

DIN 4074, Part 1, December 1958, "Wood for Timber Buildings, Requirements for Lumber (Conifers)"

DIN 4074, Part 2, December 1958, "Requirements for Round Construction Lumber (Conifers)"

Both of these publications contain standards and quality requirements for conifer lumber and round timbers whose cross sections are determined by design, that is, for wood designed according to DIN 1052 or other regulations. DIN 68365, "Wood for Carpentry, Quality Requirements" is valid for other sawn or round lumber.

DIN 4074, parts 1 and 2, contains the requirements for grade III wood with regard to general conditions, moisture content, minimum weight, width of yearly rings, knots, and curvature. Also given are grades for lumber, dimensional tolerances, and skew of grain.

DIN 68365, November 1957, "Wood for Carpentry"

This standard regulates wood used for nonstructural carpentry. It establishes in general form the requirements for the quality of sawn and round timbers, rough and planed boards, strips and dimension lumber, and sawn and round hardwood timber. The data on allowable defects are only qualitative since quality grading is based more on appearance than on strength. New editions of DIN 4074 and 68365 will strive to unify all the quality requirements for timber.

DIN 68705, Part 1, January 1968, "Plywood; Concepts, General Requirements, Testing"

This standard applies to veneer and furniture plywood and establishes concepts, requirements, and testing procedures which are applicable to all types of plywood regardless of application. Important in this context are the requirements for gluing of interior grade plywood (IF 20) and exterior grade plywood (AW 100), the testing of these requirements, and rules on quality certification and marking.

DIN 68705, Part 2, September 1968, "Plywood for General Use; Quality Requirements"

This standard establishes the requirements for surface veneers of panels intended for interior nonstructural use. There are three quality grades, and requirements vary with the type of wood.

DIN 68705, Part 3, January 1968, "Plywood: Construction Veneer Panels"

This standard is valid only for construction plywood that is generally applied rough. It contains the requirements for floor and subfloor veneers, panel construction, gluing, bending strength, moisture content, and wood preservatives. Quality certification and markings are also presented.

DIN 68705, Part 4, July 1968, "Plywood; Construction and Furniture Panels, Quality Requirements"

Given here are the requirements for construction and furniture panels, their veneers, fillers, and glues, as well as general requirements similar to those for construction veneer panels.

DIN 68763, September 1973, "Wood-Chip Boards, Flat-Pressed Panels for Construction; Concepts, Properties, Testing, Control"

While DIN 68761 and 68762 treat flat-pressed panels for general purposes, such as furniture and acoustical or decorative wall or ceiling coverings,

DIN 68763 treats flat-pressed panels that are used as structural or stiffening members in structures. It contains a classification of panel types according to their glues or wood preservation additives, their minimum quality requirements, and testing, including quality control and markings.

DIN 68764, Part 1, September 1973, "Wood-Chip Boards, Extruded Press Boards for Structures; Concepts, Properties, Testing, Control"

This standard encompasses rough boards and extruded panels laminated on both sides, all of them used for load-carrying and stiffening purposes.

DIN 68764, Part 2, September 1974, "Wood-Chip Boards, Extruded Press Boards for Structures, Laminated Press Boards for Panel Structures"

This standard deals with extruded press boards laminated on both sides, consisting of 12- to 16-mm-thick raw panels conforming to DIN 68764, part 1, and laminates of at least 1-mm-thick beech veneers or minimum 2-mm-thick hardwood-particle boards. Based on the requirements of part 1, this standard gives minimum bending strengths in both directions of the panels and thus facilitates their best structural use.

DIN 68771, September 1973, "Wood-Chip Boards as Subflooring"

This standard is valid for wood-chip boards used as subflooring in rooms intended for permanent human occupancy. It treats the three most common types of application, the requirements for substructure, and humidity protection. In addition, the standard gives the rules for the installation of panels, maximum spans for linear supports, and floor coverings.

DIN 68754, Part 1, February 1976, "Dense and Medium-Dense Wood-Particle Boards for Structures; Wood Products Grade 20"

This standard is valid for panels used in structures for load-carrying or stiffening members in rooms with generally lower humidity, that is, in applications for wood products grade 20, according to DIN 68800, part 2. A special standard is being prepared for grades 100 and 100G. Given are the allowable dimension tolerances and minimum values for bending and shear strengths as well as swelling. Fabrication should be subject to quality control.

DIN 68800, May 1974, "Wood Preservation in Buildings"

Part 1: General. This standard applies to the protection of wood or wood products against destructive influences of fungi, insects, or fire. It analyzes the significance of structural or chemical protective measures against fungi, insects, or fire in buildings, and details appropriate planning and construction methods.

Part 2: Preventive detailing measures. This standard gives the rules for preventive detailing methods and materials needed for the preservation of wood and wood products. It also gives the required grades of wood products for load-carrying or stiffening structural members, depending on their area of application.

Part 3: Preventive chemical treatments of solid wood. Preventive chemical treatments of wood are given here. These treatments are classified according to their composition (water-soluble or oil-based, foam-building) and their effectiveness (against fungi, insects, or fire). Penetration methods and minimum deposition quantities are also given.

Part 4: Protective measures against fungi and insects. This standard describes required measures to combat an actual occurrence of fungus or insect decay. It describes possible structural or chemical methods and the manner of testing the completed work.

DIN 18334, August 1974, "Carpentry and Woodworking," VOB Part C: "General Technical Rules for Workmanship"

The standard contains introductory rules for describing the workmanship to be applied in specific cases. The main part encompasses the applicability of rules for materials and building components (differentiating between those that are only to be sampled and those that have to be furnished and installed), installation, secondary uses, and estimating. Materials and building components for which there are DIN standards must conform to their quality and dimension requirements. Those for which a permit is needed must be officially approved and must correspond to their permit requirements. Others may be used only with the owner's consent. Contractors should prove before undertaking the work that they are capable of performing that type of work. The standards are applicable to the workmanship itself.

The section on secondary work lists work that is included under contract even without being mentioned in the specifications. Finally, rules are given for the payment of building components for which the performance is generally described on the drawings. If the drawings are not available, the work is to be measured.

Large Halls and Roof Structures

JULIUS NATTERER

In collaboration with:
Johannes Goehl
Gunter Henn

FUNDAMENTALS

This part presents 166 examples of assembly halls and roof structures built with timber and representing various categories of construction. The spans of these structures vary from 10 to 100 m, and the shapes of their structural members range from straight beams to free-form shells; their uses vary from kindergarten buildings to assembly halls with 15,000 seats. At first glance, this may seem a bewildering wealth of forms, ideas, and information.

The main task of this presentation is to highlight the real differences between various types of construction and to have each structure reveal itself, so that we can discern the great number of options that are available in design. Both the engineer and the architect are given information as to the manner in which these structures were conceived and constructed.

This presentation is arranged according to the principles of statics, a sequence familiar to the engineer, but less so to the architect. Straight beams are presented in the beginning, to be followed by trusses, frames, arches, and suspension structures. Finally, described on the later pages are grids, folded plates, domes, and shells.

It would have been possible to classify these structures according to their use, the shape of their roofs, or the length of their spans. However, none of these criteria would be as meaningful and unequivocal as their classification according to structural type.

A close examination of timber structures from the point of view of their type of construction and structural system is particularly meaningful because among the various materials of construction, such as steel, reinforced concrete, and timber, timber is probably the most difficult to use. The difficulty lies not so much in the details of execution as in the fact that loads on timber sections are determined readily and every resulting change in a timber section or in its connections becomes very visible. Timber design considerations influence not only the structure but also the appearance of a building. In reinforced concrete, for example, it is always possible, provided stresses in a section allow it, to "add a couple of bars" without changing the dimensions or the form of a beam. In timber construction, on the contrary, every change in design becomes visible and the resulting changes in size cannot be avoided.

Timber thus forces us in a very special way to carefully select the right structural system and detail it accurately. It is not by accident that this book stresses the engineering aspects of construction.

Timber as a material for large halls and roofs allows us to create many architectural forms and space structures, but it also demands an engineering approach. The often taunted but always desirable cooperation between engineer and architect becomes indispensable in timber construction. Indeed, it must be present right from the beginning of the design process.

Structural Systems

The left column of each example in the following sections contains a description of the structural form of each building and an outline of its loading type. Its static behavior is described in terms of bending, shear stresses, and deflections; the general layout of the building is also described.

Isometric drawings and cross sections show possible alternatives to each structural system. Looking at the left columns it could be said that a structural system can be recognized from the cross section of a building.

Some building types and span lengths dictate the structural system: a span of 4 m with a flat roof can have beams resting on columns; a span of 100 m with a high ceiling certainly suggests the use of a three-hinged arch.

The engineer must collaborate with the architect and find the structural system best suited for the purpose. Most of the time certain data are given, such as the plan, the intended use of the building, the ceiling height, and the overall cross section. It then becomes necessary to develop a structural system for this generally defined from. Decisive in the choice of the structural system is not only the ceiling height but also the outer envelope of the building and the room left for supports. The space between the ceiling and the outer envelope is available for the structural framework.

The main task of the engineer is to examine several alternative supporting systems and choose the one best suited for the available construction space. In this developmental phase the engineer has to consider carefully whether any change in the architectural form is warranted.

A structural system is not only a building form but also a mathematical model. A hall spanned by a frame is really a hall spanned by a continuous beam.

The question as to which structural system is the most appropriate for a given situation naturally depends not only on the length of a span or on ceiling height, but also on the architectural form intrinsic in the building.

Theoretically, all supporting systems can be applied to any length of span. However, when economy is taken into account, the longer the span and thus the greater the loads carried by it, the more a structural system has to follow the resultant of the loads. The best use of timber in a structural system is obtained by making it resist mainly compression forces and only some bending forces.

The relationship between the length of span and the narrowing of the structural system toward the path of resultant forces is well illustrated in the examples: uniformly loaded continuous beams for short spans, trusses for intermediate spans, and finally hinged beams, frames, arches, and shells for spans of up to 100 m.

Construction

The choice of a structural system cannot be made without considering construction details. If a roofing system, such as a three-hinged arch, is considered, it immediately becomes necessary to think of the way of constructing its spring and crown bearings and its tie connections. Right columns of the examples in this book show in isometric projection the construction details of bearings, supports, truss elements, connections, and shell assemblies (see index on page 172).

If these details, taken from current construction practice, are compared with traditional wood connections used in carpentry, it becomes clear that techniques have been subject to major developments, due mostly to the introduction of steel in connections and to the fabrication of laminated beams. Available in the past were only rectangular timber sections, to be connected by means of half-lap joints, pins, dovetail joints, and mortise and tenon joints. The size of timbers was limited by the thickness of the logs, and only limited tensile forces could be transmitted through a joint because connections caused considerable weakening of the timber section. On the contrary, today it is possible to construct laminated beams from glued planking up to a cross section of 30 × 240 cm, these maximum measurements being presently dictated by the size of available planing machines. Present limits are not set by the size of logs; cross sections can be made narrow and deep, depending on the requirement of the structural design.

Steel connections, such as bolts, nails, screws, dowels, and nail plates, cause only minor weakening of a cross section and can transfer larger compressive and tensile forces than was possible with earlier connections. Steel connections transfer forces in a more centered and concentrated way so that the components of trusses and the supports of three-hinged arches can be designed as truly hinged members. Such connections do not transfer deformations from one member to another and thus do not generate secondary stresses.

Structural Systems

Every building contains one or more structural elements. The overall structural system is created by joint action of these elements, which generally consist of the main framework, secondary members, roofing, stiffeners, and foundations. They form a three-dimensional system made to resist vertical and horizontal loads. Each element is connected to another, but they are designed in succession.

Once the layout, the span, and the interior space of a building are determined, the structural design begins with the computation of the roof. If an insulated roof structure is chosen, the roof decking can consist of concrete or timber planking, particle board, plywood, or corrugated sheet metal. Each of these materials has its most economical length of span. On the other hand, in an uninsulated roof the direction of ventilation may be a determining factor in orienting rafters.

The areas between the main girders are taken by a secondary system of uniformly loaded elements. If the girders are close to each other, roof planking can span the distance directly. Medium distances between girders can be spanned economically by timber rafters, depending on their structural type: in the simplest case, simple beams between the girders, otherwise continuous beams or Gerber beams (continuous beams with intermediate pinned joints) resting on main girders. Larger spans require glue-laminated beams or trussed rafters. The distance between these secondary elements depends again on the maximum economic spans of roof decking.

Single elements of the secondary systems resist additional compressive and tensile stresses when they are used as members or chords of a horizontal truss which serves as a stiffener against horizontal loads. Loads in the roof decking, secondary system, and lateral stiffeners are transferred to the main girders vertically and horizontally. Loads on main girders depend also on their spacing and on the arrangement of the lateral stiffeners.

The main girders can be subject to many different load configurations, depending on various alternative designs of roof decking, secondary systems, and stiffeners. Design requires a choice between alternatives. Structural elements subject to bending stresses should preferably have a deep and narrow cross section because such a section has the largest moment capacity. Such girders must still be stiffened against buckling and against local folding of roof decking. Stabilizing forces provided by stiffeners pass across the secondary system into shear walls.

These complex and many-sided considerations make it difficult to choose the best structural system. Such considerations demand that the designer visualize a three-dimensional flow of forces. But structural optimization cannot be the only criterion in the choice of a system and in the comparison of alternatives. The arrangement depends also on several other functional requirements. For example, heating, ventilating, and sprinklers may dictate the use of trussed members, lighting may govern the structural plan, and loudspeakers or lighting fixtures may provide additional loads. Such considerations, together with those of architectural form, influence the choice of a structural system. In timber construction, as elsewhere, there is no arbitrary freedom of design. In fact, timber dictates design discipline and logic in structural design much more than other materials do. The design process must from the beginning adapt itself to this special material and to its complexity. However, a comparison of structural alternatives and the weighing of their merits and demerits solely on the basis of structural computations and without the assistance of creative imagination can never produce good construction and good architecture.

Building an architectural model becomes an indispensable tool in the development of a particular structure. Especially in the design of large timber halls and roofs a model can be most useful in representing form, structure, and color. The model can even be made from the same timber as the planned building.

Finishes

The easy and neat workability of wood, together with the development of machines for sawing, routing, gluing, planing, and turning, lends itself to a high degree of workmanship in actual practice. Today's laminated girders are put together in a special but repetitive manner on an assembly line. After drying the boards in a drying room, the process continues until finger jointing of their ends, cutting the boards to the required lengths, gluing, pressing the boards into desired cross sections, planing, connecting, painting, and shipping. The cross section of laminated beams is limited by the available planing machines, which at present can handle a maximum cross section of 30 × 240 cm. Deeper girders have to be put together by joining smaller cross sections. Bending the girders for camber or for a significant vertical curvature is possible at no additional cost. Only the doubly curved or twisted laminated girders, such as those used as girts for a shell, result in a higher cost because of more difficult workmanship.

Transportation

The cost of transportation may have a substantial influence on the choice of a structural system and its connections. For example, two-hinged arches must generally be constructed with field splices because individual arches cannot be transported by train or truck due to their overall dimensions. Rail transport limits the width of a horizontally lying girder to 2.50 m and the height to 2.80 m. The length of a girder, depending on the rail line, cannot exceed 50 or 60 m. In special cases the width of transport up to 6 m is possible by means of wide trucks and deep loaders. A length of 40 m can be exceeded only by special license. Of the maximum height of 4.40 m for loaded trucks, the usable height is only 2.80 m after subtracting the height of the loading platform, which equals 1.60 m. The usable height is increased to 3.40 m in deep loading trucks. During their transportation the timber girders are well protected by cushioning and covers so that generally excellent protection against humidity and dirt is assured.

Erection

Erection should preferably be entrusted to a contractor that has experience in erecting and connecting timber. It should be based on appropriate construction sequence plans and on a knowledge of erection forces.

Possibly, the manner of erection may influence the choice of a structural system, or at least the design of columns, structural members, or details of construction.

During erection of individual members it is especially necessary to provide appropriate bracing because the effectiveness of the stiffening members in a building comes into play only after all the components of the building have been assembled.

166 Examples

As already mentioned, the examples in this book are arranged according to their structural systems. The aesthetic criteria therefore do not appear dominant. Often simple, economically oriented industrial and storage buildings are presented side by side with other buildings in which an overall architectural concept of space and structure was an essential element of design. This arrangement facilitates the understanding of structural systems since it leads to their comparison.

The examples show only existing structures. The wealth of information and the drawings and photographs intend, above all, to illustrate the complexity of engineered timber construction and of its architecture. In timber construction less may be more, but not necessarily in a book that aims at a comprehensive view of large halls and roofs.

Aesthetic, structural, construction, and economic criteria change often. They should be disregarded here, so that a reader's own critique may come into play. If such criteria are purposely set aside, it will become worthwhile to examine a stimulating general concept or a special detail shown in this book whenever a problematic structure is being studied.

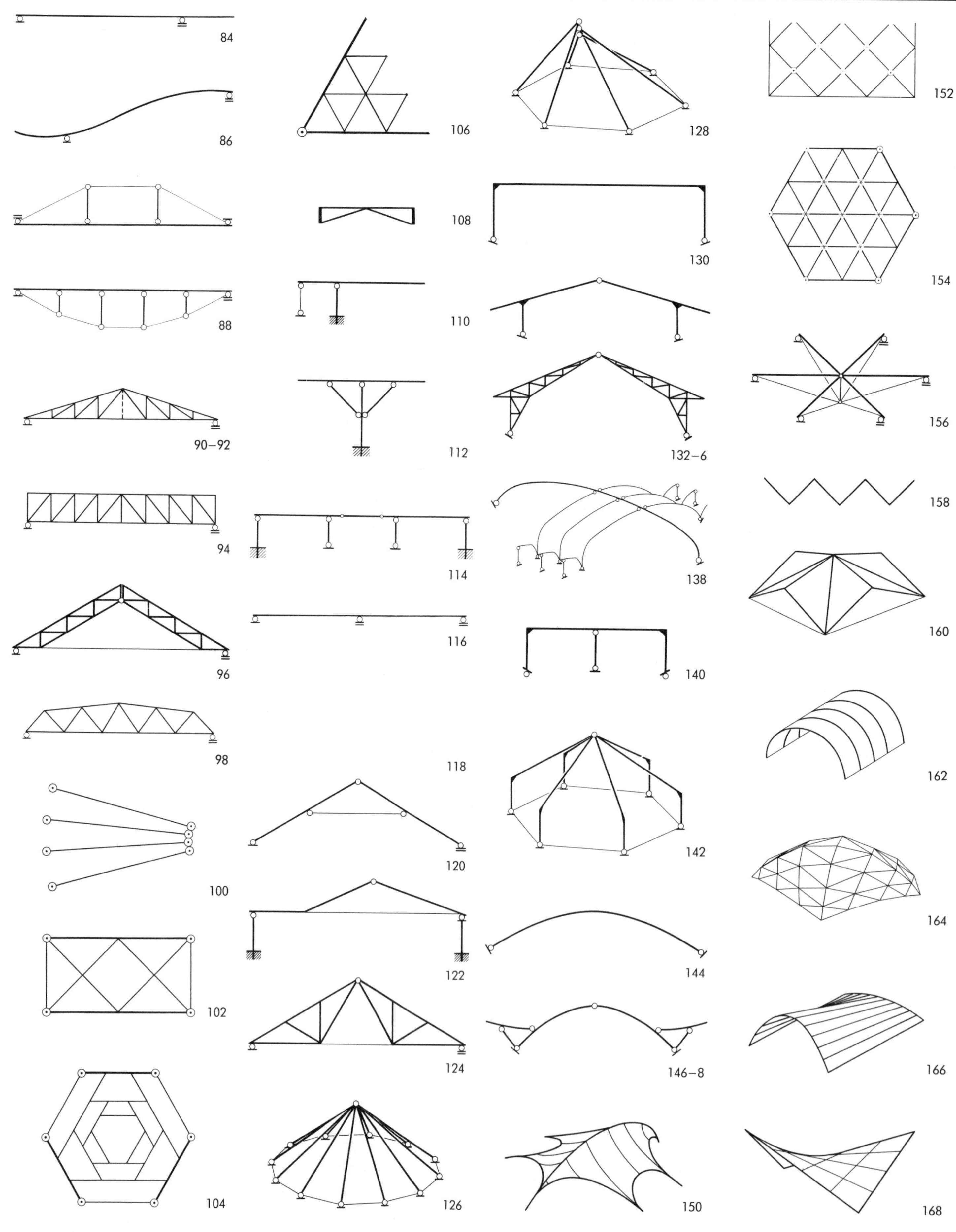
84
86
88
90–92
94
96
98
100
102
104
106
108
110
112
114
116
118
120
122
124
126
128
130
132–6
138
140
142
144
146–8
150
152
154
156
158
160
162
164
166
168

Structural System	Type of Structure	Item	Structure	Location	Country
Simple-span beams	Straight solid girders	1	Sports arena	Ladenburg	W. Germany
		2	Ice skating rink	Bad Reichenhall	W. Germany
		3	Gymnasium	Hannover	W. Germany
		4	Agricultural building	Weihenstephan	W. Germany
	Bent or sloped solid girders	5	Factory	Neustadt	W. Germany
		6	Firehouse	Regensburg	W. Germany
		7	Synagogue	Wallingford	G. Britain
		8	Industrial hall	Minden	W. Germany
	Stayed or propped girders	9	School for the handicapped	Thanet	G. Britain
		10	Chapel	Silton	Canada
		11	Indoor swimming pool	Kochel	W. Germany
		12	Ice skating rink	Ingolstadt	W. Germany
	Trusses	13	Triangular truss		
		14	Triangular truss with raised bottom chord		
		15	Triangular truss with raised eaves		
		16	Triangular truss		
		17	Triangular truss with raised eaves		
		18	Triangular truss		
		19	Mountain church	Winkelmoosalm	W. Germany
		20	Parish community hall	Gossau	Switzerland
		21	Riding hall	Meissenheim	W. Germany
		22	Storage shed	Rosenheim	W. Germany
		23	Nursery school	Erdweg	W. Germany
		24	Ice skating rink	Grefrath	W. Germany
		25	Ice skating rink	Dortmund	W. Germany
		26	Sports hall	Cramond	Scotland
		27	Exhibition pavilion	Grafenau	W. Germany
		28	Church	Munich-Waldperlach	W. Germany
		29	Ice skating rink	Lahr	W. Germany
		30	Church	Munich	W. Germany
		31	Sports hall	Weinfelden	Switzerland
		32	Ice skating rink	Bülach	Switzerland
	Radial arrangements	33	Parochial center	Gossau	Switzerland
		34	Indoor swimming pool	Neustadt	W. Germany
		35	Dolphin house	Hamburg	W. Germany
	Beam grids 90°	36	Office building	Ballerup	Denmark
		37	Cafeteria	Twente	The Netherlands
		38	Central hall of bank	Lippstadt	W. Germany
		39	Ice skating rink	Middletown	United States
	Beam grids, special forms	40	School gymnasium	Aachen	W. Germany
		41	Sports and recreation center	Wasserburg	W. Germany
		42	Exhibition hall	Montreal	Canada
		43	Multipurpose hall	Roseburg	United States
	Beam grids 60°	44	Gasoline station	Wetterau	W. Germany
		45	Tennis clubhouse	Kelkheim	W. Germany
		46	Exhibition hall	Nürnberg	W. Germany
	Various arrangements of secondary girders	47	Community center	Freiburg-Landwasser	W. Germany
		48	Lumber yard roof	Essen-Werden	W. Germany
		49	Research laboratory	Vancouver	Canada
	Cantilever beams	50	Grandstand	Krefeld	W. Germany
		51	Grandstand	Dielsdorf	Switzerland
		52	Grandstand	Munich-Riem	W. Germany
		53	Loading shed	Boulogne	France
		54	Olympic cycling stadium	Munich	W. Germany
		55	Grandstand	Metz	France
		56	Church	Lech	Austria

Summary of Structures and Projects

Multiple-span beams	Hinged beams	57	Industrial building		W. Germany
		58	Storage shed	Dorsten	W. Germany
		59	Storage shed		W. Germany
		60	Printing plant	Paderborn	W. Germany
	Continuous beams	61	Dressing rooms	Langenfeld	W. Germany
		62	Student cafeteria	Würzburg	W. Germany
		63	Boat sheds	Feldmoching	W. Germany
Hinged frames	Three-hinged frames	64	Stable	Munich-Riem	W. Germany
		65	Church	Fawley Court	G. Britain
		66	Swimming pool	Fornasette	Switzerland
		67	Riding hall	Villingen	W. Germany
		68	Church	Kempten-Wetzikon	Switzerland
	Three-hinged frames with tie	69	Storage shed	Oberhausen	W. Germany
		70	Golf clubhouse	Hilton Head Island	United States
		71	Riding hall	Pompadour	France
		72	Riding hall	Lausanne	Switzerland
		73	Ice skating rink	Deggendorf	W. Germany
		74	Riding hall	Marbach	W. Germany
	Three-hinged truss frames	75	Ice skating rink	Freiburg	W. Germany
		76	Concert hall	Snape	G. Britain
	Space frames	77	Exhibition pavilion	Berkeley	United States
		78	Church	Bensberg	W. Germany
		79	Open-air church	Stuttgart	W. Germany
		80	Circus building	Munich	W. Germany
		81	Church	Recklinghausen	W. Germany
		82	Church	Altendorf	W. Germany
		83	Church	Windach	W. Germany
Continuous frames	Two-hinged frames	84	Tennis hall	Ulm	W. Germany
		85	Industrial building		
		86	Nursery school	Munich	W. Germany
		87	Church community center	Flamatt	Switzerland
	Three-hinged frames	88	Storage shed	Kaufbeuren	W. Germany
		89	Riding hall		
		90	Riding hall		
		91	Church	Bocholt	W. Germany
		92	Storage shed	Nordenham	G. Britain
		93	Storage shed		France
		94	Storage shed		
		95	Storage shed		
		96	Storage shed		
		97	Storage shed		
		98	Storage shed		
		99	Riding hall	Gerolstein	W. Germany
		100	Riding hall	Munich-Riem	W. Germany
		101	Indoor swimming pool	Gstaad	Switzerland
		102	Slaughterhouse	Paris	France
		103	Market hall	St. Etienne	France
		104	Swimming pool	Créteil	France
		105	Swimming pool	Griesheim	W. Germany
		106	Exhibition hall	Epinal	France
	Propped or buttressed frames	107	Agricultural building	Rifferswil	Switzerland
		108	Riding hall	Munich-Riem	W. Germany
		109	Riding hall	Hamburg-Volksdorf	W. Germany
		110	Storage shed	Hamburg	W. Germany
		111	Storage shed	Kandel	W. Germany
	Radial frames	112	Exhibition hall	Poitiers	France
		113	Exhibition hall	Kortrijk	Belgium
		114	Church	Wildegg	Switzerland
		115	Church	Livermore	United States

Arches	Two-hinged arches	116	Multipurpose hall	Nantes	France
		117	Ice skating rink	Bern	Switzerland
		118	Multipurpose hall	Leiden	The Netherlands
	Three-hinged arches	119	Ice skating rink	Selb	W. Germany
		120	Exhibition hall	Klagenfurt	Austria
		121	Sports stadium	Turku	Finland
		122	Multipurpose hall	Biebesheim	W. Germany
		123	Sports stadium	Joinville	France
		124	Storage shed	Weichach	Switzerland
		125	Ice skating rink	Porrentury	Switzerland
		126	Ice skating rink	Langnau	Switzerland
		127	Covered market	Wangs	Switzerland
Suspended beams		128	Exhibition hall	Alençon	France
		129	Sports hall	Poitiers	France
		130	Ice skating center	Munich	W. Germany
Beam grids	Solid web beams 90°	131	Administration office	Garching	W. Germany
		132	Residence	Straubing	W. Germany
		133	Church	Kolbermoor	W. Germany
		134	Building supply center	Bamberg	W. Germany
	Solid web beams 60°	135	Church	Greding	W. Germany
		136	School	Gurtweil	W. Germany
		137	Civic center	Bischofsheim	W. Germany
		138	All-weather zoo	Münster	W. Germany
	Trusses	139	Youth center	Gozenyama	Japan
		140	Church	Benet Lake	United States
		141	Auditorium	Weihenstephan	W. Germany
Folded plates	Parallel	142	Storage shed	Apeldoorn	The Netherlands
		143	Shopping center	Würzburg	W. Germany
		144	Convalescent center	Freilassing	W. Germany
	Radial	145	School	Wellington	G. Britain
		146	Church	Uitikon	Switzerland
		147	Music pavilion	Montreal	Canada
Vaulted shells		148	Barrel vault shell	Winnepeg	Canada
		149	Railroad yard shed	Coventry	G. Britain
Rotational domes		150	Ribbed construction	Köln-Volkhofen	W. Germany
		151	Sports arena	Bozeman	United States
		152	Sports arena	Salt Lake City	United States
Geodesic domes		153	Geodesic dome	Munich	W. Germany
		154	Geodesic dome	Säckingen	W. Germany
Vaulted domes		155	Multipurpose hall	Mannheim	W. Germany
Conoid shells		156	Institutional building	Delft	The Netherlands
		157	Market hall	Yeovil	G. Britain
		158	Railroad station	Manchester	G. Britain
Hyperbolic paraboloid shells		159	Pavilion	Freiburg	W. Germany
		160	Reception hall	Honolulu	United States
		161	Sports hall	Paris	France
		162	School	Ipswich	G. Britain
		163	Information pavilion	Brussels	Belgium
Cantilever shells		164	Ribbed shell	Munich	W. Germany
		165	Ribbed shell	Rosenheim	W. Germany
Suspended shells		166	Suspended shell	Dortmund	W. Germany

For an index of the structural details of each category (right columns) and the building functions see page 172.

The loads on a single-span beam cause deformations, and these in turn cause bending and shear stresses. The design of the beam may be governed by bending stresses, shear stresses, or deflections, depending on the cross section of the beam, the type of load, and the length of span. Lateral buckling may govern the size of slender beams (width to height ratio = 1:4).

Fixed bearing Expansion bearing

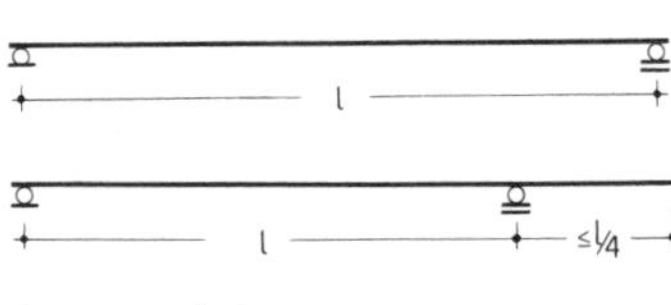

Solid wood purlins
a = 0.5 to 2.0 m (spacing)
l = 1 to 7 m
Distance between purlins depends on the type of roofing, load, etc.

As main girders
a = 5 to 7 m

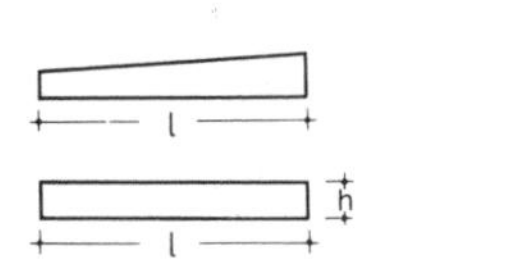

With glued web plates, nailed or glued flanges, or webs	l = 7 to 30 m h = l/8 to l/14
Laminated wood beams	l = 7 to 40 m h = l/10 to l/20

1 Sports Arena in Ladenburg, West Germany

Architect: R. Mockler, Heilbronn
Engineer: H. Stadtelmeyer, Mannheim

Triple gymnasium 31.00 × 45.00 m. Space can be subdivided by means of two curtains, each of which can be raised into the interstice within a main girder. Girder consists of two beams 20/215 cm, spaced at 60 cm, capped by a web which prevents buckling. Secondary beams 16/72 cm, 15.40 m long, span between girders and carry purlins, sheathing, and a "warm" (nonvented) roofing structure.

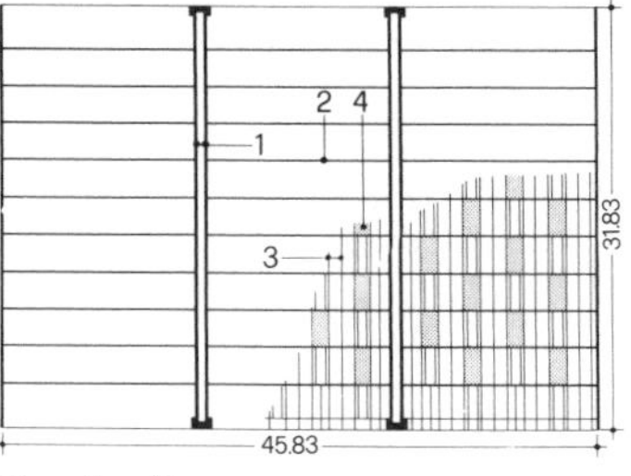

Plan of roof beams

1 Main girder 2 × 20/215
2 Secondary beams 16/72 cm
3 Purlins 8/12 cm
4 Skylights

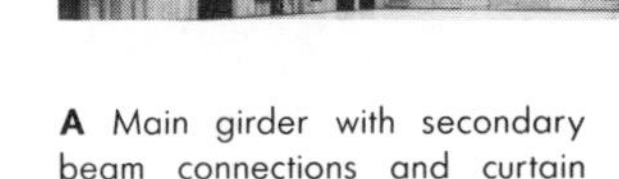

A Main girder with secondary beam connections and curtain

Longitudinal section

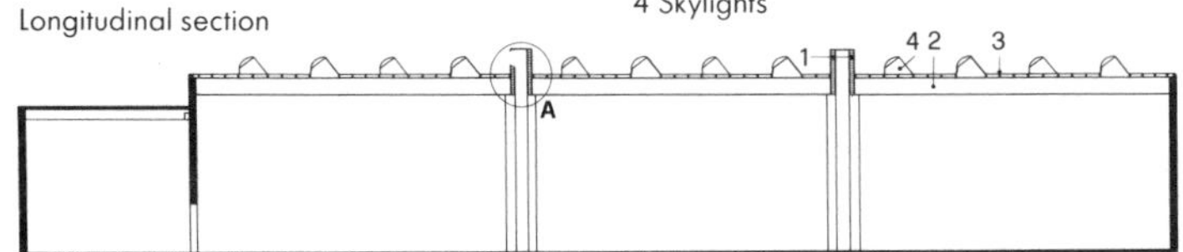

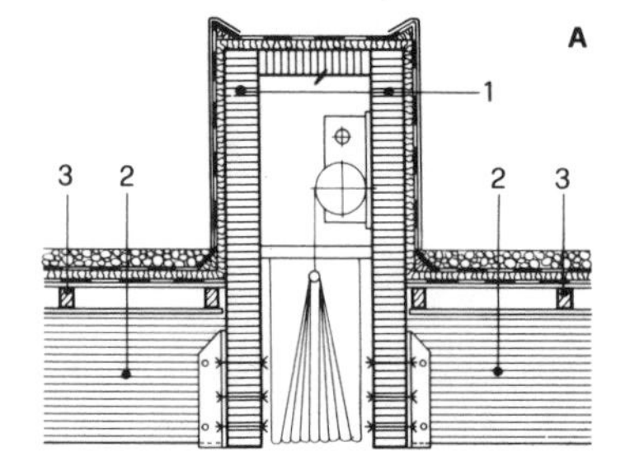

2 Ice Skating Rink in Bad Reichenhall, West Germany

Architect: H.-J. Schmidt and Partner, Munich
Engineer: Timber Construction Contractor

Overall size 75.00 × 48.00 m. Transverse box girders are 2.87 m high, 40.00 m long, spaced at 7.5 m, and are cantilevered 4.00 m at each end. Box girder webs are laminated wood panels, flanges are laminated wood. Purlins 12/46 cm, spaced at 3.17 m, rest on metal beam seats. Box girders are braced at every purlin by interior stiffeners and at every third purlin by vertical K frames; the latter appear also at roof fascia and impart to roof its characteristic appearance.
Reference: *Deutsche Bauzeitschrift* 10/1975, p. 1159; *Detail* 6/1974, illustrations

Partial view of main girder and detail **A**

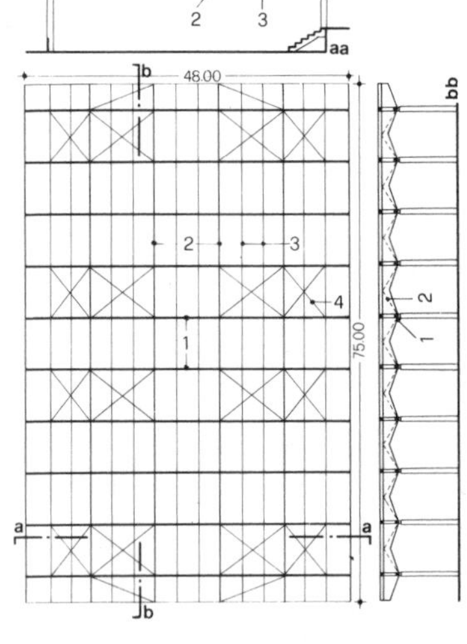

Layout of beams with wind bracing and cross sections.

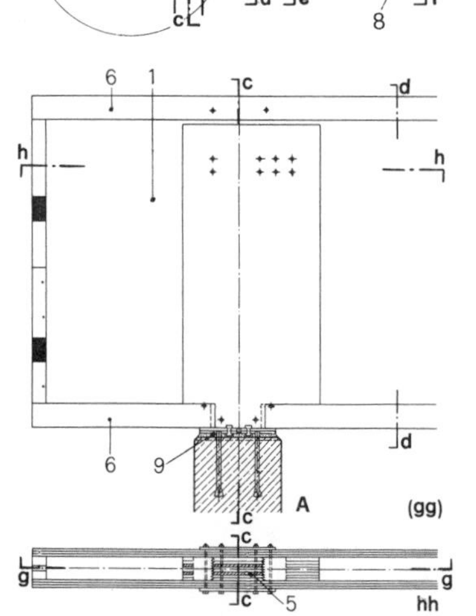

1 Main girder 28/287 cm
2 Diaphragms of laminated panels with wood fillers
3 Purlins 12/46 cm
4 Wind bracing, round steel bars at roof beam level
5 Laminated wood panels 6.5 cm
6 Flanges 20/20 cm
7 Stiffeners 6/12 to 8/12 cm
8 Bearing stiffener at diaphragm
9 Elastomeric bearing

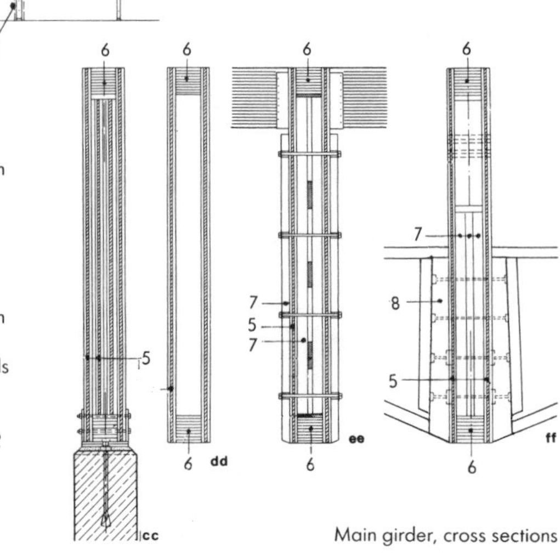

Main girder, cross sections

3 Gymnasium in Hannover, West Germany

Architect: W. Ziegemeier and H. Pfitzner, Hannover
Engineer: Rosenbusch and Detlau, Hannover

Roof 40.00 × 90.00 m with double main girders, spaced at 11.40 m, U cross-section 2 × 30/275 cm, spaced at 50 cm. Top flange of girder horizontal. Room can be partitioned into three parts. Air ducts within main girders. Roof beams are haunched on top and rest on girder shoes, giving a trapezoidal shape to roof and facade. Horizontal bracing is given by prestressed concrete columns.

Layout of beams

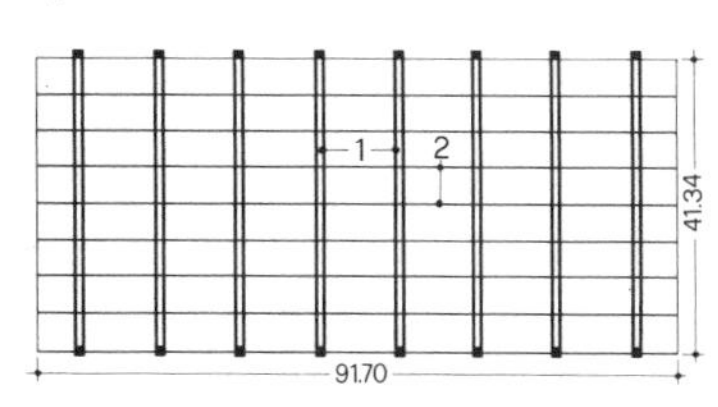

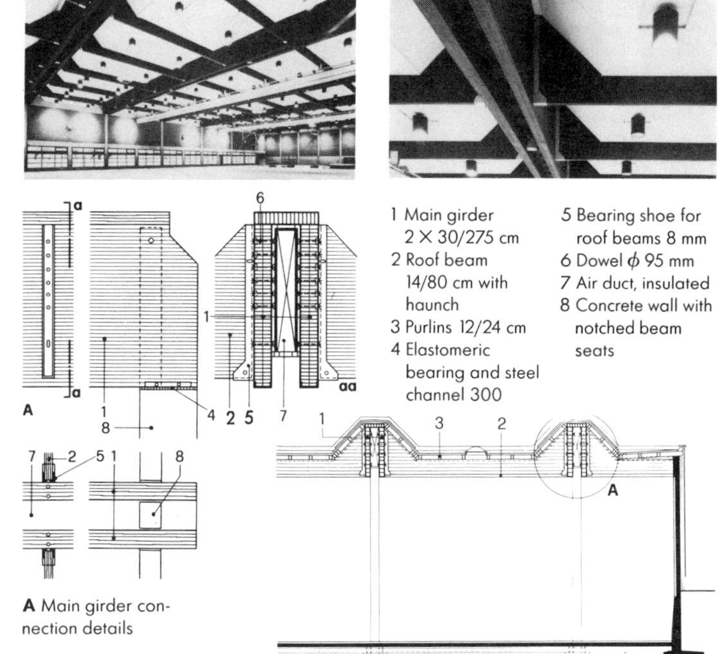

1 Main girder 2 × 30/275 cm
2 Roof beam 14/80 cm with haunch
3 Purlins 12/24 cm
4 Elastomeric bearing and steel channel 300
5 Bearing shoe for roof beams 8 mm
6 Dowel ϕ 95 mm
7 Air duct, insulated
8 Concrete wall with notched beam seats

A Main girder connection details

Partial longitudinal section

4 Typical Building for Agricultural Cooperative, Weihenstephan, West Germany

Engineer: K. März, Munich

Agricultural building with gable roof supported by box girders. Structure is so standardized that it can be built by handymen using ordinary materials. Girders are spaced at 5.00 m and span 12.50 m. Each box girder consists of upper and lower flanges 10/17.4 cm, vertical web timbers 14/17.4 cm, and 1.3 cm thick plywood sheets nailed on both sides. Solid wood columns 20/26 cm are attached to girders with timber gussets and to foundations with steel plates, the latter forming a moment connection. Longitudinal purlins 14/16 cm or purlins 6/16 cm lapped at supports are secured to girders with steel angles. Roofing is corrugated asbestos-cement sheeting.

Buckling and wind bracing are provided by 4/10 cm timber diagonals placed in every sixth bay.

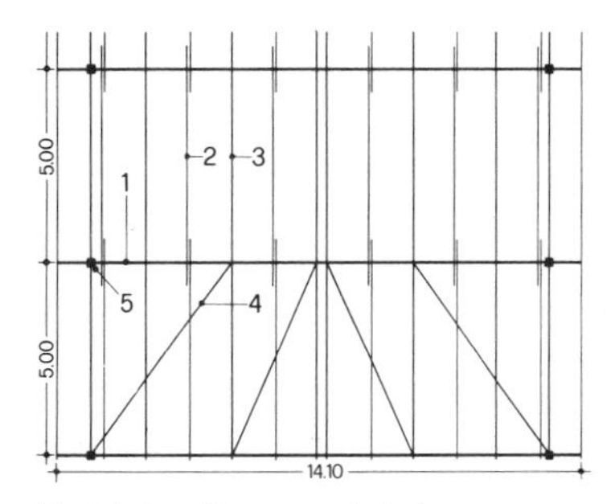

Partial plan of beams and wind bracing

Partial cross section and view of gable

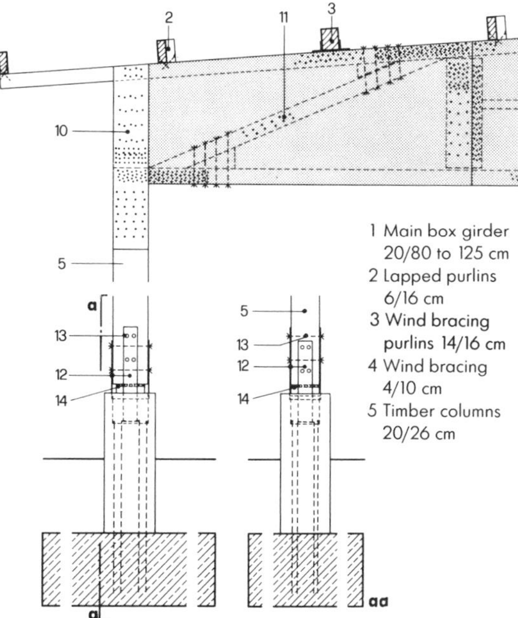

1 Main box girder 20/80 to 125 cm
2 Lapped purlins 6/16 cm
3 Wind bracing purlins 14/16 cm
4 Wind bracing 4/10 cm
5 Timber columns 20/26 cm
6 Flanges 10/17.4 cm
7 Stiffeners 6/17.4 cm
8 Web splice fillers 14/17.4 cm
9 Plywood panels 13 mm each side
10 Connection timbers 4/26 cm
11 Diagonal timbers 10/17.4 cm
12 Steel connection plates
13 Steel bolts ϕ 20 mm
14 Bituminous building paper

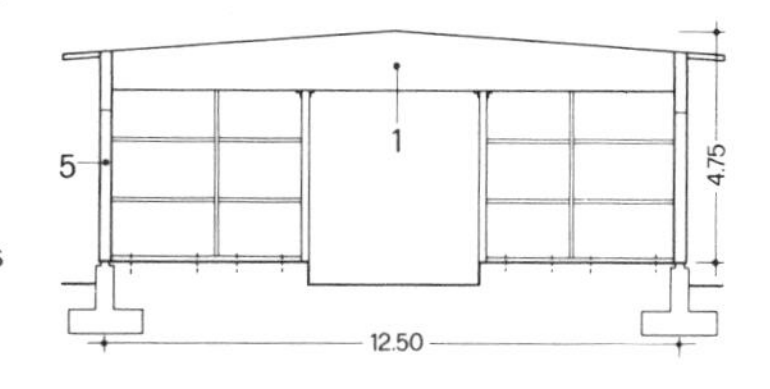

Bearing of Girder on Column

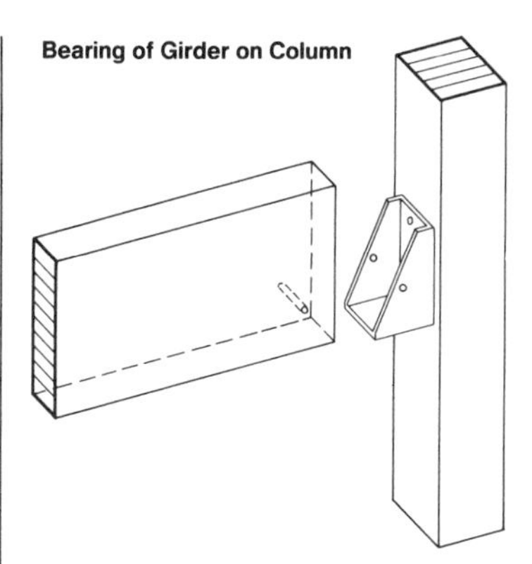

Girder in steel shoe, which is nailed or bolted to column.

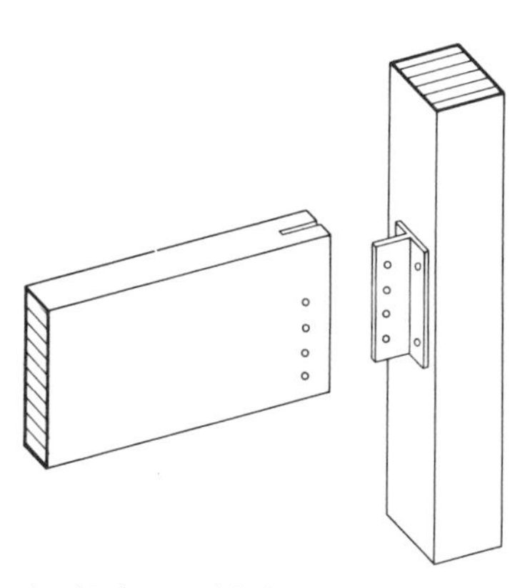

Steel T shape with bolts on column in single shear. Girder is slit and connected with bolts.

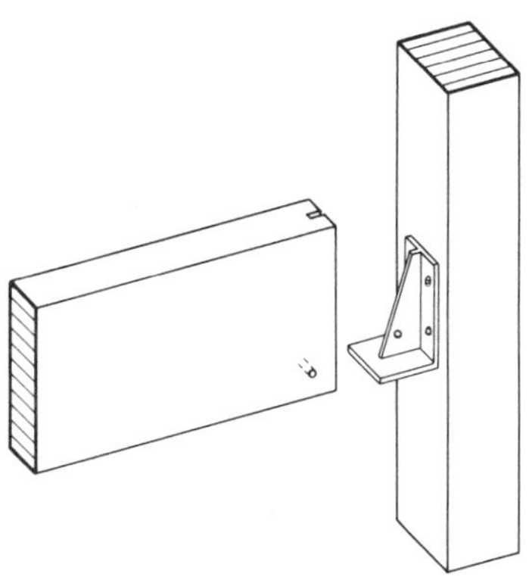

Girder rests on steel angle with stiffener.

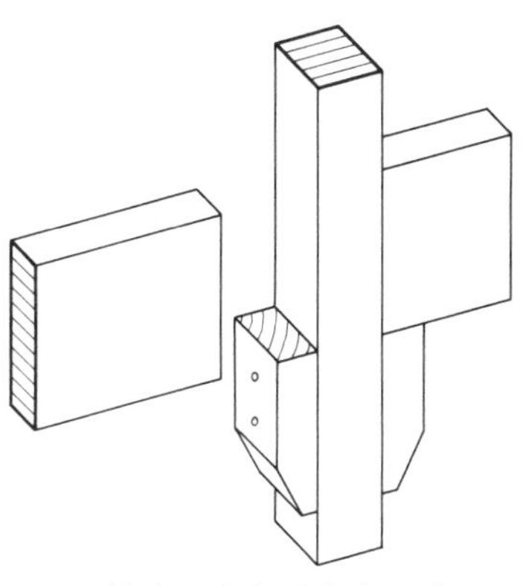

Bearing blocks nailed or bolted to column.

Vertical loads generate only vertical bearing reactions, even if simply supported beams have a bent or curved axis. In addition to deflection and bending or shear stresses, the design is governed by transverse compressive or tensile stresses created at points of curvature.

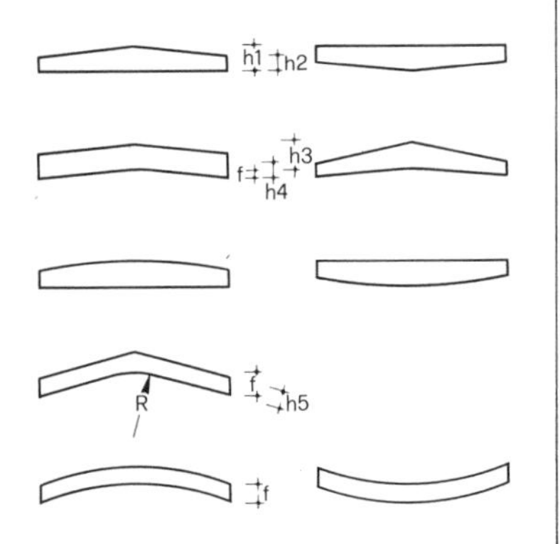

Alternatives of beam configurations (dimensions for laminated wood)

$h_1 = l/14$ to $l/18$
$h_2 = l/18$ to $l/22$
$h_3 = l/14$ to $l/18$
$h_4 = l/30$ to $l/50$
$h_5 = l/14$ to $l/18$

$\sphericalangle = 6$ to $15°$
$R \geq 6$ m
$f \leq l/5$ to $l/10$

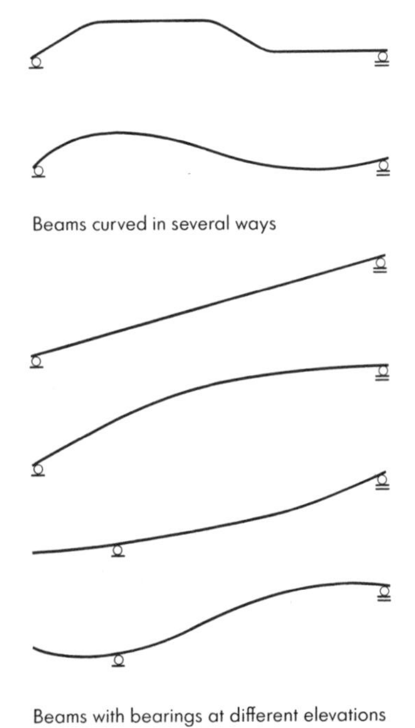

Beams curved in several ways

Beams with bearings at different elevations

5 Factory in Neustadt, West Germany

Architect: Girndt and Wagner, Coburg
Engineer: J. Natterer, Munich

Overall plan size 48.00 × 48.00 m. A central stairwell serves as shear wall and as central support for main girders 2 × 22/192 cm, which divide building in half.

Layout of girders and wind bracing

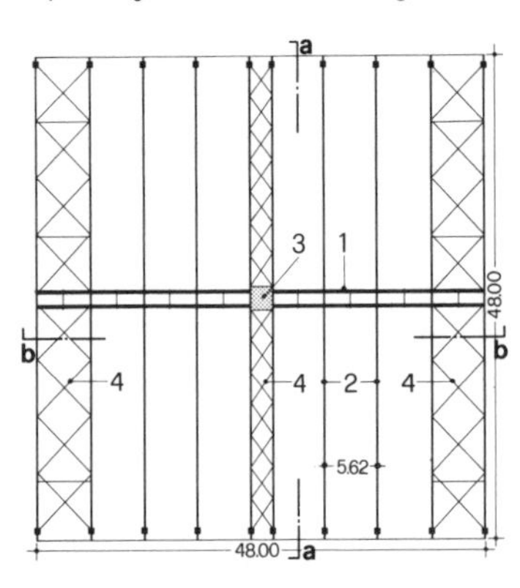

Secondary beams 16/135 cm, spaced at 5.62 m, span normal to girders. On their outer ends secondary beams rest on reinforced-concrete columns; on their inner ends they rest on steel shoe or struts supported by main girders. Secondary girders are curved upward in order to provide clerestory windows. Secondary beams are covered by trapezoidal sheet metal. Horizontal wind bracing of roof is provided by round steel bar diagonals.

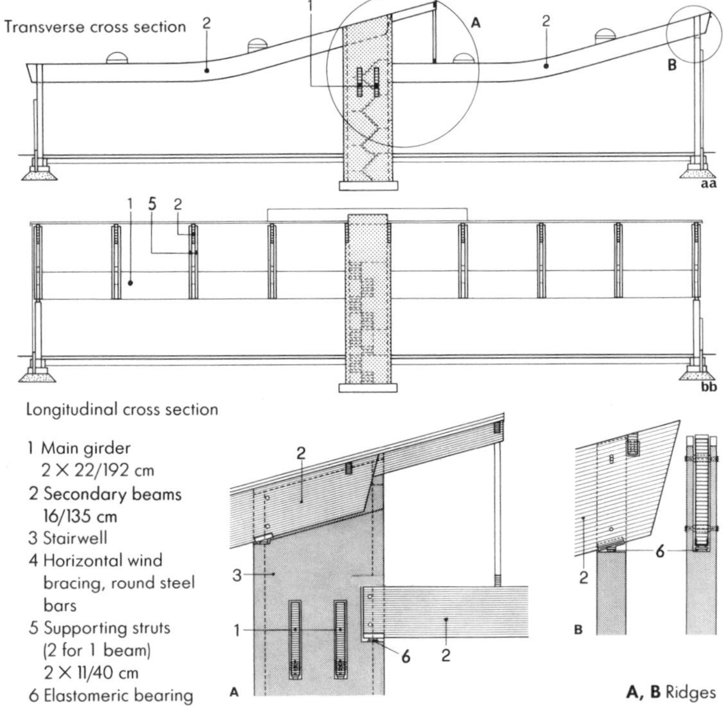

Longitudinal cross section

1 Main girder 2 × 22/192 cm
2 Secondary beams 16/135 cm
3 Stairwell
4 Horizontal wind bracing, round steel bars
5 Supporting struts (2 for 1 beam) 2 × 11/40 cm
6 Elastomeric bearing

A, B Ridges

6 Firehouse in Regensburg, West Germany

Architect: County Building Office
Engineer: D. Filus, Pentling

Training hall for a firemen's school. Shape is required by need to allow fire drills with ladders. This called for a bent roof shape, which could be achieved with curved laminated beams 24/210 cm. These main girders are spaced at 3.50 m and span over 40 m. Between girders there are steel tubes, crossed in both plan and elevation, which serve not only as beam stiffeners and wind bracing, but also as supports for purlins.

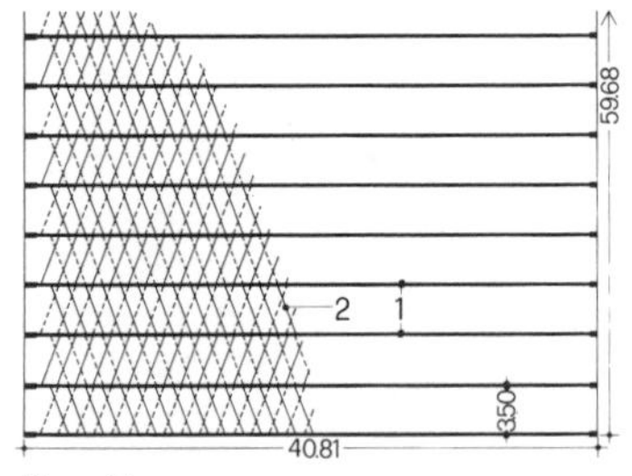

Plan of beams

Horizontal stiffening with purlins

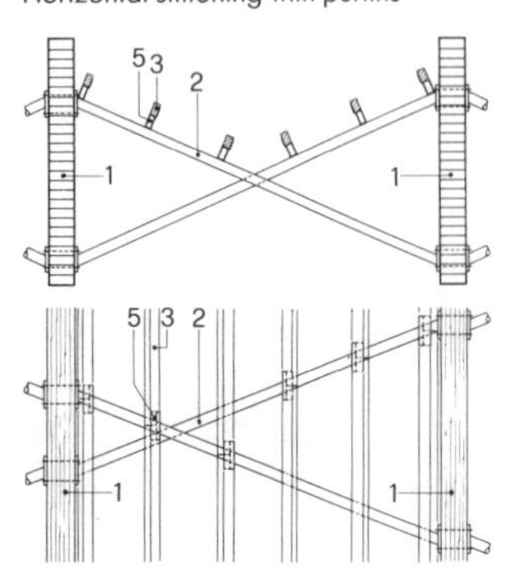

1 Main girders 24/210 cm
2 Crossed steel tubes ϕ 88.9 × 6.3 mm
3 Purlins 6/10 cm
4 Suspended supports for stairs and mezzanine
5 Strut supports for purlins
6 Steel dowels and tightening bolts ϕ 20 mm
7 Elastomeric bearing

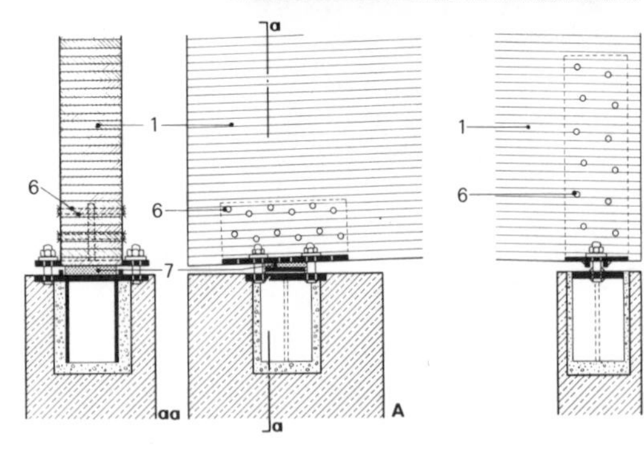

A Expansion bearing, **B** Fixed bearing

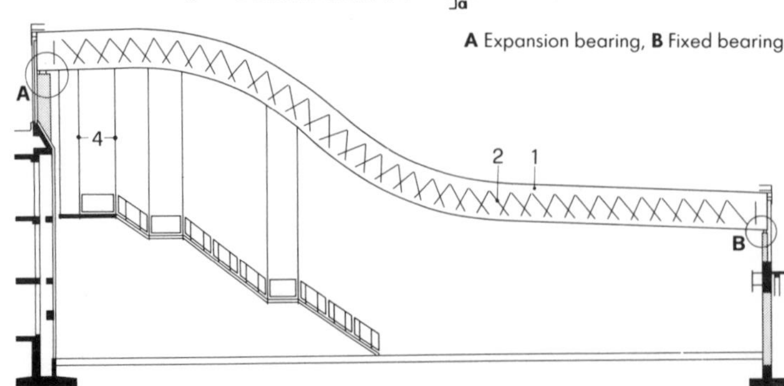

7 Synagogue in Wallingford, Great Britain

Architect: T. Hancock, London
Engineer: Gifford and Partner, Southampton

Synagogue is spanned longitudinally by four curved laminated wood girders. In the east, they rest on a curved masonry wall, in the west, on low round columns. These main girders 18/61 to 153 cm span over 22 m and are cantilevered on lower side 9.50 m. Bearings are steel gusset plates with ϕ 100 mm bolts.

Rafters 6.4/23 cm rest on girders and are stiffened by diagonal planking. K-type frames between girders serve as wind and lateral bracing.
Reference: *Bauen mit Holz* 7/1964, p. 304

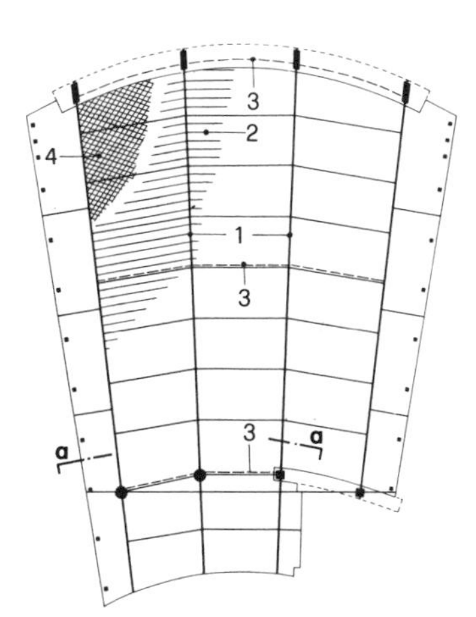

Plan of girders and wind bracing

Partial section aa with lateral bracing

Bearing on concrete column

Longitudinal section

9.50 — 23.50

1 Main girder 18/61 to 153 cm
2 Rafters 6.4/23 cm
3 Lateral bracing
4 Diagonal planking 2 × 16 mm
5 Timber ledger for rafters
6 Bolts ϕ 100 mm
7 Steel gusset bearing

Bearings, Girder on Column

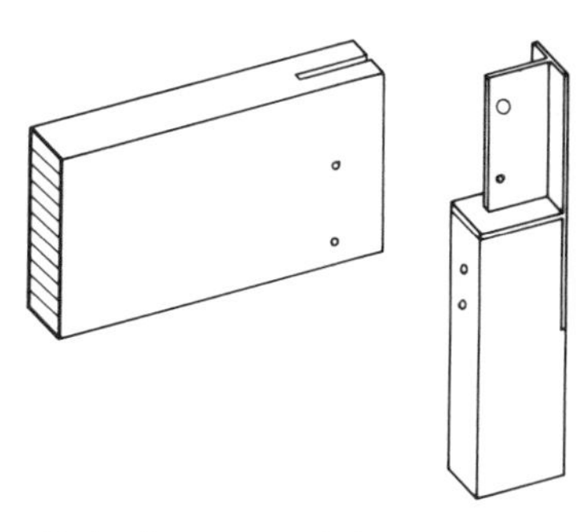
Girder slit, set on steel shoe, concrete, or steel columns. Lateral bracing through steel stiffener.

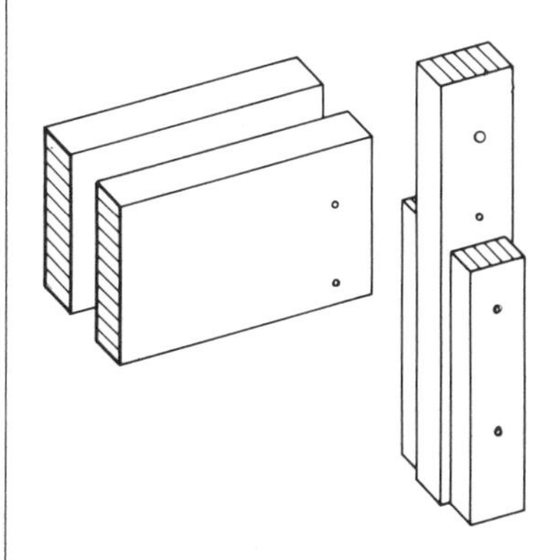
Double girder resting on column timber blocks.

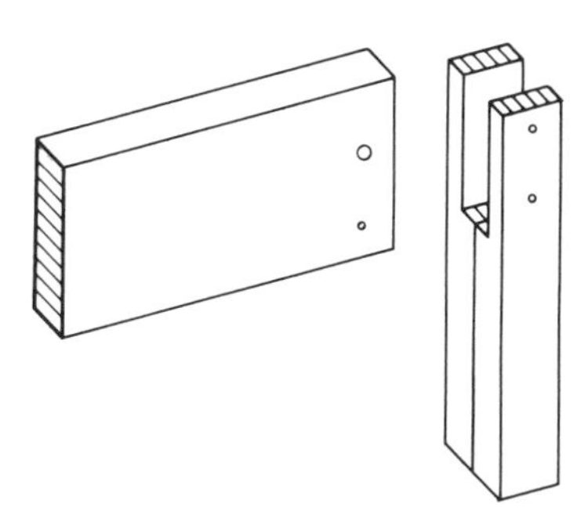
Bearing and lateral bracing by forked top of column.

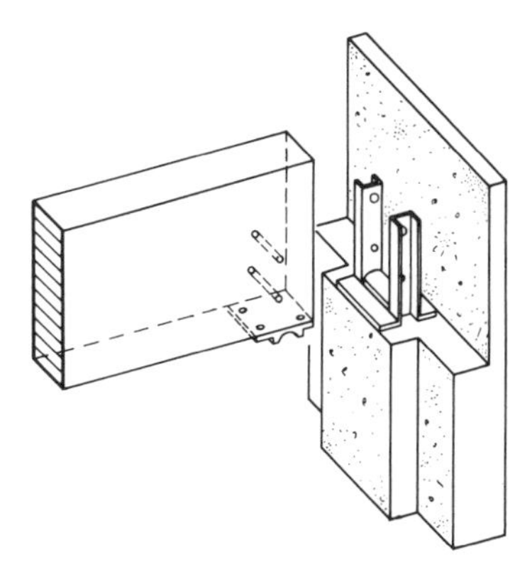
Heavily loaded girder on reinforced concrete wall (or column); steel plates with cylindrical bearing seat. Lateral bracing through vertical steel shapes.

8 Industrial Hall in Minden, West Germany

Engineer: Timber Construction Contractor

Transverse main girders 18/61 to 153 cm, spaced at 6.82 m span 25.00 m and are cantilevered 8.00 m on each side. Forked bearings in prestressed concrete columns. Coupled rafters 6/20 to 11/20 cm span longitudinally. Round steel bars stiffen roof diagonally. Wind loads are taken by concrete columns.

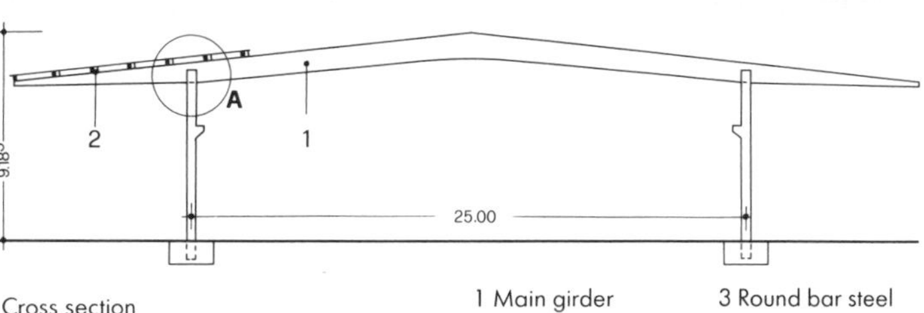

Cross section

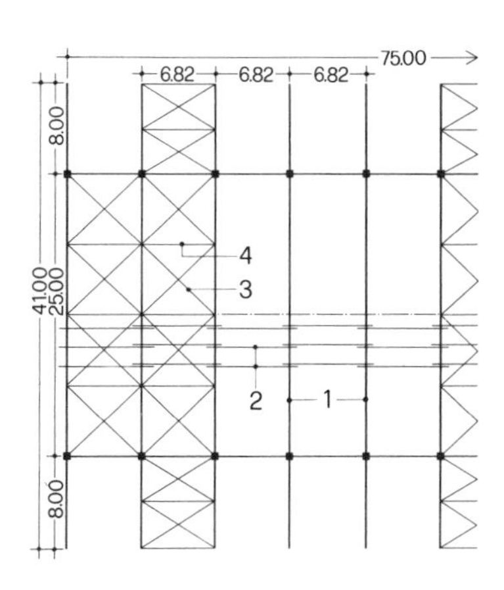

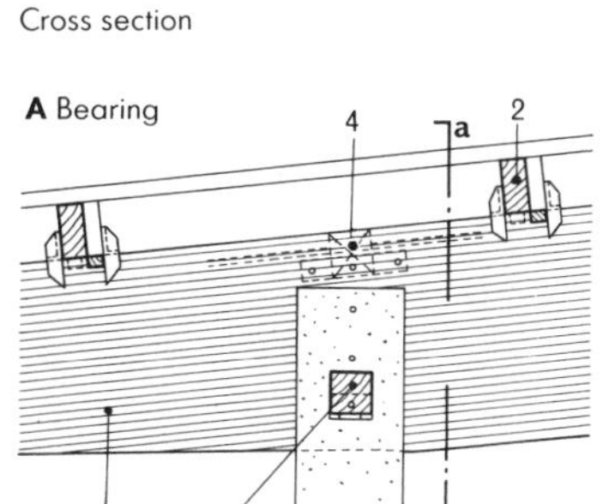

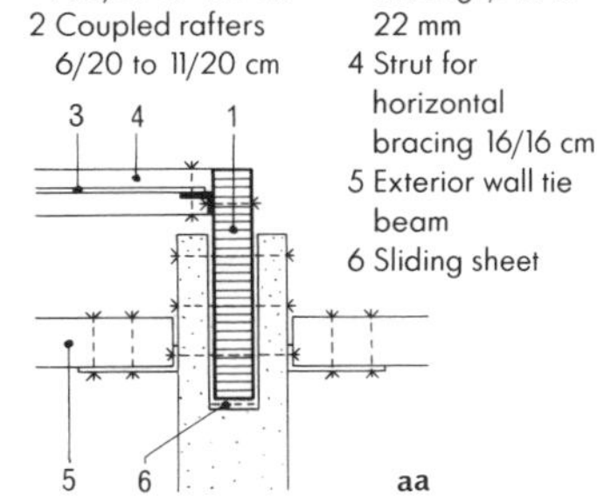

1 Main girder 14.6/20 to 100 cm
2 Coupled rafters 6/20 to 11/20 cm
3 Round bar steel bracing ϕ 16 to 22 mm
4 Strut for horizontal bracing 16/16 cm
5 Exterior wall tie beam
6 Sliding sheet

A stayed or propped girder represents a transition from a simple beam to a linked truss.

Staying or propping provides an intermediate bearing point and thus reduces bending moments in the girder. A stayed or propped girder can be treated as a continuous beam in preliminary design.

However, there are also corresponding axial stresses in the girder and in the stays and props.

9 School for the Handicapped in Thanet, Great Britain

Architect: R. Halter and Associates, London

School for the handicapped with three areas for therapy grouped around a multipurpose central hall. Roof of multipurpose hall consists of four propped single-span girders, spanning over approximately 12.00 and 20.00 m. Girders are double, props are steel tubes, and lower ties are twin steel shapes. Purlins span transversely to girders. Roof is raised on one side to provide a clerestory window.

Reference: *Deutsche Bauzeitung* 2/1968, p. 113; *Baumeister* 7/1968, pp. 776 ff., *Architectural Review* Jan. 1970

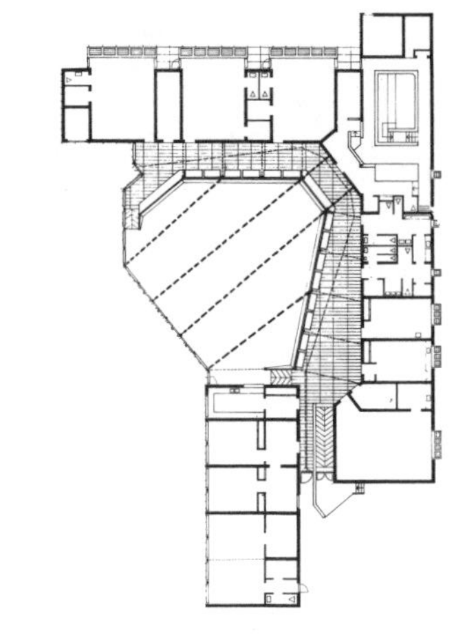

Structural framework

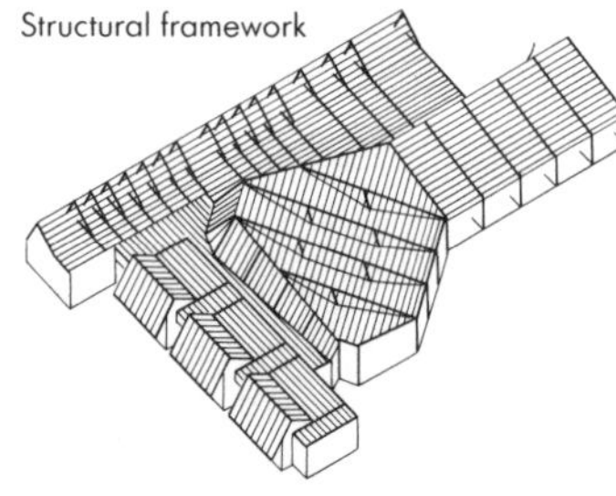

Longitudinal section

~ 20.00

Main girder with steel and ties

Bearings as on page 84

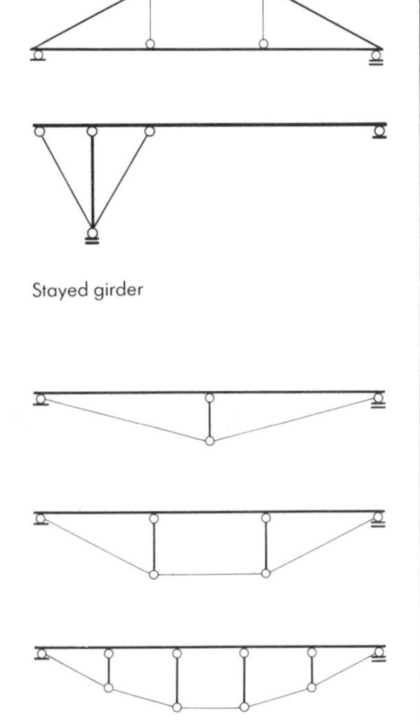

Stayed girder

Propped girder, especially economical for very long spans

10 Chapel in Silton, Canada

Architect and engineer: C. Wiens, Regina

Plan of the structural element is cross-shaped. Main girders 28/78 cm rest outside of building on concrete pillars and are hinged at crossing point by means of a steel cross, which is suspended by a tension bar ϕ 57 mm. This tension bar transfers the downward pull to the roof peak and from there again to the girder. Hip roof rests on ridge beams 2 × 5/25 cm, peripheral beams 33/42 cm, and purlins 5/25 cm. Free corners of hip roof are connected to roof peak by means of ϕ 19 mm tension bars.

Reference: *Plywood World* 4/1970, p. 12

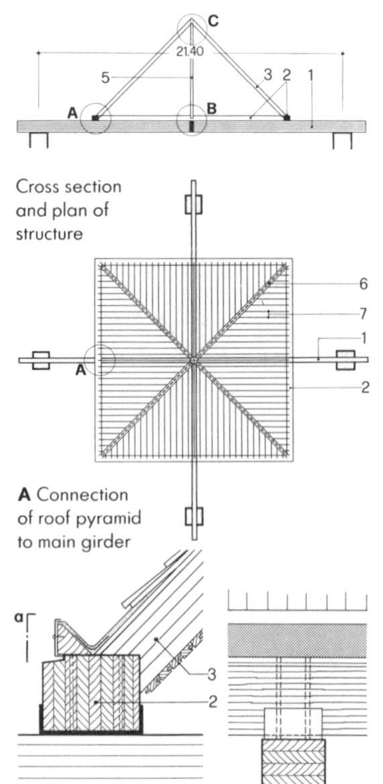

Cross section and plan of structure

A Connection of roof pyramid to main girder

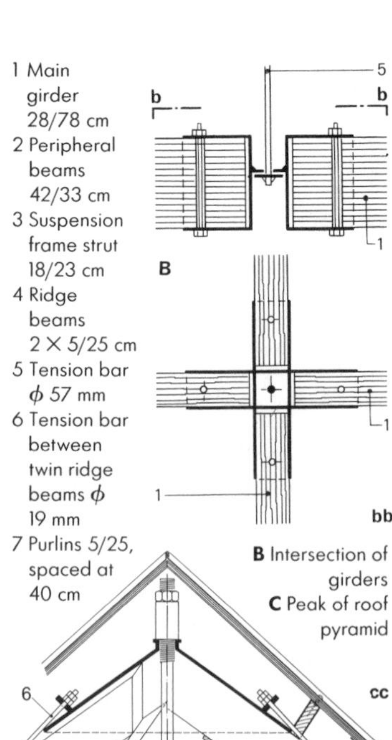

B Intersection of girders
C Peak of roof pyramid

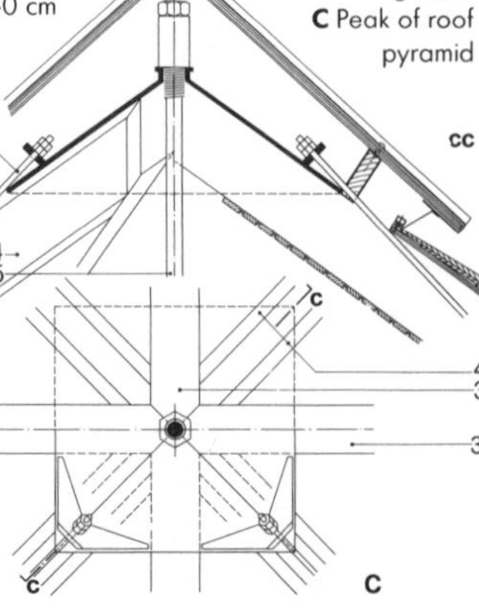

11 Indoor Swimming Pool in Kochel am See, West Germany

Architect: P. Seifert, Munich
Engineer: D. Herrschmann, Munich

Restaurant and entrance are covered by trusses (spans 6.00 and 9.00 m). Swimming pool area 18 × 27 m is roofed by means of girders subtensioned by bars running in two directions. Twin subtensioned girders 2 × 10/20 cm span in the shorter direction and support similar twin girders placed longitudinally. Props are 16/16 cm timbers. Tension and diagonal bars are stainless steel, connected to props by means of grooved stainless-steel pins. Columns in window areas are 2 × 10/26 cm. Layout of orthogonally subtensioned girders (over a swimming pool area having a 1:1.5 ratio of sides) represents a transition from one-way subtensioned girders to a two-way grid of subtensioned girders of unequal stiffness in each direction. Reference: *Detail* 5/1972, illustrations; *Baumeister* 2/1974, p. 80

1 Subtensioned girder
2 Truss
3 Planking for walkway
4 Roofing
5 Air space for ventilated roof
6 Thermal insulation
7 Upper girders 2 × 10/20 cm, laminated wood
8 Props 16/16 cm, laminated wood
9 Subtensioning stainless-steel bars and turnbuckles
10 Round steel pins with grooves for bar connections

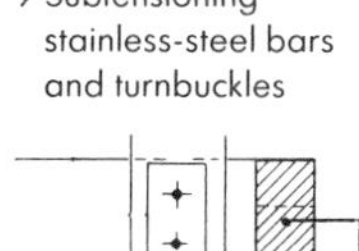

Layout of girders and lateral bracing

Ground floor plan, scale 1:1000

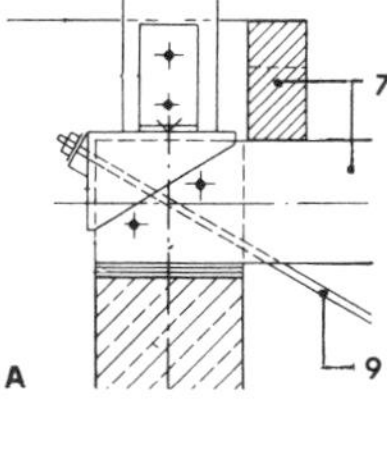

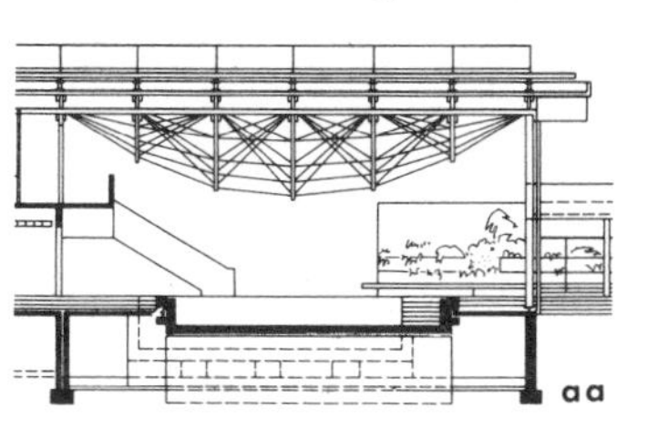

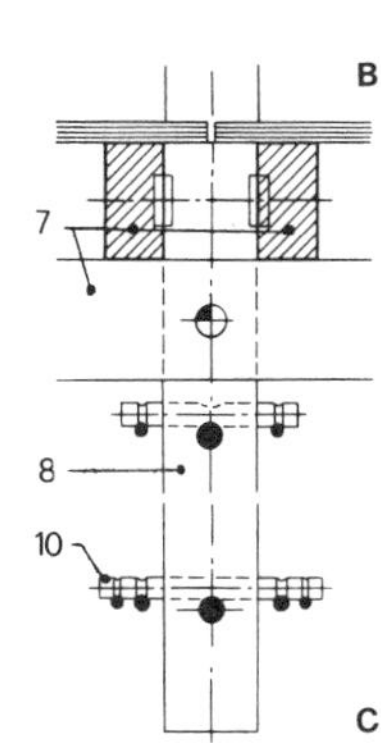

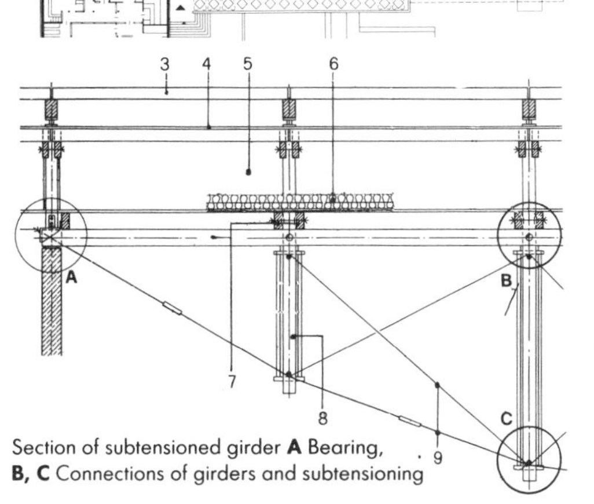

Section of subtensioned girder **A** Bearing, **B, C** Connections of girders and subtensioning

Connection of Subtensioning to Girder

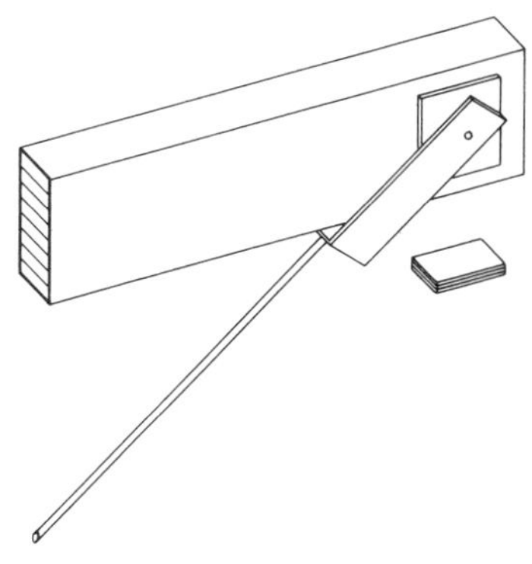

Side connection to girder by means of nail plates and bolt.

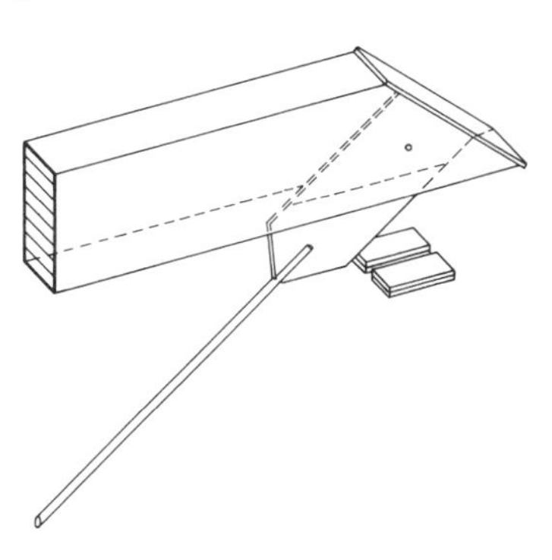

Slit girder, one-plate connection with rear anchorage plate.

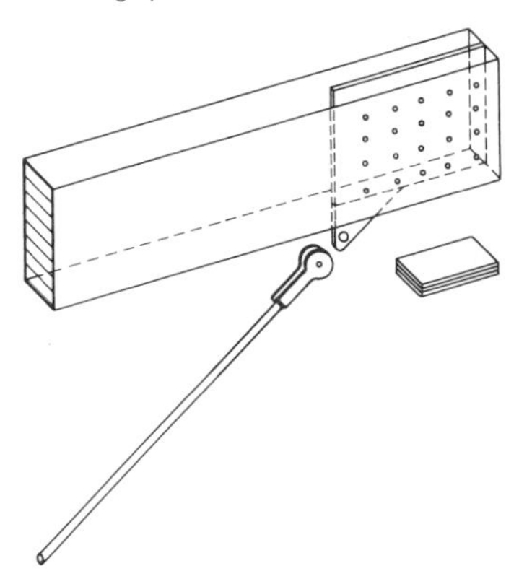

Steel plate in girder slit, steel dowels.

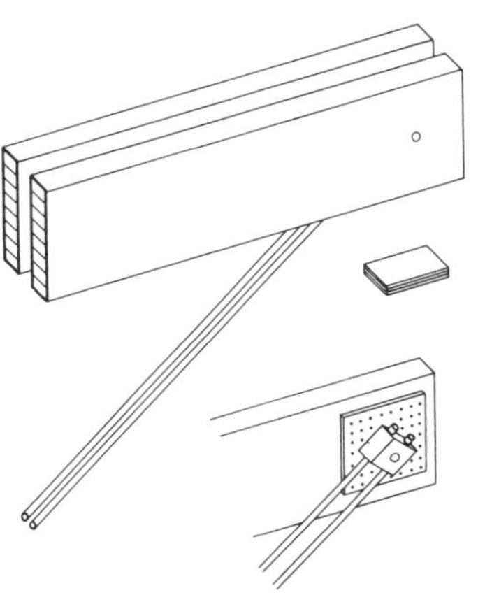

Connection to twin girder through steel box, tightening bolts, and nail plates.

12 Ice Skating Rink in Ingolstadt, West Germany

Architect: H. Stich, Ingolstadt
Engineer: Fries and Schittig, Ingolstadt

Six transverse laminated wood box girders, each composed of two 12/190 cm beams and 3 cm thick nailed plywood plates top and bottom, stayed from steel columns. Purlins 16/48 cm span longitudinally. Horizontal bracing through torsional resistance of box sections and tied columns.

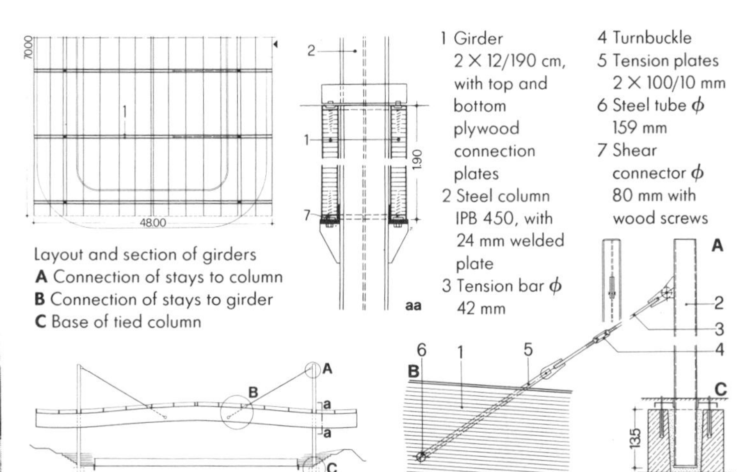

Layout and section of girders
A Connection of stays to column
B Connection of stays to girder
C Base of tied column

1 Girder 2 × 12/190 cm, with top and bottom plywood connection plates
2 Steel column IPB 450, with 24 mm welded plate
3 Tension bar ϕ 42 mm
4 Turnbuckle
5 Tension plates 2 × 100/10 mm
6 Steel tube ϕ 159 mm
7 Shear connector ϕ 80 mm with wood screws

Trusses are girders which have been reduced to an assembly of simple struts connected by pin connections. Struts are stressed either in tension or in compression. Under the same exterior loads, the bearing reactions and the bending or shear forces in a truss are the same as in a girder. Bending moments are resolved into compressive and tensile forces in the chords. Shear forces create tension in diagonals which rise to the bearings, and compression in those diagonals that descend to the bearings.

The size of compression members is generally governed by buckling, while the size of tension members is controlled by tensile stresses at the weakest points, which are generally at connections. Because of this, it may be necessary to increase the cross-sectional area of a member in order to obtain a sufficient connecting surface or cross section at connections. The design of deflections must take into account the slippage of connections.

The top chords of a truss are braced against buckling by lateral bracing. In order to avoid additional bending stresses in truss members, the loads preferably should be applied at nodes, which governs the spacing of cross beams and nodes.

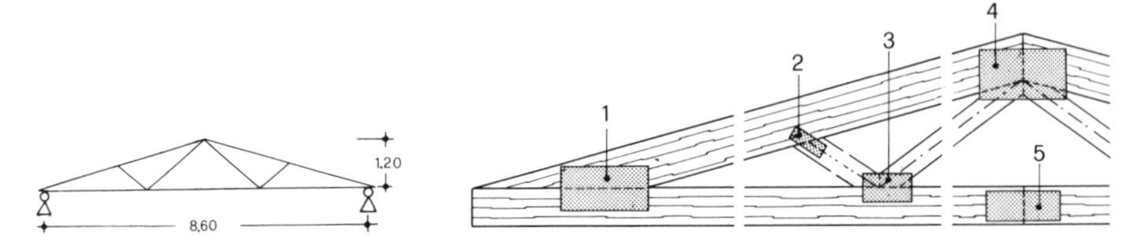

13 Triangular Truss

Truss spacing 1.25 m; top chord 5/12 cm, bottom chord 5/10 cm, diagonals 5/6 cm. Connections: pressed nail plates (Gangnail system, Twinaplate, etc.).—1 GN 14-114/233 mm, 2 GN 14-38/100, 3 GN 14-76/133, 4 GN 14-133/233, 5 GN 14-76/200.

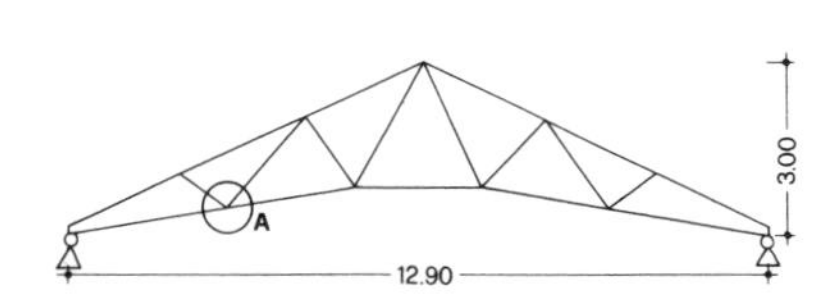

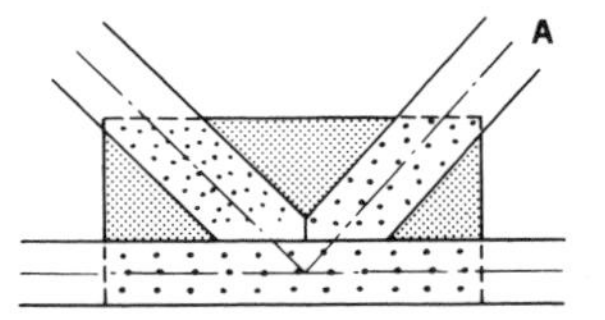

14 Triangular Truss with Raised Bottom Chord

Top chord 2 × 8/16 cm, bottom chord 2 × 8/12 cm, diagonals 2 × 4/14 cm. Connections: plywood panels and nails—Connection **A:** Nodal plate 700/350/14 mm, bottom chord nails 2 × 33 N46/130, left diagonal 2 × 42 N34/90, right diagonal 2 × 23 N31/70.

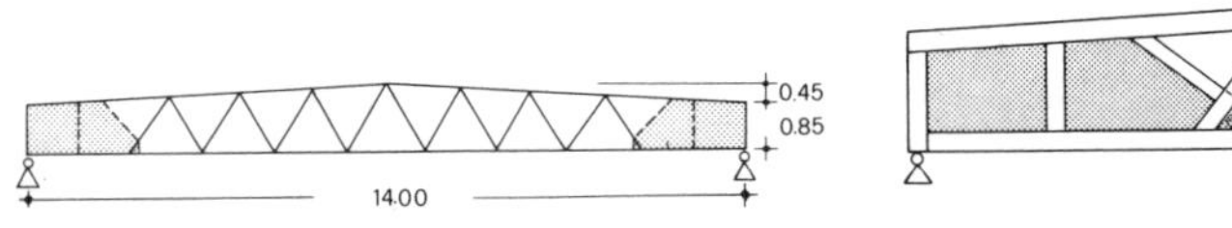

15 Triangular Truss with Raised Eaves

Connections: plywood panels and nails. At bearings there is a transition to an I cross section with plywood web.

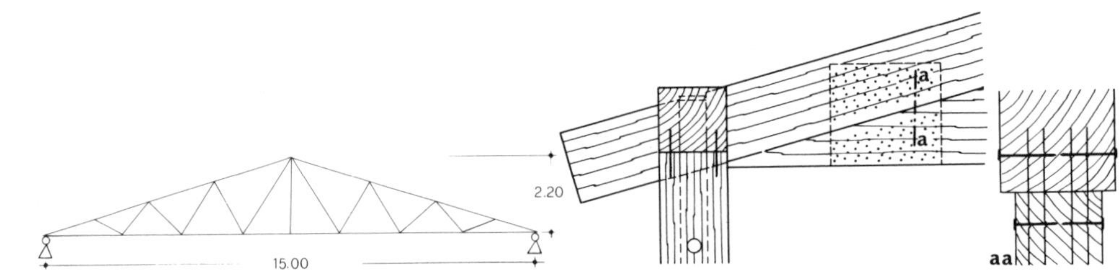

16 Triangular Truss

Truss spacing 2.50 m, top and bottom chords 16/20 cm, diagonals 6/12 to 10/12 cm. Connecting hardware: steel plates set in slits and through-nailed (Greim system, Borg system, etc.). Plates at bearing: 4 × 320/280 cm with 120 N31/80.

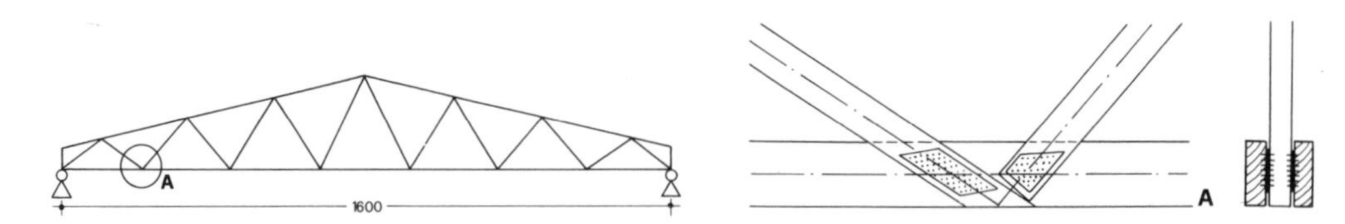

17 Triangular Truss with Raised Eaves

Trusses spaced at 5.55 m, upper chord 2 × 6/23 cm, lower chord 2 × 6/17 cm, compression diagonals 1 × 6/12 to 3 × 6/16 cm, tension diagonals 1 × 6/8 to 1 × 6/12 cm. Connection hardware: plastic plates with impressed double dowels (Menig system).—Connection **A:** Left diagonal 6/10 cm with two nail plates 80/200 mm, right diagonal 6/12 cm with two nail plates 100 × 70 to 170 mm.

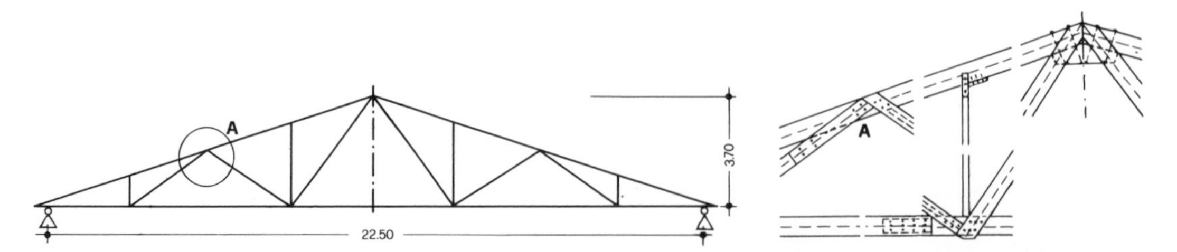

18 Triangular Truss

Trusses spaced at 6.25 m, upper chord 18/28 cm, lower chord 2 × 12/26 cm, compression diagonals 18/18 cm, tension diagonals 2 × 6/18–6/24 cm, vertical struts 8/18 cm. Connection hardware: steel dowels.—Connection **A:** 4 steel dowels ϕ 20 mm.

Wind Bracing and Lateral Bracing

Wind bracing must transfer wind loads to the foundation. Lateral bracing not only gives an overall stability to the building but also braces individual structural members against buckling. Bracing forms trusses which stiffen the structure against buckling and at the same time resist wind. Horizontal bracing is contained in roof surfaces, vertical bracing conveys lateral loads to the foundation.

Horizontal bracing may consist of supporting struts (wind struts), crossed or parabolic tension strips, trusses, or stiff panels. Vertical bracing of a structure occurs through diagonal struts, K braces, trusses, frames, plates, or solid shear walls.

Vertical Bracing (in Wall Plane)

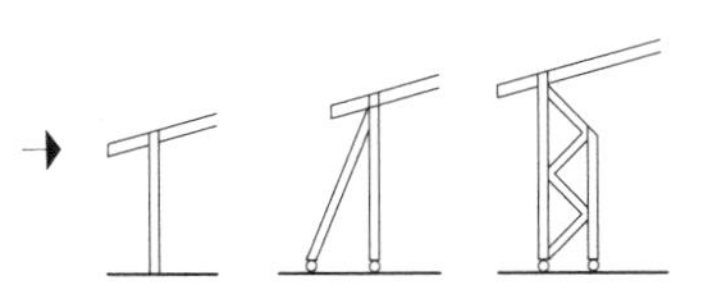

Diagonal struts or K braces

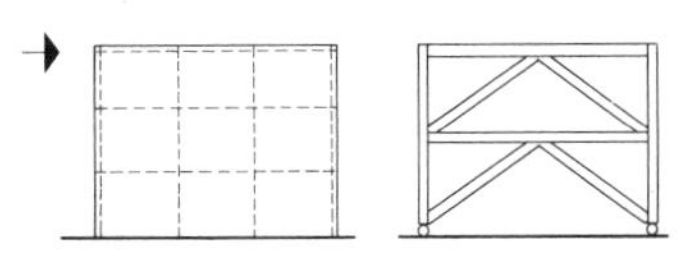

Plates

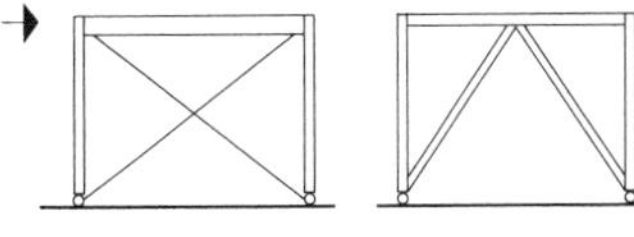

Trusses

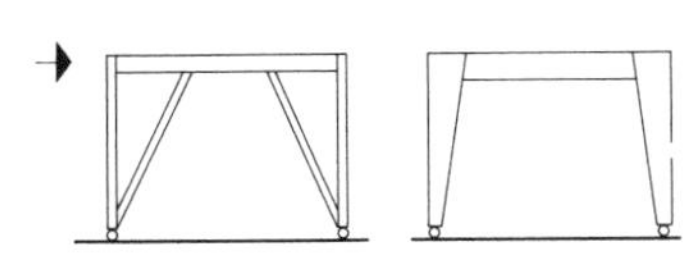

Frames

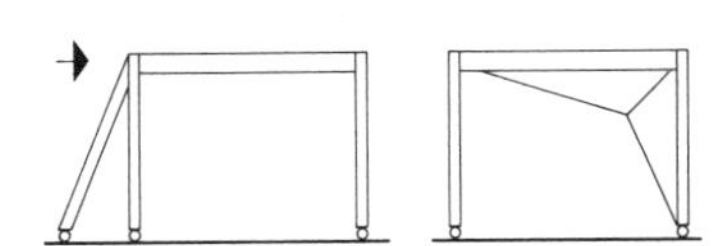

Half-frames

Horizontal Bracing (in Roof Plane)

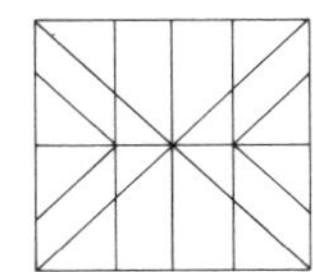

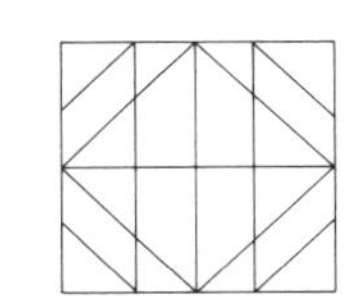

Wind bracing studs (for smaller buildings)

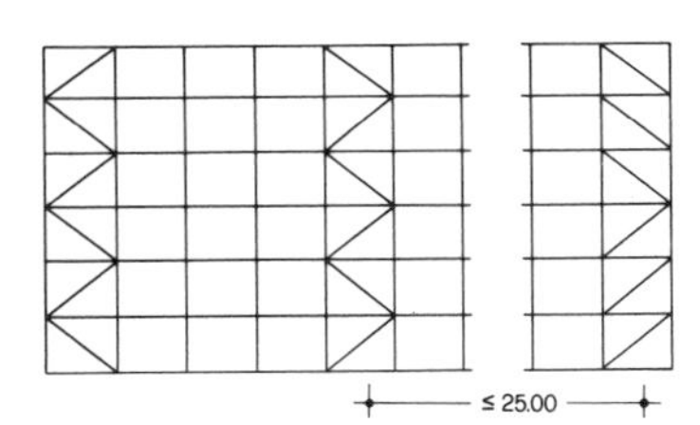

Compression diagonals

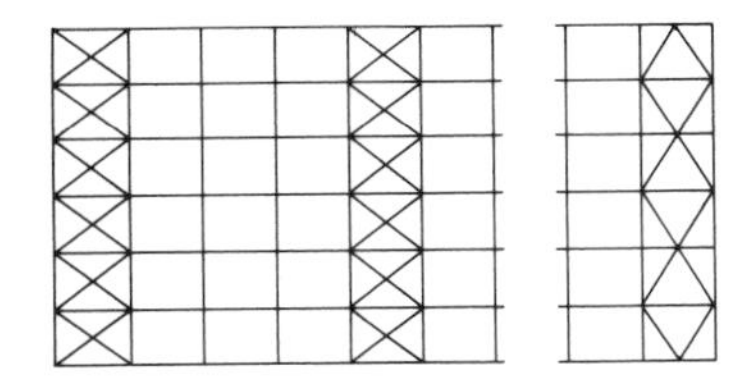

Tension diagonals

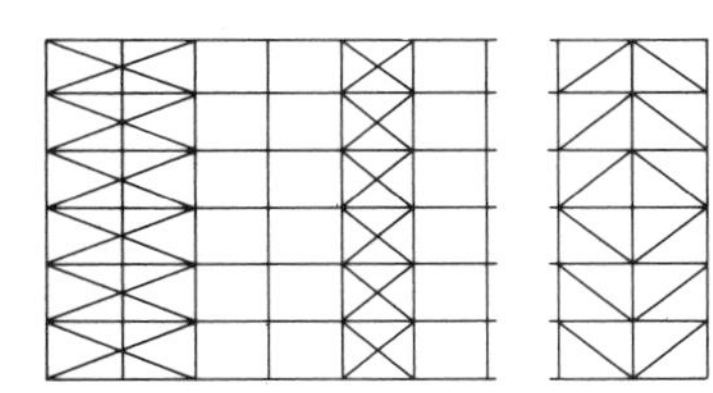

Diagonals over two bays

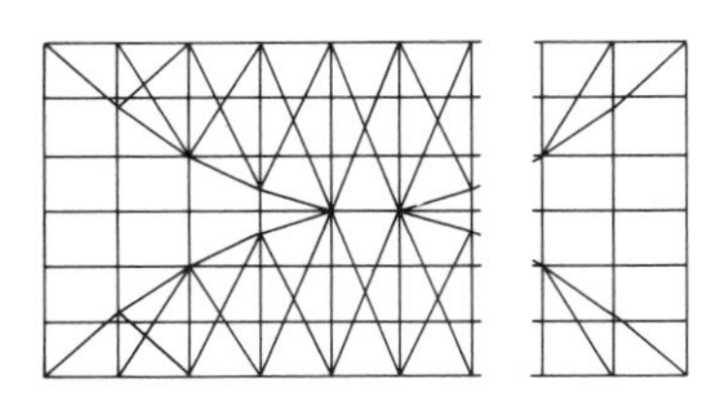

Parabolic bracing

Connection of Timber Wind Bracing to Main Girder

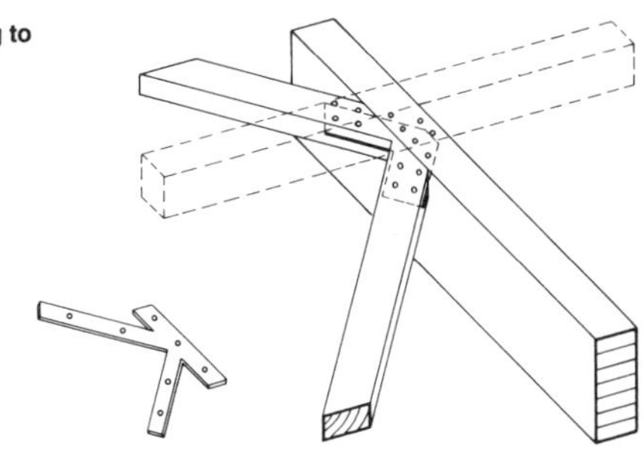

Diagonals and main girder slit horizontally, steel plates nailed or doweled.

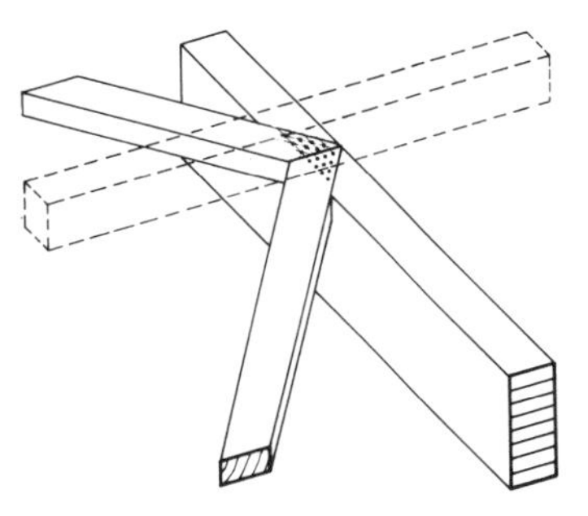

Main girder cut out, diagonals nailed. This arrangement weakens the girder.

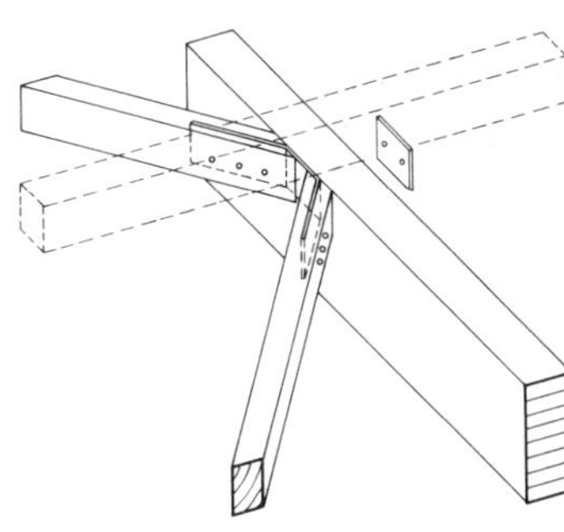

Diagonals slit vertically, steel plates attached with dowels.

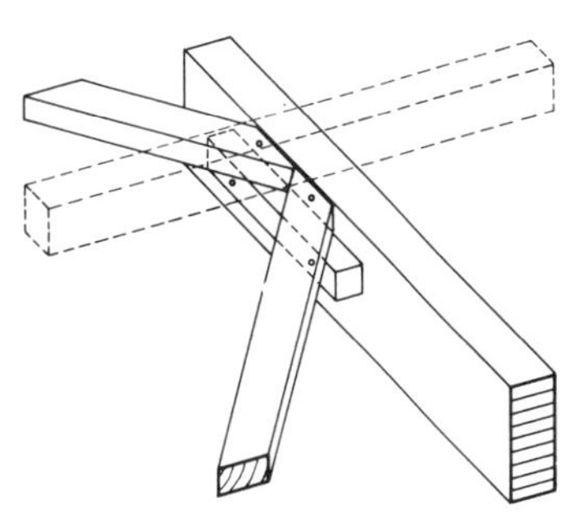

Diagonals rest on timber ledger, attached with dowels.

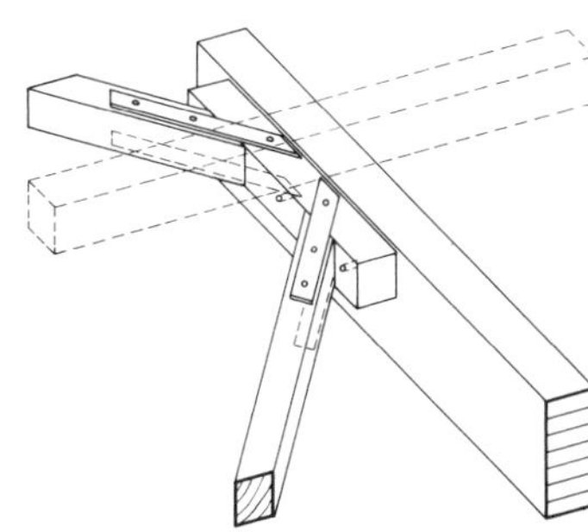

Diagonals rest on timber ledger, attached with two-sided gussets and dowels.

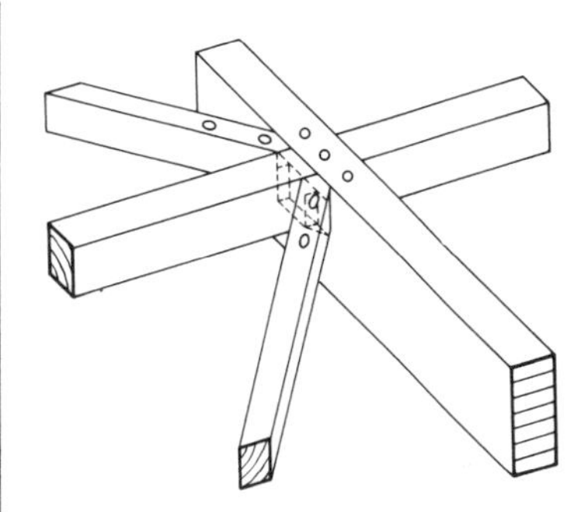

Lateral bracing struts and diagonals rest on steel seat, connections with steel dowels and gussets.

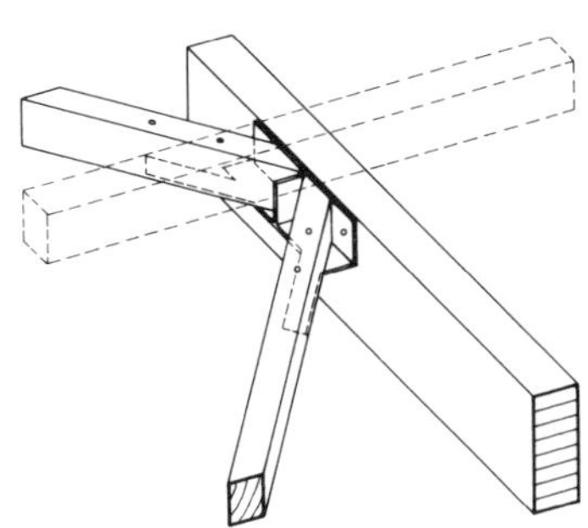

Diagonals rest on steel angle support, attached with steel gussets and dowels.

Sloped truss made of planks
a = 0.8 to 1.25 m (spacing)
l = 5 to 15 m
∢ ≥ 15
h = l/8

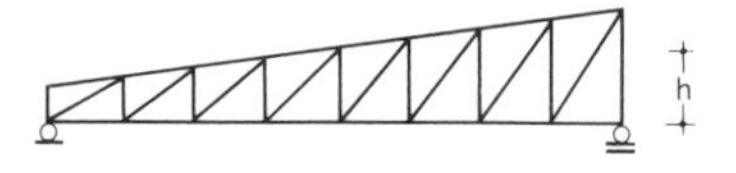

Sloped truss made of planks, raised eaves; trussing alternatives as above
h = l/9 to l/10

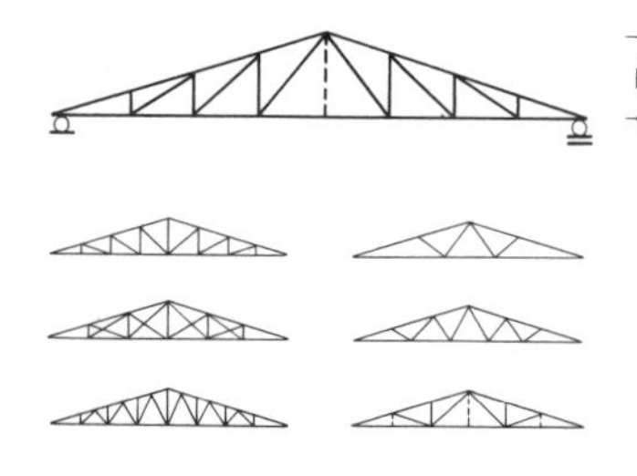

Gable roof made of planks
∢ ≥ 15°
h = l/7 to l/8
Additional vertical supports for suspended ceiling shown dashed

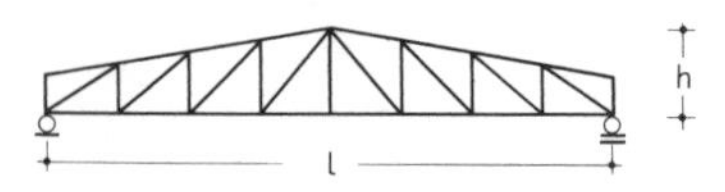

Gable roof with raised eaves; trussing alternatives as above or as parallel chord truss
a = 0.8 to 1.25 m, l = 5 to 15 m (made of planks)
a = 2.5 to 6 m, l = 5 to 35 m (made of solid lumber)
h = l/9 to l/10

19 Mountain Church on Winkelmoosalm, West Germany

Architect: J. Wiedemann, Munich
Engineer: H. Schlaegel, Munich

Church with interior court and sloped roof over church, inclined at 30°. Roof structure consists of four trusses which have single timber top and bottom chords 24/24 cm, double compression struts 2 × 12/22 cm with filler woods, and steel tension diagonals ϕ 30 to 42 mm, St 52.

Tension diagonals are drilled through upper and lower chords and bolted against a steel washer. On their lower side, trusses rest on a masonry wall. On their high side, which contains a window, they rest on a timber frame, which is braced by steel diagonals.

Purlins 14/20 cm, spaced at 80 cm, are attached to upper chords with ϕ 16 mm bolts and carry a vented roof. Roof has exposed planking on underside. Over that it has diagonally laid out planking for wind and lateral bracing, and on top of that, insulation, air space, two-way nailers, and three layers of larch shingles.

Reference: *Detail* 2/1975, illustrations

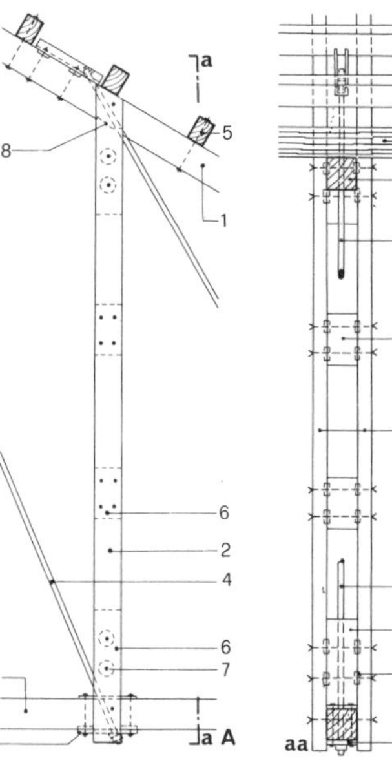

A, aa Truss section

Cross section and plan with girder layout

Truss section over church

1 Upper and lower chords 24/24 cm, solid wood
2 Struts 2 × 12/22 cm
3 End struts 24/28 cm
4 Tension diagonal ϕ 30 to 42 mm
5 Purlins 14/20 spaced at 80 cm
6 Filler wood
7 Steel dowel ϕ 115 mm
8 Double notch
9 Anchor washer 25 mm, two dowels ϕ 115 mm

20 Parish Community Hall in Gossau, Switzerland

Architect: Bächtold and Baumgartner, Rorschach
Engineer: W. Menig, St. Gallen

Roof construction of parish hall consists of four trusses with fanlike diagonals. Spacially arranged diagonals support secondary girders parallel to trusses and are resting on lower chord of trusses. Connection of 13 diagonals converging to one point of twin lower chord is made with a steel shoe and welded dowels. Roof planking 32 mm thick spans transversely to girders.

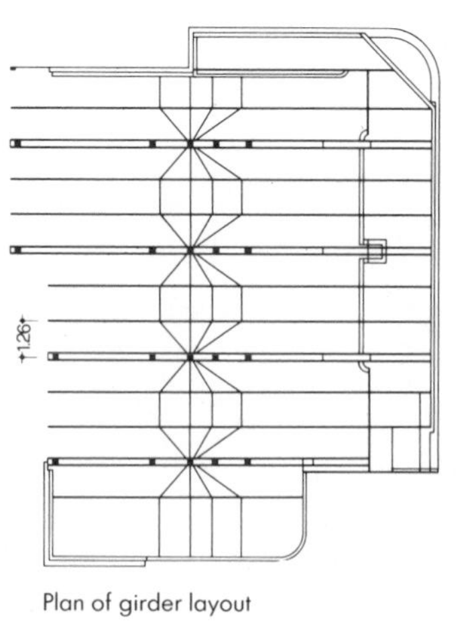

Plan of girder layout

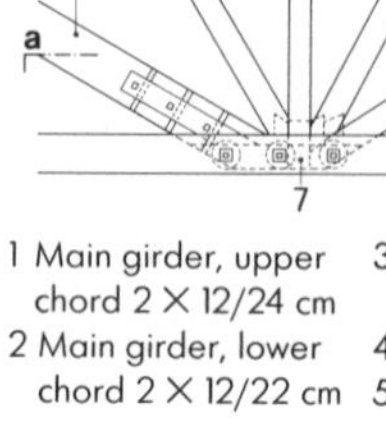

General cross section

1 Main girder, upper chord 2 × 12/24 cm
2 Main girder, lower chord 2 × 12/22 cm
3 Diagonals 12/12 to 12/14 cm
4 Diagonal 12/26 cm
5 Secondary girders 16/24 cm
6 Frame header 12/12 cm
7 Steel shoe with welded dowels ϕ 160 mm

21 Riding Hall in Meissenheim, West Germany

Architect: C. Langenbach, Lahr
Engineer: N. Kopp, Lahr

Eight trusses with skylight additions cross the hall transversely, spanning over 17.00 m. Top and bottom truss chords are triple, while diagonals and struts are double. Connections have steel dowels. Fixed bearings on one side consist of braced columns; their bracing rests on bleachers. On opposite longitudinal side there are two building additions housing stables and a restaurant.

Purlins 10/18 to 20/24 cm, run longitudinally. In both end bays there is wind bracing consisting of timber diagonals 6/8 to 16/24 cm.

Reference: *Bauen mit Holz* 9/1970, p. 424

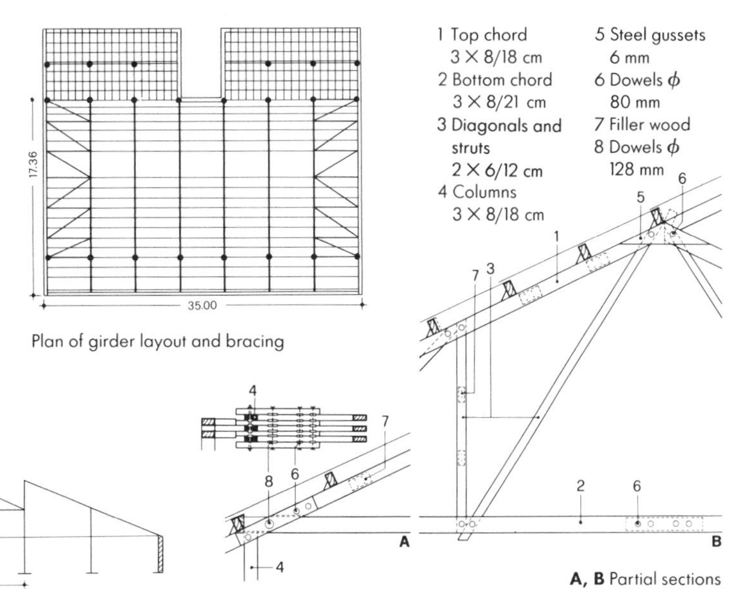

Plan of girder layout and bracing

General cross section

17.36

A, B Partial sections

Truss Connections, Single-Member Chords

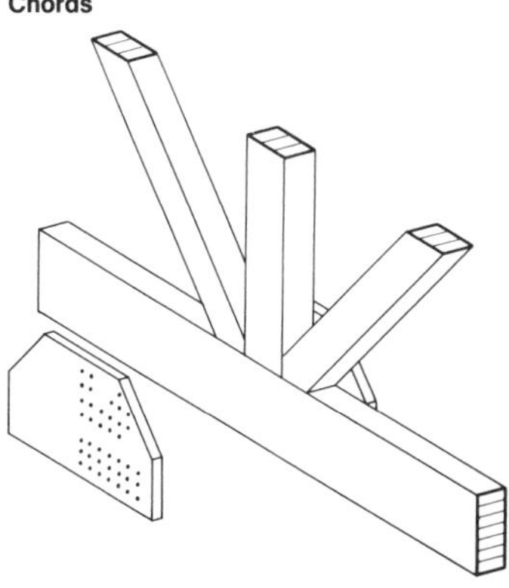

Side gussets of plywood or steel, nailed.

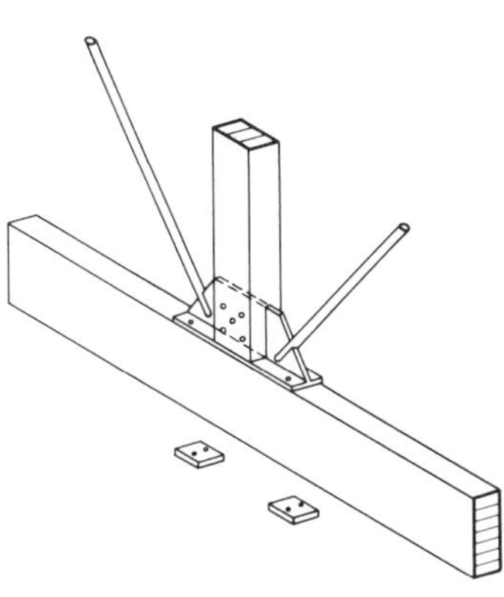

Steel tension diagonals, welded to a T steel shape. Connection to chord with one-sided shear connectors, anchor plate, and bolts.

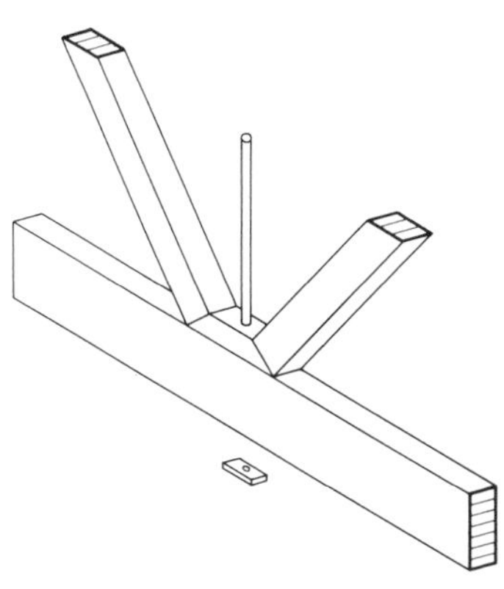

Compression diagonals with notch, tension bar, and anchor plate.

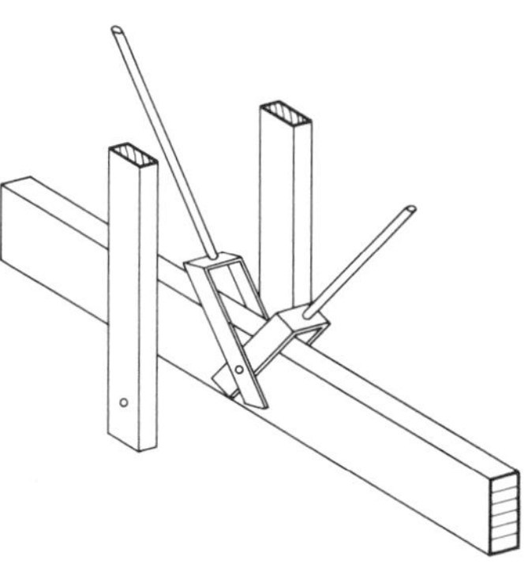

Side connection of tension diagonals with steel plates, nailplates, and pin bolts.

22 Storage Shed in Rosenheim, West Germany

Engineer: K. Sailer, Munich

Covered area 1530 m². Eight trusses spaced at 6.43 m span transversely over 34 m. Top and bottom chords consist of two plywood webs with glued dimension lumber. Diagonals and struts are multiple dimension lumber. The last two panels in the vicinity of bearings are made into box girders, with plywood panels resisting shear. This avoids highly stressed diagonals at bearings. Purlins 12/16 to 12/18 cm are placed longitudinally and have hinged joints.

Horizontal bracing is provided in end panels. Compression diagonals 10/10 to 10/22 cm are tied to upper chords in notches of attached ledgers. Tension members are two ϕ 16 mm steel bars. Vertical bracing is provided by braced steel columns in gable walls. Tension bars of horizontal bracing are attached to columns.

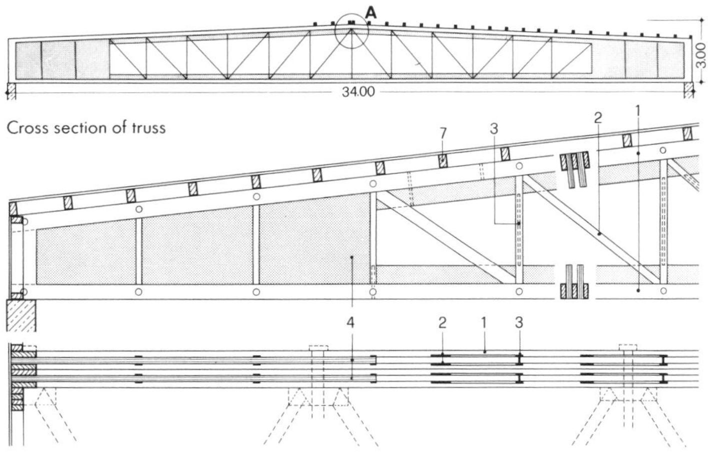

Cross section of truss

Partial section and plan of truss

1 Upper and lower chords as double-T cross section of glued lumber 8/20 cm with plywood webs 8/45 cm
2 Tension diagonals 2 × 2.4/12 to 16 cm
3 Compression struts as in 2, with filler wood
4 Bearing area, 2 plywood panels 8 cm
5 Compression struts 10/10 to 12/22 cm for wind bracing
6 Tension bars 2 × ϕ 16 mm for wind bracing
7 Hinged purlins 12/16 to 18 cm

Plan of girder layout with wind bracing

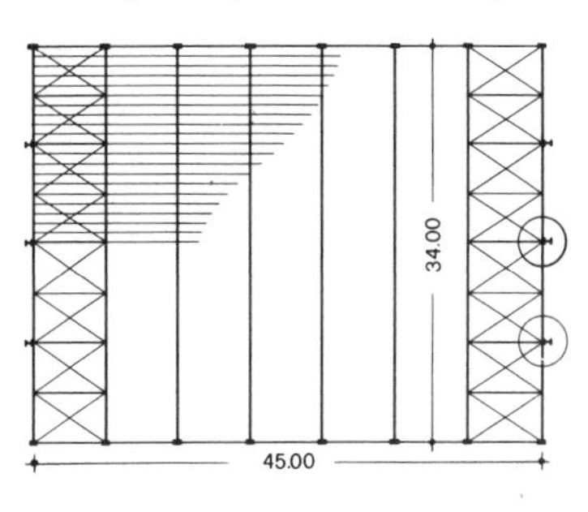

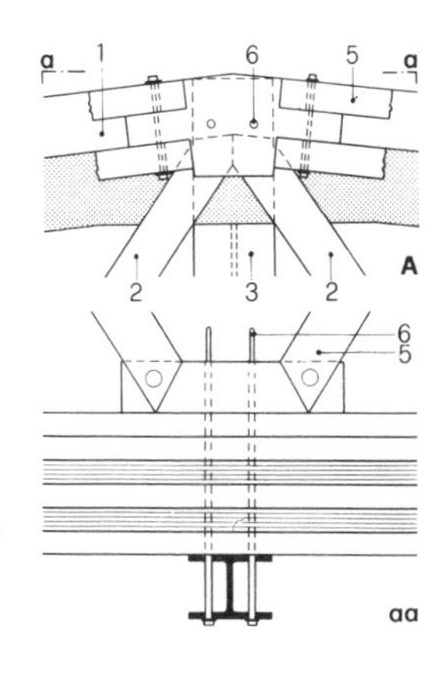

A Ridge point with wind bracing connection

B Isometrics of wind bracing connection

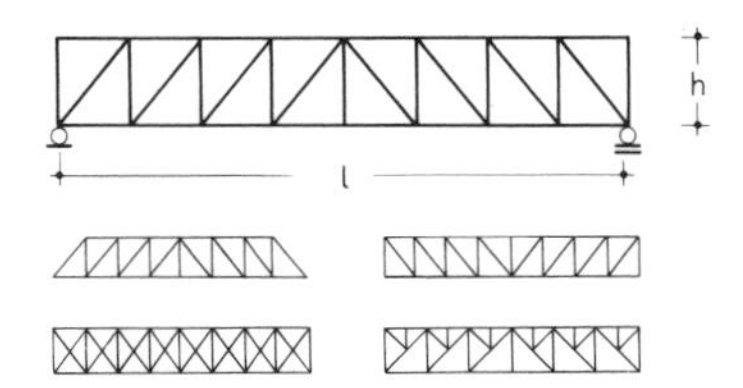

Trusses with parallel chords, vertical struts, and diagonals.

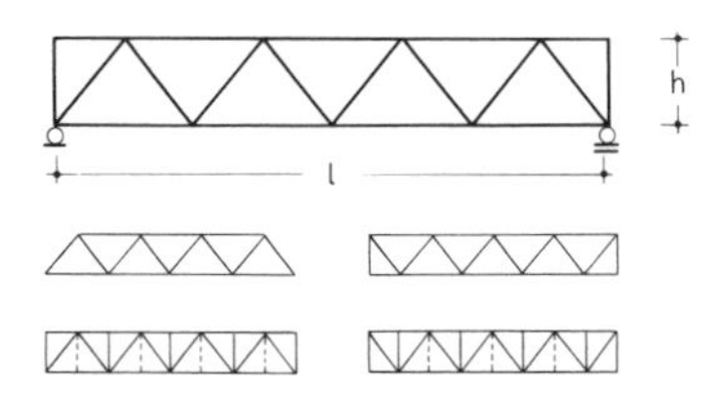

Trusses with parallel chords and diagonals (For special trusses Trigonit and DSB, see page 90.)

Upper chord slope 0 to 4°
As secondary trusses
$a = 0.8$ to 1.25 m, $l = 5$ to 15 m, $h = l/8$ to $l/12$, where a = spacing

As main trusses
$a = 2.5$ to 6 m, $l = 5$ to 25 m, $h = l/10$ to $l/14$

Laminated wood alternative
$a = 10$ to 20 m, $l = 40$ to 80 m, $h = l/12$ to $l/16$

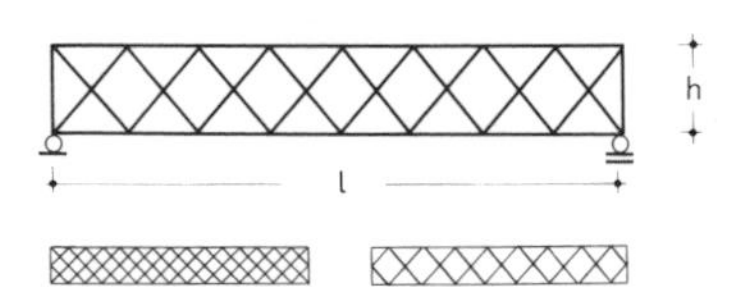

Trusses with parallel chords and crossed diagonals
$a = 2.5$ to 6 m, $l = 20$ to 50 m, $h = l/10$ to $l/14$

Trusses with parallel chords and rigidly connected rigid struts (Vierendeel truss as special shape for shorter spans)

23 Nursery School in Erdweg, West Germany

Architect: O. Steidle and Partner, Munich
Engineer: J. Natterer, Munich

Building has flat roof and roof overhang. Three rows of timber columns 15.6/15.6 cm are spaced at 8.40 m. Trusses 0.70 m deep span between them, spaced at 2.40 m. Top and bottom chords are double, while diagonals and vertical struts are steel tubes flattened at their ends. Connections between twin chords are two one-sided shear connectors. Planking 4.2 cm thick spans distance of 2.40 m between trusses. Horizontal bracing is achieved by a peripheral truss in plane of roof; vertical bracing is by diagonal steel tubes between columns and by timber struts in the middle of column rows.
Reference: *Detail* 5/1977, illustrations

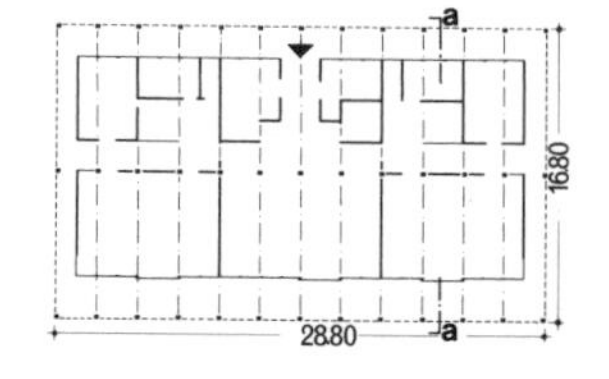

1 Column 15.6/15.6 cm
2 Truss
3 Horizontal wind bracing (Gangnail system)
4 Vertical bracing, timber
5 Nonvented roof
6 Top and bottom chords 2 × 7/15 cm, laminated wood
7 Diagonals and struts, tubes ϕ 38/2.5 mm
8 Shear connectors ϕ 80 mm

Plan, perspective with wind bracing.
A Detail of truss

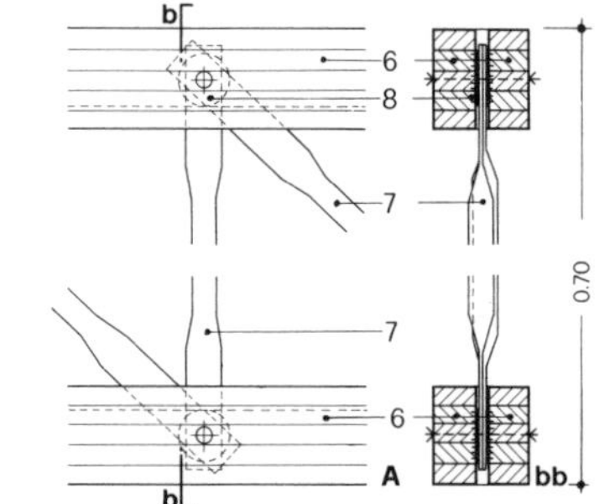

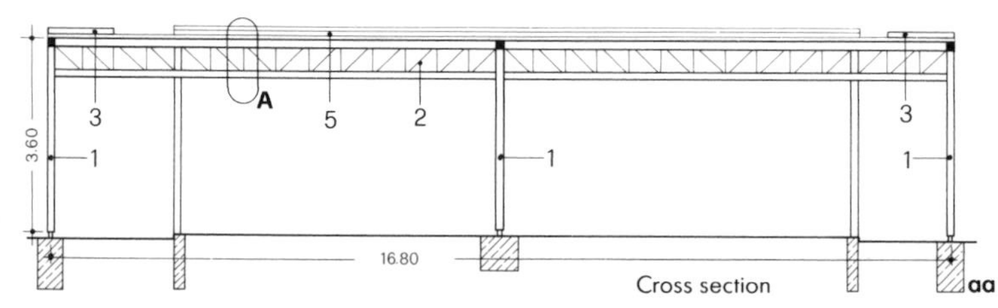

Cross section

24 Ice Skating Rink in Grefrath, West Germany

Architect: L. Limmer, Düsseldorf
Engineer: Timber Construction Contractor
Structural consultation, hinge details: J. Natterer, Munich

The main structural system of this 61.20 × 66.50 m roof consists of four trusses spaced at 13.20 m and spanning 60.00 m. Top and bottom chords are triple. Diagonals are double and built as I sections. The small depth of truss, only 4.10 m at centerline, results in high member stresses (up to 740 kN in diagonals and 2350 kN in chords). The structural problem caused by these high stresses was solved by pin connections of diagonals to chords. Connections are made with nail plates and steel pins.
Reference: *Bauen und Wohnen* 6/1974; *Bauen mit Holz* 8/1971, p. 382

1 Truss
2 Purlins 12/75 cm
3 Horizontal bracing
4 Top chord 2 × 12/84 and 17/84 cm, laminated wood
5 Bottom chord 2 × 8.5/81 and 17/81 cm
6 Filler wood
7 Diagonals 2 × 12 and 13.6 cm, height 80 to 34 cm
8 Nail plates with welded reinforcement plates
9 Bolts ϕ 42 mm in tube ϕ 108 mm
10 Roof planking
11 Horizontal bracing 11.5/8 cm

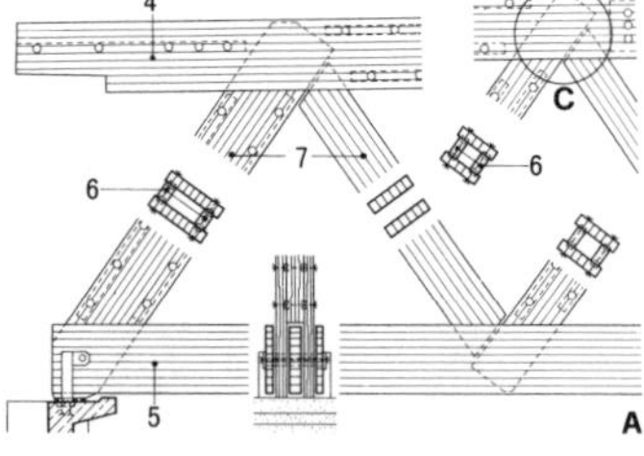

A Bearing of truss, **B** Connection of rafter and horizontal bracing to upper chord

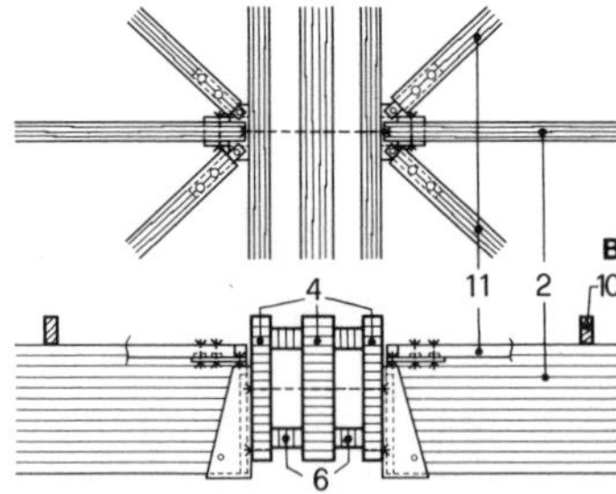

Girder layout and wind bracing

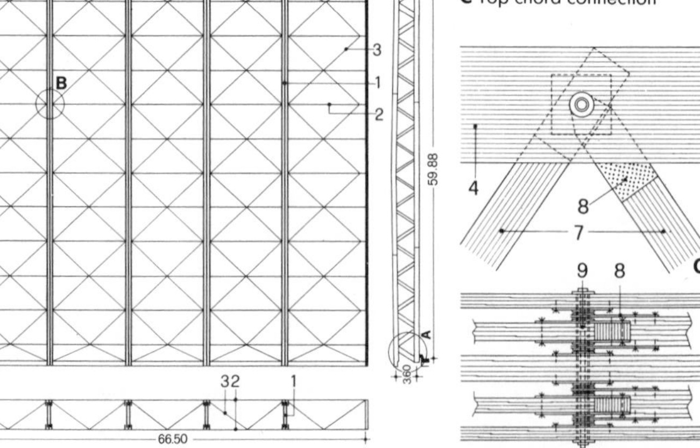

C Top chord connection

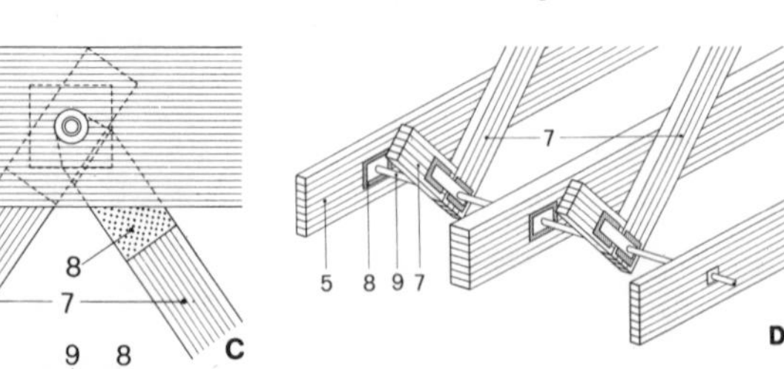

D Connection of diagonals to lower chord

25 Ice Skating Rink, Dortmund, West Germany

Architect: W. Funke, Dortmund
Engineer: E. Sänger

Roofed area 49.00 × 74.00 m with bleachers along long side. Layout and surrounding buildings allowed access to construction from one short side only. The roof therefore consists of six segments, which are placed on longitudinal walls from one short side and are then pushed to their final position (see erection sketch). Each segment consists of two 4.00 m deep trusses with 2 × 10.5/42 cm chords of glued planking. Steel pipe diagonals and struts are connected to chords by means of nail plates and steel pins. Between trusses are braced purlins with a rigid connection at center of span. Underside of roof is exposed planking.
Reference: *Detail* 6/1973, illustrations

Longitudinal cross section

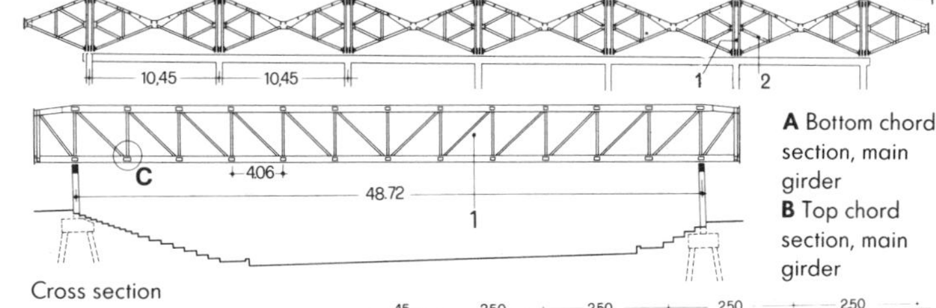

Cross section

A Bottom chord section, main girder
B Top chord section, main girder

1 Truss
2 Secondary system
3 Top and bottom chords 2 × 10.5/42 cm, glued planking
4 Steel diagonals and struts ϕ 108 to 152.4 mm
5 Upper and lower secondary systems 2 × 7.5/22.5 cm
6 Diagonals 7.5/22.5 cm
7 Rigid connection laminated wood gussets 7.5 cm
8 Connection plates
9 Steel plate fastened to 3 by wood screws
10 Steel pipe with M20 bolts

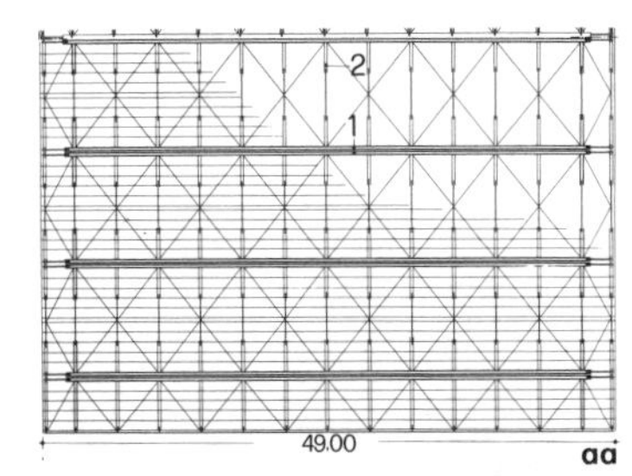

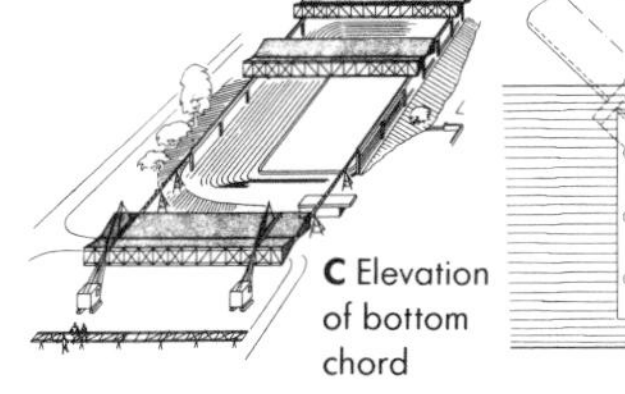

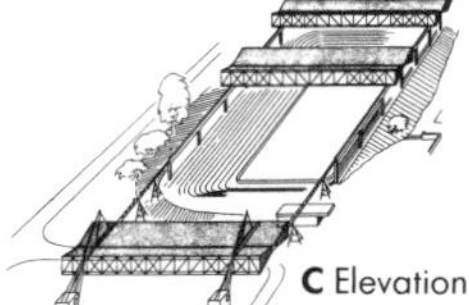

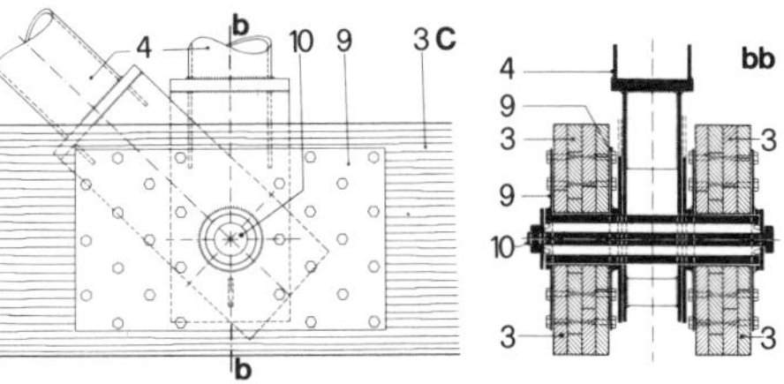

C Elevation of bottom chord

26 Sports Hall in Cramond, Scotland

Architect: Matthew, Johnson-Marshall, Edinburgh
Engineer: H. Haddow

Roof consists of coupled trusses which are contained within nonvertical planes and span transversely over 14.70 m. Double top chords 2 × 7.5/20 cm and bottom chords of ϕ 38 mm round bars are offset in plan by half truss spacing. Diagonals 2 × 5/15 cm are skewed in both directions and are so arranged that four diagonals originating from one point of bottom chord radiate to top chords. Bottom chords are braced laterally.

1 Top chord 2 × 7.5/20 cm transverse
2 Diagonals 2 × 5/15 cm
3 Longitudinal bracing ϕ 38 mm
4 Bottom chord, steel pipe ϕ 50 mm
5 Purlins 7.5/25 cm
6 Steel plates or angles, shear connectors with bolts
7 Shear connector ϕ 100 mm

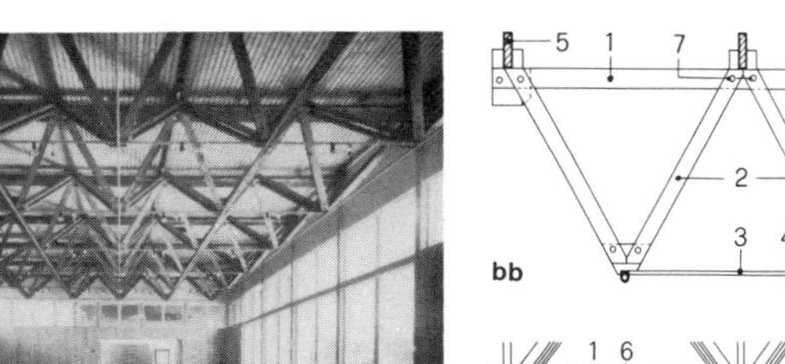

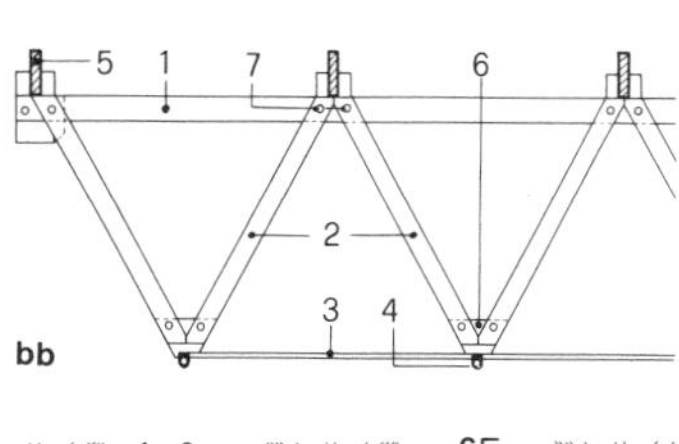

aa Cross section
bb Elevation of truss
cc Truss cross section

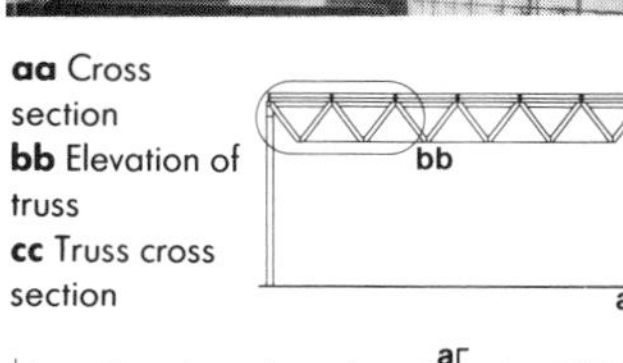

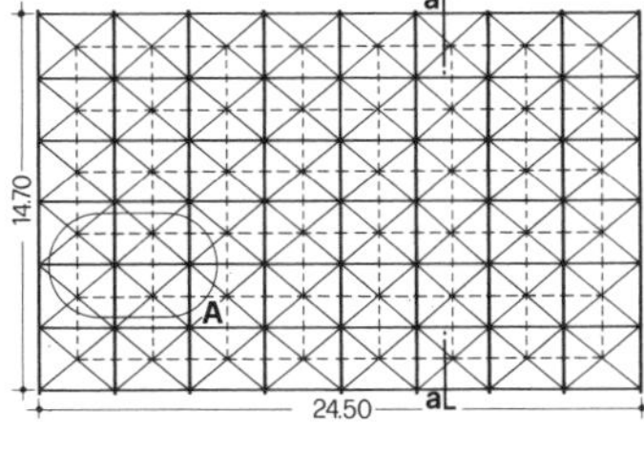

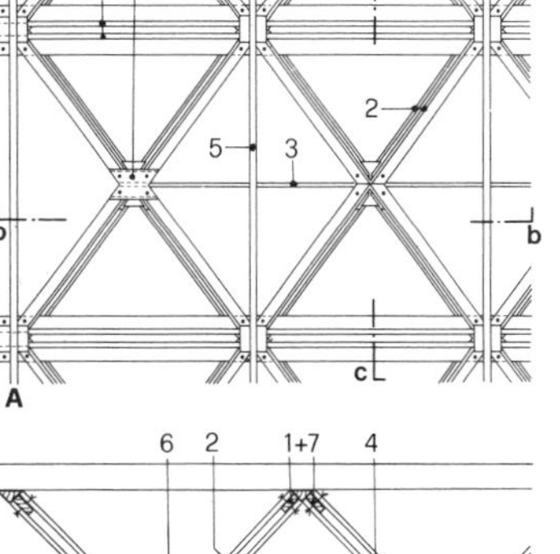

Truss Connections, Double Chords

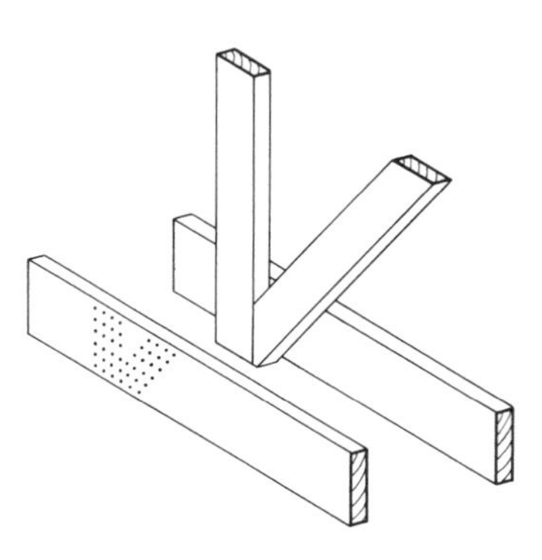

Chords nailed or shear-connected to diagonals and struts.

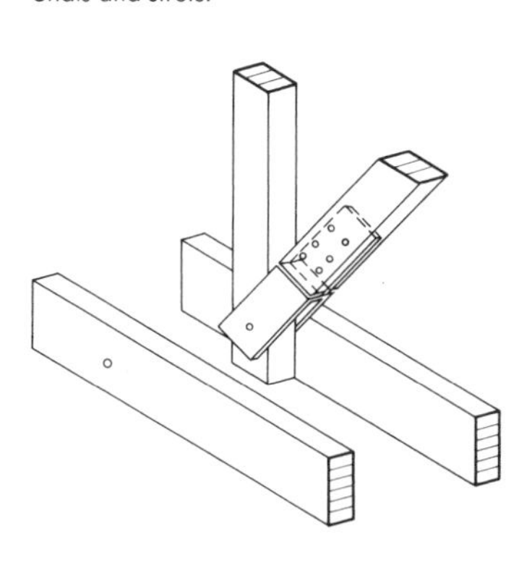

Connection with shear connectors and steel pins, diagonals (or struts) connected with steel plates and steel dowels.

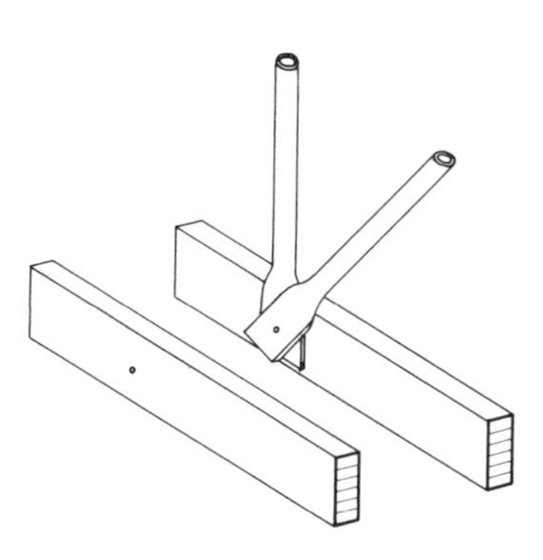

Steel tube diagonals and struts flattened at connections.

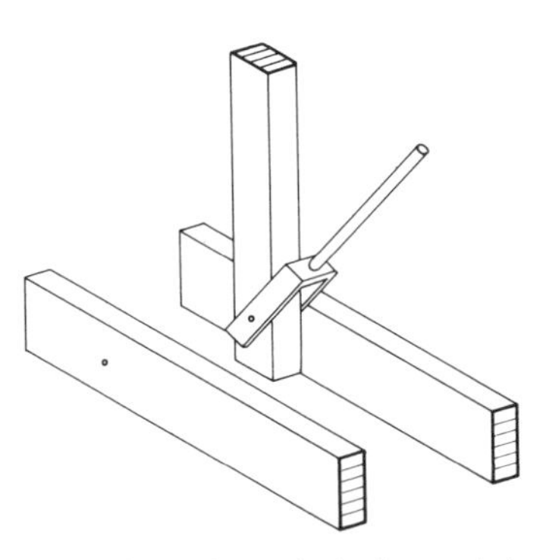

Tension diagonals attached with one-sided shear connectors. Vertical struts attached with two-sided shear connectors.

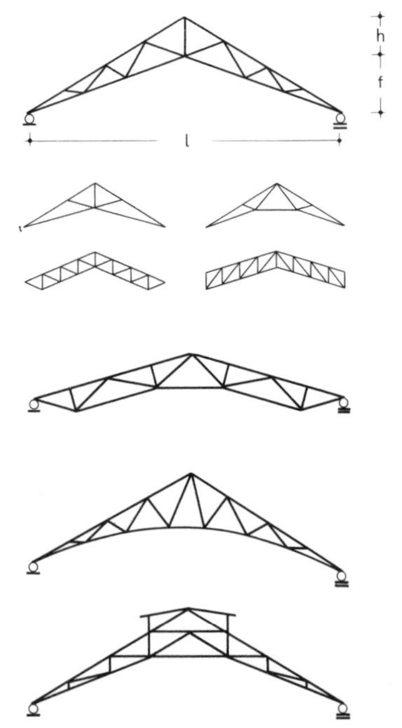

Triangular trusses with raised bottom chord. If both bearings are fixed against translation, trusses may be two- or three-hinged arches (see pages 118–125).
$f \leq l/4$ to $l/7$

For dimensioning see page 92.

27 Exhibition Pavilion in Grafenau, West Germany

Architect: Schuster and Gerlach, Munich
Engineer: J. Natterer, Munich

Exhibition pavilion in the Bavarian Forest National Park. Two half-circular buildings contain exhibition and movie halls, a library, a waiting room, offices, and service rooms. Roof consists of radial trusses, spanning 27.00 m, with snow load equal to 5kN/m². Multicomponent chords, struts, and diagonals of trusses are round timbers. Connections with nail plates and bolt pins. Truss supports round purlins with unvented roof and wood shingles.

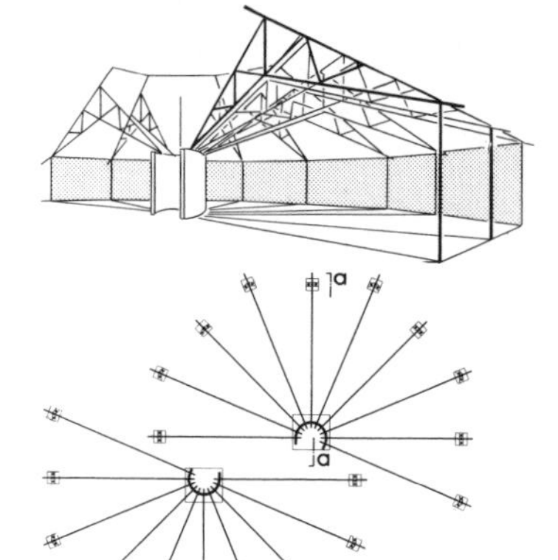

Truss layout

1 Top chord 3 × ϕ 37 cm
2 Diagonals 2 × ϕ 25 cm
3 Bottom chord 3 × ϕ 25 cm
4 Purlins ϕ 20 cm spaced at 40 cm
5 Eave beams
6 Wood shingles on unvented roof
7 Nailed steel plates with reinforcement rings
8 Bolts ϕ 63 mm

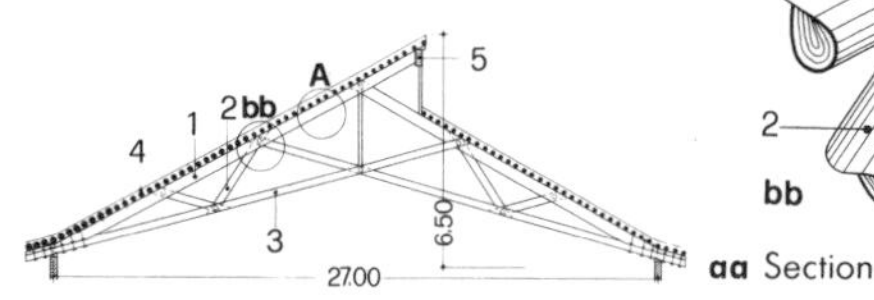

aa Section

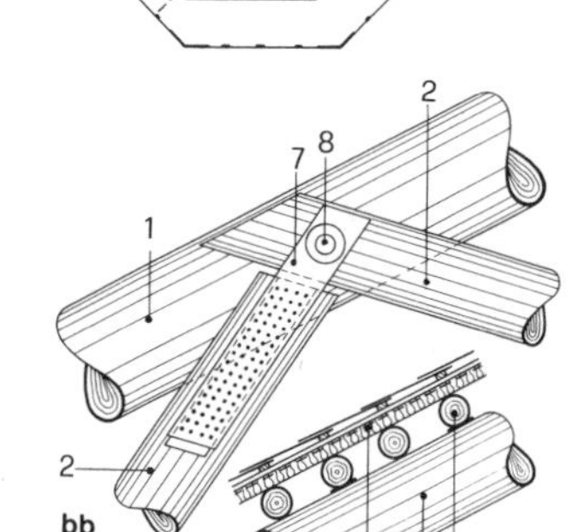

A Roof section
B Top chord connection

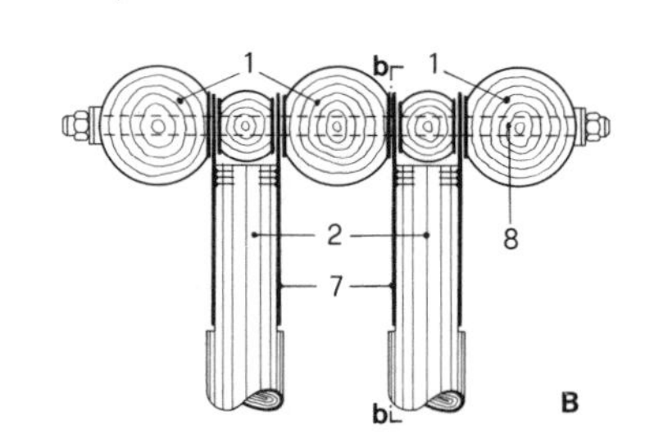

28 Church in Munich-Waldperlach, West Germany

Architect: J. Wiedemann, Munich
Engineer: W. Christmann, Munich

Roof in shape of two opposing sloping trusses with timber struts and steel diagonals. Top chords are double (2 × 14/26 cm), struts are single (14 × 14 cm), bottom chords and diagonals are round steel bars ϕ 33 to 42 mm. Timber struts contain steel U shapes to which tension members are welded. Struts and steel diagonals are connected between double top chords over U shapes or steel plates. Lateral bracing in outer bays. Lower chords are braced normal to truss axes.
Reference: *Bauen mit Holz* 7/1974, p. 338

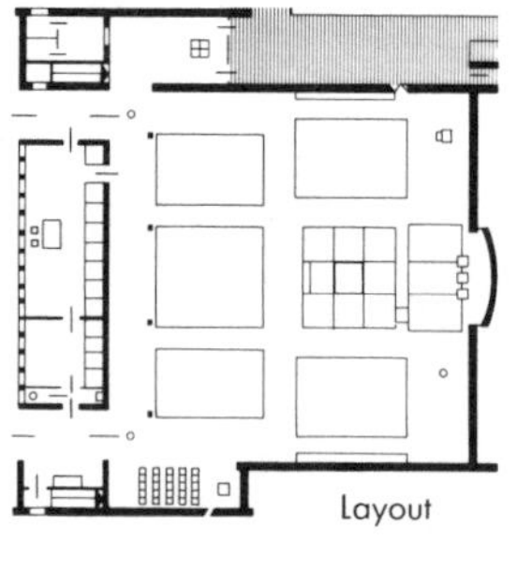

Layout

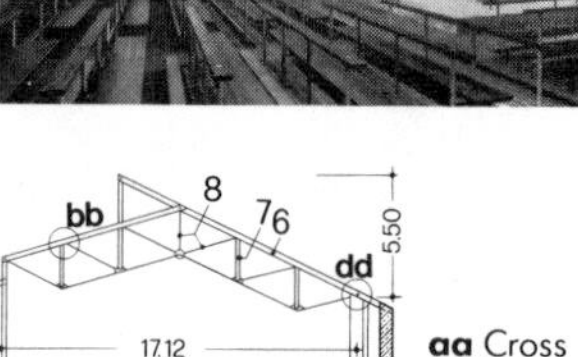

aa Cross section

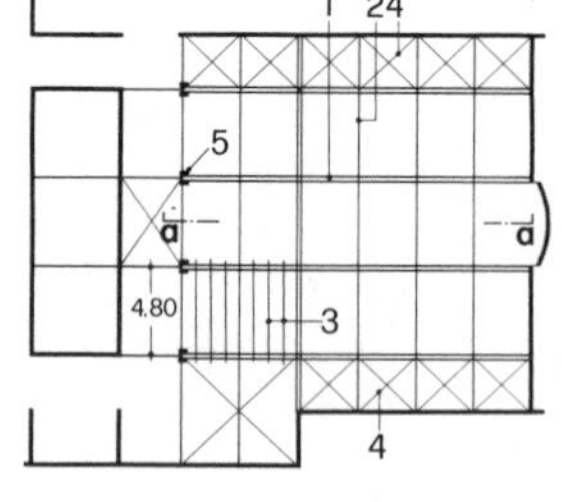

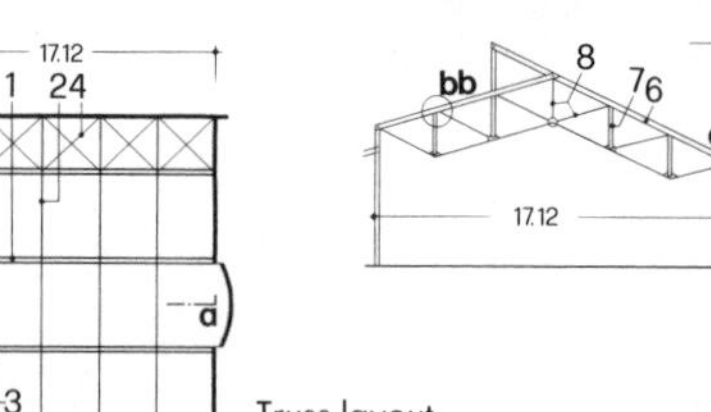

Truss layout with wind bracing

1 Truss
2 Bracing purlins 14/20 cm
3 Purlins 14/20 cm
4 Wind bracing, flat steel 50/10 mm
5 Struts 2 × 14/26 cm
6 Top chord 2 × 14/26 cm
7 Struts 14 × 14 cm
8 Tension members ϕ 33 to 42 mm
9 Shear connectors ϕ 95 mm

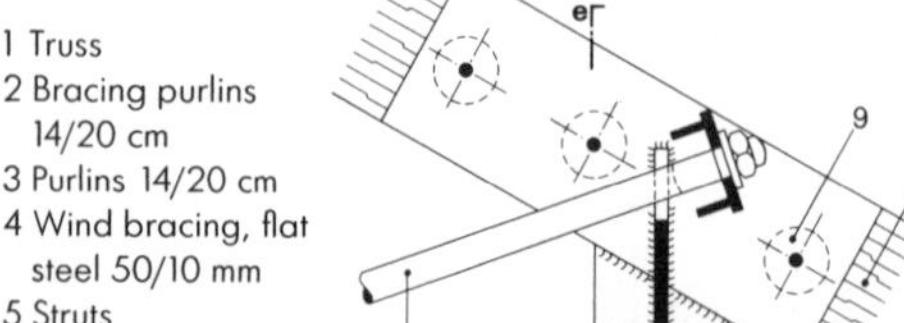

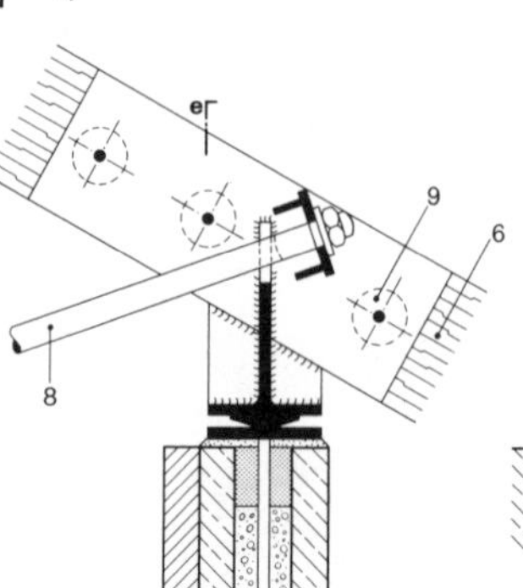

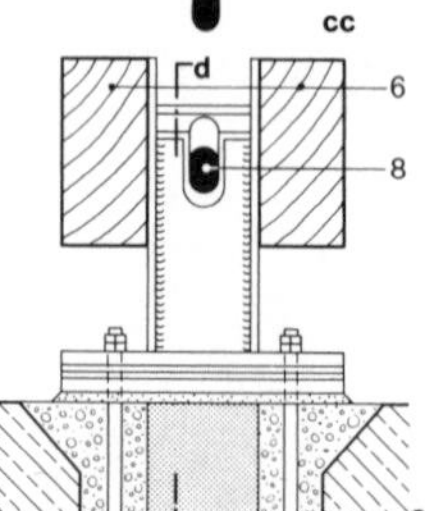

bb, cc Truss connections
dd, ee Bearing

29 Ice Skating Rink in Lahr, West Germany

Architect: C. Langenbach, Lahr
Engineer: N. Kopp, Lahr

Roof covers an area of 76.00 × 35.50 m. All girders are wood trusses with parallel chords, raised 2.40 m. Trusses are cantilevered 4.40 m at each end, spaced at 5.85 m. Top and bottom chords each have three components; diagonals and struts have two components in the middle and four near bearings. Connections of multiple members are shear connectors, ϕ 65 to 190 mm. Multiple members offer sufficient connecting surfaces even for large forces.

Lateral wind bracing of top flanges is achieved by diagonal trussing within roof structure. Purlins 12/28 cm, spaced at 116 cm, run longitudinally. Roofing is corrugated asbestos-cement sheathing. Hall is lit through skylight at the ridge.

The eccentricity of connections in trusses and lateral bracing must be considered in design of members. Trusses were assembled at construction site and were erected with two mobile cranes.
Reference: *Bauen mit Holz* 6/1969, p. 269

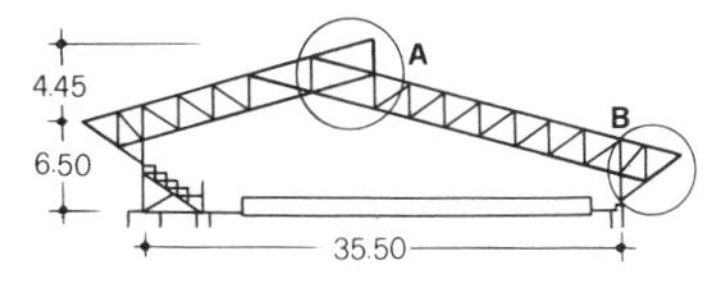

Cross section

Truss layout with lateral wind bracing

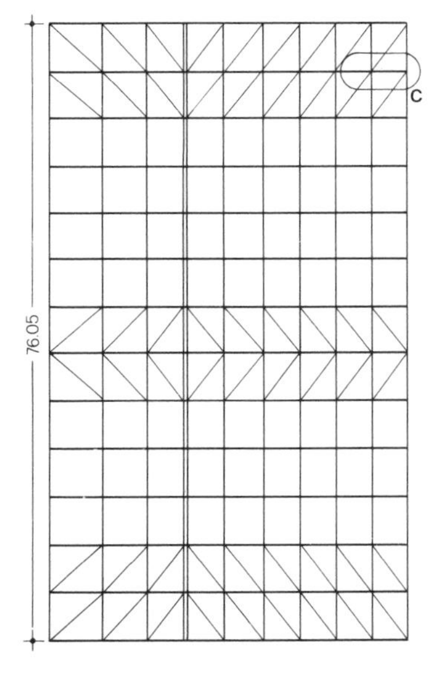

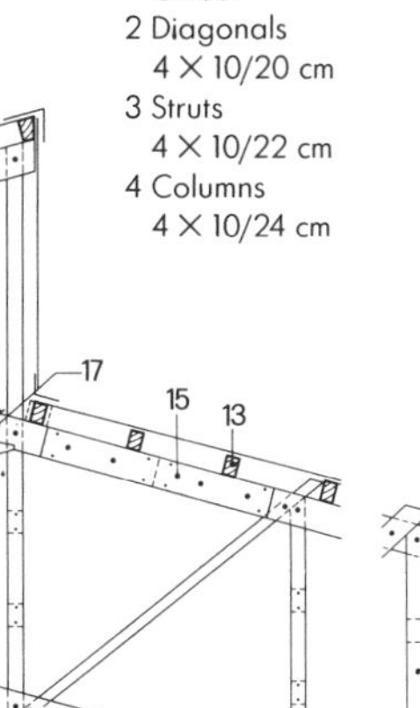

1 Top and bottom chords 3 × 12/28 cm lumber
2 Diagonals 4 × 10/20 cm
3 Struts 4 × 10/22 cm
4 Columns 4 × 10/24 cm
5 Knee brace 2 × 12/20 cm
6 Struts 12/12 cm
7 Diagonals 2 × 12/12 cm
8 Extension chord 2 × 12/28 cm
9 Ridge strut 4 × 10/24 cm
10 Saddle plate, triple laminated wood 12 cm thick with ϕ 190 mm shear connectors
11 Nodal connection plate 8 cm thick with ϕ 80 and 150 mm shear connectors
12 Lateral bracing purlins 18/18 cm
13 Purlins 12/18 cm
14 Wind bracing 6/12 to 18/18 cm
15 Field splice with 4 gussets 10/28 cm and dowels
16 Shear connectors ϕ 65 mm
17 Bolts ϕ 12 mm
18 Shear connectors ϕ 95 mm
19 Anchor bolts M20 × 390

A Truss joint
B Bearing
C Connection of wind bracing

Truss Connections, Double or Multiple Chords

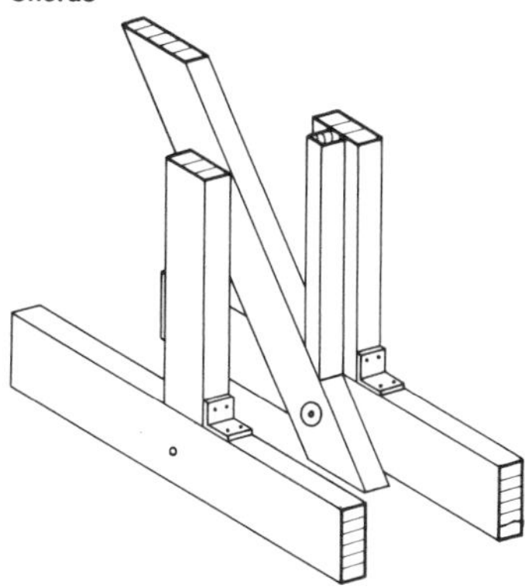

Single-piece diagonals, connected with shear connectors; double compression struts.

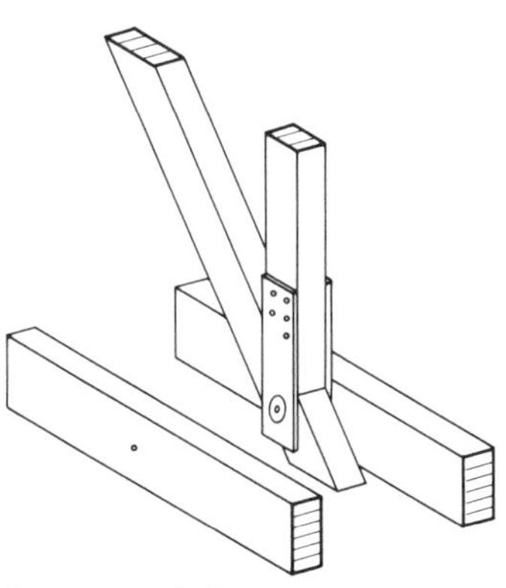

Connection with shear connectors and pin bolts; struts and diagonals connected with metal gusset plates and bolts.

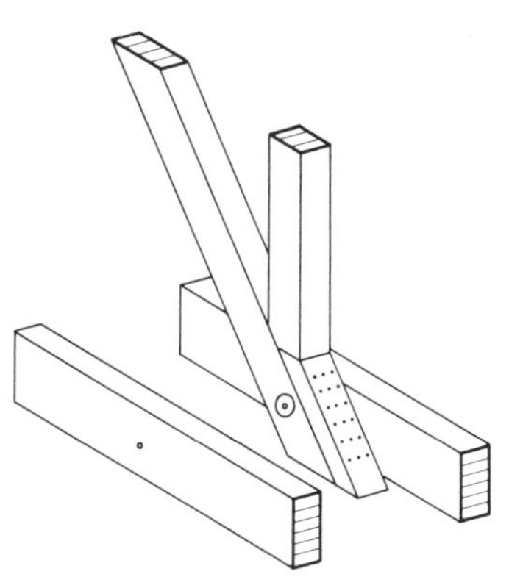

Connection with shear connectors and pin bolts; compression struts and diagonals joined over a nailed timber block.

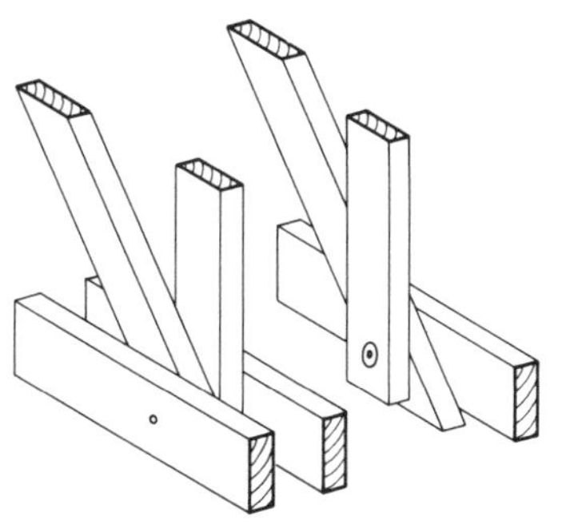

Triple chords, double struts and diagonals with shear connectors and pin bolts.

Mansard and arched trusses
$a = 2.5$ to 6 m (spacing)
$l = 20$ to 50 m
$h = l/6$ to $l/8$

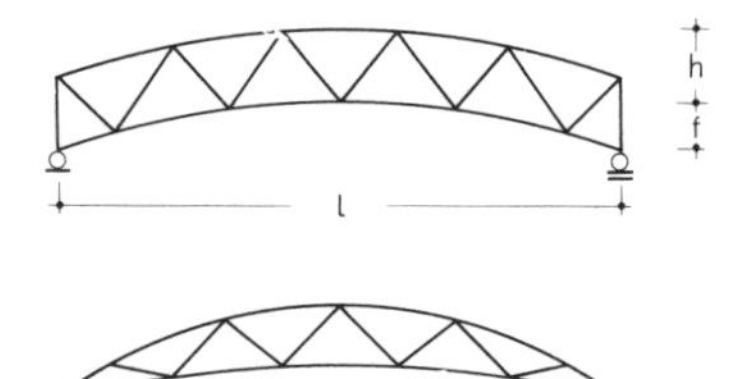

Arched trusses with curved chords or sickle-shaped forms. Transition to two- or three-hinged arches (see pages 144–149)
$f \leq l/4$ to $l/7$
$a = 2.5$ to 6 m
$l = 20$ to 50 m
$h = l/10$ to $l/14$

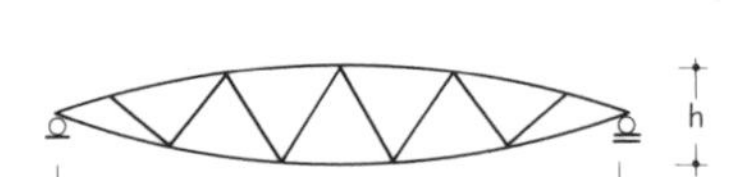

Fish-shaped truss
$a = 2.5$ to 6 m
$l = 20$ to 50 m
$h = l/8$ to $l/10$

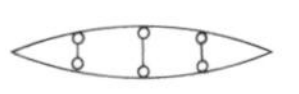

Special shapes. For stayed girder, see pages 88 and 89; for subtensioned girder, see pages 144 and 149.

30 Church of St. Ansgar in Munich, West Germany

Architect: E. M. Lang, Munich
Engineer: J. Natterer, Munich

Square church nave with sloped roof. Roof supported by five trusses, each with 20.00 m span and depth 1.94 to 5.00 m. Upper and lower chords are double, struts are single members. Connections with nail plates and pin bolts. Purlins 2 × 10/26 cm, bracing by K frames. Light through large skylights made in plywood covered by planking on inner side.

Length of trusses made field splices necessary. Compression splice in top chord has filler wood, tension splice in bottom chord is made with ϕ 50 mm steel bar, which is attached to bottom chord by steel plates and bolts.

1 Truss
2 Tension bar ϕ, 50 mm St 52
3 Top and bottom flanges 2 × 12/21 cm
4 Diagonals 2 × 10/15 cm
5 Diagonals 2 × 10/18 cm
6 Struts 10/15 cm
7 Nail plates
8 Bolts ϕ 83 mm

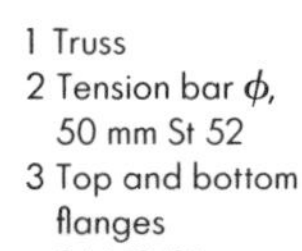

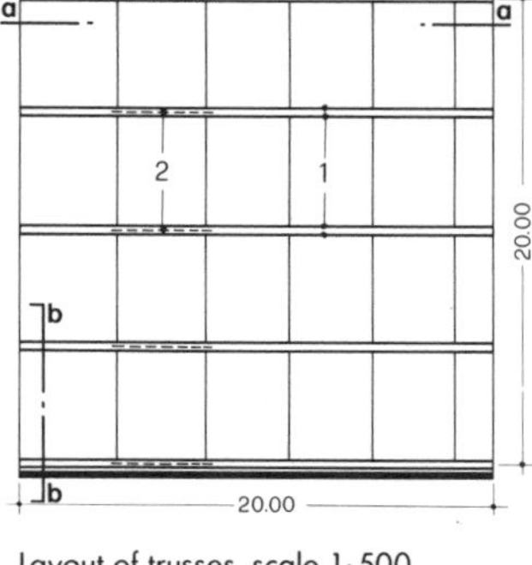

Layout of trusses, scale 1:500

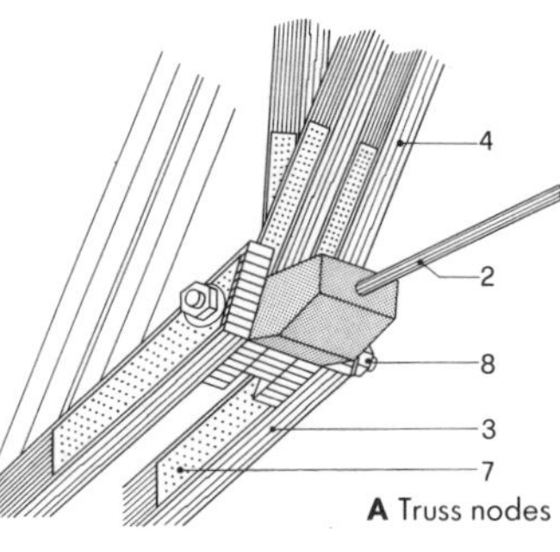

A Truss nodes

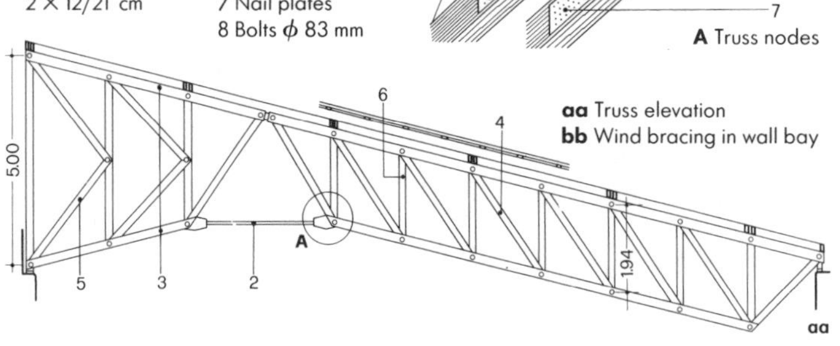

aa Truss elevation
bb Wind bracing in wall bay

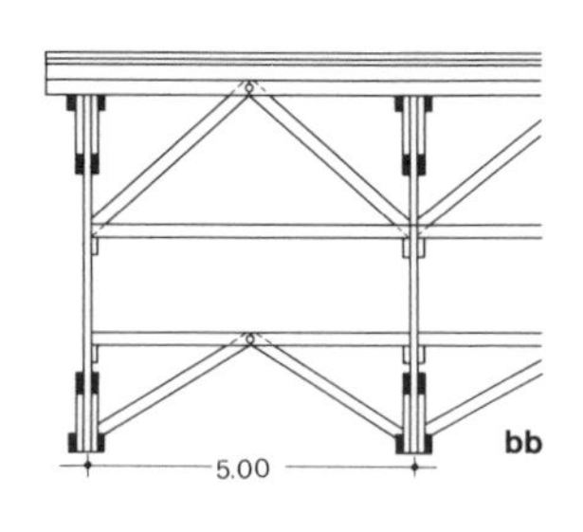

31 Sports Hall in Weinfelden, Switzerland

Architect: R. and E. Guyer, Zurich
Engineer: W. Menig, St. Gallen

17 trusses span the subdividable hall and are cantilevered on the bleacher side by 7.50 m (grandstand) and by 2.50 m for sun protection on the other side. Trusses span 25.00 m and are spaced at 3.00 m; depth of truss varies from 1.70 to 2.30 m. Trusses have six-element top and bottom chords and triple diagonals. Connections are by means of nailed steel plates (5.88 m² per truss). Top chord is straight; bottom chord is parabolic to follow moment diagram. Purlins 10/14 cm run longitudinally and support 24 mm sheathing. Trusses were erected in two days by means of two mobile cranes. Reference: *Holzbau* 4/1973, p. 101

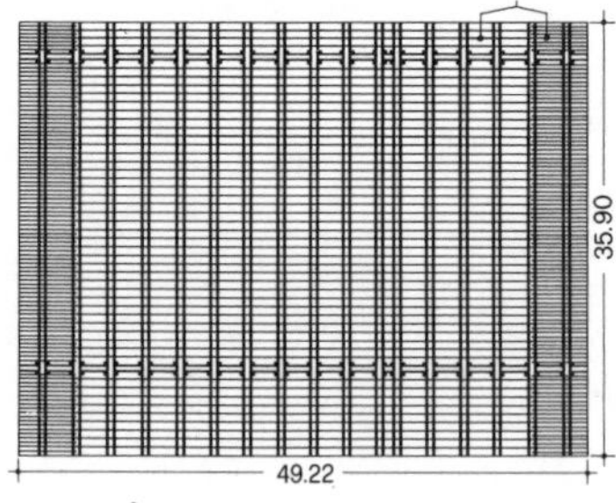

Layout of trusses

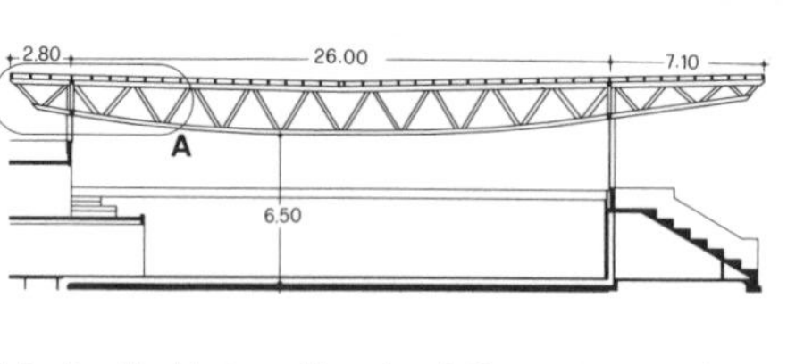

Cross section, scale 1:600

1 Purlins (double in end bays)
2 Top and bottom flanges, quadruple
3 Triple diagonals
4 Nail plates
5 Connection trough six one-sided connectors ϕ 115 mm
6 Bearing plate 40 mm with 8 mm side plates

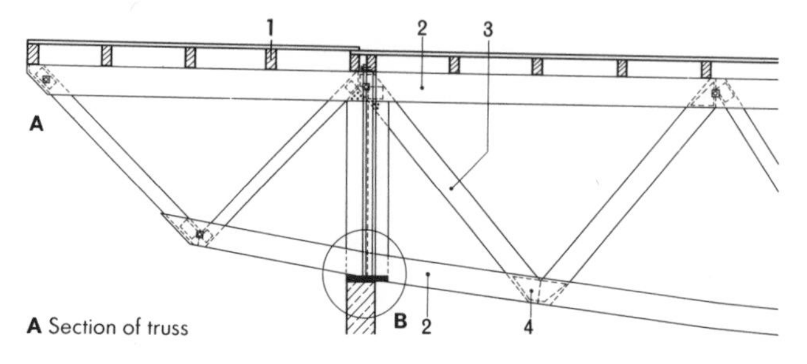

A Section of truss

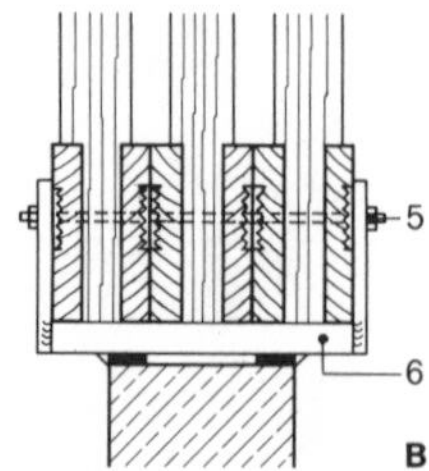

B Lower chord bearing on concrete column, section and isometric view

32 Ice Skating Rink in Bülach, Switzerland

Architect: Oberli, Bülach
Engineer: W. Menig, St. Gallen

Roof over ice rink (60.00 × 40.00 m) and bleachers (60.00 × 14.00 m) is spanned transversely by trusses which rest on exterior reinforced-concrete columns and on longitudinal girders in the interior. Trusses over rink are spaced at 5.00 m and span 40.00 m; they have six-element double top and bottom chords and triple diagonals and struts. Trusses over bleachers are spaced at 2.50 m and span 14.00 m; they have double top and bottom chords and single diagonals and struts. Connections are Menig system nodal plates. Coupled rafters 8/16 to 14/16 cm rest on trusses. Each span of longitudinal girder (3 spans at 20.00 m) serves as support for three trusses over rink (180 kN reaction each) and seven trusses over bleachers (30 kN reaction each). Girder is 4.45 m high truss with top chord of 2 × 14/92 cm and diagonals of 28/50 cm. Each diagonal can support a load of 600 kN. In order not to obstruct the spectators' view, columns supporting the longitudinal truss are slender steel shapes 360 × 360 mm.

Lateral bracing of top and bottom truss chords occurs through prestressed roof panels at outer columns on both sides.
Reference: *Holzbau* 1/1975

Plan of trusses with lateral bracing, scale 1:1000

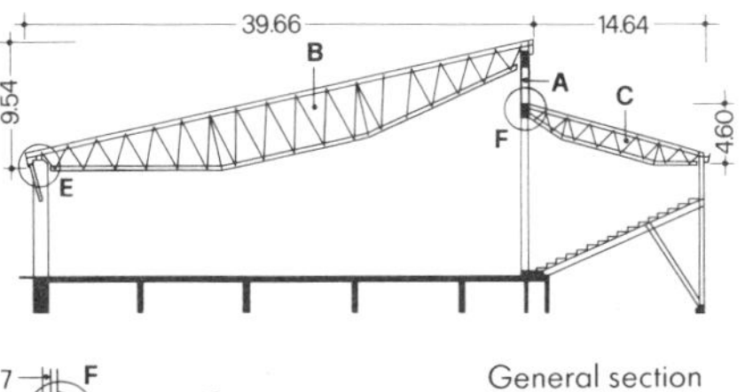

General section

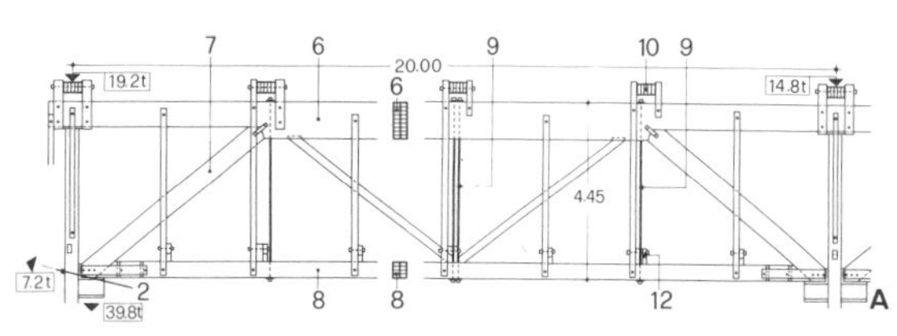

A Longitudinal girder

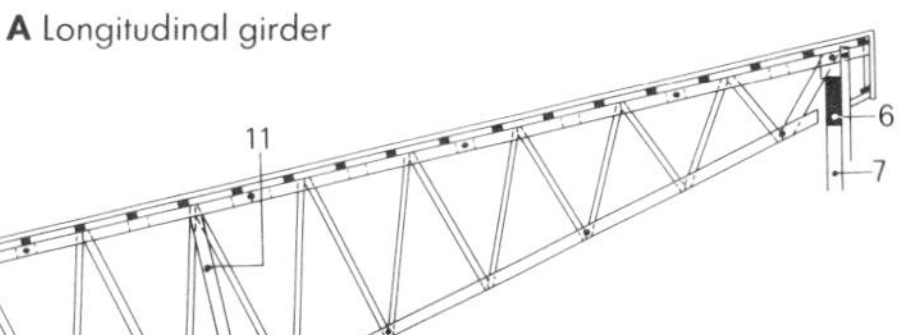

C Transverse truss over bleachers
B Transverse truss over rink

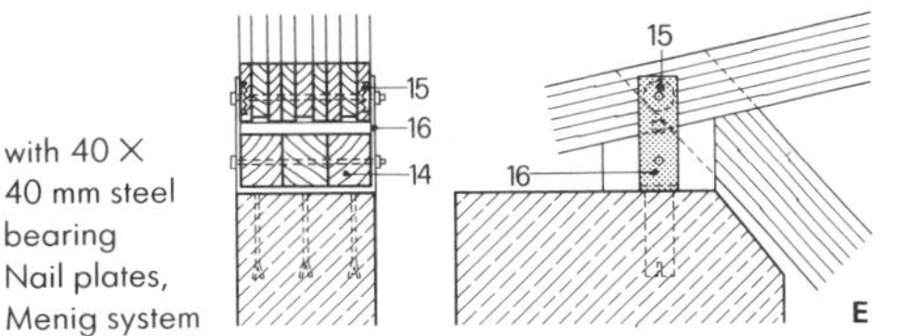

E Bearing of transverse truss **B** on outer column

1 Coupled rafters 8/16 to 14/16 cm
2 Stabilizing bar for bottom chord
3 Stabilizing bars for top chord
4 Compression diagonals
5 Square tube 360/360/9.5 mm
6 Upper chord 2 × 14/92.5 cm
7 Diagonals 28/50 cm
8 Lower chord 2 × 14/40 cm
9 Tension bars ϕ 40 mm
10 Upper and lower chords 6 × 5/24 cm
11 Diagonals and struts, triple
12 Top and bottom chords 2 × 6/22 cm
13 Single diagonals and struts
14 Bearing wedges with 40 × 40 mm steel bearing
15 Shear connector ϕ 117 mm
16 Steel bearing shoe, 14 mm steel plate
17 Nail plates, Menig system

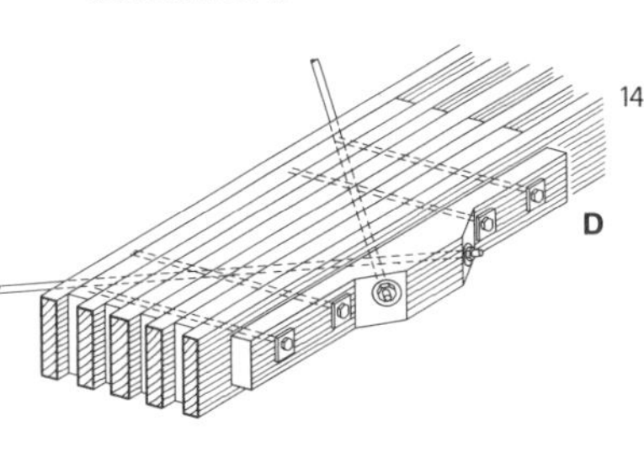

D Connection of bracing bars (3) to top chord of truss **B**

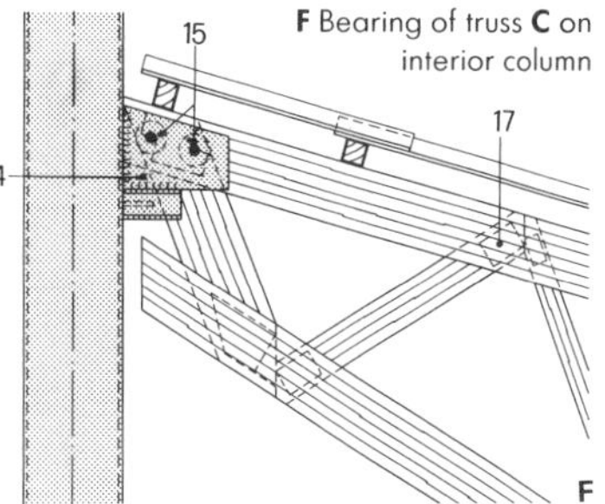

F Bearing of truss **C** on interior column

Industrially Produced Trusses

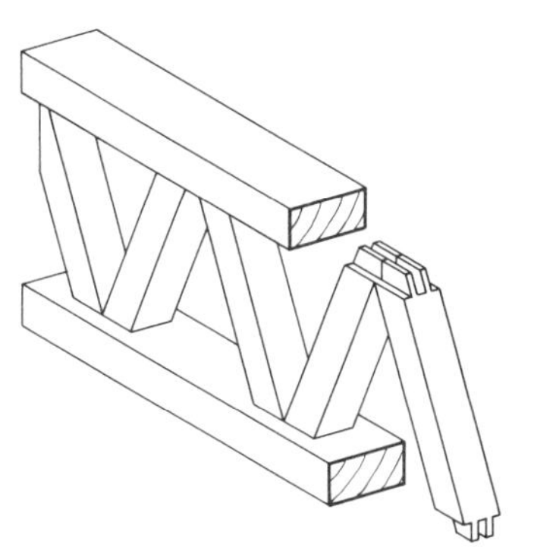

Triangular system (DSB). Diagonals mortised and tenoned into chords and glued.

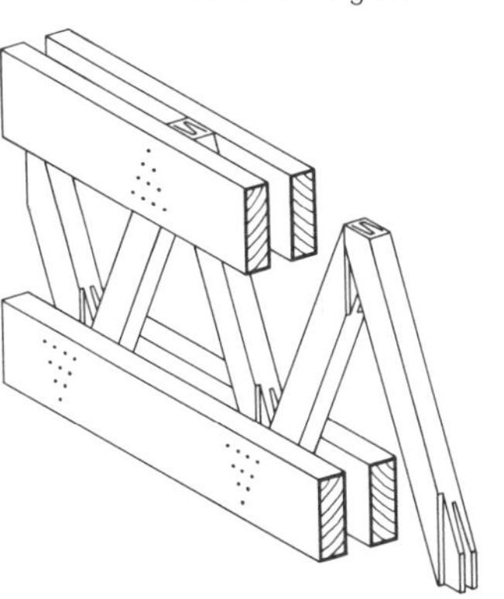

Trigonit system. Diagonals finger-jointed, glued, and nailed between double chords.

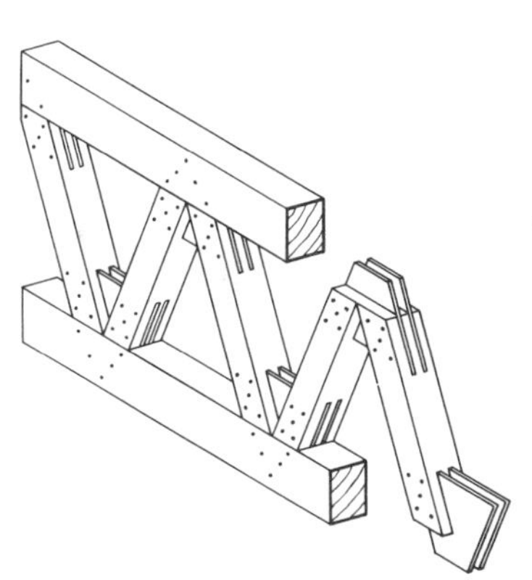

Greim system. Connection plates nailed in slits of diagonals and chords.

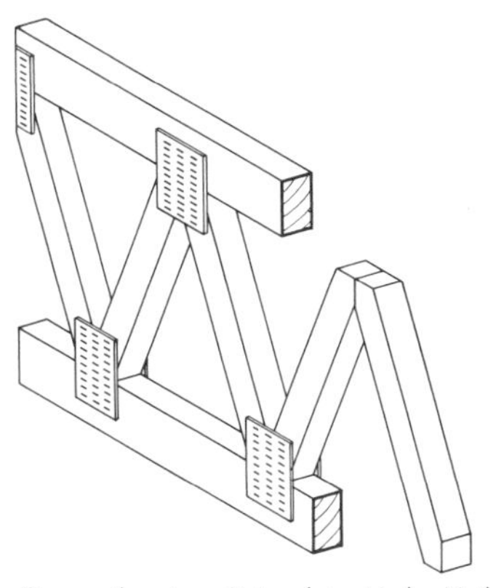

Gangnail system, Twinaplate, Hydro-Nail, etc. Sidewise connection plates pressed as nail plates.

Radial layout of girders allows many alternatives over various plan arrangements. Fitting of rafters over variable spans is made by varying either their size or their spacing.

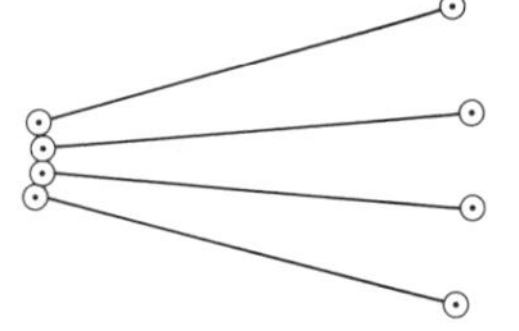

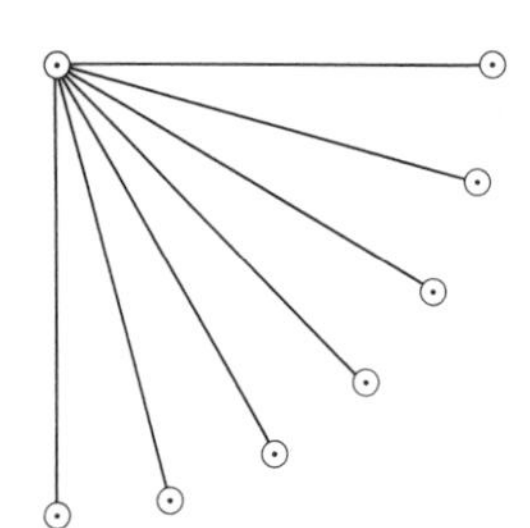

Circular plans

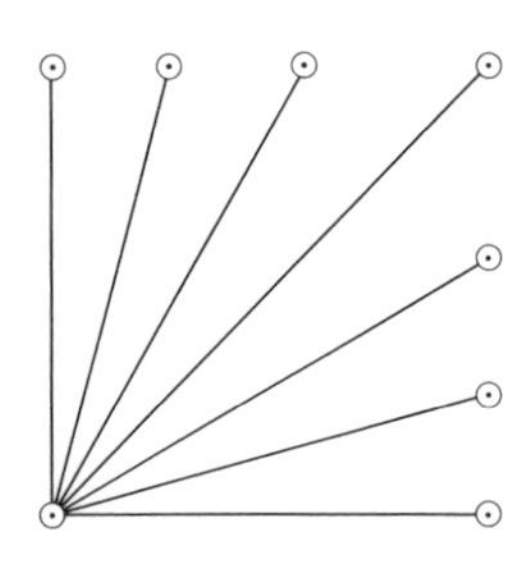

Square plans

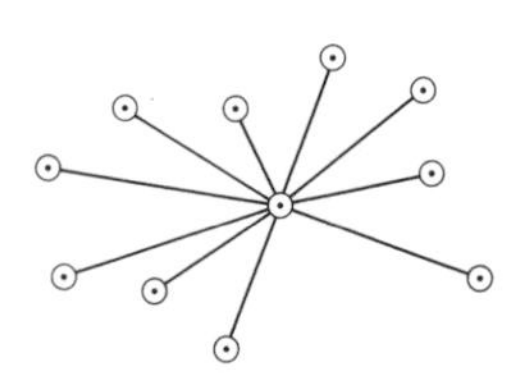

Variable-perimeter layout

33 Parochial Center in Gossau, Switzerland

Architect: Bächtold and Baumgartner, Rorschach
Engineer: W. Menig, St. Gallen

Semicircular church with 15.00 m radius. Roof is half-cone, approximated by plane triangular surfaces between radial girders. Timber girders are 18/80 cm; on the outside they rest on a semicircular solid wall, on the inside on a central column. Central bearing is a cantilevered shelf with a triple-tension member and a double-compression member. Connection is by nail plates, Menig system, and bolts. Vertical load from roof is maximum 380 kN, which creates a tension of 380 kN and a compression of 530 kN on the bearing strut.

Purlins are parallel to perimeter. Underside is planking. Above purlins are insulation, nailers, and asbestos-cement panels.
Reference: *Holzbau* 10/1973, p. 4

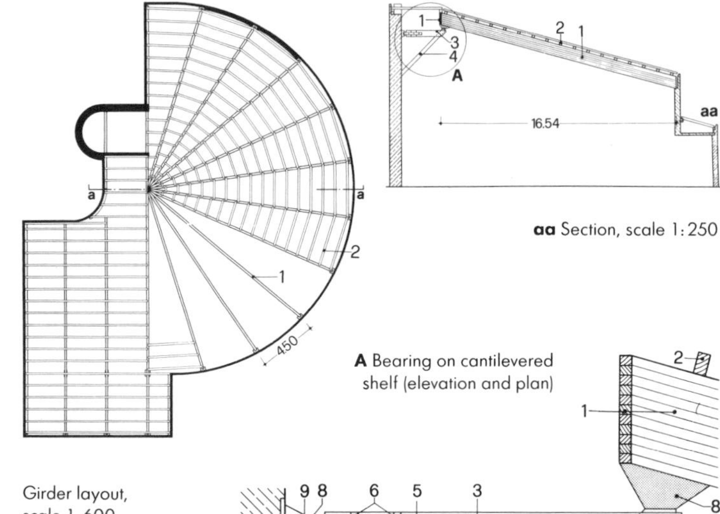

aa Section, scale 1:250

Girder layout, scale 1:600

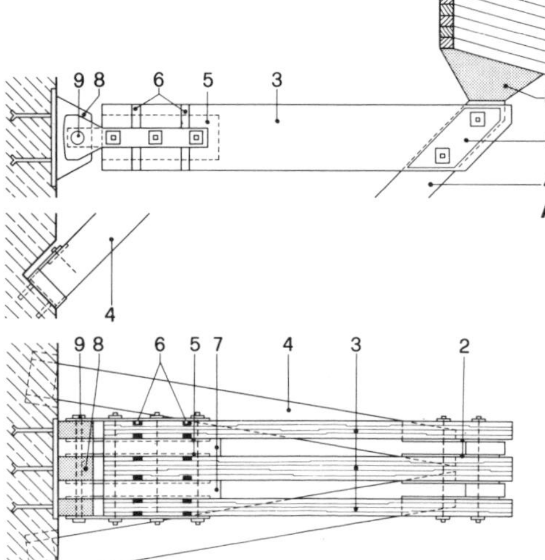

A Bearing on cantilevered shelf (elevation and plan)

1 Radial girder 18/80 cm
2 Rafters 10/12 to 14/18 cm
3 Tension beam 3 × 12/44 cm
4 Compression strut 2 × 11/26 cm
5 Connection plates Menig system, with bolts
6 Shear connectors welded to steel plates
7 Filler wood 12/30 cm
8 Bearing box, steel plates
9 Steel pin

34 Indoor Swimming Pool in Neustadt/Saale, West Germany

Architect: G. Harkort, Leinburg
Engineer: Timber Construction Contractor

Plan has shape of a quarter-circle. Main girders fan out from a low central bearing **(A)** to high outer columns, which are highest in the middle. Roof thus has tentlike appearance.

Central and outer supports are of reinforced concrete; outer ones have a forked bearing seat.

Radial girders are 22/175 cm and support rafters 16/20 cm, placed parallel to perimeter. Acoustical panels are suspended between girders.
Reference: *Sport + Bäderbauten* Oct. 1973, p. 672

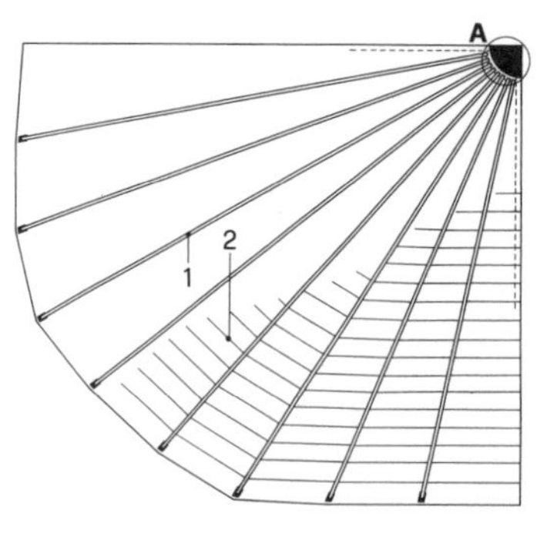

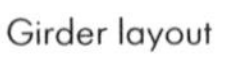

Girder layout

1 Radial girder 22/175 cm
2 Rafters 16/20 cm
3 Hardwood spacers
4 Steel plate 8/80 mm with ϕ 30 mm bolt connection to bearing
5 Drain leader

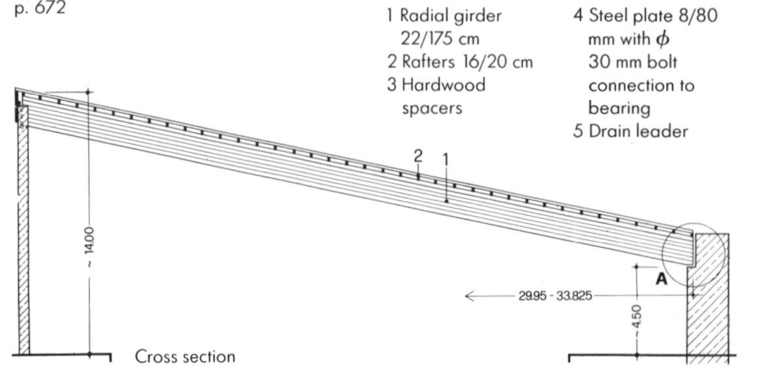

Cross section

A Bearing

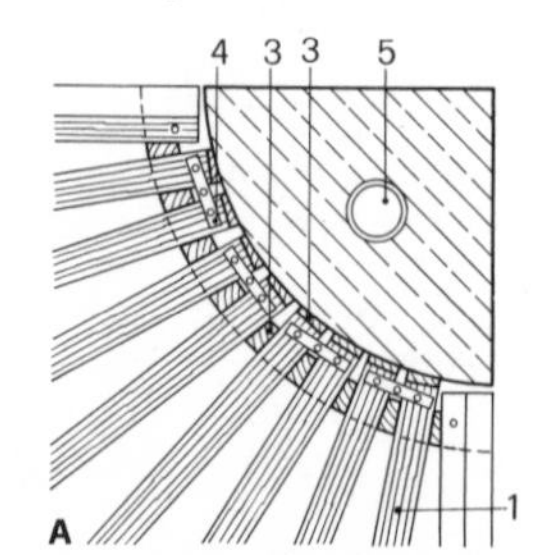

35 Dolphin House in Hamburg Zoo, West Germany

Architect: Neve and Partner, Hamburg
Engineer: Timber Construction Contractor

Dolphin house with exhibition hall and utility rooms. Exhibition hall plan is a segment of a circle. Hall contains a pool and bleachers. Roof consists of 12 radial girders which rest on nearly level supports and have a curve with a rise of 4.18 m. Such a high rise results in rather high lateral deflection. Bearings are therefore neoprene expansion bearings with slotted hole connections.

Exposed planed purlins span between girders. Diagonal planking and nonventilated insulated roof rest on purlins.
Reference: *Detail* 4/1971, illustrations; *Deutsche Bauzeitung* 8/1971

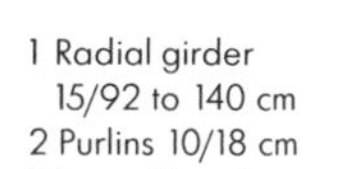

1 Radial girder 15/92 to 140 cm
2 Purlins 10/18 cm
3 Lateral bracing
4 Diagonal planking
5 Steel channel 220 mm
6 Steel angle 100/100 mm
7 Elastomeric bearing
8 Nail plate as tension gusset

Plan

Cross section

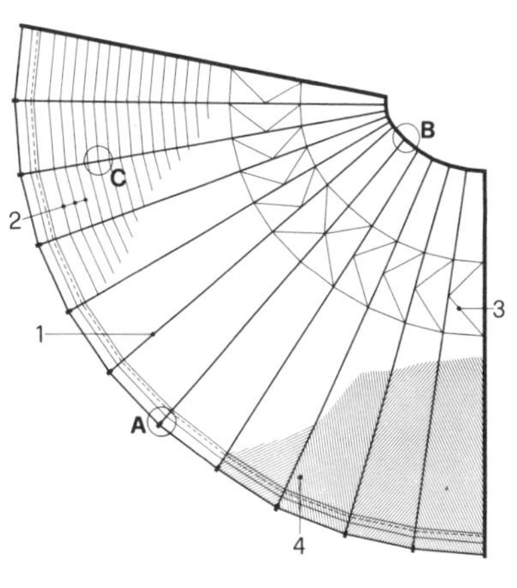

Layout of girders and lateral bracing

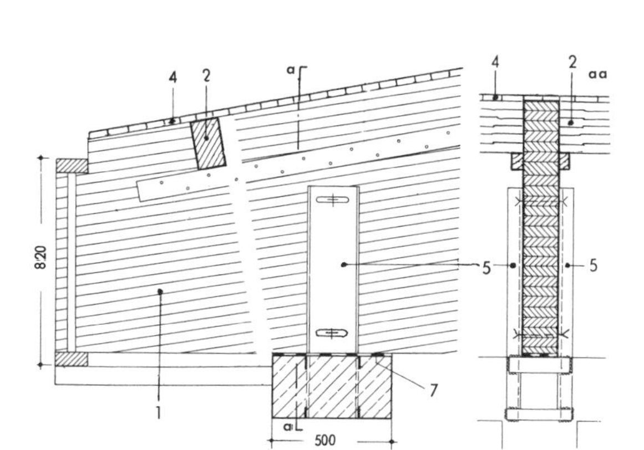

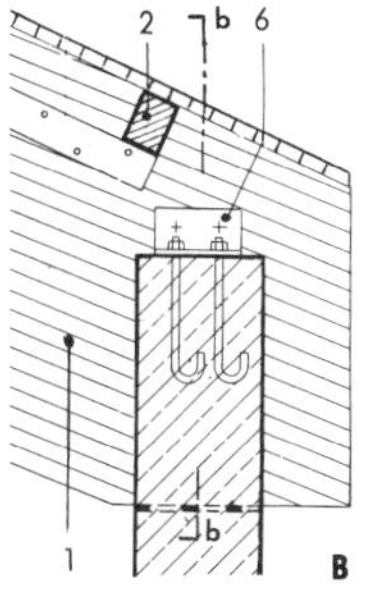

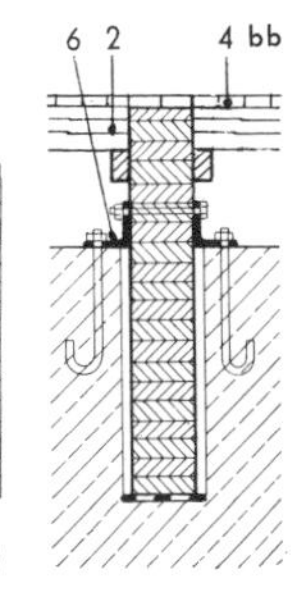

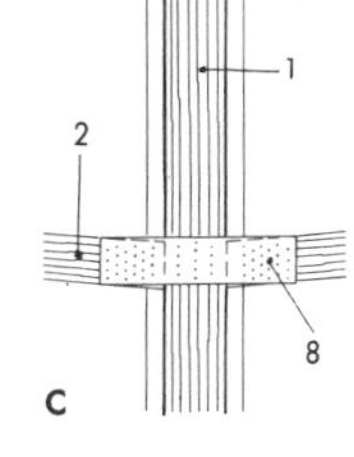

A, B Bearings, **C** Connection of purlins

Main Girder, Central Bearing, Radiating Girders

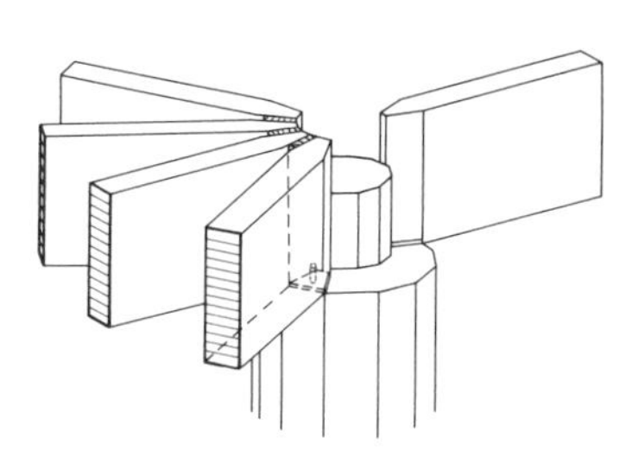

Concrete column. Elastomeric bearing with safety dowel, hardwood core spacer between girders.

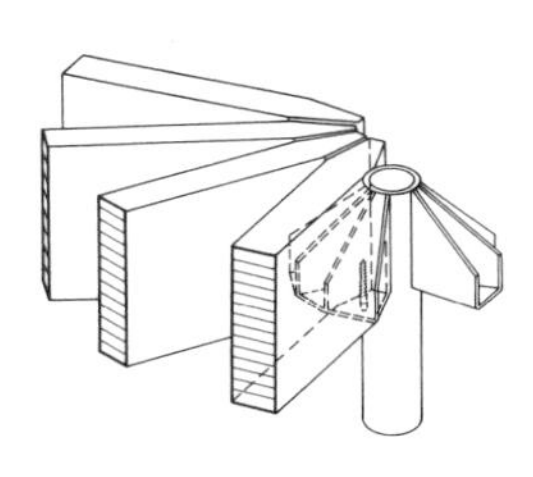

Steel tube column with welded bearing shoes.

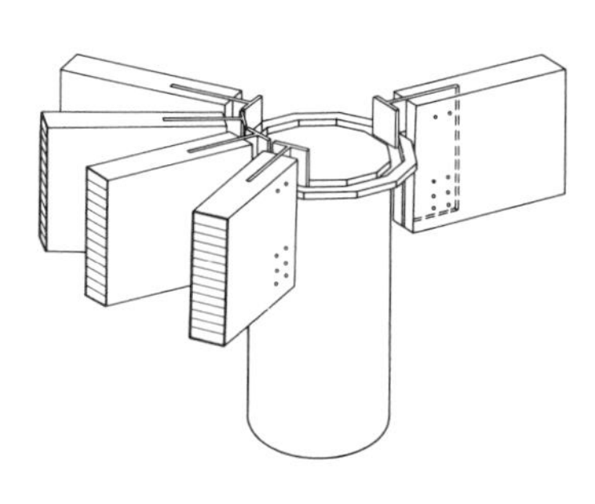

Timber, reinforced concrete, or steel column with bearing ring. Girders hooked on by bolted steel plates.

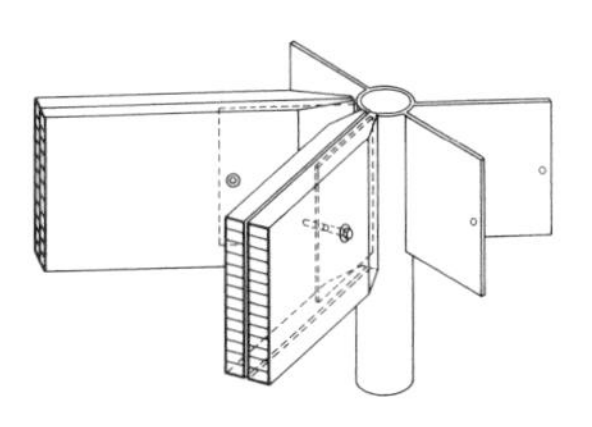

Steel tube column with welded bearing plates. Twin girders with nail plates and pin connection bolts.

Beam grids consist of one-span beams, pin-connected in the main and secondary directions. A uniform mesh layout and/or uniform sizing of main and secondary beams results in a uniform beam grid in all directions.

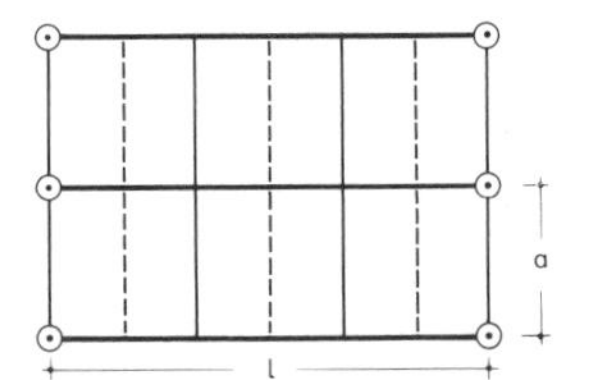

Linear system, main and secondary beams have same appearance. Ceiling looks like a box grid.

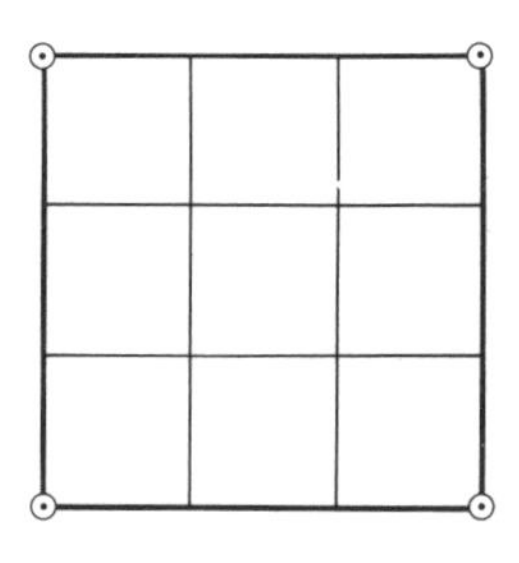

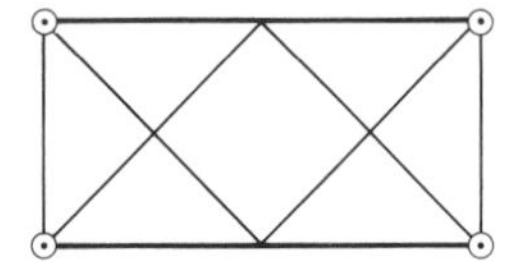

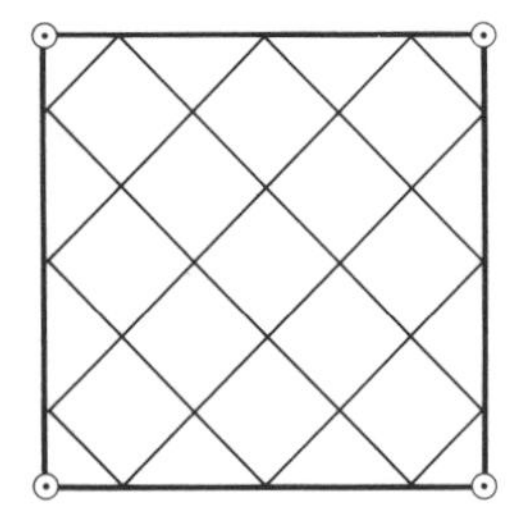

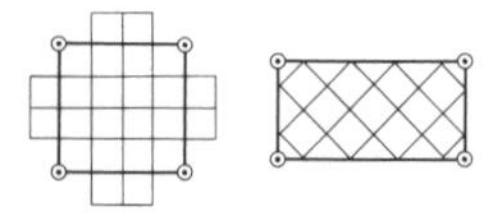

Main beams on the outside. Secondary beams may be either parallel or diagonal; if diagonal, they form lateral wind bracing.

36 Office Building in Ballerup near Copenhagen, Denmark

Architect: FDBs arkitektkontor, Glostrup
Engineer: J. O. Eriksen

One-story building with vestibule and hall. Timber columns 13.5/27 cm are placed on grid of 4.80 × 4.80 m. Main girders 14/36 cm span longitudinally on centerline of columns. Secondary girders are placed transversely at 2.40 m.

Secondary girders are connected to main girders by means of tension bolts attached through a threaded bar. This secures secondary girders against overturning. Purlins are 6.5/10 cm spaced at 48 cm and support sheathing and insulation.

Reference: *Arkitektur DK* 8/1974, p. 317

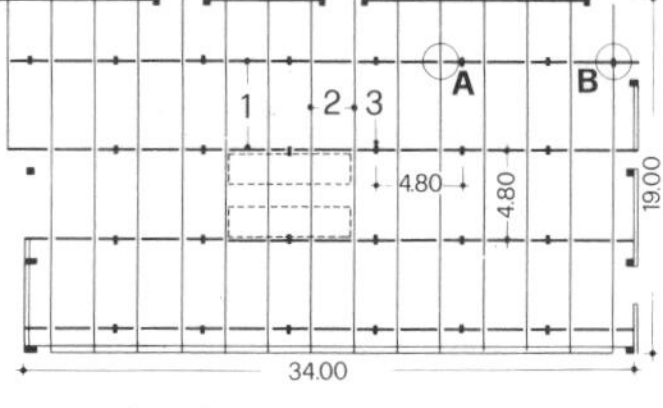
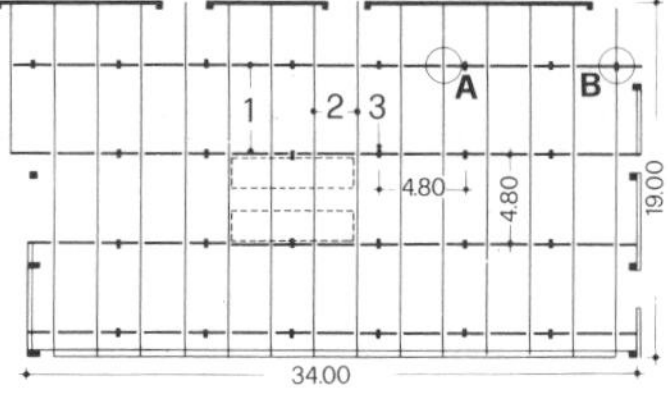

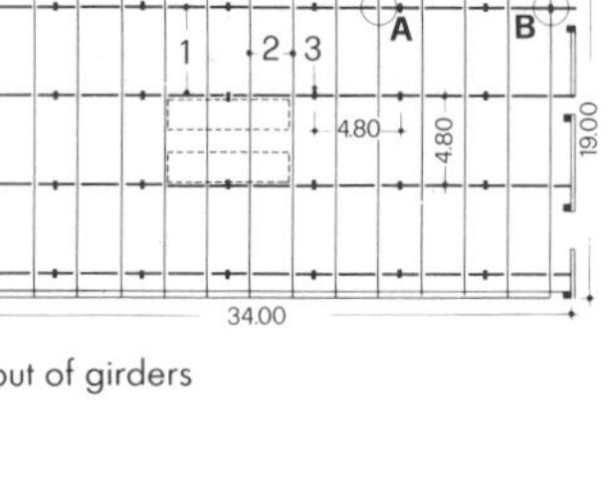

Layout of girders

1 Main girder 14/36 cm, laminated wood
2 Secondary girder 9/40 cm, laminated wood
3 Column 13.5/27 cm, laminated wood
4 Purlins 6.5/10 cm, laminated wood, spaced at 48 cm
5 Steel bar ϕ 36 mm with threaded hole
6 Bolt ϕ 16 mm
7 Filler wood
8 Steel angle and wood screws

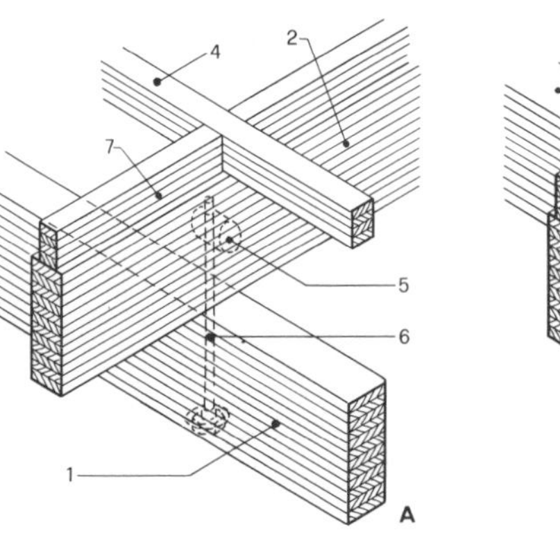

A Bearing, secondary to main girder

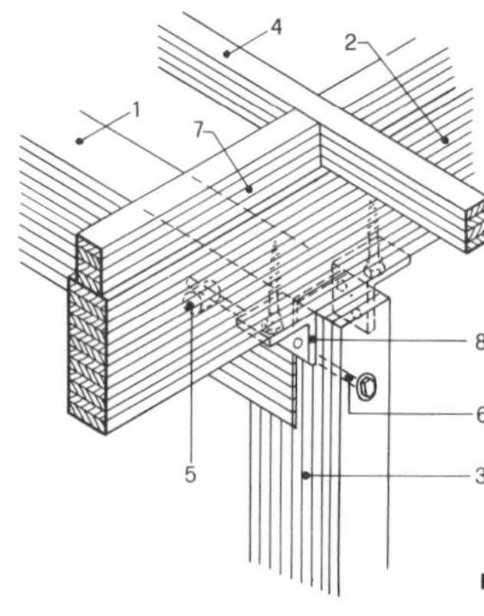

B Bearing, end post

37 Cafeteria of Technical Faculty in Twente, The Netherlands

Architect: J. van Stigt
Engineer: Oosterhoff, Tjebbes und Barends, Arnheim

Cafeteria for university personnel, consisting of central entrance, food counters, and peripheral dining areas. Main girders 61 cm deep are spaced at 5.60 m in two directions on a square grid. Girders in one direction are continuous, in the other direction simply supported. Square bays are spanned by 9/9 cm lumber, covered with planking top and bottom. Columns 2 × 8.5/22 cm with forked bearings are located in middle of bay so that intersections of girders are visible and girders cantilever 2.80 m in both directions.

Reference: *Wood* Oct. 1966; *Detail* 4/1970, illustrations

Photo and view of structure

1 Girder 10/67 cm, laminated wood
2 Lumber 9/9 cm
3 Planking 26 mm
4 Columns 2 × 8.5/22 cm, laminated wood, forked bearings

Detail of girder

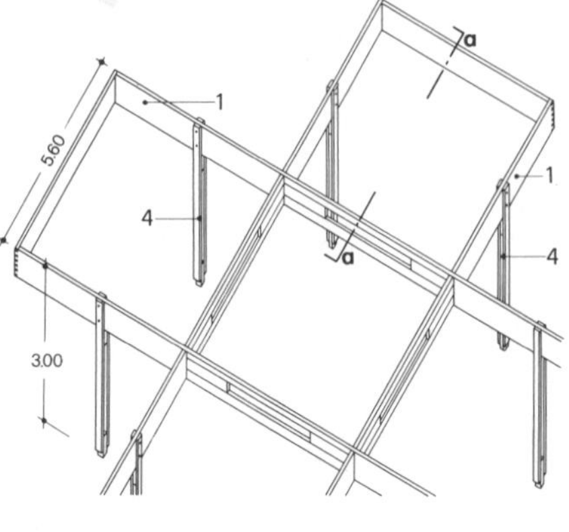

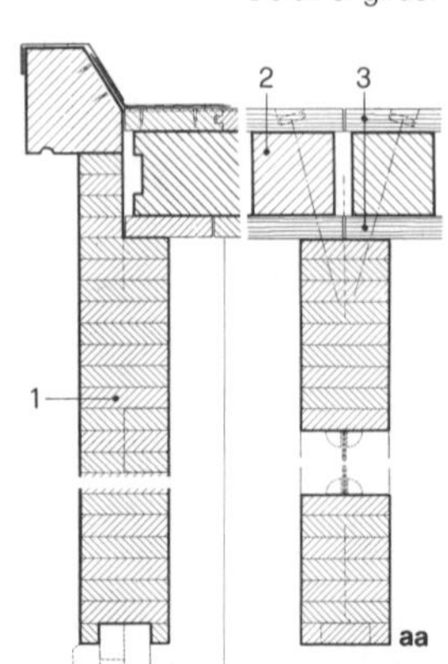

38 Central Hall of a Savings Bank in Lippstadt, West Germany

Architect: R. Mumme, Lippstadt
Engineer: Timber Construction Contractor

Roof over two-story-high central hall. Roof is a girder grid spanning 21.00 m; girders are simple beams 22/80 cm; secondary girders, simply supported between them, are same size. Girders are spaced at 1.80 m in both directions. In each panel there is a double-panel skylight which rests on raised frames. A peripheral girder is 22/108 cm. At connection of peripheral girder to main girder, shear bolts act as suspension rods. Secondary girders are tightened together on site by means of ϕ 16 mm tensioning rods. Connection is through shear connectors in girder end faces.

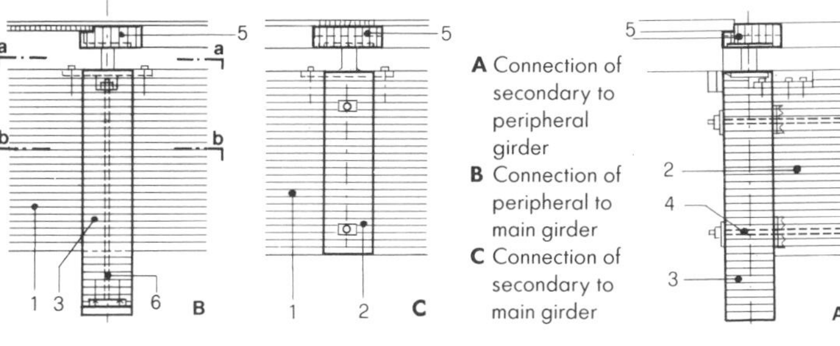

A Connection of secondary to peripheral girder
B Connection of peripheral to main girder
C Connection of secondary to main girder

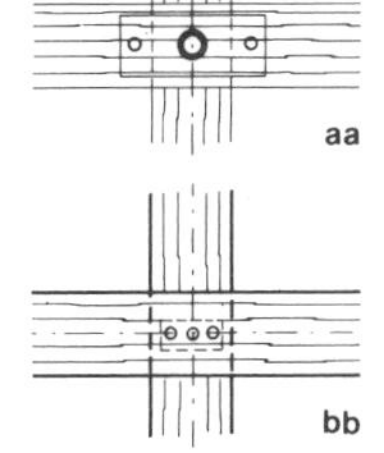

1 Main girder 22/80 cm
2 Secondary girder 22/80 cm
3 Peripheral girder 22/108 cm
4 Tension rod ϕ 16 mm
5 Upstanding frames for skylights
6 Shear bolts acting as suspension rods

Girder layout and cross section

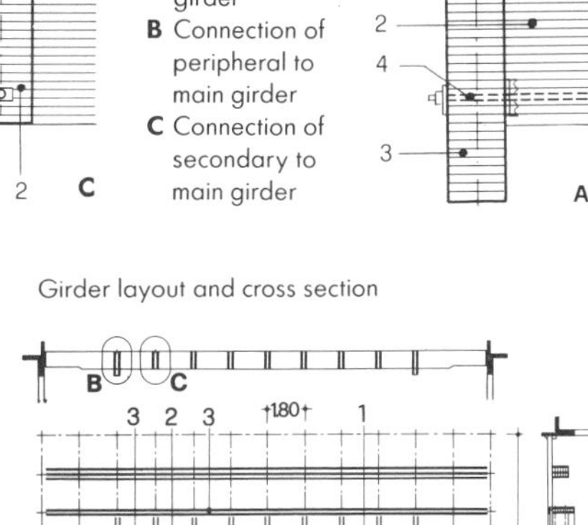

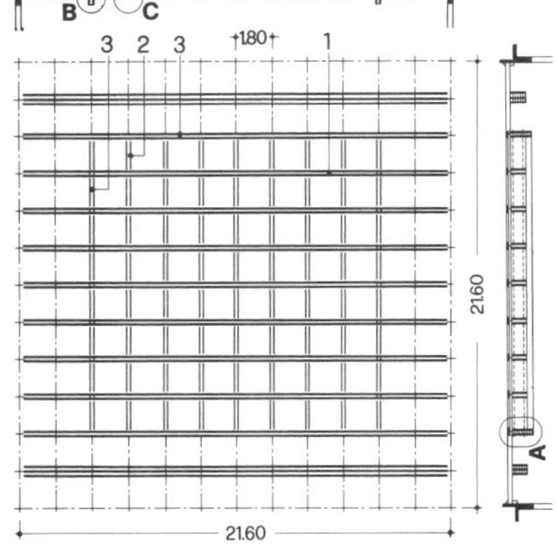

39 Ice Skating Rink in Middletown, United States

Architect: Warner, Burns, Toan, Lunde, New York
Engineer: H. Berger, New York

Ice rink with bleachers along long side. Roof consists of subtensioned girders in which tendons lie within column axes and girders span diagonally 49.00 m from one bearing to the opposite one. Tendons are parallel to floor and then rise, following incline of bleachers. There is a strut at each bend in the tendon to the crossing point of two girders.

Wind bracing is achieved through diagonal girders and through lateral bracing within plane of roof rafters.

Reference: *Progressive Architecture* 4/1971, p. 86; *Architecture and Engineering* 3/1969

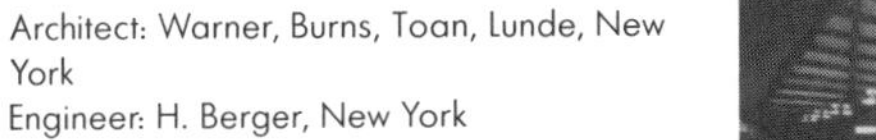

1 Main girder 30/107 cm, laminated wood
2 Purlins 15/46 cm, laminated wood
3 Compression strut ϕ 200 mm, extra-strength pipe
4 Tendon ϕ 52 mm
5 Tendon ϕ 45 mm
6 Connection plates 3.8 mm
7 Lateral bracing

Section of structural system

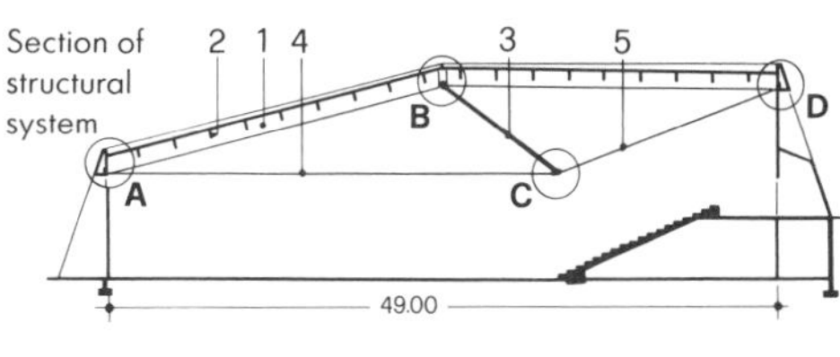

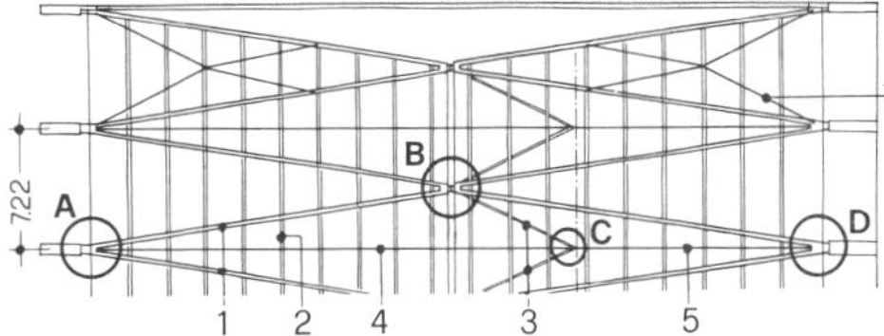

Partial plan of structure

A, D Bearings
B Connection at ridge
C Connection of tendons

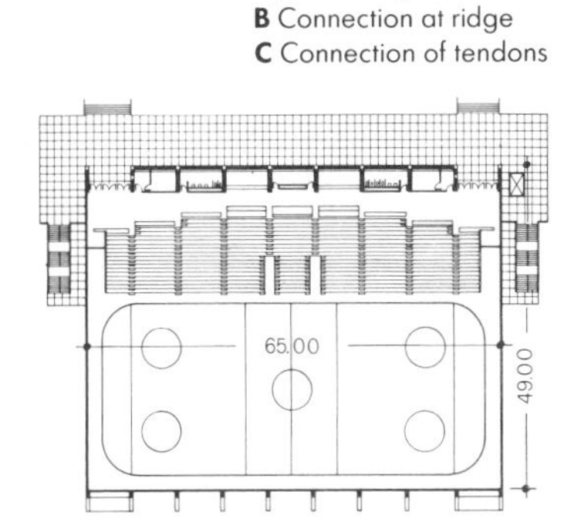

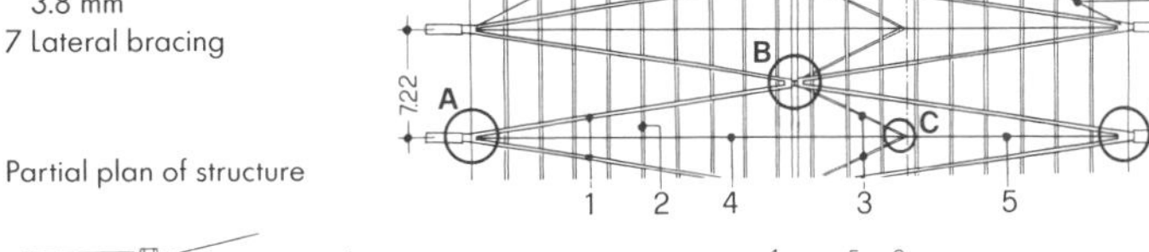

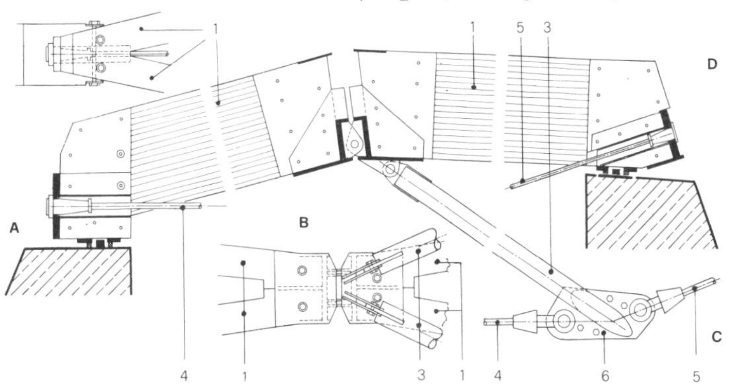

Bearing of Secondary Girder on Main Girder

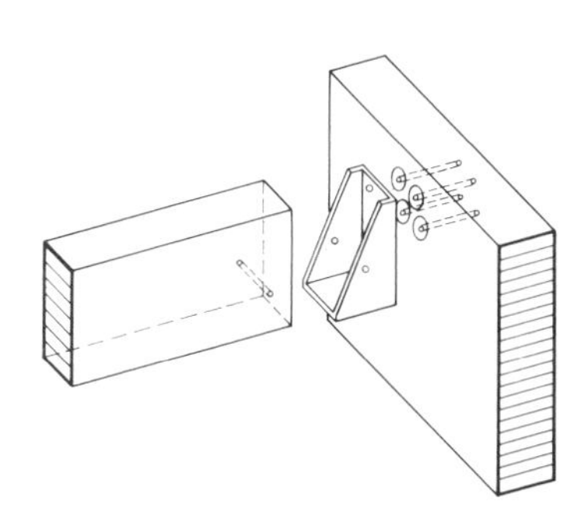

Beam shoe on main girder, nailed or shear-connected.

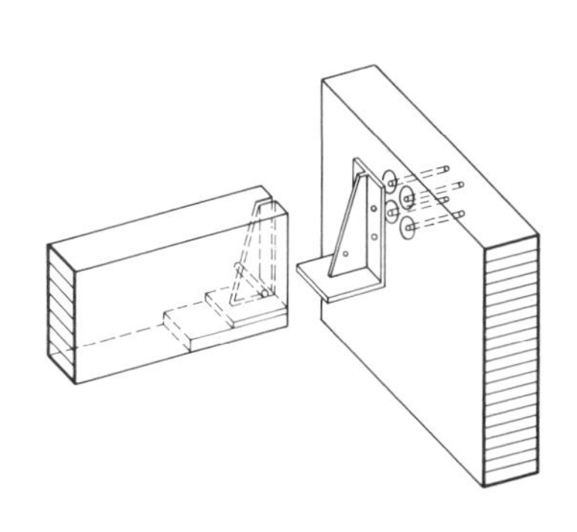

Secondary girder resting on recessed angle with stiffener.

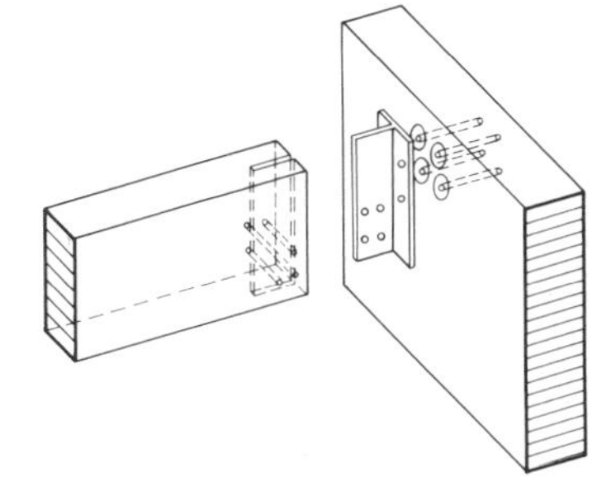

Steel T-shape shear connector attached to main girder; nailed or doweled to secondary girder.

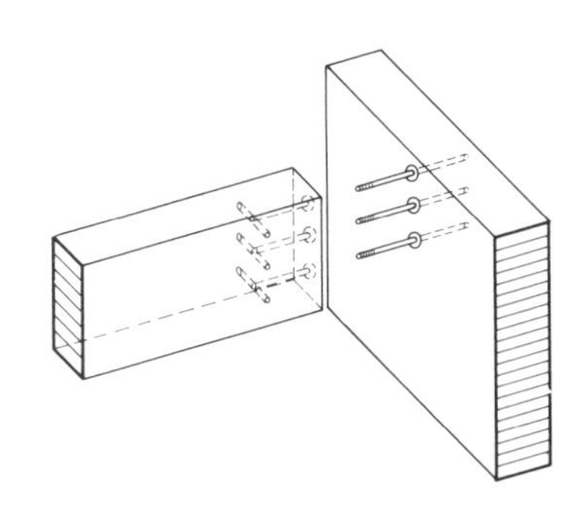

End grain bolts screwed into threaded transverse round bars.

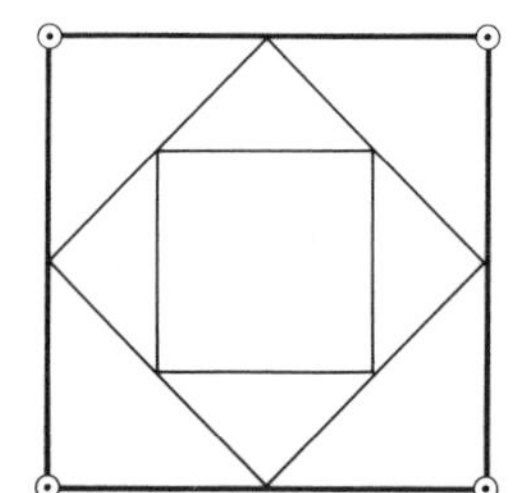

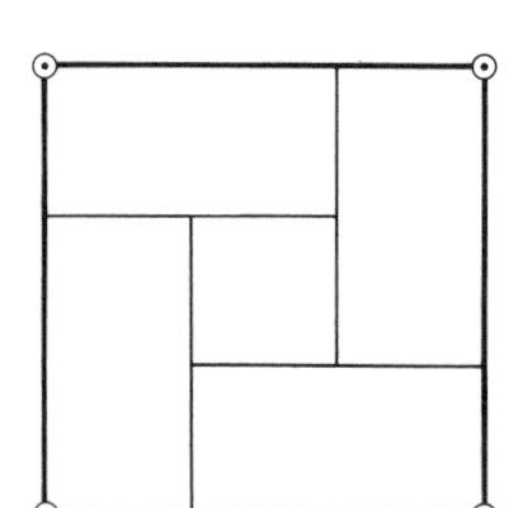

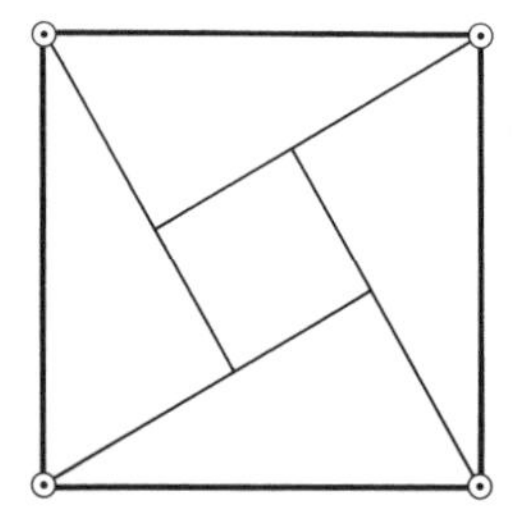

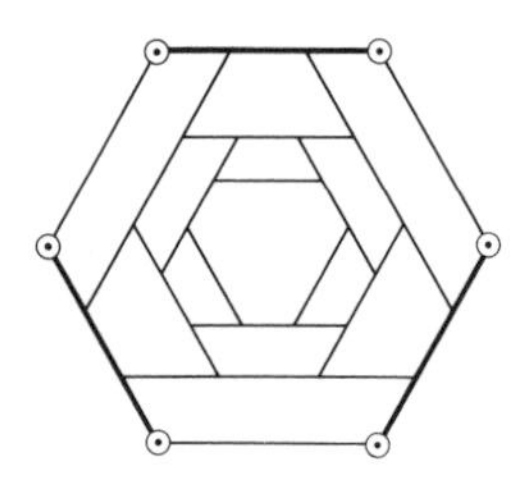

Main girders at 90 and 60°, secondary girders enclosed with varied arrangement and in different directions.

40 School Gymnasium in Aachen, West Germany

Architect: E. Meissen, Stolberg
Engineer: J. Natterer, Munich

Plan area 27.50 × 15.50 m. Main girders on diamond layout, 15 m span. Lateral bracing is achieved by diagonal girder layout.

Secondary girders span between main girders longitudinally and transversely; connections by means of steel angles and bolts. Roofing is trapezoidal sheet metal.

1 Main girder 18/90 cm
2 Edge beam 14/150 cm
3 Secondary girder 14/60 cm
4 Secondary girder 14/42 cm

Plan and view of girder layout

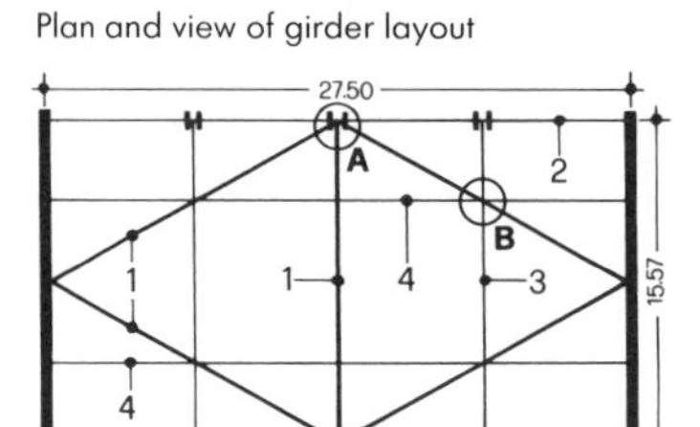

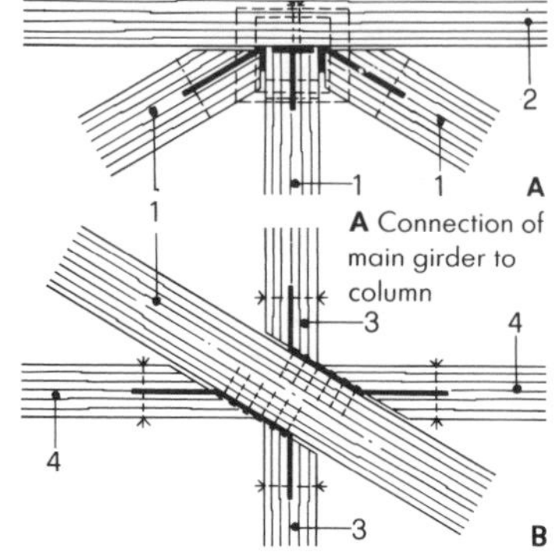

A Connection of main girder to column

B Connection of secondary to main girder

41 Sports and Recreation Center in Wasserburg, West Germany

Architect: P. Seifert, Munich
Engineer: D. Herrschmann, Munich

Triple hall 29.50 × 44.50 m. Roof structure, using shallowest possible depth of girders, is meant to create uniform looking grid and a lively room. Secondary girders carry partitions.

Main girder system is a grid, subtensioned in one direction and having moment connection splices. Laminated transverse girders are 30/220 cm, spaced at 15.00 m, and longitudinal ones are 30/232 cm, spaced at 9.80 m. Moment connections at nodes have steel plates in compression and steel bolts in tension. Compression splices are by contact over steel compression plates. Shear transfer is by steel plates with shear connectors. Transverse girders are subtensioned with two steel tendons ϕ 32 mm.

Secondary structural system consists of diagonally arranged subtensioned beams, which makes special wind bracing unnecessary. Over this there are purlins with framed skylights.

1 Transverse girder 30/232 cm, subtensioned
2 Longitudinal girder 30/230 cm
3 Secondary system, upper chord
4 Struts
5 Secondary system, lower chord

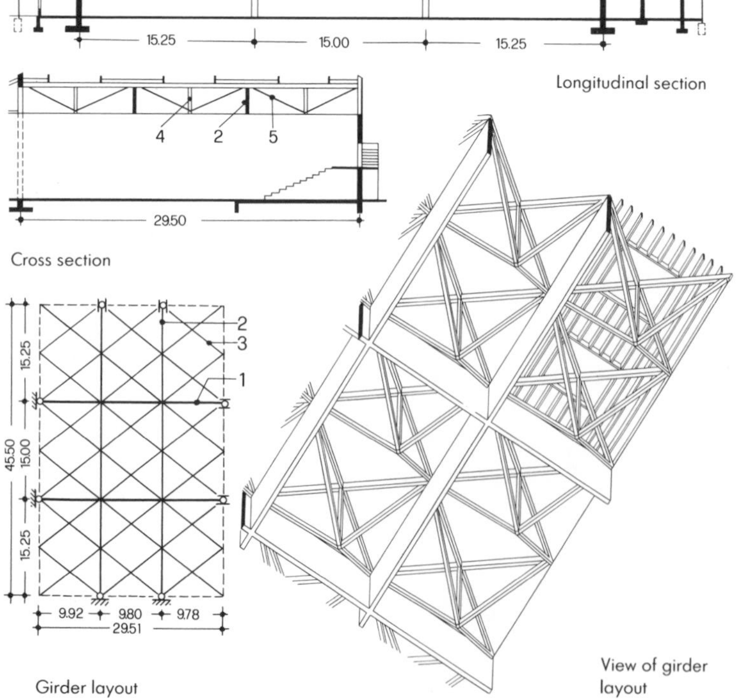

Longitudinal section

Cross section

Girder layout

View of girder layout

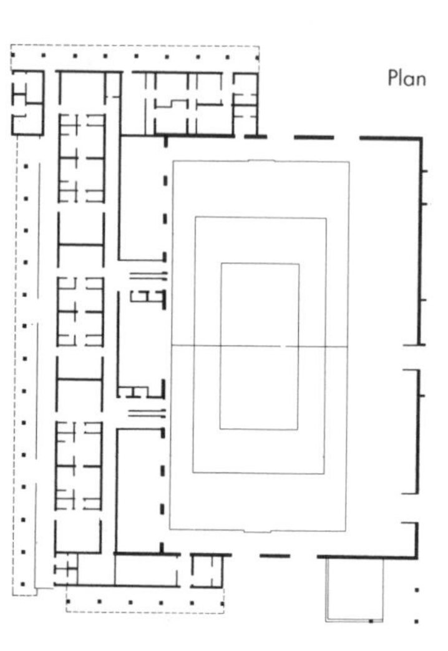

Plan

42 Exhibition Hall in Montreal, Canada

Architect: Erickson and Massey, Vancouver
Engineer: J. Baracs

Exhibition pavilion "Man in the Community" as part of the World's Fair of 1967 in Montreal. Pavilion consists of stacked hexagonal tiers of beams, whose ends rest in center of underlying beams. This creates a hexagonal pyramid with a curved profile. Beams are plywood box girders with four webs on lower tiers and two on upper ones.

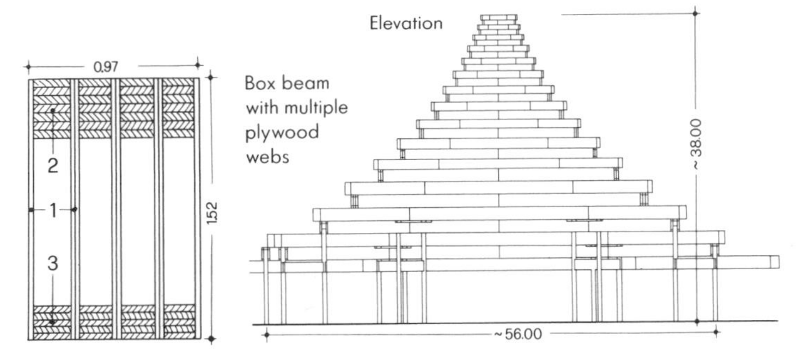

1 Plywood 3.18 cm
2 Upper flanges 18/33 cm
3 Lower flanges 18/22 cm

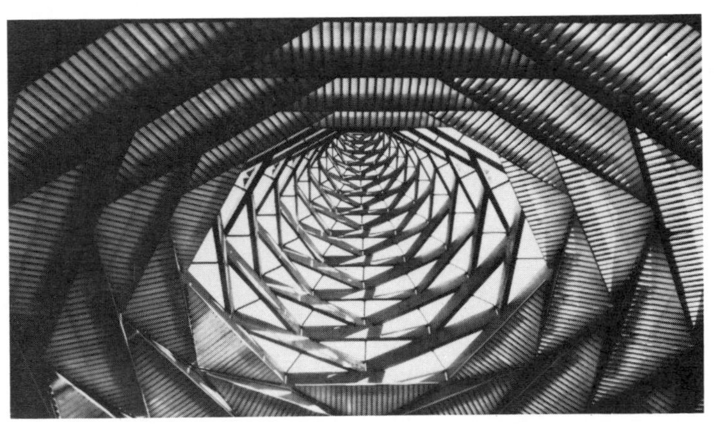

43 Multipurpose Hall in Roseburg, Oregon, United States

Architect: Backen, Arrigoni, and Ross

Multipurpose hall 46.50 × 46.50 m for sports, concerts, fairs, and assemblies. Structural system consists of trusses arranged on a square in plan view, lying alternately parallel or diagonally to walls; smaller squares are inscribed inside larger ones. In this manner, loads of inner truss are always transferred to center of next outer truss.
Reference: *Progressive Architecture* 12/1971, p. 61

Plan with layout of trusses

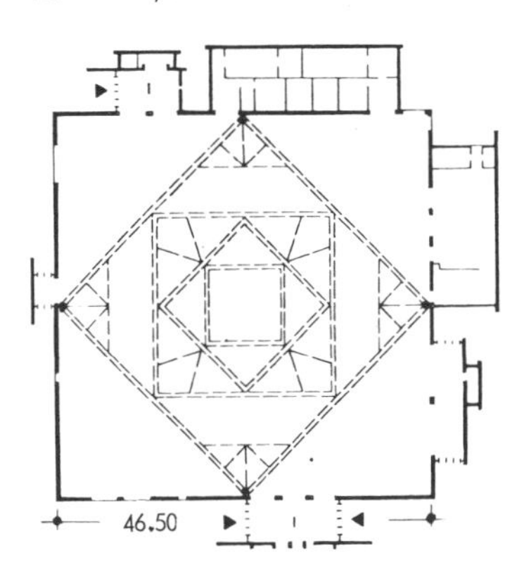

Perspective view

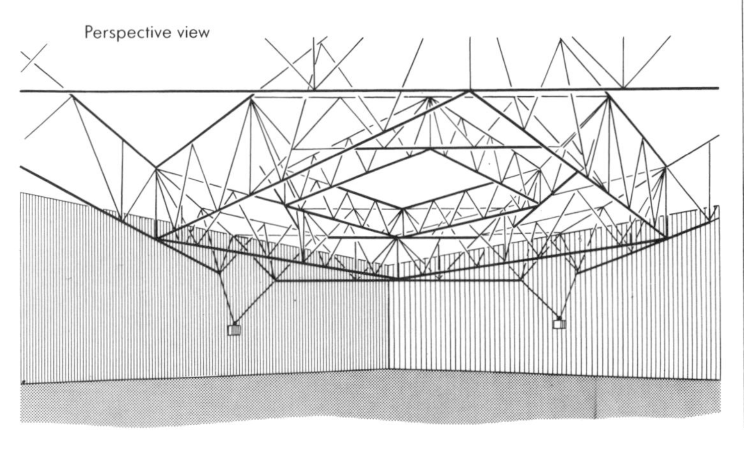

Bearing of Purlins

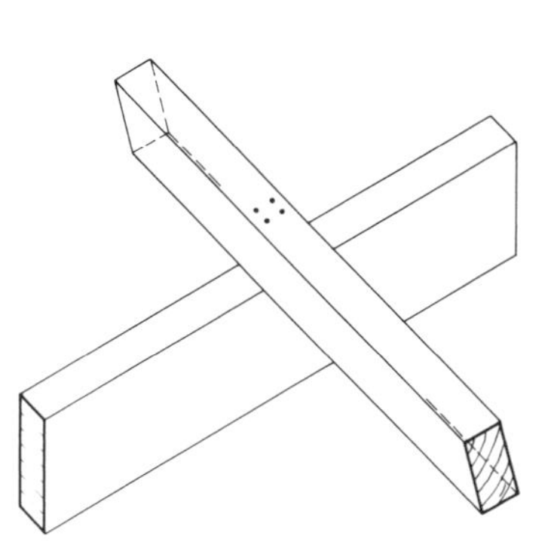

Purlins on flat slope secured by nails or screws.

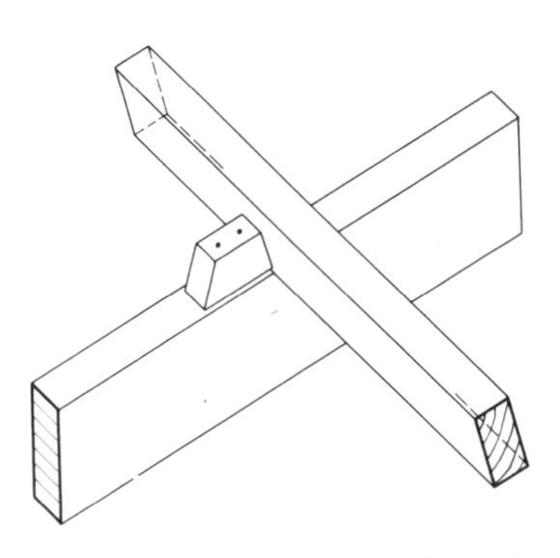

Purlins on steeper slopes secured by side blocks.

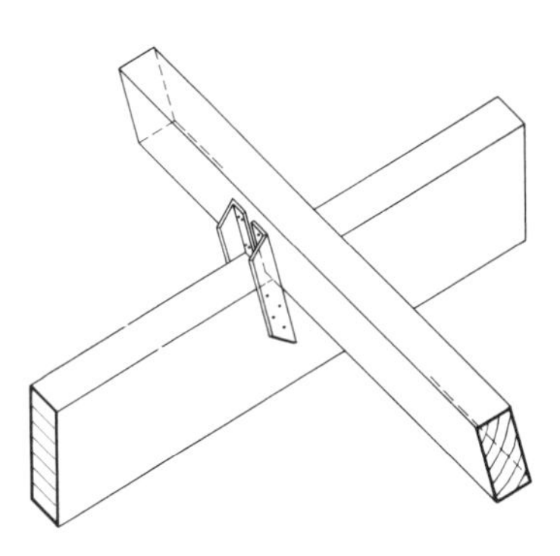

Nailed steel angles or plates, or commercial specialty anchors, prevent uplift.

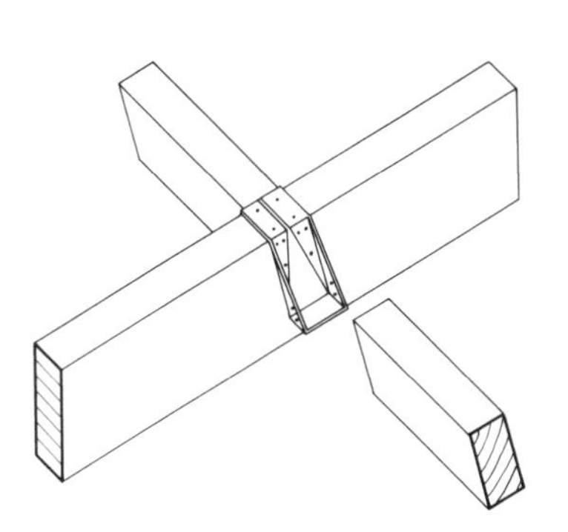

Nailed steel sheet-metal bearing seat.

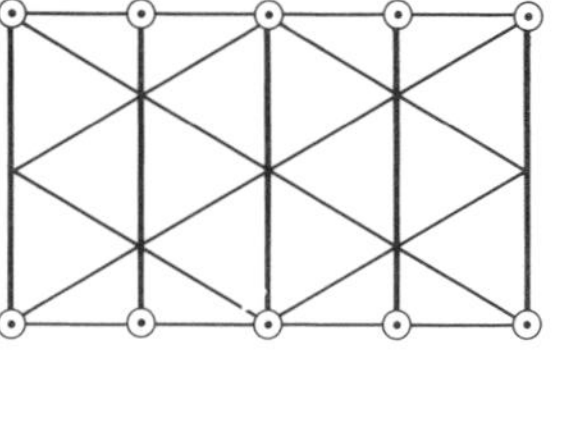

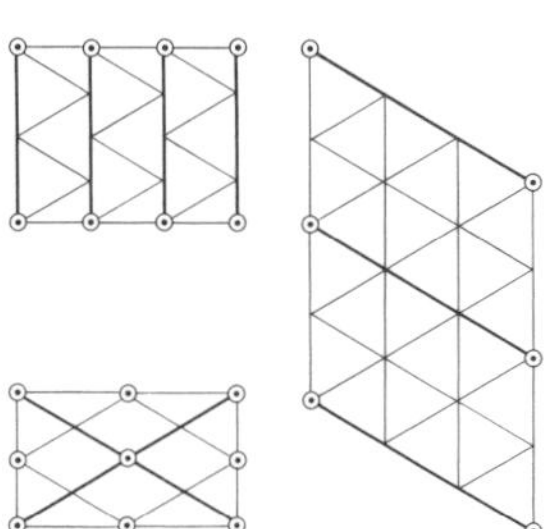

Linear systems with main or secondary beam arrangement at 60°.

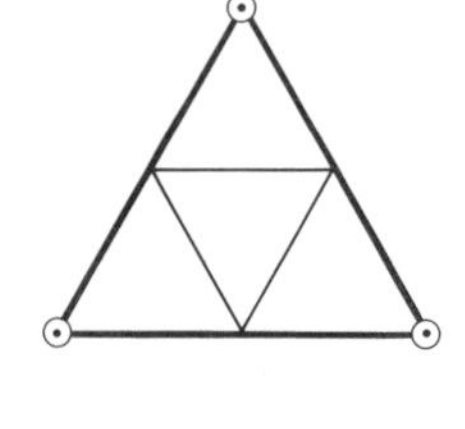

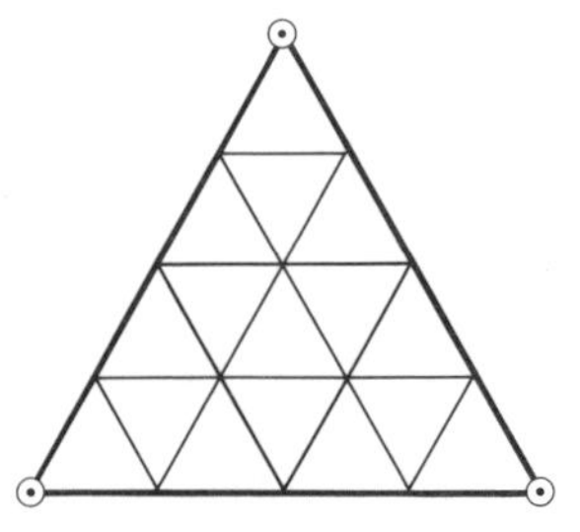

Main girders at 60°. Secondary beams on various layouts. Horizontal triangular trusses for wind bracing.

44 Gasoline Station Wetterau, West Germany

Architect: S. Wüstner, Friedberg
Engineer: G. Thürauf, Frankfurt

Roof is a beam grid with main and secondary beam layout at 60°. Underside appearance is that of equilateral triangles. Main beams 12/70 cm span 12.50 m between peripheral beams, which are 12/150 cm. Main beams are braced laterally by secondary beams 12/70 cm, placed at 60°. The 5 cm thick tongue and groove planking rests on beam grid, covered by several plies of bituminous paper and a layer of gravel.

Roof was prefabricated on the ground in three parts and was lifted with two movable cranes. Lateral bracing consists of triangular beams on fixed columns.
Reference: *Bauen mit Holz* 6/1971, p. 284

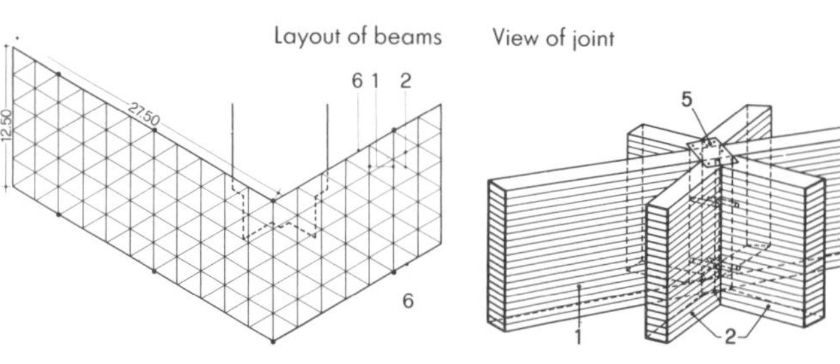

Layout of beams View of joint

aa, bb Section and plan view of main and secondary beam connection

1 Main beam 12/70 cm
2 Secondary beam 12/70 cm
3 Tongue and groove planking 5 cm
4 Steel bolt ϕ 20 mm
5 Steel plate
6 Edge beams 12/150 cm

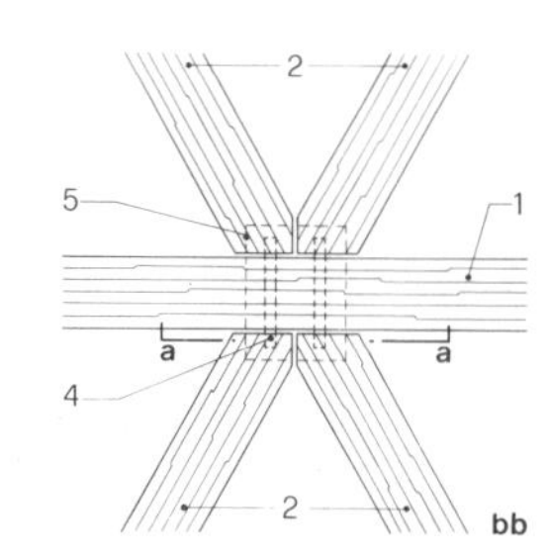

45 Tennis Clubhouse in Kelkheim, West Germany

Architect: F. Rosenberg, Kelkheim
Engineer: P. Klockenhoff, Wiesbaden

Clubhouse with dressing rooms, restaurant, and service rooms for open-air tennis club. It consists of two wings at an angle of 120° facing tennis courts. Plan is laid out on a 60° grid, which can be seen in the arrangement of beams. Beams are spanning from an outer wall to the next connecting beam, which is supported indirectly. Beam sections are therefore designed to carry their individual loads. Beam sections vary from 6/10 to 14/24 cm and are exposed so that they reveal the roof structure.

Horizontal bracing occurs through the 60° arrangement of beams and the 5 cm thick layer of planking.
Reference: *Detail* 2/1976, p. 175; *Deutsche Bauzeitschrift* 7/1973, p. 160

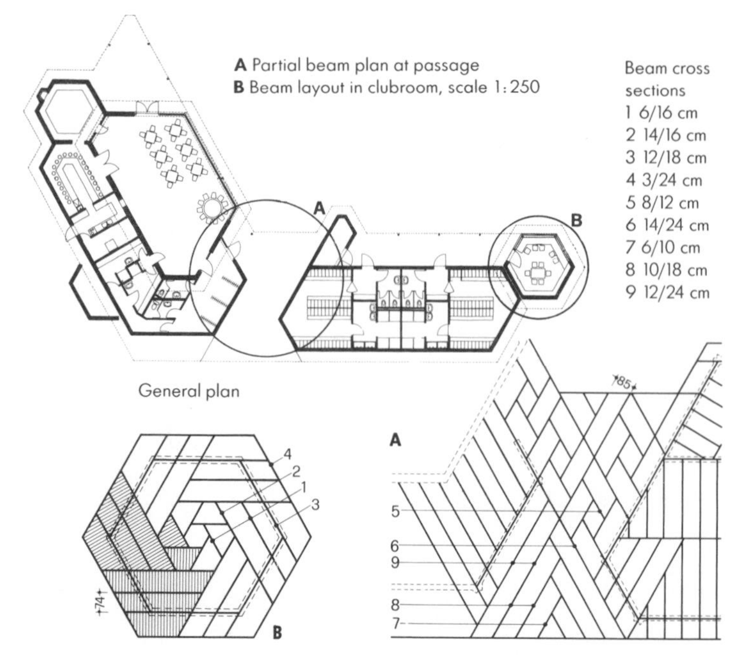

A Partial beam plan at passage
B Beam layout in clubroom, scale 1:250

General plan

Beam cross sections
1 6/16 cm
2 14/16 cm
3 12/18 cm
4 3/24 cm
5 8/12 cm
6 14/24 cm
7 6/10 cm
8 10/18 cm
9 12/24 cm

46 Exhibition Hall in Nürnberg, West Germany

Architect: Plan GmbH, Munich
Engineer: J. Natterer and K. März, Munich

Overall covered area is 60,480 m². Layout of 10 partially interconnected buildings is based on 168 equilateral triangles with 28.80 m long sides. Roof is a statically determinate system with main girders 18/190 cm spanning 28.10 m, and secondary girders 12/114 cm and 14/70 cm spanning between main girders. Because of utilities, network of 14/25 cm purlins is supported above main girders on 16/16 cm posts. A trapezoidal sheet-metal structure on an insulated roof rests on purlins. Triangular structure of girders and purlins constitutes lateral bracing and transfers loads to reinforced-concrete columns.

At bearings, horizontal loads of 120 kN are transferred to concrete support through a steel nail plate. Vertical loads of 132 kN are transferred through a steel bolt glued into laminated wood girder.

This allows column to be very slim and without cantilevered bearing seats. The 168 triangular roof components were preassembled on the ground, including purlins, and were set on columns by a mobile crane.

Reference: *Zentralblatt für Industriebau* 5/1974, p. 160; *DBZ* 6/1975, p. 149

Connections of Secondary Beams to Main Beam at 60°

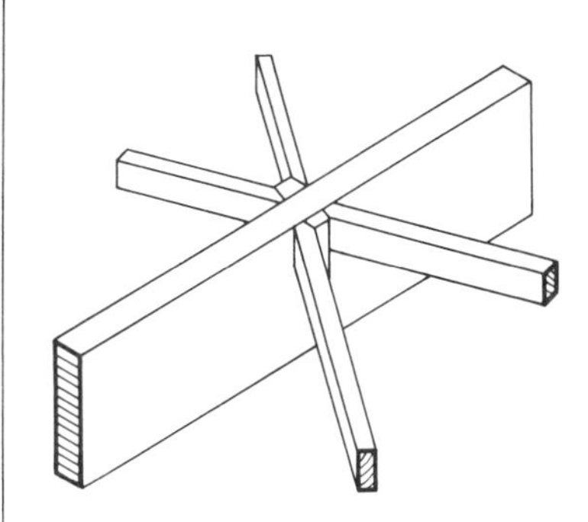

Nailed to shear-connected wood insert.

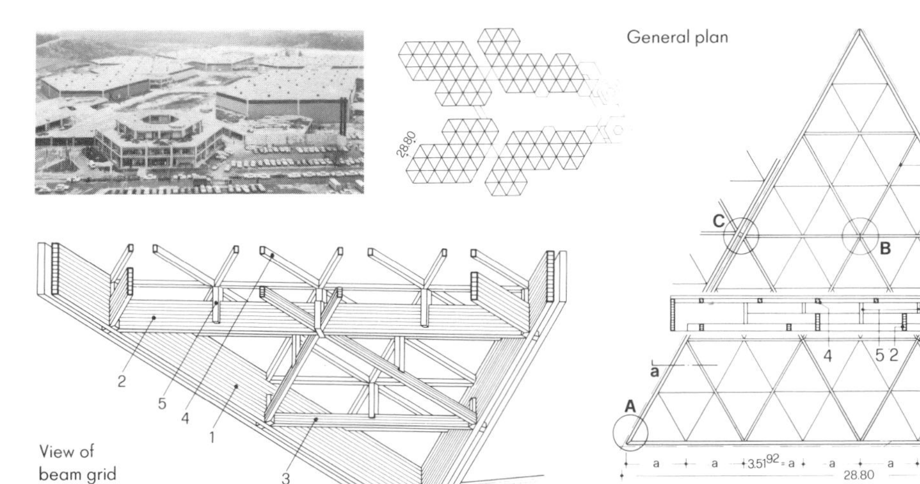

General plan

Plan and section of system

View of beam grid

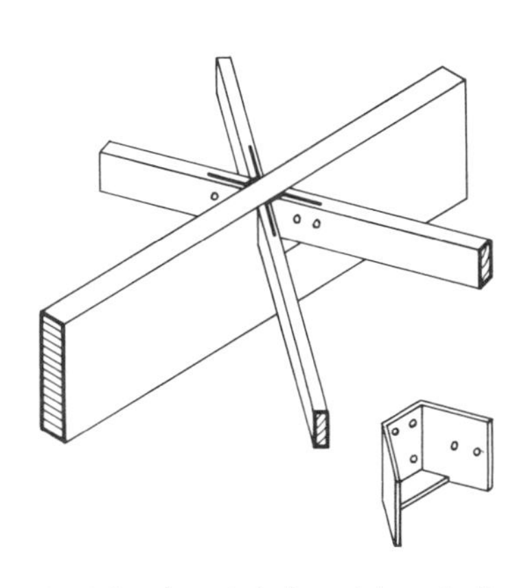

Steel plate shape bolted to main beam in slit of secondary beams.

Beam connection to column

A Bearing of main girder

1 Main girder 2 × 18/190 cm
2 Secondary girder 12/114 cm
3 Secondary girder 12/40 cm
4 Purlins 14/25 cm
5 Posts 16/16 cm
6 Connection and filler wood 20/20 cm
7 Plywood panel 5 mm
8 Shear connector ϕ 65 mm
9 Glued-in bolt
10 Bearing plate for 9
11 T shape welded to 10, grouted in pocket
12 Nail plate

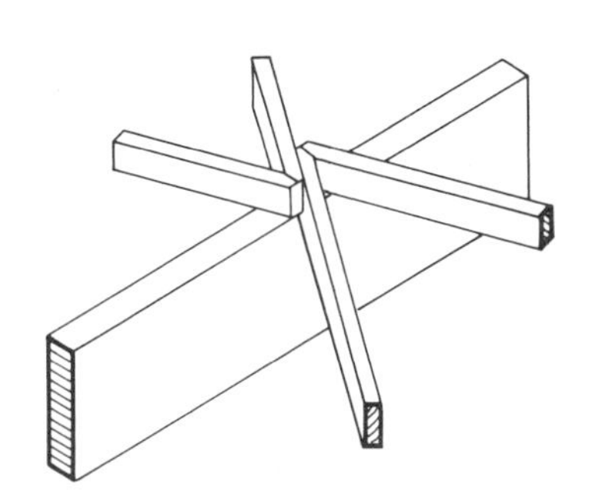

Secondary beams spliced over main beam.

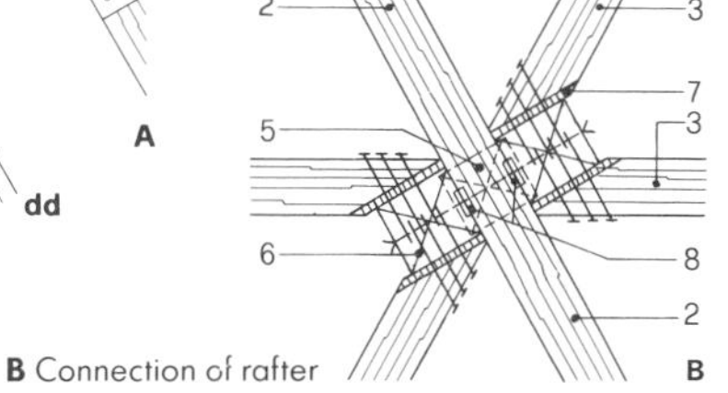

B Connection of rafter

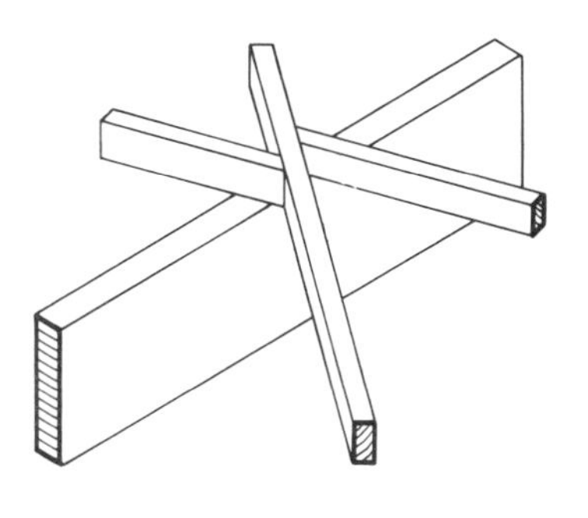

Secondary beam continuous or spliced over main beam.

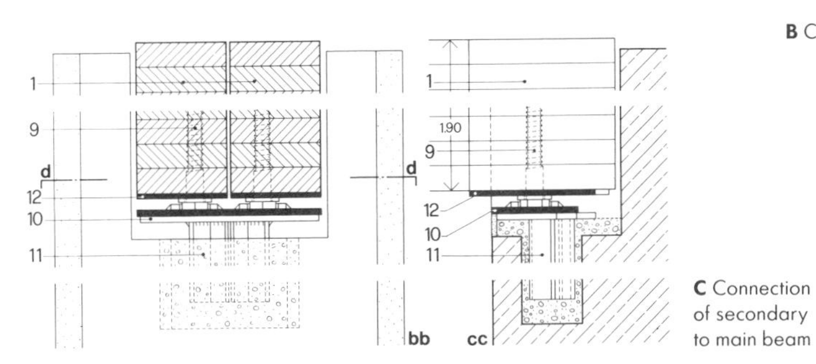

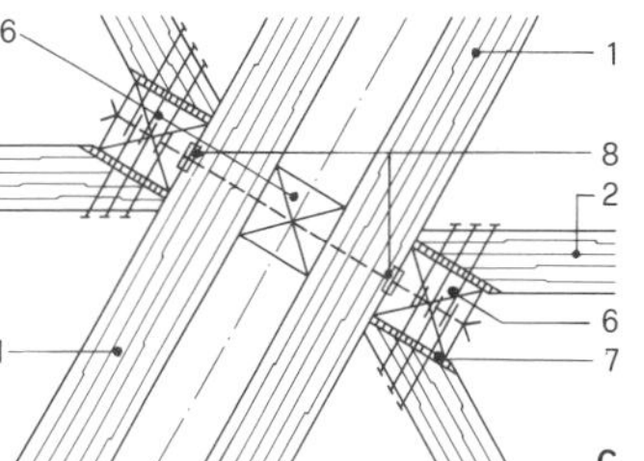

C Connection of secondary to main beam

47 Community Center in Freiburg-Landwasser, West Germany

Architect: Gruppe F 70, Freiburg
Engineer: M. Scherberger, Freiburg

Community center with main hall, cafeteria, club rooms, nursery school, and service rooms. A specific hallmark of this one-story building group is its sequence of gabled roofs. Column grid is on 7.20 × 7.20 m spacing. In area outside of main hall, main girders 14/80 cm lie under gutters. Rafters act as a three-hinged frame because there is no ridge beam. Horizontal forces resulting from uniform vertical loads cancel out over columns. One-sided loads and horizontal loads in end bays are transferred to columns by means of truss works lying within plan of roof. Steel ties in column line take up these horizontal loads from one end of the building to the other. Wind loads in both directions are taken by fixity of columns. In area of main hall there are main girders on every column line at 3.60 m spanning entire hall.

Purlins span parallel to main girders. Girders in main hall are 14/100 cm, elsewhere 14/80 cm. Rafters are 6/20 cm. Columns are double. Connection to girders is with ϕ 190 mm shear connectors. Purlins and rafters are connected with sheet metal anchors. Horizontal steel ties are flat steel shapes. Trussing in roof plane is by planks 2.4/12 to 22 cm.
Reference: *d-extrakt* 14, p. 16.

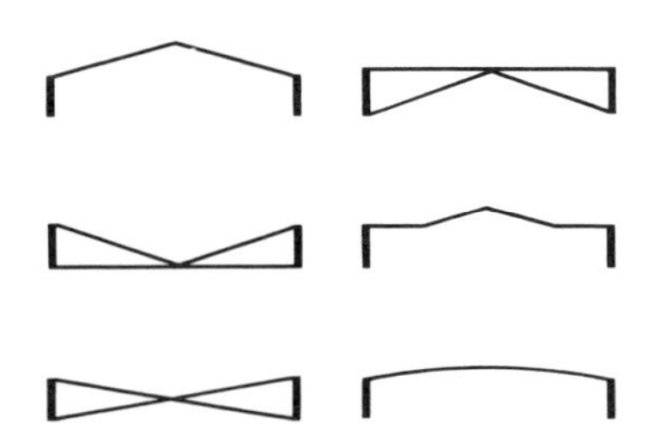

Bent, curved, or composite secondary beam systems allow the use of various structural configurations.

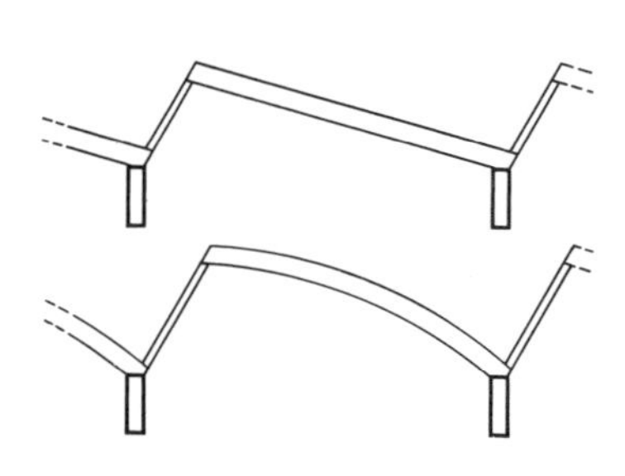

Secondary system in the form of a three-hinged frame with straight or curved members creates a shed roof.

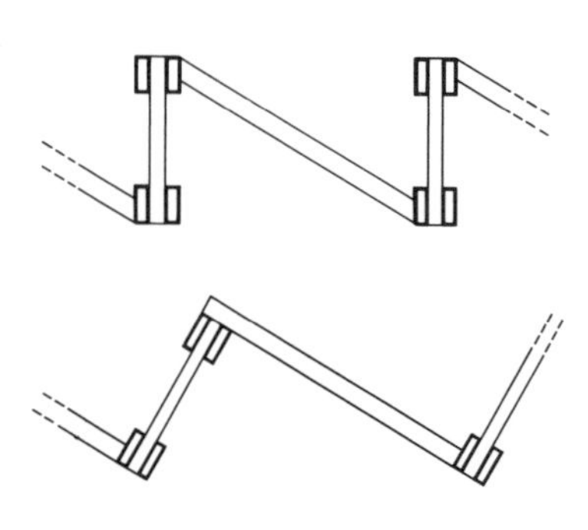

Inclined secondary members with vertical or inclined main girder systems represent a transition to folded roof concepts. (See pages 158 and 159.)

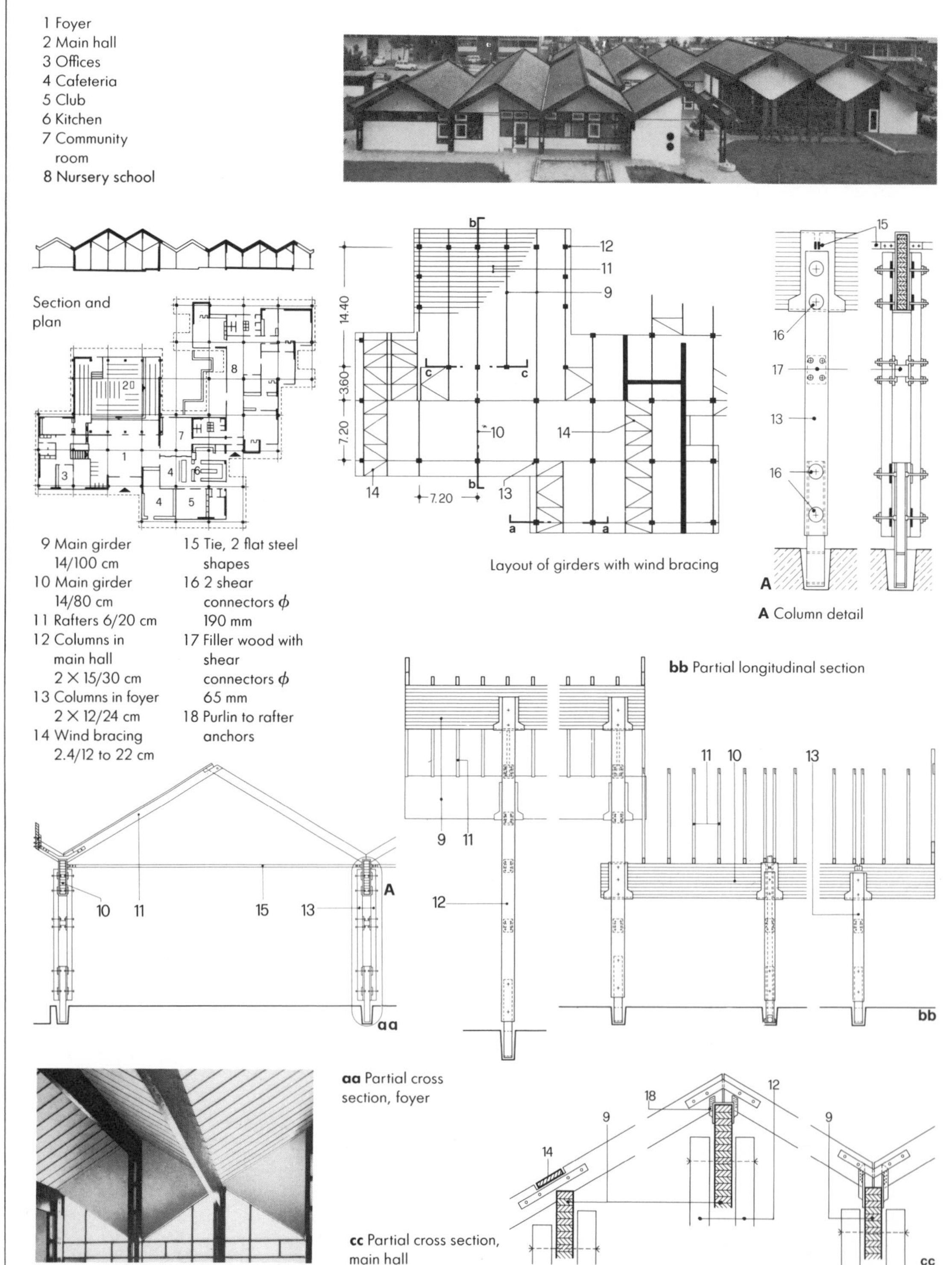

Section and plan

Layout of girders with wind bracing

A Column detail

bb Partial longitudinal section

aa Partial cross section, foyer

cc Partial cross section, main hall

48 Lumber Yard Roof in Essen-Werden, West Germany

Architect: F. Gildemeier
Engineer: Timber Construction Contractor

Main girders of laminated wood 16/100 cm, spaced at 10 m, span 12 m between reinforced-concrete fixed columns transverse to building and cantilever 6 m at each end. Roof shape is achieved through diagonally crossed secondary beams 12/25 cm, which are sloped at 14° between top flange of main girder and the 16/16 cm lower flange, suspended on tie rods ϕ 16 mm. Secondary beams are joined at intersecting point through finger jointing. The crossing forms an intermediate support which reduces the span. In addition, crossed beams act as diagonal bracing and create sloped roof surfaces.
Reference: *Detail* 1/1977, illustrations

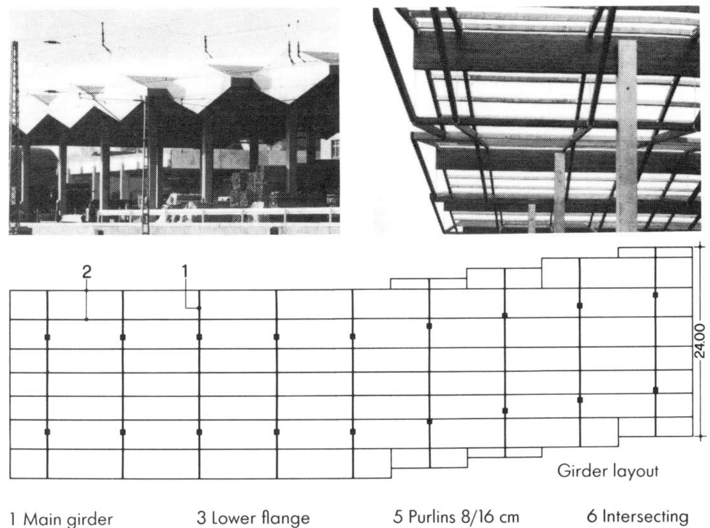

Girder layout

1 Main girder 16/100 cm
2 Crossed secondary beams 12/25 cm
3 Lower flange 16/16 cm
4 Suspension rod for lower flange ϕ 16 mm
5 Purlins 8/16 cm resting on metal beam seats support 25 mm plywood panels
6 Intersecting point, finger-jointed

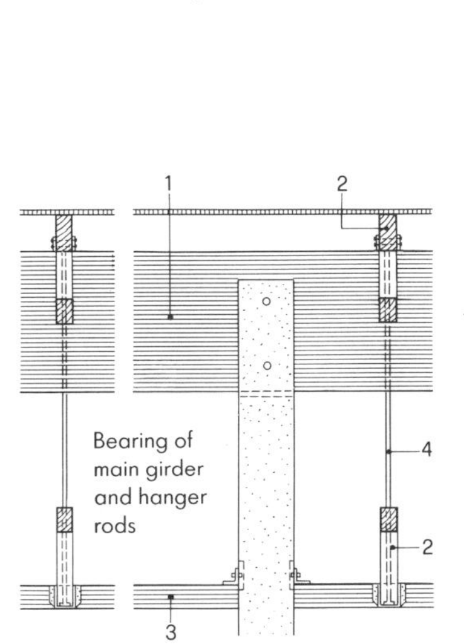

Bearing of main girder and hanger rods

Longitudinal section

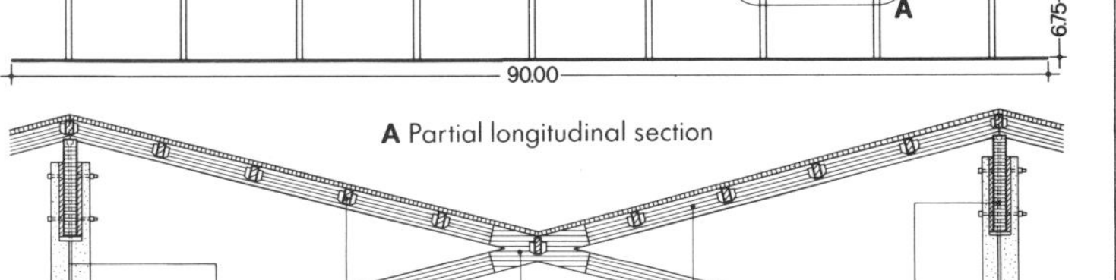

A Partial longitudinal section

49 Research Laboratory in Vancouver, Canada

Architect: R. J. Thom
Engineer: J. O. McCatcheon

Research laboratory for plywood products has a main hall and mezzanine. Outside dimensions 18.00 × 41.00 m, height of roof 7.00 m. The exterior characteristics of this building are its hip roofs made from triangular and trapezoidal plate elements. These elements consist of 19 mm plywood on wood frames 10/10 or 10/15 cm, exterior insulation, and a plastic coating as exterior water proofing. Spacial configuration stiffens the roof. Main girders are transverse and consist of a combination of laminated wood and timber (spans 18.00 m, spaced at 4.50 m). They are freely supported on concrete columns.
Reference: *Wood* 12/1962, p. 476

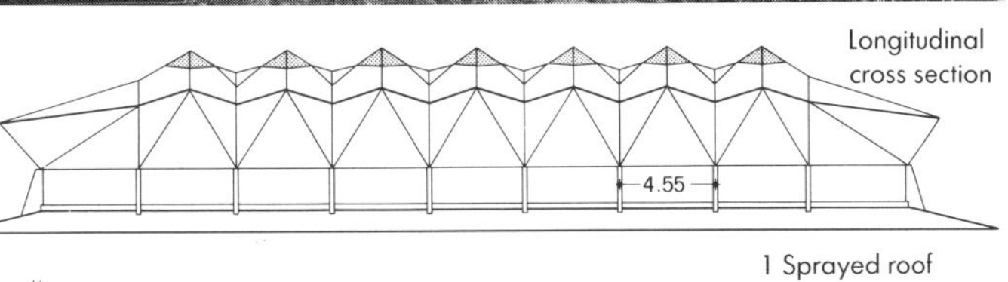

Longitudinal cross section

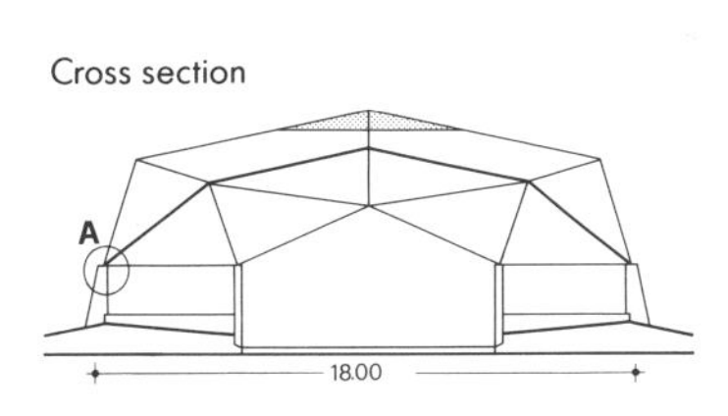

Cross section

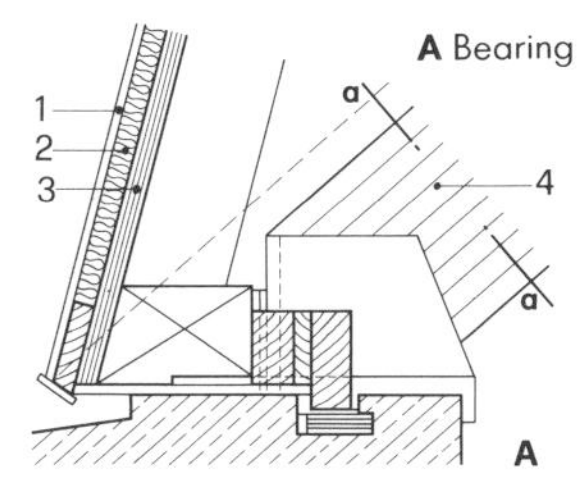

A Bearing

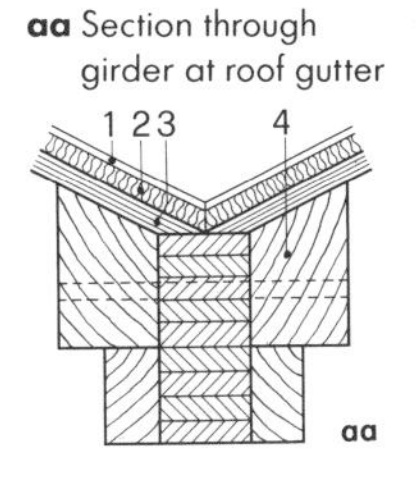

aa Section through girder at roof gutter

1 Sprayed roof coating
2 Hard-foam insulation
3 Plywood 19 mm
4 Connection section laminated wood 10/20 cm, solid lumber 2 × 5/10 and 2 × 10/15 cm

Secondary Beam Alternatives

Single-piece secondary beam on main girder.

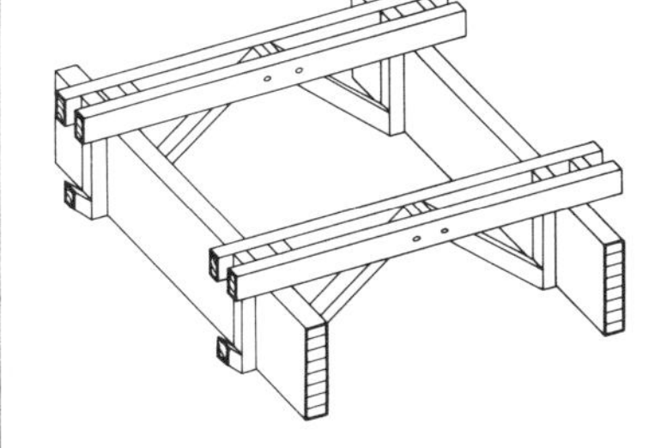

Double secondary beam with K-shaped struts as intermediate supports.

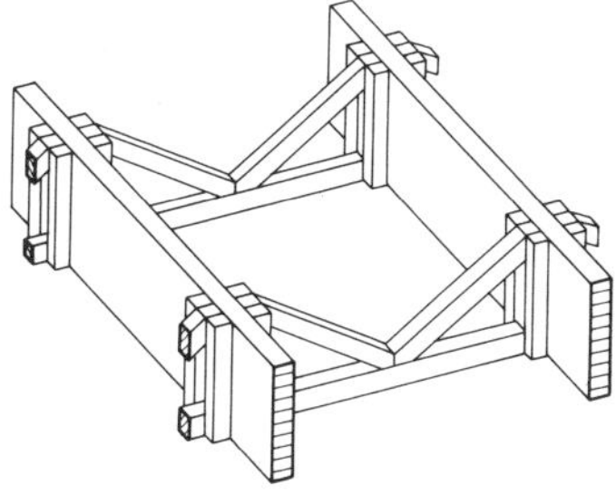

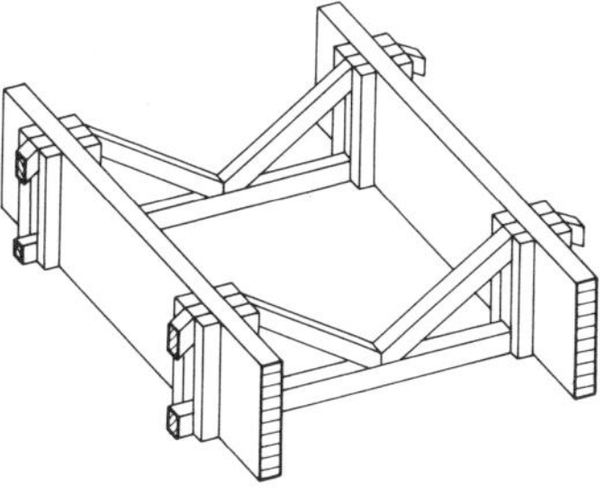

Gutter between main girders. K-shaped secondary beams on straight lower beams.

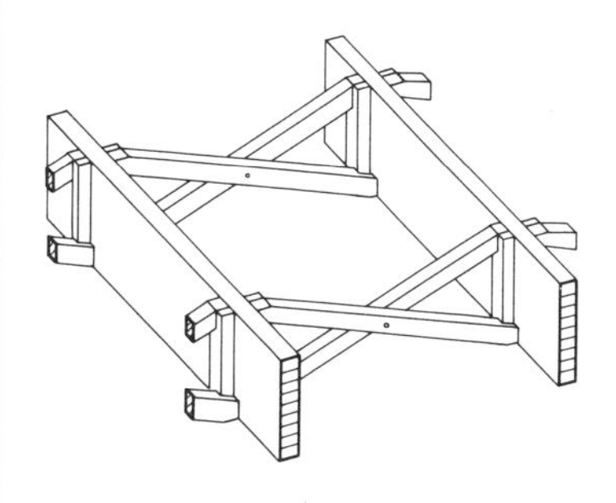

Gutter between main girders, crossed secondary beams.

Cantilever beams are statically determinate beams fixed at one end. The fixed end moment is resolved into a force couple and is taken up by compression and tension members. These members must be designed for both compression and tension because the dead load of the cantilever is generally smaller than the wind uplift. The design is governed by bending and shear forces at the fixed end, and by vertical displacements at the free end due to wind.

Laminated wood cantilevers
$a = 3$ to 8 m (spacing)
$l = 5$ to 20 m
$h = l/8$ to $l/10$ (depth of beam)

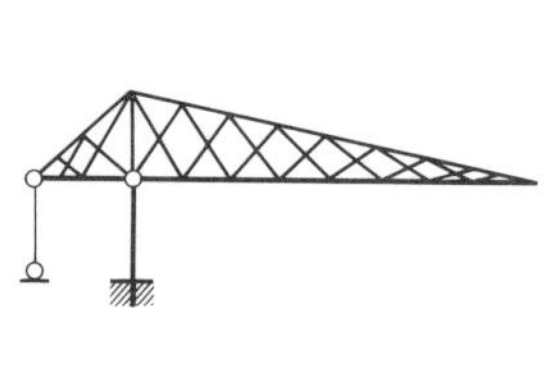

Truss cantilevers
$a = 6$ to 12 m
$l = 10$ to 40 m
$h = l/4$ to $l/6$

50 Grandstand in Krefeld, West Germany

Engineer: A. Grage, Herford

Girders for grandstand and columns are reinforced concrete. Roof cantilevers 28.90 m and is supported by timber box girders with glued flanges varying from 70/100 to 70/248 cm. Depending on bending moment, box girder has two or three webs.

1 Cantilever box girder 70/100 to 248 cm, webs and flanges 18.5 cm glulam
2 Lapped purlins 6/22 to 16/25 cm
3 Wind bracing, steel ϕ 16 to 42 mm, St 37
4 Lateral bracing, steel ϕ 48 mm, St 52
5 Flanges 18.5/70 cm
6 Web 18.5 cm
7 Connection holes for lateral bracing
8 Diagonal bracing ϕ 38 mm
9 Flange bracing steel IPB 180
10 3 tension rods ϕ 26.5 mm, St 80/105
11 IPB 180 for connecting tension rods

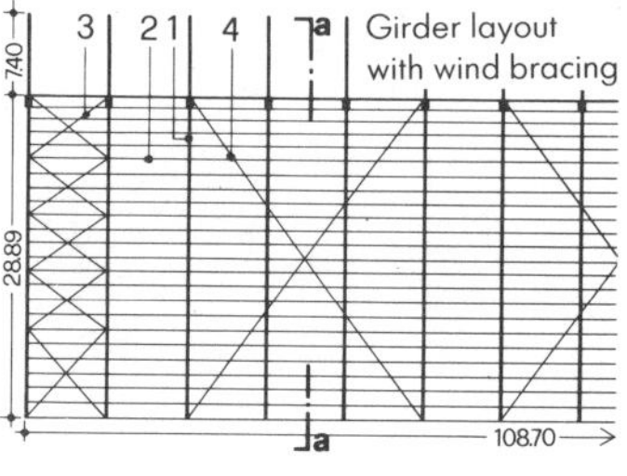

Girder layout with wind bracing

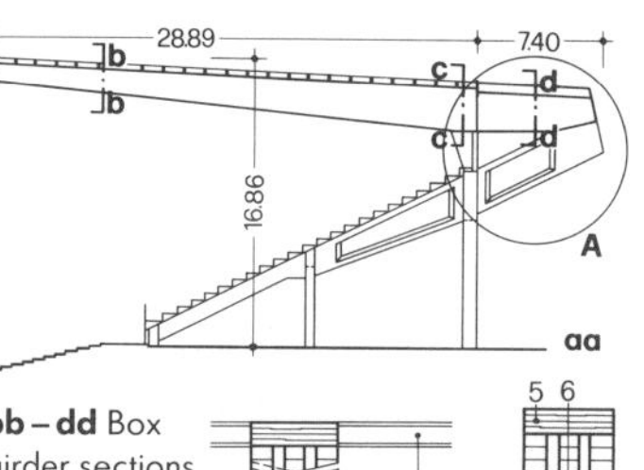

aa Cross section

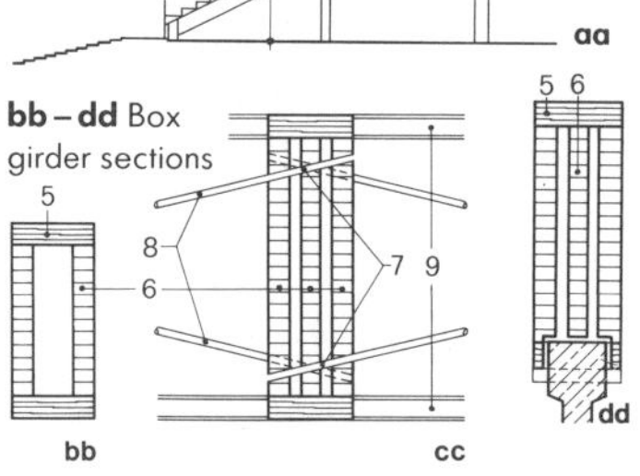

bb – dd Box girder sections

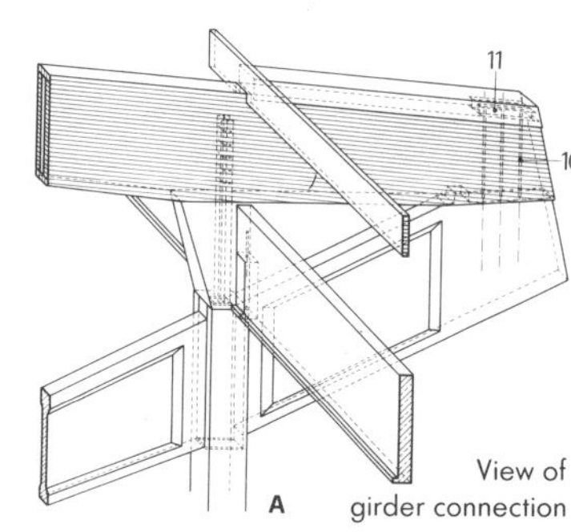

View of girder connection

51 Grandstand in Dielsdorf, Switzerland

Architect: Th. Laubi, Zurich
Engineer: M. P. Kämpf, Rupperswil

Grandstand for 1200 spectators at race track. Roof cantilevers 10.30 m and is supported by 15 glue-laminated wood girders, which rest on columns and are anchored in rear to a tension–compression post. Laminated wood girders are 16 cm wide and vary in depth from 30 cm at cantilever end to 120 cm at support. Compression column has I cross section and serves as support for a laminated girder supporting the bleachers. Tension columns are double, with filler wood. Connections are steel dowels and safety bolts.

Lapped purlins are 10/16 cm, spaced at 1.20 m, placed longitudinally. Roofing is corrugated asbestos-cement sheeting. Roof is braced horizontally with 6/14 cm diagonal planks, connected to main girders with nailed gusset plates.

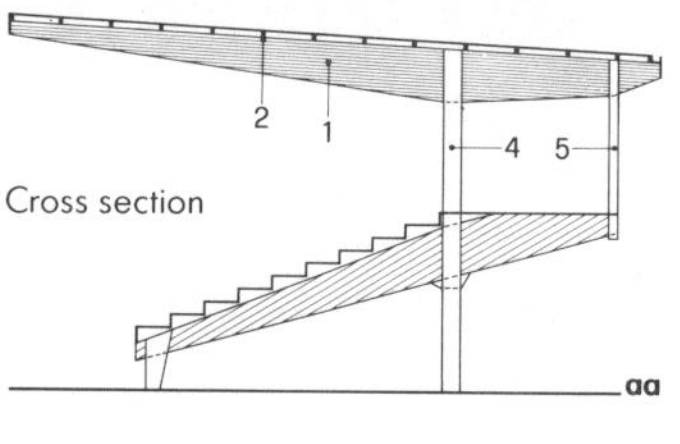

Cross section

1 Cantilever girder 16/30 to 120 cm
2 Lapped purlins 8/16 to 16/16 cm
3 Wind bracing 6/14 cm
4 Column I shape, 2 × 10/44 + 2 × 12/18 cm
5 Column I shape, 2 × 10/20 + 2 × 12/8 cm
6 Steel dowels ϕ 20 mm
7 Gusset plates, 35 mm plywood
8 Nails 5/130
9 Shear connectors ϕ 95 mm

Girder layout

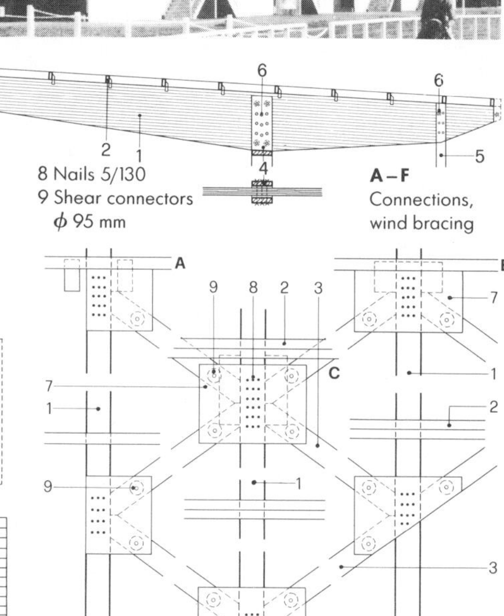

A – F Connections, wind bracing

52 Grandstand in Munich-Riem, West Germany

Architect: Atelier Kleineichenhausen
Engineer: Rüter, Minden

The feature of this grandstand for 7000 spectators is a variable slope of cantilevers, which form a saddle-shaped surface. Each one of 25 laminated wood cantilevers is up to 2.52 m deep and spans up to 27.00 m. They rest on twin compression and tension columns and are connected with steel dowels ϕ 24 mm for a maximum tensile force of 560 kN and compressive load of 1180 kN. Lateral bracing of deep girders is given by wood plank diaphragms at the ends and centers of the cantilevers, and at column lines. Wind and lateral bracing is provided by steel shapes IPB 100 placed diagonally.

Wind forces are transferred to foundation by frames between columns consisting of vertical steel shapes IPB 140 and diagonal steel tubes 90 × 90 × 9 mm.
Reference: *Detail* 4/1972, p. 727

1 Cantilever girder 3 × 14.5/130 to 252 cm
2 Purlins 16/22 cm
3 Wind bracing IPB 100
4 Compression column 43.5/120 cm, triple
5 Tension column 43.5/64 cm, triple
6 Steel dowels ϕ 24 mm
7 Tightening bolts ϕ 16 mm

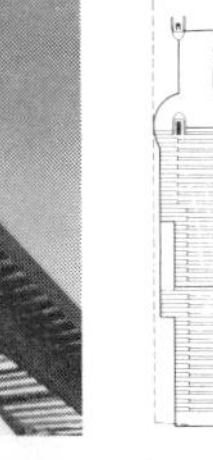

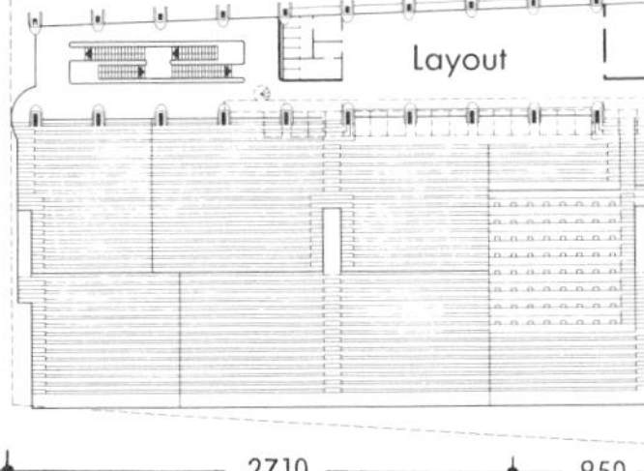

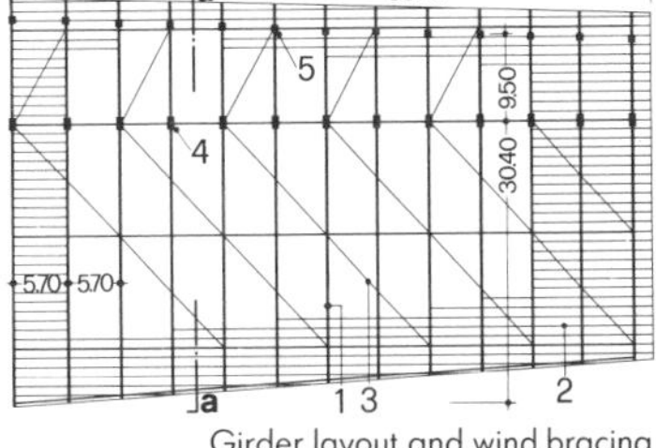

Girder layout and wind bracing

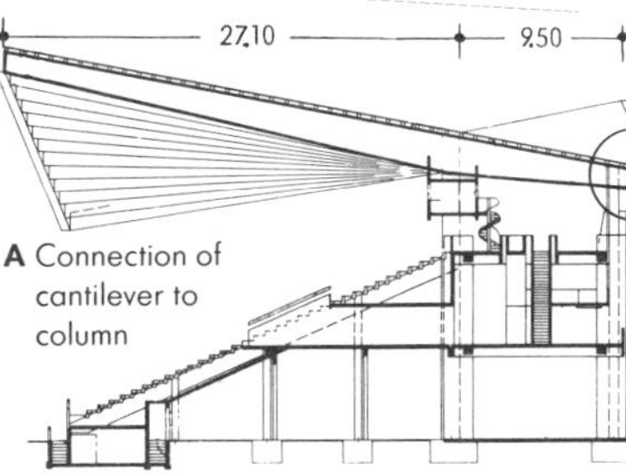

A Connection of cantilever to column

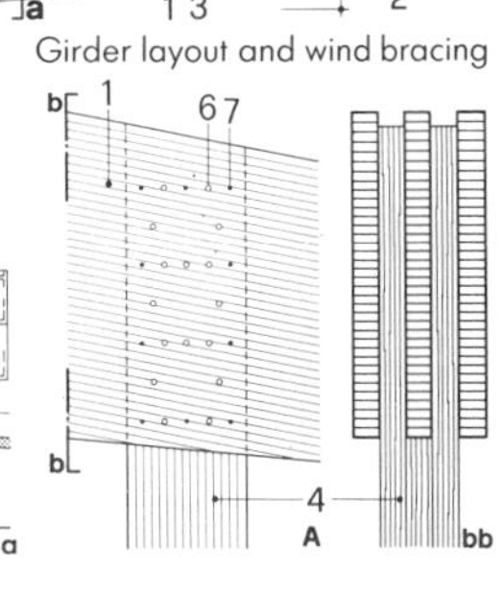

53 Loading Shed in Boulogne, France

Engineer: G. Dubrulle, Boulogne

Cantilever roof for a shipping pier. Cantilevered main girders span 13.00 m and rest on reinforced concrete columns spaced at 13.30 m. Tension and compression connections are made with steel channel sections and shear connectors. Purlins 6.5/18 cm, connected by steel angles, run longitudinally and are braced at midspan.

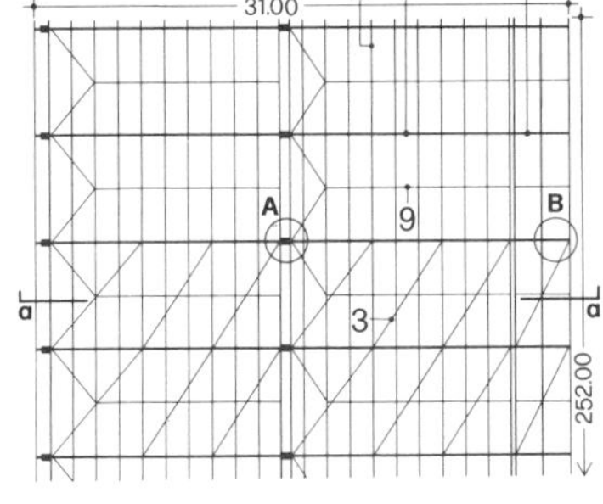

Girder layout and wind bracing

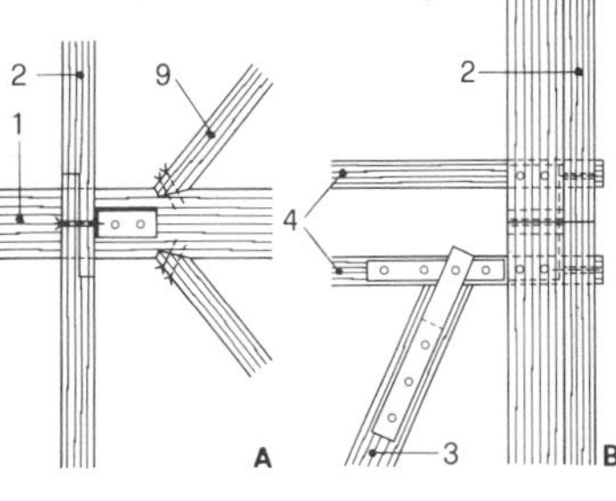

1 Cantilevered girder 16.6/39 to 168 cm
2 Purlins 6.5/18 cm
3 Wind bracing 6.5/6.5 to 6.5/11 cm
4 Front roof beam 2 × 6.5/53.5 to 79 cm
5 Reinforced-concrete column
6 Shear connector ϕ 95 mm
7 Shear connector ϕ 128 mm
8 Steel dowels and bolts ϕ 20 mm
9 Lateral bracing for rafters 6.5/11 cm

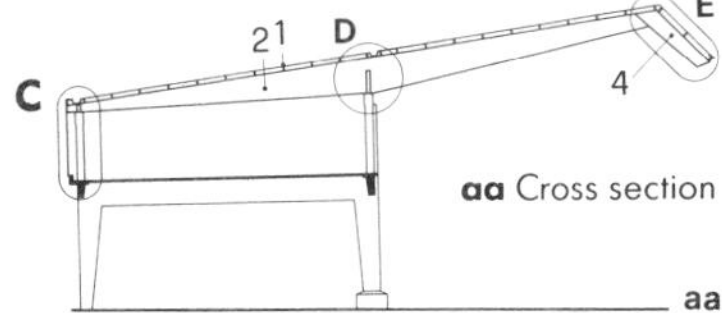

aa Cross section

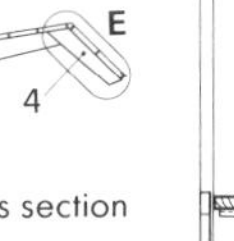

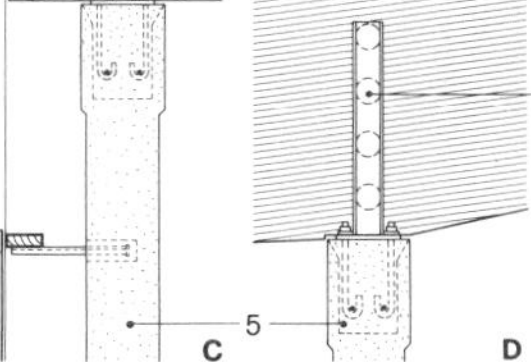

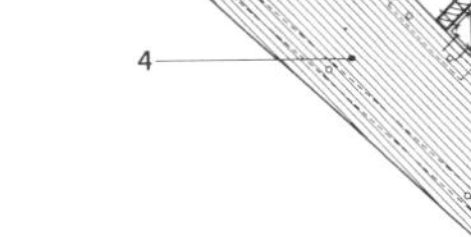

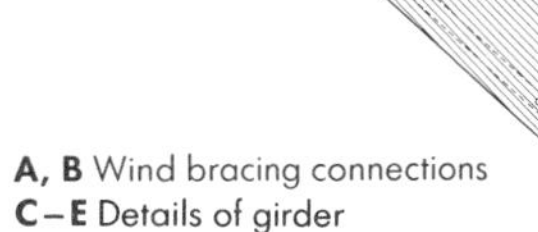

A, B Wind bracing connections
C–E Details of girder

Main Girder with Lateral Bracing and Secondary Beams

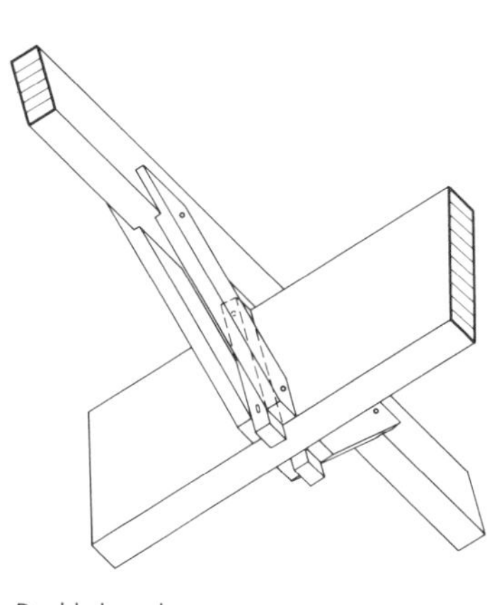

Double knee brace

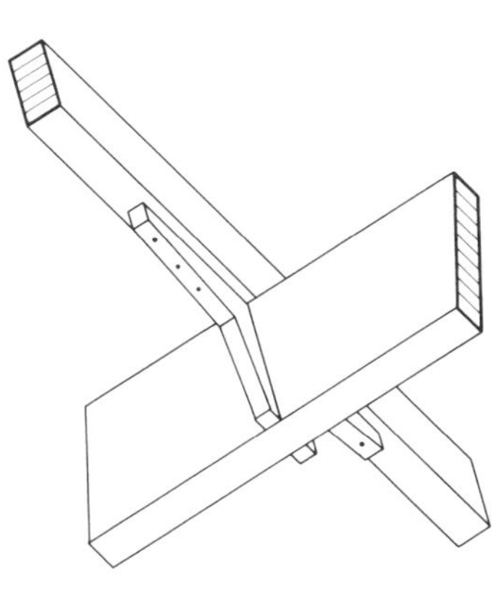

Finger-jointed timber angle

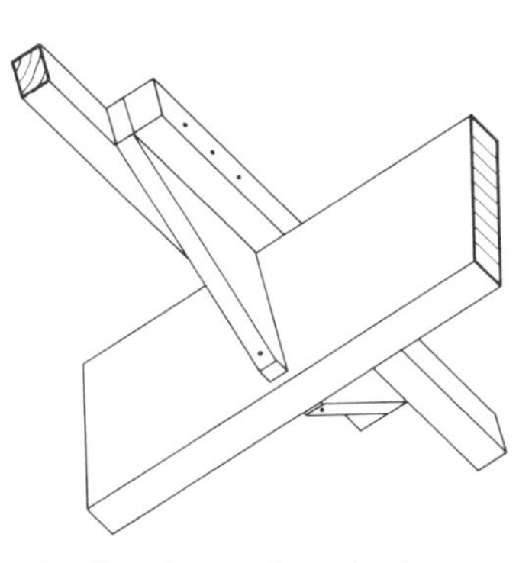

Web stiffener between lapped purlins

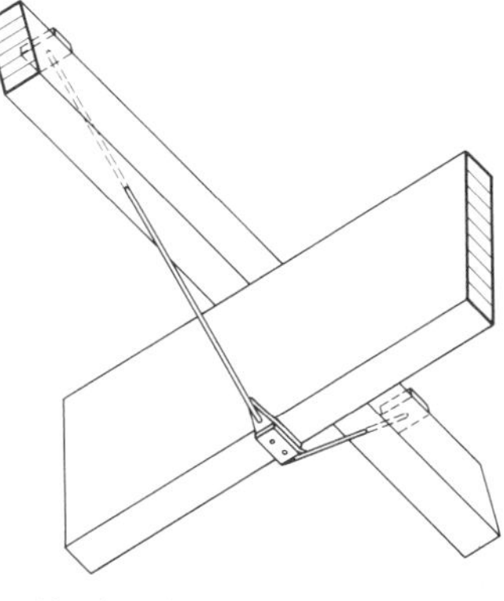

Steel bar knee brace

Cantilever beams can be built also as frames with one elbow. The frame is fixed at the base or is braced. The elbow frame may be rigid or braced. (See also pages 130 to 138, Frames.)

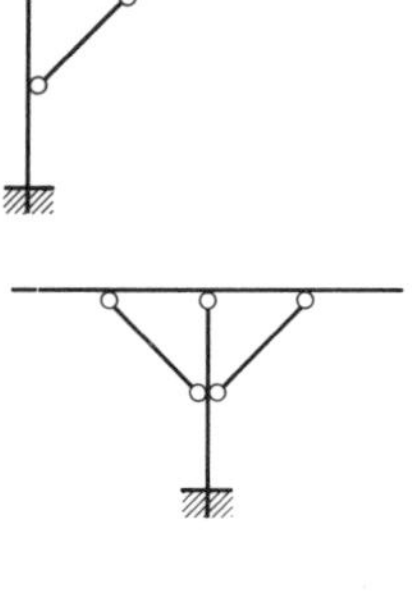

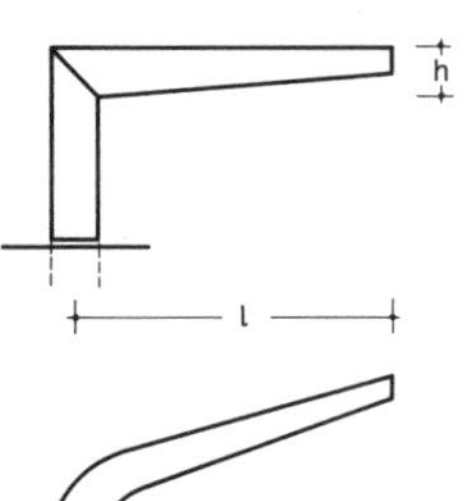

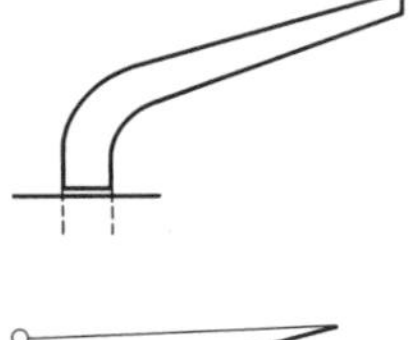

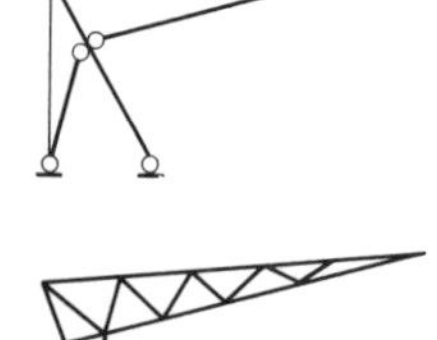

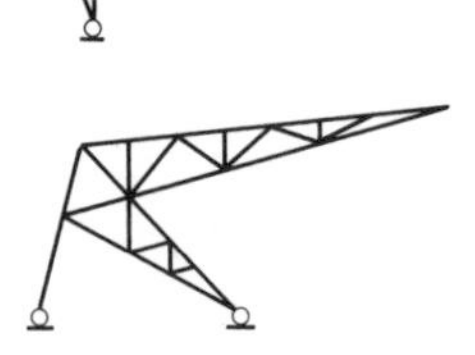

a = 3 to 6 m (spacing)
l = 5 to 20 m
h = l/5 to l/10

54 Olympic Cycling Stadium in Munich, West Germany

Architects and engineers: Beier, Dahms, Grube, Harden, Kaiser, and Laskowski, Braunschweig
Structural consultation: J. Natterer Munich

Roof for a cycling track and grandstand for 4700 spectators (1972 Munich Olympic Games). 56 elbow frames cantilevering from 11.00 to 24.00 m and spaced at 6.00 m surround cycling track. Each frame consists of a lower and an upper member. The lower one supports the grandstand and rests on circular reinforced-concrete beams, the upper one supports the roof. Each frame consists of 16 to 23 cm wide double girders, 140 to 220 cm deep at fixed end and 60 cm deep at free end. Upper and lower girders are connected by a triple compression strut and by a rear tension member, thus forming a frame. The tension member consists of steel boxes and adjustable tension bars. Load transfer between wood members occurs through steel nail plates and bolts. Connection of compression strut is also through steel plates and bolts in order to obtain true pin connections and provide for cantilever adjustment.

Lateral and wind bracing of roof is obtained by web plates 10 cm thick and up to 2.40 m deep, placed between frames at compression struts. Steel tubes provide bracing in cantilever.
Reference: *Detail* 4/1972, illustrations

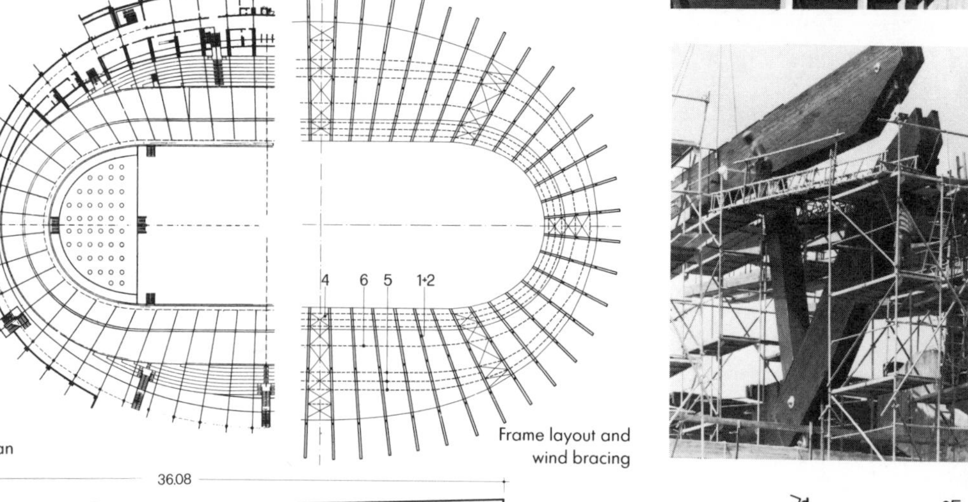

Half-plan

Frame layout and wind bracing

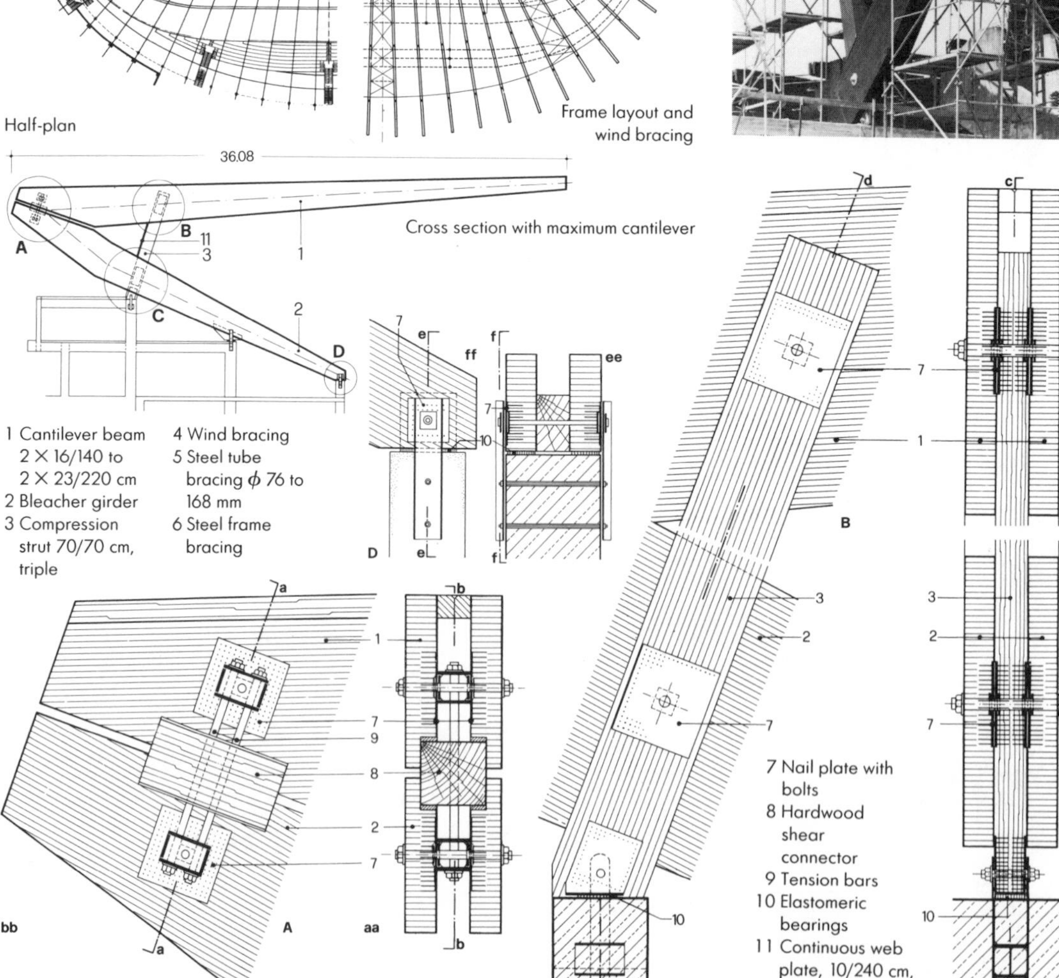

1 Cantilever beam 2 × 16/140 to 2 × 23/220 cm
2 Bleacher girder
3 Compression strut 70/70 cm, triple
4 Wind bracing
5 Steel tube bracing ϕ 76 to 168 mm
6 Steel frame bracing
7 Nail plate with bolts
8 Hardwood shear connector
9 Tension bars
10 Elastomeric bearings
11 Continuous web plate, 10/240 cm, for bracing

A – D Frame connections

55 Grandstand in Metz, France

Architect: L. Feher and B. Beau, Paris

Grandstand roof for spectators at a sports field. Girders cantilevering 16.00 m have dimensions 13.5/35 to 122 cm and rest on framed supports. They are anchored in the rear with steel members IPB 140. Framed timber supports have I section and are rigidly connected to girder with ϕ 90 mm shear connectors. Vertical bracing is round steel bars, horizontal bracing in roof plane is lumber 7/10.5 cm.

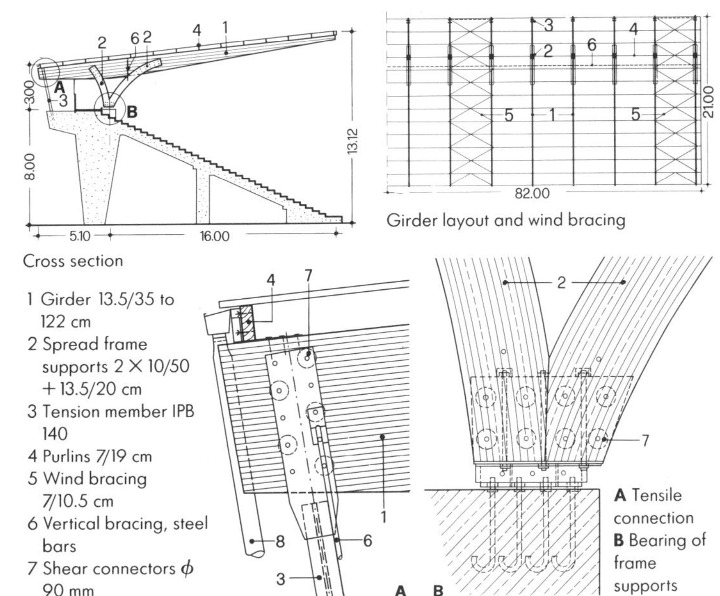

Cross section

Girder layout and wind bracing

1 Girder 13.5/35 to 122 cm
2 Spread frame supports 2 × 10/50 + 13.5/20 cm
3 Tension member IPB 140
4 Purlins 7/19 cm
5 Wind bracing 7/10.5 cm
6 Vertical bracing, steel bars
7 Shear connectors ϕ 90 mm
8 Roof drainage

A Tensile connection
B Bearing of frame supports

56 Church in Lech, Austria

Architect: R. Ostertag, Stuttgart
Engineer: J. Natterer, Munich

Interior of this church is dominated by exposed, double girders, 1.86 m high. This depth, large for roof girders spanning 20.00 m and spaced at 4.33 m, is determined by a snow load equal to 10 kN/m². A statically determinate four-hinged frame was selected because of this high snow load. Structure braced transversely and longitudinally against horizontal and vertical loads by steel trussing in roof and in outer walls. Hinges in frame prevent any secondary stresses from developing as a result of rotation under high loads. A main girder and the mezzanine girder at the valley are supported by a fascia girder (4) because there is no column at the bend.
Reference: *Baumeister* 3/1977, p. 253

1 Main girder 2 × 20/186 cm
2 Column 20/100 cm
3 Column 2 × 17/120 cm
4 Fascia girder 2 × 18/180 cm for support of valley girder
5 Cantilever of mezzanine
6 Mezzanine support 20/85 cm with hinge bolts and slotted holes
7 Wind bracing in roof plane, flat steel 12/130 mm
8 Vertical bracing
9 Connection plate, fascia girder, and hanger bar
10 Nail plate
11 Bolts ϕ 55 to 185 mm
12 Spacer pipe

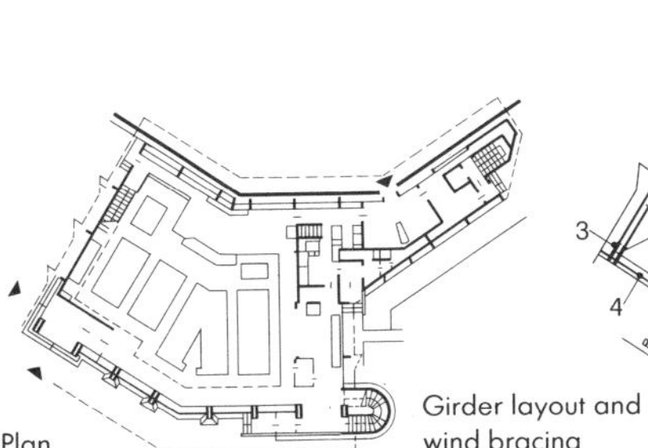

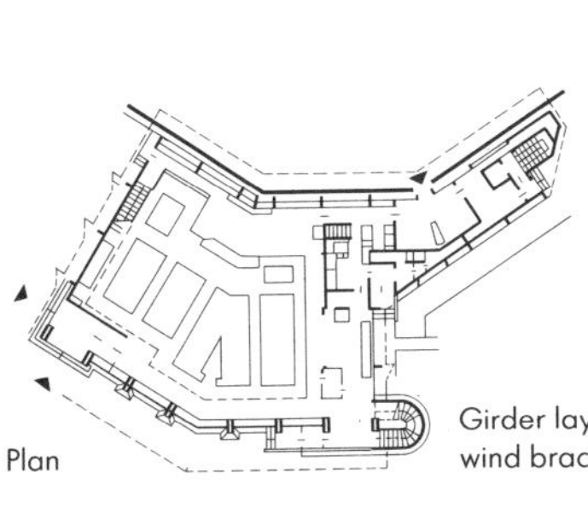

Plan

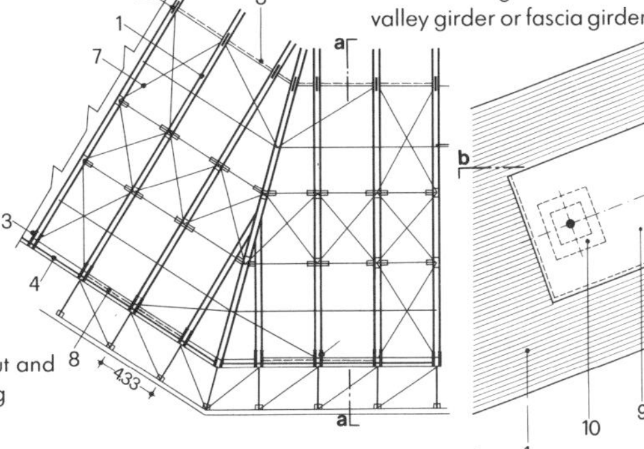

Girder layout and wind bracing

A Detail of hanger bar and valley girder or fascia girder

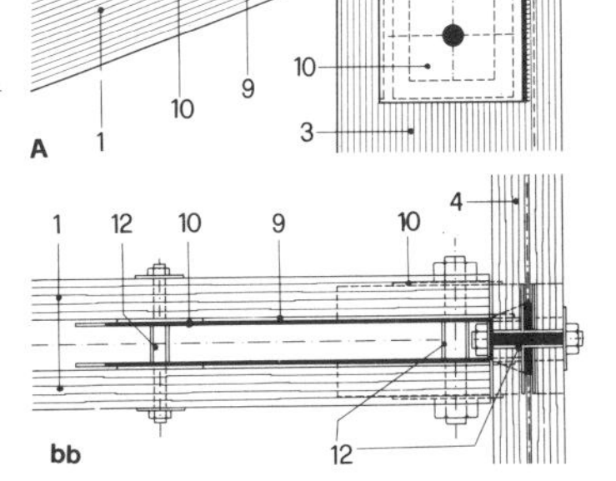

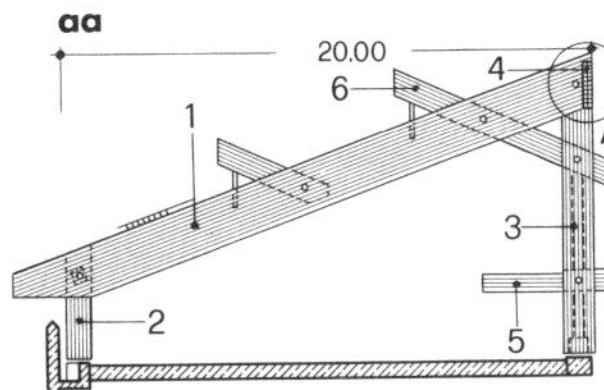

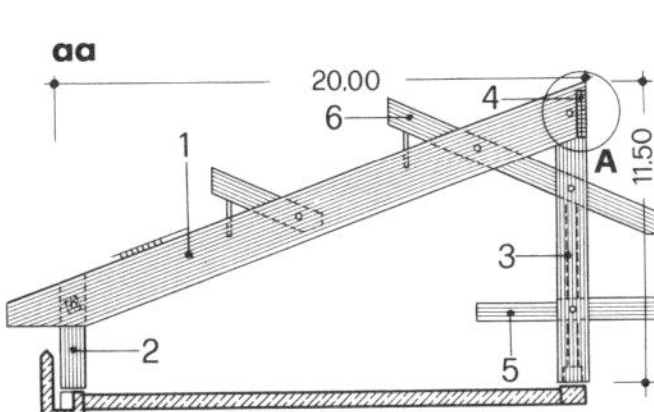

Columns Fixed in Concrete Foundation

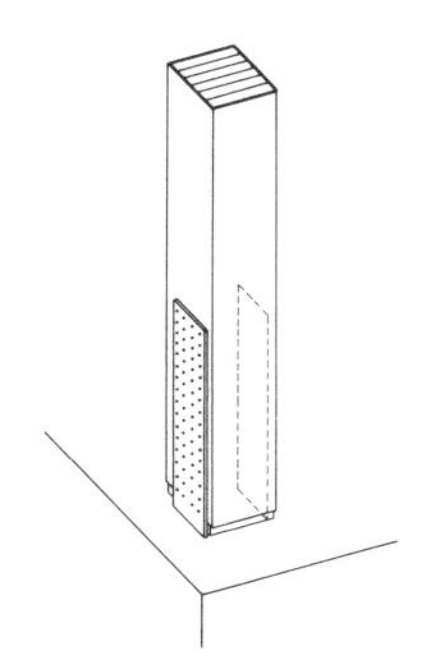

Steel plates nailed sidewise.

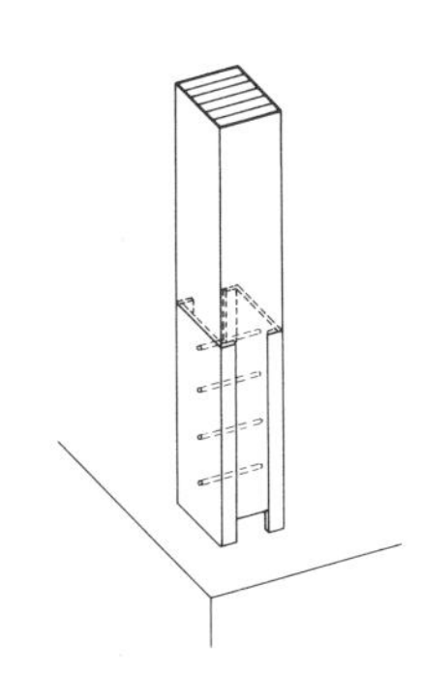

Steel U shapes nailed sidewise as fixed support in two directions.

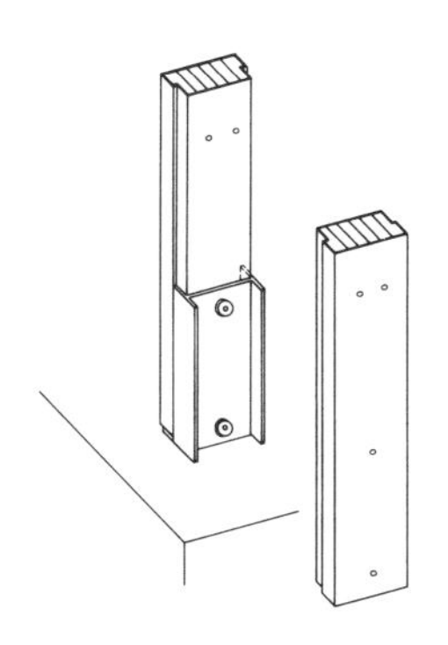

Interior I shape for double column.

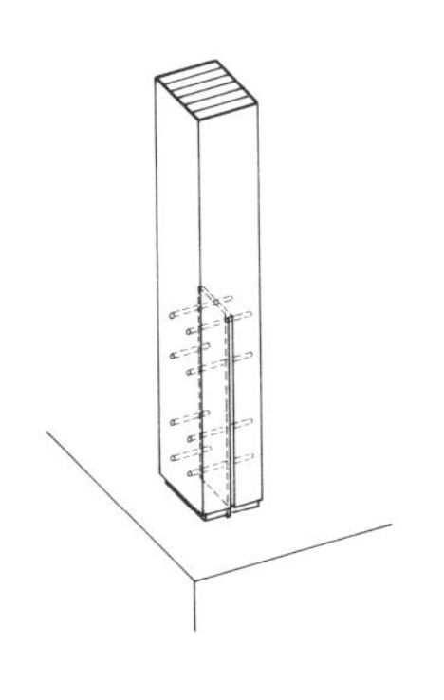

Doweled steel web in column slit.

Continuous beams with hinges are multispan beams which are hinged together in certain spans. These hinges can transfer only beam reactions but no bending moments. This results in zero moment at the hinges. An arrangement of moments suited to the available depth and length of beams is possible through an appropriate layout of hinges. If the number of hinges is 2 less than the number of supports, the beam is determinate. The size of beam is governed, as in single-span or cantilever girders, by the bending moment, the shear, the deflection, and the dimensions of the hinges.

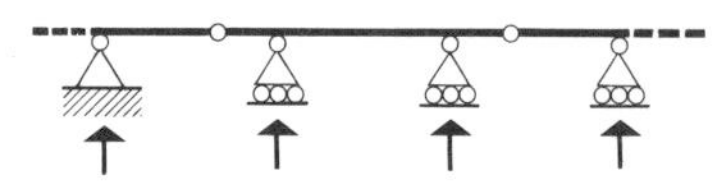

Bearing reactions are the same as for single beams

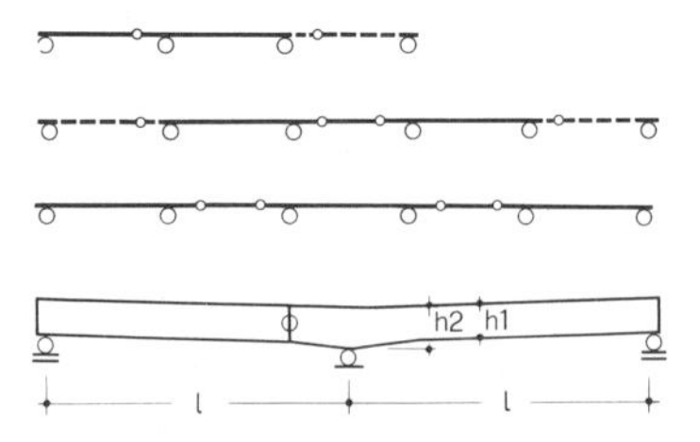

For solid timber
a = 0.5 to 1.5 m (spacing)
l = 4 to 8 m

For laminated wood
a = 2 to 6 m
l = 10 to 30 m
$h_1 = l/24$
$h_2 = l/16$
Haunch slope ≤ 1:8

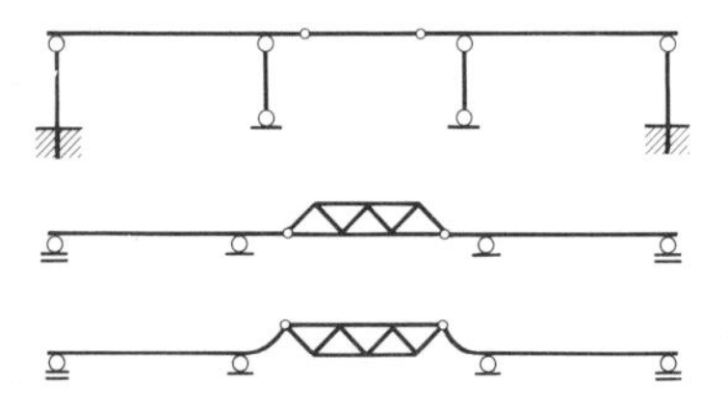

Suspended beams are often used in multibay buildings; the type of suspended beam varies.

57 Industrial Building, West Germany

Engineer: Rüter, Minden

Floor area 27,000 m². Hinged beams over four bays span transversely; one interior field has two hinges, the other has one. One-piece girders are haunched at columns. Outer columns are solid lumber, interior ones are laminated wood, double, fixed at the bottom, and connected to girder with two rows of shear connectors. Roofing is trapezoidal sheet-metal decking with insulation and no purlins, spanning 6.25 m between girders. In each sixth or seventh bay there is diagonal bracing of crossed flat steel bars, working together with sheet-metal roofing.
Reference: *Bauen mit Holz* 12/1968

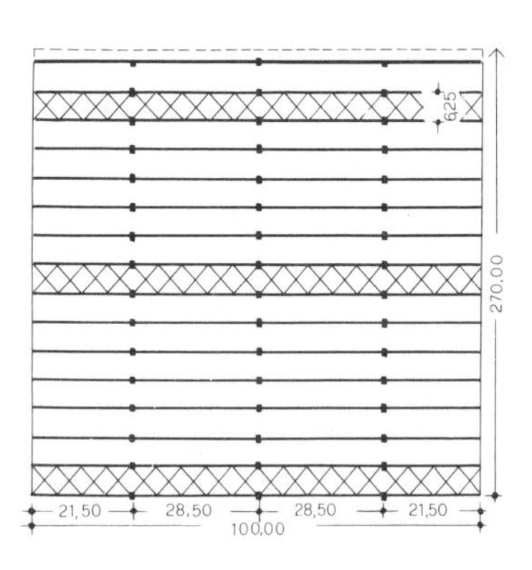

Partial cross section

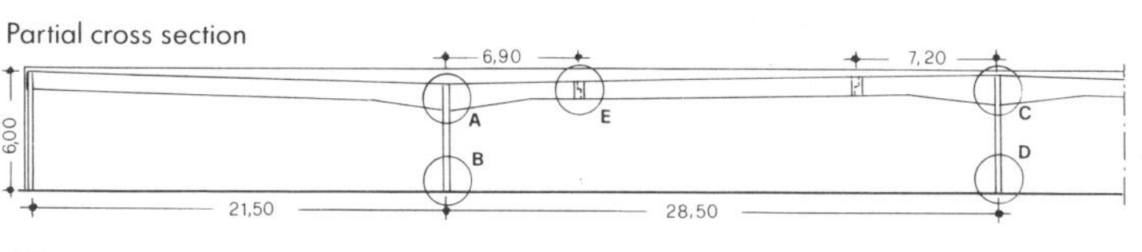

E Hinge

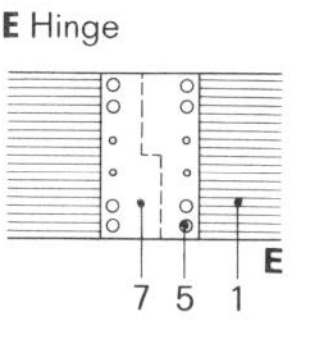

1 Girder 14/85 cm, at column 14/145 cm
2 Column 2 × 13/40 cm
3 Column 2 × 13/26 cm
4 Shear connections ϕ 80 mm in columns at 1/3 points
5 Shear connector ϕ 65 mm
6 Shear connector ϕ 80 mm
7 Steel plate 6 mm
B Column, fixed at base
D Base of hinged column

A, C Connection of girder to column

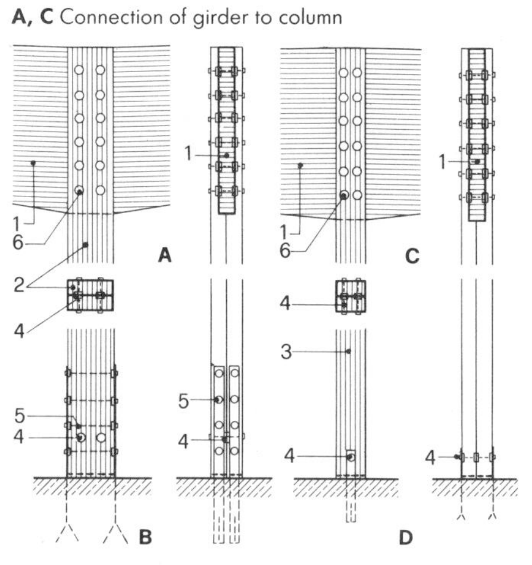

58 Storage Shed in Dorsten, West Germany

Engineer: Rüter, Minden

Floor area 13,000 m² divided into three parts by reinforced-concrete walls. Continuous girders 12/71 cm, haunched at columns. Spacing at 6.60 m, span 18.30 m, but 15.20 m in end bays. Columns are shear-connected, double 2 × 12/20 cm, attached to girders with shear connectors ϕ 80 mm.

Horizontal bracing of roof through steel diagonals. Wind loads transferred to foundation through knee-brace struts of lumber nailed in shape of double T and designed for bending. Main girders are fixed in fire wall to retain continuity.

Girder layout and wind bracing

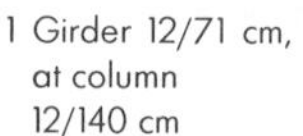

1 Girder 12/71 cm, at column 12/140 cm
2 Purlins 7/28 cm, laminated wood
3 Knee brace as I section, 3 × 6/12 cm
4 Fire wall, 24 cm reinforced concrete
5 Horizontal fire skirt, reinforced concrete
6 Columns 2 × 12/20 cm, laminated wood
7 Columns at wind brace 2 × 16/20 cm
8 Shear connectors ϕ 80 mm
9 Shear connectors ϕ 95 mm
10 Bearing timbers 2 × 3/13 cm, glued and nailed

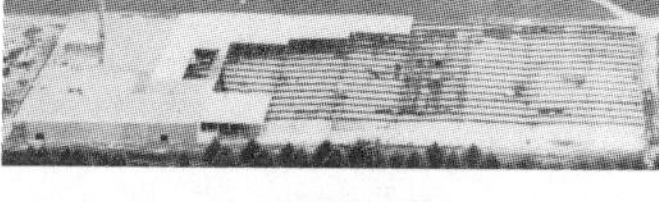

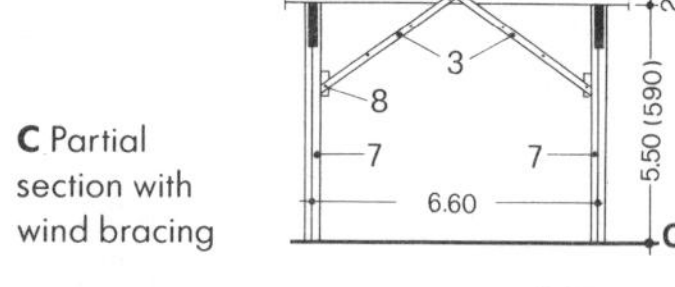

C Partial section with wind bracing

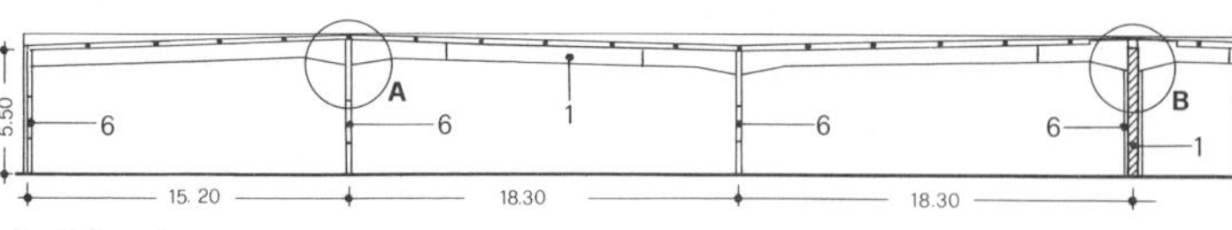

Partial section

A Connection, girder to column

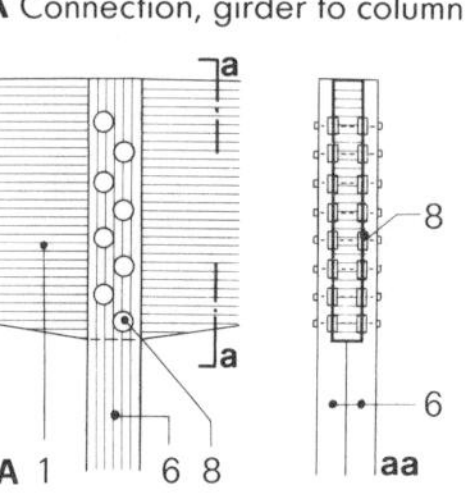

B Moment connection, girder to fire wall

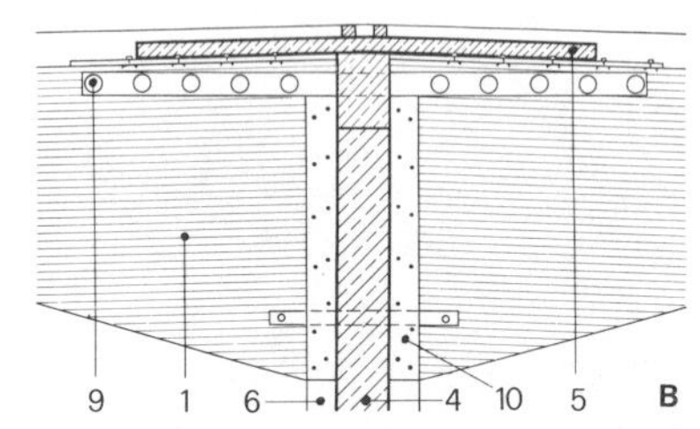

59 **Storage Shed, West Germany**

Architect: H. Holzer, Augsburg
Engineer: Timber Construction Contractor

Fixed reinforced-concrete columns support simply supported girders with cantilever and with a hinge that carries adjacent span. Column bearings are forked to support girders laterally. Hinge is a bolted steel plate within a slit. Lapped purlins span 6.00 m between girders.
Reference : *Bauen mit Holz* 10/19, p. 484.

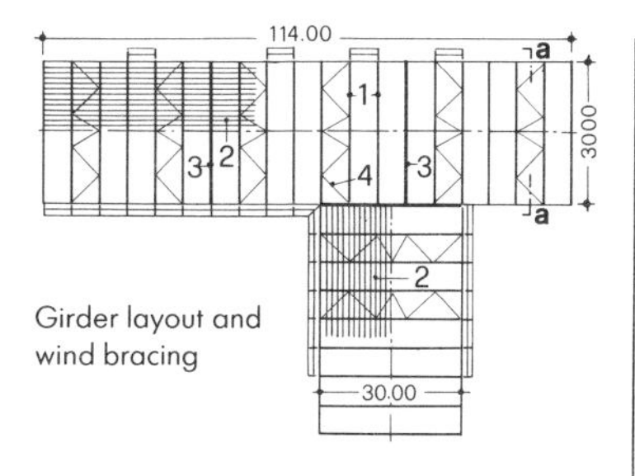

Girder layout and wind bracing

A Hinge

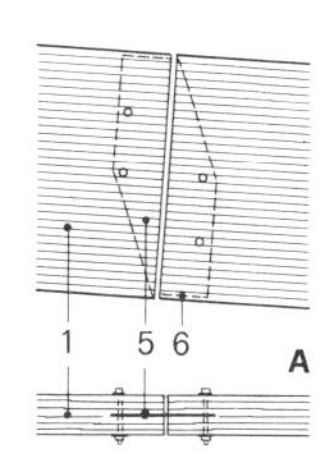

1 Girder 14.5/84 cm
2 Lapped purlins 7 to 14/18 cm
3 Fire wall
4 Wind bracing 6/12 cm
5 Hinge, 15 mm steel plate in slit, bolts ϕ 16 mm
6 Bearing seat

aa Cross section

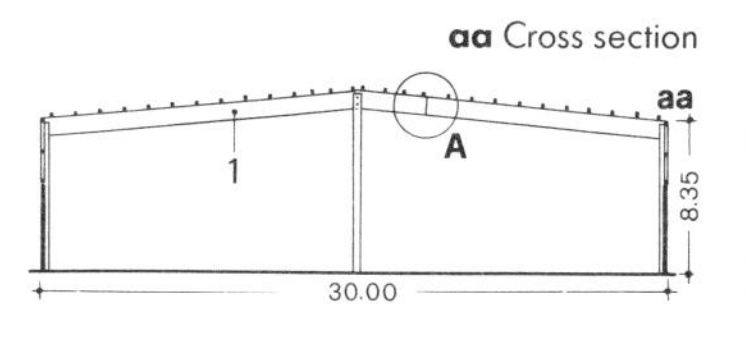

Hinges

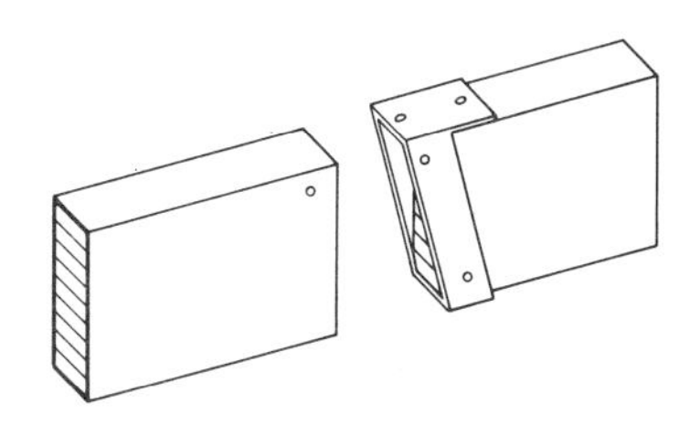

Steel seat with overhanging supporting plate, good for small tensile forces (from wind, for example).

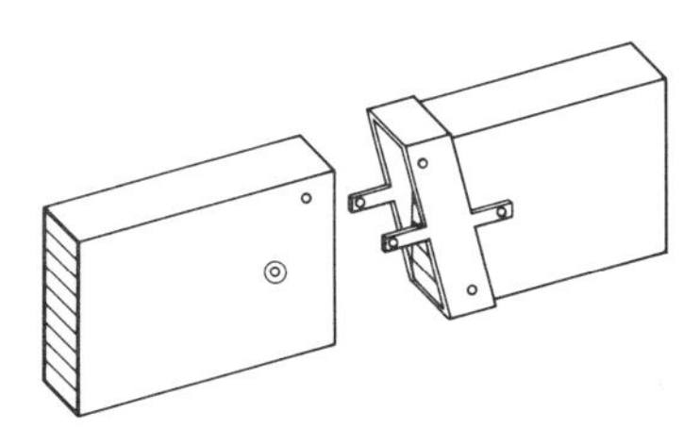

Steel seat with side plates and shear connectors for transfer of larger tensile forces (from wind, for example).

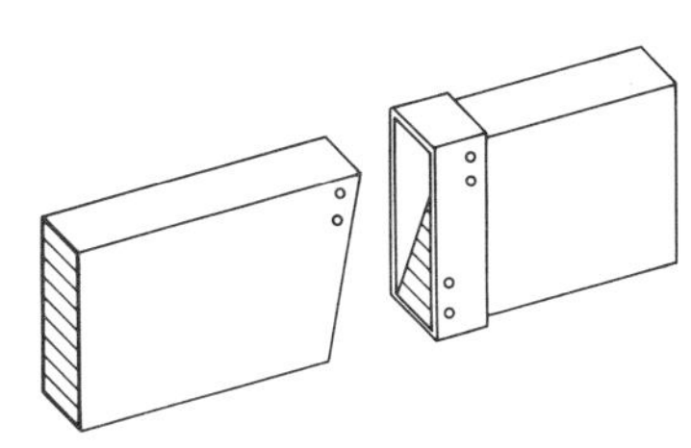

Steel seat for transfer of shear only.

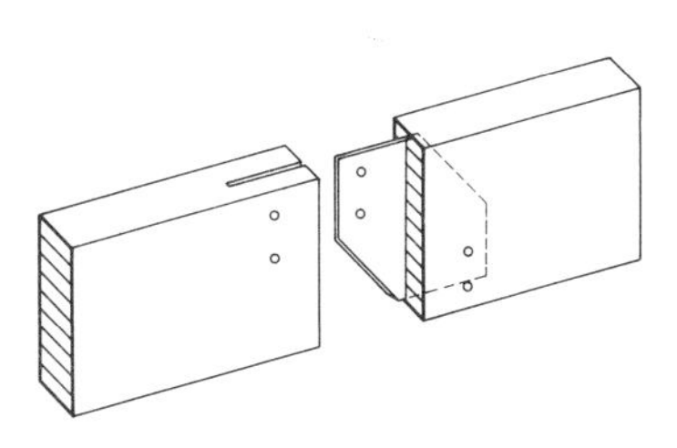

Doweled steel plate in slit.

60 **Printing Plant in Paderborn, West Germany**

Architect: Peter C. v. Seidlein and Horst Fischer, Munich
Consultant: Hansjörg Kramer, Lothar Tenge
Engineer: Seeberger and Friedl, Munich

Large hall, 5000 m² area, divided into typesetting room, printing shop and bookbinding area, and service room, as well as paper storage area separated by a fire wall. Column grid on 21.00 × 10.50 m. Main girders span longitudinally over four spans with a hinge in each end span. Secondary beams, spanning transversely and spaced at 3.50 m, are overlaid with trapezoidal sheet-metal roofing and insulation. Timber columns of cross-shaped sections are fixed to foundation with steel anchors. Column tops are forked to support girders laterally. Horizontal and wind bracing is achieved by means of diagonal trussing in two roof bays and column fixity.
Reference: *Detail* 4/1976, illustrations

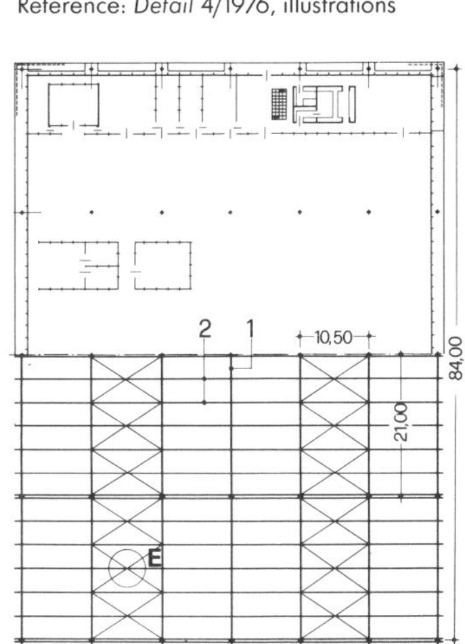

1 Main girder
2 Secondary beam
3 Cross-shaped column
4 Steel plate
5 Key
6 Connection plate
7 Steel bearing plate
8 Threaded bar ϕ 15 mm
9 Stiffener in slit
10 Tightening bolts
11 Steel dowel
12 Connection plate
13 Steel bearing
14 Anchor bolt
15 Leveling nut

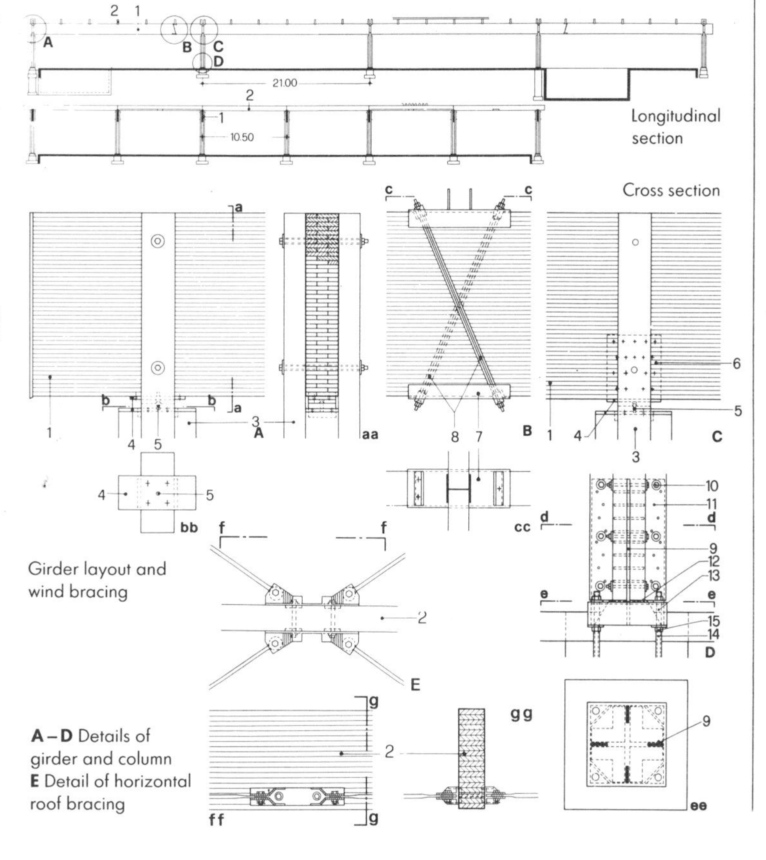

Girder layout and wind bracing

A–D Details of girder and column
E Detail of horizontal roof bracing

A beam continuous over several spans is statically indeterminate. The loading of even one span causes deformations in all of them because of the beam's continuous resistance to bending. All spans and supports take the load. Deflections are smaller than in statically determinate multispan beams with hinges or in simple spans. Design is governed by bending and shear stresses, while their distribution is determined by the length of spans and the cross section of the beam.

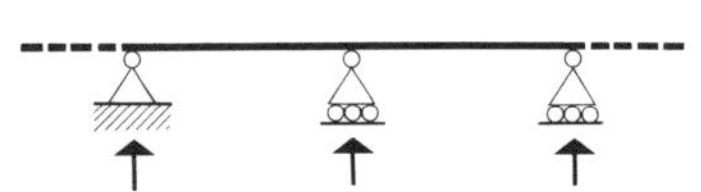

All reactions are vertical

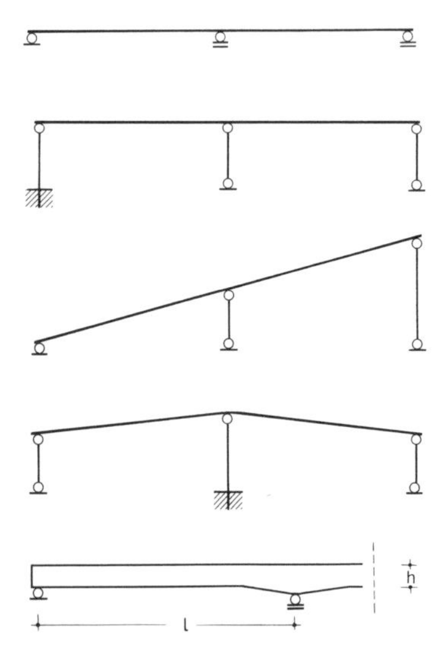

Solid wood beams (coupled rafters)
a = 0.5 to 1.5 m (spacing)
l = 4 to 10 m
h = l/16 to l/20

Laminated wood beams
a = 2 to 6 m (spacing)
l = 10 to 30 m
h = l/18 to l/22
Haunch slope ≤ 1:8

61 Dressing Rooms in Langenfeld, West Germany

Architect: H. Retzki, Dortmund
Engineer: Timber Construction Contractor

Dressing rooms, ticket office, and toilets for an open-air public pool. Continuous beams 14/60 cm over two spans are placed transversely to building at 5.00 m spacing. Columns are spaced at 10.00 m and 7.50 m. Beams are cantilevered 2.50 m on one long side of building. Double shear-connected columns 2 × 13/16 cm are fixed with steel shapes. Purlins 10/16 cm run longitudinally. Central passage is lit through a continuous skylight. Horizontal loads are absorbed by fixed columns and masonry walls on short sides of building.
Reference: *Bauen mit Holz* 12/1968, p. 586; *Detail* 1/1971, illustrations

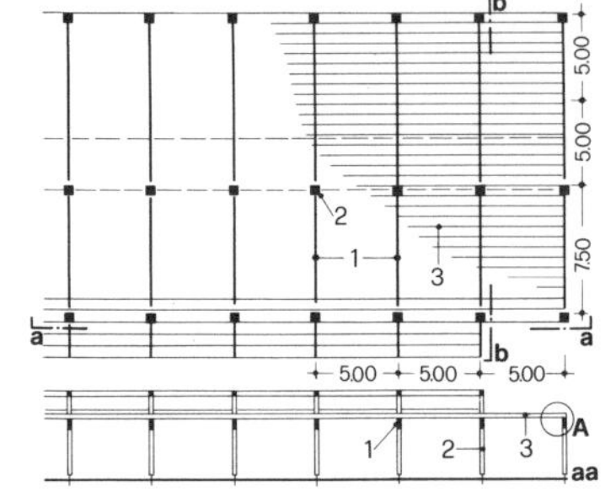

1 Main girder 14/60 cm
2 Columns 2 × 13/16 cm
3 Purlins 10/16 cm
4 Column base, fixed, I 240

Layout of girders
aa Longitudinal section

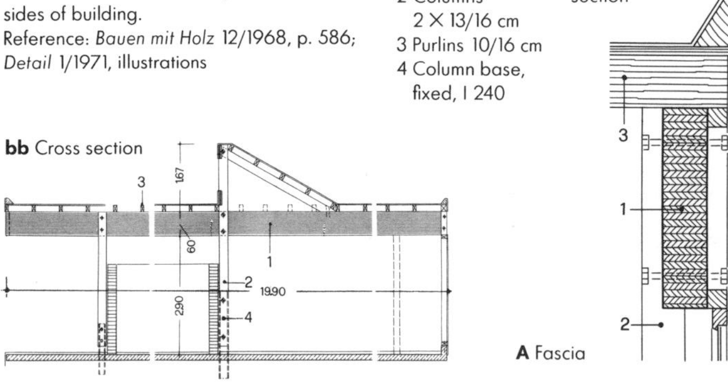

bb Cross section

A Fascia

62 Student Cafeteria in Würzburg, West Germany

Architect: A. Freiherr v. Branca, Munich
Engineer: J. Natterer, Munich

Flat roof, stepped in elevation and plan. Main girders are double continuous girders spaced at 8.40 m, spanning over 3 to 5 spans, plus cantilevers. They are bent up at midspans, where they are rigidly attached to a pair of secondary girders, between which run air ducts. A cantilevered structure is made possible around corners by girders crossing at the same level. A moment connection of main girders is achieved by means of shear connectors and steel U shapes, which transfer forces at midspan to a steel IPB shape.

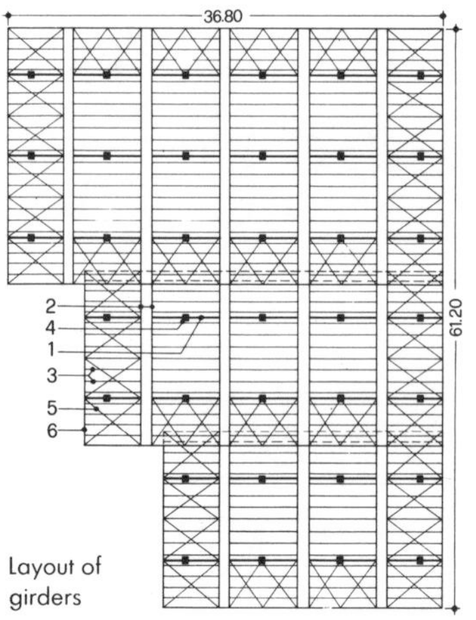

Layout of girders

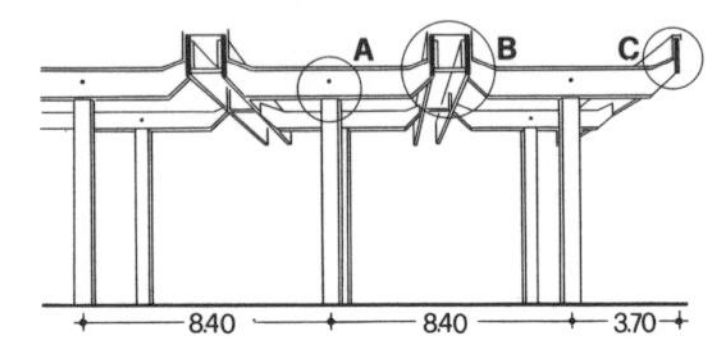

Perspective diagram

1 Main girder 2 × 20/93 cm
2 Secondary girder 16 × 135 cm
3 Bent rafters 15/45 cm
4 Reinforced-concrete columns 70/70 cm
5 Wind bracing, flat steel bars
6 Fascia girder 16/90 cm
7 Finger jointing
8 2 U shapes 320 mm
9 Shear connectors ϕ 160 mm
10 IPB 200
11 Shear connectors ϕ 65 mm
12 Nail plate with steel tube and bolts ϕ 50 mm
13 2 U shapes 160 mm girder bearing

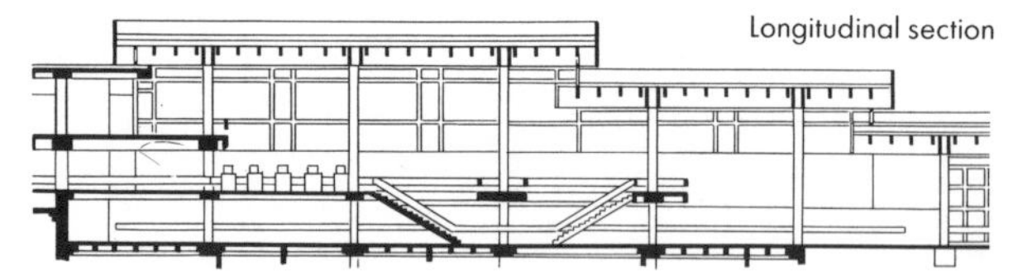

Longitudinal section

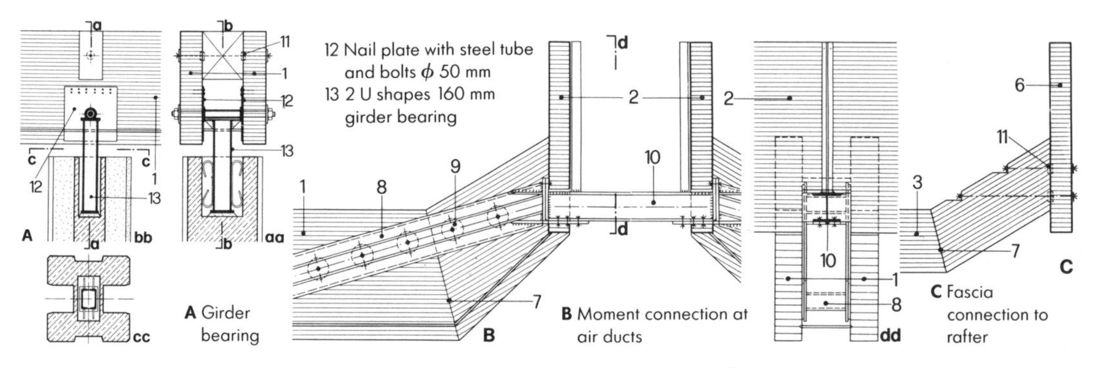

A Girder bearing

B Moment connection at air ducts

C Fascia connection to rafter

63 Boat Sheds in Feldmoching near Munich, West Germany

Architect: Eberl, Weippert, Heym, Leitner, Munich
Engineer: H. and W. Held, Munich

Boat sheds were built for the 1972 Olympic Games in Munich and contain boat storage, workshop, dressing rooms, and toilets. Main girders 2 × 22/112 cm reach transversely over two 13.60 m long spans. They rest on fixed reinforced-concrete columns with side brackets. These girders support purlins 18/56 cm which span 6.40 m.

Upper floor has a valley-shaped roof built in traditional post and beam construction.

Horizontal bracing is by diagonals and fixed columns.

Reference: *Detail* 4/1972, p. 740

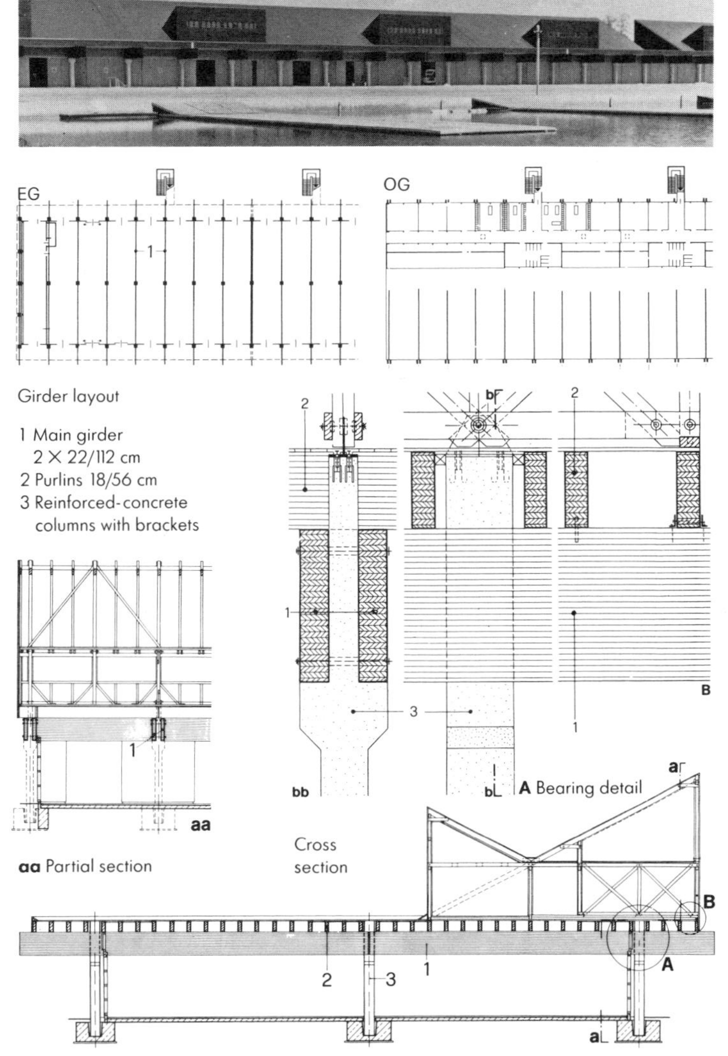

Girder layout

1 Main girder 2 × 22/112 cm
2 Purlins 18/56 cm
3 Reinforced-concrete columns with brackets

aa Partial section

Cross section

64 Stable in Munich-Riem, West Germany

Architect: Atelier Kleineichenhausen
Engineer: Rüter, Minden

Stable with 48 horse stalls and service rooms erected for the 1972 Olympic Games in Munich. Roof structure consists of two-span girders 11/84 cm, spanning 14.80 and 17.00 m in the transverse direction. Center row of fixed columns consists of ϕ 324 mm steel pipes; outer columns are timber. Lapped purlins are 8/22 cm in interior bays and 10/22 cm in both outer bays.

Reference: *Detail* 4/1972, p. 734

1 Main girder 11/84 cm
2 Lapped purlins 8/22 to 10/22 cm
3 Steel pipe columns ϕ 324/8.8 mm
4 Screw ϕ 16 mm
5 Timber columns 2 × 15/26 cm
6 Timber columns 26/29 cm
7 Roof wedge for drainage

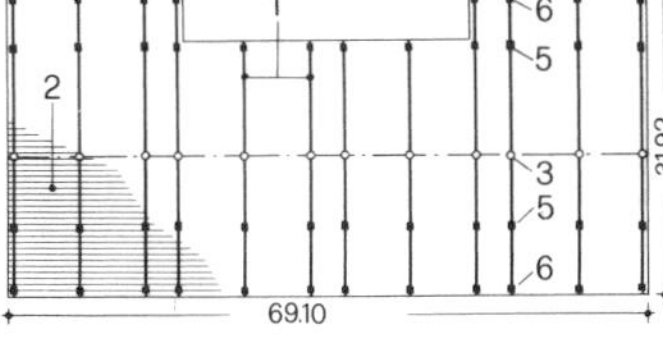

Girder layout

A Center bearing, **B** Bearing detail

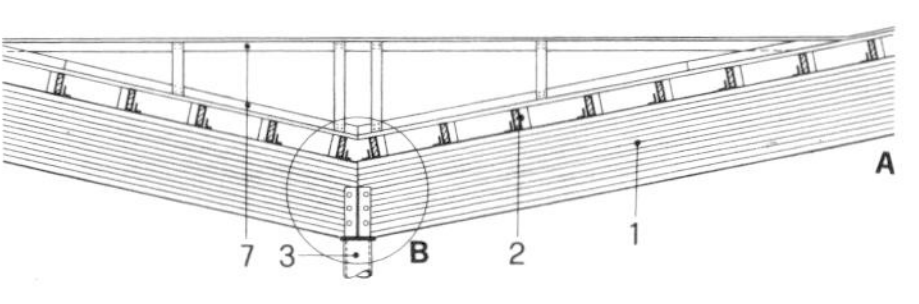

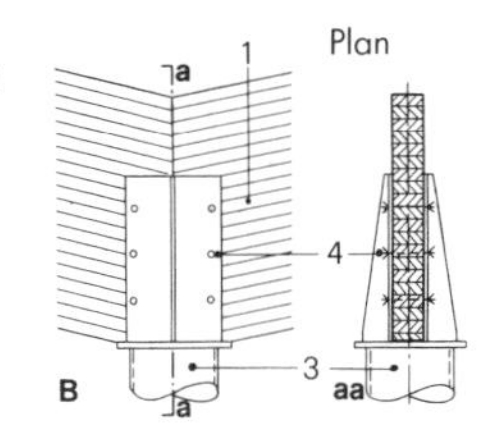

Cross section

Bearing for Continuous Beam

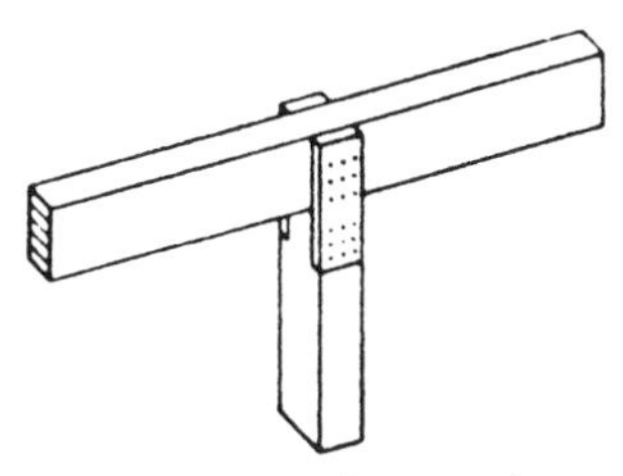

Without girder strengthening at bearing, connection with steel gussets and shear connectors or nails.

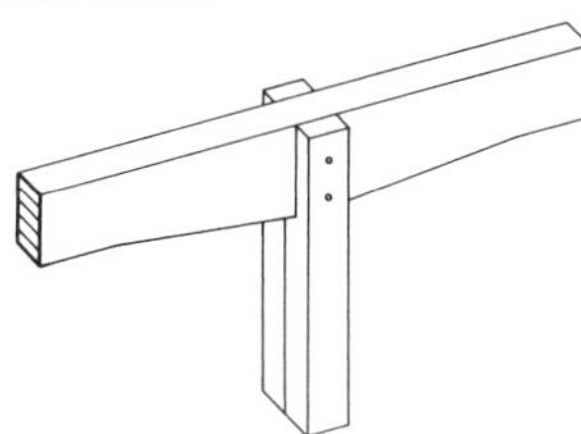

Reinforcing of girder through haunches (slope < 1:10).

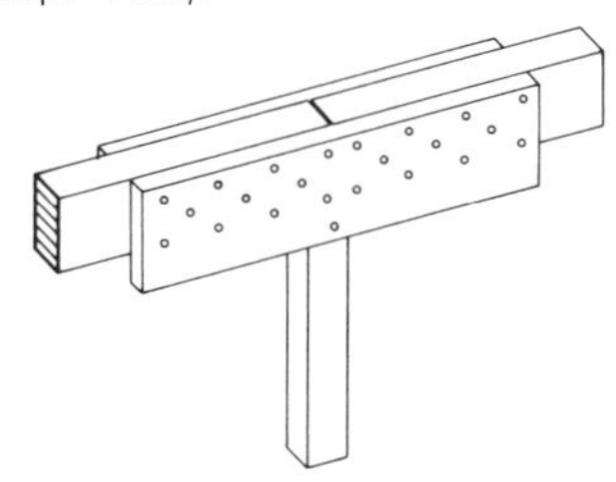

Sidewise reinforcing with shear connectors or nails.

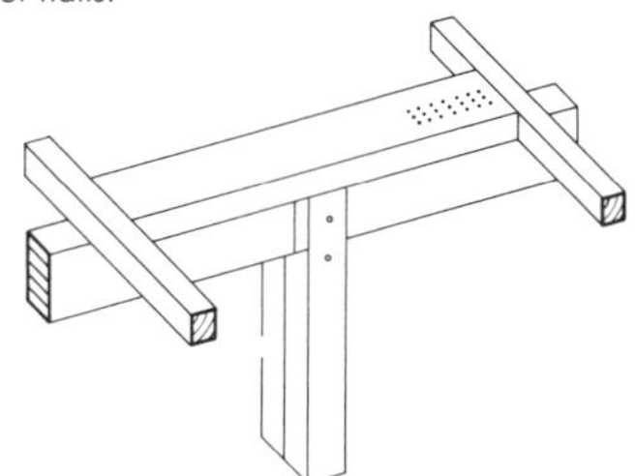

Upper reinforcing plank, nailed.

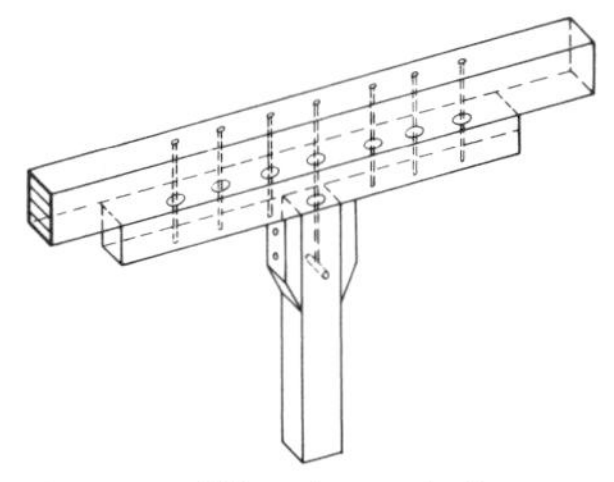

Reinforcing saddle timber under beam, with shear connectors and brackets.

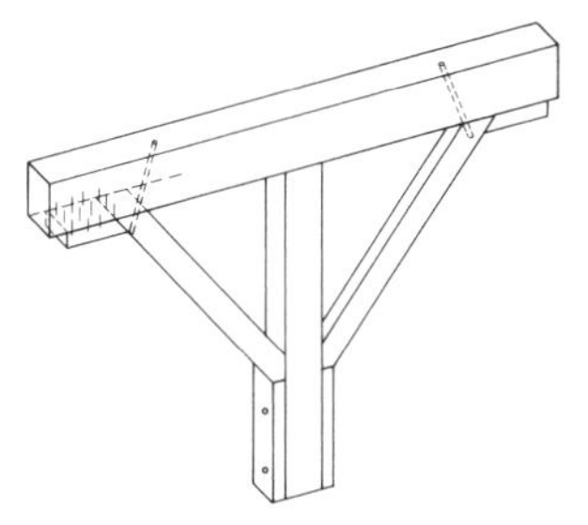

Knee brace with brackets or notches serves to reduce span.

Three-hinged frames are statically determinate and consist of two inclined straight members, which are hinged together at the crown and rest on hinged bearings. Exterior loads are conveyed to bearings through compressive and bending stresses in members. A steeper inclination of members results in larger compressive stresses and lesser bending. The redirection of forces through hinges results in skewed reactions at bearings. The vertical component of these skewed reactions is equal to the vertical load, while the horizontal component depends on the slope of the members; it is larger for flatter slopes.

Design of members is governed by bending and compressive stresses, but for slender members buckling may govern.

Skewed reactions at bearings, nonyielding supports

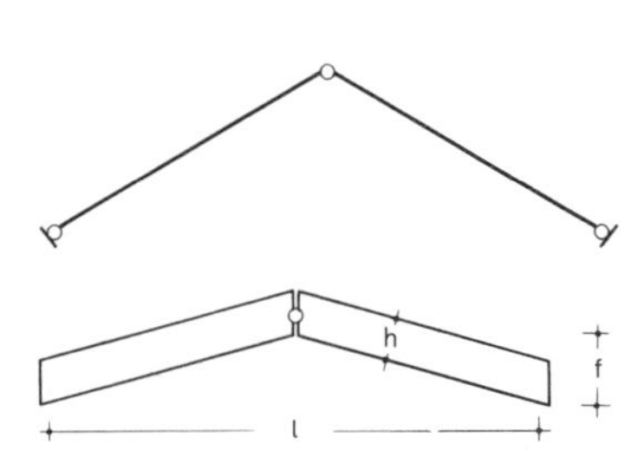

a = 5 to 8 m (spacing)
l = 15 to 50 m
h = l/30 to l/50
$f \geq l/3$

65 Church in Fawley Court, Great Britain

Architects: Crabtree and Jarosz, Hampton Court
Engineer: Timber Construction Contractor

Plan is in the shape of two offset trapezoids. Roof consists of three-hinged beams with crown heights of 8.00 to 22.00 m. One-piece main girders have parabolic profiles corresponding to moment diagram. Maximum depths vary from 33 to 92 cm, depending on span. Girders rest on bearing shoes, joined at crown by steel I shapes with shear connectors. Solid wood wind bracing is exposed to view. Wind bracing diagonals meeting at various angles are connected through special hinges. Two steel gussets bolted to diagonals grip a steel sphere which is connected to girder by a bracket.

1 Main girder 12/33 to 12/92 cm
2 Wind bracing 7.6/20 cm
3 Connection of wind bracing: spherical joint with 2 steel gussets
4 Steel angle with bolts and anchor bolts
5 Crown hinge, I shape with shear connectors
6 Cross beam 10/24 cm

Plan

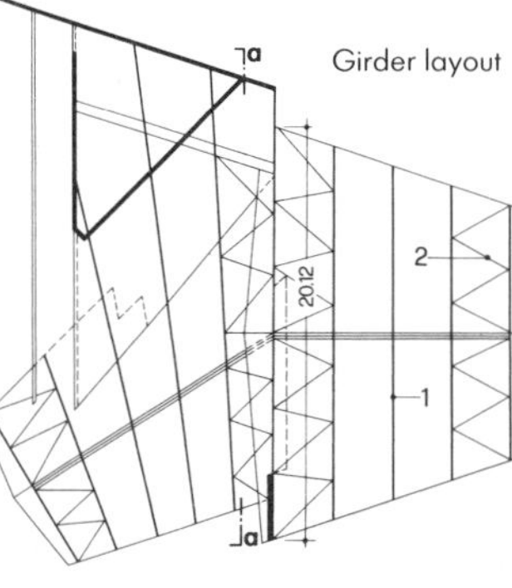

Girder layout

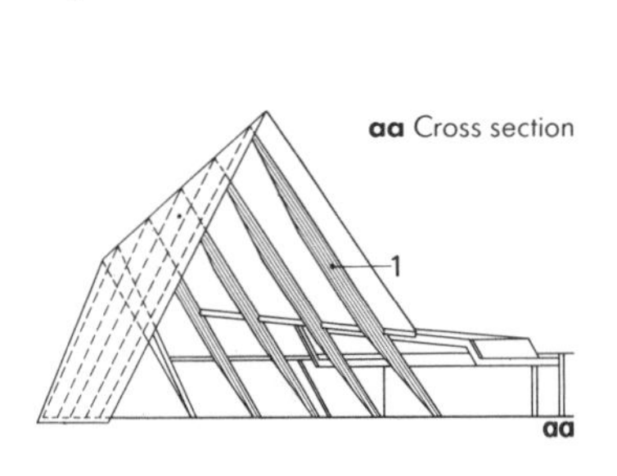

aa Cross section

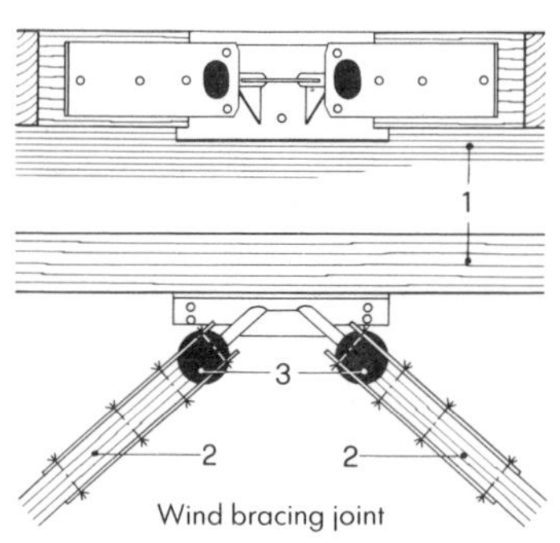

Wind bracing joint

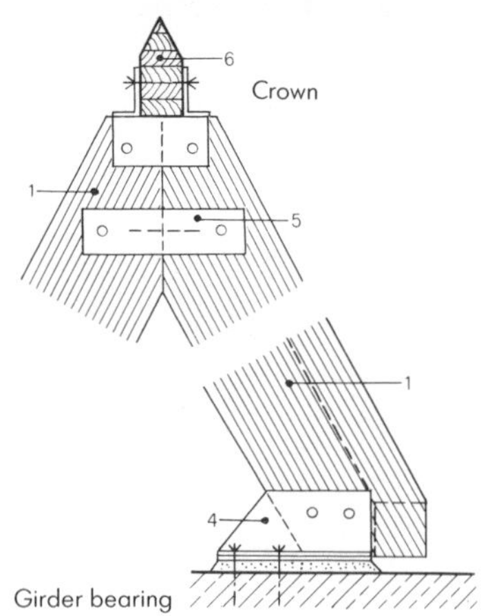

Crown

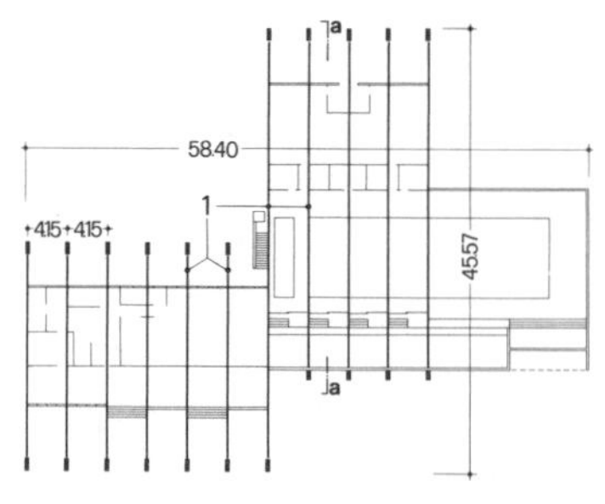

Girder bearing

66 Swimming Pool in Fornasette, Switzerland

Architect: J. Dahinden, Zurich
Engineer: Prantl and Gaschen, Thun

Three rectangles in plan are covered by sloped roofs. Roof structure consists of three-hinged beams 14/80 cm. Concrete footings take horizontal girder forces. Crown joints are exposed steel gussets and dowels. Purlins of 12/14 cm lumber rest on girders; 24 mm diagonal planking and a vented roof rest on rafters. A 14 mm layer of planking supporting thermal insulation is screwed onto underside of rafters.
Reference: *Deutsche Bauzeitung* 5/1971, p. 552; *Werk* 1/1971, p. 34

Plan and girder layout

1 Main girder 18/80 cm
2 Purlins 12/14 cm
3 Crown joint with steel dowels
4 Glued-on wedge

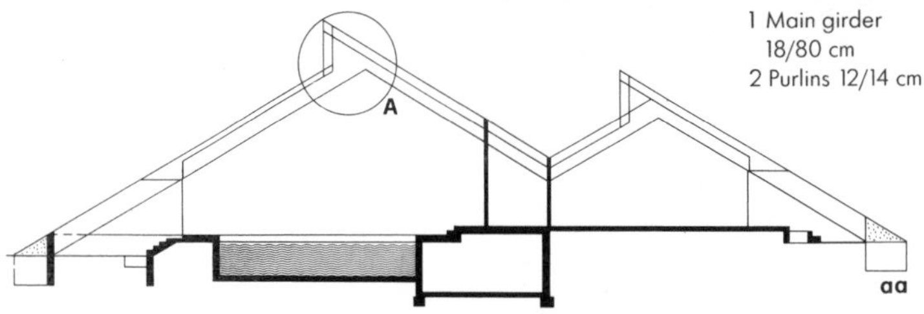

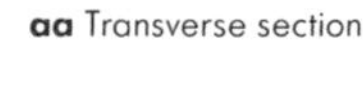

aa Transverse section

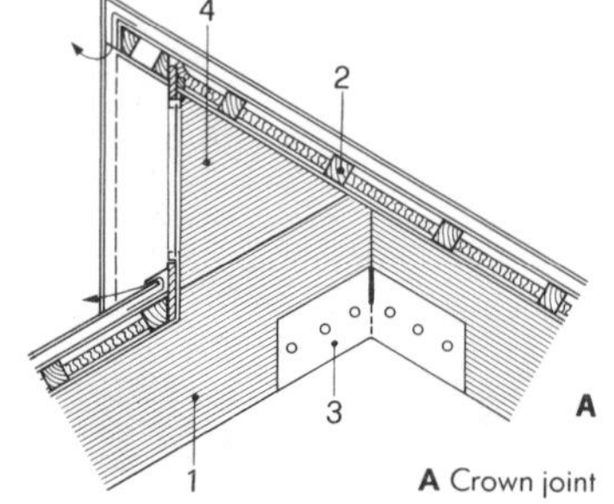

A Crown joint

67 Riding Hall in Villingen, West Germany

Architect: U. Schnitzer

Roofed riding track 20 × 40 m. Eleven three-hinged frames form a gable roof and span 25.00 m transversely to building. Depth of 14/80 cm laminated wood members tapers to 40 cm at footings. Reinforced-concrete counterforts support bearings. Crown joints contain a hardwood pin and a plywood safety key.

Purlins are Gerber beams 12/16 and 16/16 cm connected to frames by anchors to prevent uplift. Filler inserts between purlins anchor purlins against sliding. Every other bay contains timber diaphragms for lateral and wind bracing. Frames are assembled on ground in pairs, together with purlins and diaphragms. After they are erected, purlin lap joints are bolted together.

1 Main frames 14/40 to 80 cm
2 Purlins 12/16 to 16/16 cm
3 Wind bracing 6/12 to 6/14 cm
4 Hardwood 16/16 cm
5 Plywood key 6/20/25 mm nailed

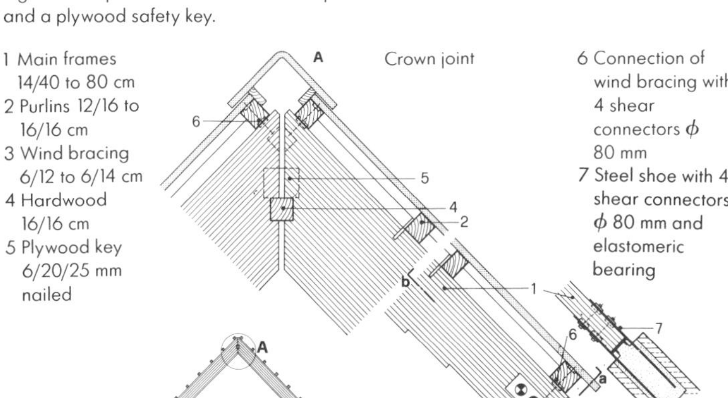

Crown joint

6 Connection of wind bracing with 4 shear connectors ϕ 80 mm
7 Steel shoe with 4 shear connectors ϕ 80 mm and elastomeric bearing

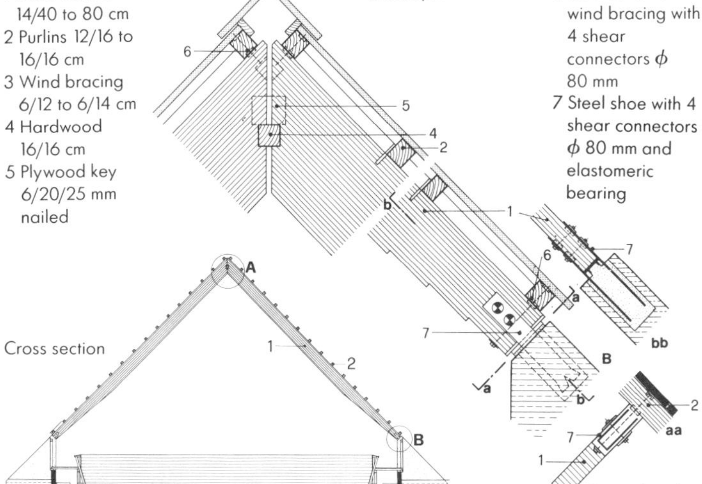

Cross section

Frame bearing

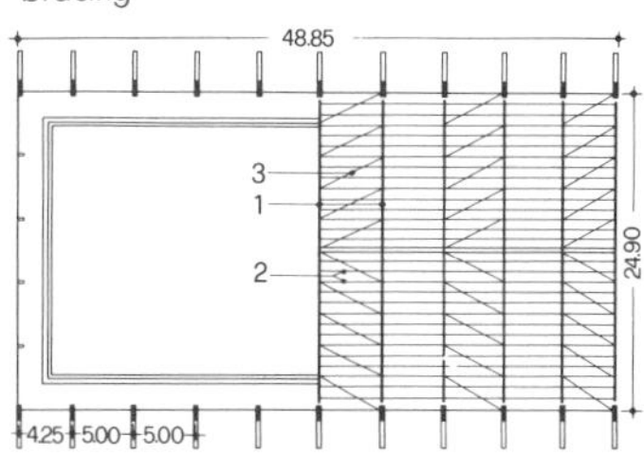

Plan with girder layout and bracing

68 Church in Kempten-Wetzikon, Switzerland

Architect: R. Krieg, Zurich
Engineer: W. Wyss, Ettemhausen-Wetzikon

Rectangular plan. Hip roof continues to ground. Main structure consists of three-hinged frames with 18/82 cm straight members and hip beams 18/100 cm, all connected on top by ridge beam 18/126 cm. This configuration provides two triangular side supports which resist horizontal forces. Frame bearings consist of interlocking web plates and steel pins. Prefabricated roof elements rest between girders, measure 3.60 × 2.82 m, and consist of grid beams 62 cm deep, insulated, and planked on both sides.

Reference: *Raum und Handwerk* 1/1976

1 Hip beams 18/100 cm
2 Rafters 18/82 cm
3 Ridge beam 18/126 cm
4 Steel T section, placed in slit
5 Steel-plate bearing with steel pin and cotter pins

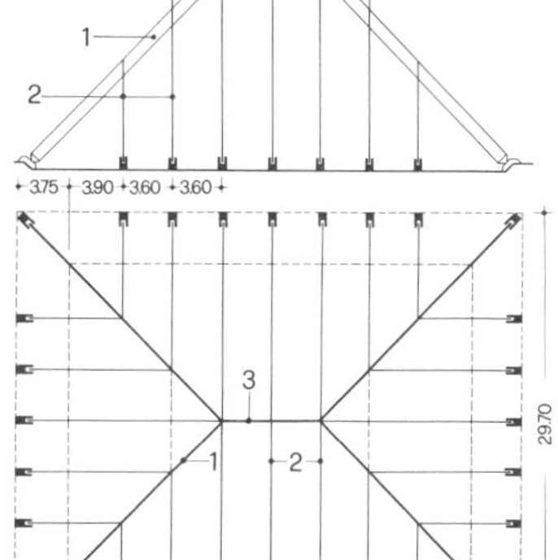

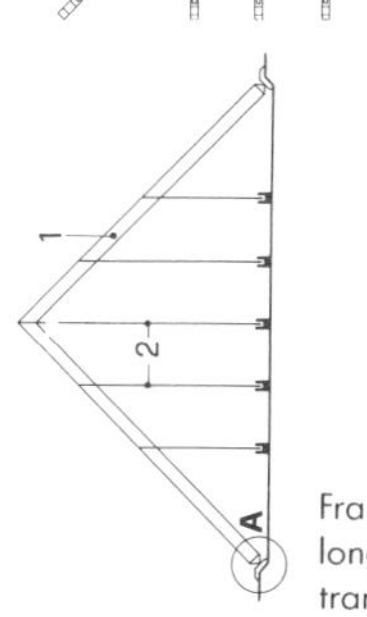

Plan

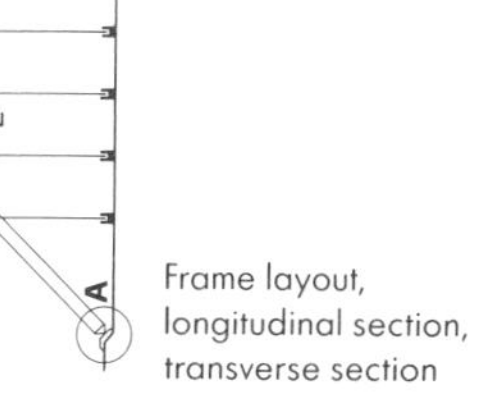

Frame layout, longitudinal section, transverse section

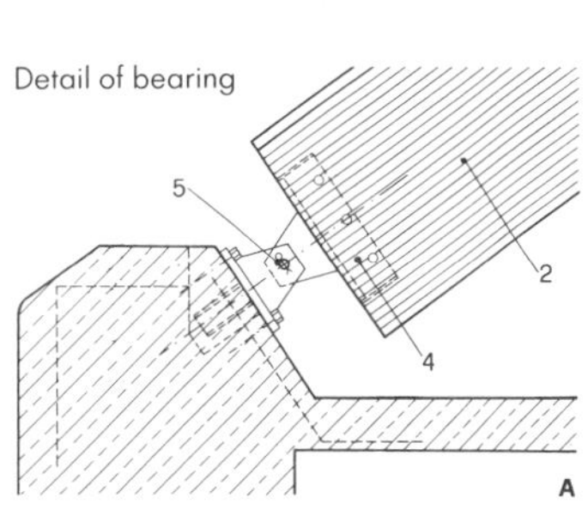

Detail of bearing

Heavy Crown Hinges

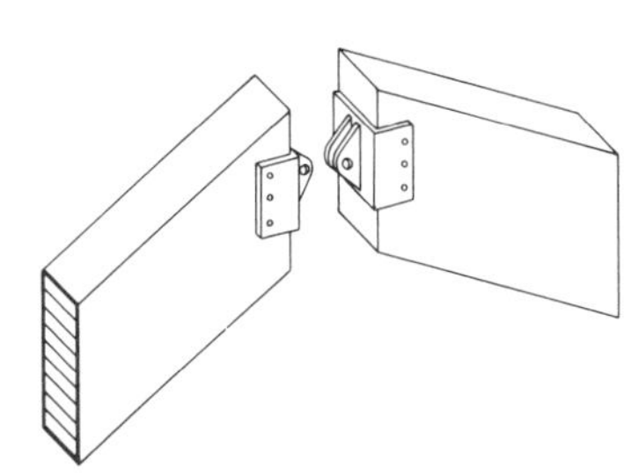

Side steel connection with steel pin.

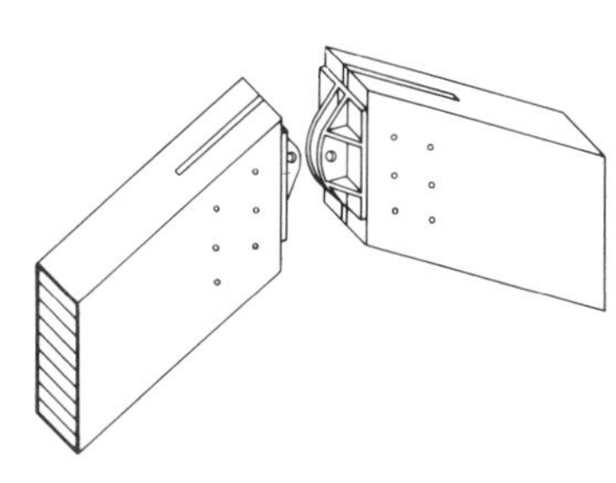

Steel plates placed in slit and doweled; head plate, webs, and steel pin.

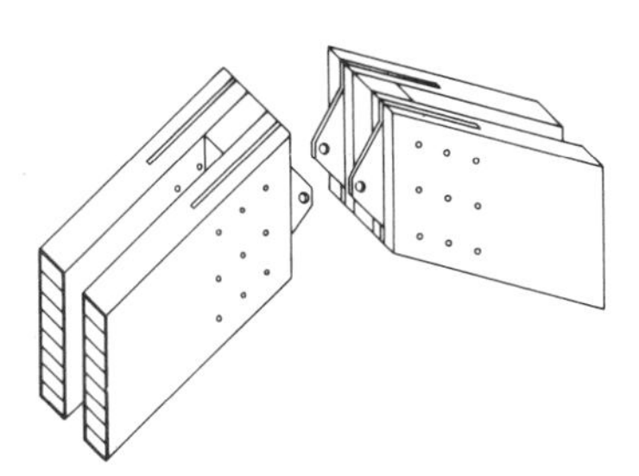

Steel bearing with pin for twin beams.

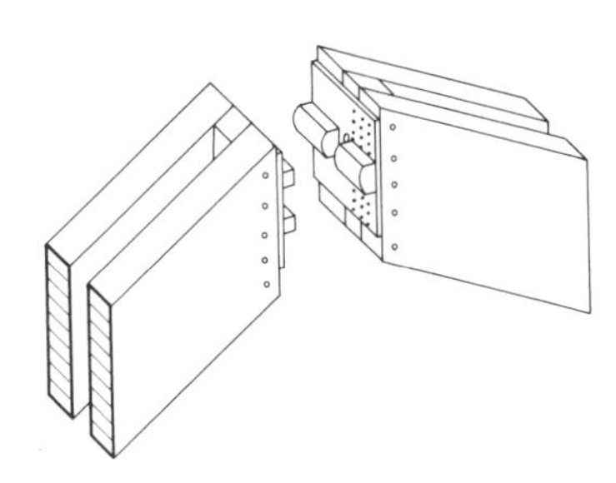

Head plate with cams for twin beams. Joint secured by bolt through wood fillers. Filler connected by steel dowels.

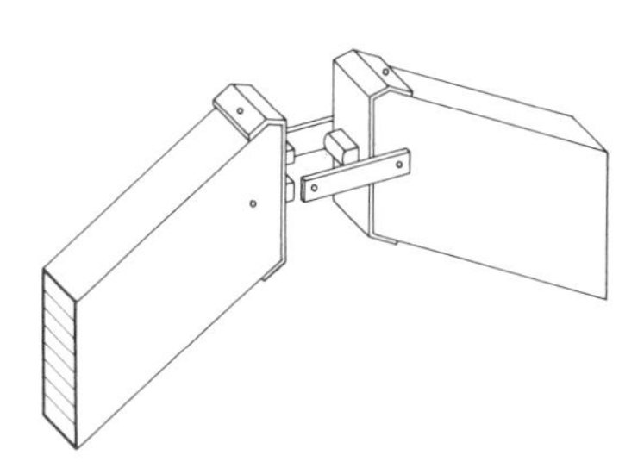

Head plate with bearing knobs and lateral safety anchor plates.

Tied three-hinged frames balance the horizontal bearing forces generated by vertical loads through timber or steel ties. Frame forces are determined in the same way as in frames without ties.

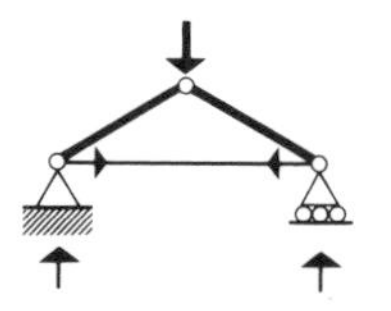

Horizontal bearing reaction is absorbed by tie

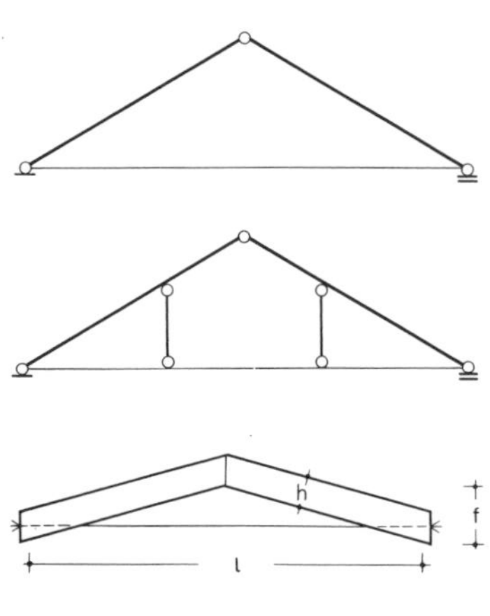

a = 5 to 8 m (spacing)
l = 15 to 50 m
h = l/30 to l/50
$f \geq l/6$

If the tie is placed above the bearing hinges, there are additional bending moments in the frame members. These bending moments can be avoided if the bearings can resist lateral forces or if the tie can resist compressive forces (collar beam rafters).

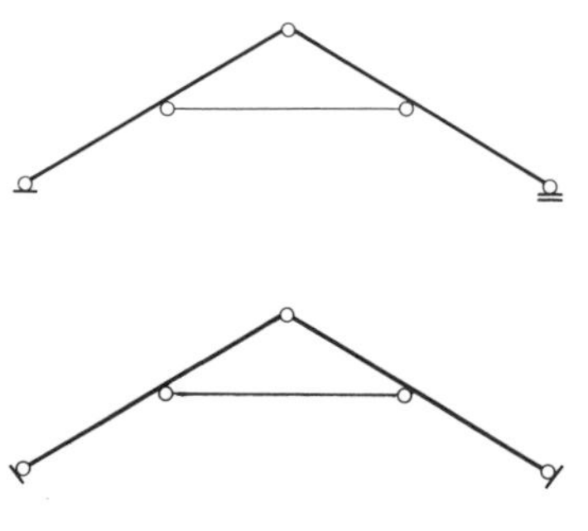

69 Storage Shed in Oberhausen, West Germany

Engineer: Timber Construction Contractor

Two-bay shed with covered surface of 80.00 × 40.00 m. Each bay has a 40.00 m span. Roof beams are built as tied triangular trusses and are spaced at 6.00 m. Beam dimensions vary from 14/90 to 14/140 cm, ties are ϕ 32 mm steel. Coupled purlins are 8/18 to 12/18 cm. Wind bracing provided by diagonals in roof, and lateral loads are transferred to foundations through reinforced-concrete columns.

Crown joint consists of a steel plate in beam slit and a head plate. Load is transferred through steel bearing plates welded to head plates and secured through a forked seat. Ties are secured at bearings through 50 mm thick anchor plates.
Reference: *Bauen mit Holz* 10/1971, p. 474

A Bearing, concrete column to beam, with tie anchor

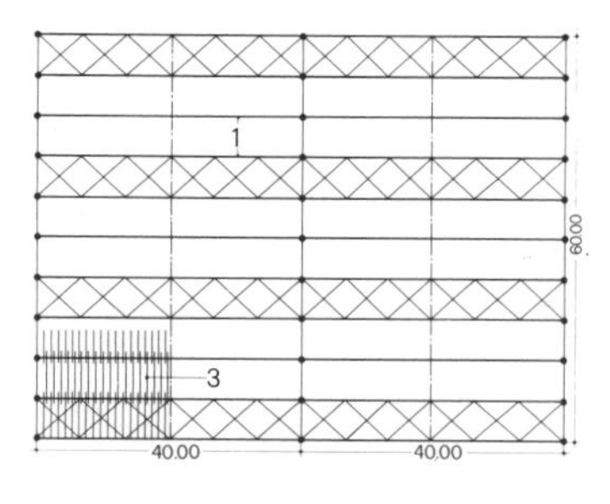

Beam layout and bracing

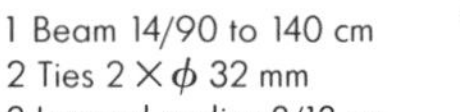

1 Beam 14/90 to 140 cm
2 Ties 2 × ϕ 32 mm
3 Lapped purlins 8/18 cm interior, 12/18 cm end bays
4 Reinforced purlins for wind bracing 14/18 cm
5 Turnbuckle
6 Web plate in slit and head plate
7 Bolts ϕ 20 mm
8 Anchor plate with bolts

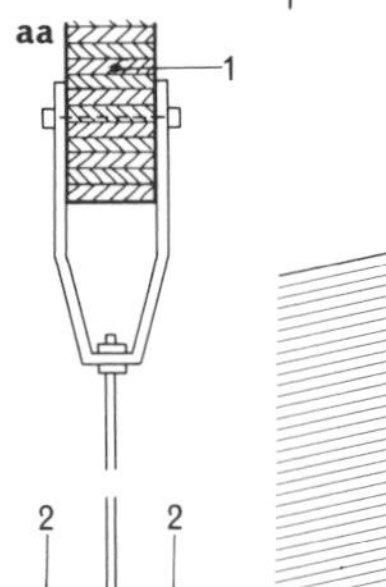

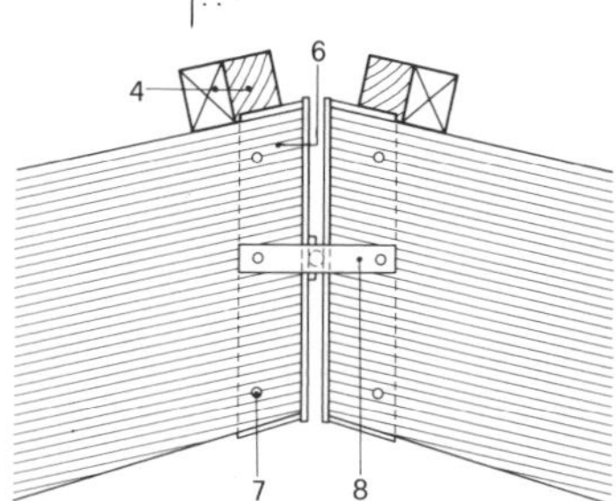

B Ridge joint

aa Suspension of tie rods

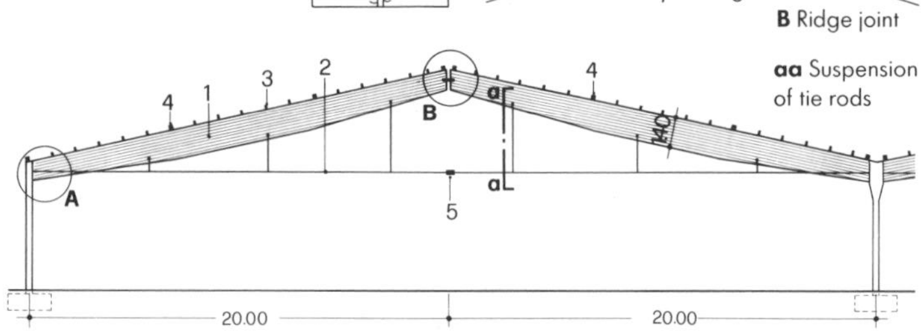

70 Golf Clubhouse at Hilton Head Island, United States

Architect: Copelin and Lee, New York
Engineer: Butterfield, New York

Clubhouse, dressing rooms, offices, restaurant, and store on ground floor. Utility rooms in a concrete basement. Roof over ground floor is supported by three-hinged frames with ties, offset in elevation. Spacing of frames is 5.50 m, spans are 5.50 and 11.00 m. Roof is supported by 21 fixed round reinforced-concrete columns. Roof consists of planking, insulation, and wood shingles on roofing felt.
Reference: *Detail* 6/1973, illustrations

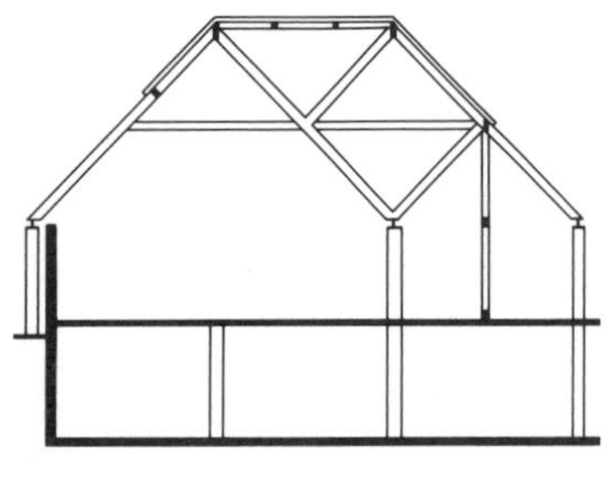

Cross section of building, scale 1:600±

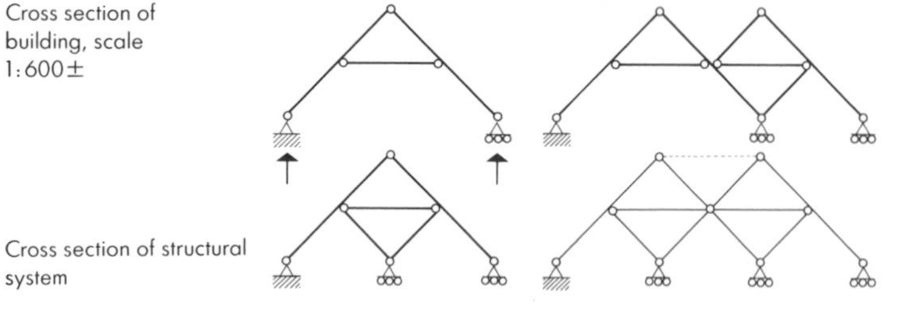

Cross section of structural system

71 Riding Hall in Pompadour, France

Architect: R. Deknuydt, Paris
Engineer: Censi, Rodez

Roof is supported transversely by three-hinged frames with elevated timber collar beam, which is suspended from ridge. Frame spans 22.60 m and its members are 36 to 92 cm deep. Collar beam is 2 × 8/18 cm. Roof dormers in the longitudinal direction are similarly formed by three-hinged frames with a tie beam. These dormers provide efficient illumination and ventilation. Purlins are longitudinal, except at dormers, where they are laid transversely. They are always normal to roof slope.

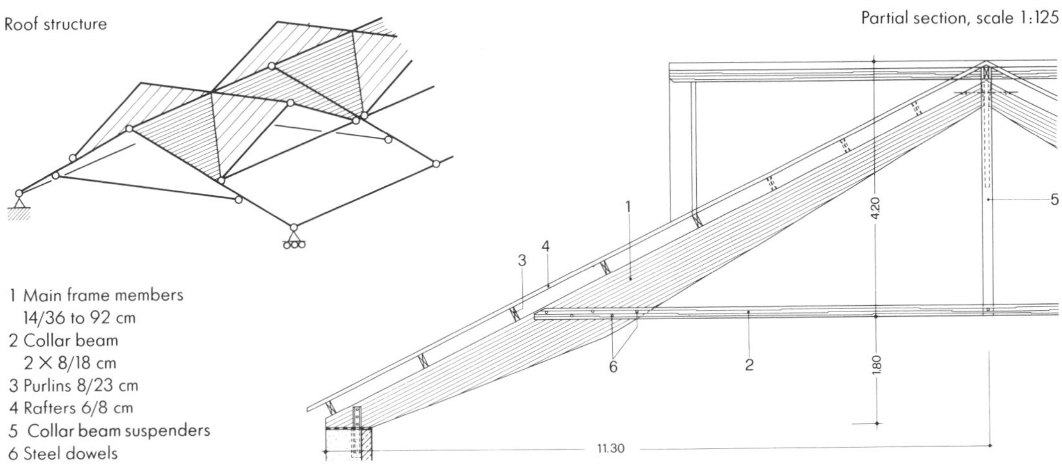

Roof structure

Partial section, scale 1:125

1 Main frame members 14/36 to 92 cm
2 Collar beam 2 × 8/18 cm
3 Purlins 8/23 cm
4 Rafters 6/8 cm
5 Collar beam suspenders
6 Steel dowels

Tie Beam Connections at Bearing

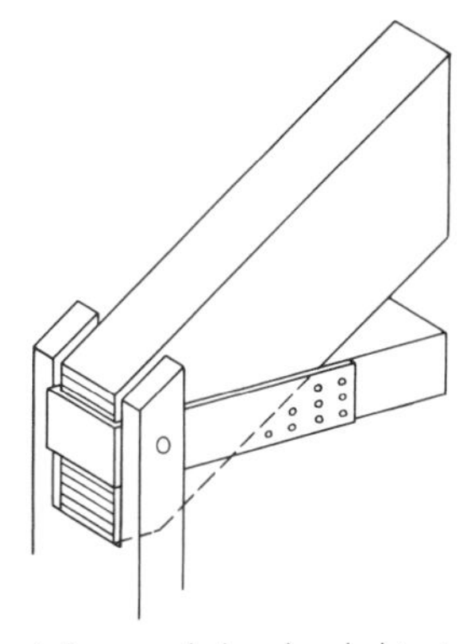

Timber tie beam nailed or doweled to side gusset plates welded to head plate.

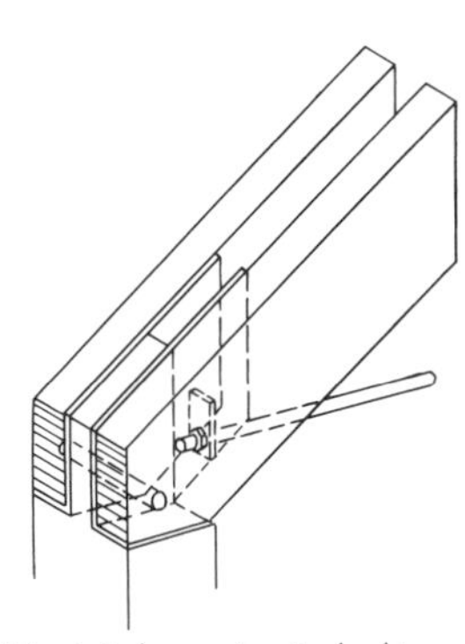

Tie rod for twin beams is attached to web welded to connection plate. Column top has dowel.

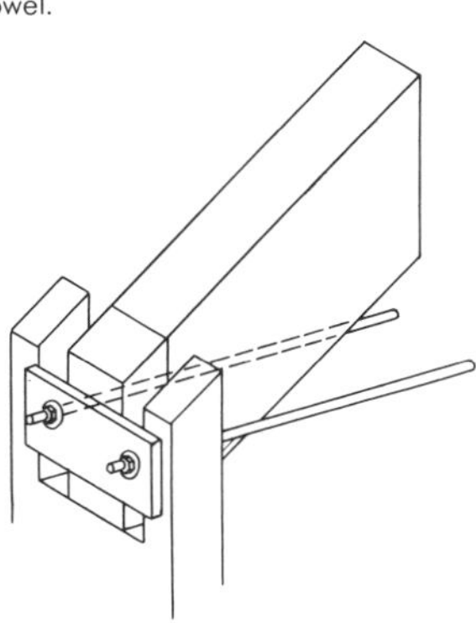

Steel tie rods are adjacent to beam and are bolted to anchor plate.

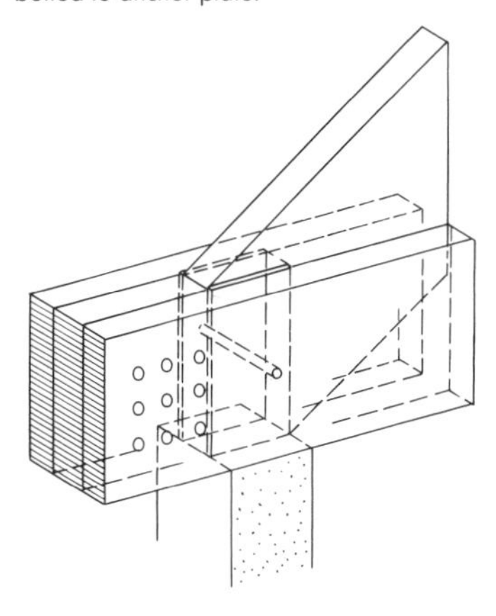

Double tie beam bolted to filler wood.

72 Riding Hall in Lausanne, Switzerland

Architect: F. Brugger, Lausanne
Engineer: Janin and Girard, Lausanne

The importance of this riding school, with its riding hall, stables, and living quarters, is stressed by conspicuous hip roofs. The great riding hall, measuring 25.00 × 75.00 m, is covered by a 17.00 m high roof supported by 13 three-hinged frames with collar beams. Depth of frame beams varies from 30 to 60 cm, their spacing is 5.60 m, and they span 33.00 m. Collar beams and facade columns are double. Purlins are 10/14 cm.

Horizontal bracing is by means of diagonals in end bays and sloped hip roofs at both ends of building.
Reference: *Werk* 9/1966

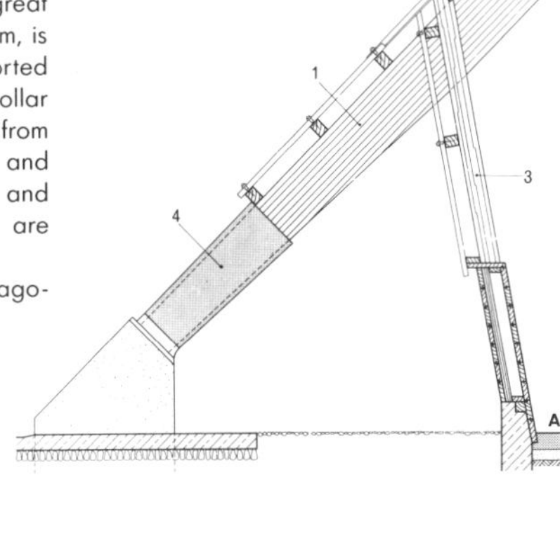

A Beam bearing and exterior wall connection

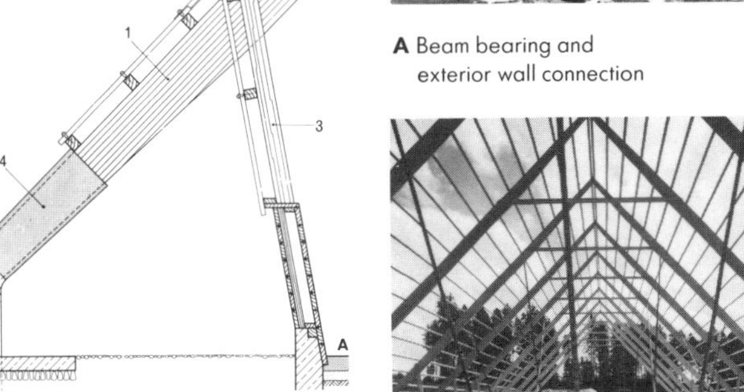

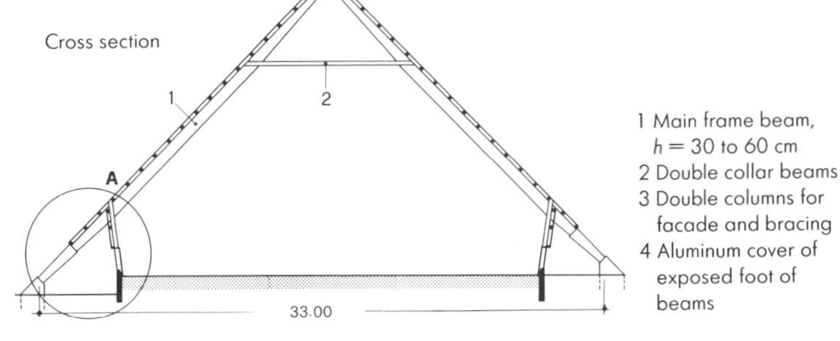

Cross section

1 Main frame beam, $h = 30$ to 60 cm
2 Double collar beams
3 Double columns for facade and bracing
4 Aluminum cover of exposed foot of beams

If frame members are bent or if the tie beam is sloped, the three-hinged frames become special structures in which bending moments at connection or bent points become critical for design.

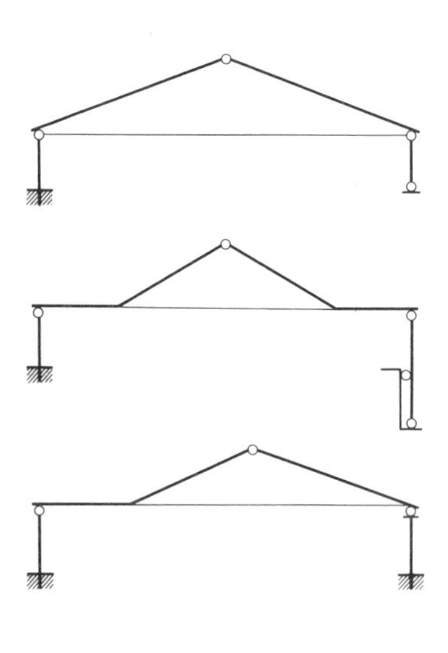

A transition to subtensioned beams or frames is represented by special structures having crossed or sloped ties, or ties which are suspended or propped in the middle.

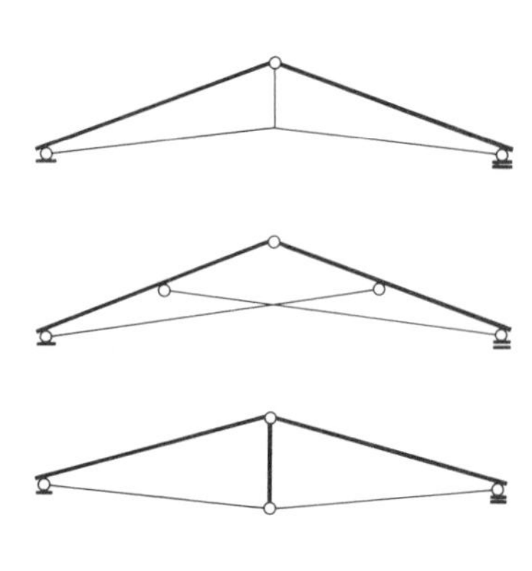

Transition to subtensioned beams (pages 88 and 89)

73 Ice Skating Rink in Deggendorf, West Germany

Architect: City of Deggendorf
Engineer: J. Natterer, Munich

Roof over an existing ice rink. Three-hinged frames with tie rods are spaced at 8.50 m and span 48.00 m. Twin frame members are unequal. One of them is bent to suit an existing building. Tie rods are sloped and are protected by fire-retardant coating.

Purlins 16/26 cm are crossed, spaced at 2.50 m, and support ribbed 19 mm plywood panels. This configuration creates a statically efficient folded roof, which distributes the overturning and wind loads to several fixed reinforced-concrete columns. Visually, the configuration minimizes the bulk of 2.25 m high frame members. It also provides good drainage.

Cross section

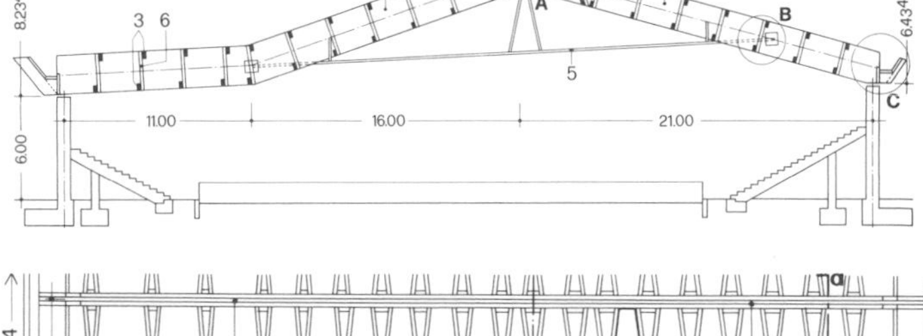

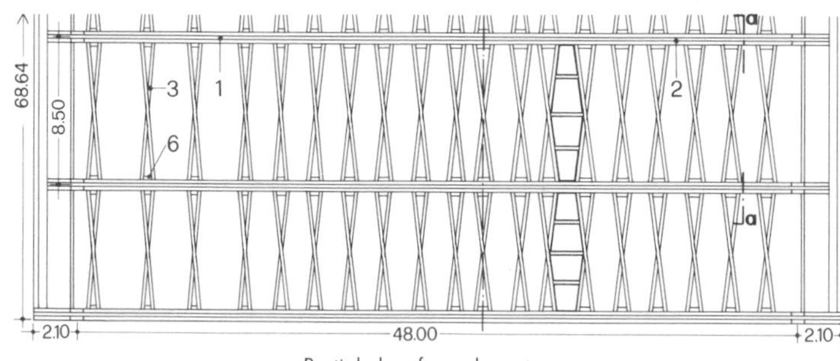

Partial plan, frame layout

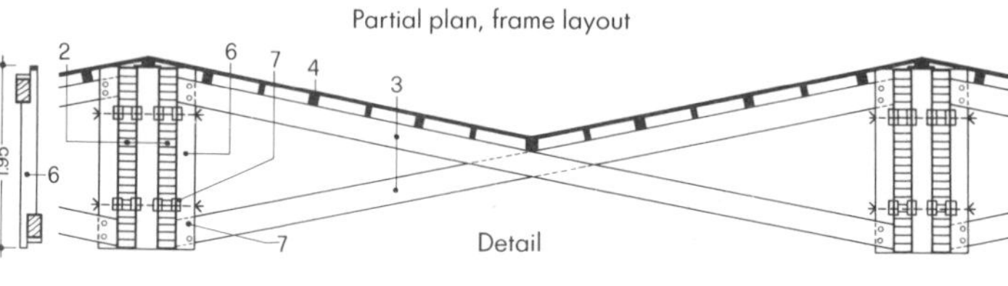

Detail

1 Main frame 2 × 22/225 cm
2 Main frame 2 × 22/195 cm
3 Purlins 16/26 cm
4 Plywood panels 19 mm, with ribs 10/10 and 6/10 cm
5 Double steel bar tie
6 Connection timbers for crossed purlins 16/20 cm
7 Shear connector ϕ 65 mm
8 Nail plate with reinforcement
9 Pin bolts ϕ 80 mm
10 Elastomeric bearing
11 Threaded rod for shear connectors ϕ 65 mm
12 Lockwashers
13 Linkage bolts ϕ 70 mm
14 Nuts
15 Filler wood 20/25 and 22/25 cm
16 Steel plates in slit, with bearing knobs
17 Dormer beam 2 × 20/85 cm

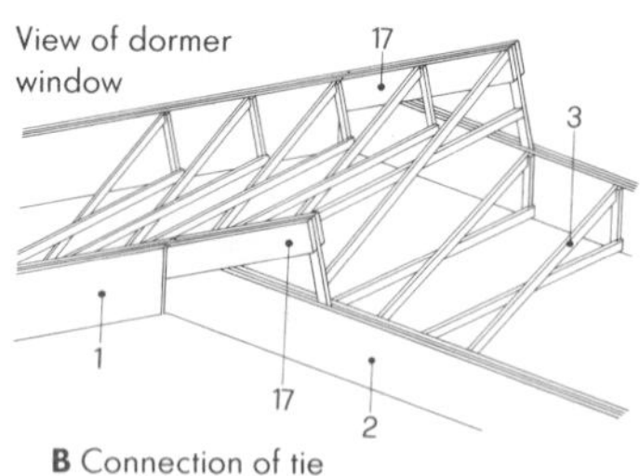

View of dormer window

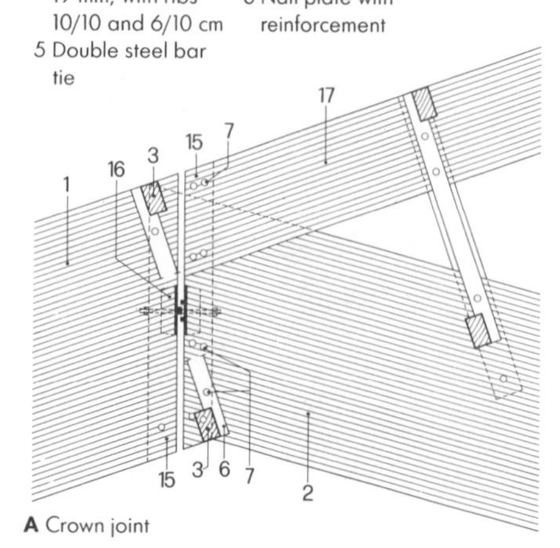

A Crown joint

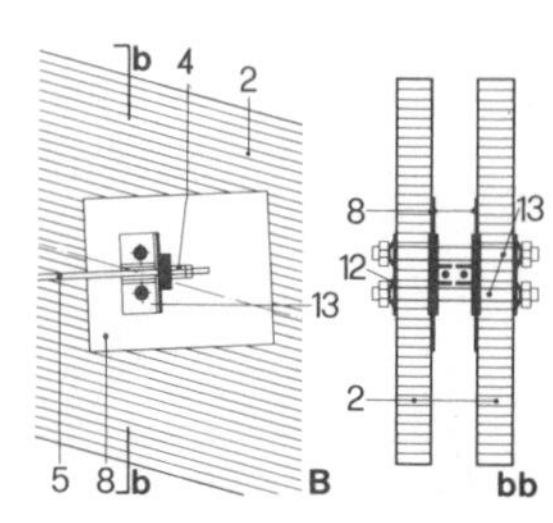

B Connection of tie rods

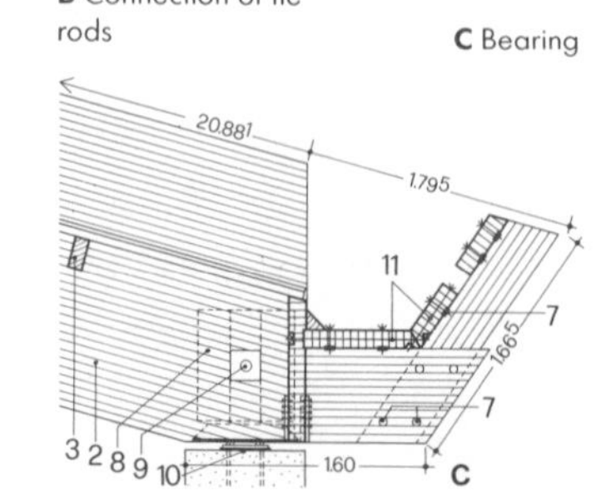

C Bearing

74 Riding Hall in Marbach, West Germany

Architect: State Building Department, Reutlingen
Engineer: J. Natterer, Munich

Main frames are bent girders with ties, twin construction, placed transversely to building at 7.15 m. Girders are deepest at bends, where moments are largest. Steel ties are 2 × ϕ 38 mm, St 52, with turnbuckle, anchored to girders with bolts, and nail plates between twin girders.

Purlins 18/26 cm run normal to roof slope, are supported by metal beam seats, and are subject to lateral forces due to their side slope. These forces are resisted by 5/60 mm flat steel bars reaching to ridge. These bars at the same time stiffen the purlins against buckling at one-third span points.

Laminated wood columns 22/90 cm are fixed on one side and pinned on other side. Fixed columns are on top of a reinforced-concrete frame and the foundation of the basement. Large lever arm results in smaller connection forces. At pinned end, wind forces are transferred from wood to concrete through a nail plate and a steel dowel. End roof bays contain diagonal flat steel bar bracing.

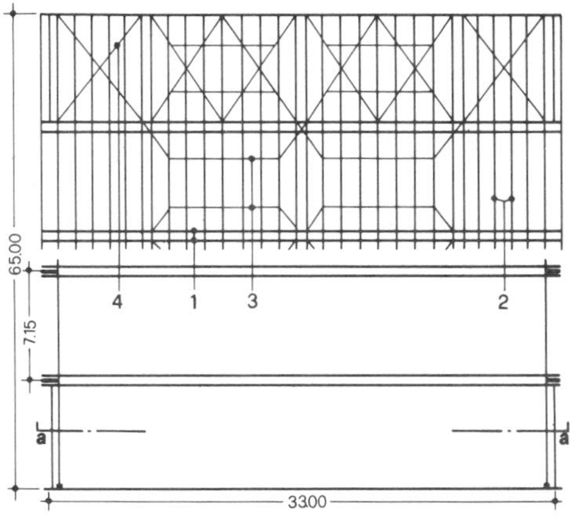

Plan of frames, purlins, and bracing

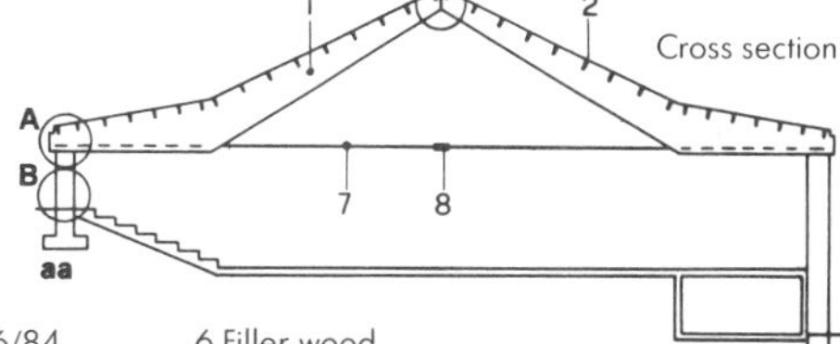

Cross section

1 Main frame 16/84 to 200 cm
2 Purlins 18/26 cm
3 Lateral support and bracing of purlins, flat steel 5/60 mm
4 Wind bracing, flat steel 5/120 mm
5 Column 22/90 cm
6 Filler wood 22/22 cm
7 Steel tie 2 × ϕ 38 mm, St 52
8 Turnbuckle
9 Nail plate
10 Steel box as bearing and tie anchorage
11 Elastomeric bearing
12 Steel plate, in slit, nailed
13 Steel dowel ϕ 36 mm
14 Steel dowels and bolts ϕ 24 mm
15 Shear bolt ϕ 36 mm

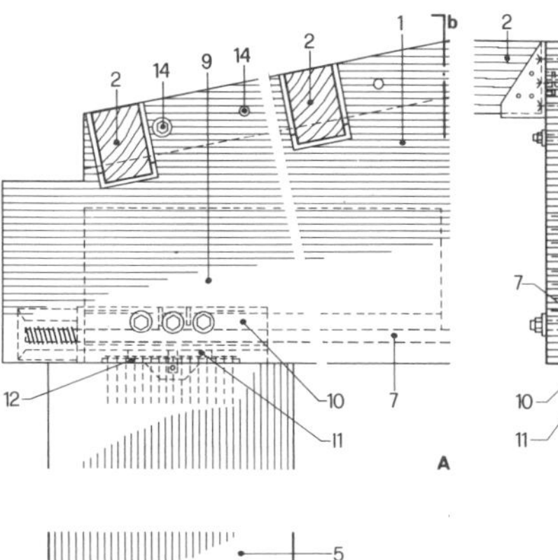

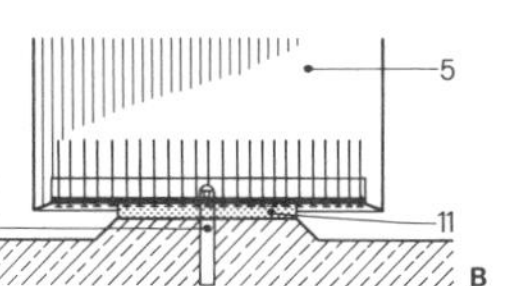

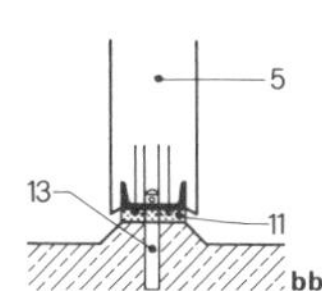

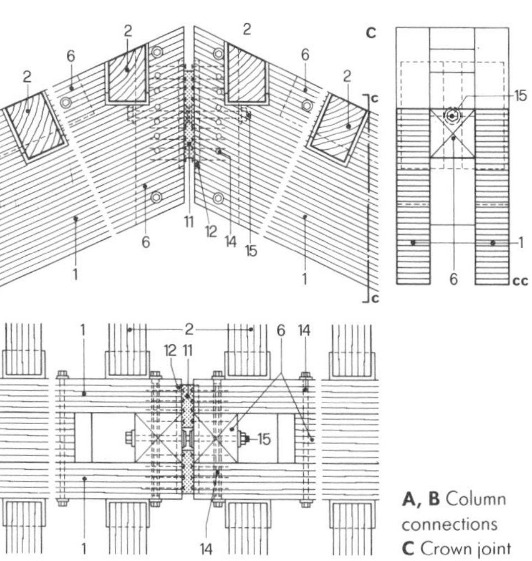

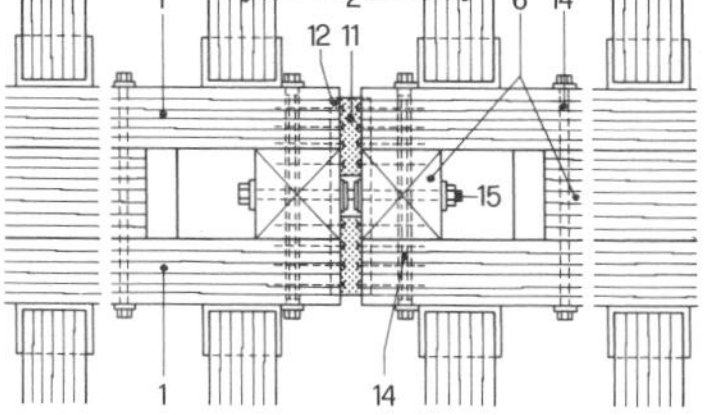

A, B Column connections
C Crown joint

Collar Beam Connections

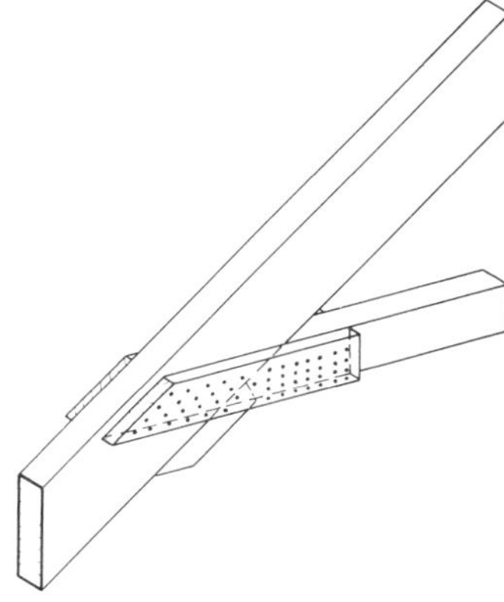

Side timbers, nailed, timber block for shear.

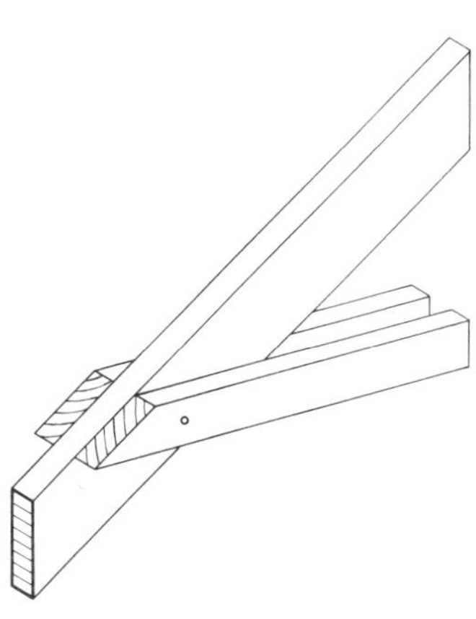

Twin-collar beam with shear connectors (and bolts).

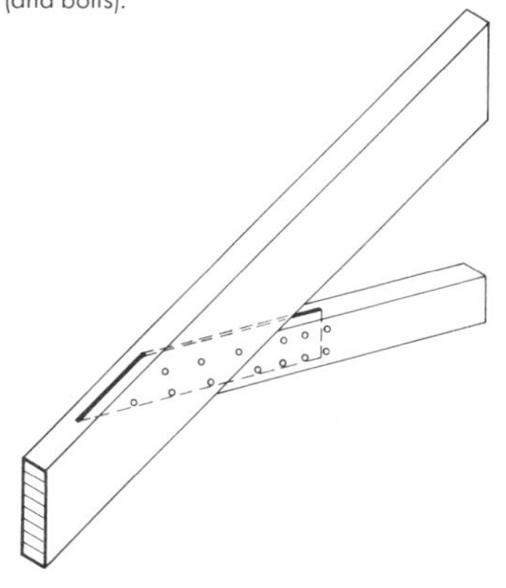

Steel plate in slit.

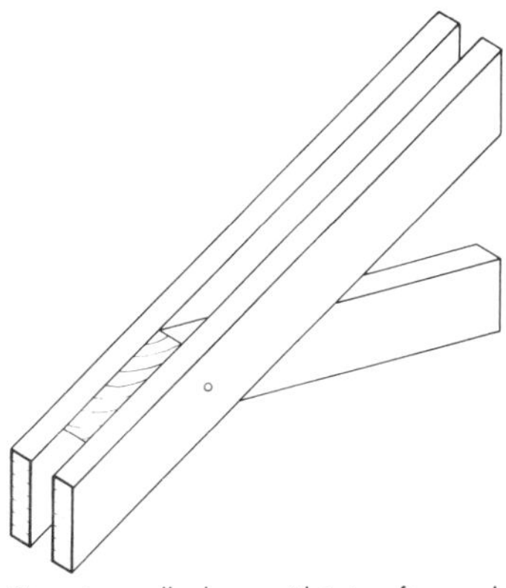

One-piece collar beam with twin rafters and shear connectors (and bolt).

Three-hinged frames composed of trusses are structurally similar to frames composed of beams. Design of trusses is governed by the choice of connections and their flexibility. Truss frame construction allows lighter roof construction, but attention must be paid to securing the system against uplift from wind forces.

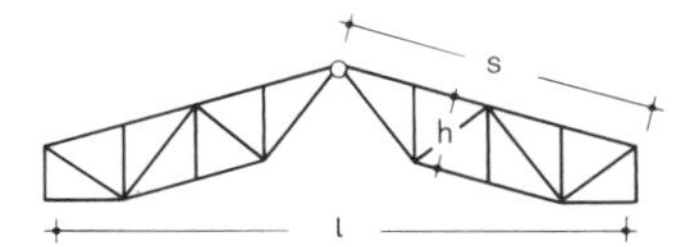

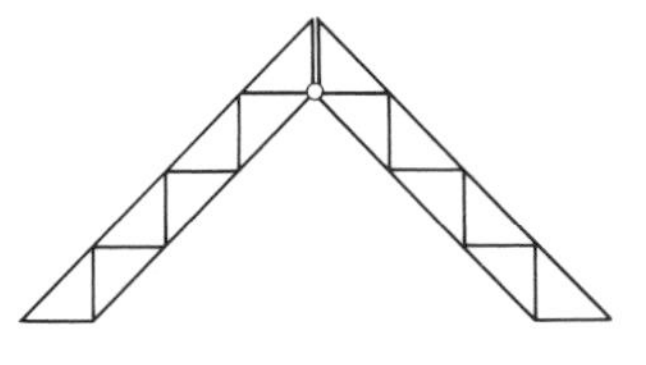

a = 5 to 8 m (spacing)
l = 15 to 50 m
h = l/15 to l/25

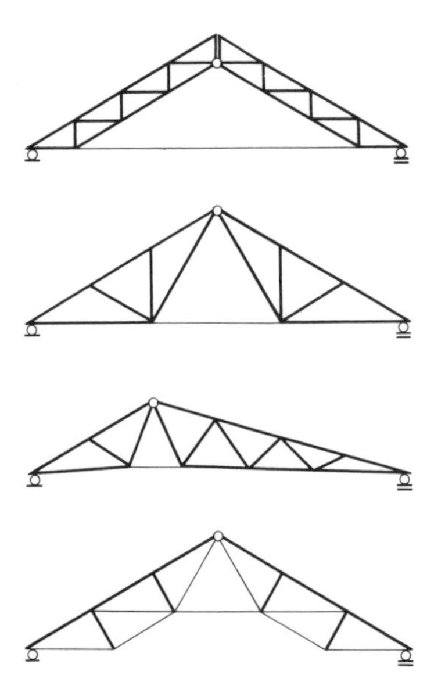

75 Ice Skating Rink in Freiburg, West Germany

Architect: C. Langenbach, Lahr
Engineer: N. Kopp, Lahr

Roof over an existing ice rink of 30.00 × 60.00 m surface. Earth embankment supports concrete bleachers for about 4500 spectators, sitting or standing. In transverse direction the main structural system consists of six three-hinged trussed frames with timber ties. Span is 42.00 m, frame spacing is 9.00 m, cantilevers on both ends are 4.00 m; total covered surface area is 50.00 × 76.00 m. Parallel upper and lower truss chords are triple, diagonals and struts are double. Joints contain shear connectors ϕ 80 mm. Sloping secondary trusses spaced at 1.00 m span between main frames. Secondary trusses are supported on one side on upper and lower chords of truss frames, on other side they rest on upper chord. This arrangement creates four clerestory windows. Main frames slope 23°, secondary trusses 15°. Roofing is corrugated asbestos cement. Wind forces in roof are transferred through central bay bracing, vertically through wind struts in end walls and through half-frames in end bays of end walls.

Reference: *Bauen mit Holz* 9/1970, p. 426; *Bauwelt* 29/1972, p. 1120

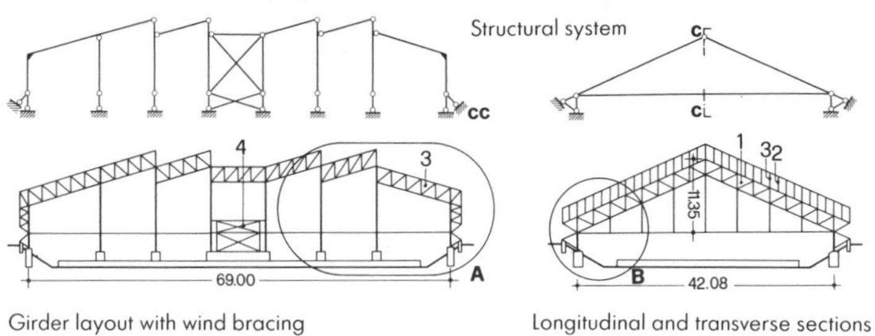

Girder layout with wind bracing

Longitudinal and transverse sections

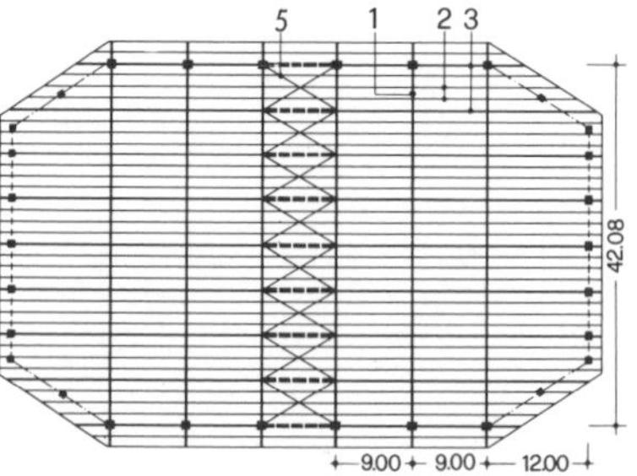

1 Main frame, dimension lumber
2 Secondary truss
3 Reinforced secondary truss as longitudinal bracing or half-frames in end bays
4 Vertical bracing
5 Wind bracing
6 Upper and lower chords 3 × 12.5/28 cm
7 Tie 2 × 10/30 cm
8 Diagonals and struts 2 × 10/10 to 24 cm with shear connectors ϕ 80 mm
9 Columns 2 × 10/24 + 2 × 6/24 cm
10 Filler wood with ϕ 12 mm bolts
11 Anchor plate of U shape 400 mm reinforced as tie beam
12 Steel gussets 4 × 240 × 800 × 10 mm with ϕ 190 mm shear connectors
13 Each gusset 2 welded M30 screwed onto 11
14 Wind load struts
15 Corrugated asbestos-cement panels

B Partial transverse section

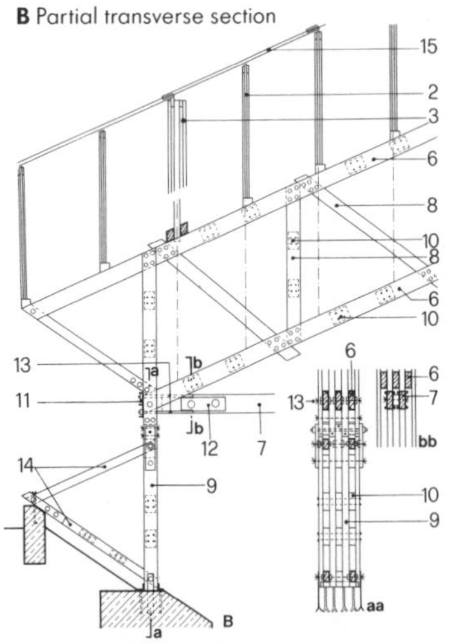

A Partial longitudinal section

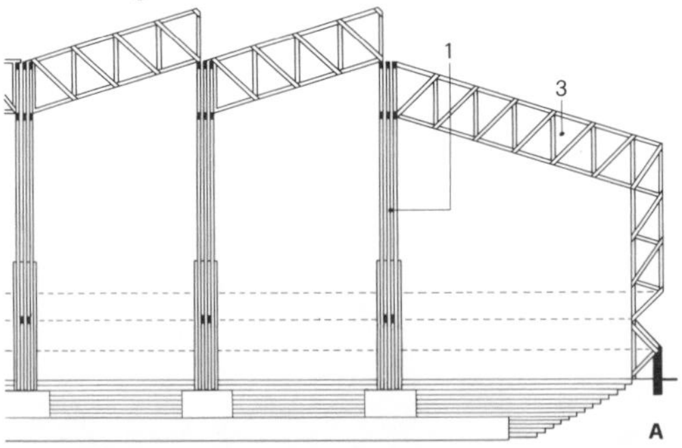

76 Concert Hall in Snape, Great Britain

Architects and engineers: Arup Assoc., London

During remodeling of old malt house into concert hall with 840 seats, perimeter walls were raised and stabilized by means of a reinforced-concrete ring. Original roof shape was retained as well as four large timber ventilation shafts.

Through these measures the historic character of malt houses in this region was retained. Beam frames span transversely 18.30 m. They consist of two sloped subtensioned beams connected at ridge by a horizontal beam. Ridge bay is subtended by two crossed ties, so that system represents a transition from a subtensioned three-hinged frame to a truss.

Frames are spaced at 3.80 m. Upper chords are double, compression struts are single, both of dimension lumber. Ties are round steel bars. Purlins run longitudinally. Two layers of crossed planking, together with hip roof ends, brace roof.

Reference: *Baumeister* 3/1968, p. 225

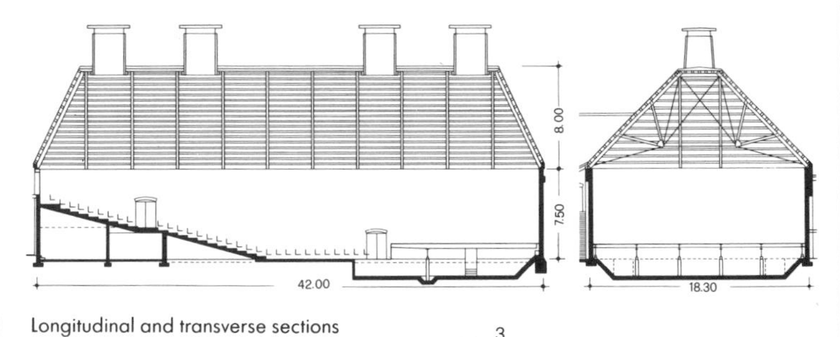

Longitudinal and transverse sections

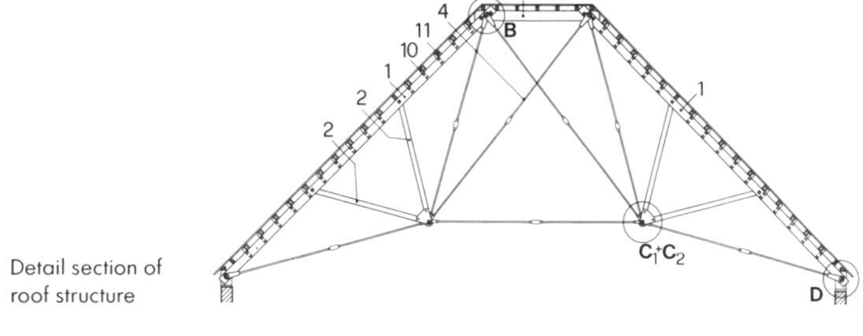

Detail section of roof structure

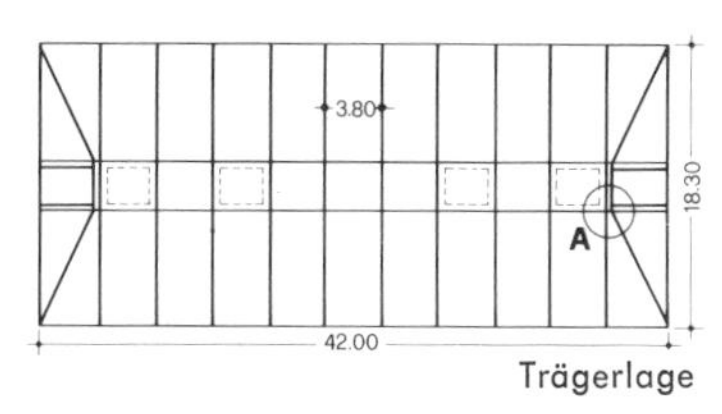

Trägerlage

A Connection of hip rafters
B Ridge with tie rods
C_1, C_2 Nodal points, tie rods, and compression struts
D Bearing

1 Upper chord 2 × 4.5/23 cm lumber
2 Compression struts 9.5/11 cm lumber
3 Compression struts 9.5/23 cm lumber
4 Tie rods ϕ 19 mm
5 Hip rafters 2 × 4.5/23 cm in hip roof surface
6 Shear connectors ϕ 100 mm
7 Connection plate
8 Cover plates
9 Bolts ϕ 50 mm
10 Filler wood
11 Purlins

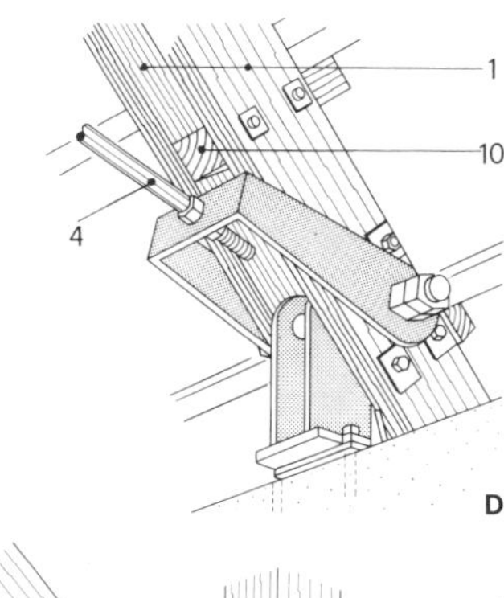

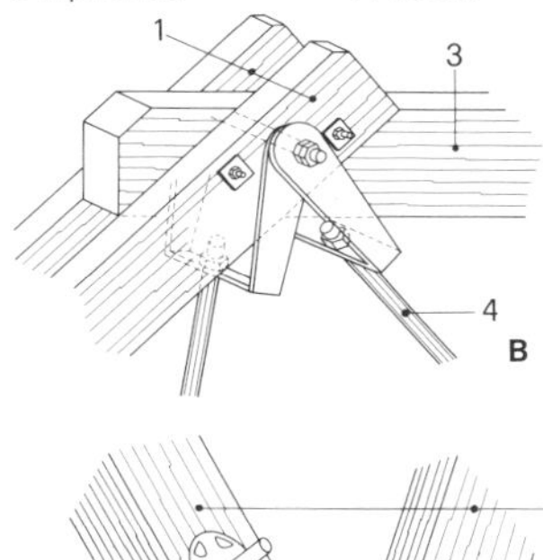

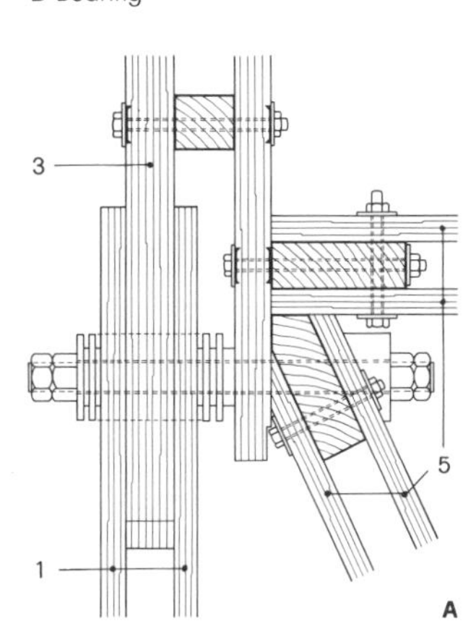

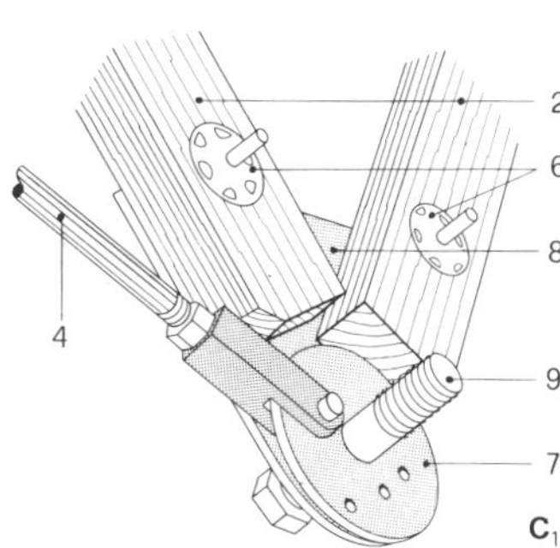

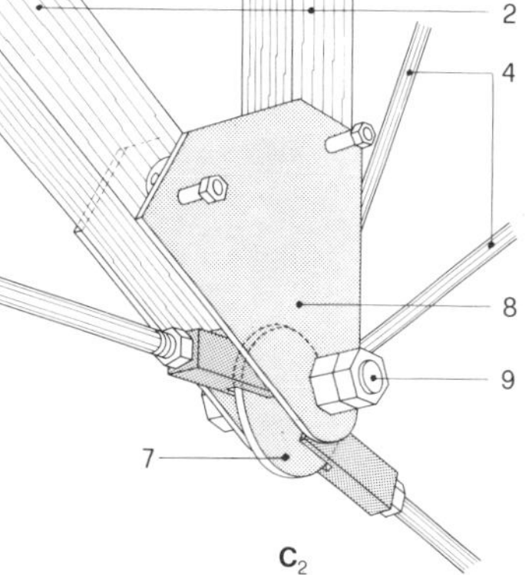

Connections of Subtensioning to Compression Posts

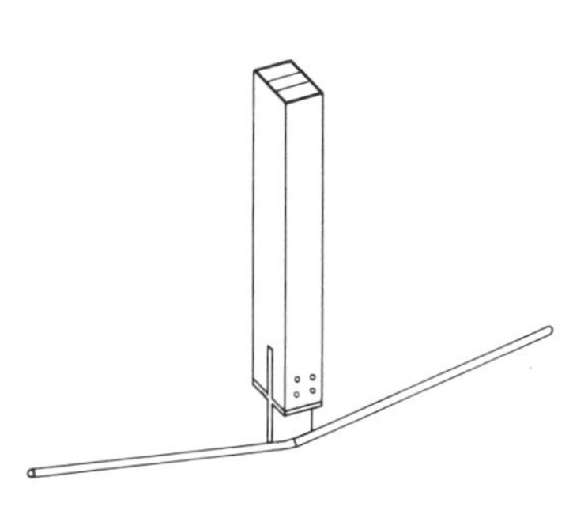

Steel plate in slit, with compression plate; welded tie rod.

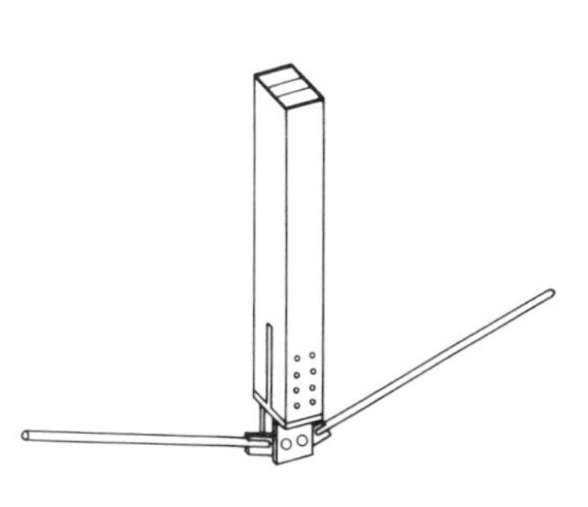

Steel plate in slit, with compression plate; tie rod linked.

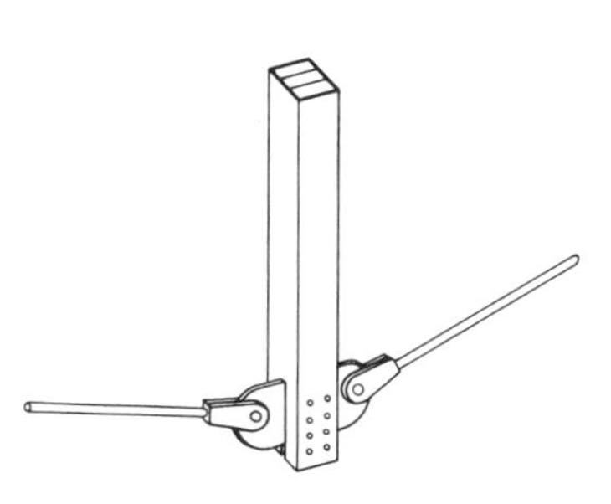

Steel plate in slit, with link connectors.

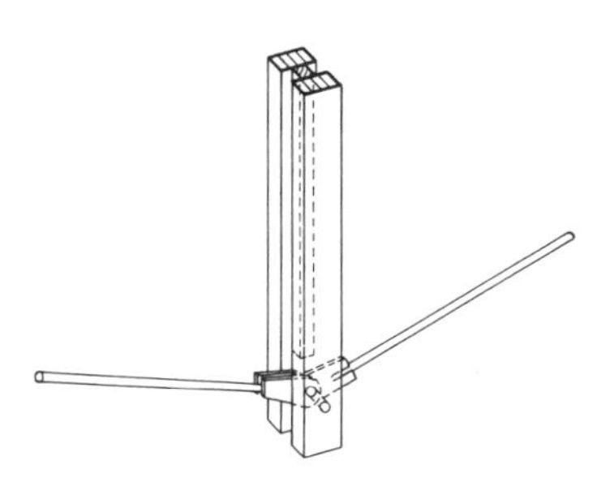

Link connection on double struts, with bolt and shear connectors.

Spacially arranged hinged beams consist of statically determinate three-hinged beams with a common crown joint, but arranged in plan and elevation in different ways. In spite of a spacial configuration, the load is supported through a planar arrangement in which to each beam corresponds another one in the opposite direction. Various horizontal forces generated in each plane can be resisted by individual footings or can be balanced by ties connecting individual footings. If a peripheral ring is used for that purpose, attention must be paid to unsymmetrical wind or snow loads causing high lateral stresses in the tension ring.

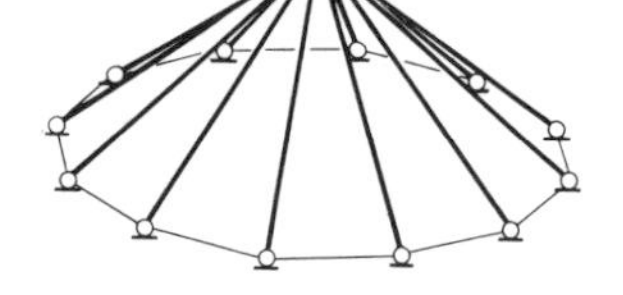

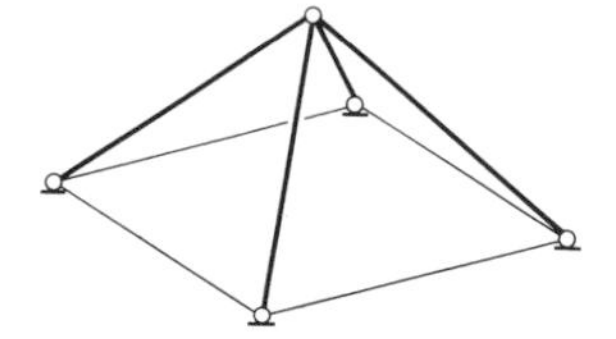

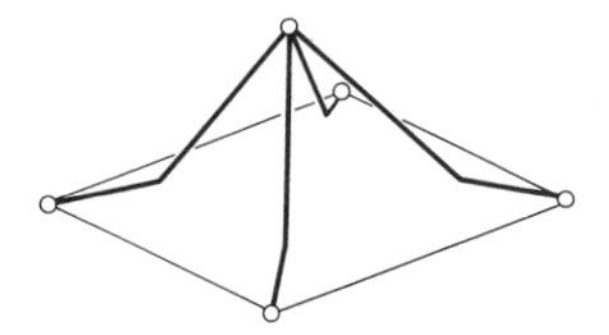

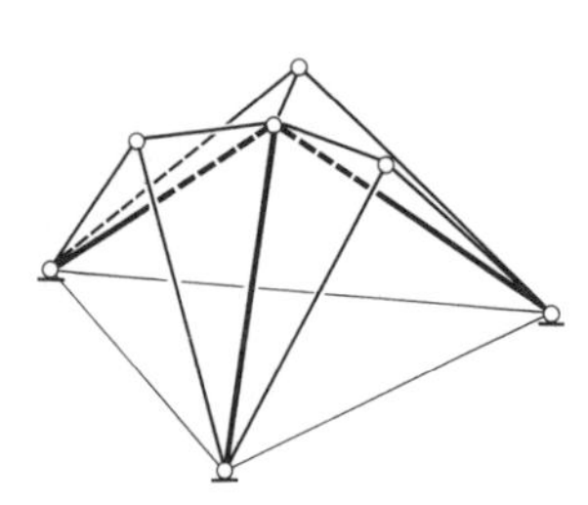

Symmetrical arrangement

77 Exhibition Pavilion in Berkeley, United States

Architects: Ratcliff, Slama, Cadwalader

Roof of exhibition pavilion is a space system of three-hinged beams. Longitudinally, the center field has crossed diagonals.

In order not to interrupt natural grades, building is set up on round timber columns which pierce the cantilevered platform and support the roof. Exterior walls are behind columns so that columns are exposed in their full length, thus giving a marked character to the building. Columns (ϕ 30 cm) are pressure-treated; they are fixed at foundation and platform levels because platform is laterally supported by walls. Timber platform is a box structure, with plywood flanges, solid wood webs, and cross ribs.

Reference: *Detail* 6/1976, illustrations

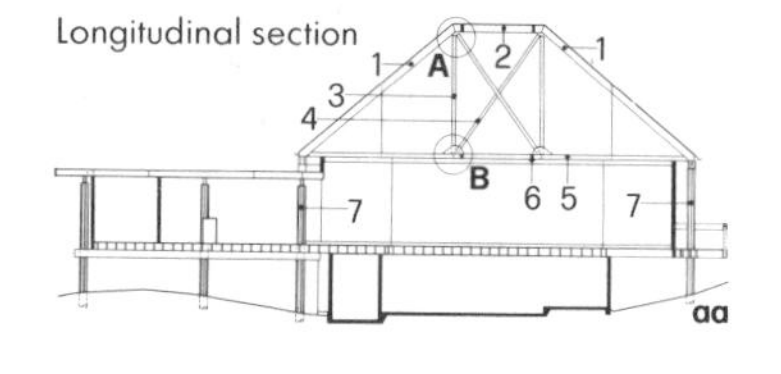

Longitudinal section

bb Cross section

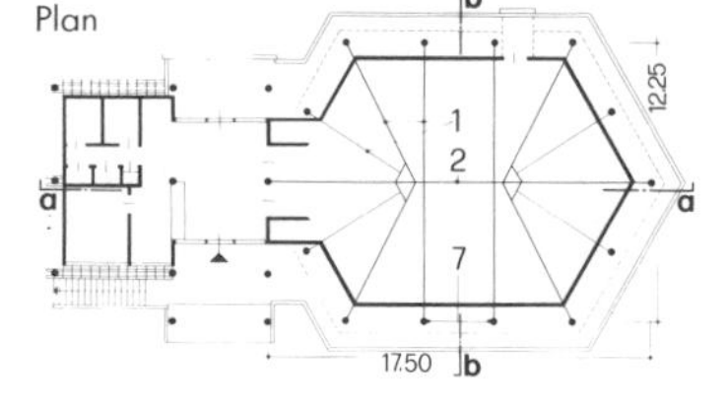

Plan

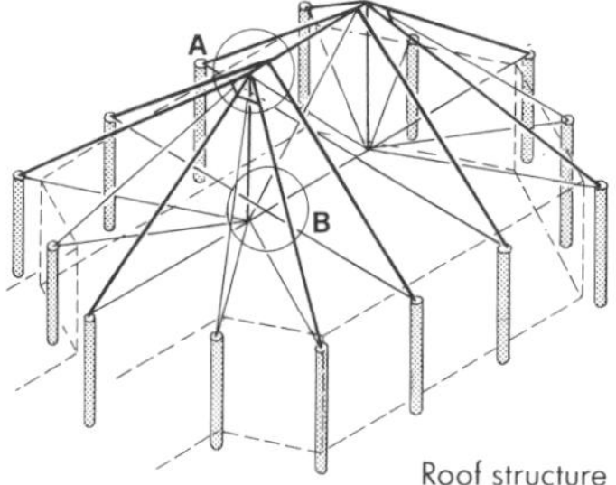

Roof structure

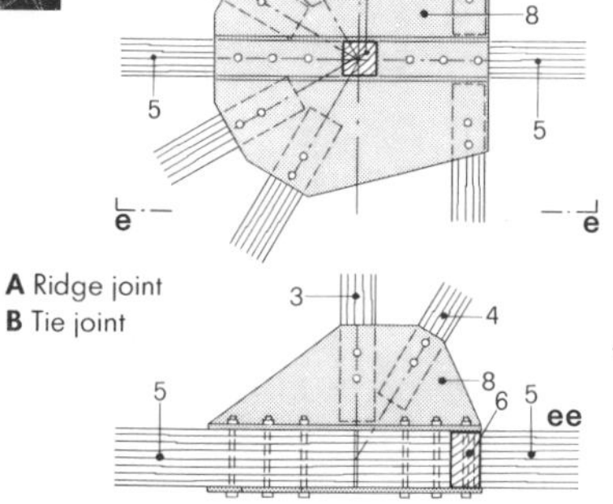

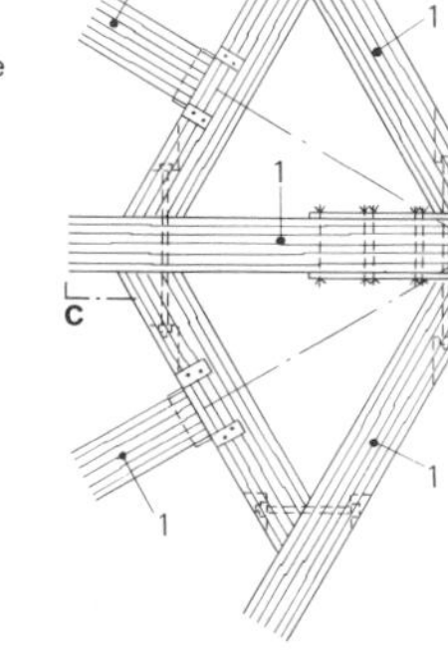

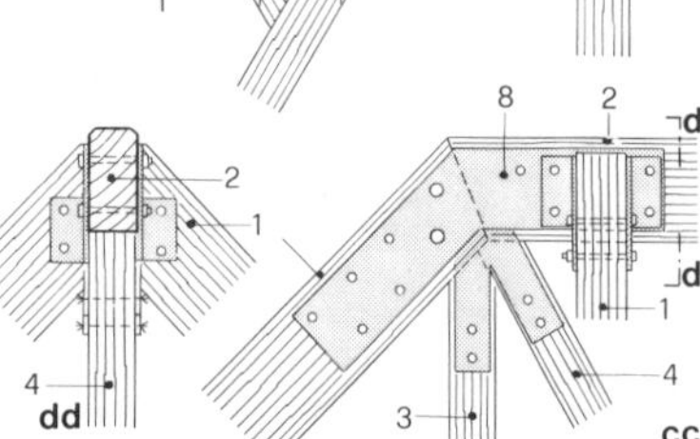

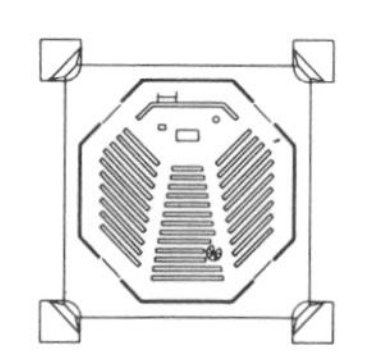

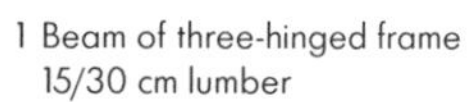

1 Beam of three-hinged frame 15/30 cm lumber
2 Ridge beam
3 Struts
4 Diagonal bracing
5 Tie beam, longitudinal
6 Tie beam, transverse and radial
7 Round timber columns ϕ 30 cm
8 Gusset plate

A Ridge joint
B Tie joint

78 Church in Bensberg, West Germany

Architect: G. Rasch, Cologne

Three-hinged frames are arranged over a square plan of 25.00 × 25.00 m such that roof shape is composed of four diamond-shaped planes. Walls of octagonal church appear as low reinforced-concrete panels with clerestory windows reaching to roof.

Four individual footings are tied together with reinforced-concrete grade beams, and serve as support for seven frames, one of which reaches the peak and others the hips. Purlins run horizontally and are planked underneath. Roofing is bituminous paper and copper sheathing. The stand-up seams of roofing are so arranged that drainage is guided through the center of each roof surface to foundation.

Reference: *Detail* 2/1972, illustrations; *Bauen mit Holz* 4/1970, p. 168

Plan

Beam layout

25.00

View of structural system

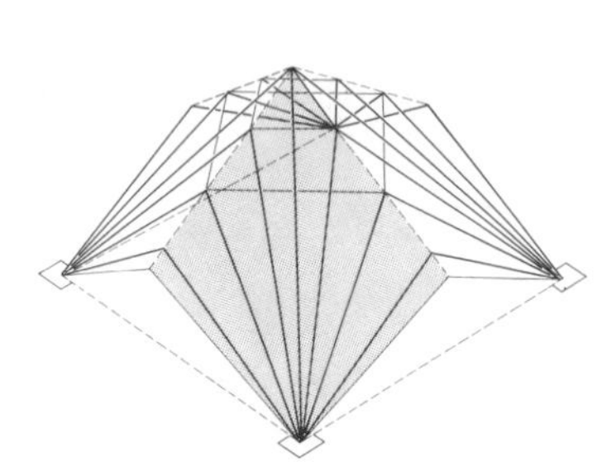

79 Open-Air Church in Stuttgart, West Germany

Architect: Beck-Erlang, Ulm
Engineer: P. Scherr, Ulm

Open-air church, for occasional use, is built in form of a pyramid with a roof in its upper area. Triangular box beams are made of web plates and laminated wood flanges. They span a length of 37.26 m and are 46.00 m long. Beam cross section varies and follows moment diagram. Beams are tied together at crown through bearing shoes of which two are fixed and one is pinned. In roof area beams are joined by purlins 14/70 to 2 × 14/115 cm and a bottom laminated wood beam 18/95 to 150 cm.

1 Triangular box beam, web plates, and laminated wood
2 Purlins 14/70 to 2 × 14/115 cm
3 Bottom beam 18/95 to 150 cm
4 Bridging by web plates
5 Web plate 8 cm
6 Splice backup
7 Laminated wood 14 cm
8 Lumber 10/14 cm at 4.00 m
9 Tie 2 × 3/14 cm
10 Joint shoe with one-sided shear connectors

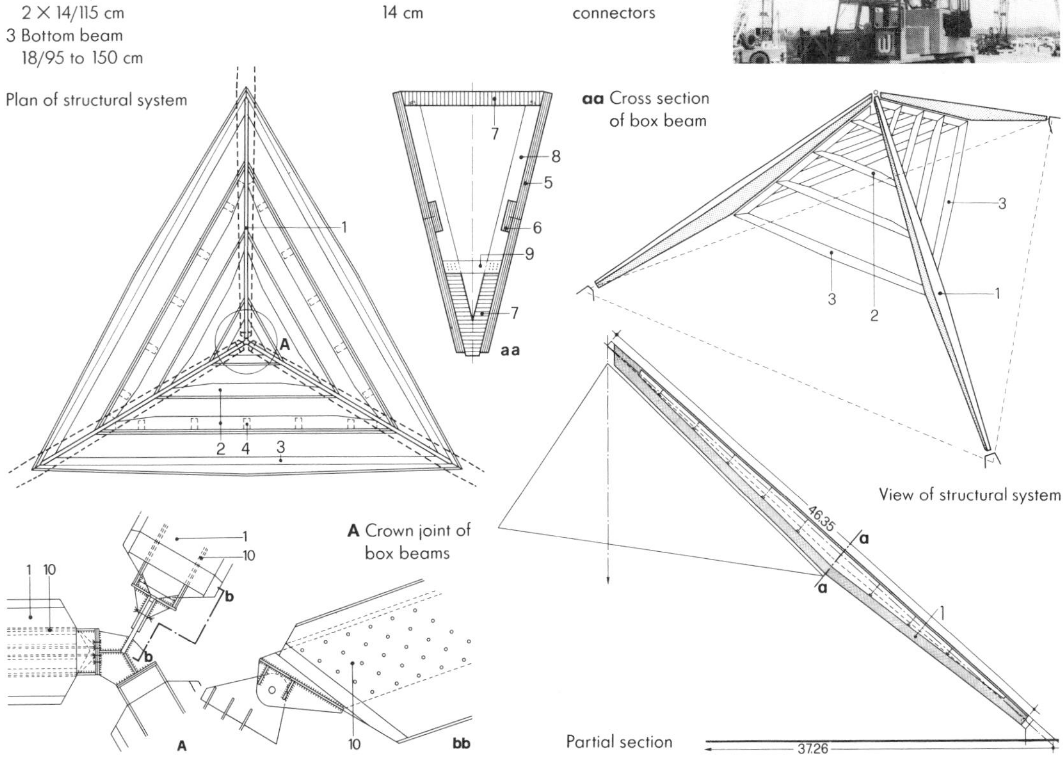

Plan of structural system

aa Cross section of box beam

View of structural system

A Crown joint of box beams

Partial section

80 Circus Building in Munich, West Germany

Architect: Galitz, Munich
Engineer: Reger, Munich

Circus dome consists of 24 radial laminated wood girders 18/105 cm. At bearings they are spaced at 6.25 m. Crown consists of a steel ring with bearing plates to which each beam is attached in a semirigid manner. Purlins 8/16 to 12/20 cm are arranged tangentially to steel ring. Radial beams are supported on a concrete wall by a steel shoe fitted in a beam recess. Roof slope is 23°. Purlins support planking and roofing.
Reference: *Bauen mit Holz* 4/1964, p. 156

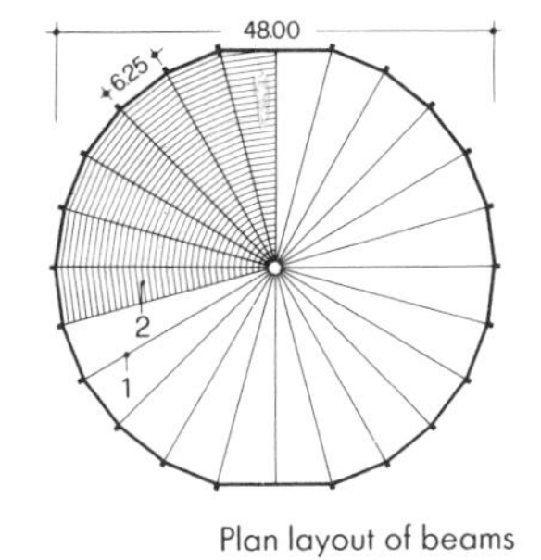

Plan layout of beams

1 Radial beams 18/105 cm
2 Purlins 8/16 to 12/20 cm
3 Beam shoe with bearing angle

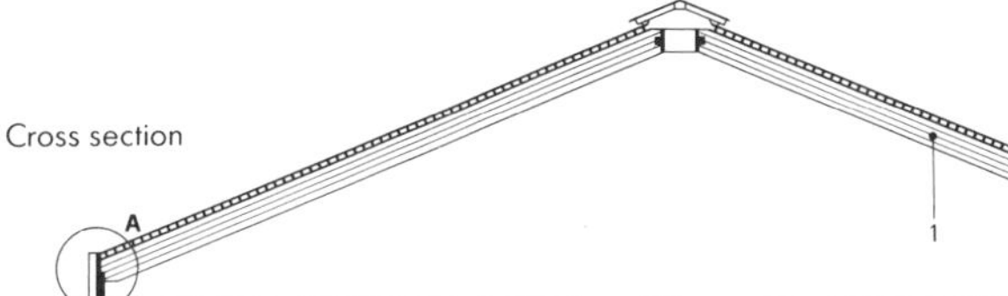

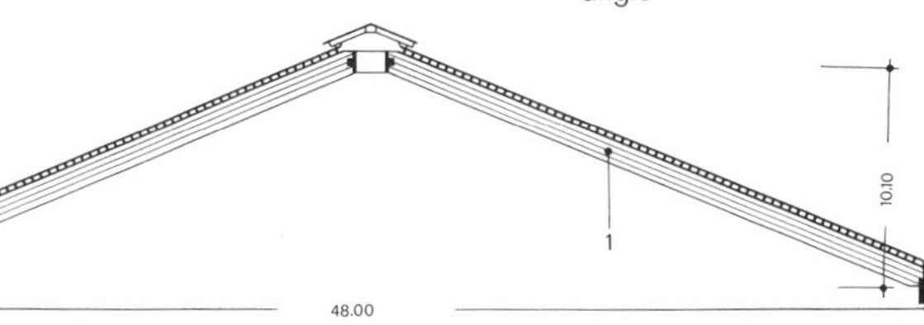

Cross section

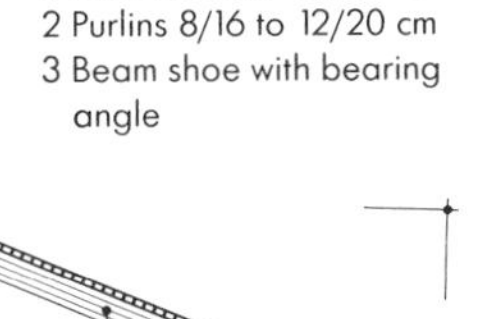

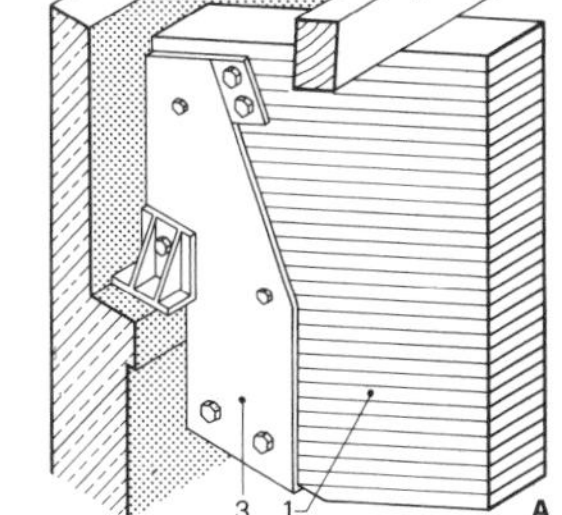

A Bearing

Roof Decking

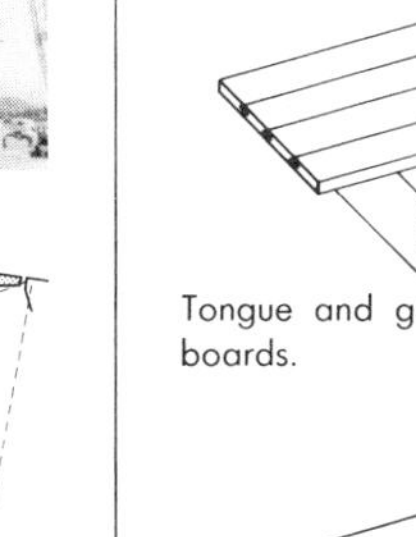

Fabric or plastic roof on braced beams.

Tongue and groove planking or splined boards.

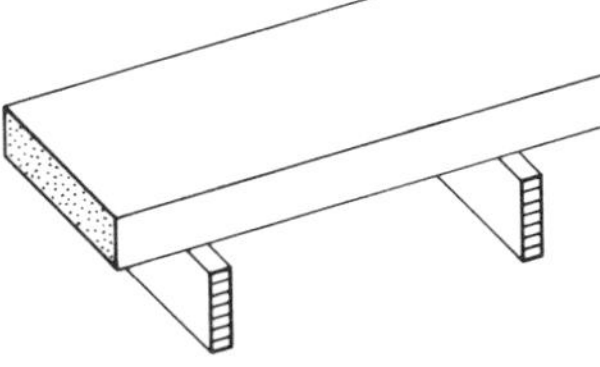

Planking of lightweight concrete or composite materials.

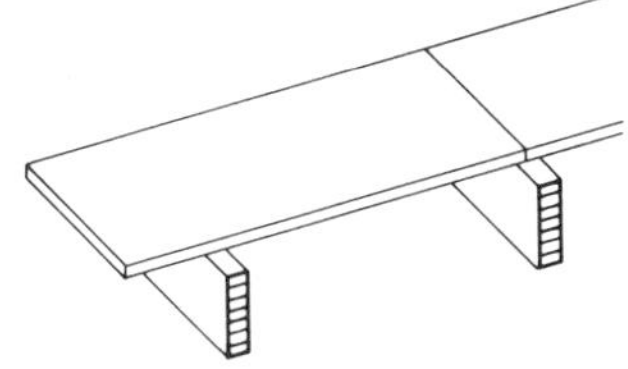

Wood-chip boards, plywood, or furniture panels.

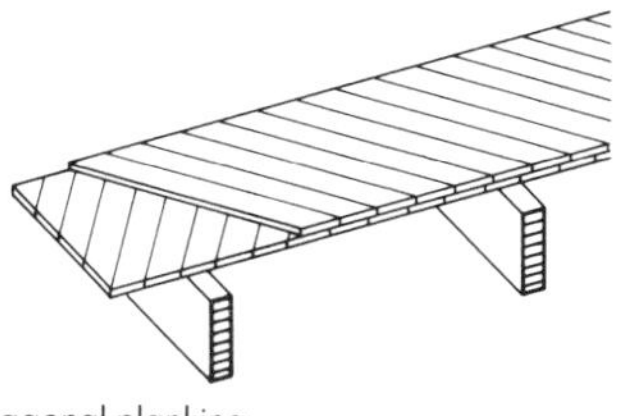

Diagonal planking.

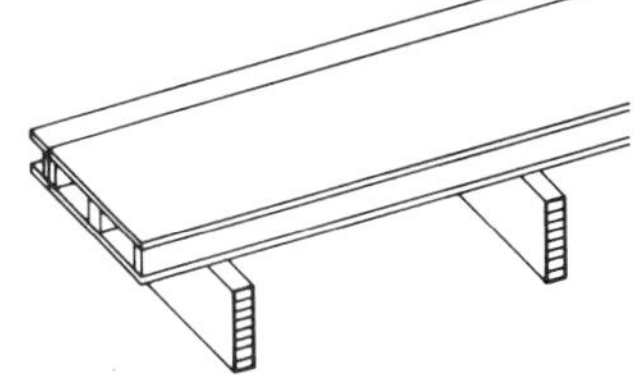

Panel elements of timber slats and sheathing.

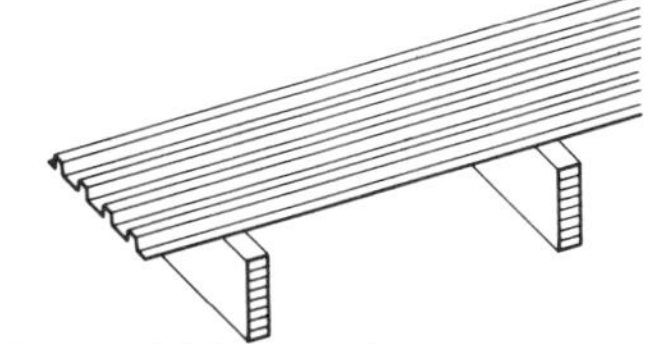

Trapezoidal sheet metal.

Schemes 3 to 7 may be used as rigid-plate elements for wind bracing and stiffening against lateral buckling.

When crowns of three-hinged frames do not meet in one point, the frame joints must be designed to maintain the stability of the structure.

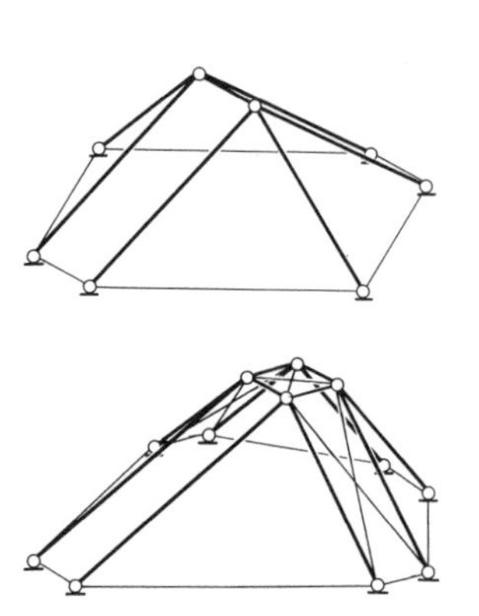

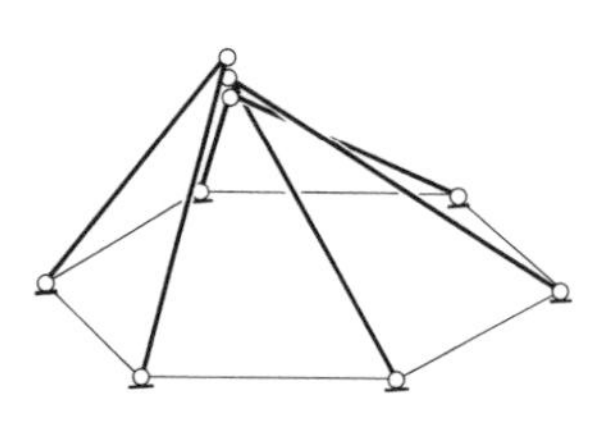

Unsymmetrical and scattered arrangement

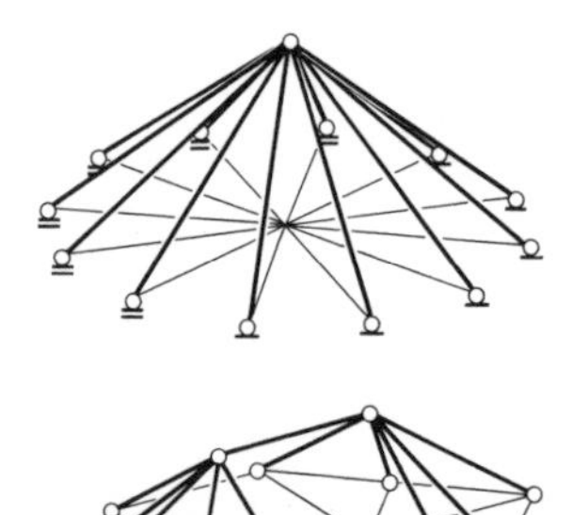

Frames with interior ties

81 Church in Recklinghausen, West Germany

Architect: F. Gantefüh- rer and F. Hannes, Recklinghausen
Engineer: E. Krabbe, H. Kintrup

Pyramid-shaped roof rises over hexagonal plan. Roof is supported by six hip beams hinged top and bottom and supported by walls. Crown point does not lie over the center of hexagon, but is offset 4.20 m. Result is a roof of variable slopes and beams of different lengths. Twin beams 2 × 17/100 to 150 cm are connected at supports by steel shoes, dowels, and pins. At crown, they are joined through plates and shear connectors to a steel tube. In addition, beams are supported at gutter line by laminated wood box columns. This reduces the beam span.

Purlins are placed parallel to gutter line and have dimensions 12/38 to 12/50 cm, depending on span. They support 2.4 cm sheathing and corrugated asbestos-cement panels over bituminous felt and nailers. Roof is stiffened by flat steel diagonals, which are connected to beams by steel plates and one-sided shear connectors.

During erection a tripod was set up by two mobile cranes; crown joint was rigidly affixed to one beam. After this, successive beams and purlins could be attached without temporary supports.

Reference: *Bauen mit Holz* 7/1973, p. 377

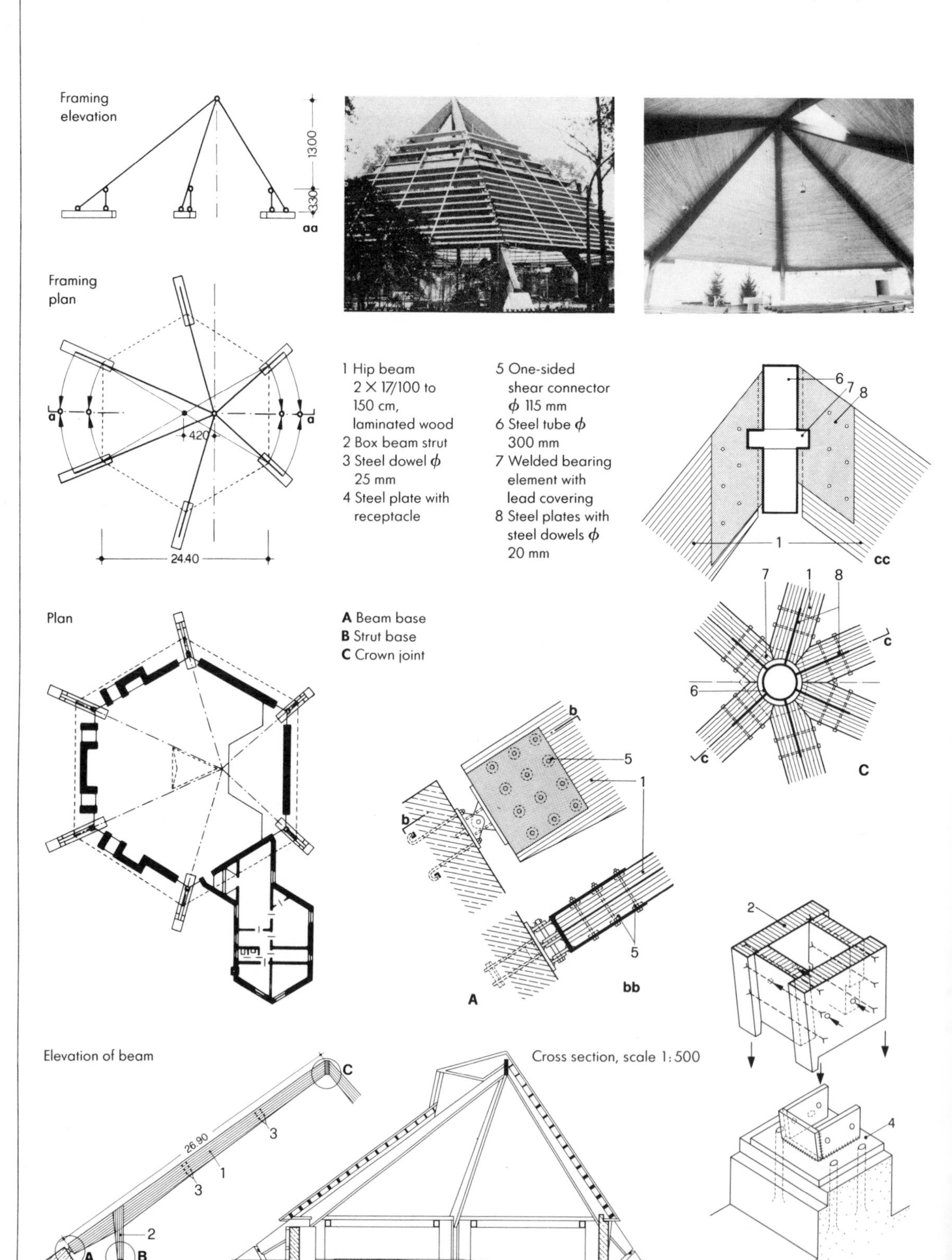

82 Church in Altendorf, West Germany

Architect: M. Ludes, Dorsten
Engineer: A. Sondermann, Dorsten

Roof has the shape of skewed pyramid and rises over trapezoidal plan with cut-off corners. Main beams are coupled and spaced 2.80 m apart; they are located at the hips. A square field of 2.80 × 2.80 m is formed at crown. Beams have a moment connection on one side of crown square, and a pin on the other, so that there is a three-hinged frame in each plane.

Horizontal bracing is through diagonal steel bars between beams. Secondary beams 12/30 to 15/58 cm span between main beams and gutter. Purlins 10/10 cm run parallel to gutter and carry 2.4 cm thick roof sheeting and corrugated asbestos-cement panels.

Reference: *Deutsche Bauzeitschrift* 7/1974, p. 1249

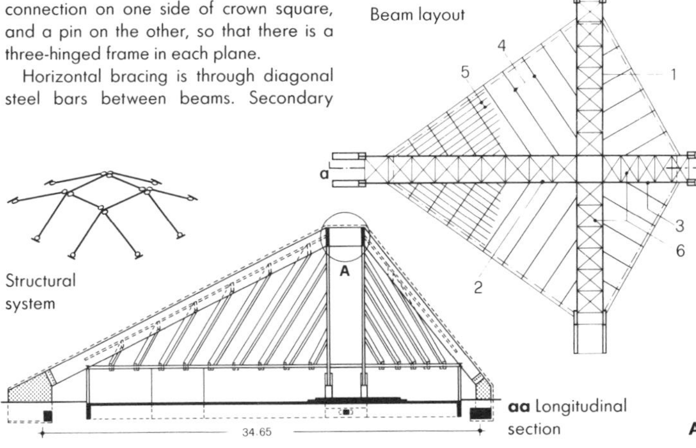

Beam layout

Structural system

aa Longitudinal section

1 Beam 20/120 cm
2 Beam 20/132 cm
3 Beam 20/92 cm
4 Rafters 12/30 to 15/58 cm
5 Purlins 10/10 at 52 cm, with planking 2.4/12 cm, tongue and groove
6 Wind and lateral bracing
7 Fixed joint
8 Pinned joint

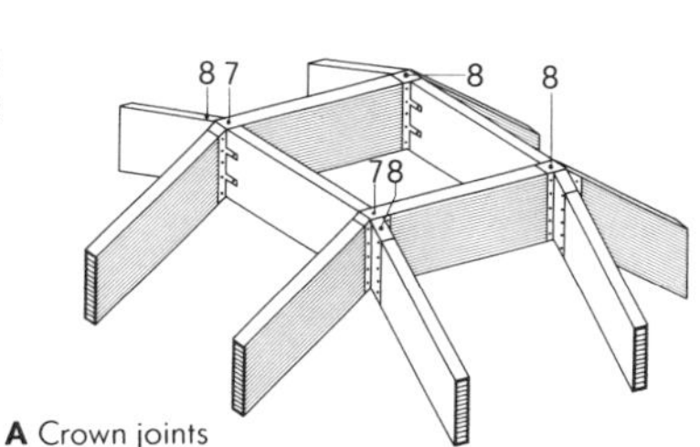

A Crown joints

83 Church in Windach, West Germany

Architect: J. Wiedemann, Munich
Engineer: C. Michael, Munich

Twelve radially arranged beams form tent-like roof 25.00 m high. Base of beams is pinned at concrete footing and is secured against lateral movement by a steel plate. At crown, beams are joined by steel pins, which are offset and spiral upward, but each pin joins two beams lying in a plane, so that each pair of beams forms a three-hinged frame.

Purlins are parallel to gutters and span between beams; they are 8/28 to 32/28 cm, spaced from 58 to 124 cm. Purlins are supported by timber ledgers, attached to each side of beams. Diagonal planking, nailers, counternailers, and corrugated asbestos-cement panels rest on purlins. Underside of roofing is sheathed. Roof surfaces are set off from ground by continuous row of windows.

Reference: *Bauen mit Holz* 7/1973, p. 382

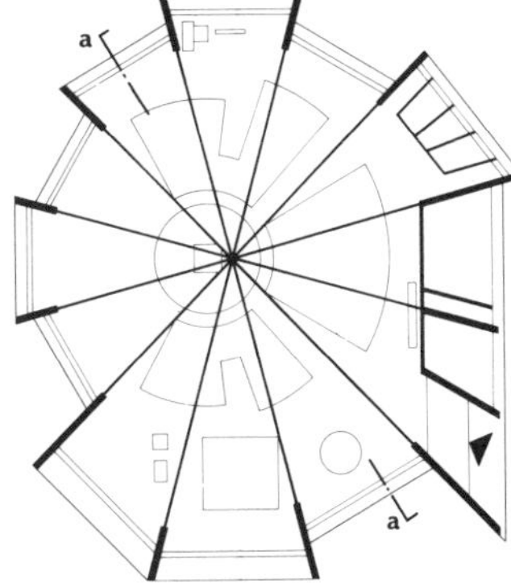

Beam layout

1 Bearing angle with 20 mm steel dowel
2 Joint shoe with ϕ 65 mm shear connector and wood screws
3 Welded steel joint spur
4 Steel pin ϕ 48 mm

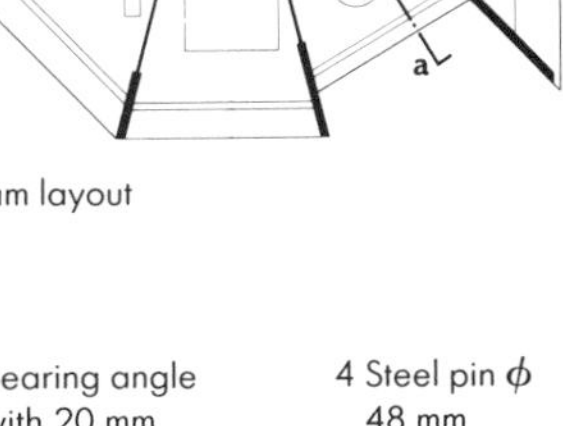

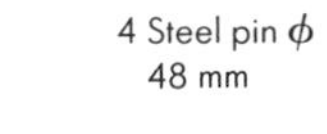

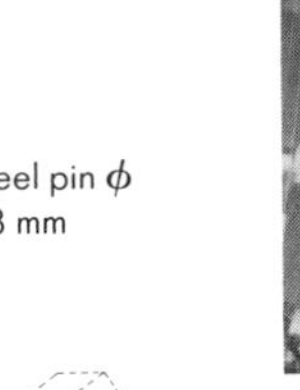

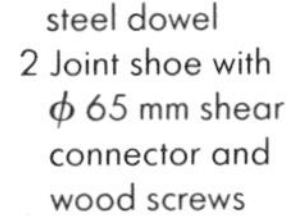

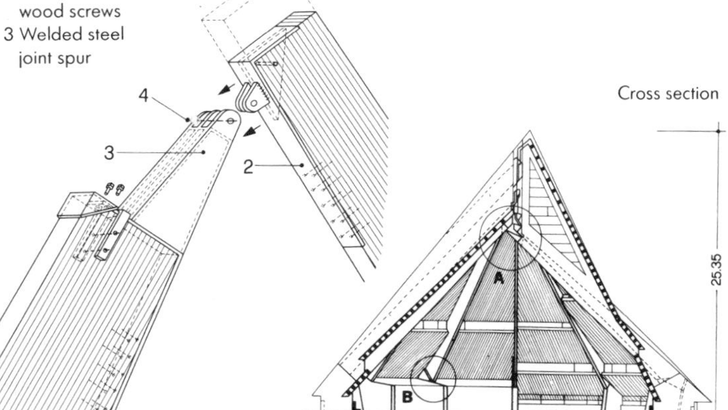

B Bearing

A Crown joint

Cross section

Field Connections of Purlins at Different Angles

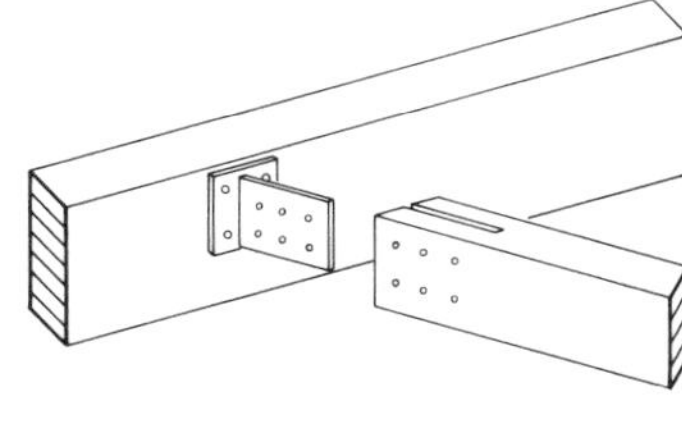

Exterior metal plates welded to shear-connected base plate.

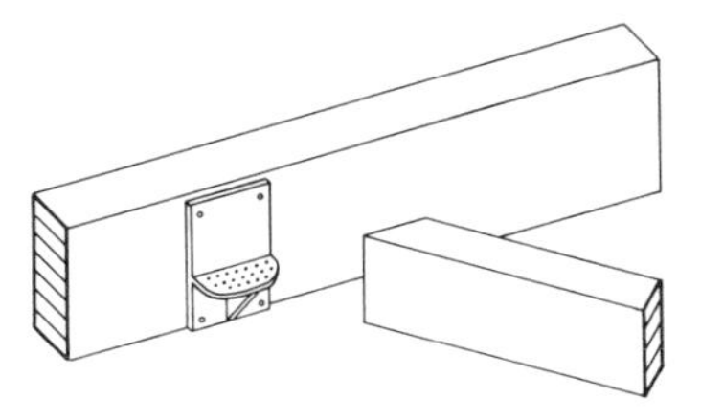

Web welded to base plate and doweled in purlin slit.

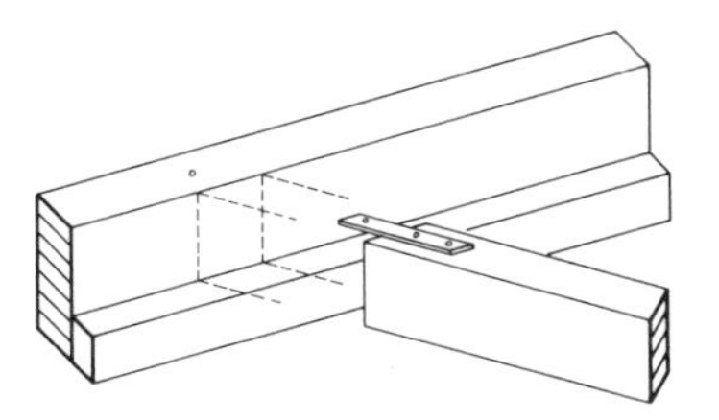

Bearing angle with stiffener.

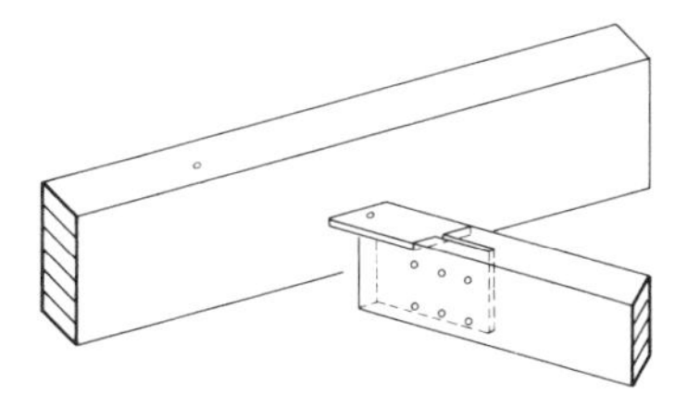

Timber ledger shear-connected to beam. Purlin secured by upper steel gusset.

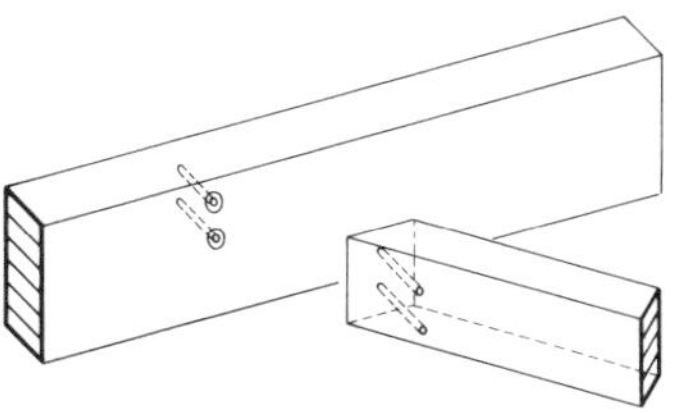

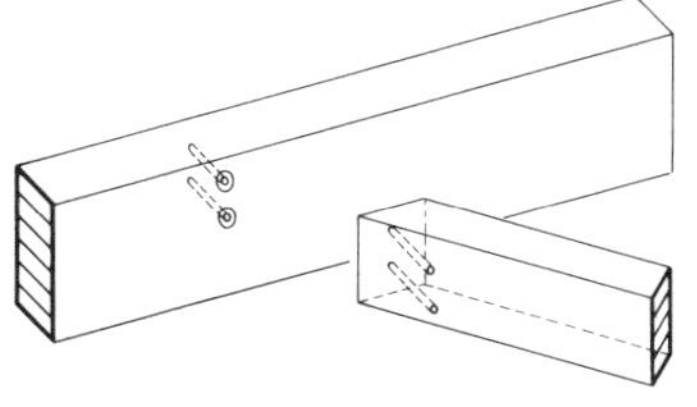

Pin connection with doweled steel plate.

Dowels in end face of purlins.

A two-hinged rigid frame is statically indeterminate to one degree and consists of two vertical legs hinged on bottom and a top beam rigidly connected to them. The moment connections of the beam to the frame legs transfer beam moments to legs. As a result, there are horizontal forces in the legs even if the exterior load is vertical. The design is governed not only by the bending in the beam and the legs, but also by the shears in the frame elbows. The stability of the frame must be analyzed because of compression forces, which are present both in the beam and in the legs of the frame.

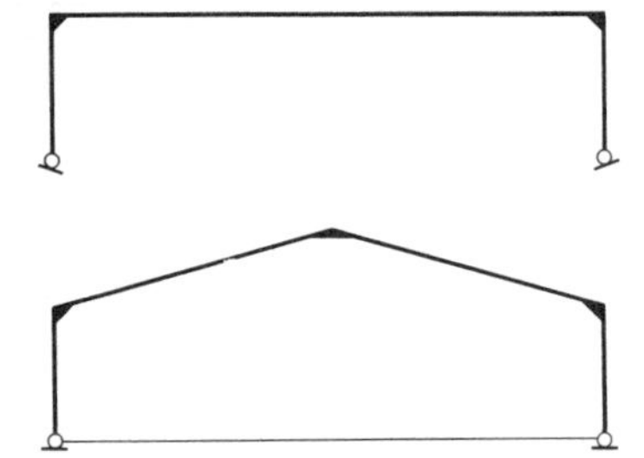

Frame-type legs corresponding to bearing reactions

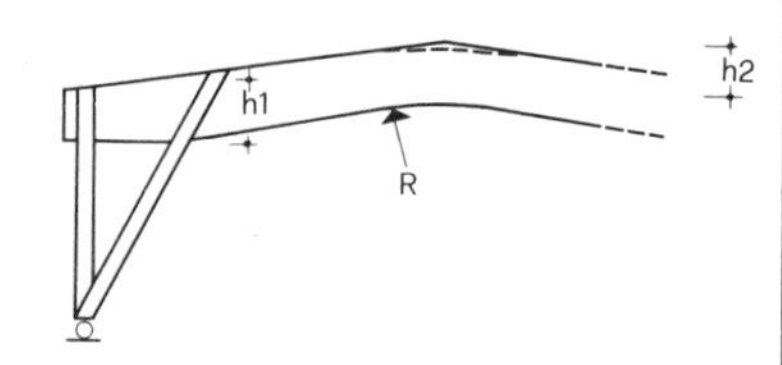

a = 4 to 6 m (spacing)
l = 10 to 35 m
$h_1 = l/20$ to $l/30$
$h_2 = l/15$ to $l/20$
$R \geq 10$ m

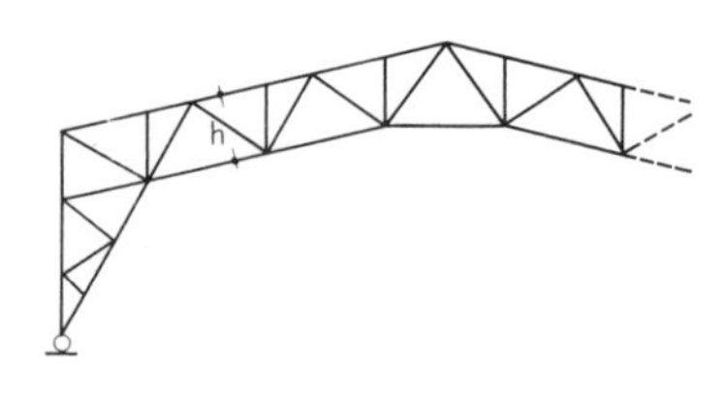

a = 4 to 10 m (spacing)
l = 10 to 50 m
$h = l/10$ to $l/15$

84 Tennis Hall in Ulm, West Germany

Architect: Reuter, Ulm
Engineers: J. Natterer and K. März, Munich

Multicourt tennis hall with overall surface of 70.00 × 31.00 m. Two-hinged frames placed transversely to building consist of single-component top beams 16/144 cm and framed legs. The 16/80 cm core layer of three-layer compression leg is notched into top beam. Tension leg 2 × 10/28 cm is connected to upper part of beam with shear connectors ϕ 115 mm. Roof is trapezoidal sheet metal spanning 5 m between frames in longitudinal direction. Wind and lateral bracing consist of trapezoidal sheet metal and flat steel bar diagonals, which connect to adjacent concrete structures.

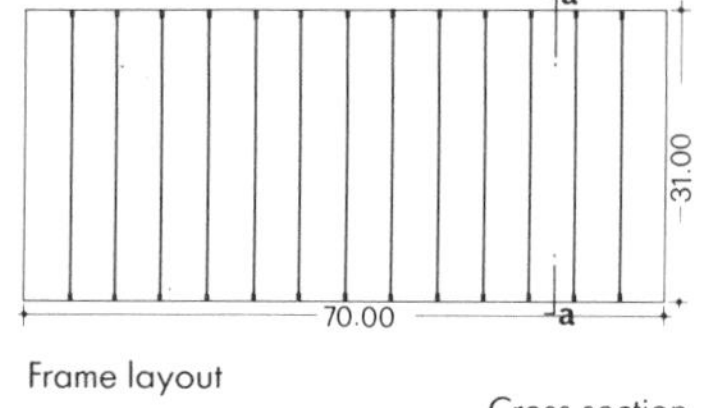

Frame layout

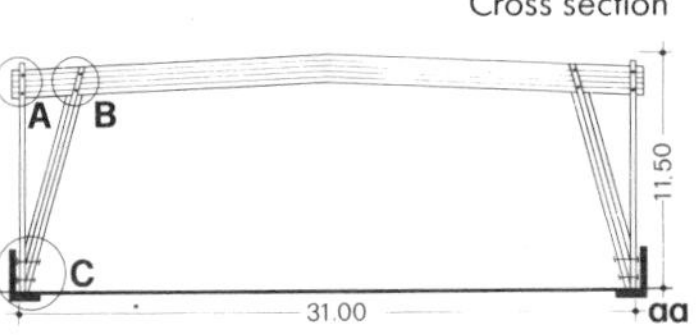

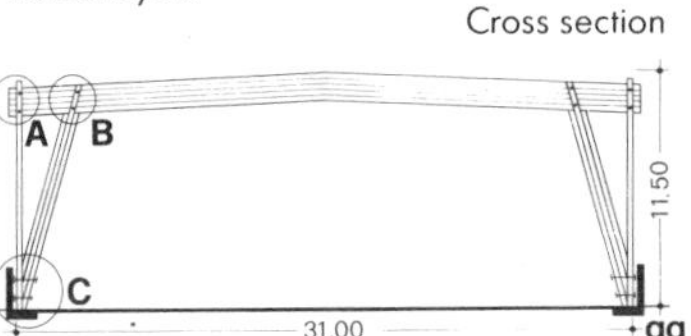

Cross section

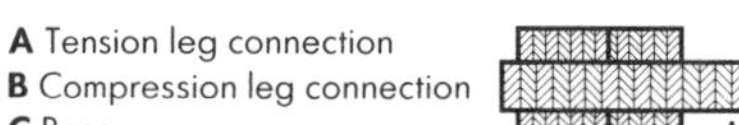

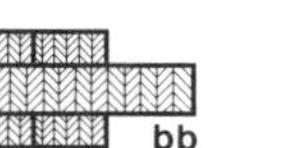

A Tension leg connection
B Compression leg connection
C Base

1 Top beam 16/144 cm
2 Tension leg 2 × 10/28 cm
3 2 × 4 shear connectors ϕ 115 mm
4 Bolts ϕ 16 mm, slotted holes
5 Compression leg 16/80 cm with side boards 10/28 cm
6 Bolts ϕ 16 mm
7 U shape 200 mm for horizontal shear
8 Bituminous felt

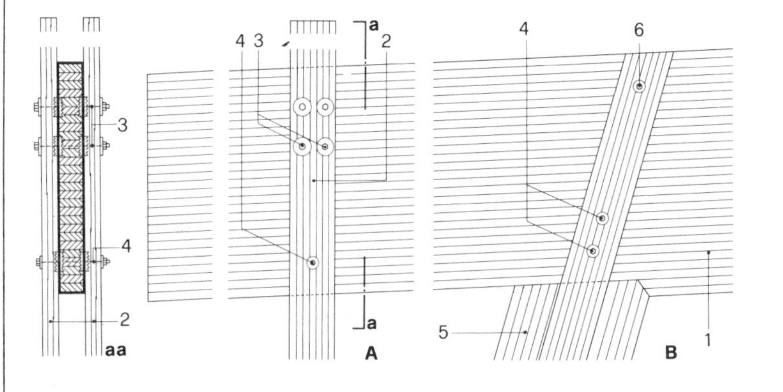

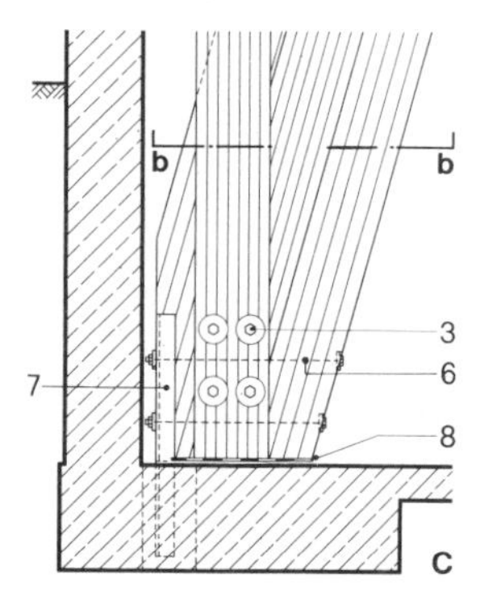

85 Industrial Building

Engineer: Timber Construction Contractor

Covered area 73.75 × 26.55 m, spanned transversely by two-hinged frames, spaced at 5.25 m, and longitudinally by lapped purlins; roof is corrugated asbestos cement sheeting.

Frames consist of one-piece beam with twin laminated wood legs; legs are joined by glued filler wood. Beams and legs were joined on site with shear connectors ϕ 65 mm arranged in a circle to form a rigid elbow. Three wind and lateral bracing trusses are made from lumber and are connected eccentrically by nails.

Reference: *Bauen mit Holz* 9/1969, p. 413

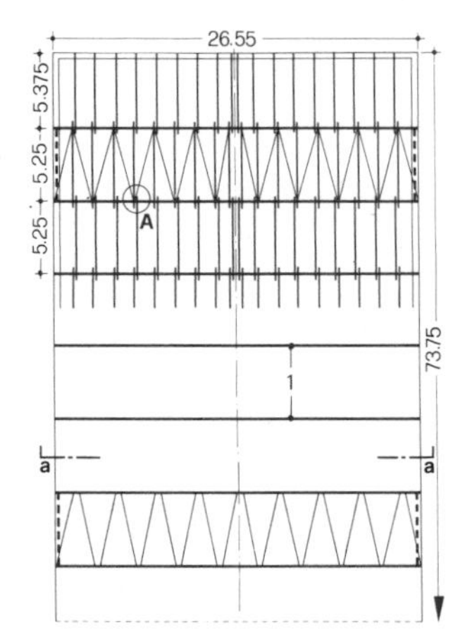

Frame layout with wind bracing

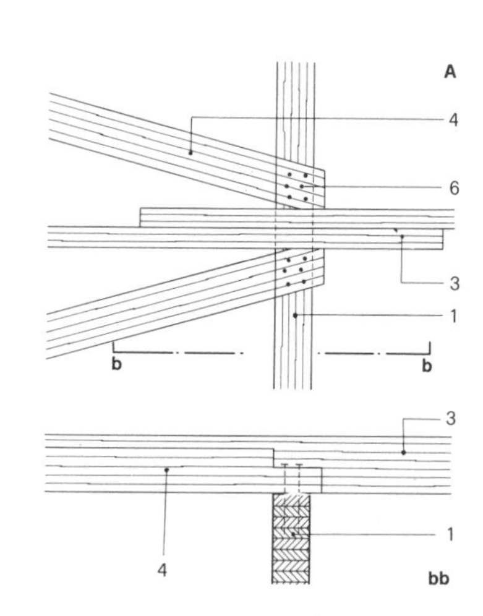

aa Partial section

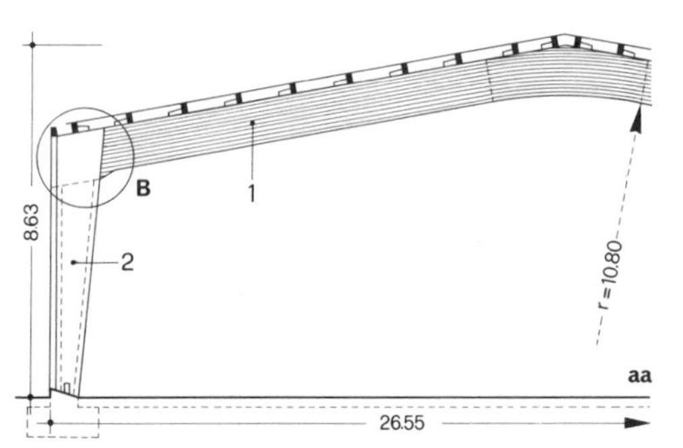

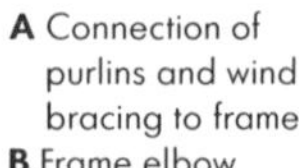

A Connection of purlins and wind bracing to frame
B Frame elbow

1 Frame beam 12/110 cm
2 Frame leg 2 × 6.5/58 to 110 cm
3 Lapped purlins 6/18 cm
4 Wind bracing 14/14 cm
5 88 shear connectors ϕ 65 mm, in circle
6 6 nails N70/210

86 Nursery School in Munich, West Germany

Architect: J. Kraus, Munich
Engineer: J. Natterer, Munich

Building consists of two parallel wings for group activities and an intermediate area for services. Wings are covered by opposite sloping roofs.

Both wings are spanned by two-hinged frames spaced at 4.00 m. Spans are 6.00 m. Frame has a one-piece beam and twin legs, rigidly connected on site by nailing and nail-plate inserts. Purlins 4/15 cm span longitudinally and support a vented roof with corrugated asbestos-cement roofing. Underside of roof is planked. Wind bracing and stiffening in both directions is provided by frame action; in longitudinal direction such rigid connection is provided by nailing end purlin to frames.

Reference: *Detail* 6/1973, illustrations

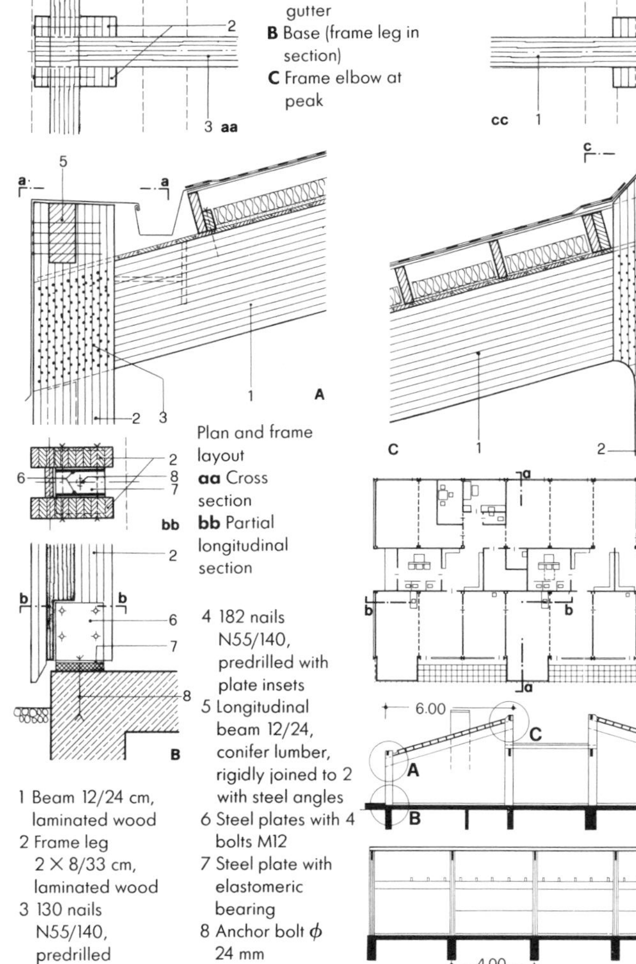

A Frame elbow at gutter
B Base (frame leg in section)
C Frame elbow at peak

Plan and frame layout
aa Cross section
bb Partial longitudinal section

1 Beam 12/24 cm, laminated wood
2 Frame leg 2 × 8/33 cm, laminated wood
3 130 nails N55/140, predrilled
4 182 nails N55/140, predrilled with plate insets
5 Longitudinal beam 12/24, conifer lumber, rigidly joined to 2 with steel angles
6 Steel plates with 4 bolts M12
7 Steel plate with elastomeric bearing
8 Anchor bolt ϕ 24 mm

Frame Legs, Divided

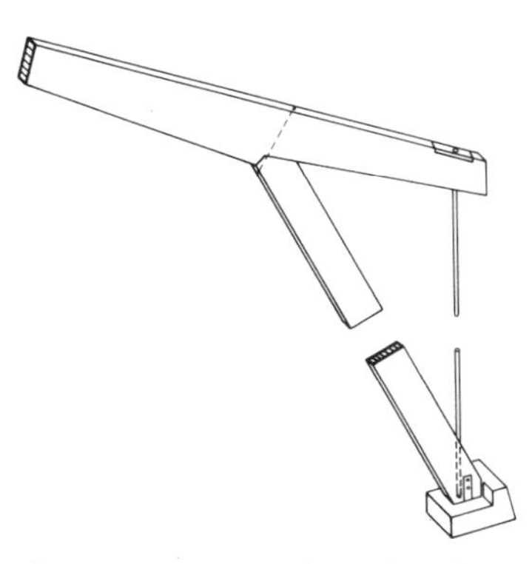

One-piece compression leg with notch on one-piece beam. Tension leg is steel bar with compression plate.

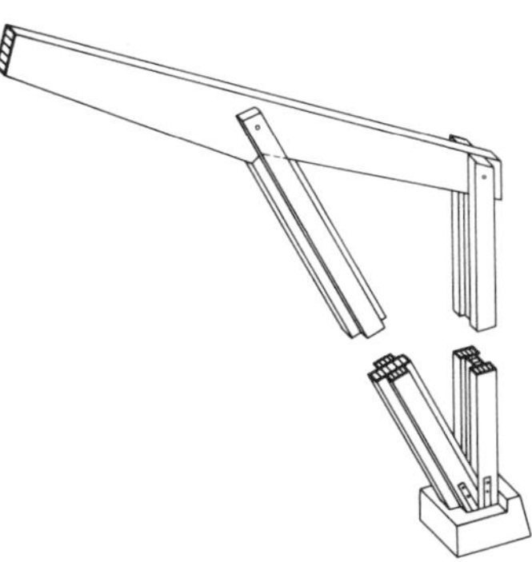

One-piece compression leg with side boards attached to a one-piece beam. Tension leg is double, with filler wood (good also for compression in alternative stress conditions).

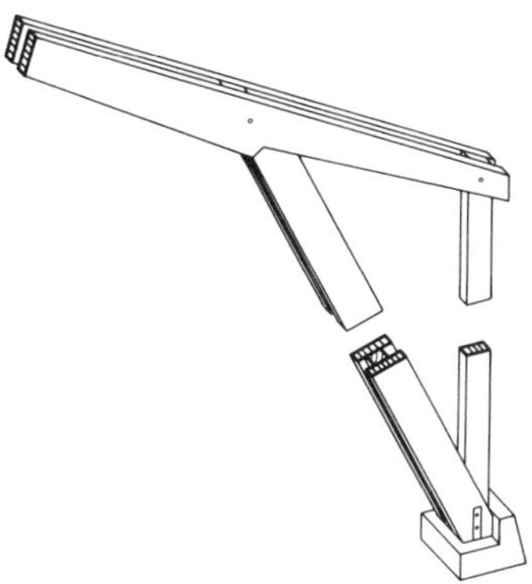

Double compression leg with filler wood and notch in double beam. One-piece tension leg.

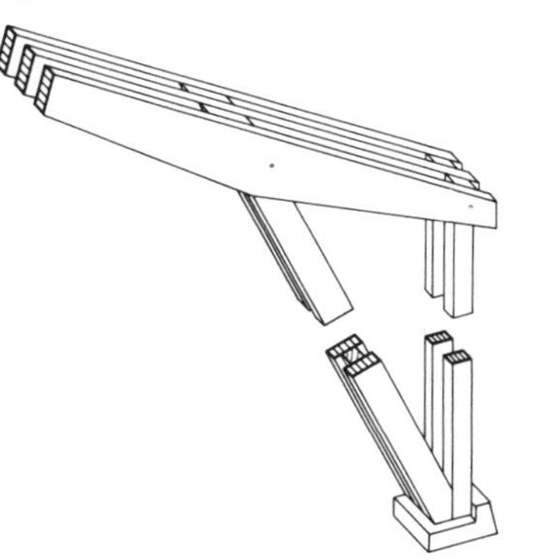

Double compression and tension legs between a triple beam.

87 Church Community Center in Flamatt, Switzerland

Architect: Atelier 5, Bern
Engineer: H. Vogel, Bern

Worship hall with 380 seats. Construction of flat roof consists of five transversely placed main girders 16/100 cm, which span 14.40 m and are spaced at 6.00 m. Center girder is double in order to carry a partition curtain. Two-piece posts 2 × 14/30 cm are rigidly connected to girders and to their bases. However, this rigid frame is designed to transfer only lateral wind forces. For vertical loads beams are designed as simple beams.

Four secondary girders 14/55 cm span between main girders and are attached to them with steel plates in slits. Purlins 10/22 cm at 60 cm span 4.66 m between secondary girders.

Reference: *Holzbau* 2/1974

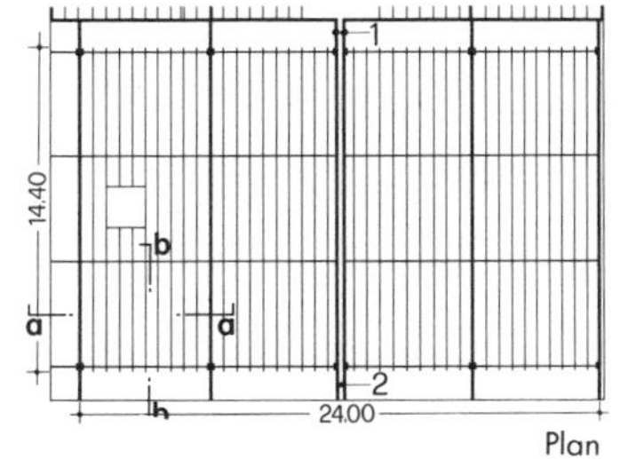

Plan

1 Frame beam 16/110 cm
2 Suspended curtain
3 Frame legs 2 × 14/30 cm
4 Secondary girder 14/55 cm
5 Purlins 10/22 cm
6 Struts for insulation
7 Shear connector ϕ 200 mm

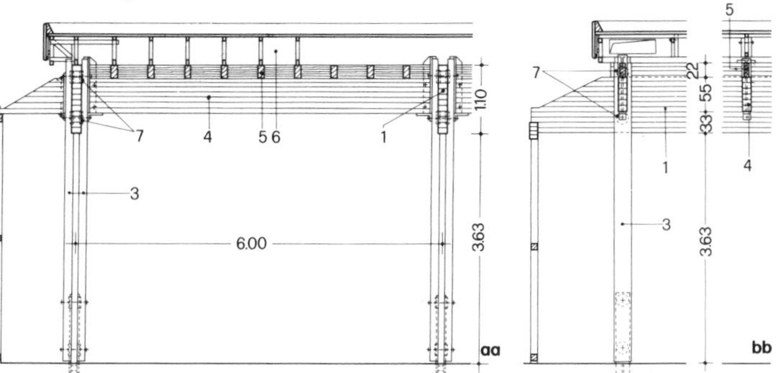

aa Partial longitudinal section
bb Partial transverse section

Three-hinged frames are statically determinate. The loads are carried through bending and shear stresses in frame bents and legs. Rigid corners of a frame transfer the moments from the upper frame bent to the legs. This creates vertical and horizontal reactions at supports, the same as in three-hinged beams. The size of the horizontal component depends on the relation between the height and the span of the frame. The higher the height, the smaller the horizontal reaction. The hinge at the middle of the frame reduces the moment at that point to zero, so that the largest moments occur at the elbows of the frame. Bending and shear stresses in the elbow govern the design. Compression in the bent and the legs may be critical for the stability of the frame.

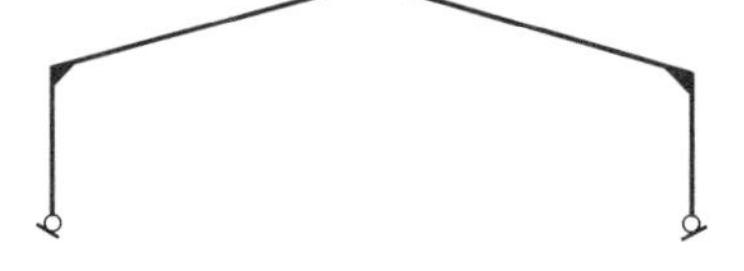

Bearing oriented to resist forces

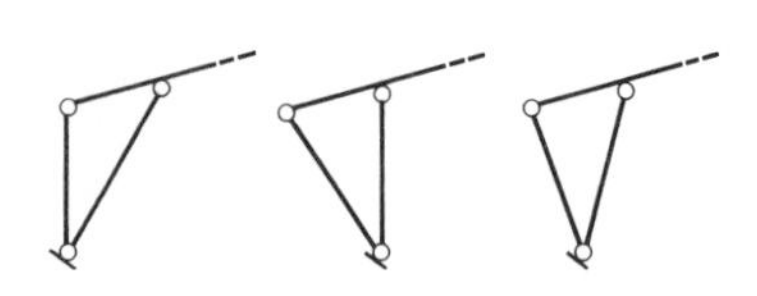

Frame legs as articulated members

88 Storage Shed in Kaufbeuren, West Germany

Engineer: Timber Construction Contractor

Covered surface 17.50 × 35.00 m. Three-hinged frames transverse to building consist of one-piece beams 14/50 to 105 cm and articulated legs. Compression leg is double, tension leg is a single member, joined by shear connectors ϕ 65 mm. Crown joint is a steel shoe made with 10 mm thick plates, screws, and pin. Lapped purlins longitudinal. Corrugated asbestos-cement roofing. Wind bracing in both gable ends absorbs horizontal longitudinal loads.

Frame layout with wind bracing

Partial section

A Wind bracing connection
B Crown joint

1 Frame beam 14/50 to 105 cm
2 Compression leg 14/28 +2 × 12/28 cm
3 Tension leg 2 × 12/22 cm
4 Lapped purlins 7/18 cm
5 Wind bracing 9/16 cm
6 Plywood gusset 4 cm, nailed
7 2 blocks 4/14 cm, nailed
8 Steel shoe, 10 mm steel plate with ϕ 22 mm screws, ϕ 30 mm pin bolt
9 Shear connector ϕ 65 mm

89 Riding Hall

Architect: Steybe, Böblingen, West Germany
Engineer: Timber Construction Contractor

Covered surface 53.00 × 40.00 m. Three-hinged frames at 6.50 m span transversely 31.80 m. They consist of one-piece beams 16/82 to 128 cm, compression and tension legs each 2 × 18/30 cm, joined by shear connectors. Lapped purlins longitudinal. Frames braced laterally at compression leg by bridging. Wind bracing in three roof bays.
Reference: *Bauen mit Holz* 3/1971, p. 106

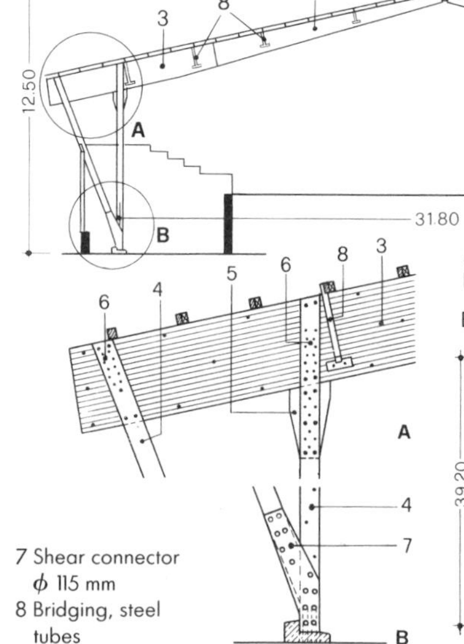

Cross section

A Connections of legs to beam
B Base

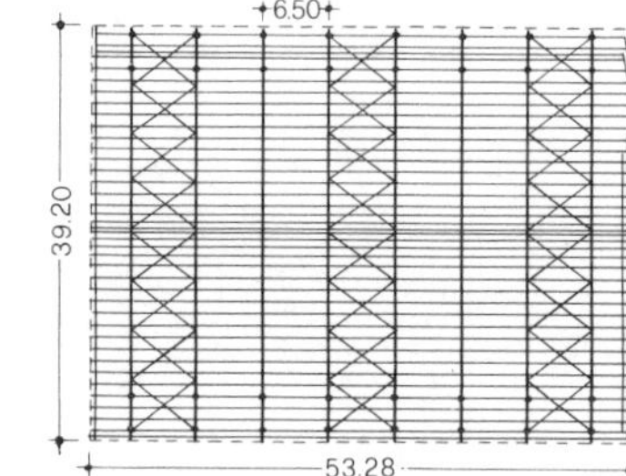

Beam layout and wind bracing

1 Beam 16/82 to 128 cm
2 Beam section 16/170 cm (haunch)
3 Section widening to 32/128 cm (2 × 8 cm)
4 Compression and tension legs 2 × 18/30 cm
5 Bearing blocks, laminated wood
6 Steel dowel ϕ 24 mm
7 Shear connector ϕ 115 mm
8 Bridging, steel tubes

90 Riding Hall

Engineer: Timber Construction Contractor

Three-hinged frames with one-piece beams and double legs; laminated wood box beams. Frame elbow assembled with three circles of shear connectors. Double columns receive beam in a forked bearing and brace it in its compression area against buckling.
Reference: *Bauen mit Holz* 12/1969, p. 587

Partial section (frame spacing 6.80 m)

A Frame elbow

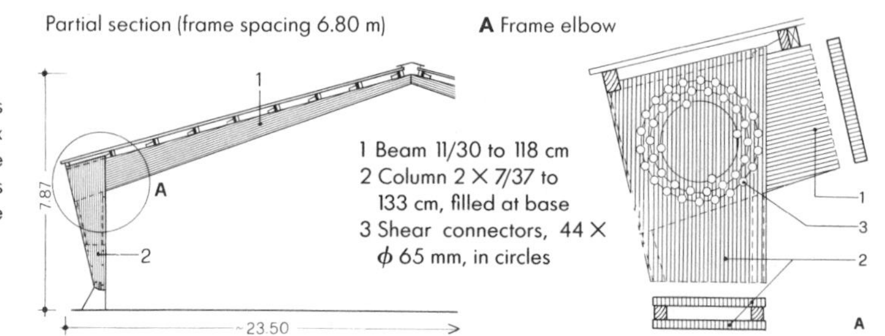

1 Beam 11/30 to 118 cm
2 Column 2 × 7/37 to 133 cm, filled at base
3 Shear connectors, 44 × ϕ 65 mm, in circles

91 Church in Bocholt, West Germany

Architect: P. Hübotter, B. Ledeborr
Engineer: F. Schroeder, Hannover

Church nave 28.00 m long, 14.75 m wide. Three-hinged frames span transversely; they consist of one-piece beams 18/18 to 55 cm and articulated legs. Compression leg is 18/22 cm and tension leg a ϕ 22 mm round steel bar. Compression leg is notched into beam. Tension leg is embedded in a 18/18 cm laminated wood strut for possible reversal of stresses. Purlins are longitudinal.
Reference: *Bauen mit Holz* 7/1964, p. 300

Partial section (frames spaced at 5.00 m)

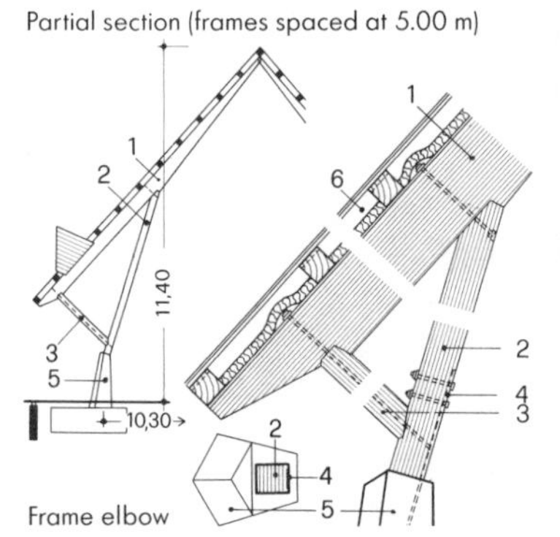

Frame elbow

1 Beam 18/18 to 55 cm
2 Strut 18/22 cm
3 Tenon 18/18 cm with ϕ 22 mm bar
4 Steel 120/14 mm, bolts ϕ 22 mm
5 Concrete base
6 Copper roofing

92 Storage Shed in Nordenham, Great Britain

Engineer: Surveyer, Nenninger and Chénevert, Montreal; Denzinger, Gelsenkirchen

390.00 m long raw materials storage shed for asbestos fibers. Main frames 16/79 to 16/188 cm. Base and crown joints have steel shoes and pin bolts. A conveyor is supported by a collar beam connected to frames with nail plates and pin bolts. Wind forces are transferred to gable walls by diagonals 8/10 to 14/18 cm in six bays, so that loads can be transferred to several footings. In addition, bridging and bracing of diagonal lumber is formed into trusses with purlins as struts.
Reference: *Zentralblatt für Industriebau* 3/1976, p. 90

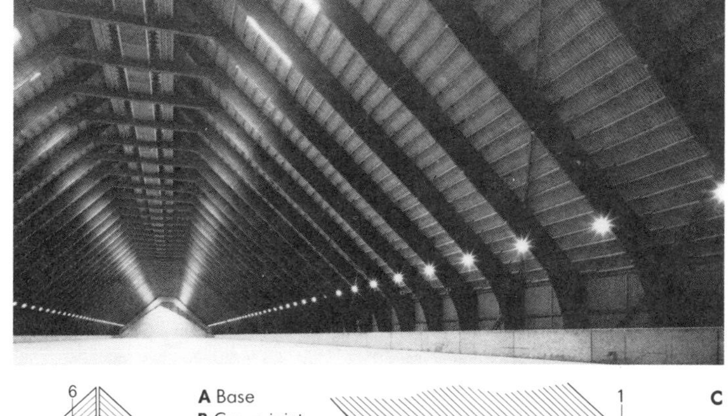

Layout of frames and wind bracing

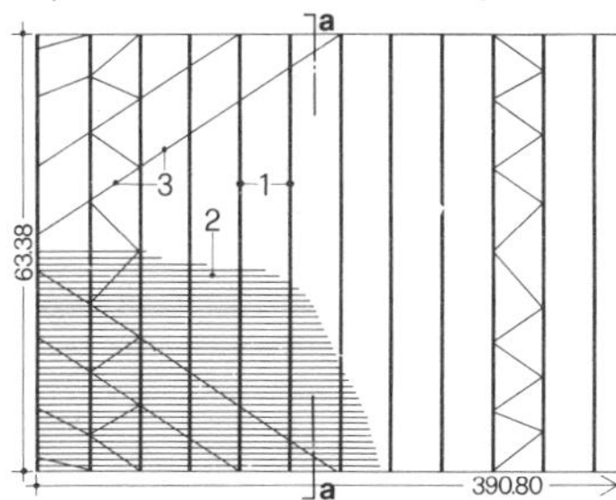

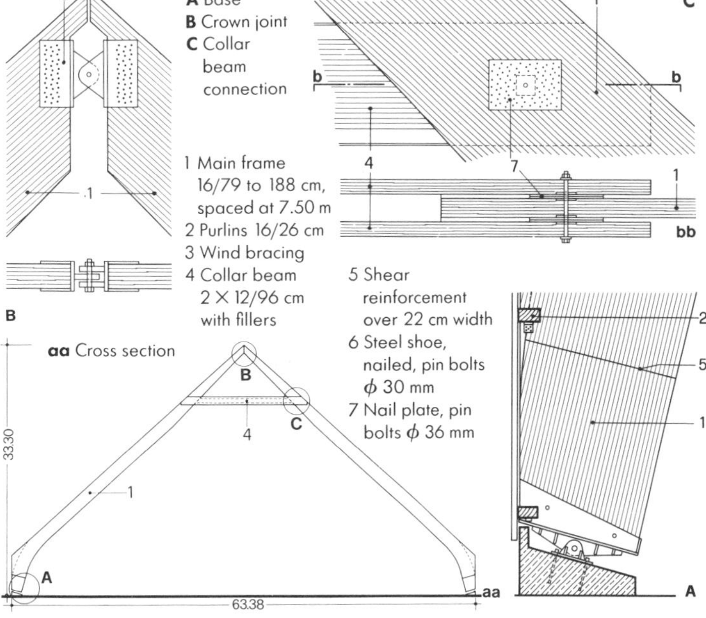

93 Storage Shed in France

Double shed, each span 33.34 m with a 5.00 m cantilevered canopy on one side. Three-hinged frames with cross sections 14/44 to 14/160 cm are offset by one frame width and overlap on center bearing. Lapped purlins 10/28 cm, span 7.50 m. Cantilevered canopy beams are 2 × 6/80 cm, each with four shear connectors ϕ 128 mm.

Horizontal loads in roof plane are resisted by timber diagonals; longitudinal ones by diagonal struts 12/18 cm.
Reference: *Bauen mit Holz* 2/1968, p. 66

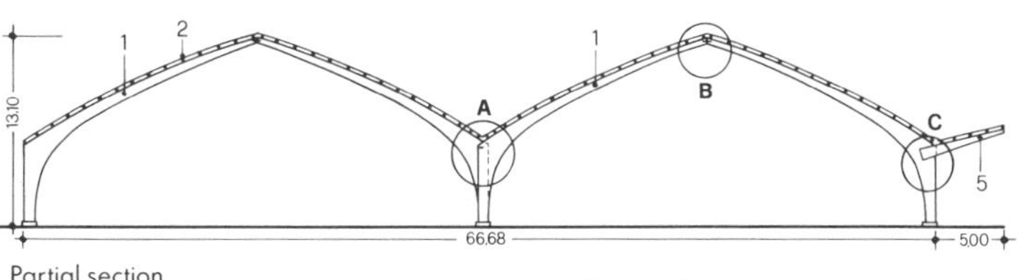

Partial section

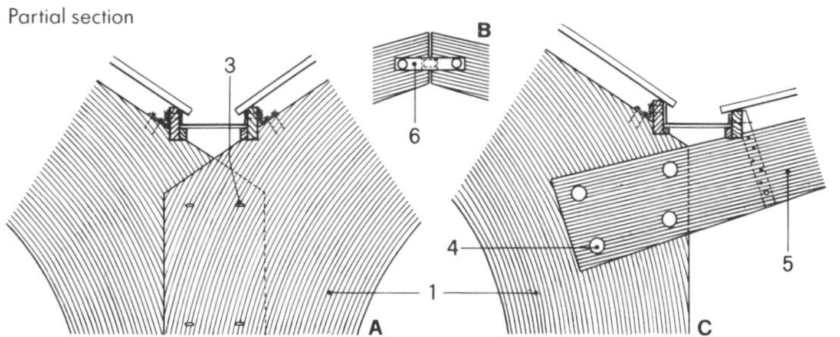

1 Main frame 14/44 to 160 cm at 7.50 m
2 Purlins 10/28 cm
3 Bolts ϕ 20 mm, slotted holes
4 Shear connectors ϕ 128 mm
5 Cantilever, 2 × 6/80 cm maximum
6 Steel tie with ϕ 95 mm shear connector

Frame Legs, Single Members

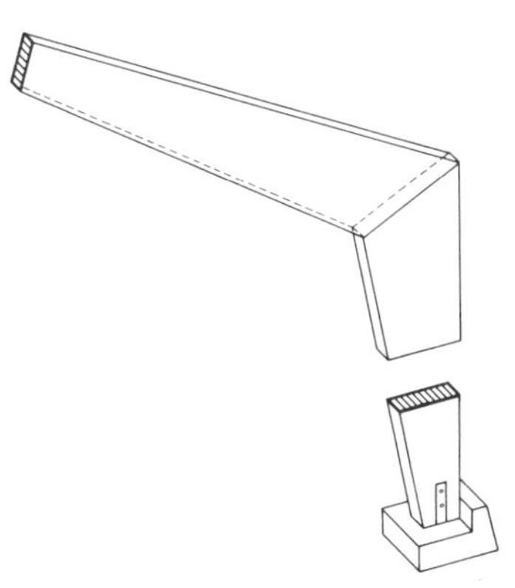

Frame elbow with finger jointing.

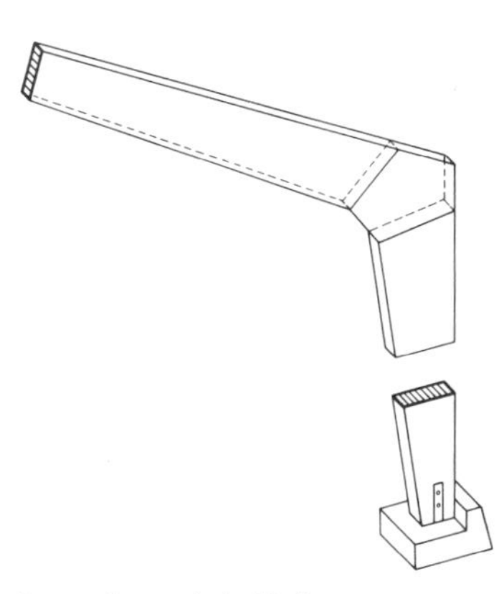

Frame elbow with double finger jointing.

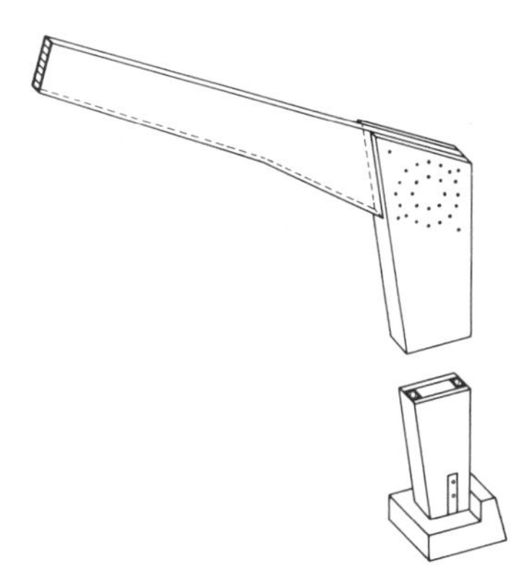

Connection of frame elbow, shear connector circles, and tightening bolts.

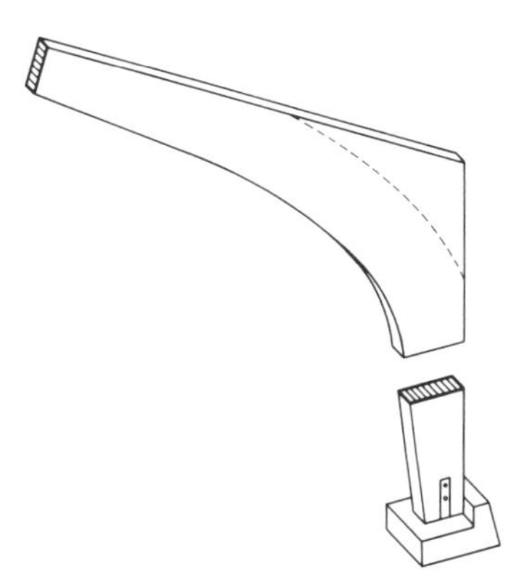

Bent frame. Outer wedge without structural function.

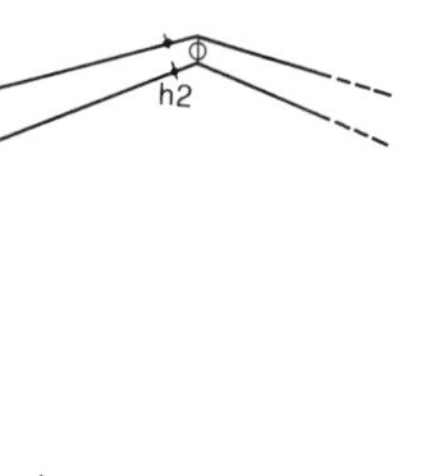

Laminated wood
a = 5 to 10 m (spacing)
l = 10 to 50 m
$h_1 = l/20$ to $l/40$
$h_2 = l/30$ to $l/60$

Trusses
a = 7 to 10 m (spacing)
l = 15 to 50 m
$h = l/8$ to $l/18$

94 - 98 Storage Sheds for Bulk Goods

Bulk storage of minerals and grains requires a roof shape conforming to the natural shape of the heap. In most cases choice fell on three-hinged bent frame whose profile departs from parabolic axial force diagram. Wood is especially resistant to many aggressive chemicals. It was therefore chosen as the right material for sheds storing chemicals such as salts and fertilizers. Steel connections have been avoided as much as possible. If necessary, stainless steel was used.

Frames differ mainly in their departure from the parabolic axial force diagram and the details of connections or wind bracing. Bending moments in frame elbows are also different. Wind bracing and stability of building are secured by diagonal trussing in single-frame bays, or by diagonals that radiate over entire roof surface. One such arrangement engages all footings in resisting wind forces.

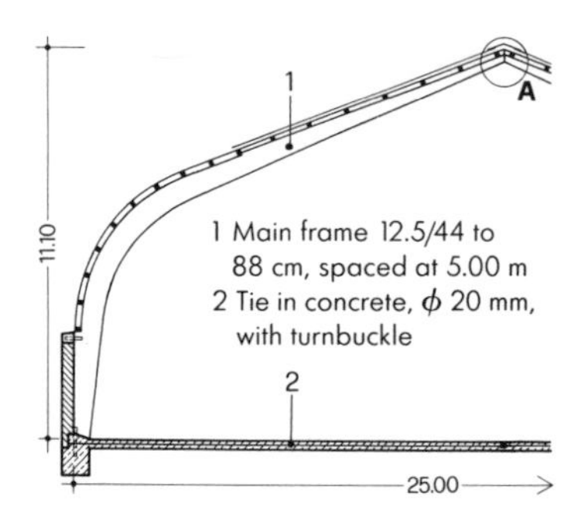

1 Main frame 12.5/44 to 88 cm, spaced at 5.00 m
2 Tie in concrete, ϕ 20 mm, with turnbuckle

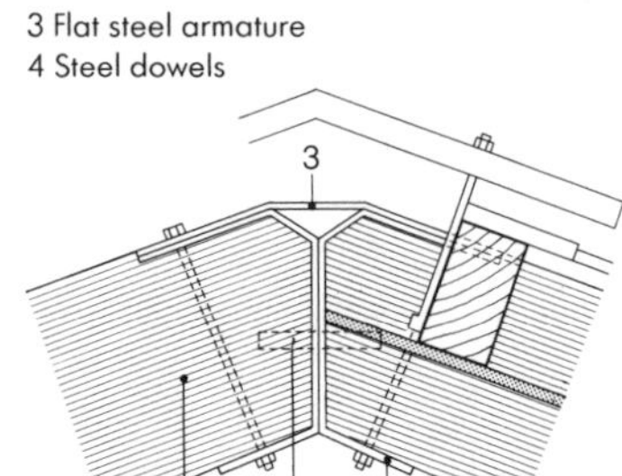

3 Flat steel armature
4 Steel dowels

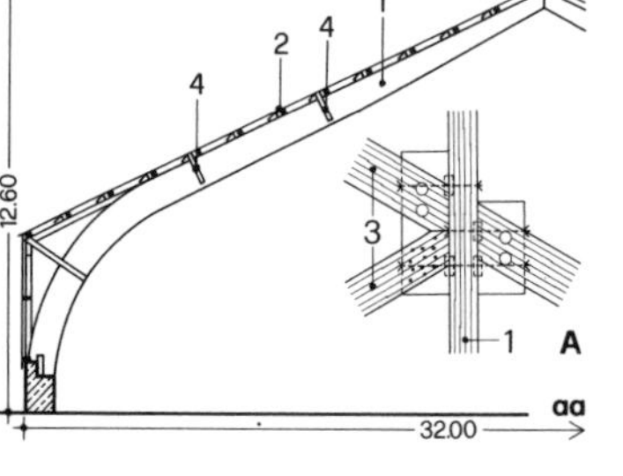

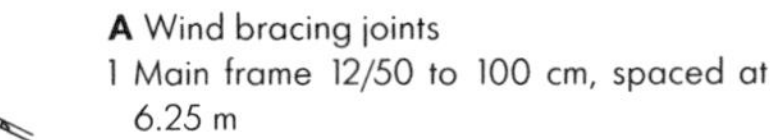

A Wind bracing joints
1 Main frame 12/50 to 100 cm, spaced at 6.25 m
2 Lapped purlins 9.5/16 cm
3 Wind bracing 7/16 to 7/20 cm
4 Bridging 6/10 cm

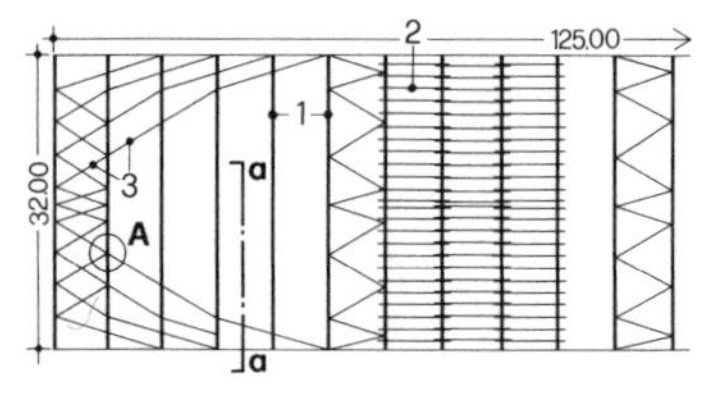

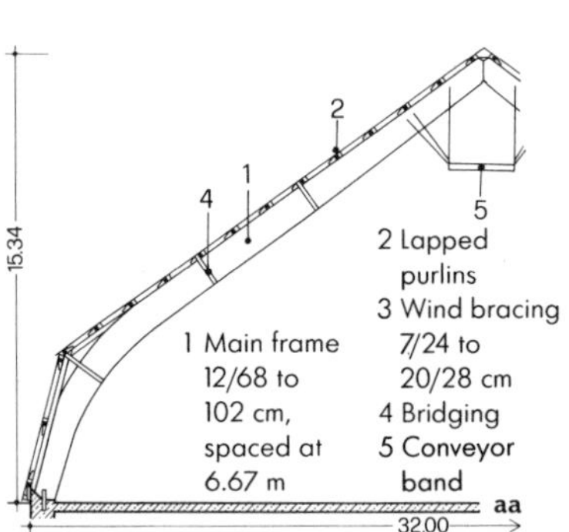

1 Main frame 12/68 to 102 cm, spaced at 6.67 m
2 Lapped purlins
3 Wind bracing 7/24 to 20/28 cm
4 Bridging
5 Conveyor band

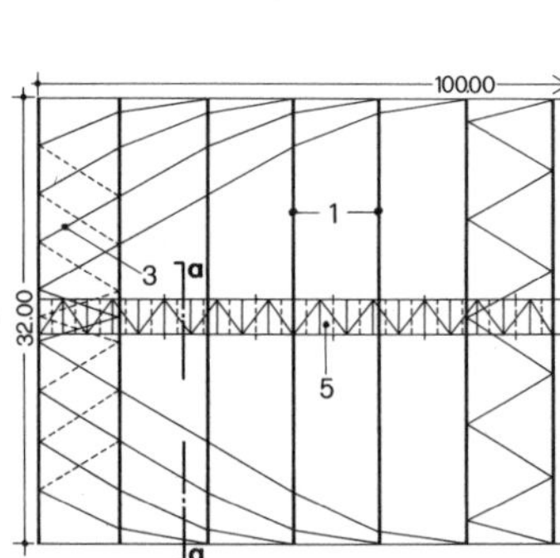

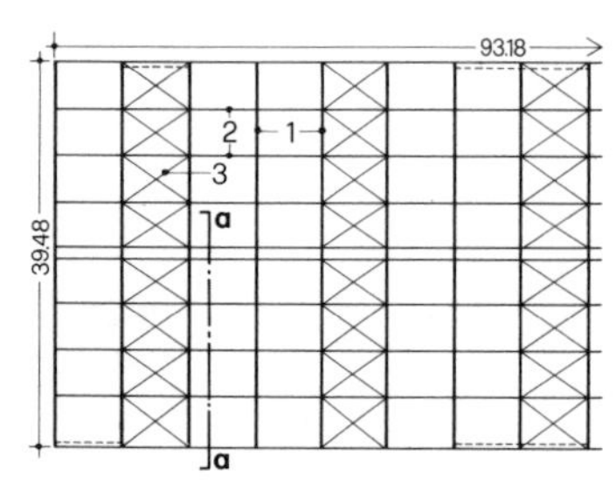

1 Main frame 16/65 to 125 cm, spaced at 7.20 m
2 Purlins 20/36 cm

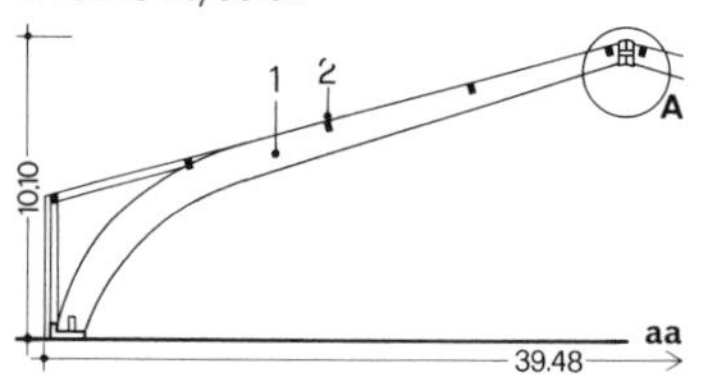

3 Wind bracing, ϕ 16 to 20 mm steel bars
4 Steel shoe

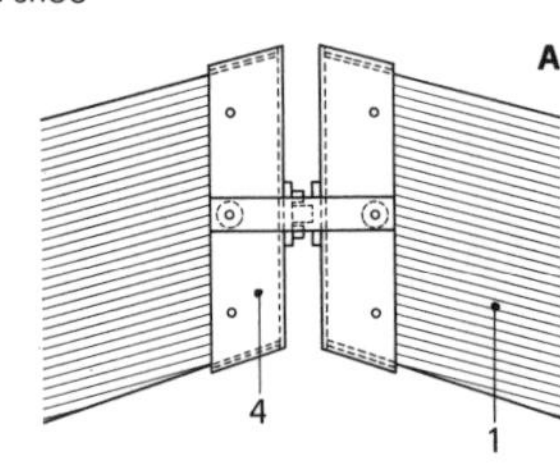

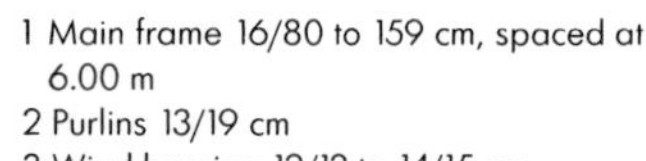

1 Main frame 16/80 to 159 cm, spaced at 6.00 m
2 Purlins 13/19 cm
3 Wind bracing 12/12 to 14/15 cm
4 Flat steel cross with shear connectors ϕ 80 mm as crown hinge
5 Materials container baffle
6 Steel shoe

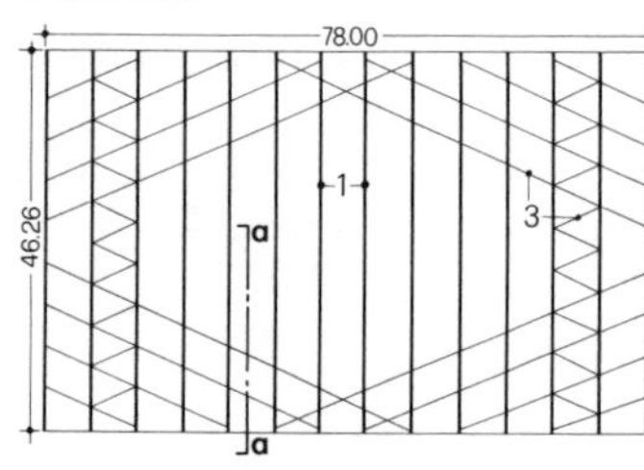

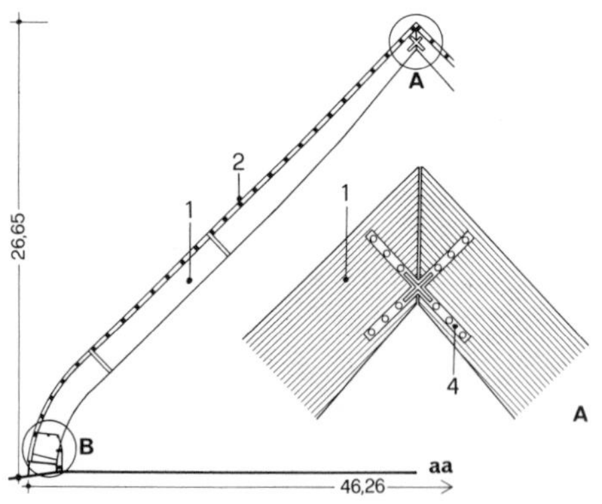

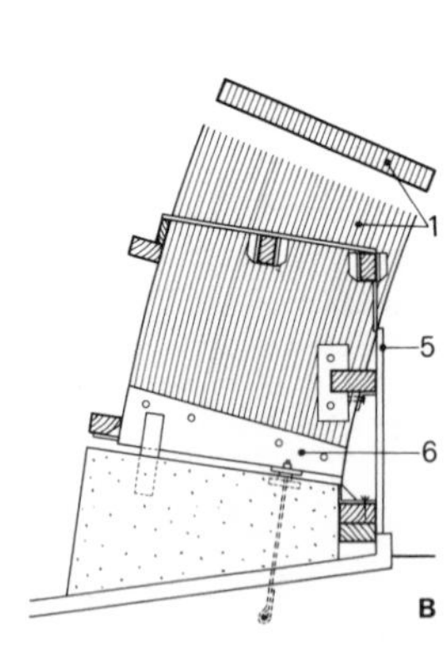

99 Riding Hall in Gerolstein, West Germany

Architect: U. Schnitzer, W. Heinichen, and H. Lüsing, Karlsruhe
Engineer: A. Bruder, Karlsruhe

Three-hinged truss frames with parallel chords, double struts, and single diagonals with shear connectors. Compression struts in notched joints. Compression leg is double, tension leg is single. Crown hinge is at lower chord. Horizontal loads taken longitudinally through wind trussing in roof and sloped struts in plane of compression legs (see illustration). Purlins are longitudinal, spaced at 1.15 m. Both gable walls contain bracing.
Reference: *Bauen mit Holz* 4/1976, p. 175

Frame layout with wind bracing

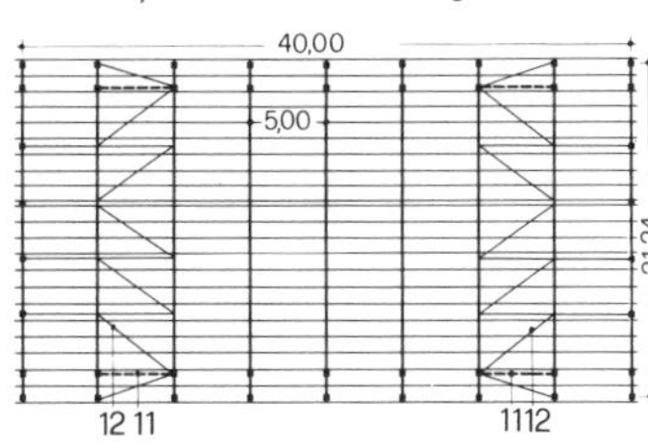

A Frame elbow

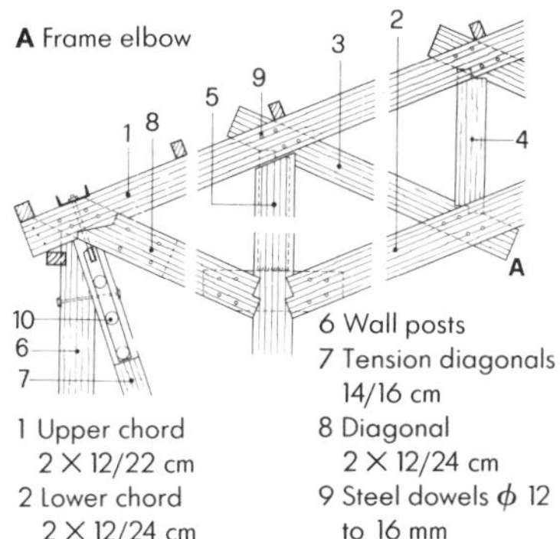

1 Upper chord 2 × 12/22 cm
2 Lower chord 2 × 12/24 cm
3 Diagonals 10/14 to 20 cm
4 Struts 10/12 to 18 cm
5 Compression frame leg 2 × 12/24 cm
6 Wall posts
7 Tension diagonals 14/16 cm
8 Diagonal 2 × 12/24 cm
9 Steel dowels ϕ 12 to 16 mm
10 One-sided shear connector ϕ 95 mm on tension leg 80 × 8 mm
11 Wind bracing strut
12 Wind bracing 6/10 to 16 cm

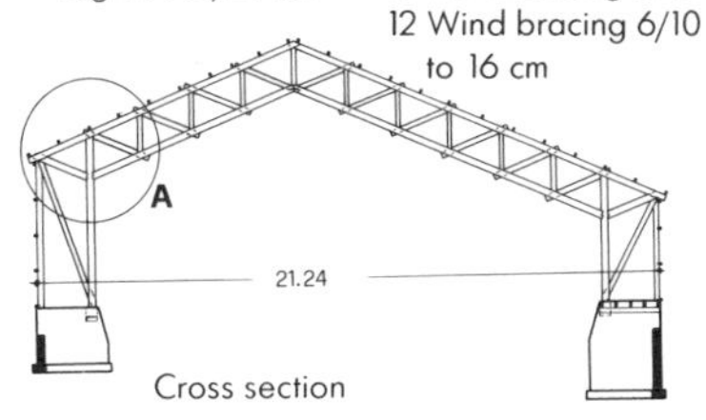

Cross section

Light Crown Hinges

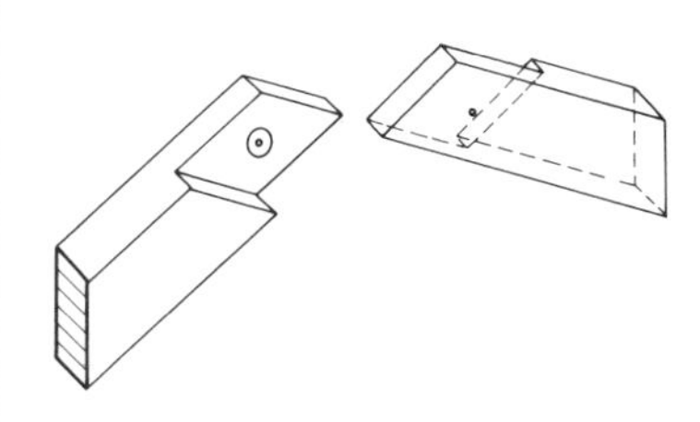

Lap joint with shear connector.

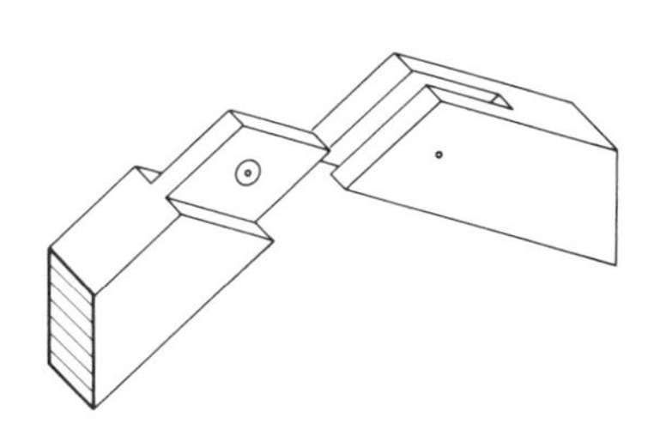

Forked lap joint with shear connector.

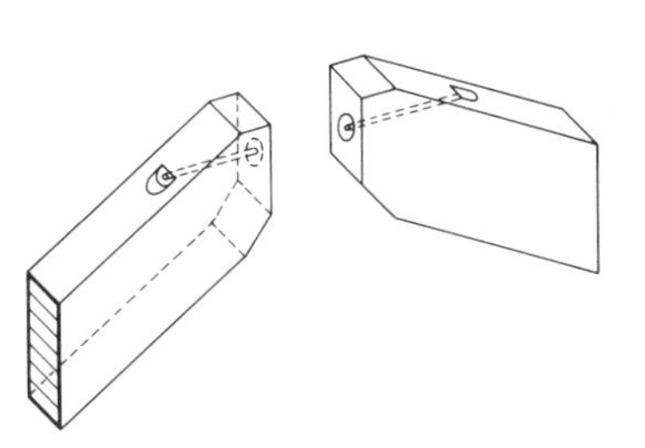

Elastomeric bearing plate with end-grain shear connectors.

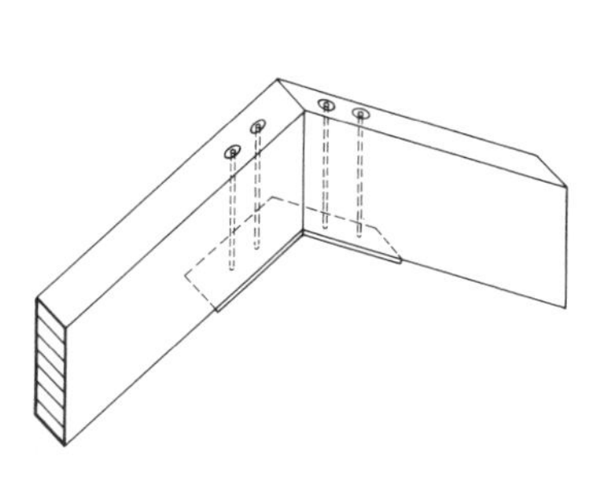

Underlying steel gusset plate with bolts.

100 Riding Hall in Munich-Riem, West Germany

Architect: G. and I. Küttinger, Munich
Engineer: J. Natterer, Munich

Three-hinged frames transverse to building. Double upper and lower chords. Single diagonals and struts. Connections through steel plate strips in slits (Borg system). Tension leg single, compression leg double. Purlins longitudinally span 7.00 m and are braced in the middle by bridging. Horizontal resistance to wind and bridging shears is provided by round pressure-treated timbers at each gable end. Truss frames are braced laterally by diagonals in plane of roof and articulated half-frames in plane of tension legs.
Reference: *Detail* 2/1976, illustrations; *Bauen mit Holz* 11/1976, p. 519

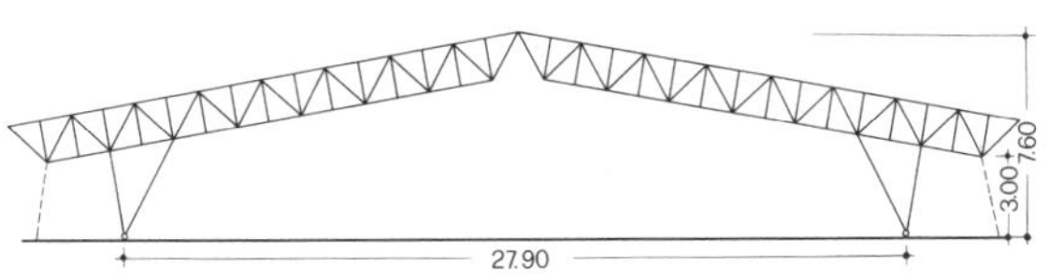

Section of structure

Partial frame layout and wind bracing

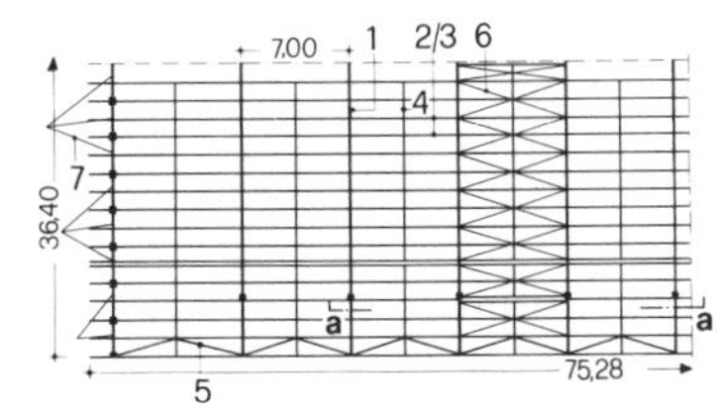

1 Truss frame
2 Purlins 12/14 cm
3 Diagonals, bracing purlins
4 Laterals, bracing purlins transversely
5 Diagonals for bracing 4
6 Flat steel lateral bracing
7 Counterforts ϕ 14 to 21 cm round timbers
9 Facade posts

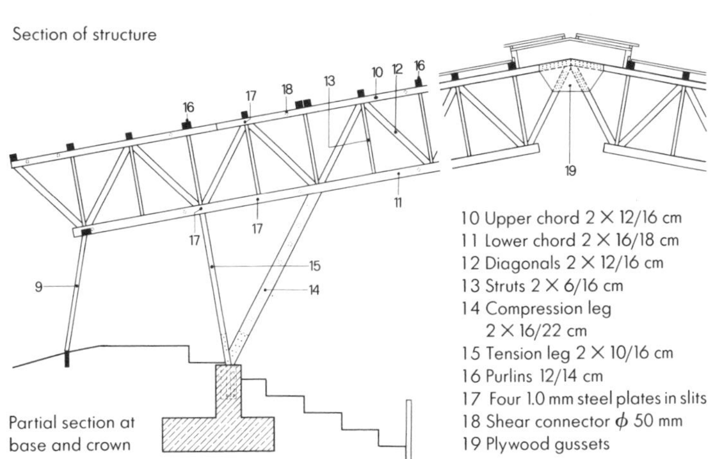

Partial section at base and crown

10 Upper chord 2 × 12/16 cm
11 Lower chord 2 × 16/18 cm
12 Diagonals 2 × 12/16 cm
13 Struts 2 × 6/16 cm
14 Compression leg 2 × 16/22 cm
15 Tension leg 2 × 10/16 cm
16 Purlins 12/14 cm
17 Four 1.0 mm steel plates in slits
18 Shear connector ϕ 50 mm
19 Plywood gussets

Frames with canopies

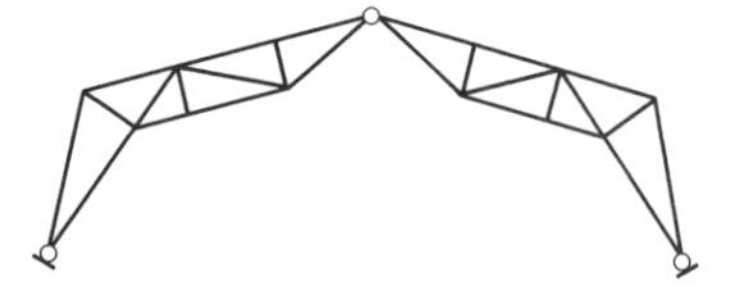

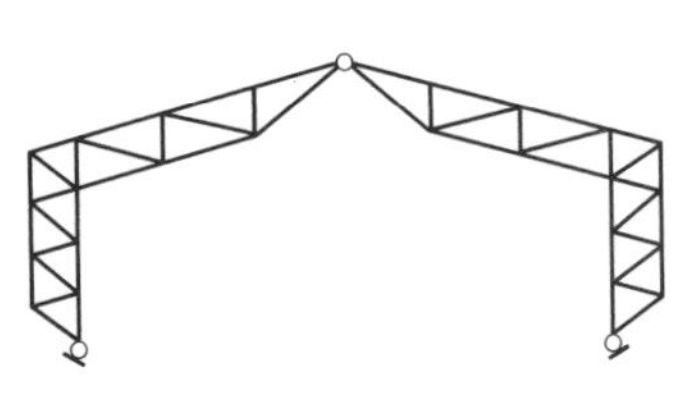

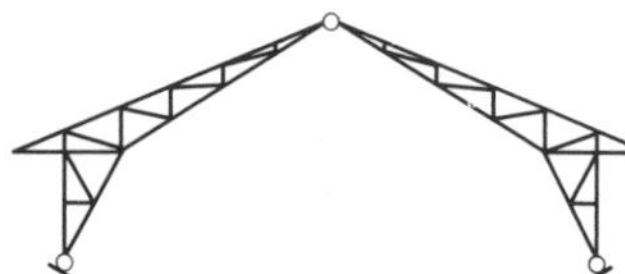

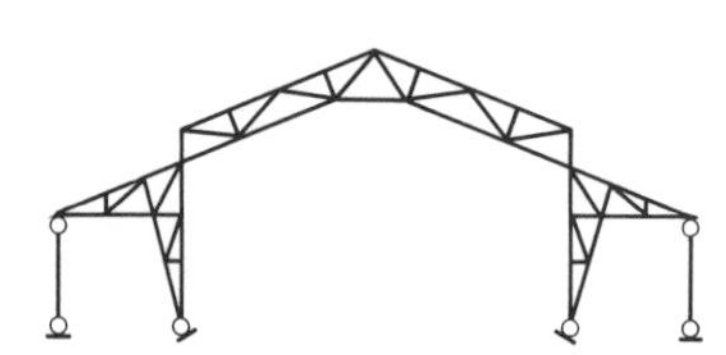

Truss frames

101 Indoor Swimming Pool in Gstaad, Switzerland

Architect: F. Anderegg, Meiringen, and M. Schweitzer, Muri
Engineer: H. Banholzer, Luzern

Covered swimming pool, beginner's pool, restaurant and dressing rooms. Roof consists of three-hinged frames, offset in plan, spaced at 4.50 m, and spanning between 21.00 and 35.00 m. Frames are laminated wood 20/70 to 35/135 cm, designed for 5 kN/m² snow load. Base and crown joints are welded steel shoes. Lapped purlins 16/24 cm rest on frames and are planked underneath.

Wind and lateral bracing is provided by diagonals connected by plywood gusset plates. Wind bracing in walls carries loads to foundation.
Reference: *Holz* 21/1972, p. 1

Plan

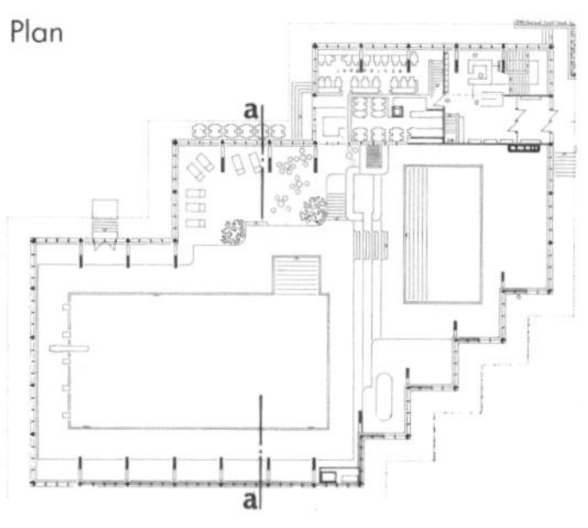

aa Cross section

9.16
3.04²
29.91⁶
3.04²

1 Main frame 20 × 35/70 to 135 cm
2 Lapped purlins 16/24 cm
3 Purlins 16/24 cm, laminated wood
4 Wind bracing 6/14 to 6/18 cm
5 Purlins skewed for air ducts, 16/30 cm
6 Plywood gussets 6 cm thick
7 Steel gusset plates
8 Shear connector ϕ 120 mm
9 Steel shoe with dowel, gussets, and shear connector ϕ 95 mm

Partial frame layout with wind bracing

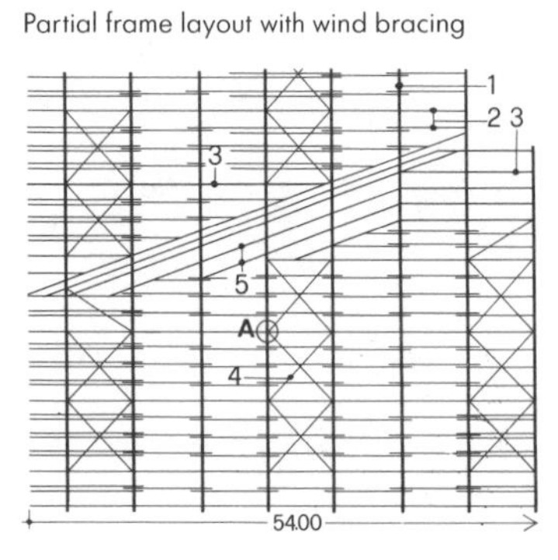

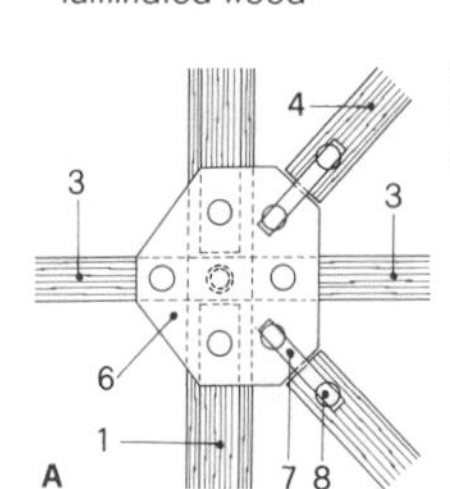

A Wind bracing connection

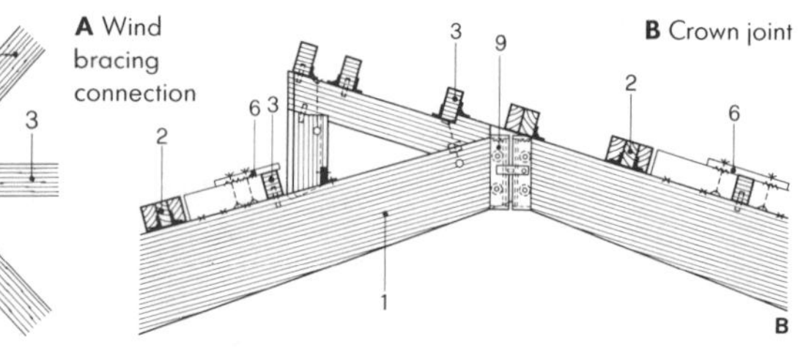

B Crown joint

102 Slaughterhouse in Paris, France

Architect: M. Lebedeff, Paris

Roof area 39.00 × 106.00 m. Three-hinged frames are spaced at 6.40 m and span 30.00 m; there are canopies on both sides. Lapped longitudinal purlins carry corrugated asbestos-cement roofing.

K-shaped wind and lateral bracing struts occupy entire gable bay; in adjacent bays they are gradually omitted, starting from crown. They transfer lateral forces to an edge beam, which conveys the forces to foundations through diagonal struts.

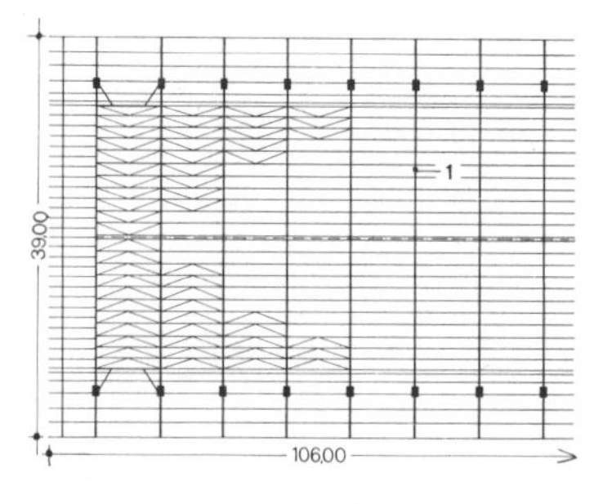

Framing layout with wind bracing

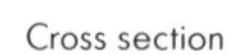

Cross section

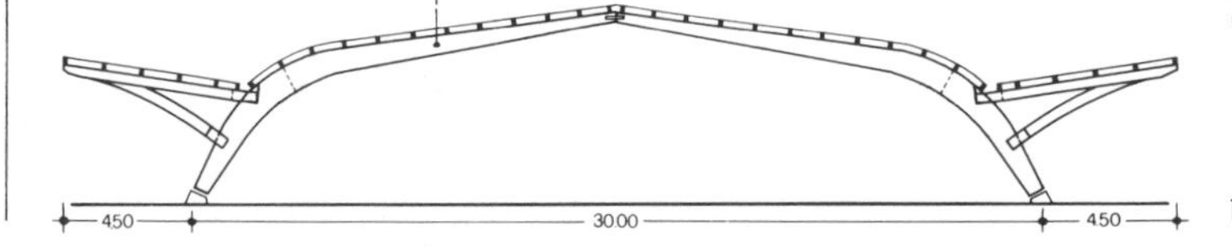

1 Main frame 16/30 to 90 cm

103 Market Hall in St. Etienne, France

Architect: R. Michard, Lorette
Engineer: Brochard, Paris

The main features of this hall are the unsymmetrical three-hinged frames which span 52.00 m transversely. Their ridge beam is discontinuous and offset in each bay, creating dormers on alternate sides. Frames are 14/80 to 14/130 cm. Along long sides there are cantilevered canopies outside and mezzanine floors inside. Purlins 8/23 cm rest on frames. Crown joint of frames is secured by side gusset plates.

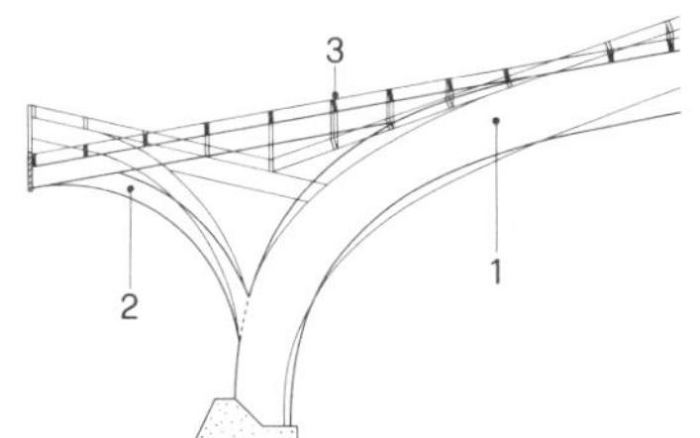

1 Main frame 14/80 to 130 cm
2 Canopies 14/40 cm
3 Purlins 8/23 cm

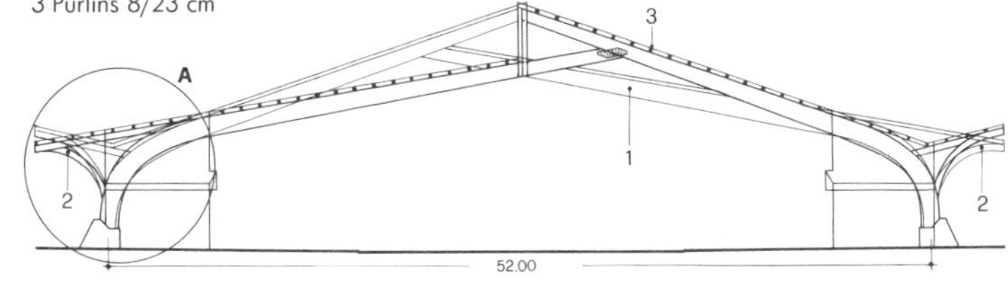

104 Swimming Pool in Créteil, France

Architect: J. Charpentier, Paris

Pool is spanned transversely by three-hinged frames, 35.00 and 33.00 m long. Offsetting the frames in plan creates an undulating exterior wall. Roof shape accentuates structure by means of diagonal frames, which rise from frame elbow to crown. The result is a sequence of folds, of skewed triangular roof planes, whose structure is made more visible by exposed purlins.

Triangular frame arrangement and hip roofs at gable ends reinforce structure laterally and convey horizontal forces to foundations.

Partial longitudinal section

1 Main frame 16/50 to 180 cm
2 Purlins

Plan

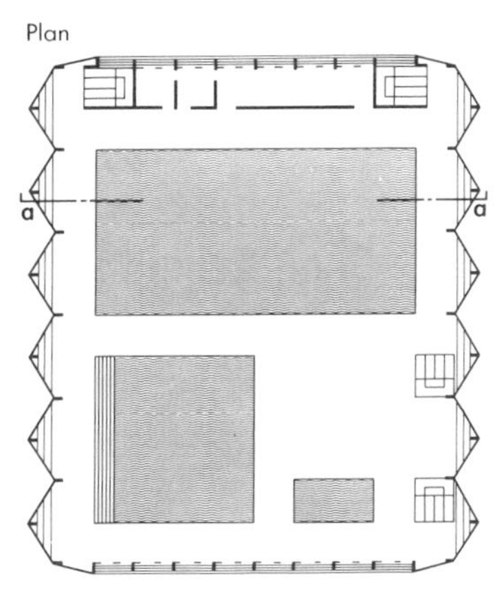

Partial frame layout

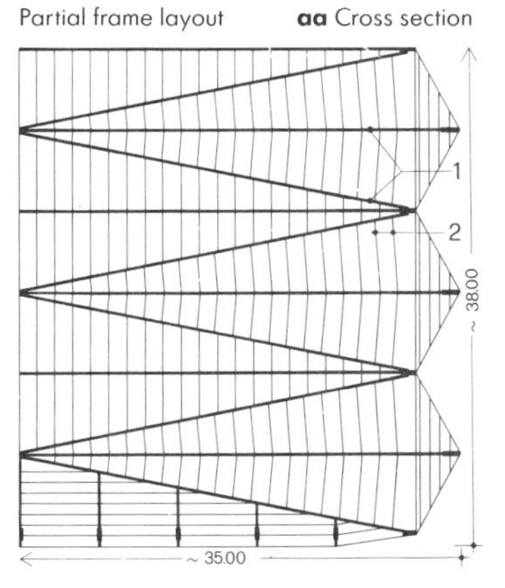

aa Cross section

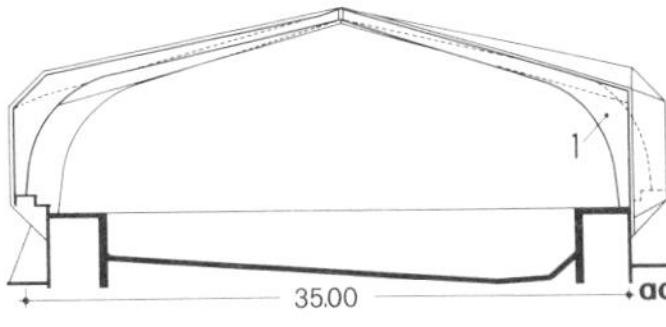

Frames, Moment Connection of Beam to Column

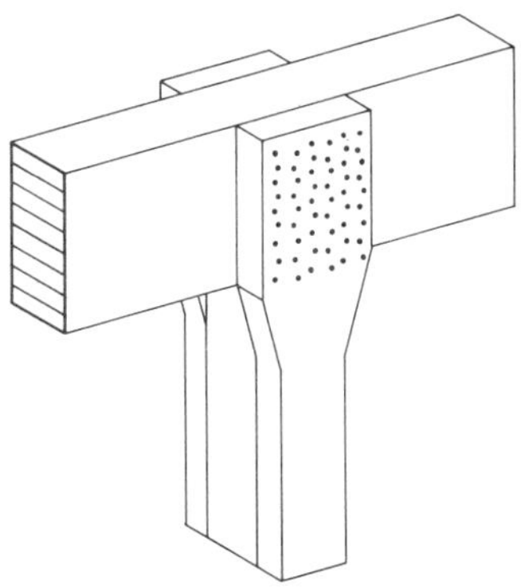

Forked construction of top of column. Nailed or doweled connection, haunch 1:10.

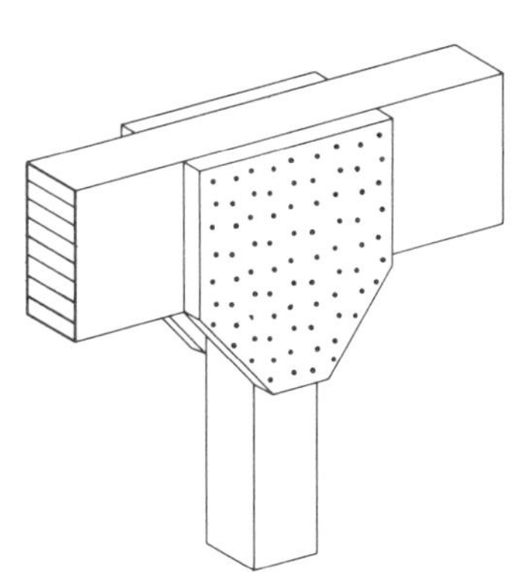

Nailed plywood or steel gusset plate.

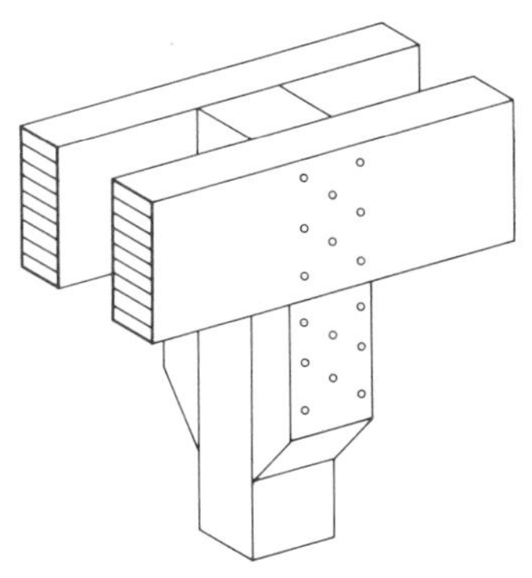

Twin beam on single column, seated on side blocks. Moment connection for small forces, steel dowels.

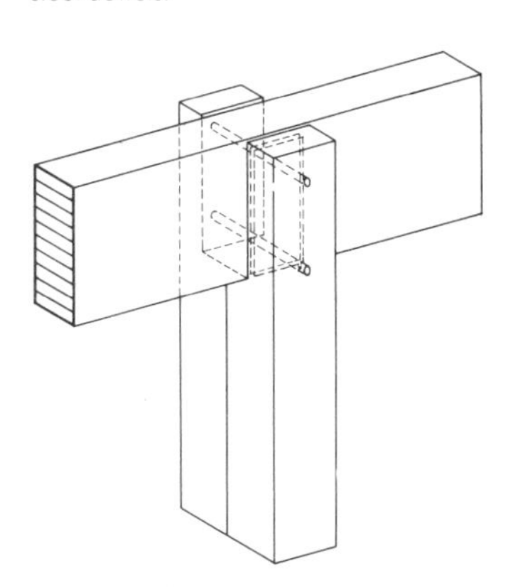

Forked top of column. Connection by means of concealed nail plates and tightening bolts.

The moment in frame elbows governs the design (page 132). Its magnitude mostly depends on the shape of the frame. The more the shape departs from a straight line connecting crown and bearing hinges, the larger is the moment in the elbow ($M \approx eA$).

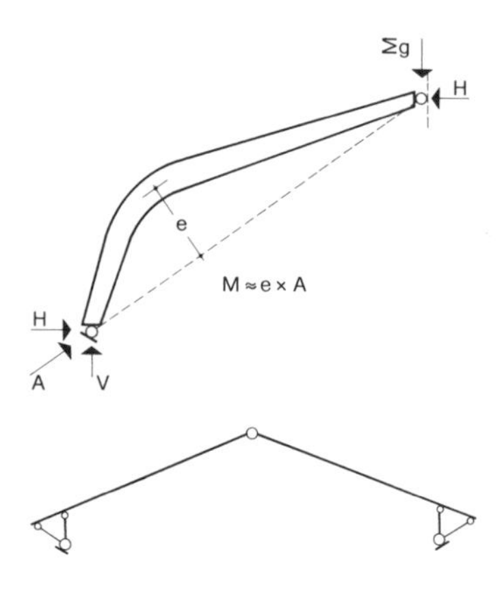

Special shapes as transitions to three-hinged beams

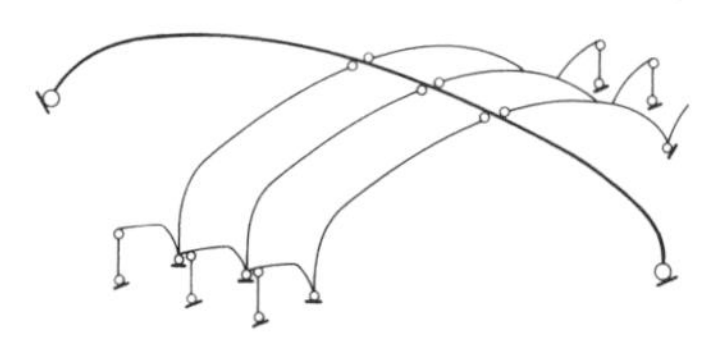

Frames in transverse and longitudinal directions as transitions to arches

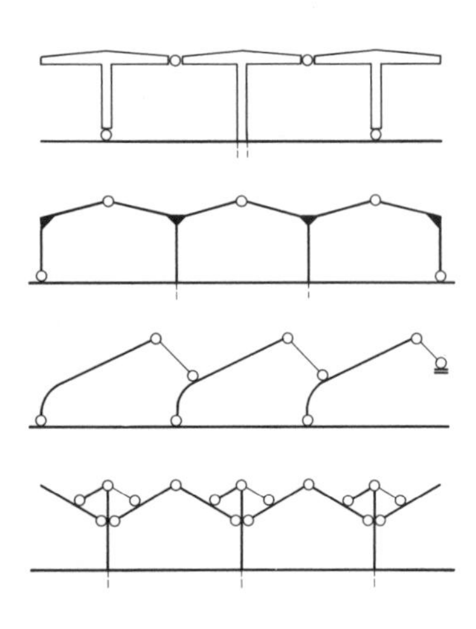

Chains of frames

105 Swimming Pool in Griesheim, West Germany

Architect: D. Loewer, Darmstadt
Engineer: Timber Construction Contractor

Indoor swimming pool with three pools, dressing rooms, sauna, cafeteria, and visitors' deck. Roof area 45.00 × 49.00 m, roof slope 17°. Three-hinged laminated wood frames 2 × 14/60 to 177 cm span 51.00 m longitudinally. They have articulated steel legs. Spacing is 5.60 and 6.00 m in end bays. Frame beam is hinged on top of an IPB 180 and is supported through a U shape on a welded shelf. Tension leg IBP 180 receives load through a steel cap and an elastomeric bearing.

Wind loads are resisted in roof plane by two exposed trusses of round steel bars and tubes. In plane of compression legs, there are crossed diagonals meeting at a steel ring. Purlins 9/20 cm rest on frames, support underside planking, and carry 5 mm woodchip boards, insulation, and corrugated asbestos-cement decking. Frame exposed to weather is protected.

1 Main frame 2 × 14/60 to 177 cm
2 Filler wood 22 cm wide
3 IPB 180
4 Tension leg IPBI 180
5 Welded steel cap
6 Two bolts ϕ 24 mm welded to IPBI 180
7 Elastomeric bearing 10 mm
8 Pin bolts ϕ 60 mm
9 One-sided shear connector ϕ 65 mm
10 Steel dowel ϕ 10 mm
11 Safety bolts with slotted hole in wood
12 Hinged steel bearing
13 Tension diagonals ϕ 36 to 42 mm
14 Compression strut ϕ 133 × 5 mm
15 Steel ring ϕ 355.6 × 25 × 150 mm

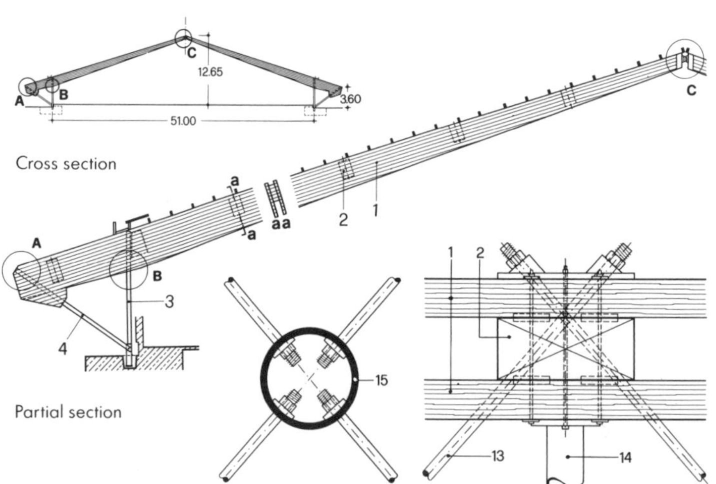

Cross section

Partial section

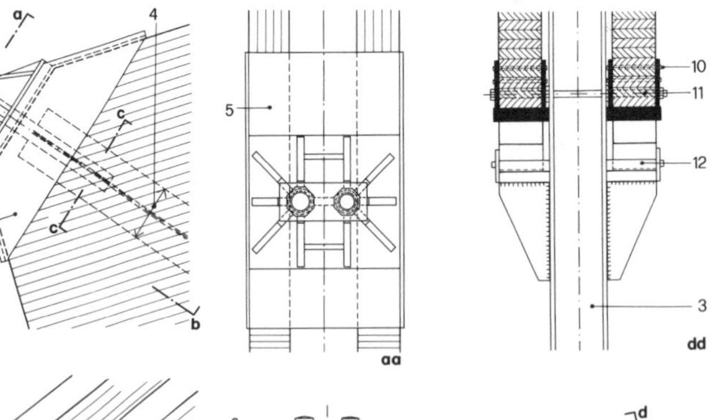
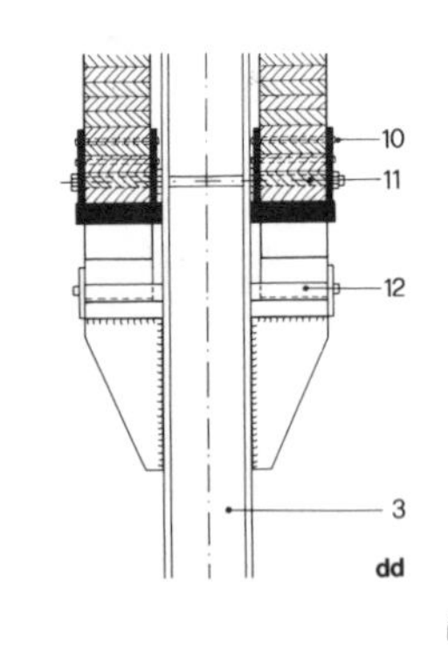
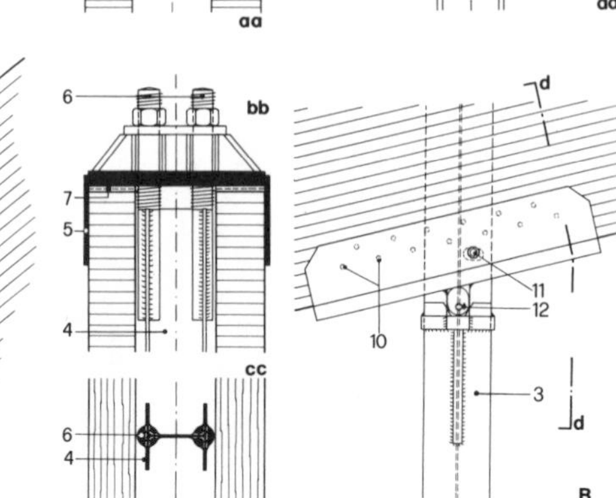

Frame layout with wind bracing

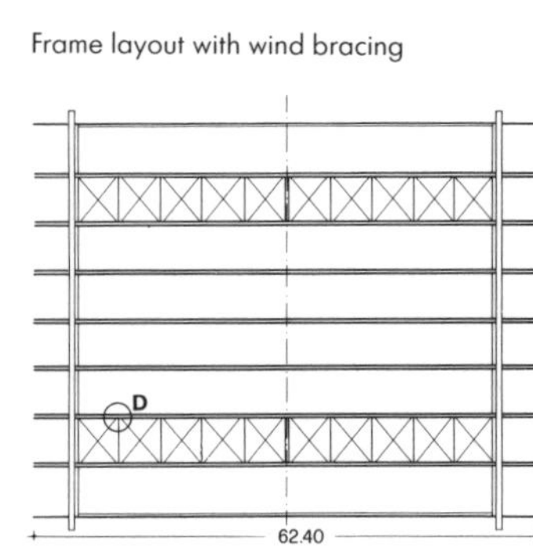

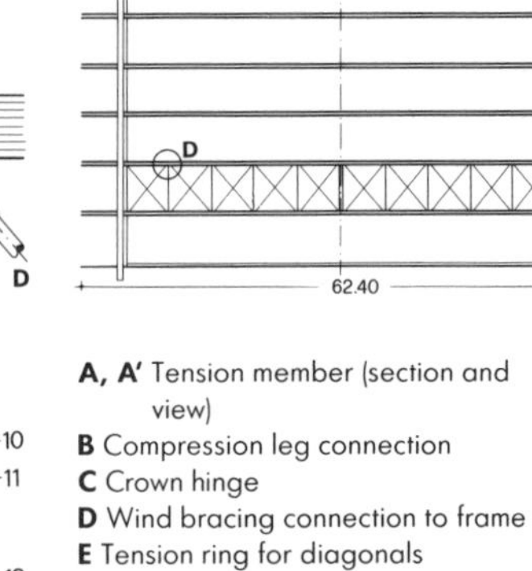

A, A′ Tension member (section and view)
B Compression leg connection
C Crown hinge
D Wind bracing connection to frame
E Tension ring for diagonals

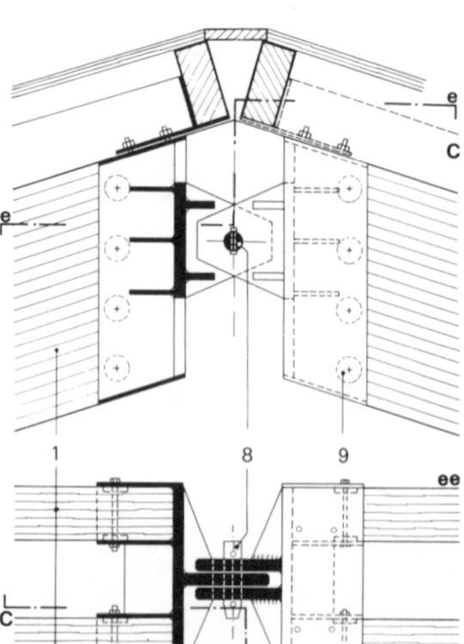

106 Exhibition Hall in Epinal, France

Architect: Houot, St. Die
Engineer: Brochard

Roof surface 125.00 × 88.00 m. Hall room is enhanced by longitudinal and transverse frames.

Longitudinally across hall there is an arch-like three-hinged frame 72.00 m long. At each end there is a two-hinged frame spanning 26.00 m. Center frames are spaced at 11.00 m, both end frames are spaced at 8.00 m. Longitudinal frames 72.00 m long are double; three-hinged transverse frames are joined to them.

Transverse frames are single members with a span of 2 × 24.00 m, or 20.00 to 26.00 m in outer bays. Frame distance is 6.00 m. Purlins between frames are hung in steel seats. Hall is illuminated through windows in outer walls, through clerestory windows, and through light strips between double longitudinal frames.

Longitudinal frames are erected first and temporarily braced. Transverse frames are erected next and attached to longitudinal frames. Wind forces are resisted in both directions by diagonal bracing.
Central exhibition hall provides a column-free room 72.00 × 48.00 m.

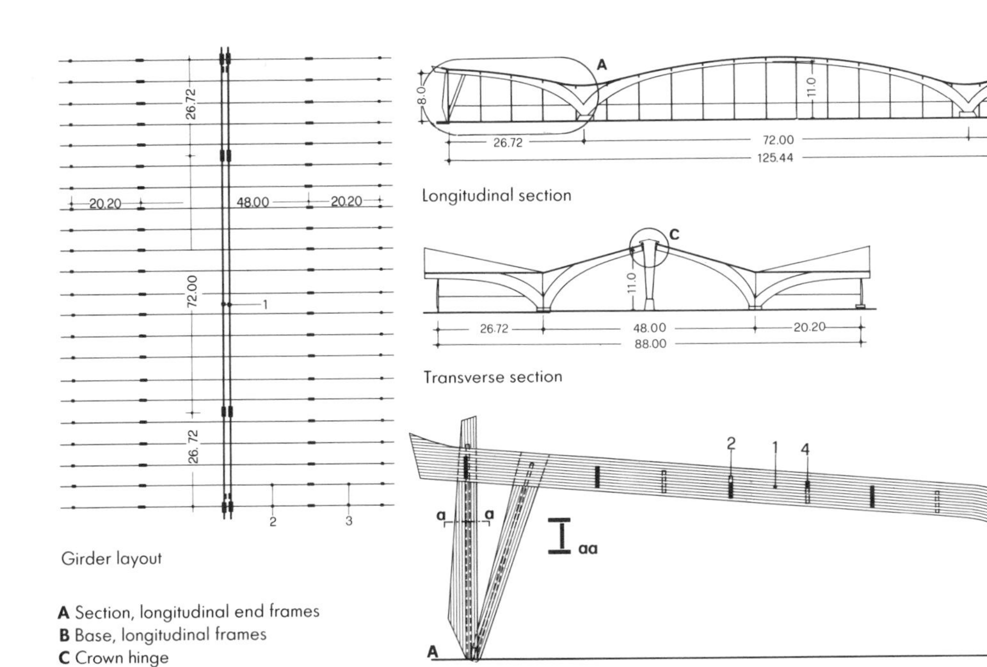

Girder layout

Longitudinal section

Transverse section

1 Longitudinal frames
2 Transverse frames, mid bay
3 Transverse frames, side bays
4 Fillers between longitudinal frames

A Section, longitudinal end frames
B Base, longitudinal frames
C Crown hinge

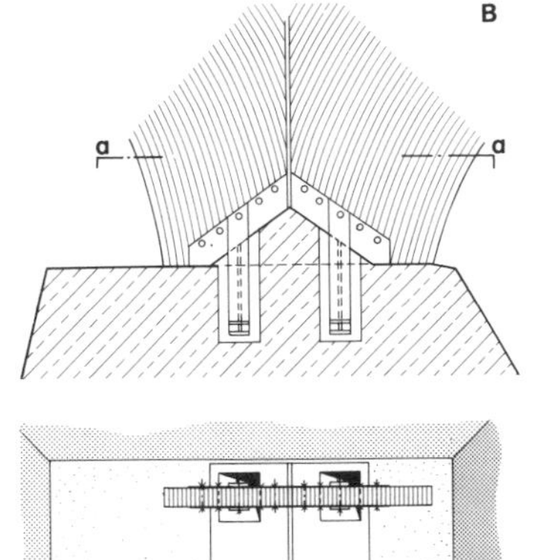

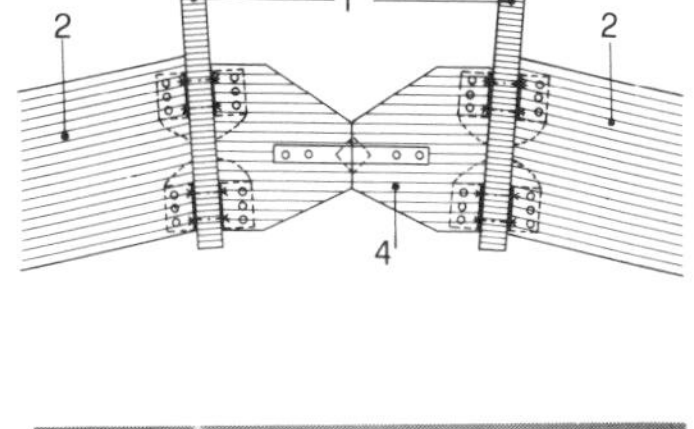

Base Hinges for Light Frames with Short Spans

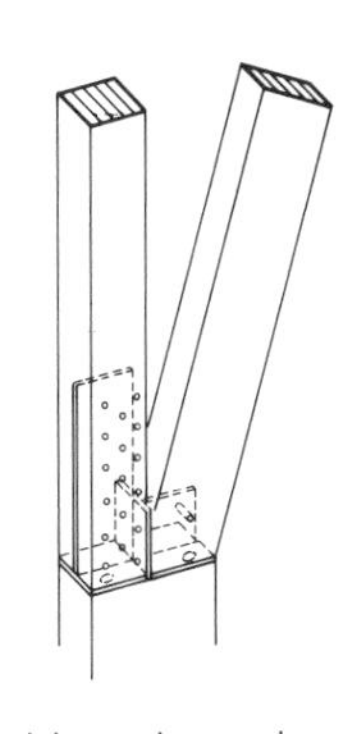

Steel shoe with base plate anchored in concrete.

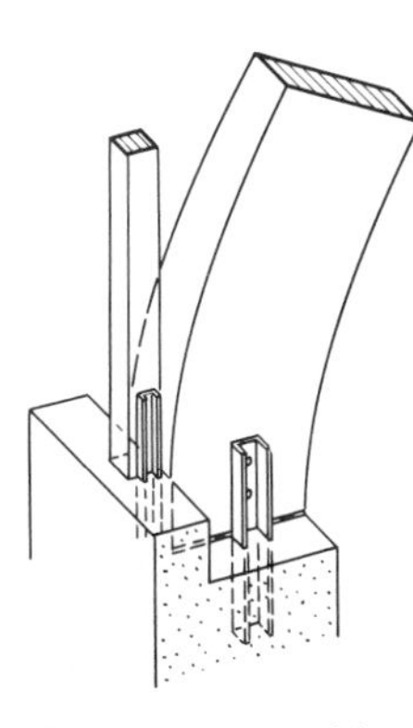

Reinforced-concrete step and lateral anchors. Lead plate on concrete. Wall post set on step.

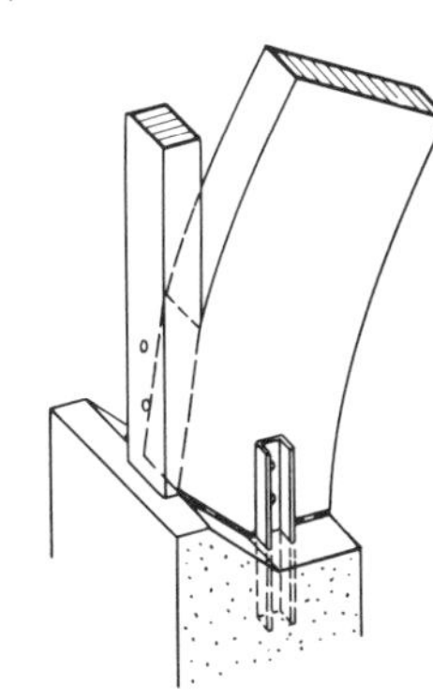

Reinforced-concrete stepped on slope and lateral erectors. Lead plate on concrete. Wall post set on step.

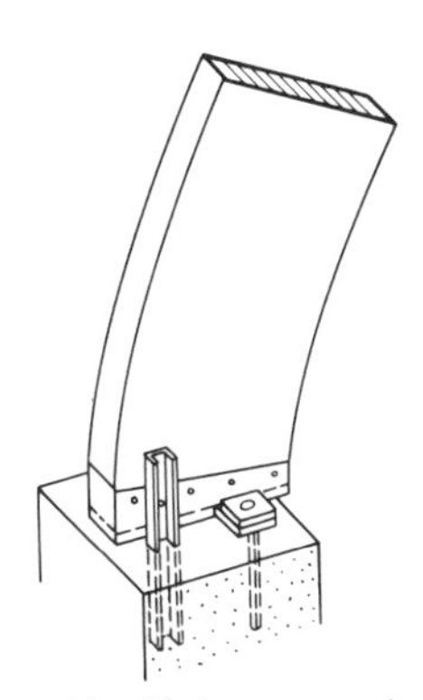

Steel shoe with welded concrete anchor and lateral anchorage member.

Propped half-frames must be able to withstand horizontal forces. Therefore, a hinged prop must be sloped, a vertical prop must be fixed at the base. Walls may be used as propping elements. A multispan structure may consist of several propped half-frames or a combination of frames and hinged struts.

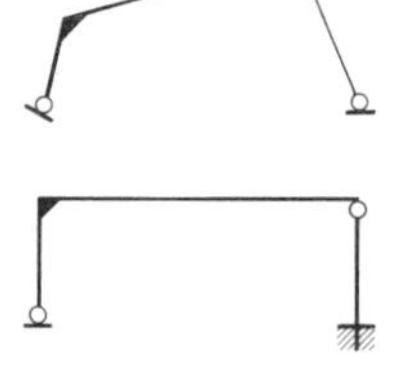

Propped half-frames

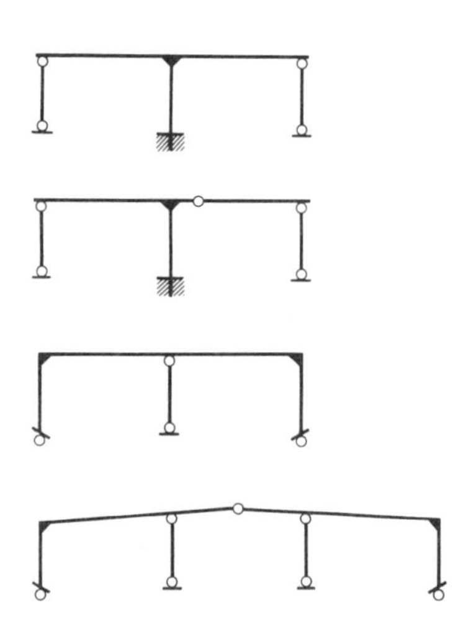

Propped frames

107 Agricultural Building in Rifferswil, Switzerland

Architect: H. Hess, Zurich
Engineer: R. Beier, Brugg

Barn with sloped roof. Plan area 23.00 × 16.80 m. Five single-elbow frames on hinged struts, placed transversely. On the lower side frames reach ground. On the high side they are supported on hinged posts 2 × 10/20 cm which rest on a solid wall of the barn. There is a 2.20 m wide cantilever on the high side of the roof.

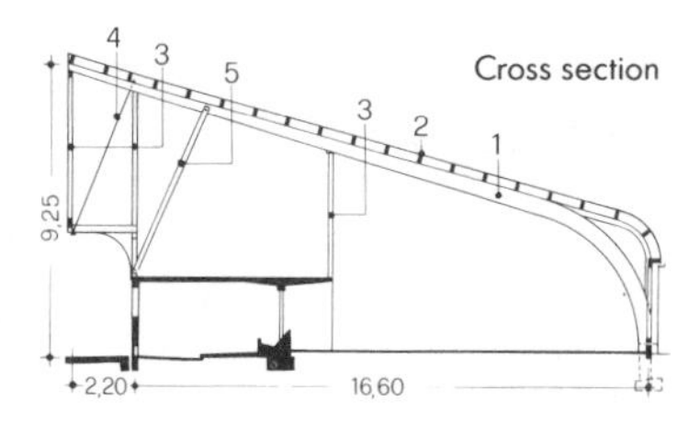

Cross section

1 Main frame 16/22 to 54 cm, spaced at 5.72 m
2 Purlins 12/22 cm
3 Posts 16/16 cm
4 Tension bar ϕ 30 mm
5 Compression strut 2 × 10/20 cm

108 Riding Hall in Munich-Riem, West Germany

Architect: Atelier Kleineichenhausen
Engineer: Rüter, Minden

Riding hall with 75.00 × 30.00 m riding track, bleachers for 2000 spectators, and service rooms. Roof is supported by single-bent frames with elbows at low side of roof and hinged columns on high side. Frame legs are box sections 36/131 to 195 cm, while frame beams are of one piece 16/184 cm; they are joined rigidly with 114 steel dowels arranged in concentric circles. To help resist high shear forces, on either side of each elbow there is a 12 mm glued beech plywood panel. Lapped purlins 7/17 cm are attached to frames with steel angles. Horizontal bracing consists of solid wood diagonals.

Reference: *Detail* 4/1972, p. 731

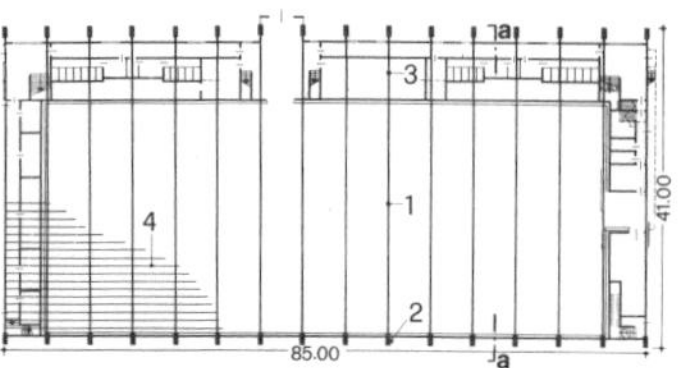

Frame layout plan (shown without wind bracing)

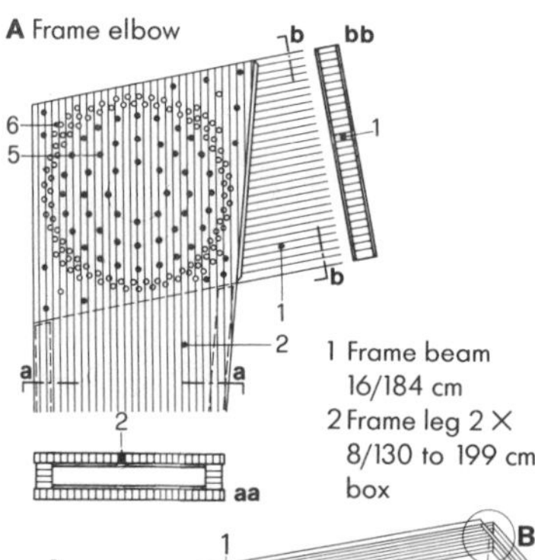

A Frame elbow

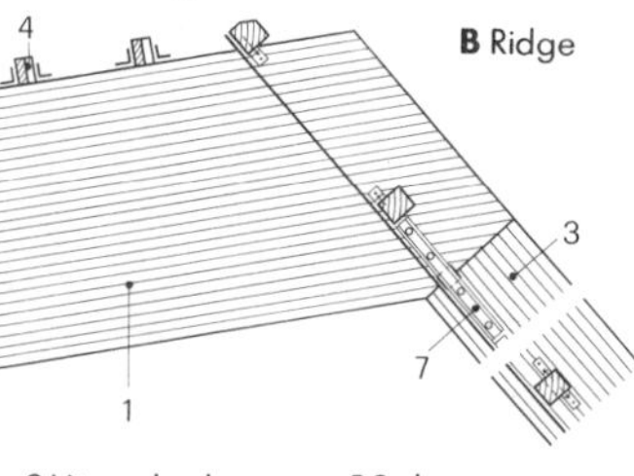

B Ridge

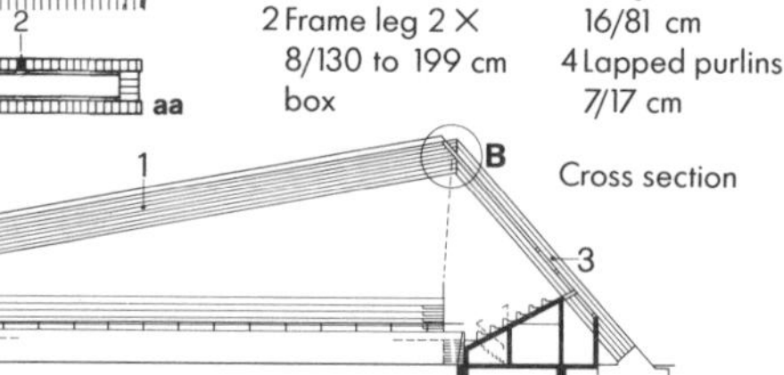

Cross section

1 Frame beam 16/184 cm
2 Frame leg 2 × 8/130 to 199 cm box
3 Hinged columns 16/81 cm
4 Lapped purlins 7/17 cm
5 3 shear connector rings with ϕ 12 mm clamping bolts
6 3 shear connector rings with 114 × ϕ 20 mm steel dowels
7 Steel U shapes with bolts and shear connectors ϕ 95 mm

109 Riding Hall in Hamburg-Volksdorf, West Germany

Architect: U. Hendewerk, Hamburg
Engineer: G. Bockelmann and H. Herrmann, Hamburg

Three-hinged frames spanning 23.50 m, spaced at 6.80 m, 9.22 m high. Three-hinged frames consist of single-bent frames with skewed hinged column. Frame beam is 1.20 m deep, and column is a 0.60 m deep I beam. Frame elbow is articulated into one compression leg 22/22 cm and a tension leg 2 × 8/20 cm. Large spacing between frames required purlins to be made out of 40 cm deep trusses. Wind bracing consists of ϕ 16 mm round bars, ϕ 24 mm in end bays. Purlins are braced by 6/14 cm diagonals in roof plane.

Reference: *Bauen mit Holz* 1/1966, p. 16

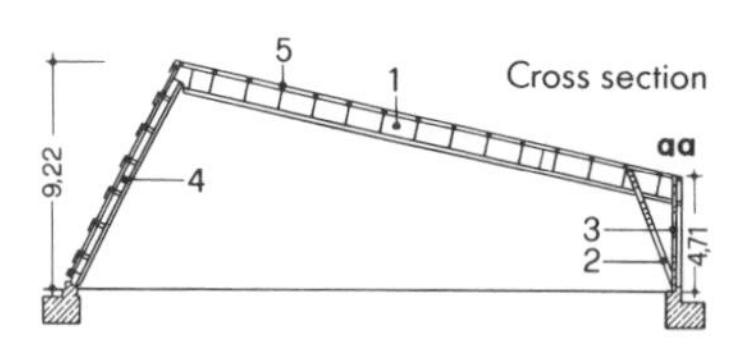

Cross section

1 Frame beam, I section, h = 120 cm, web = 6.5 cm, but 12.5 cm in frame elbow
2 Compression leg 22/22 cm
3 Tension leg 2 × 8/20 cm
4 Hinged column, I section, h = 60 cm, web = 4 cm
5 Purlins, flanges 6/14 cm, webs 3/6 cm
6 Wind bracing ϕ 16 and 24 mm
7 Lateral bracing 6/14 cm

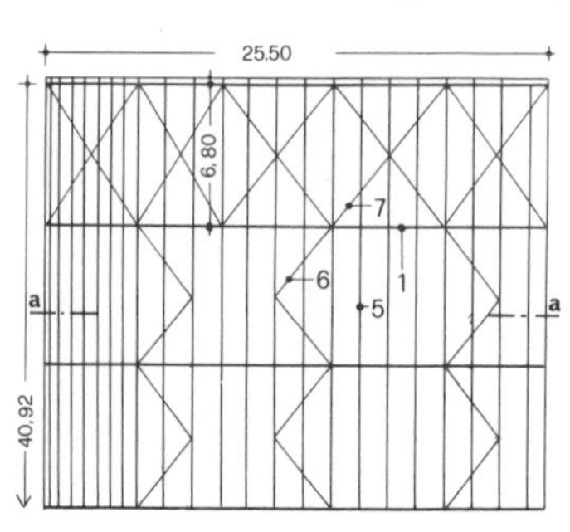

Framing plan

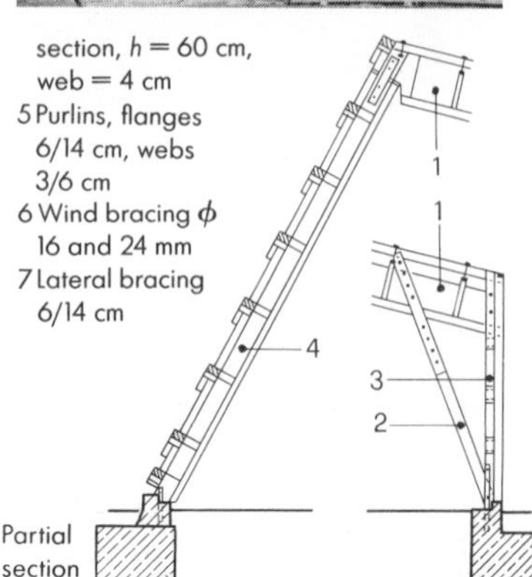

Partial section

110 Storage Shed in Hamburg, West Germany

Engineer: Timber Construction Contractor

Area 4800 m². Single-bent frames are spaced at 7.25 m, symmetrically arranged transverse to building. Frames are supported by hinged columns and from there are cantilevered another 10.00 m, so that there are three bays of 20.00 m each. Frame legs are double, with fillers; frame beam is one piece and shaped to the size of the moment (12/92 to 130 cm). Elbow is rigidly built with two circles of shear connectors ϕ 65 mm. Hinged column is 2 × 16/36 cm, connected by ϕ 65 mm shear connectors.

Wind and horizontal bracing of roof surface is provided by 6/24 cm diagonal planks. Wind loads are resisted longitudinally by two frames at each end of building, in plane of hinged columns. Hinged columns have steel base shoes.

Reference: *Bauen mit Holz* 3/1971, p. 108

Frame layout and wind bracing
Transverse and longitudinal sections

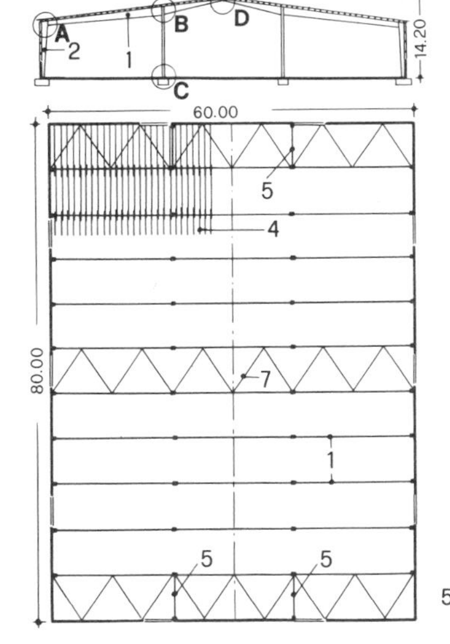

1 Frame beam 12/40 to 92 cm
2 Frame leg 2 × 7/40 to 92 cm
3 Hinged column 2 × 16/36 cm
4 Lapped purlins 8/16 cm
5 Frame beam of wind bracing 12/88.5 to 162 cm
6 Frame leg of wind bracing 2 × 7/40 to 162 cm
7 Lateral bracing 6/16 to 6/24 cm
8 Shear connector ϕ 65 mm
9 Flat steel sheath with dowel ϕ 20 mm
10 Steel shoe with shear connectors ϕ 65 mm and bolts ϕ 12 mm

E, F Wind bracing frame connections

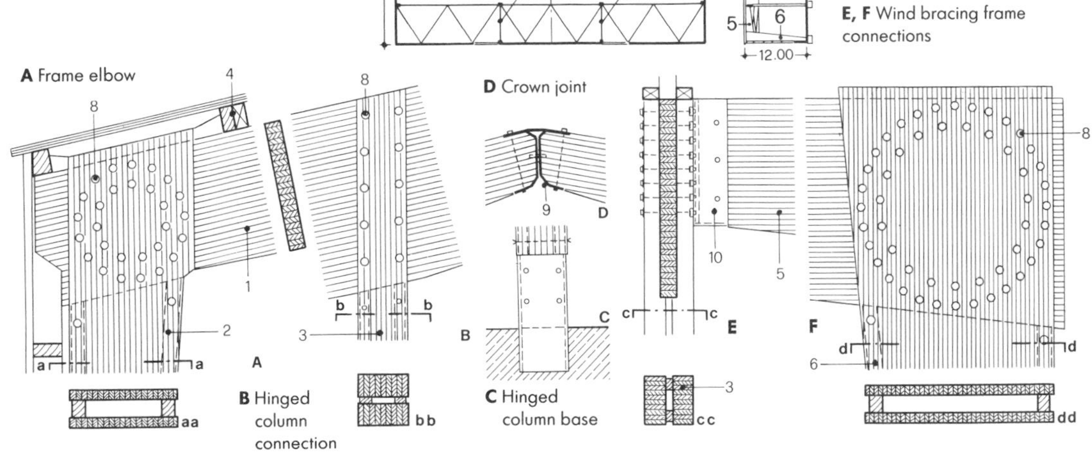

A Frame elbow

B Hinged column connection

C Hinged column base

D Crown joint

111 Storage Shed in Kandel, West Germany

Engineer: Ingenieurbüro für Holzbau, Karlsruhe

Overall size 50.00 × 200.00 m. Main structural system consists of single-bent frames at 7.45 m, hinged intermediate columns, and a central beam supported on columns. This arrangement creates four bays, two at 13.88 m and two at 11.30 m. Main frame legs are articulated into a double tension leg connected with shear connectors, and a single-piece compression leg connected with a notch joint and gusset plates. Frame beam is 14/54 to 84 cm. Hinged columns and central columns are connected to beam with blocks and gussets.

Wind bracing and horizontal stiffening are provided by diagonals in roof surfaces and walls.

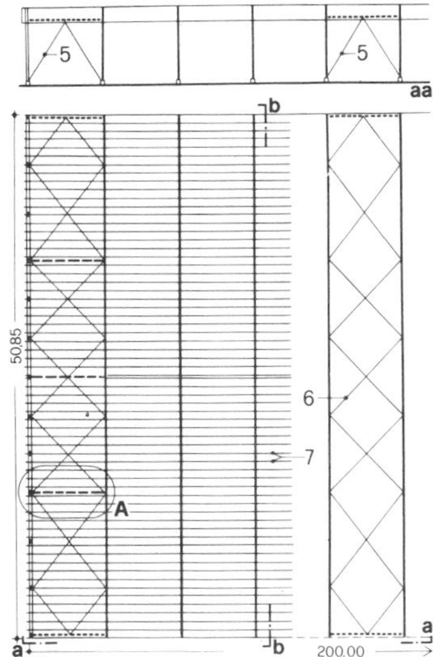

A Wind and lateral bracing

1 Frame beam 14/54 to 83.7 cm
2 Compression leg 20/24 cm
3 Tension leg 2 × 6/18 cm
4 Hinged columns 20/24 cm
5 Wind bracing 16/18 cm
6 Wind bracing 4/12 cm
7 Lapped purlins 5/18 cm

Hinged Column Bases

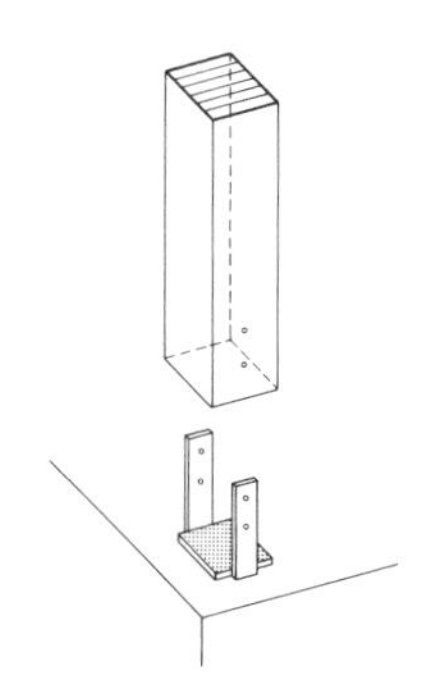

Bituminous paper and side anchors.

Steel plate with dowel.

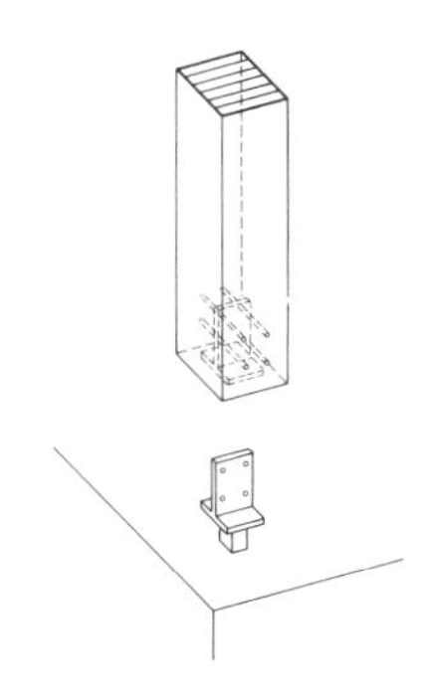

Doweled T shape on steel tube base.

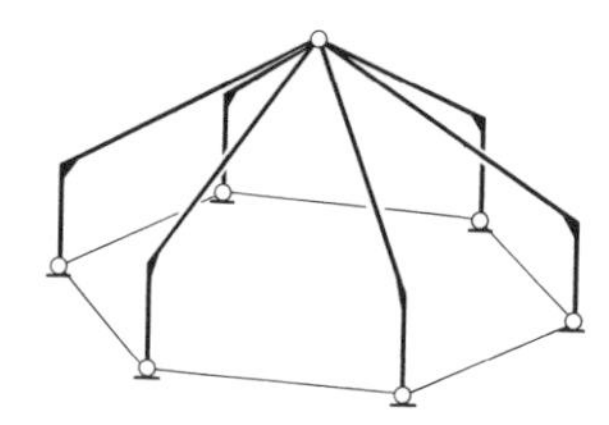

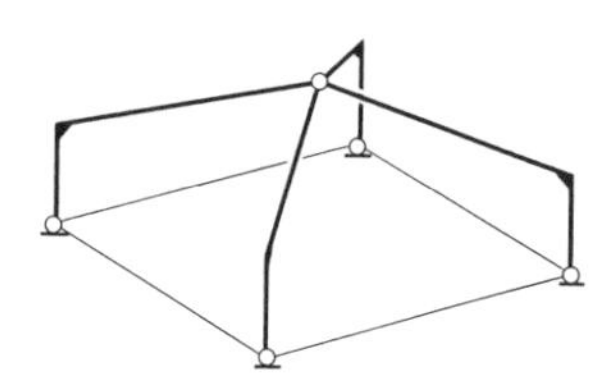

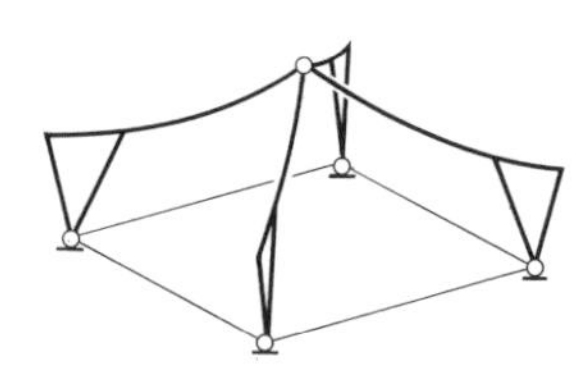

Radially symmetrical arrangement of frames

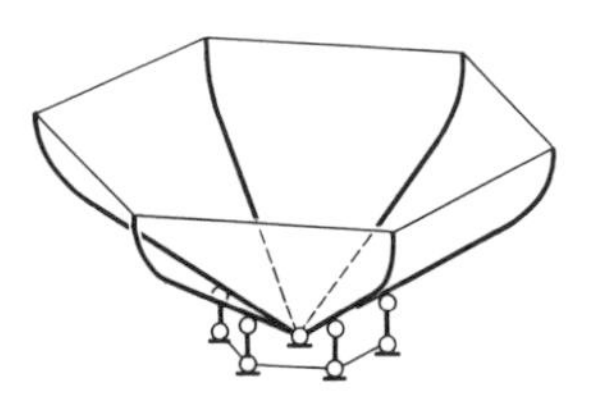

With tension ring above frames

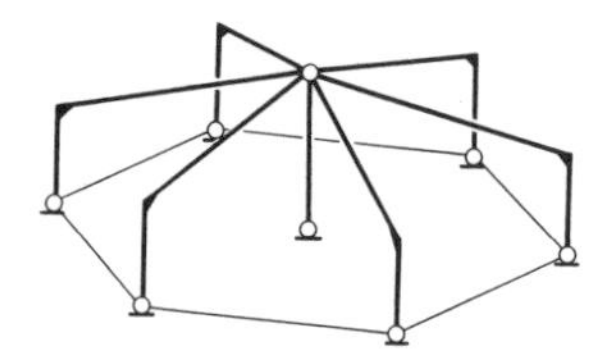

With center column

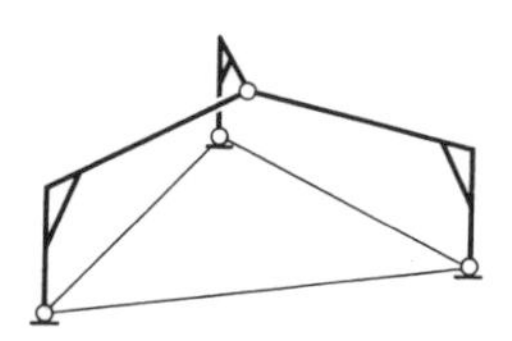

Unsymmetrical arrangement

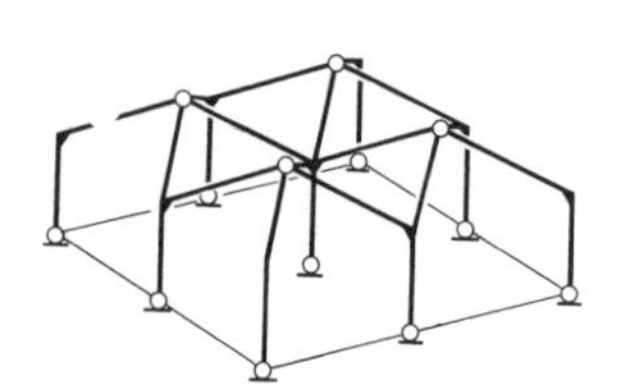

Group of radially arranged frames

112 Exhibition Hall in Poitiers, France

Architect: City Building Department, Poitiers

Round structure with a diameter of 113.30 m. Roof is divided into 16 segments, with every other segment being lower. This creates radial clerestory windows between two roof levels. Structure consists of radial three-hinged frames. Each lower segment contains three frames 12/60 to 105 cm, each higher segment contains two frames 17/80 to 120 cm. Between them are stiffening trusses supporting radial secondary frames. Purlins 8/20 cm are parallel to gutter and rest on main and secondary frames.

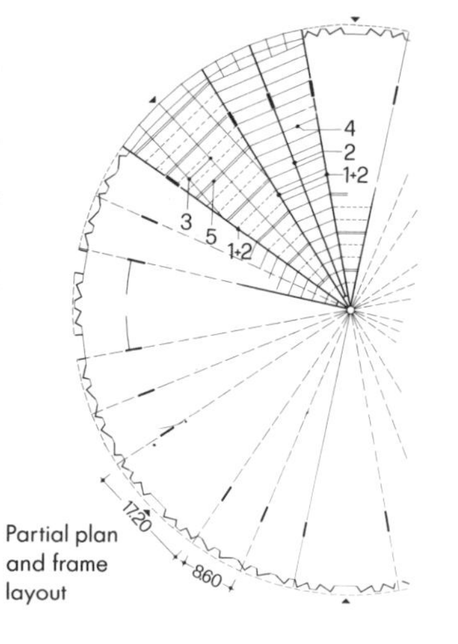

Partial plan and frame layout

Partial section

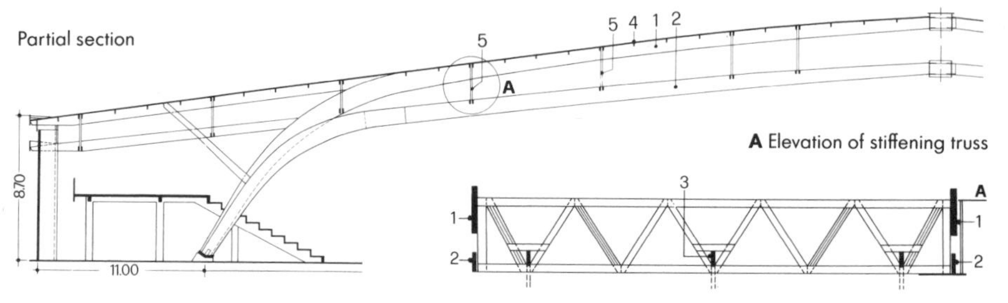

A Elevation of stiffening truss

1 Radial frames 17/80 to 120 cm
2 Lower radial frames 12/60 to 105 cm
3 Radial secondary frames 10/45 cm
4 Purlins 8/20 cm
5 Stiffening trusses

113 Exhibition Hall in Kortrijk, Belgium

Architect: G. van Oost and A. Cornelis, Kortrijk

Exhibition and assembly hall with covered surface of 68.40 × 91.20 m. Roof consists of three-hinged frames, arranged longitudinally, transversely, and diagonally. This arrangement results in eight frame legs meeting at one bearing, a mushroom-type construction. Frame spans are 22.80 m, or 32.20 m diagonally. Central room is spanned over without columns (at **A**) so that eight frames meet at crown point. Spans are 45.60 m, or 64.40 m diagonally. Horizontal bracing in both directions is achieved by spacial arrangement of frames.

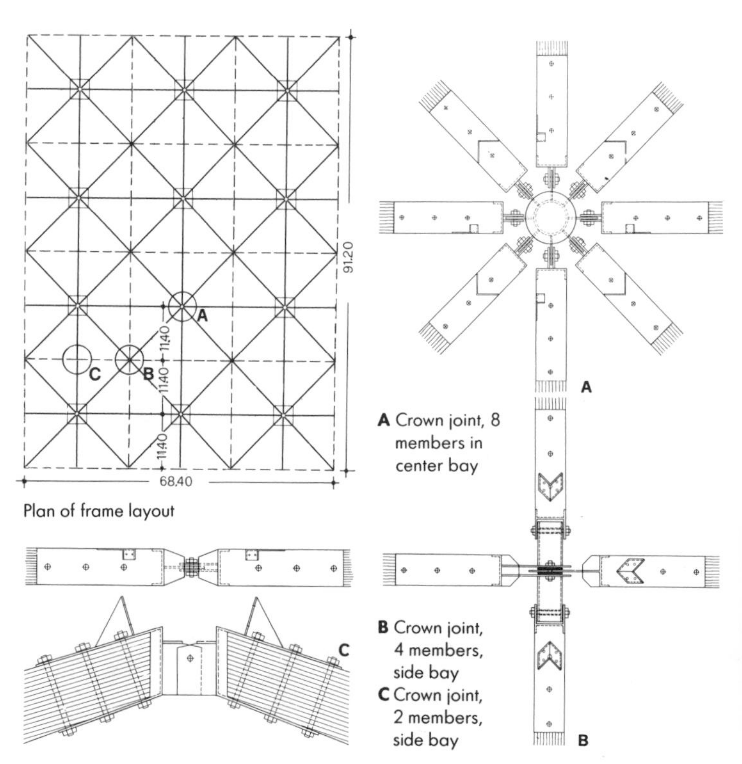

Plan of frame layout

A Crown joint, 8 members in center bay

B Crown joint, 4 members, side bay

C Crown joint, 2 members, side bay

114 Church in Wildegg, Switzerland

Architect: J. Dahinden, Zurich
Engineer: H.-P. Kämpf, Rupperswil

Church has a capacity for 350 people and is located on a hill in an exposed position. It has a stepped roof, a tower, and secondary rooms. Tentlike nave is spanned by radial, single-bent frames with an I cross section. Lower bearing is on a concrete foundation, upper one on a concrete shelf. Purlins 10/12 to 16/30 cm, depending on span, are placed parallel to gutter. Roof is vented and sheathed in copper. Underside of roof is planked so that only lower flanges of frames are exposed.
Reference: *Detail* 5/1971, p. 1013; *Werk* 12/1971, p. 810

Plan

Layout of frames

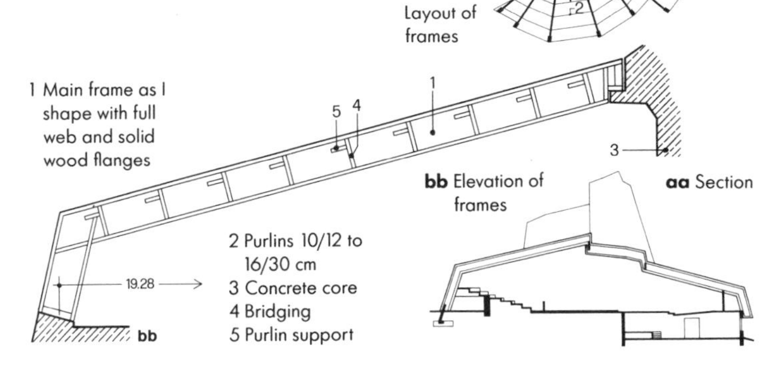

1 Main frame as I shape with full web and solid wood flanges
2 Purlins 10/12 to 16/30 cm
3 Concrete core
4 Bridging
5 Purlin support

bb Elevation of frames

aa Section

115 Church in Livermore, California, United States

Architect: Mackinlay, Winnacker, McNeil, and Partner, Oakland
Engineer: Pregnoff and Mathen, Palo Alto

Round church is spanned by 18 radial frames that cantilever 9.00 m toward center. Frames rest on a circular reinforced-concrete beam supported on columns and are held down outside by tension columns. A skylight of 6.50 m diameter is in the center. Each frame consists of single or double members, joined by shear connectors and bolts. Between frames, parallel to gutter, are 7.6 cm thick planks spanning 4.60 m maximum; 8 mm plywood nailed to planking provides shear resistance. Structure is a rigid and stable truncated cone.
Reference: *Progressive Architecture* 12/1968, p. 100

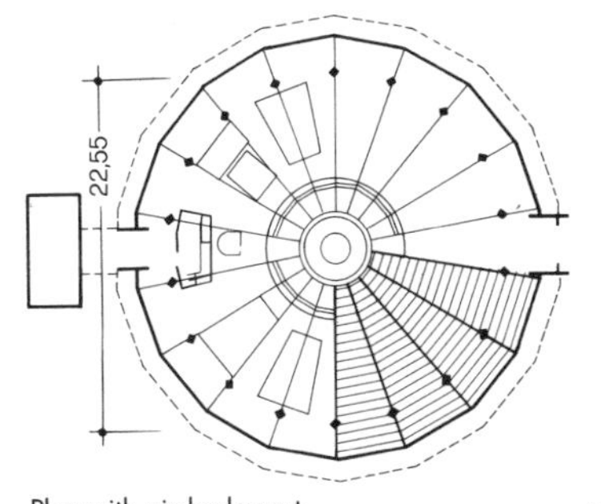

Plan with girder layout

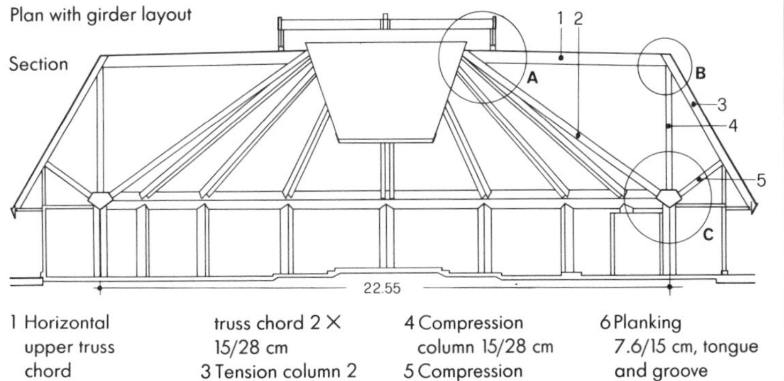

Section

1 Horizontal upper truss chord
2 Sloping lower truss chord 2 × 15/28 cm
3 Tension column 2 × 11/28 cm
4 Compression column 15/28 cm
5 Compression column 11/22 cm
6 Planking 7.6/15 cm, tongue and groove
7 Plywood 8 mm

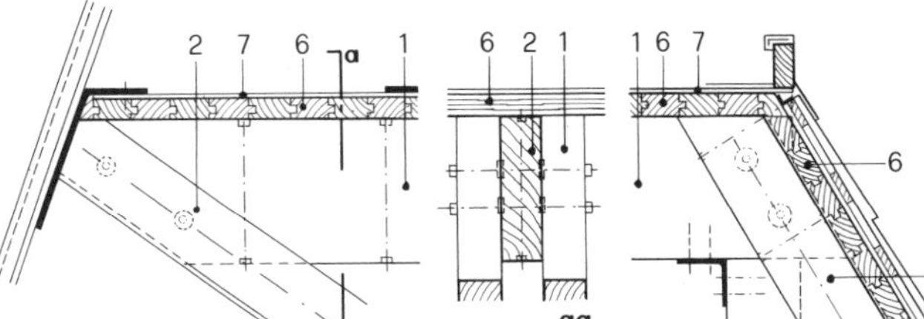

A Connection 1 to 2

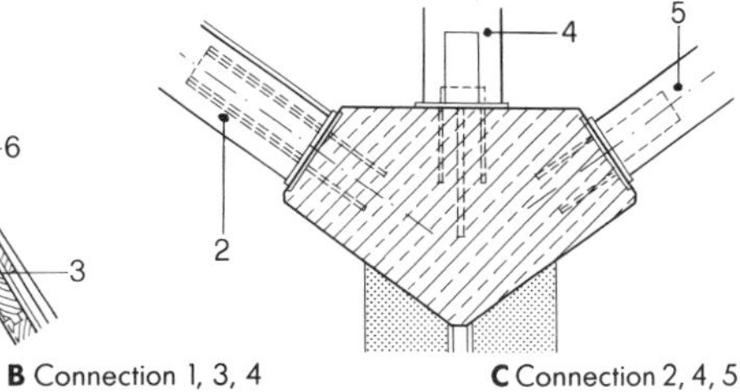

B Connection 1, 3, 4

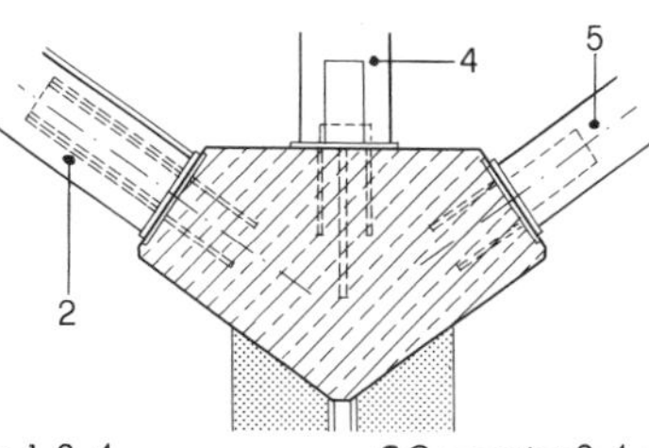

C Connection 2, 4, 5

Crown Joint of Radial Beams

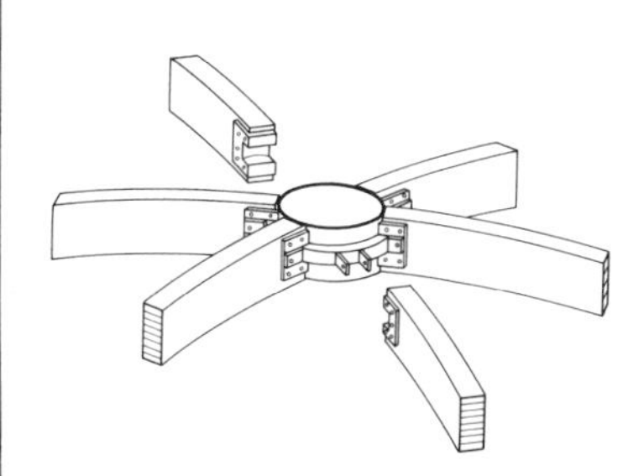

Steel ring with circular ledger and steel hardware.

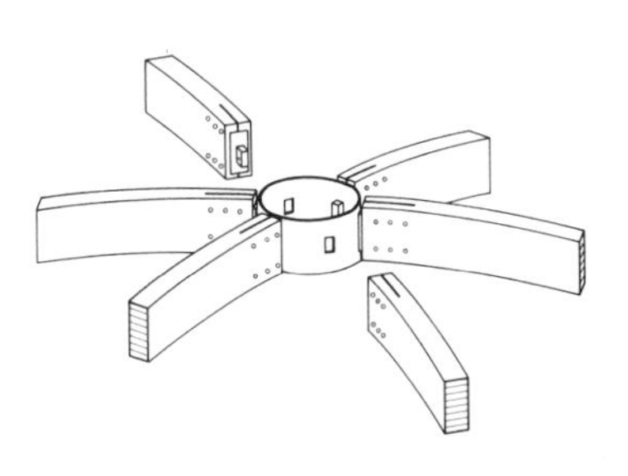

Steel ring with holes. Doweled plates, keys, and cotter pin retainers.

Upper and lower nailed gusset plates of steel or plywood. Shear transfer through shear connectors in end grain and hardwood lugs.

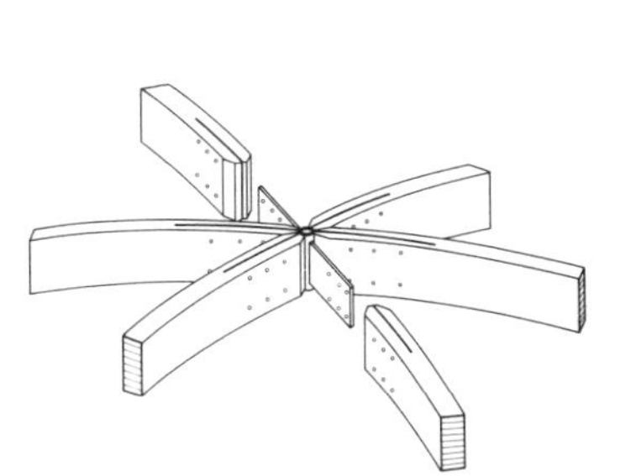

Steel tube with radially welded plates, doweled in slits.

Two-hinged arches are statically indeterminate and cause outward reactions mostly as compression forces in the direction of the arch. Unsymmetrical or horizontal loads (wind, snow) cause bending, so that the amount of horizontal thrust depends on the rise of the arch and its stiffness at the crown. The bending moment in the center and the stiffness of splices govern the design. If the bearings are subject to lateral movement, the two-hinged arch deforms and generates additional bending stresses.

q

q q

q q

Shapes of arch corresponding to resultant of compression forces for loads given above

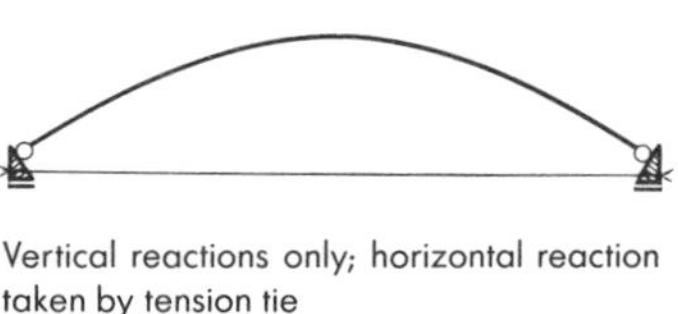

Vertical reactions only; horizontal reaction taken by tension tie

Double T, box, or solid beam sections of glue-laminated wood
a = 5 to 10 m (spacing)
l = 30 to 100 m (span)
h = l/35 to l/50 (depth)
f = l/6 to l/10 (rise)

Laminated wood trusses
a = 5 to 10 m
l = 50 to 120 m
h = l/20 to l/40
f = l/5 to l/8

116 Multipurpose Hall in Nantes, France

Architect: Y. Liberge, Nantes

Great hall, 50.00 × 110.00 m, has a lower floor and a two-story addition for assemblies and exhibitions. Hall is spanned transversely by two-hinged arches 96 cm deep, which are curved upward over two-story addition. Exterior and interior conical columns are of reinforced concrete. 60 cm deep purlins span between arches and rest on metal seats.

Roofing is trapezoidal sheet metal. Roof plane is stiffened by diagonals. Reinforced concrete deck absorbs tension stresses from arch.

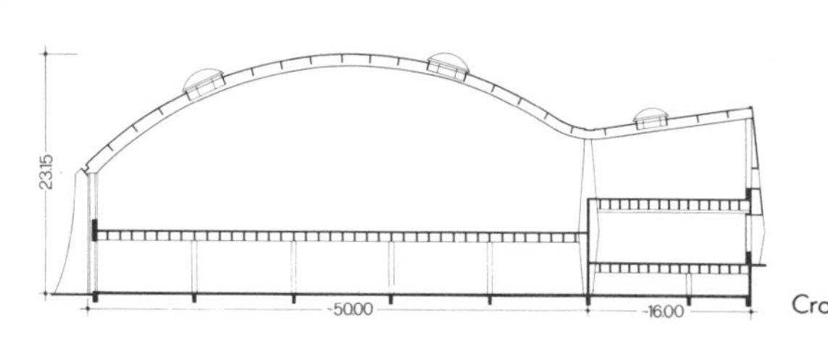

Cross section

117 Ice Skating Rink in Bern, Switzerland

Architect: W. Schwaar and F. Zulauf, Bern
Engineer: Emch and Berger, H. Vogel, Bern

Roof over an existing ice skating rink and grandstand for 16,000 spectators. Parabolic tied two-hinged arches span 75.00 to 85.00 m. Arches have box section 48.5/120 cm and flange thicknesses varying from 12 to 15 cm. Arches were delivered in three parts and were glued and bolted together on site in stepped joints. A square steel tube tie was added with a crane. Lapped purlins span longitudinally over spans varying from 1.00 to 1.15 m. Horizontal stiffening of roof is by means of I-shaped solid wood diagonals.
Reference: *Werk* 10/1971, p. 653; *Holz* no. 42-43/1970

Cross section

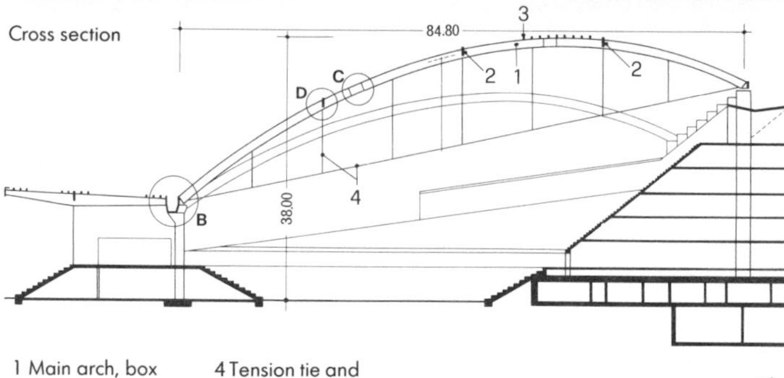

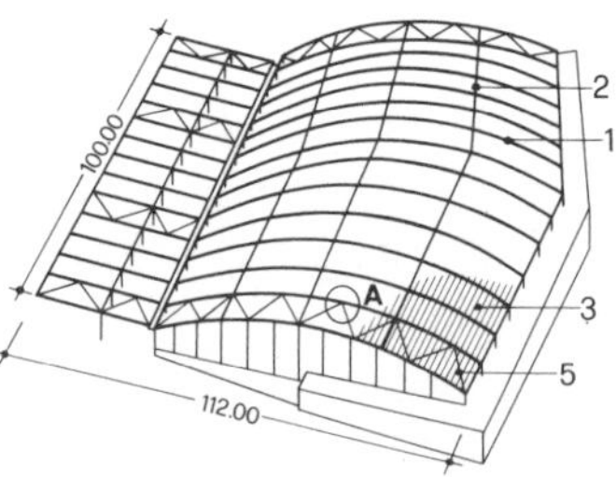

1 Main arch, box section 48.5/120 cm
2 Stiffener beam, box section with planked webs
3 Lapped purlins 7/22 to 12/22 cm
4 Tension tie and hangers 200/200/10 mm
5 Wind bracing, I-shaped lumber
6 4 bolts ϕ 52 mm welded to tension tie

A Wind bracing connection to stiffener beam
B Bearing
C Rigid field splice
D Connection stiffener beam to main arch

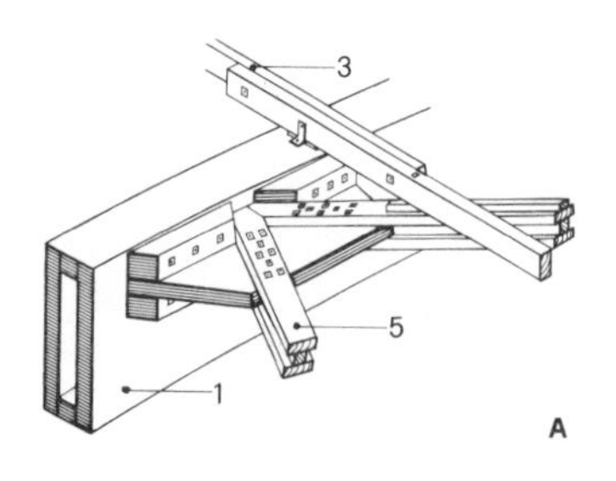

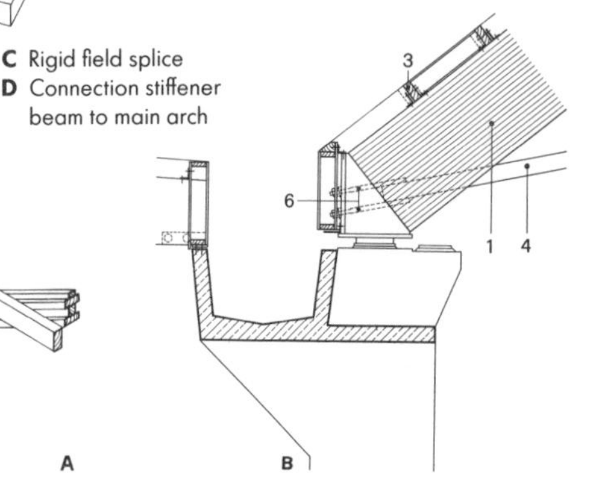

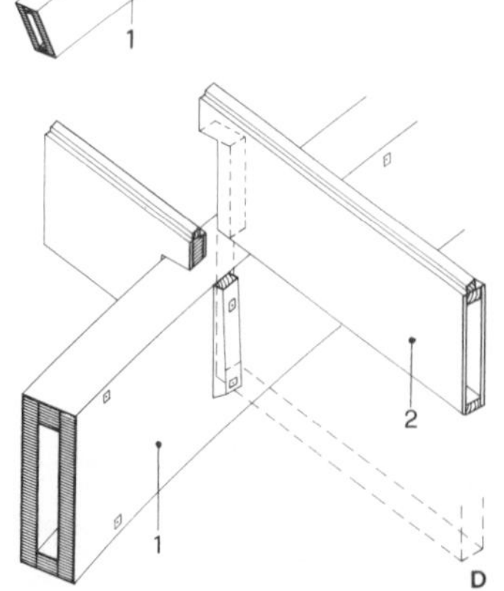

118 Multipurpose Hall in Leiden, The Netherlands

Architect: de Gruyter, Amsterdam, with v. d. Jagt and Aruhem, Leiden
Engineer: Timber Construction Contractor

Two-hinged arches, 2 × 14/100 to 230 cm, span 75.00 mm. Each arch has two splices so that each piece to be transported did not exceed 20.00 m. Purlins 7/18 cm support two layers of 24 mm planking at 55° to arch. Both layers brace upper chords of arches and transfer wind forces to foundations by means of knee braces at gutters and rigidity of twin arches in the longitudinal direction.
Reference: *Bauen mit Holz* 11/1971

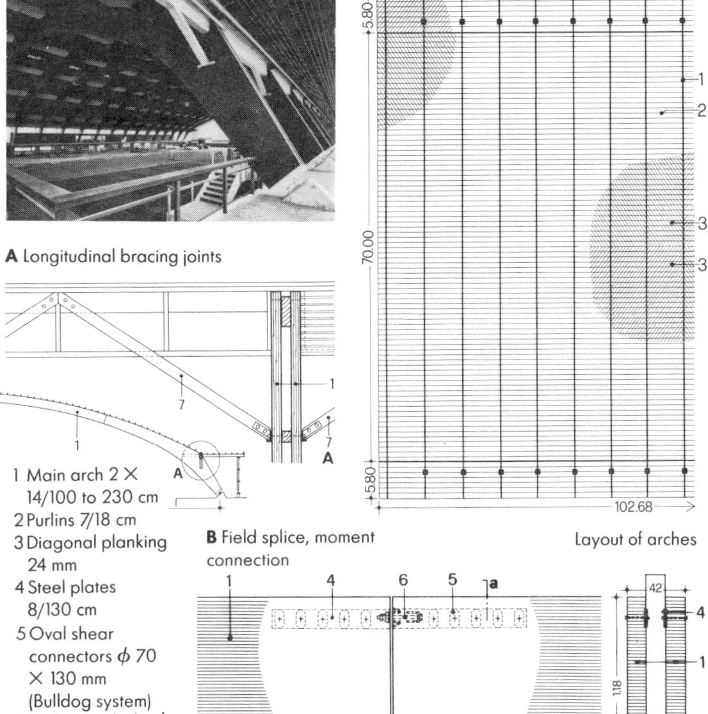

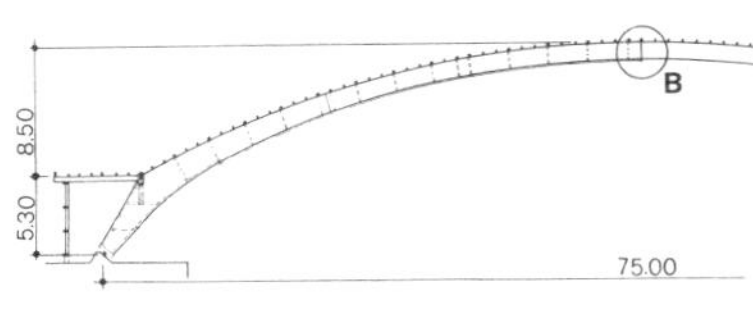

Cross section

1 Main arch 2 × 14/100 to 230 cm
2 Purlins 7/18 cm
3 Diagonal planking 24 mm
4 Steel plates 8/130 cm
5 Oval shear connectors ϕ 70 × 130 mm (Bulldog system)
6 Tightening bolts ϕ 25 mm
7 Knee brace 2 × 5.6/14 cm

B Field splice, moment connection

Moment Connection Splices, also for Arches

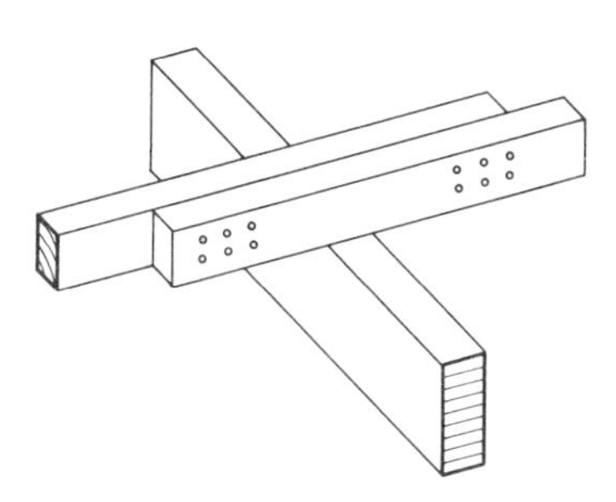

Splice of a lapped purlin; dowels or nails.

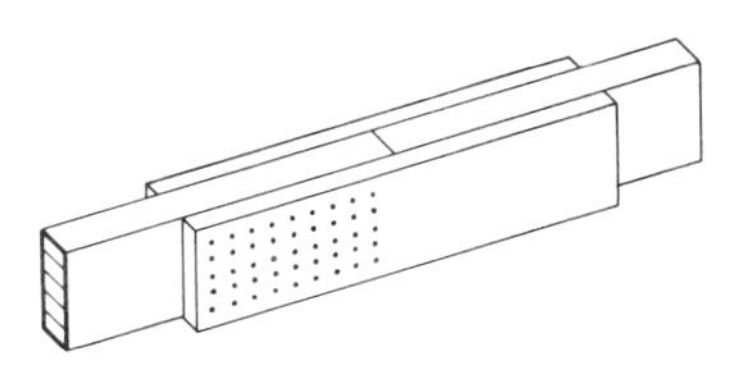

Side gussets, nailed or doweled; plywood, laminated wood, or steel plates.

Steel plates nailed top and bottom, with bolts to transfer longitudinal shear forces. Transverse shear transferred through hardwood keys.

Steel plate doweled in slits.

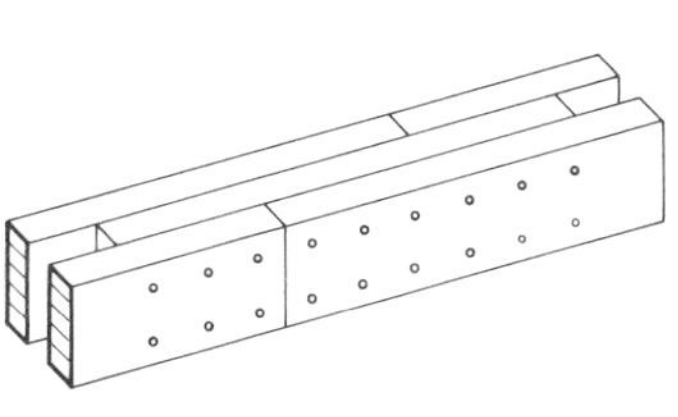

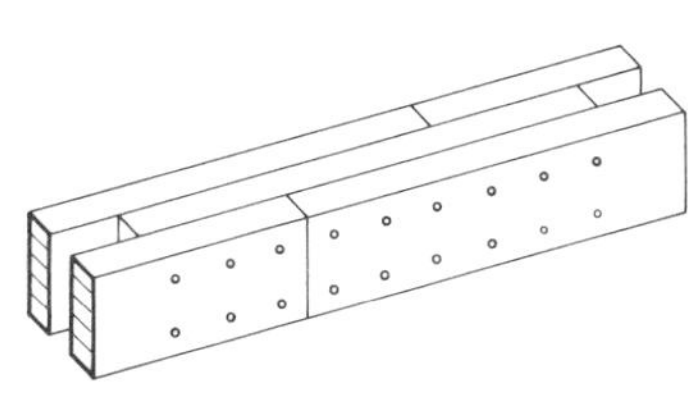

Twin beam with offset splices, doweled through filler wood.

119 Ice Skating Rink in Selb, West Germany

Architect: Hutschenreuther Planungs GmbH, Selb
Engineer: J. Natterer, Munich

Roof area 74.00 × 61.00 m. Difficult subsoil condition dictated use of a main longitudinal three-hinged arch 3 × 20/200 cm and transverse girders 20/175 cm. Main wind bracing and lateral arch support are provided by parabolic flat steel bracing placed on 35 mm planking. Transverse flat steel trussing in two roof bays braces transverse girders and resists unsymmetrical wind loads. Purlins 16/25 cm serve also as struts in wind trussing.

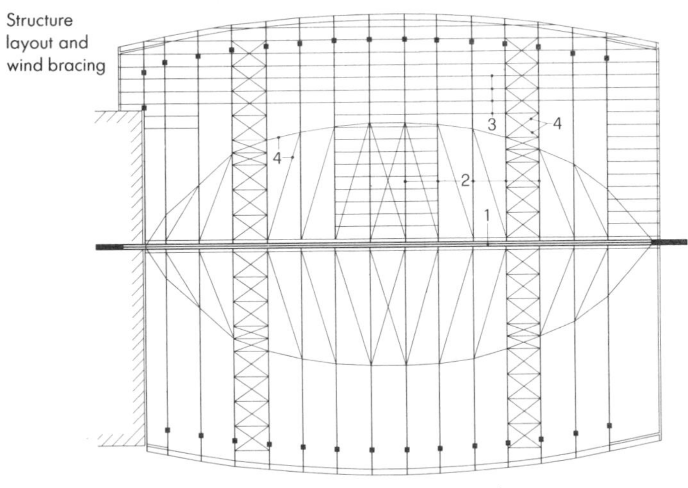

Structure layout and wind bracing

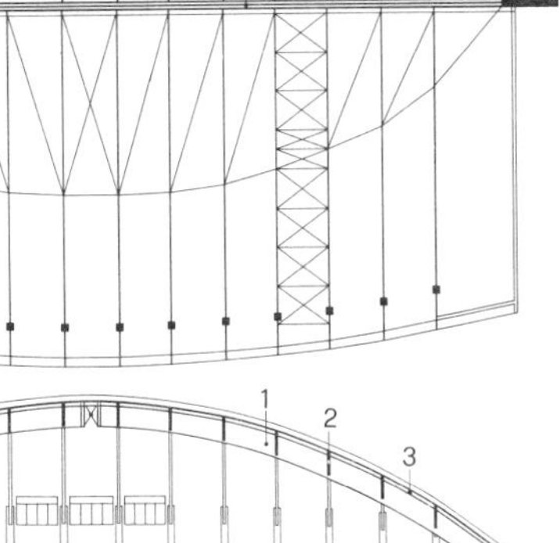

Longitudinal section

1 Main arch 3 × 20/200 cm
2 Transverse girders 20/175 cm
3 Purlins 16/25 cm
4 Main bracing
5 Transverse bracing
6 Bearing seat with dowels
7 Bearing cantilever, steel plates
8 Lateral bracing

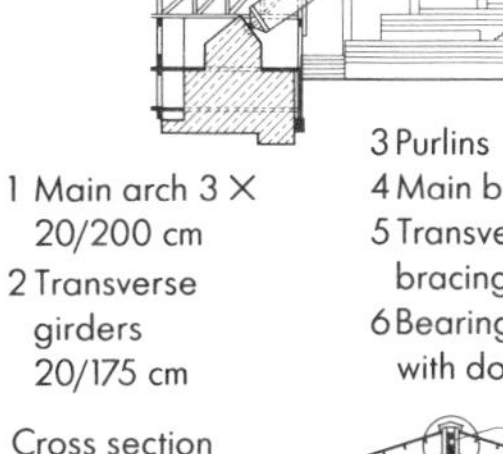
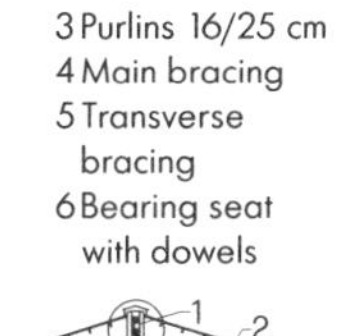

Cross section

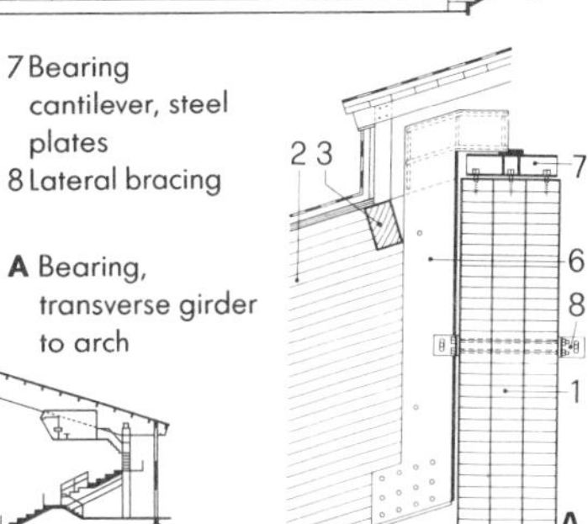

A Bearing, transverse girder to arch

Three-hinged arches are statically determinate. They resist exterior loads mostly through compression stresses in the arch. The bearing reactions are inclined, the same as for three-hinged frames or beams, and the size of horizontal forces depends on the rise of the arch. Compression and bending stresses from unsymmetrical or horizontal forces govern the design. Buckling out of the plane of the arch is also critical. Slender arches may also be subject to buckling within the plane of the arch.

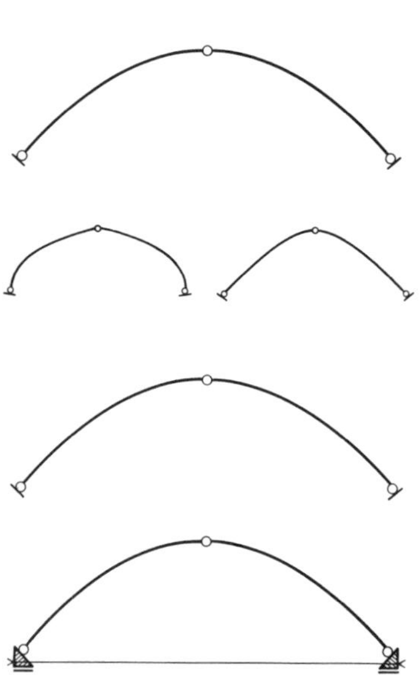

Bearing reactions are the same as for three-hinged beams. A tie may balance horizontal reactions.

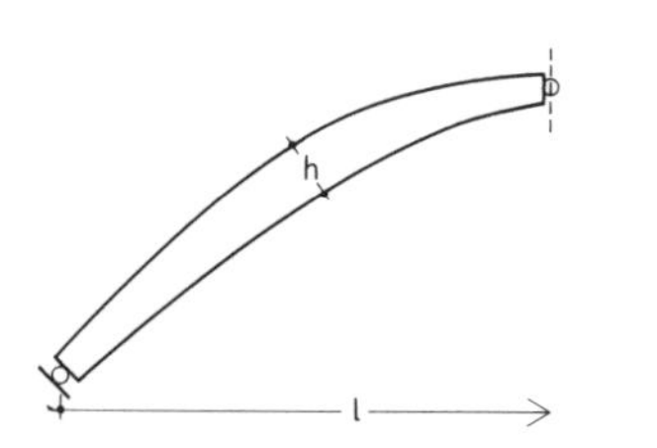

Laminated wood arch
a = 4 to 6 m (spacing)
l = 30 to 100 m
h = l/30 to l/50
f = l/5 to l/7 (rise)

120 Exhibition Hall in Klagenfurt, Austria

Architect: O. Loider, Vienna
Engineer: Timber Construction Contractor

The roof has 10 three-hinged arches spanning 96.00 m. Rise is 25.00 m. Each arch consists of two laminated wood I sections, with 2 × 16/100 to 16/187 cm webs, and upper and lower flanges as crossed planking (Kämpf system). Use of 8/22 cm lapped purlins dictated an arch spacing of 6.80 m. Purlins are braced by 8/8 cm diagonals and 3/5 cm struts in order to minimize lateral moments. At each end diagonals have a piece that is parallel to the purlin and is finger-jointed and glued to the diagonals. This permits a simple connection of diagonals to purlins. Trusswork created by diagonals, struts, and purlins extends through all bays and stiffens upper chords of arches. Lower arch chords are braced through specially framed purlins spaced at 8.80 m. End bay contains a one-sided bracing frame.

Transportation limitations required that arches be field-spliced using three sections, each 18.50 m long. Chord laminations are joined offset and glued. Web joints are spliced with lateral plates on both sides. Ten arches were assembled in 10 days.
Reference: *Bauen mit Holz* 10/1966

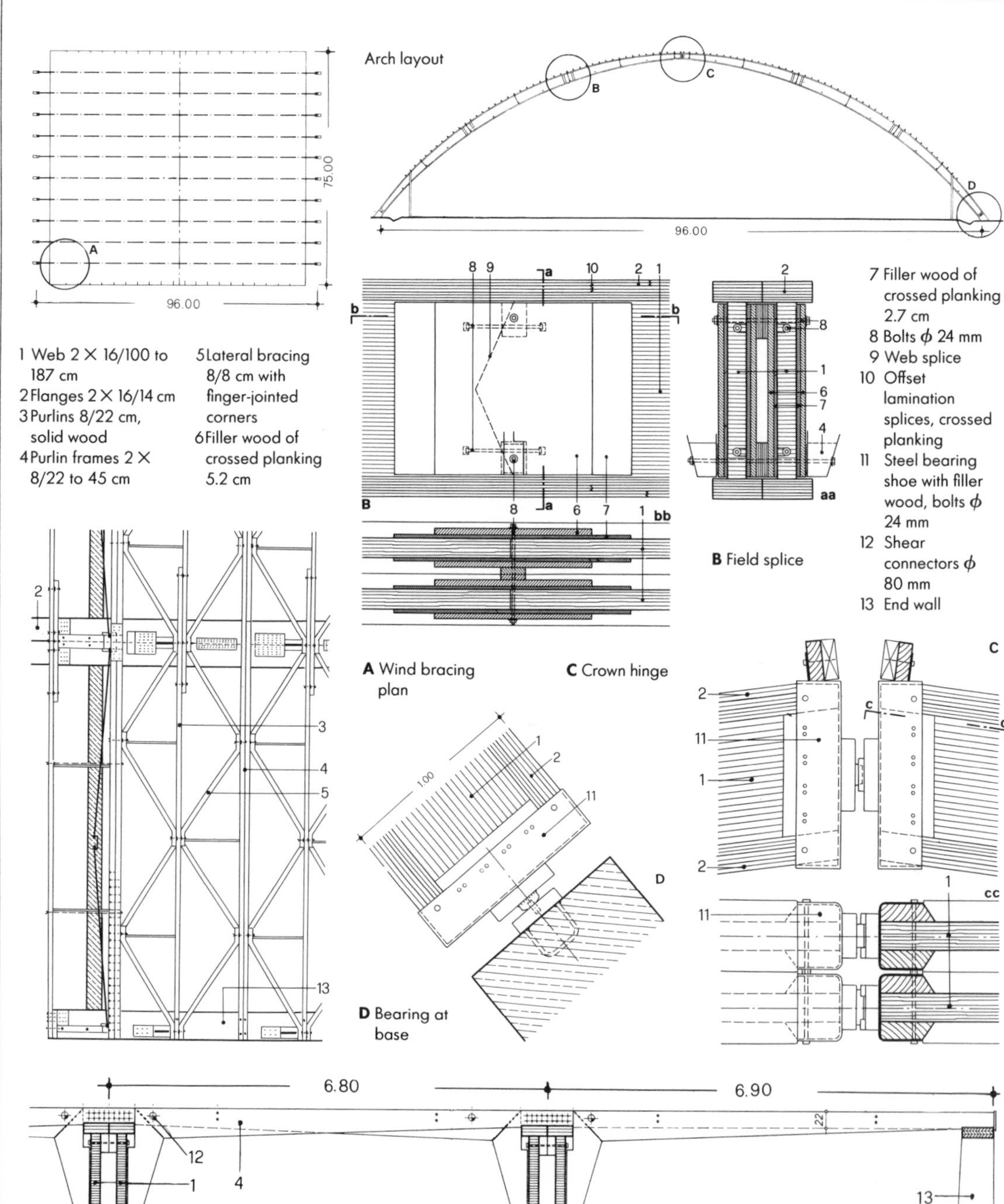

1 Web 2 × 16/100 to 187 cm
2 Flanges 2 × 16/14 cm
3 Purlins 8/22 cm, solid wood
4 Purlin frames 2 × 8/22 to 45 cm
5 Lateral bracing 8/8 cm with finger-jointed corners
6 Filler wood of crossed planking 5.2 cm
7 Filler wood of crossed planking 2.7 cm
8 Bolts ϕ 24 mm
9 Web splice
10 Offset lamination splices, crossed planking
11 Steel bearing shoe with filler wood, bolts ϕ 24 mm
12 Shear connectors ϕ 80 mm
13 End wall

A Wind bracing plan

B Field splice

C Crown hinge

D Bearing at base

Lateral bracing of arch

121 Sports Stadium in Turku, Finland

Architect: M. u. M. Jaatinen, Helsinki
Engineer: M. Sihvonen, Tapiola

Stadium is spanned longitudinally by 13 three-hinged arches of glue-laminated wood. Arches are circular with a radius of 65.50 m, span of 85.00 m, and are spaced at 3.50 m. Hinges at crown and base are steel shoes of welded steel plates and pin bolts. Transverse to arches are steel purlins in the shape of frames. Roofing is trapezoidal sheets of aluminum with 12.5 cm thick fiberglass insulation.

Arches were erected in pairs: steel purlins and bearing shoes were assembled on the ground and arches were lifted by a crane. This procedure ensured lateral stability during erection.

Reference: *Ark Finnland* 7-8/1972, p. 4

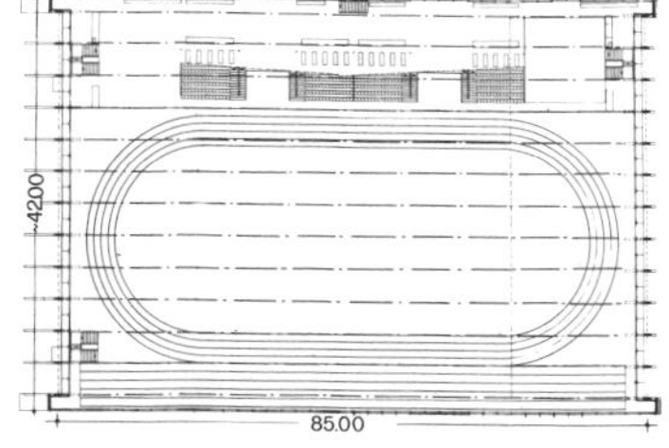

Plan and section

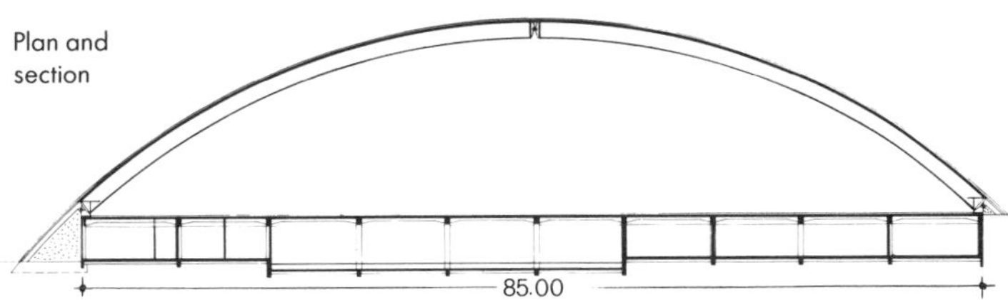

122 Multipurpose Hall in Biebesheim, West Germany

Architect: G. Kramer, Karlsruhe
Engineer: Ingenieurbüro für Holzbau, Karlsruhe

Plan area 50.00 × 55.00 m. Seven three-hinged arches span 50.00 m. They are basket-shaped in order to achieve a higher clearance. Bearings are joined by ties in floor. An arch spacing of 6.60 m requires lapped purlins of 6 to 10/18 cm size. Wind bracing is provided by trussing in one bay and by arches between bearings along both longitudinal sides. Lateral bracing of upper arch chords is provided by nailed plywood panels 1.20 × 2.40 m. Lower

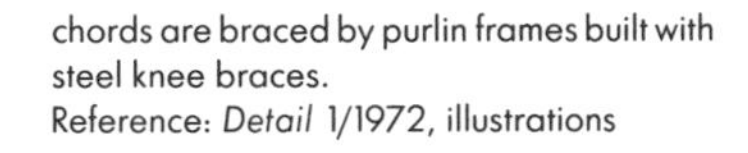

chords are braced by purlin frames built with steel knee braces.

Reference: *Detail* 1/1972, illustrations

Layout of arches

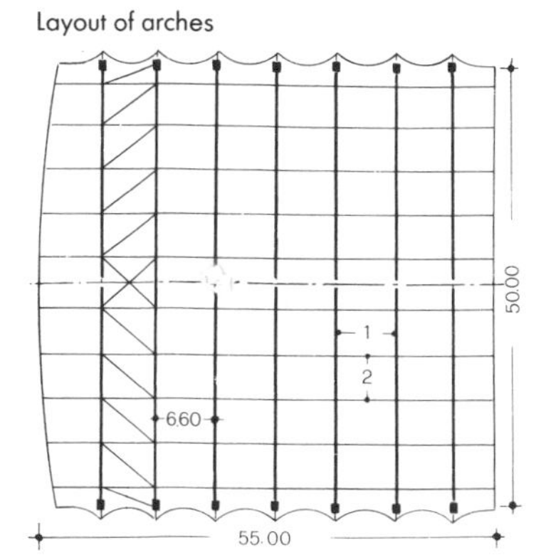

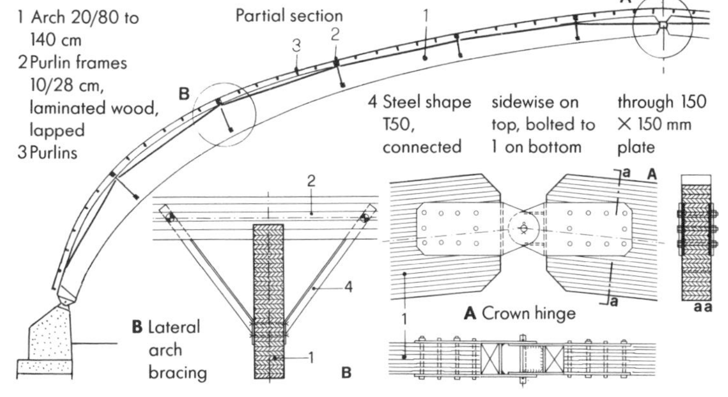

Base Bearings of Beams, Frames, and Arches

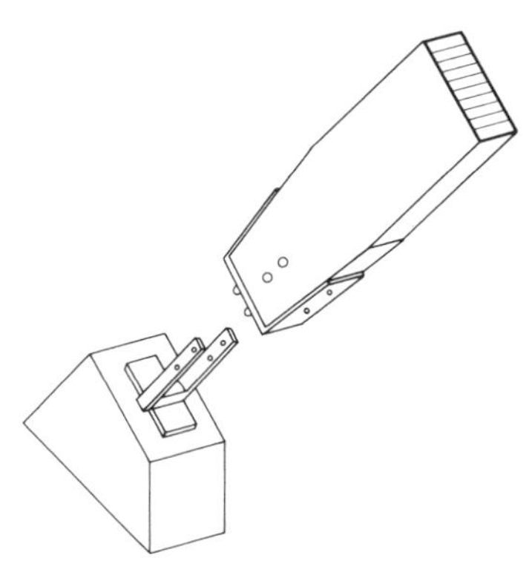

Keyed bearing with side plates.

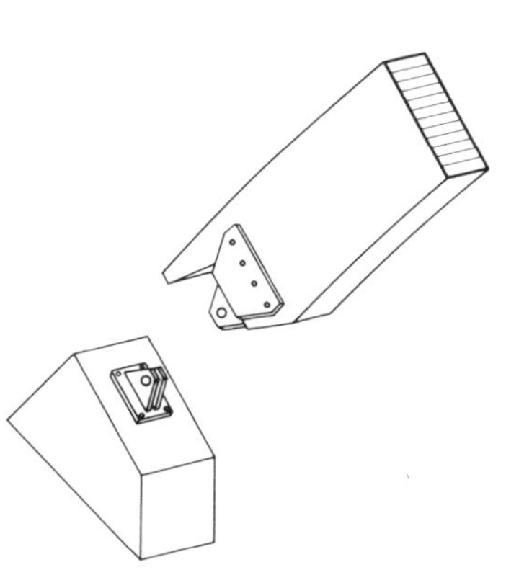

Steel shoes with pin bolt.

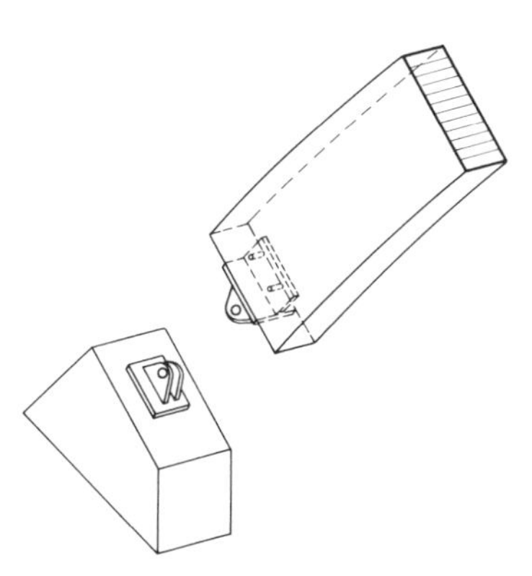

Steel plate doweled in beam slit, bearing web plates, and pin bolt.

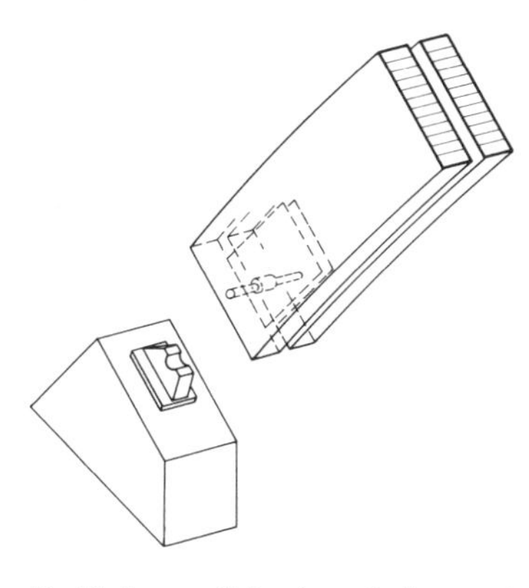

Double beam with interior nail plates and contoured hinge bearing.

123 Sports Stadium in Joinville, France

Architect: G. Bovet, Paris

Covered surface 90.00 × 145.00 m; 23 three-hinged arches span transversely. Spacing is 6.50 m, span is 89.00 m, arch rise is 18.40 m. Arches are double, with wood spacers. Base and crown bearings are steel shoes with pin bolts. Purlins are set longitudinally.

Wind force on end wall is transferred through purlins and longitudinal trussing to a transverse truss between two central arches. Wind stabilizing forces are resisted there by visible, double crossed trussing. Arches in area of gutters convey lateral loads to foundations.

Reference: *L'Architecture d'aujourd'hui* 116/1964, p. 52

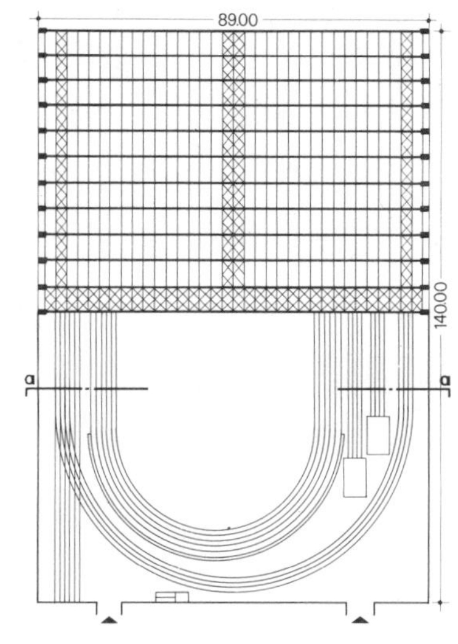

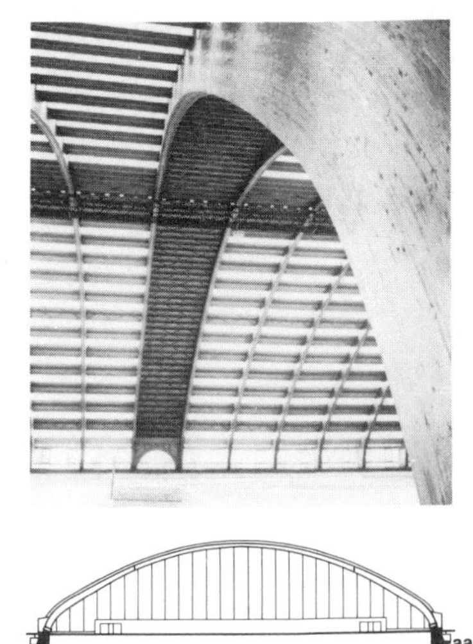

Truss arch

124 Storage Shed in Weichach, Switzerland

Engineer: Timber Construction Contractor

Open shed for sand, covered surface 44.00 × 83.00 m. Three-hinged arches span transversely 40.00 m and are spaced at 7.30 m. Arches have I cross section and shape of a polygon. I section consists of webs with crossed planking (Kämpf system) and glued flanges. Longitudinal lapped purlins carry flat asbestos-cement roofing. Diagonal timber bracing conveys wind forces to foundation.

Erection proceeded by raising pairs of arches joined by purlins and diagonals, and then field-connecting purlins and diagonals in intermediate bays. Erection of entire structure by two mobile cranes took only one day.

Reference: *Werk* 10/1971, p. 656

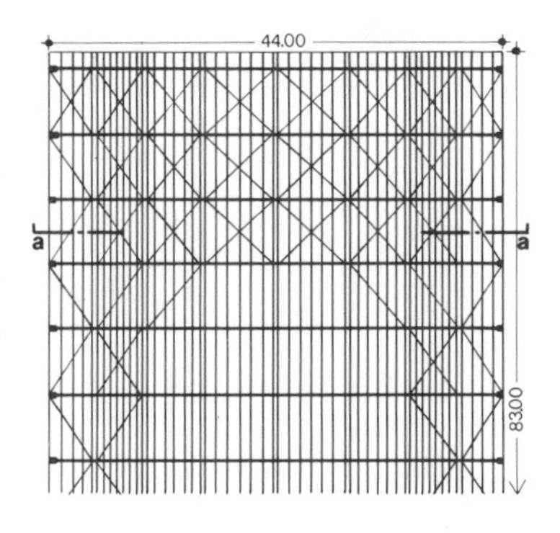

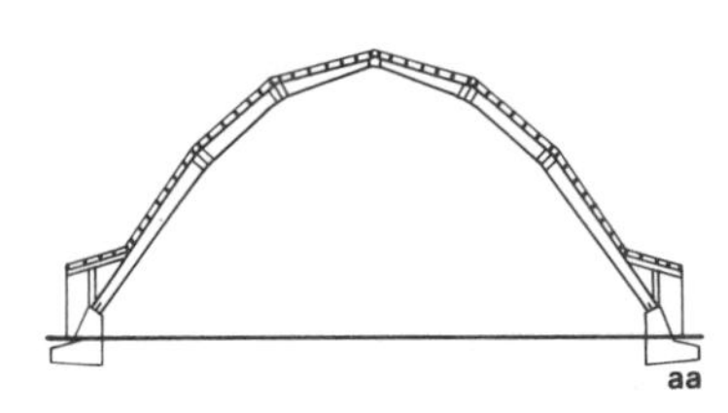

Partial plan and wind bracing
Cross section

Arch with bent beams made from steel extrusions

Arch with canopies

125 Ice Skating Rink in Porrentury, Switzerland

Architect: Gressot and Luscher, Porrentury
Engineer: G. Kämpf, Rupperswil

Covered surface 45.00 × 76.00 m. Grandstands for 3300 spectators rise on one side; on one short side there are a restaurant and service rooms. Roof construction consists of 12 three-hinged laminated wood arches spanning 45.00 m, rising from uneven elevations. Spacing is 6.80 m. Base and crown hinges are steel shoes with pin bolts. Lapped purlins in longitudinal direction. Wind bracing is timber diagonals connected to arches with steel plates.

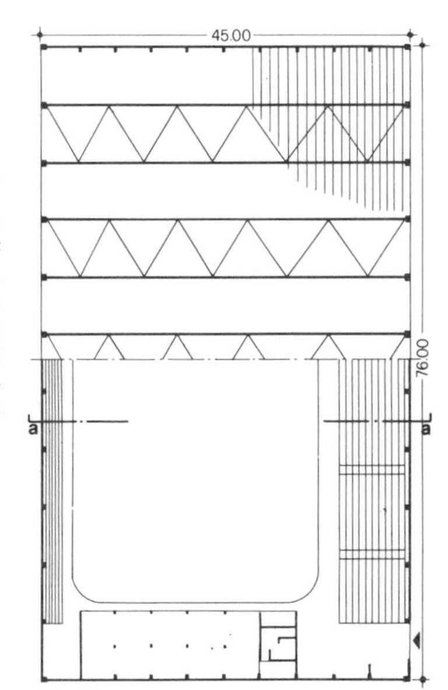

Plan, partially showing arch layout and wind bracing

Cross section

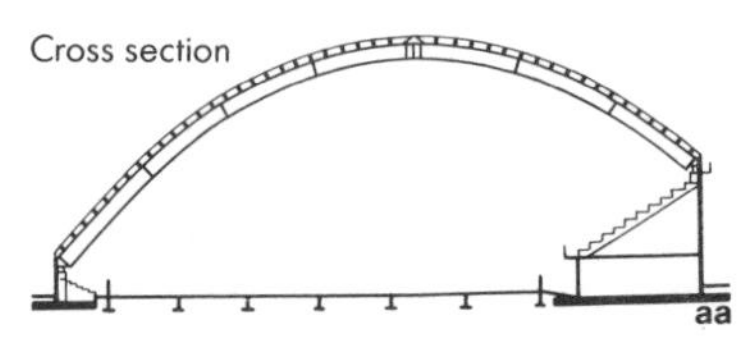

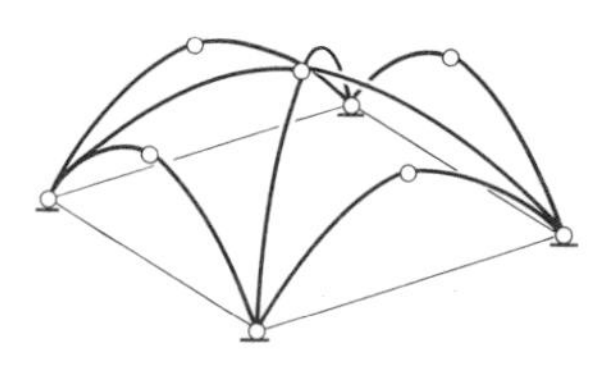

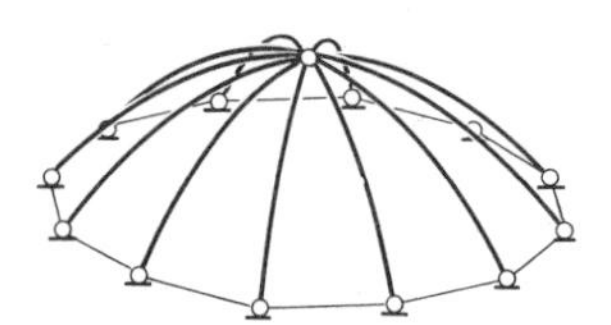

Arches in radial arrangements

126 Ice Skating Rink in Langnau, Switzerland

Architect: Hallenbad AG, Langnau-Zafingen
Engineer: H. Vogel, Bern

Roof structure consists of tied three-hinged arches. Arches are polygonal, with three plane roof surfaces on each side suitable for roofing with flat corrugated asbestos-cement panels. The largest arch cross section is 18/102.5 cm, span is 45.80 m, and spacing is 8.30 m. Tie consists of four round bars anchored at bearings with two gussets. Lapped purlins and diagonals are in all bays.

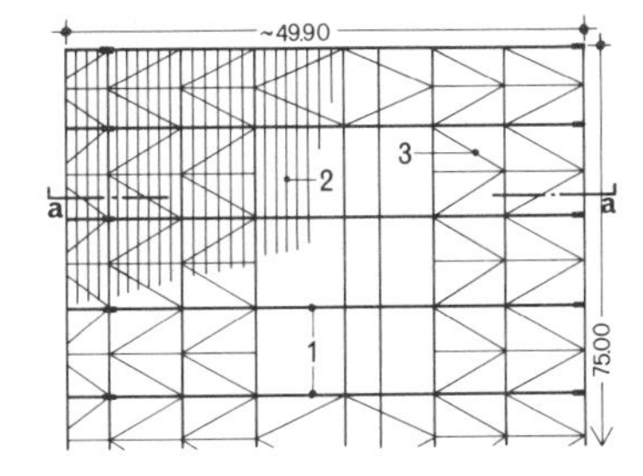

Partial plan with wind bracing

1 Arch 18/94 cm
2 Lapped purlins 8/24 to 14/24 cm
3 Wind bracing 4/12 to 4/20 cm
4 Steel bars 4 × ϕ 32 mm
5 Vertical truss bracing
6 Steel column
7 Bearing shoe
8 Plywood gussets

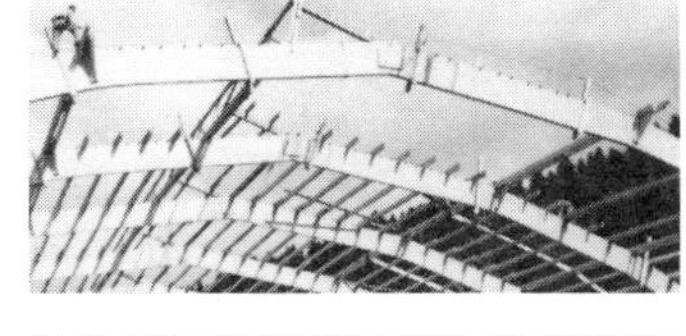

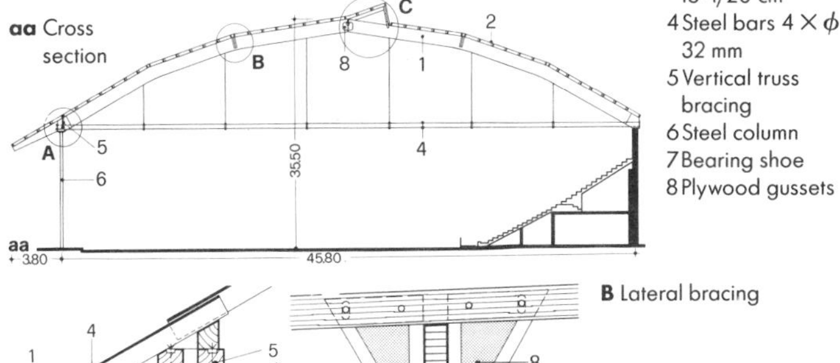

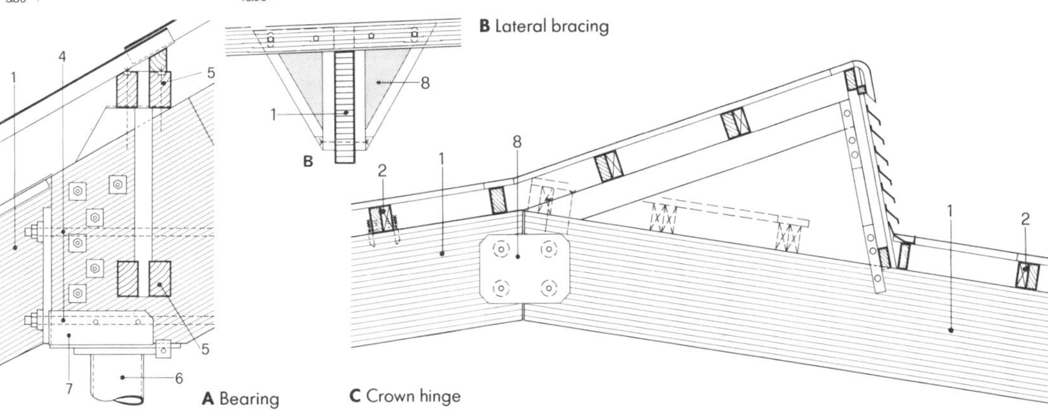

A Bearing

B Lateral bracing

C Crown hinge

Connection of Steel Wind Bracing to Main Girder

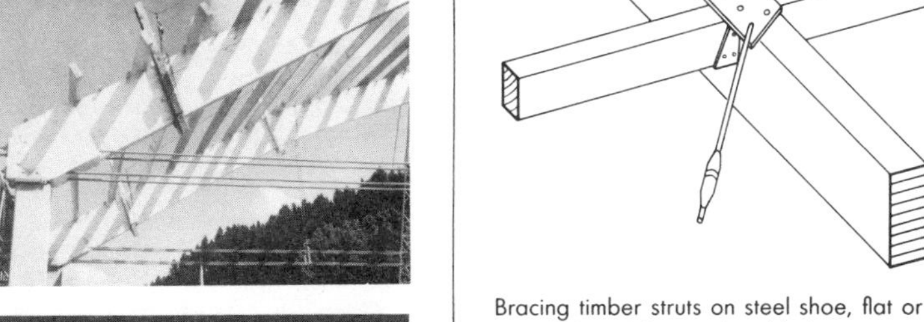

Bracing timber struts on steel shoe, flat or rounded steel diagonals welded to connection plate. Shear connectors. Turnbuckles.

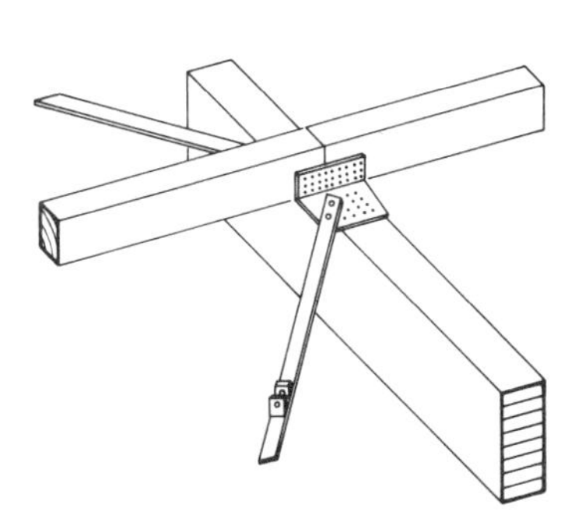

Timber bracing struts laying on main beam. Connection by steel angle. Round steel bar diagonals. Turnbuckles.

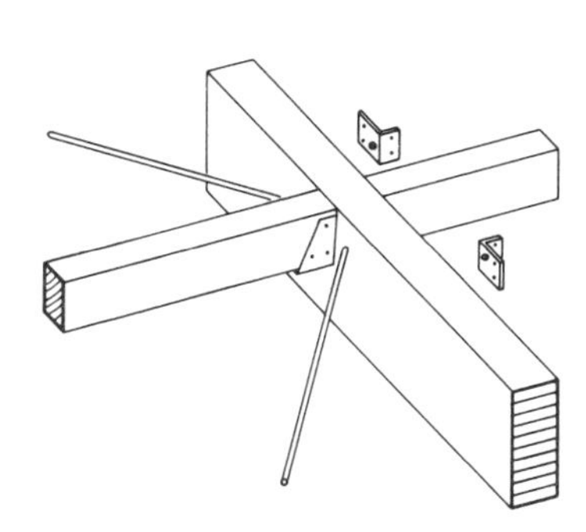

Timber bracing struts on steel shoe. Steel bar diagonals threaded and tensioned with nuts against back plate.

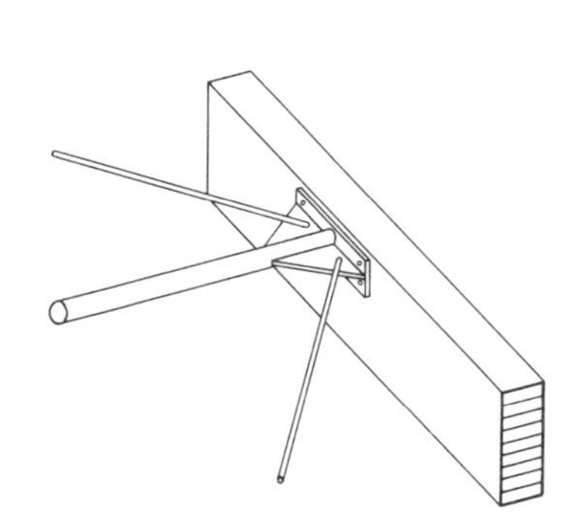

Steel pipe bracing struts. Steel bar diagonals welded or bolted to bracket.

127 Covered Market in Wangs, Switzerland

Engineer: W. Menig, St. Gallen

Two main criteria governed the choice of an economical design for this 60.00 × 72.00 m structure: hall had to have a 4.60 m vertical clearance without columns, and marshy soil did not allow horizontal forces on foundations. A tied three-hinged arch was selected; it is a timber truss arch spanning 60.00 m, 2.26 m deep, and spaced at 2.47 m. Double flanges are joined with diagonals by means of double nail plates (Menig system). Suspended tie is a steel IPBl 200. Fixed columns are rectangular steel tubes.
Reference: *Holzbau* 5/1974, p. 18

3 Lateral bracing truss
4 Upper chord 2 × 10/34 cm
5 Lower chord 2 × 4.5/26 cm
6 Diagonal 7/12 to 9/26 cm
7 Tie IPBl 200, placed flat
8 Bearing shoe
9 Gussets 2 × 6/16 cm
10 Shear connectors ϕ 117 mm
11 Steel box with bearing key

Layout of arches

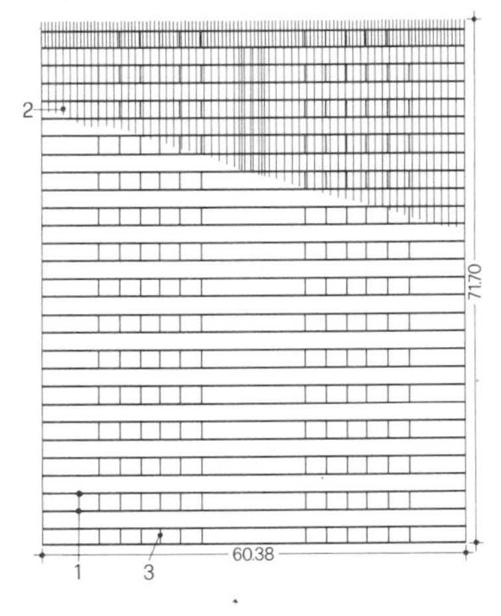

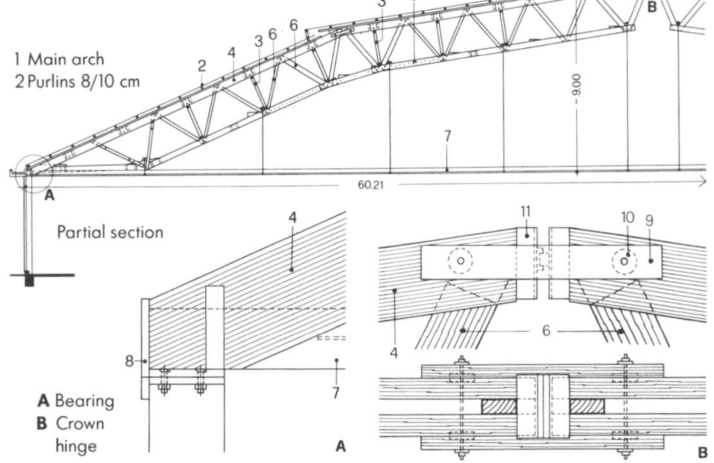

1 Main arch
2 Purlins 8/10 cm

Partial section

A Bearing
B Crown hinge

A suspended girder has the shape of an inverted arch. The loads are resisted mostly in tension. The usual and often critical stability analysis for buckling of a compressed arch does not apply here. Nevertheless, the roof has to be amply secured against wind uplift.

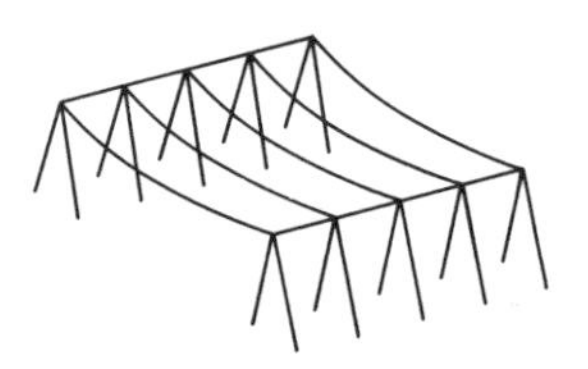

Main girders suspended, a tensioned linear system

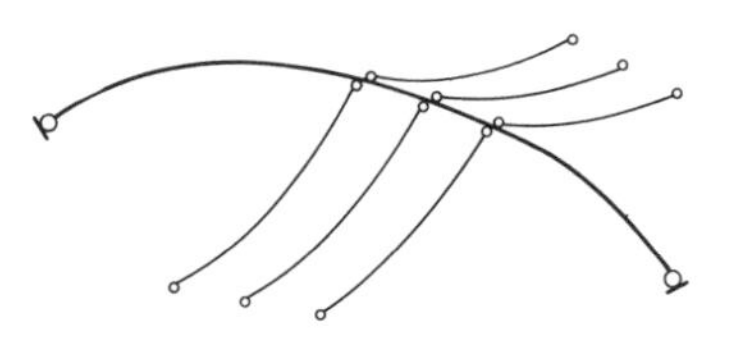

Secondary girder suspended on a longitudinal arch

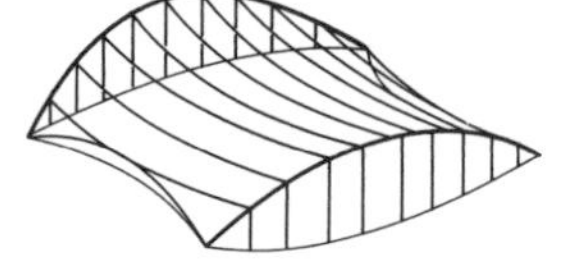

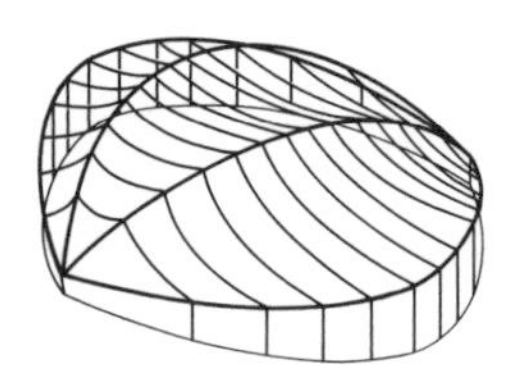

Secondary girders suspended on one to four arches

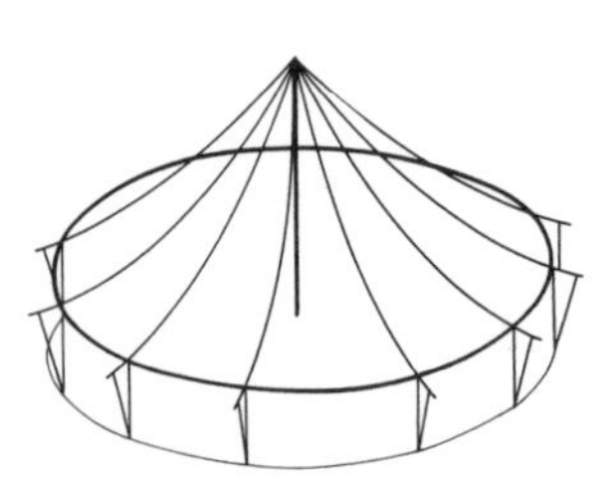

Radial suspended beam system with compression ring and center post

128 Exhibition Hall in Alençon, France

Architect: M. Azagury, Paris
Engineer: Timber Construction Contractor

Covered surface 70.00 × 107.00 m. Roof is flat on one side and rises on the other from 5.00 to 18.85 m. This allows for exhibition of larger objects and creates large end windows for good daylight illumination.

Eight parabolic suspended girders, 16/80 to 16/106 cm, are spaced at 10.00 m. In flat area of roof the girders are continuous over two spans. In sloped area they are spanning about 50.00 m and are stressed mostly in tension. One-sided loads and wind loads also cause bending. Horizontal tension is resisted by concrete walls **(C)** and tendons on high side.

Purlins 11.3/40.5 cm span between girders, connection is by steel angles. In order to limit lateral bending stresses in sloped area, purlins are suspended at midspan by ϕ 14 to 22 mm steel bars, anchored in a ridge truss lying within roof plane.

Horizontal stiffening of roof is provided by K bracing. Wind loads are transferred to foundation by concrete pylons and K braces between high compression columns.

Girder layout and wind bracing

Wind bracing of end wall

Longitudinal section

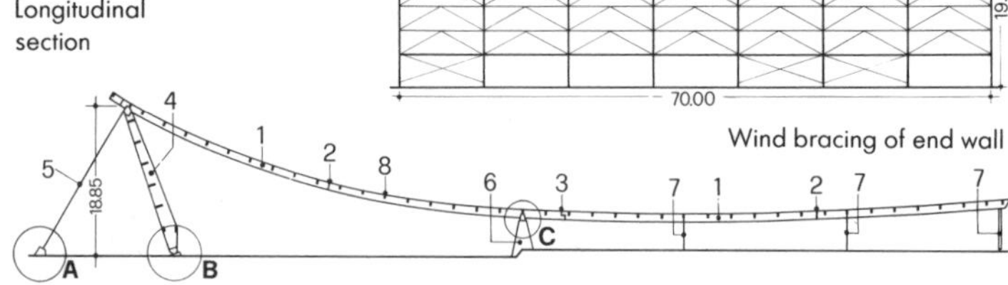

1 Suspended girder 16/80 to 106 cm
2 Rigid field splice
3 Shear key
4 Compression column 16/95 to 190 cm
5 Steel bar ϕ 100 mm
6 Concrete pylon for horizontal forces
7 Hinged columns
8 Purlins 11.3/40.5 cm
9 Wind bracing 5/15 cm
10 Purlin suspenders ϕ 14 to 22 mm
12 Spiral spring ϕ 45 mm
13 Tensioning nut
14 Bolts ϕ 24 mm
15 Steel shoe with stiffeners
16 Hinge pin ϕ 125 mm
17 Connection plate 10 mm

A Tension ties anchorage

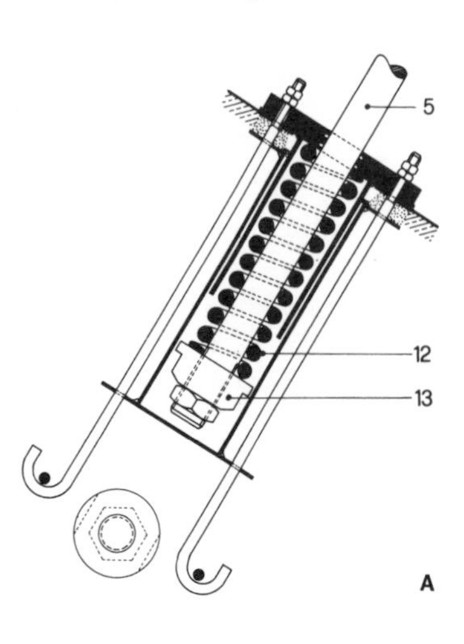

B Bearing base of compression column

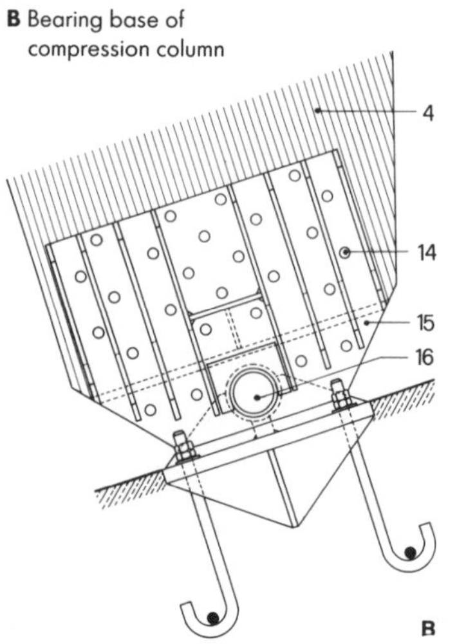

C Bearing of main girder on concrete pylon

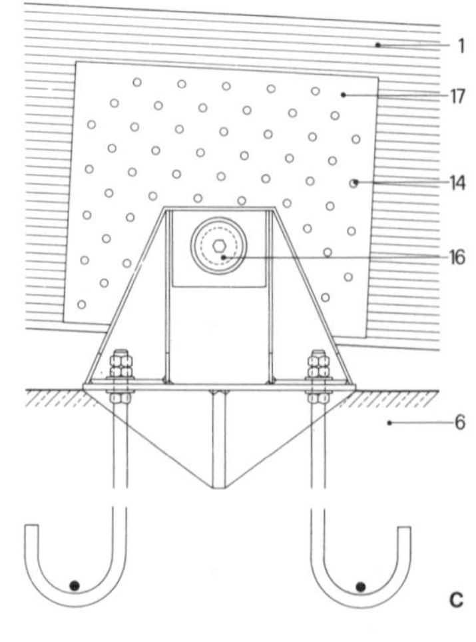

129 Sports Hall in Poitiers, France

Architect: R. Dhuit, Paris; M. Agius, Poitiers
Engineer: Uhalde-Bernier, Paris

Sports hall with arena and grandstands on both sides rising toward middle and forming an oval plan. A two-hinged central arch spans longitudinally 74.00 m. The arch is double and serves as bearing for secondary girders which rest on other end on reinforced concrete columns. Secondary girders are suspended purlins shaped concavely. They give the hall its characteristic shape.
Reference: *Technique & Architecture* 294/1973

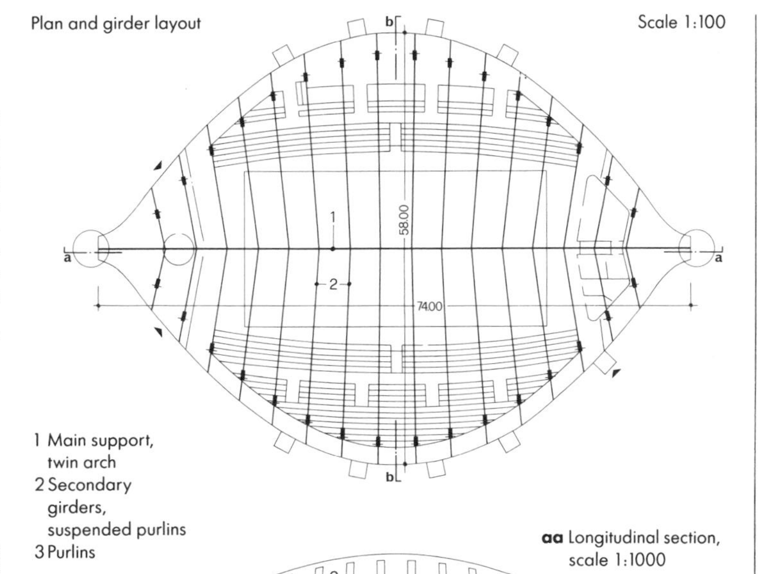

1 Main support, twin arch
2 Secondary girders, suspended purlins
3 Purlins

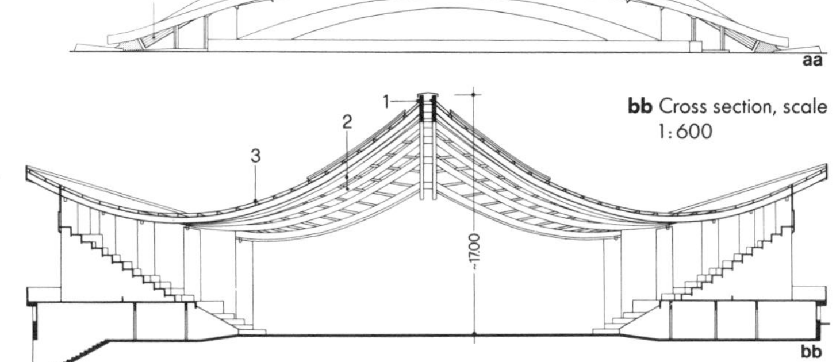

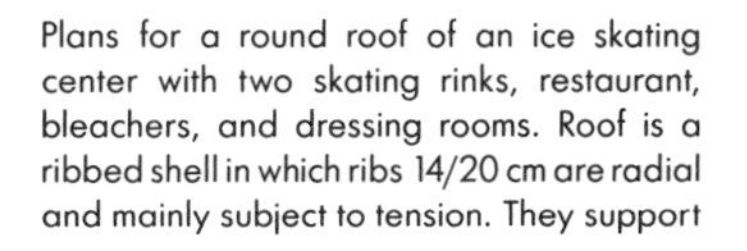

130 Ice Skating Center in Munich, West Germany

Architect: G. and I. Küttinger, Munich
Engineer: J. Natterer, Munich

Plans for a round roof of an ice skating center with two skating rinks, restaurant, bleachers, and dressing rooms. Roof is a ribbed shell in which ribs 14/20 cm are radial and mainly subject to tension. They support two layers of crossed planks. Central tower is a rotational hyperboloid made from straight, inclined, glue-laminated members 20/20 cm.

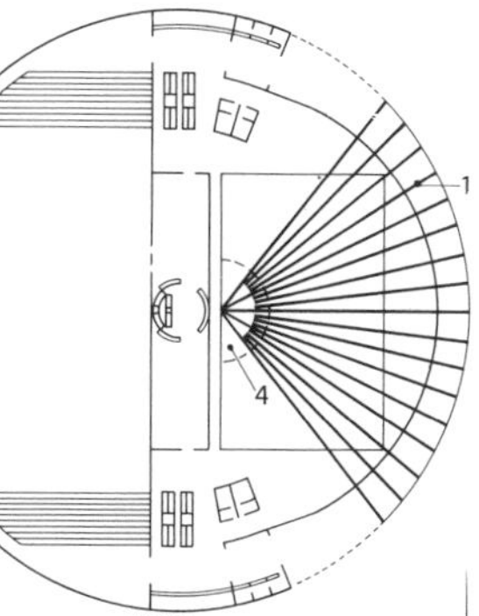

Plan with partial beam layout

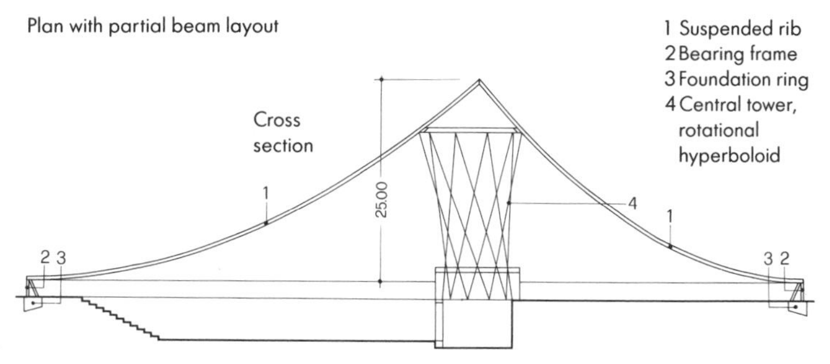

1 Suspended rib
2 Bearing frame
3 Foundation ring
4 Central tower, rotational hyperboloid

Framed Columns for Suspended Beams

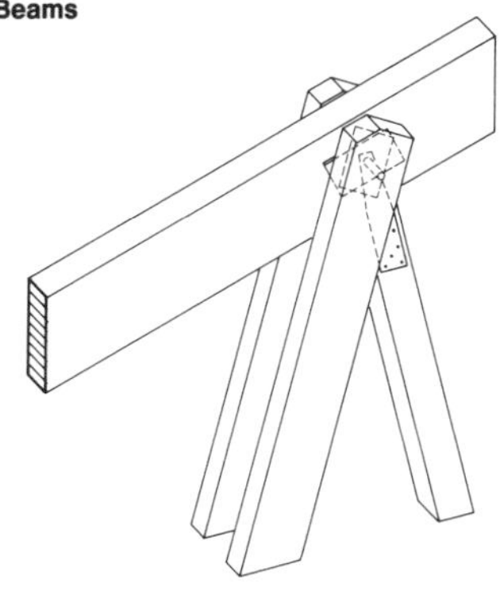

Double compression column for single beam, connected with nail plates and pin bolts. Tension column is single and connected with nail plates.

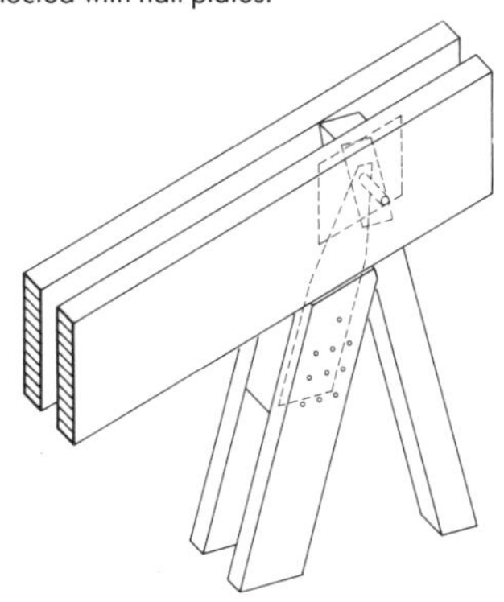

Double compression column connected with nail plate and bolt to twin beam. Tension column joined with nail plates.

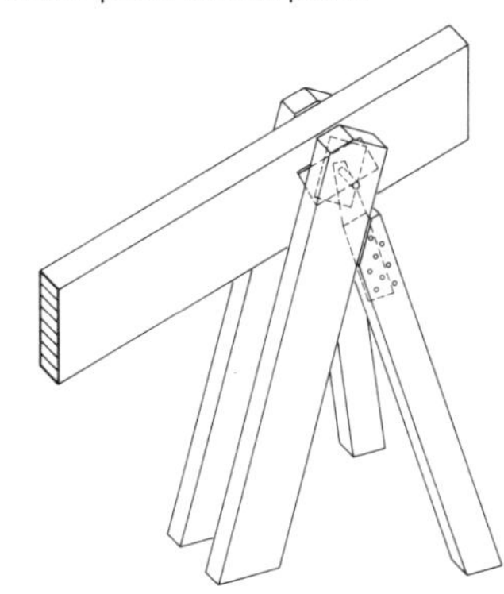

Double compression column for single beam with nail plates and pin bolts. Tension column is double and spread out.

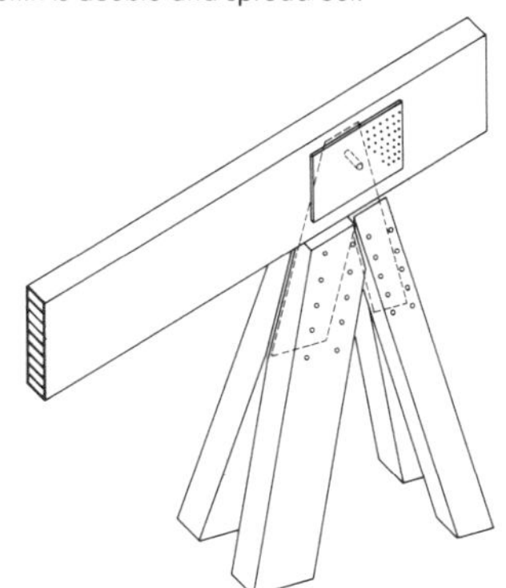

Compression and tension columns spread out.

Beam grids are plane systems of beams intersecting at 90, 60, or 45°. Beams are either continuous over intersections or joined by moment connections. These rigid joints create a highly indeterminate static system in which the loads are distributed in two or three directions. Deformation under load affects all the beams in the grid and not only the one directly supporting the load. Thus all the beams support the load with their stiffnesses and spans.

(Continued on page 154.)

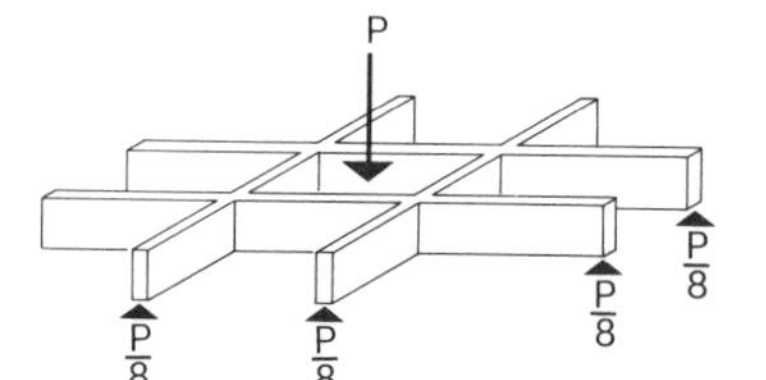

Bearing reactions

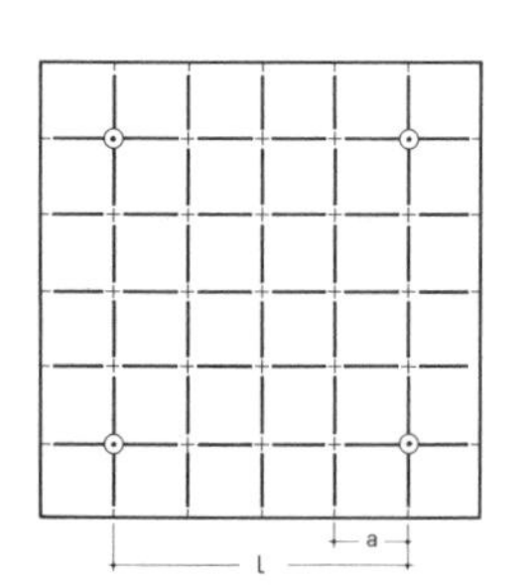

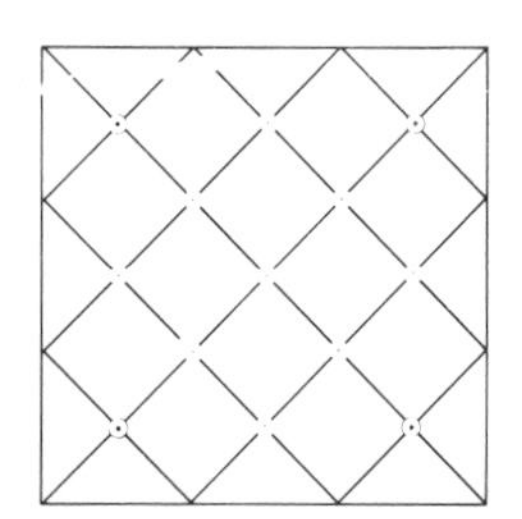

Laminated wood with steel node connections
a = 2.40 to 7.20 m
l = 12 to 24 m
h = l/16 to l/30 (beam depth)

131 Administration Office of the Munich Technical University in Garching, West Germany

Architect: Building Department of the Technical University, Munich
Engineer: J. Natterer, H. Bauler

Two-story office building for university administration. Single rooms on ground floor, office floor space on second floor. Second floor of reinforced concrete; roof is timber girders on a 7.20 × 7.20 m grid resting on steel cross-shaped columns. Square bays are spanned by grids of crossed overlapping beams. Beams are not weakened at intersections and are only secured by dowels. They are connected to girders by beam shoes. Wind bracing and stiffening is provided by round steel bar in roof surface and three shear walls in core of building.

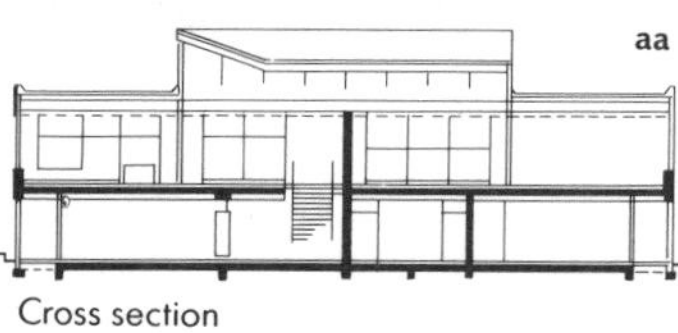

Cross section

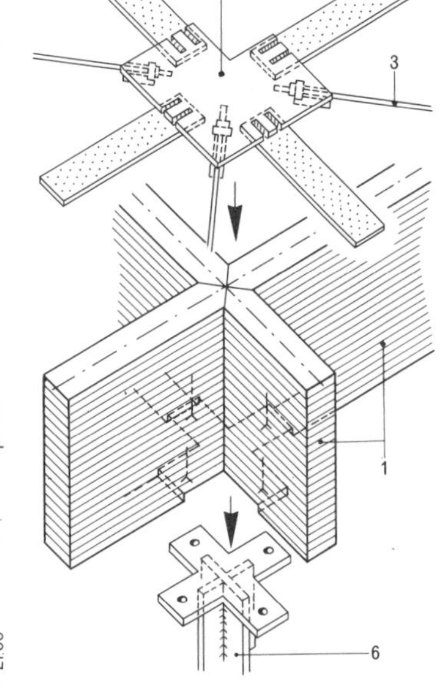

Girder bearing and connection of wind bracing

7 Steel connection plate with welded nail plates and webs for wind bracing attachment

Plan of grids

1 Girders
2 Beam grid
3 Wind bracing
4 Shear walls
5 Raised roof
6 Steel column

132 Residence in Straubing, West Germany

Architect: K. Schmidhuber, Munich
Engineer: J. Natterer, Munich

House has interconnecting rooms and a swimming pool. Roof is a grid of the so-called lamination intermesh type. Laminations of glue-laminated beams cross grid joints alternately (see **bb** below). Empty layers are filled with filler laminations. Beams are then glued and pressed together by nailing to form a solid section. This creates a uniform structural grid. Timber columns are placed freely at a maximum distance of 8.00 m. Cantilevers in two directions do not exceed 3.00 m. Wind loads are absorbed by fixity of columns.
Reference: *Detail* 1/1974, illustrations; *Bauen mit Holz* 12/1972, p. 688; *Bauwelt* 29/1972, p. 1122

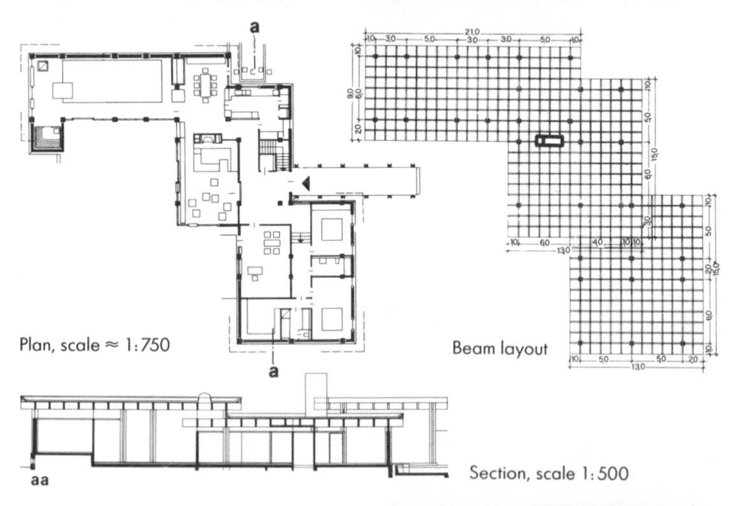

Plan, scale ≈ 1:750

Beam layout

Section, scale 1:500

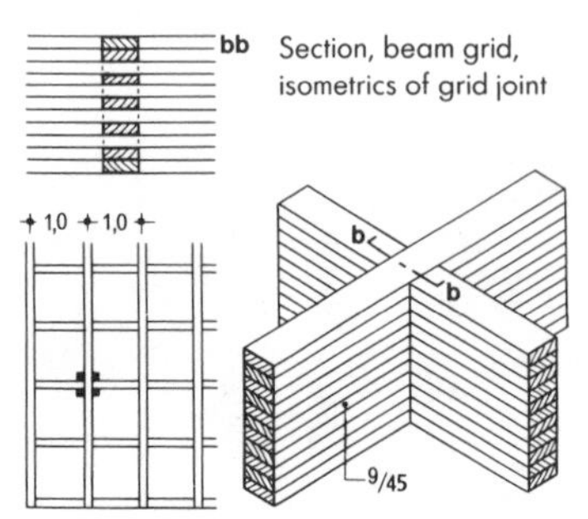

Section, beam grid, isometrics of grid joint

133 **Church in Kolbermoor, West Germany**

Architect: C. T. Horn, Munich
Engineer: J. Natterer, Munich

Square church nave. Clear span with grid of glue-laminated wood beams and steel joints. Double beams are connected to joint plates by nail plates and bolts. The economy of steel joints makes larger spacing possible. There is a secondary system of solid wood purlins, placed in each bay in alternate directions.

1 Beam grid 2 × 13/136 cm
2 Steel cross
3 Nail plate
4 Stiffeners (welded flat steel shapes)
5 Bolts ϕ 36 mm
6 Secondary beams 10/26 cm
7 Two layers of planking for stiffening
8 Exposed planking

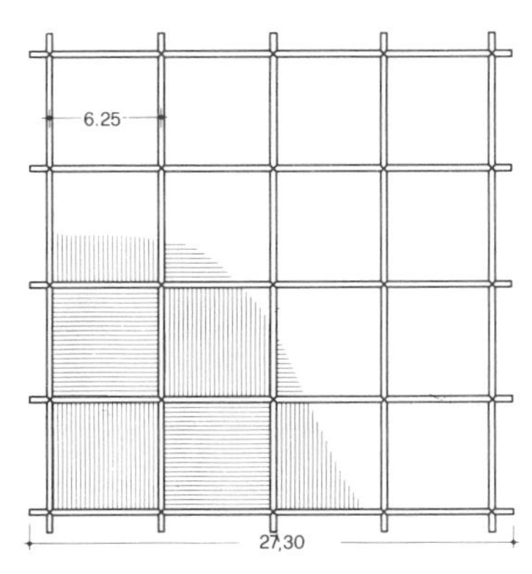

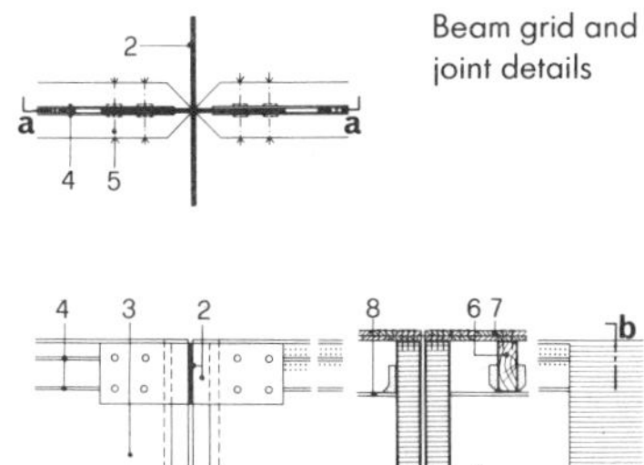

Beam grid and joint details

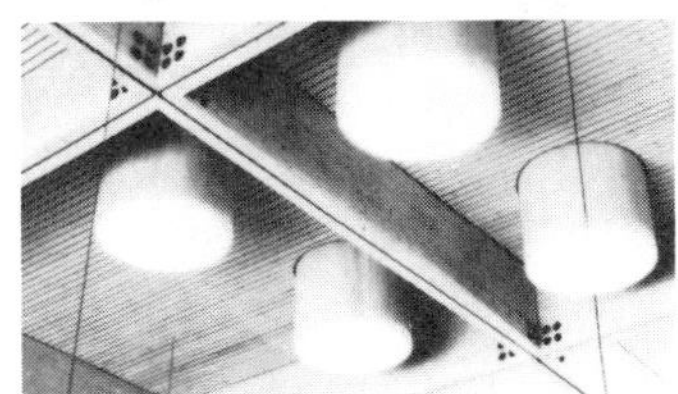

134 **Building Supply Center in Bamberg, West Germany**

Architect: Building Division BayWa, Munich
Engineer: J. Natterer, Munich

Selling area for building materials. Diagonally arranged beam grid with steel joints. Diagonal span 11.80 m, joint spacing at 5.90 m. Double beams, steel joints, bolts, and connection plates. Secondary beams are one-piece, connections are steel crosses in beam slits.

Bracing is provided by diagonal structure, its trapezoidal gussets, and concrete walls.

Diagonal arrangement of grid requires only one intermediate support **A** and five intersection points **B**; it also makes 5.00 m cantilevers possible.

A Bearing column

B Intersection point connection

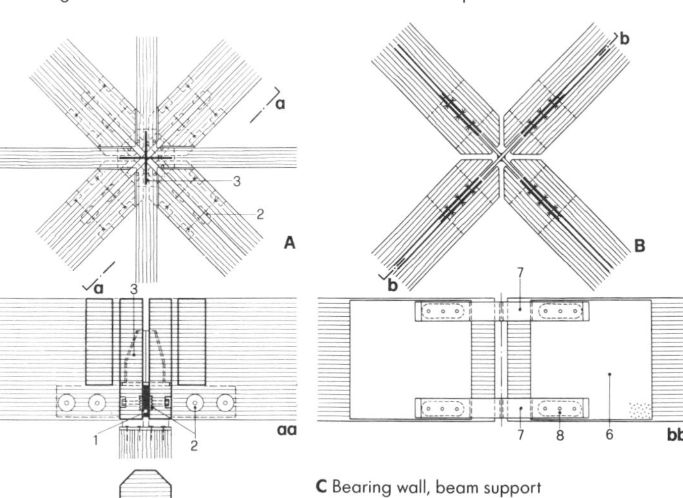

C Bearing wall, beam support

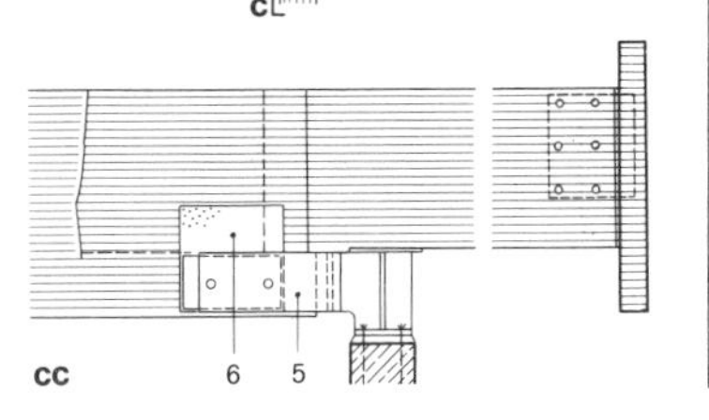

Layout of beams

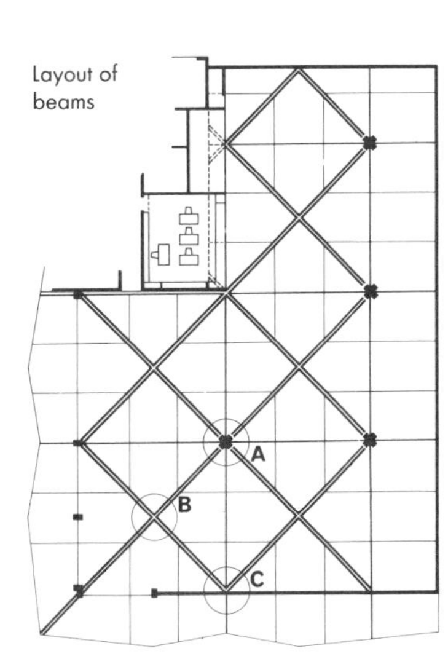

1 Main beam joint, 40 mm thick plate
2 One-sided shear connectors 2 × 2 × ϕ 160 mm
3 Secondary beam joint, 10 mm thick plate
4 IPE 300
5 Plates 25 mm thick for beam connection
6 Nail plate
7 Main beam joint, 25 mm plate
8 HV screws

Beam Grid Joints at 90°

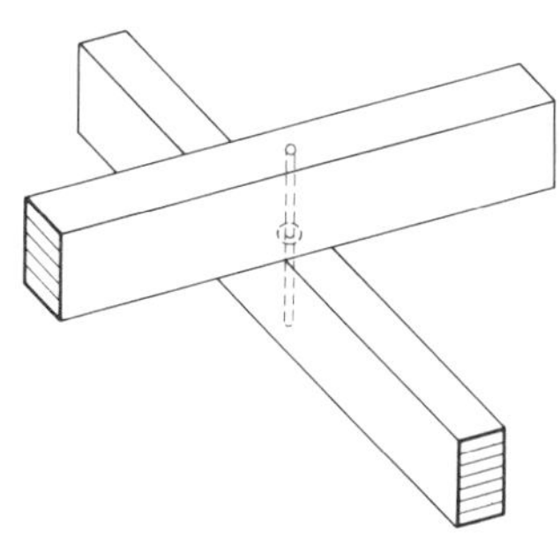

Crossed beams, one over other, with shear connector and dowel.

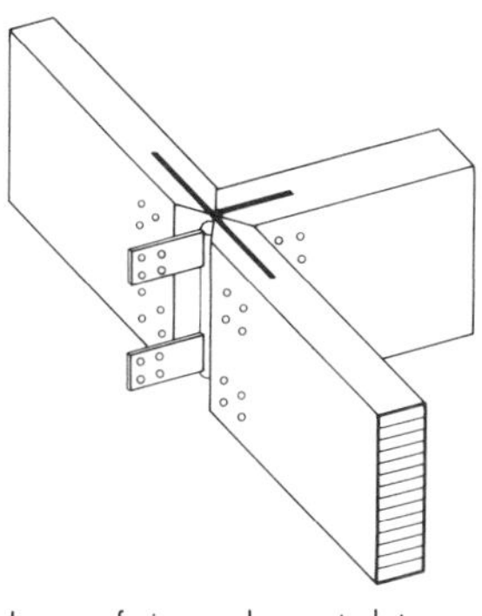

Steel cross of pipe and gusset plates, doweled in slits.

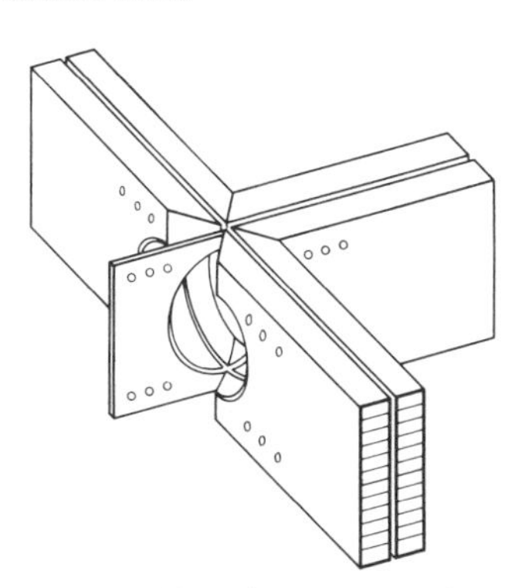

Steel cross with holes for utilities, doweled in beam slits or between beams. In double beams also gusset plates and bolts.

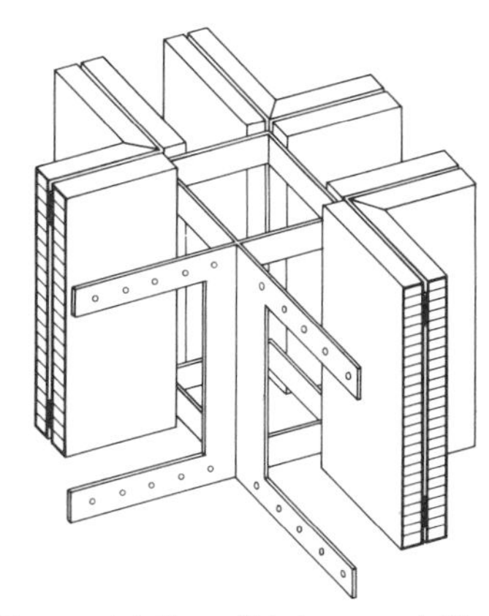

Crossover joint for multiple beams and utilities. Shear connectors or gusset plates and bolts.

(Continued from page 152.)

In solid beam grids the beams are subject to bending. Vertical shears create horizontal shears in beams. The weakened beam cross section at connections governs the design for bending and shear stresses. Deflection, usually critical for simple beams, is generally not critical for grids because of their high static indeterminacy. However, it is necessary to check the flexibility of joints in order to determine the camber of the grid. The torsional rigidity of a grid can be ignored.

For dimensioning see page 152

135 Church in Greding, West Germany

Architect: G. and I. Küttinger, Munich
Engineer: Timber Construction Contractor

Twelve-sided central church nave for 200 people. Roof consists of 12 radial laminated wood girders 2 × 5/80 cm. They bear on outside walls through steel shoes and are rigidly connected at center to steel plates by means of one-sided shear connectors. Steel plates are welded to a ϕ 100 cm steel ring. Purlins are 6/14 cm. Beams were attached to ring on the ground and were lifted by a mobile crane.
Reference: *Bauen mit Holz* 12/1972, p. 694

1 Radial beam 2 × 5/80 cm
2 Purlins 6/14 cm
3 Steel ring ϕ 100 cm
4 Steel plate 16 mm with ϕ 80 mm shear connectors
5 Stiffener

Layout of beams

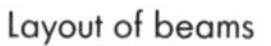

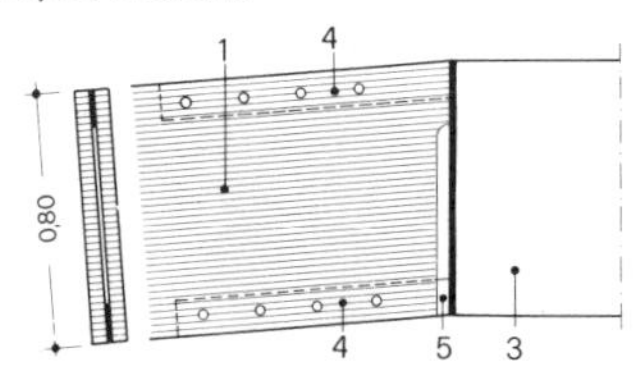

Beam connection to central ring

136 School in Gurtweil, West Germany

Architect: H. Schaudt, Konstanz
Engineer: Ingenieurbüro für Holzbau, Karlsruhe

School with 10 classrooms, all nested as hexagonal honeycombs. Roof and floor structures are beam grids at 60° angle. To reduce number of beam joints to a minimum and avoid intersecting beams, roof was divided into panels corresponding to a classroom, so that only one rigid joint becomes necessary at the crossing of six beams. Rigid joints contain steel plates on the underside of beams to take tension, and high-strength concrete in the core to act in compression. Beams are bearing on hexagonal columns by means of gussets in slits, joined by dowels.
Reference: *Bauen mit Holz* 6 and 7/1972

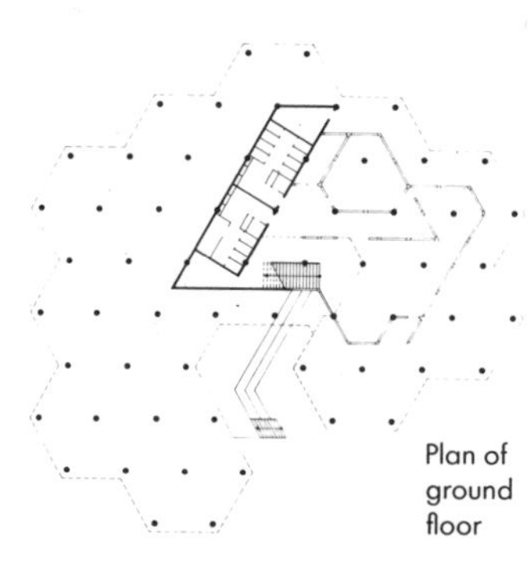

Plan of ground floor

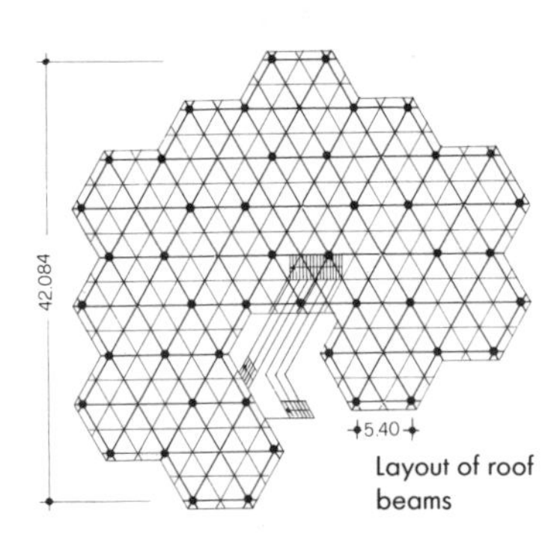

Layout of roof beams

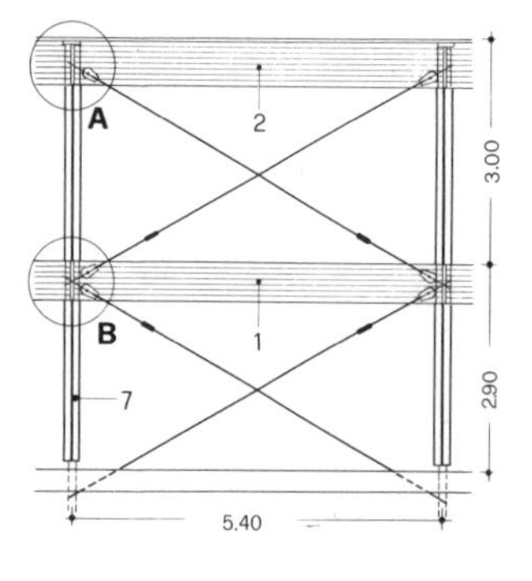

Partial section with bracing diagonals

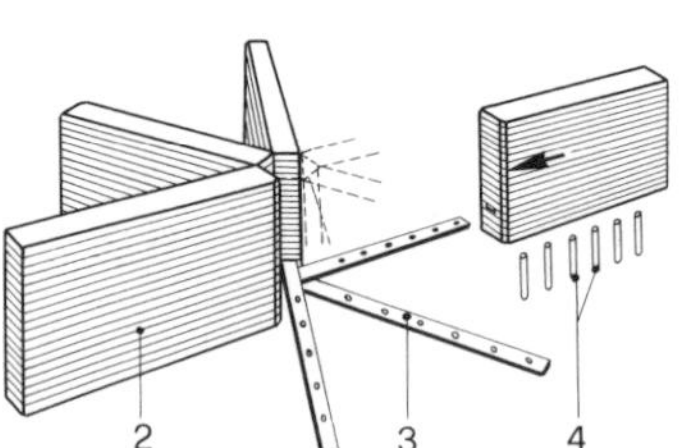

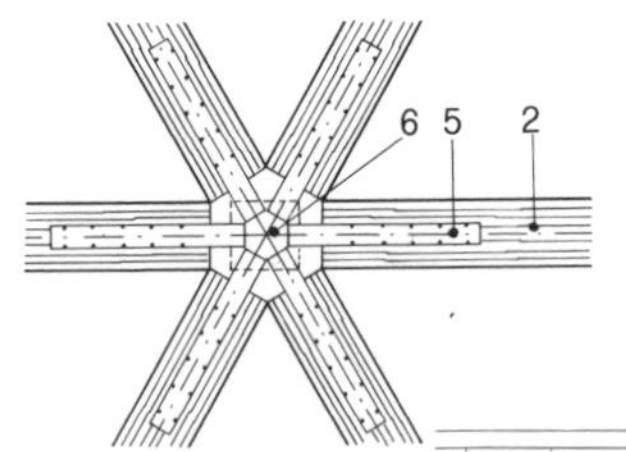

View and plan of main beam joint

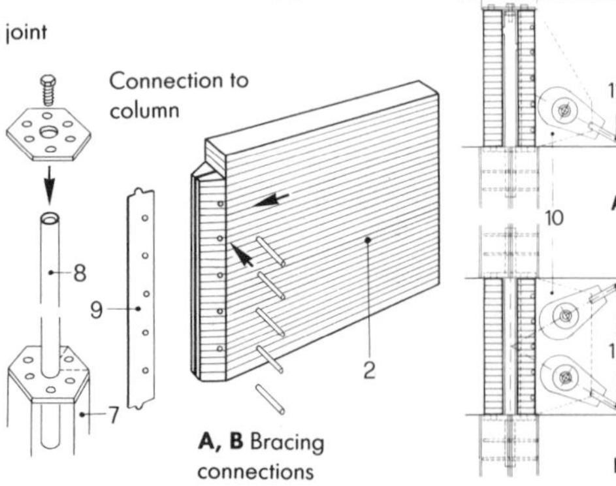

Connection to column

A, B Bracing connections

1 Beam over ground floor 12/55 cm, laminated wood
2 Roof beam 12/60 cm, laminated wood
3 Steel plates 10/80 mm
4 Steel dowels ϕ 20 mm
5 Steel plates 4/40 mm, nailed
6 Concrete compression core
7 Hexagonal timber column ϕ 21 cm, laminated wood
8 Steel tube ϕ 42 mm with base and head plates
9 Steel insert with nosing and ϕ 12 mm connection dowels
10 16 mm gusset plate with ϕ 12 mm dowels
11 Bar diagonals ϕ 24 mm

137 Civic Center in Bischofsheim, West Germany

Architect: H.-J. Kny, Frankfurt
Engineer: J. Natterer, Munich

Center has a restaurant, club rooms, a library, and a hexagonal hall for 750 persons. Roof of hall consists of beam grid spanning 24.00 m. Beam intersections are at 6.00 m. There is a lower building all around the hall.

Rigid joints consist of six star-shaped plates welded to a tube. Beam nail plates are attached to these plates with ϕ 30 mm bolts. Forces are transferred from wood to nail plates, and from there through recessed bolts to star-shaped joint plates.

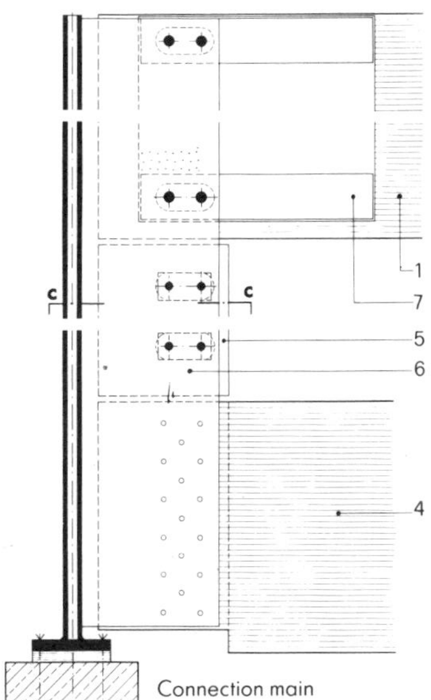

Connection main beam to peripheral beam

Layout of beams

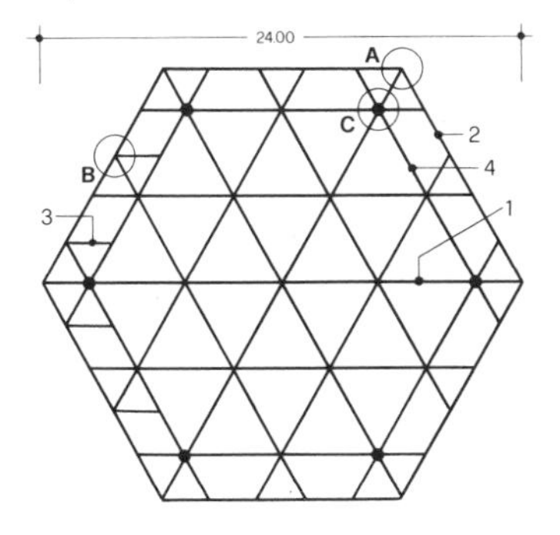

1 Main beam 2 × 12/127 cm
2 Exterior peripheral beam
3 Secondary beam
4 Interior peripheral beam
5 Filler wood
6 Star-shaped joint plates, 25 mm on ϕ 76 mm steel tube
7 Nail plates and ϕ 30 mm bolts

Plan details

Grid Joints at 60°

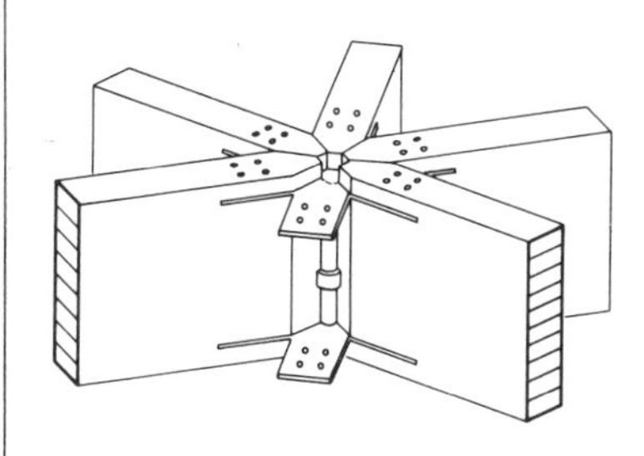

Star joint of flat gusset plates stacked on tube and bolted in beam slits. Key on tube to transfer shear.

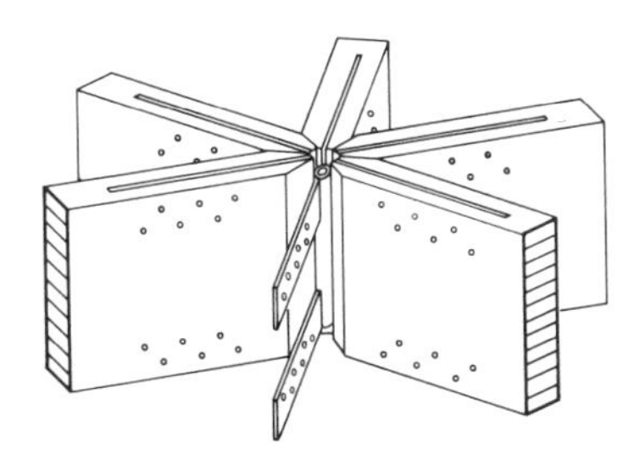

Star joint of vertical plates welded to tube and doweled in beam slits.

Overlapping steel plates in tension area. Compression forces transferred through concrete filling. Shear transferred through dowels. Tension transferred through nailed plates.

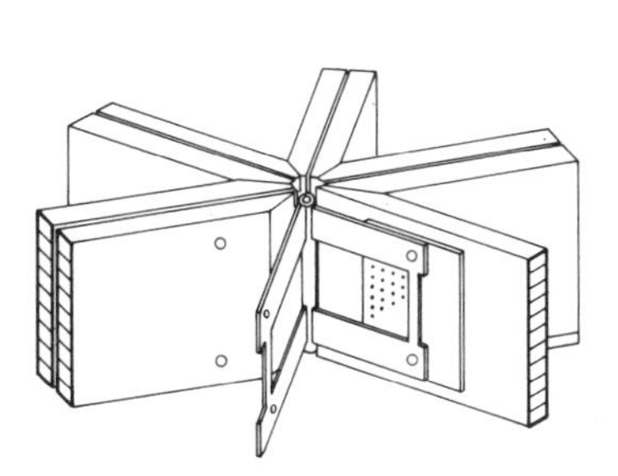

Star joint for double beams, nail plates and bolts.

138 All-Weather Zoo in Münster, West Germany

Architect: Koesters, Bahlke, and Ostendorf, Münster
Engineer: J. Natterer and K. März, Munich

Grid of equilateral triangles covering 5750 m². Roof surfaces are stepped to fit various heights of animal exhibits and provide daylight. Grid, with its 5.00 m beam length, is designed to accommodate column spacing and beam lengths of 5.00 to 20.00 m, and cantilevers in three directions up to 5.00 m. Rigid joints consist of steel tubes with welded plates. Plates are enclosed between twin beams and are attached by means of nail plates and bolts.

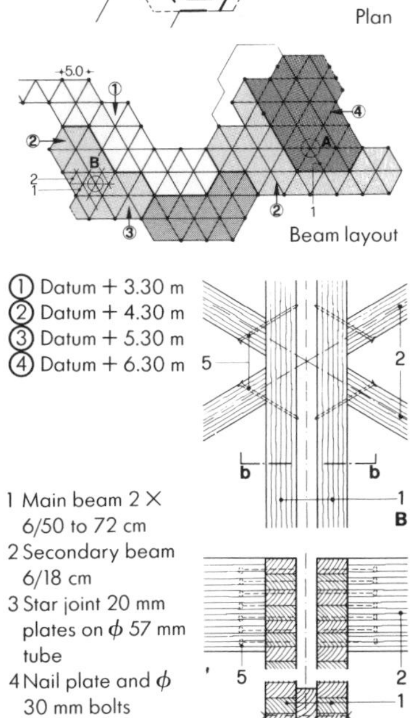

Plan

Beam layout

① Datum + 3.30 m
② Datum + 4.30 m
③ Datum + 5.30 m
④ Datum + 6.30 m

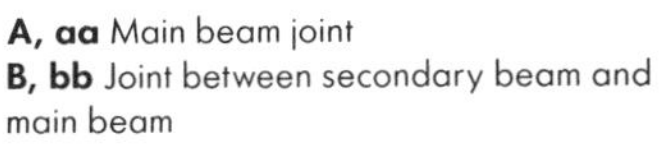

A, aa Main beam joint
B, bb Joint between secondary beam and main beam

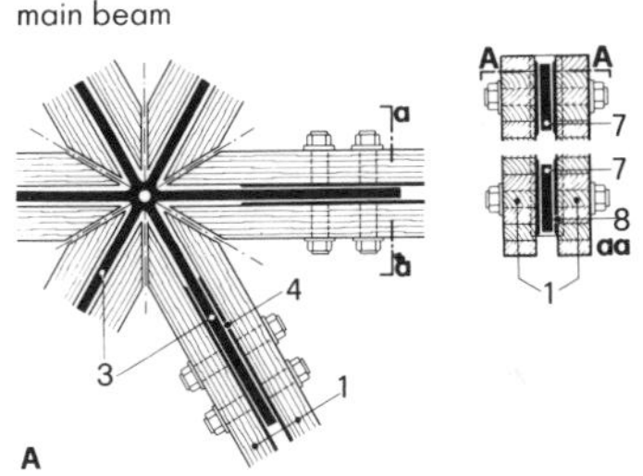

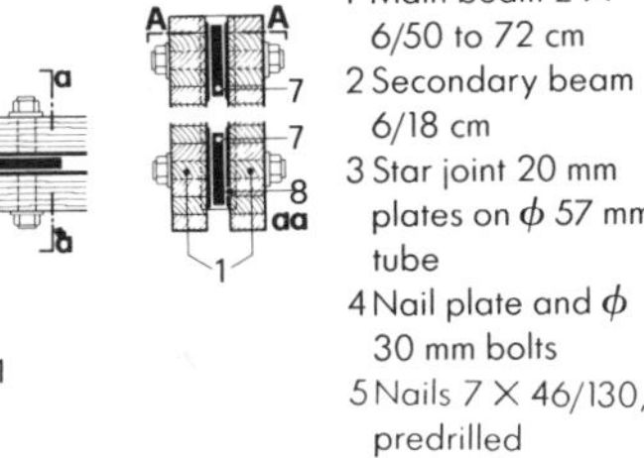

1 Main beam 2 × 6/50 to 72 cm
2 Secondary beam 6/18 cm
3 Star joint 20 mm plates on ϕ 57 mm tube
4 Nail plate and ϕ 30 mm bolts
5 Nails 7 × 46/130, predrilled

Truss grids consist of intersecting trusses. The bending moments governing the design of members and connections are decomposed into shears and axial forces in upper and lower chords. Axial forces in the diagonals are derived from shear forces.

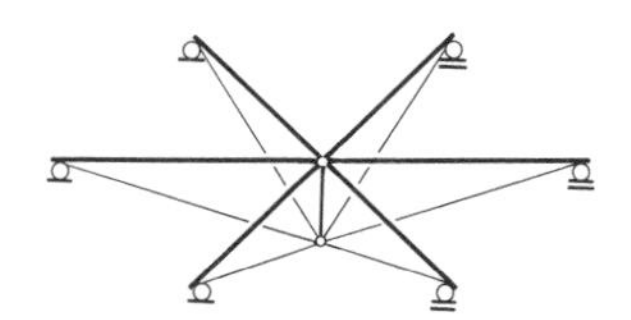

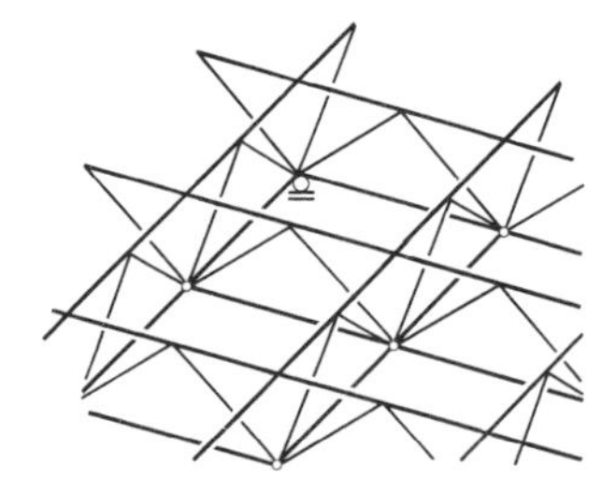

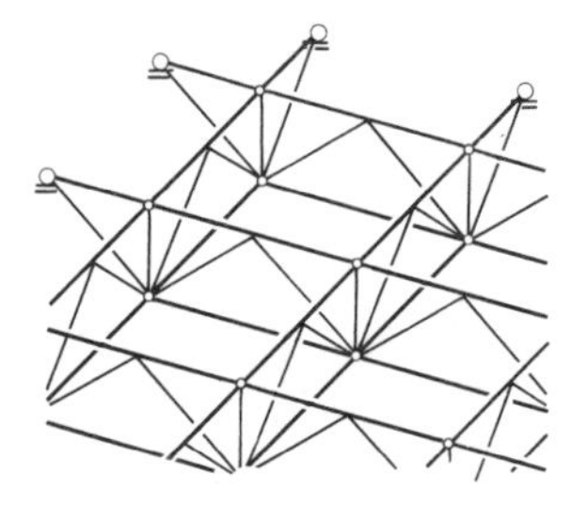

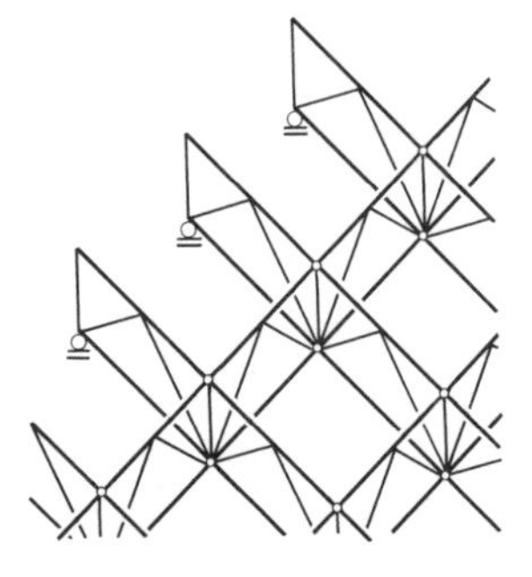

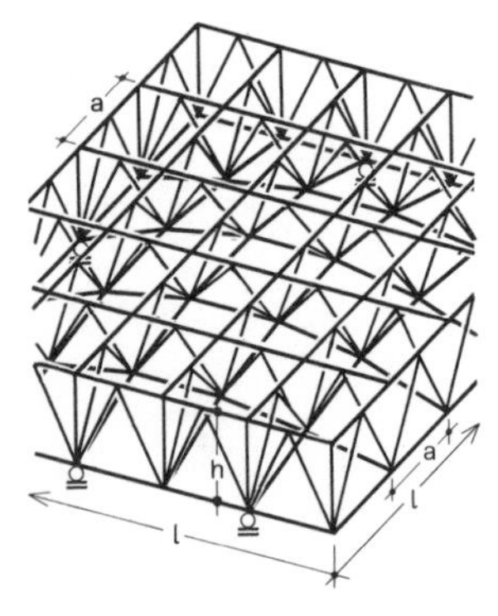

a = 1.20 to 12.00 m
l = 8 to 60 m
h = l/8 to l/16

139 Youth Center in Gozenyama, Japan

Architect: Yoshitaka Akui

House stands on a hill. Around a central room with fireplace, there are a Tatami room, a kitchen, service rooms, and a perimeter terrace. A pyramid roof is dominant; it is supported by four round timber posts which are tied by a frame to resist wind. Roof cantilevers all around. Roof is a spacial structure of round struts connected by steel joints. Three-dimensional arrangement required a hinged joint in which 12 members came to meet. A thatched roof is supported by a bamboo grid, roof top has a chimney outlet covered with asbestos-cement panels.

Reference: *Japan Architect* 9/1971, p. 233

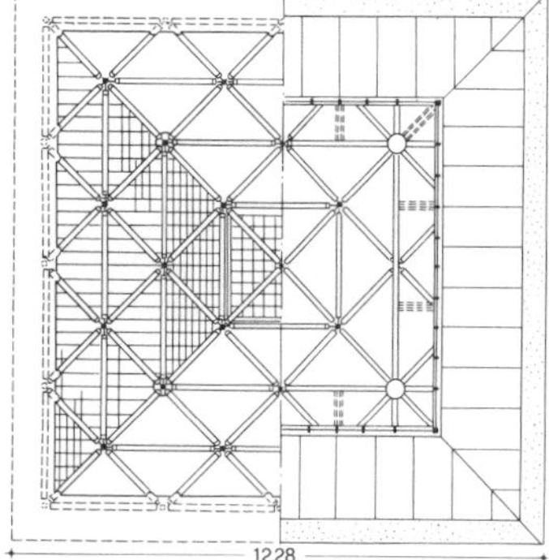

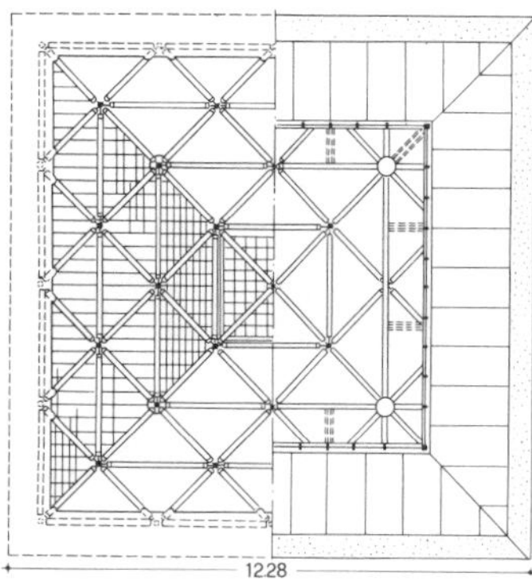

Plan of beam grid

A Joints: connection for 12 round timbers, ϕ 10.5 cm at midpoint
B, C Bearing on columns (ϕ 45.0 cm, upper bearing plate)

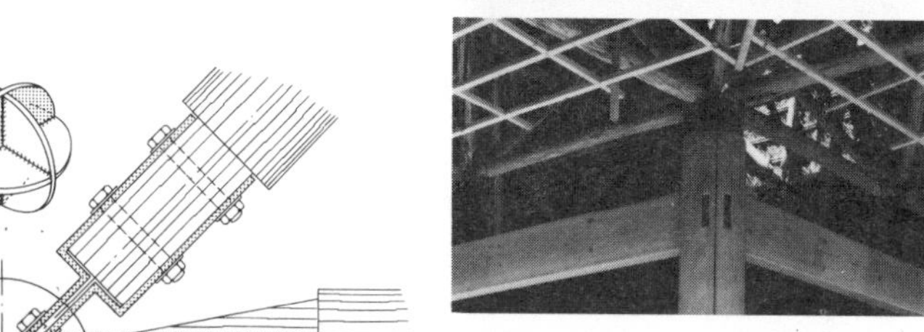

Cross section

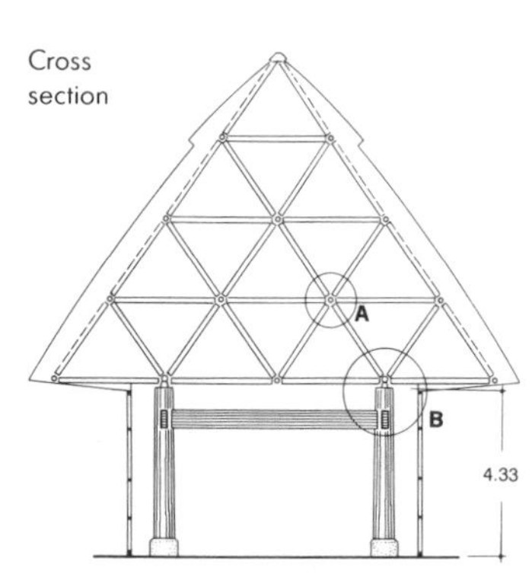

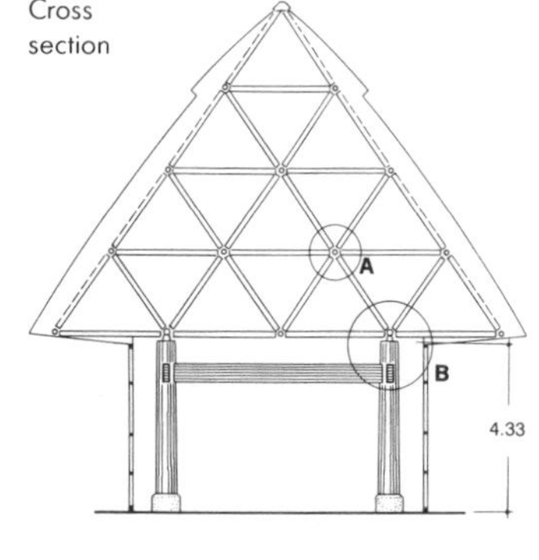

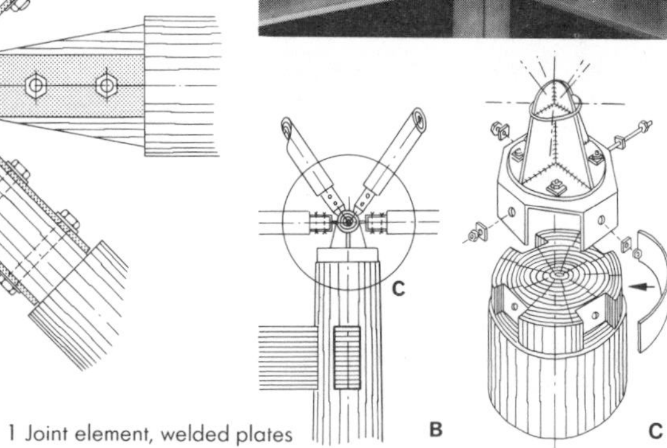

A 1 Joint element, welded plates **B** **C**

140 Church in Benet Lake, United States

Architect: S. Tigermann and Partner, Chicago
Engineer: The Engineers Collaborative, Chicago

Square community room for 300 church visitors and 30 friars within a Benedictine monastery. Finished concrete base disappears within an earth mound. Roof structure is a truss grid placed diagonally to the plan.

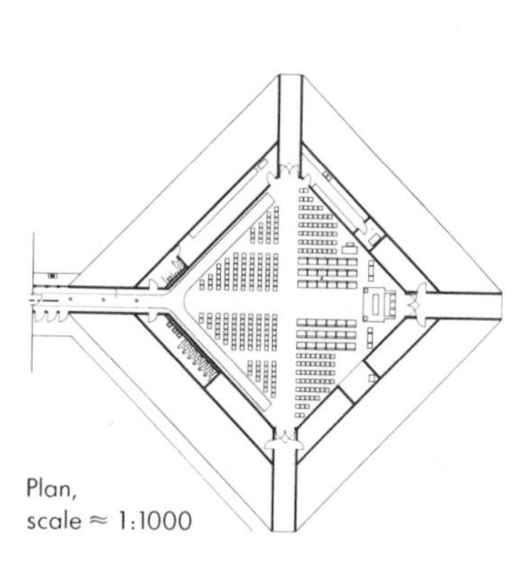

Plan, scale ≈ 1:1000

Roof structure, upper and lower chord planes

Trusses 1 and 2

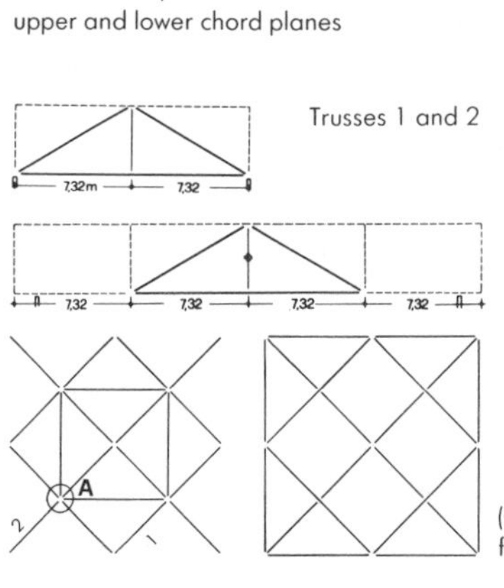

View of trusses

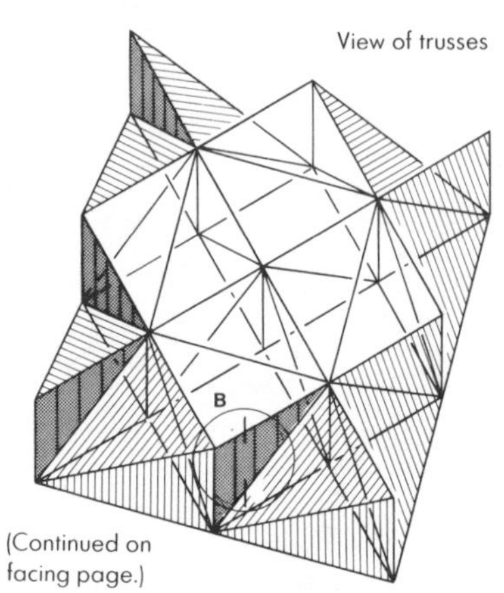

(Continued on facing page.)

Truss members are laminated wood, connections are exposed steel angles and gussets. Interior is illuminated by sloping the triangular elements of the roof on the perimeter. Sloped surfaces serve as stiffeners and are built with tongue and groove planks 7.5 × 12.5 cm each, built out of three glued boards. Roofing is sheet metal with standing seam over insulation.
Reference: *Detail* 3/1975; *A + U* 6/1973

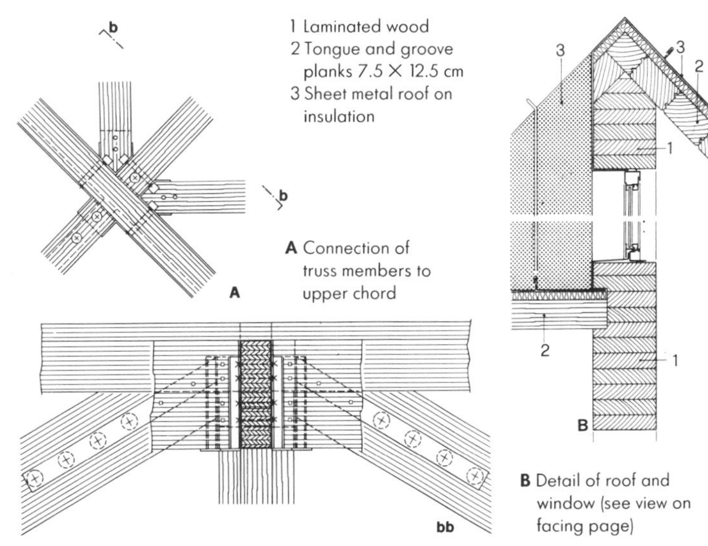

1 Laminated wood
2 Tongue and groove planks 7.5 × 12.5 cm
3 Sheet metal roof on insulation

A Connection of truss members to upper chord

B Detail of roof and window (see view on facing page)

141 Auditorium in Weihenstephan, West Germany

Architect: University Building Department
Engineer: J. Natterer and K. März, Munich

Auditorium with offices and library. Roof is a partially cantilevered truss grid resting on corner columns spaced at 9.60 × 9.60 m. Truss cantilevers 1.80 m, truss nodes are at 1.20 m, truss depth is 1.20 m. Upper and lower chords are double, diagonals single. At one lower chord node, eight 6/14 cm members of the four double lower chords and four 6/12 cm diagonals join together. Lower chord joints are steel crosses with four plates and welded shear connectors. Diagonals are attached to plates with corrugated nails. They are attached with dowels to upper chord.

The 11.40 × 11.40 m grid units were preassembled on building floor. Camber was 4 cm. Diagonals were first nailed to plates, and then upper and lower chords were attached to them with bolts and shear connectors. Grid elements were then held up by a mobile crane until columns were erected and braced.
Reference: *Detail* 4/1974, p. 666

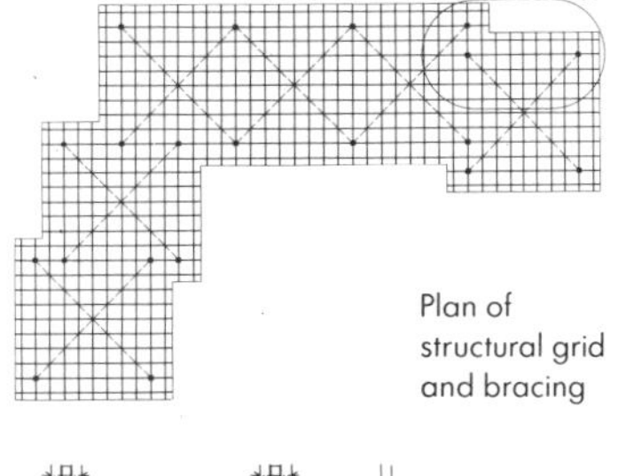

Plan of structural grid and bracing

A Partial grid plan

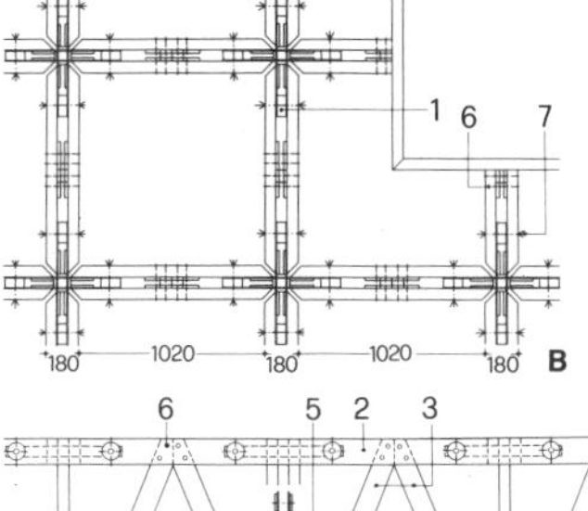

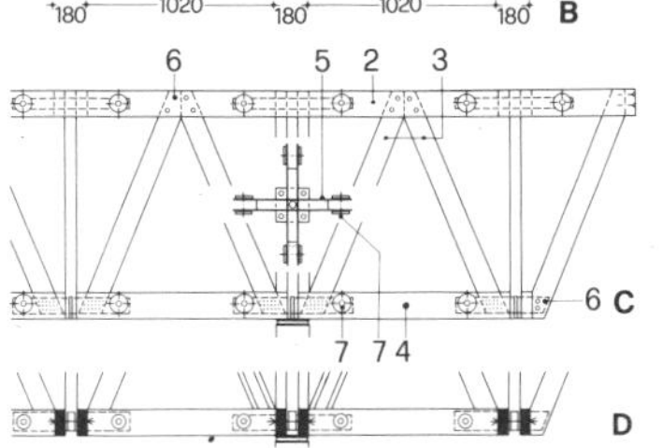

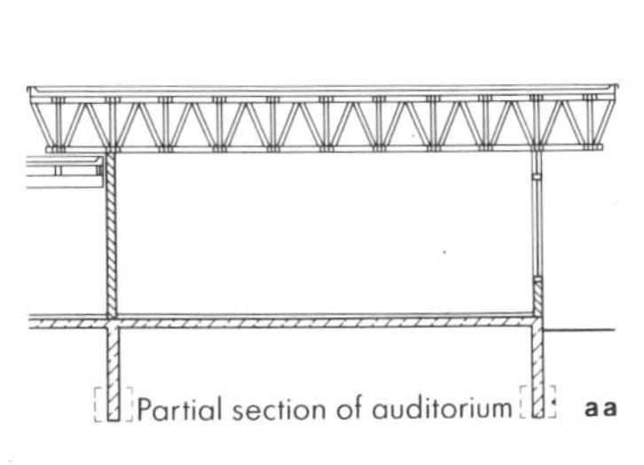

Partial section of auditorium aa

B Partial plan, upper chord
C Elevation of truss
D Lower chord section

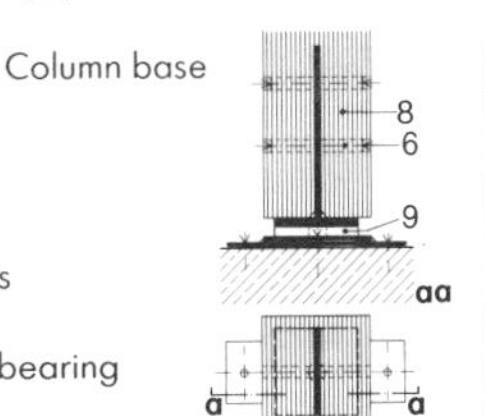

Column base

1 Filler wood
2 Upper chord 2 × 6/14 cm
3 Diagonals 6/12 cm
4 Lower chord 2 × 6/14 cm
5 Truss node, steel cross
6 Dowels
7 Bolts with one-sided shear connectors
8 Column 18/18 cm
9 Bearing plate, steel with elastomeric bearing

Truss Nodes in a Grid

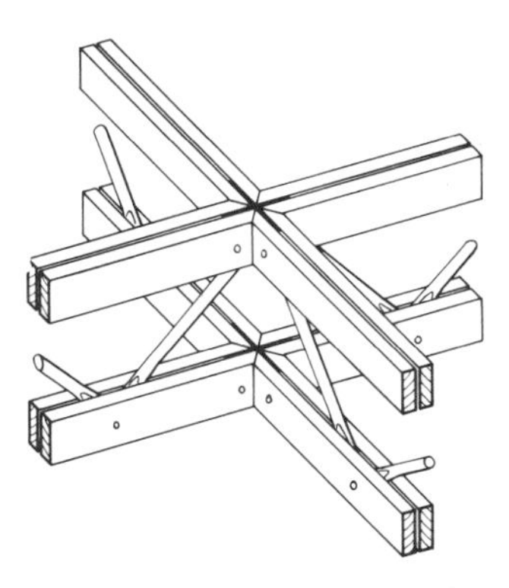

Upper and lower chords in same plane. Connections through steel crosses.

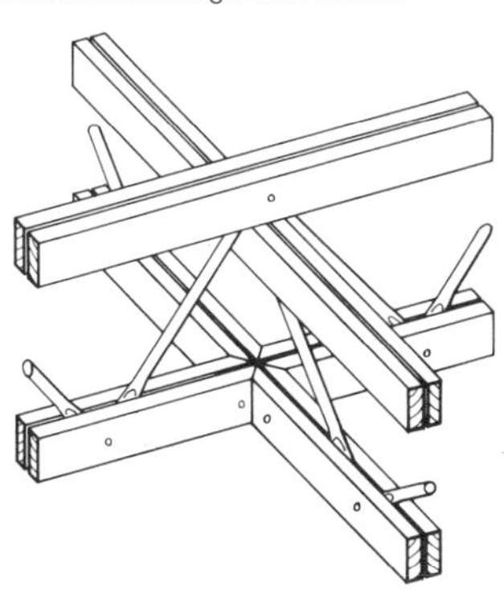

Lower chords in same plane, upper chords overlapping.

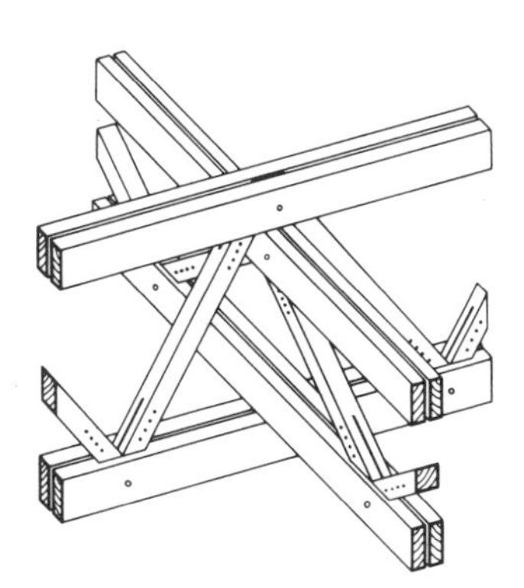

Lower and upper chords overlapping. Different depths of trusses.

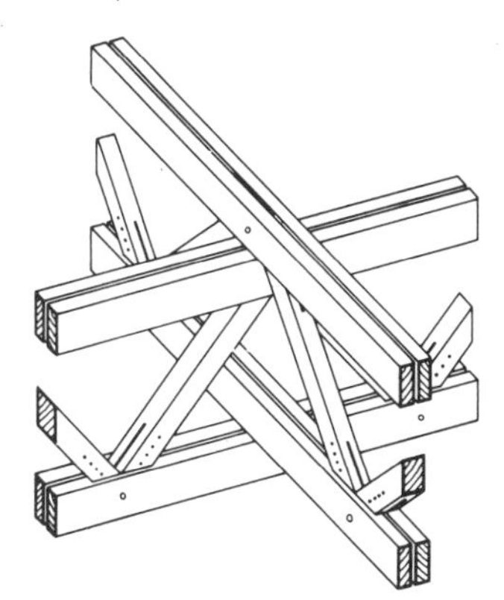

Lower and upper chords overlapping. Same depth of trusses.

Folded structures consist of sloped plane surfaces, joined together to resist shear. The load is distributed both transversely and longitudinally and is resisted by bending stresses in the planes, from valley to ridge and from bearing to bearing. Both transverse and longitudinal bending stresses govern the design.

When folded structures consist of trusses, special attention must be paid to the slippage of connections.

142 Storage Shed in Apeldoorn, The Netherlands

Architect: T. Wiarda, Apeldoorn
Engineer: Vellinga, Apeldoorn

Covered surface 50.00 × 83.00 m, columns on a 4.60 × 8.20 m grid. Roof is a folded structure of intersecting planes having the shape of a series of gable roofs. Individual panels are 8.20 m long and consist of lumber frames covered on both sides with plywood. Frames are joined to resist shear by means of hinges at valley and ridge. They are so arranged that two panels are folded together for transport. Each unit was lifted by a mobile crane, spread over gable ends, and attached to steel bearing. Wind loads are taken by fixed columns.

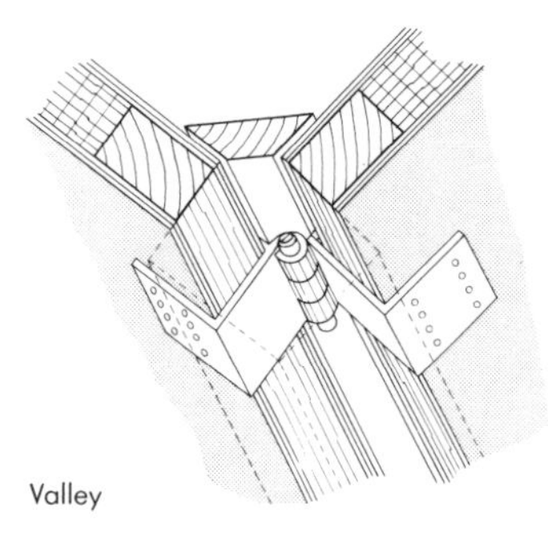

Valley

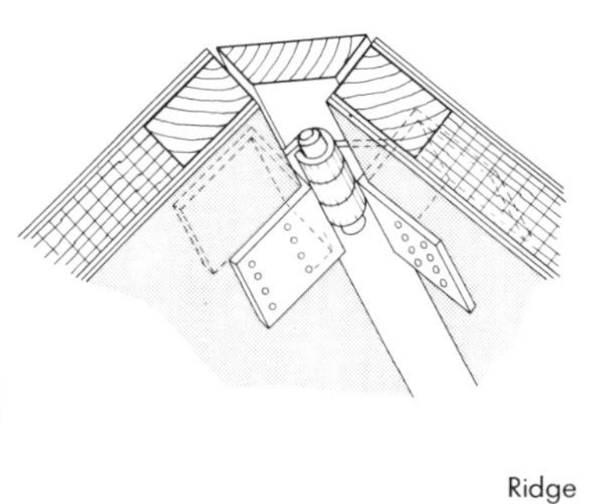

Ridge

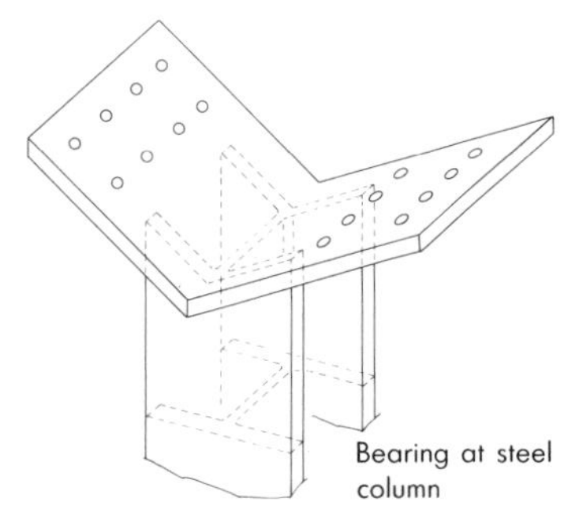

Bearing at steel column

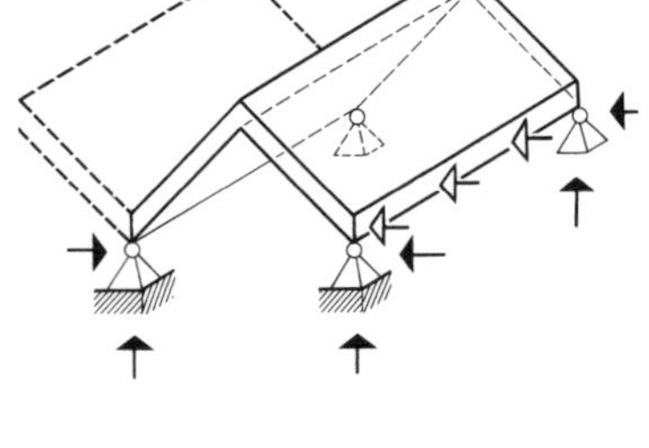

Bearing reactions

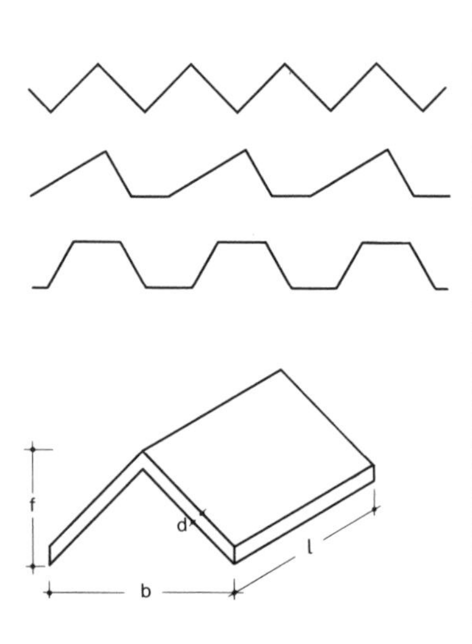

Folded structures built with crossed planking, laminated wood, or plywood, and having transverse ribs at joints, can be dimensioned as follows:
$f \geq l/8$; $\sphericalangle \geq 30°$
$d \geq h/20$ to $h/30$
where h = width of fold
For trusses,
$d \geq h/15$ to $h/25$

143 Shopping Center in Würzburg, West Germany

Architect: Schönewolff and Geisendörfer
Engineer: J. Natterer, Munich

Shopping center is located within a residential area of Würzburg. Ground floor building is covered by folds in the shape of multiple gable roofs, spanning 12.50 to 16.25 m. Folds consist of 4 cm thick crossed-plank webs and transverse ribs 7/16 and 8/16 cm, spaced at 1.90 m. Cross ribs are enlarged to 7/40 and 14/24 cm at bearings.

Folds rest on timber columns 36.5/36.5 cm, rigidly connected by means of tie beams 13.5/52 cm. These rigid connections create frames which serve as wind bracing. Horizontal forces in end bay are resisted by cantilevered half of a fold.

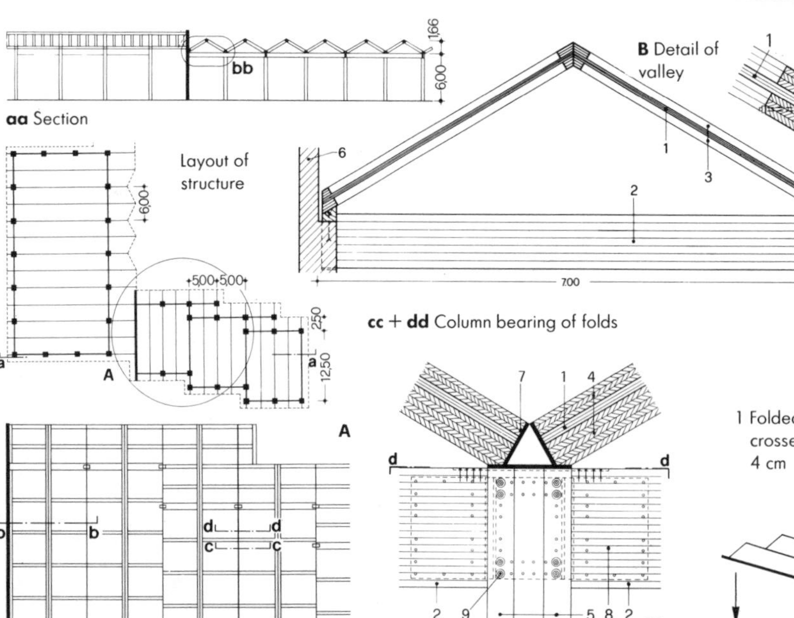

aa Section

Layout of structure

A Partial plan of structure

B Detail of valley

cc + dd Column bearing of folds

bb Partial section

1 Folded plate, crossed planking, 4 cm
2 Tension beam 13.5/52 cm
3 Transverse ribs 7/16 and 8/16 cm, spaced at 1.90 m
4 Ribs enlarged at bearing 7/40 and 14/24 cm
5 Columns 36.5/36.5 cm with recess for drain
6 Bearing at fire wall
7 Steel bearing wedge
8 Steel plate 10 mm with ϕ 10 mm dowel
9 Bolt with nut and washer

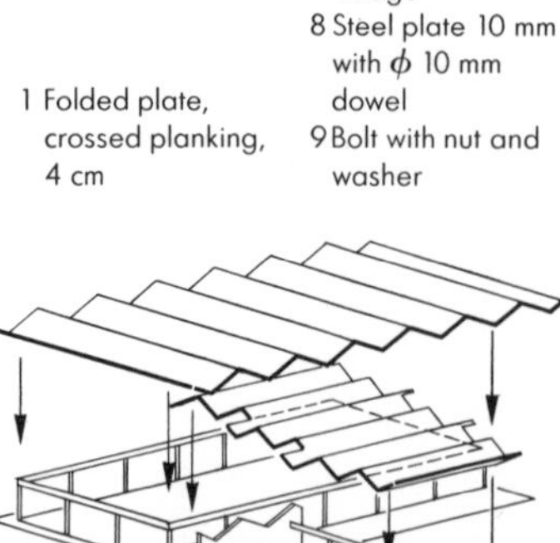

144 Convalescent Center in Freilassing, West Germany

Architect: H. Caspari, Munich
Engineer: J. Natterer, Munich

Restaurant, swimming pool, and gymnasium are covered with longitudinal shed roofs used for windows and acting as load-carrying folded plates. One shed roof over swimming pool has a 27.00 m span. Two others over gymnasium have spans of 15.00 and 45.00 m. The larger widths of this roof, some 30.00 m over swimming pool, are spanned transversely to sheds by relatively small cross beams 1.20 m high. This makes such construction economical because the enclosed space is smaller. Folded shed roof consists of crossed-plank web girders in roof plane, and of trusses in area of clerestory windows. Frame members serve as window frames while steel diagonals remain barely visible. Folded roofs rest on reinforced-concrete walls on both sides.

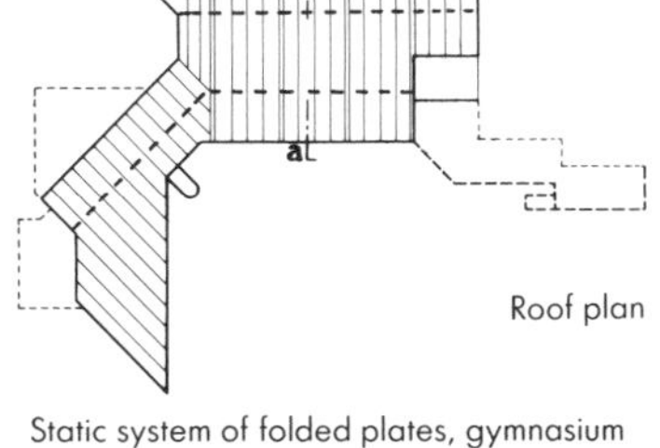

Roof plan

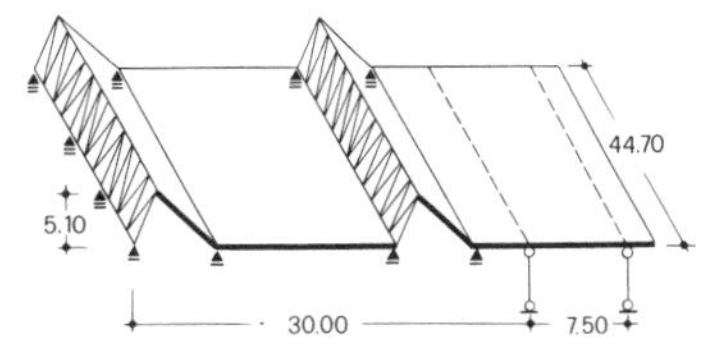

Static system of folded plates, gymnasium

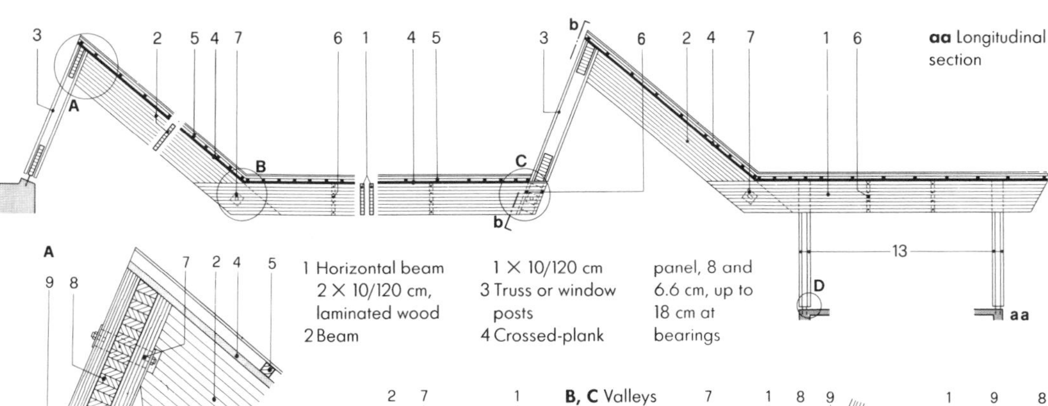

aa Longitudinal section

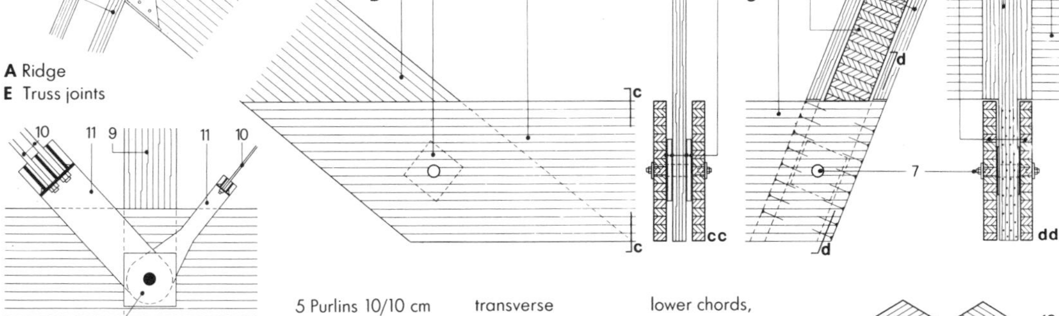

A Ridge
E Truss joints

B, C Valleys

1 Horizontal beam 2 × 10/120 cm, laminated wood
2 Beam 1 × 10/120 cm
3 Truss or window posts
4 Crossed-plank panel, 8 and 6.6 cm, up to 18 cm at bearings
5 Purlins 10/10 cm
6 Filler wood
7 Hinged joint of truss and transverse beam, nail plates, and bolts
8 Upper and lower chords, 12/120 cm at truss with intermediate columns, 32/120 at 44.7 m span
9 Posts 2 × 12/45 cm
10 Steel St 52 diagonals from 1 × ϕ 16 mm to 4 × ϕ 57 mm at bearings
11 Steel plate connection
12 Recess for curtain
13 Cross-shaped column

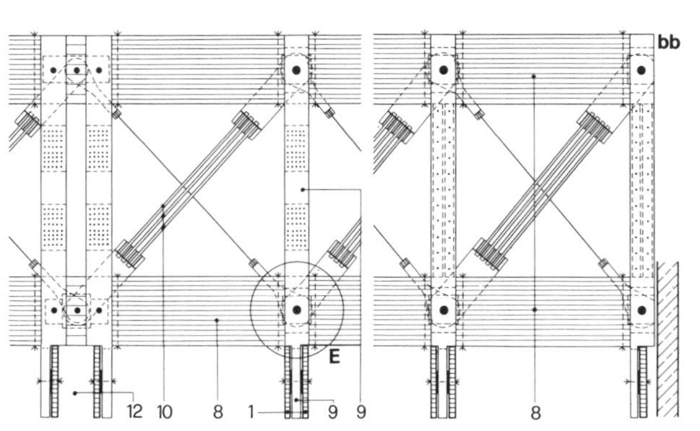

bb Truss over gymnasium

D Column base

Folded Plate Joints

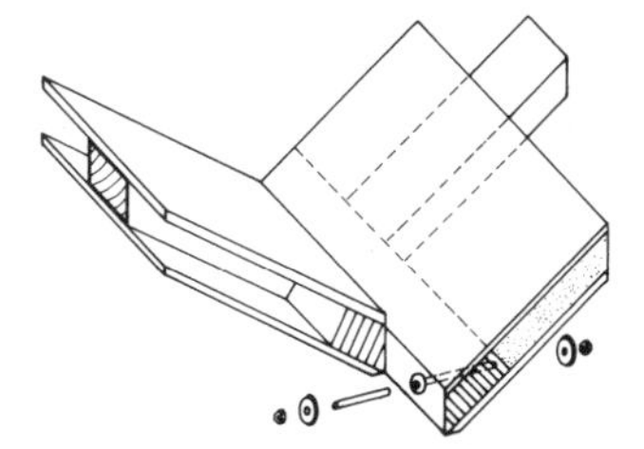

Longitudinal ribs, bolted.

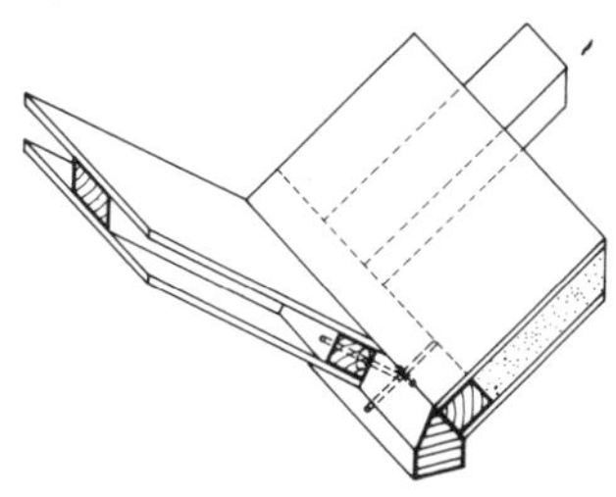

Longitudinal ribs, doweled to valley beam.

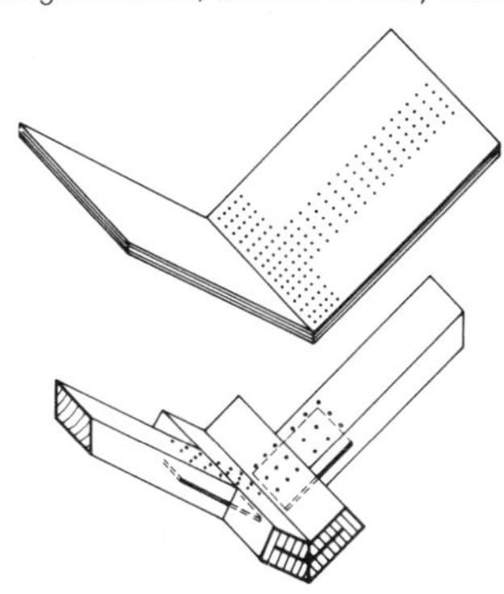

Cross ribs nailed or doweled to recessed plates.

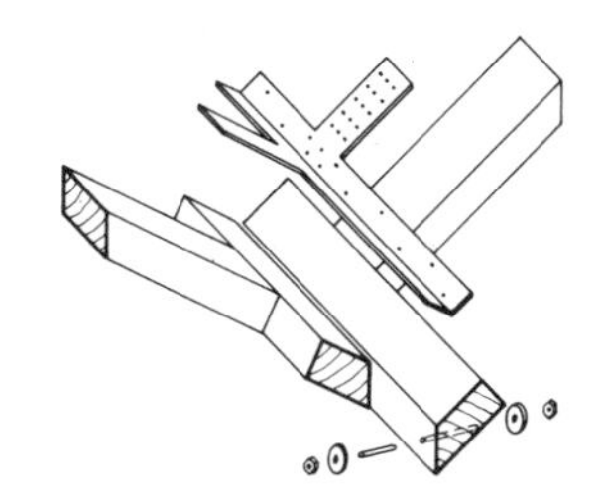

Connecting plates for longitudinal and transverse ribs. Ribs joined by bolts and shear connectors.

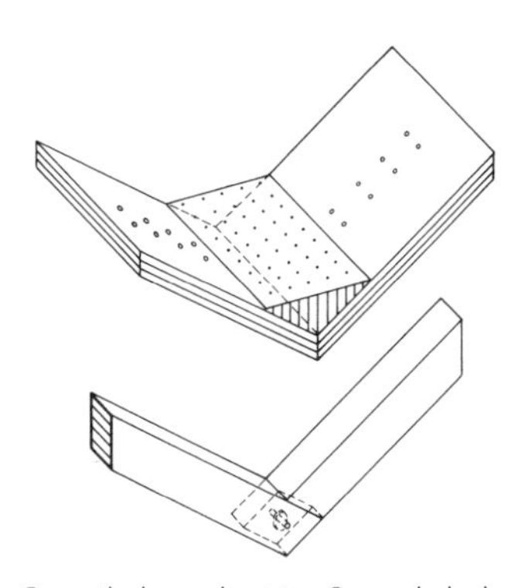

Cross ribs lapped at joint. Crossed-plank or plywood panels nailed to ribs. Valley rib also nailed longitudinally.

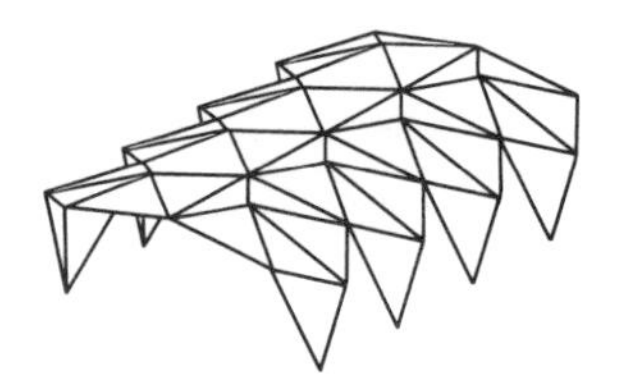

Folded-plate frames

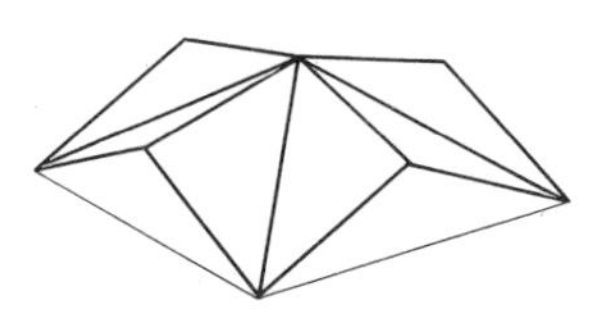

Folded-plate arches

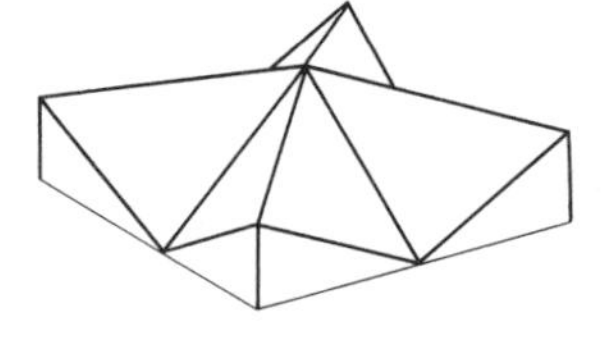

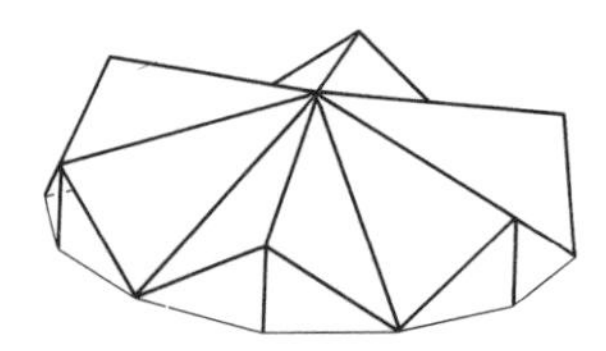

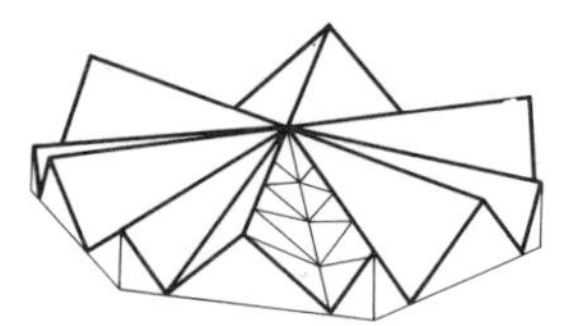

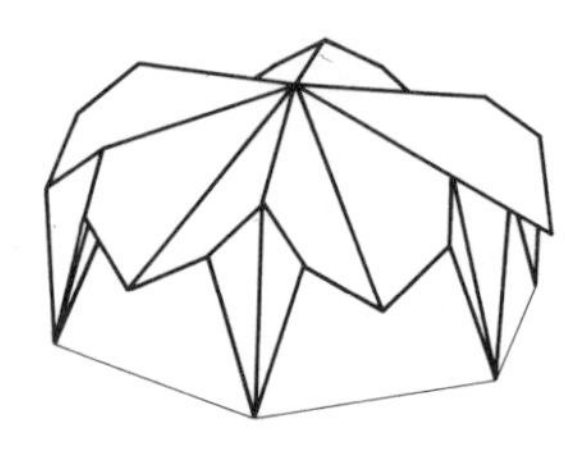

Folded plates arranged radially

145 School in Wellington, Great Britain

Architect: R. Crowe, Shrewsbury
Engineer: Ove Arup, London

Assembly or sports hall of a school, 12.00 × 14.00 m. Roof consists of folded plates arranged radially. Folded panels consist of lumber frames 4/10 cm sheathed on both sides with 10 mm plywood. Columns are double 2 × 8/24 cm with filler wood. These columns are connected with steel U shapes to walls, foundation, and flooring. Columns are connected with peripheral tension bar ϕ 30 mm in order to resist horizontal stresses in folded roof; there is a turnbuckle for adjustment. Wind loads resisted by folded roof and fixed columns.
Reference: *Plywood World* 1/1965

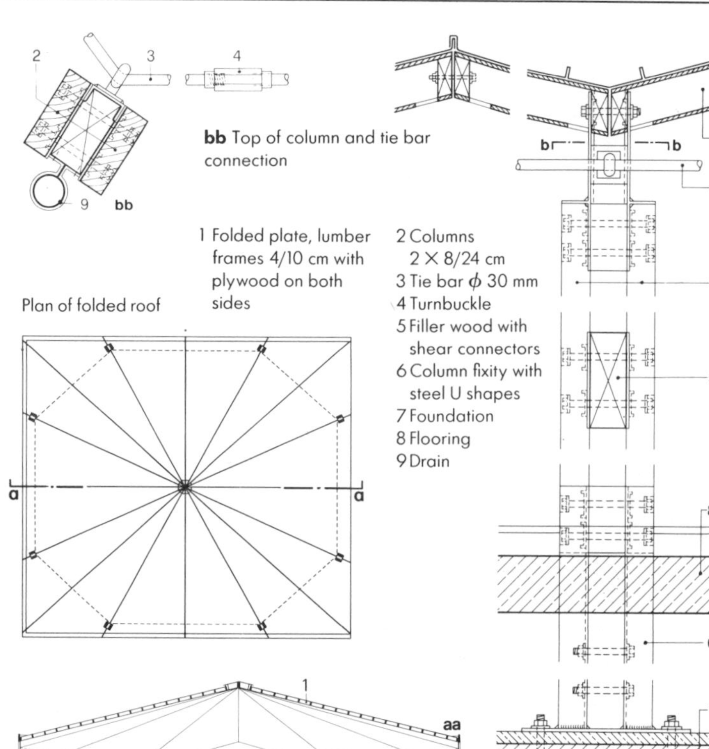

bb Top of column and tie bar connection

Plan of folded roof

1 Folded plate, lumber frames 4/10 cm with plywood on both sides
2 Columns 2 × 8/24 cm
3 Tie bar ϕ 30 mm
4 Turnbuckle
5 Filler wood with shear connectors
6 Column fixity with steel U shapes
7 Foundation
8 Flooring
9 Drain

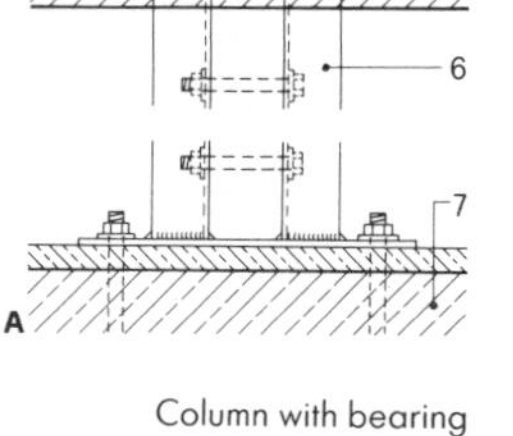

Column with bearing

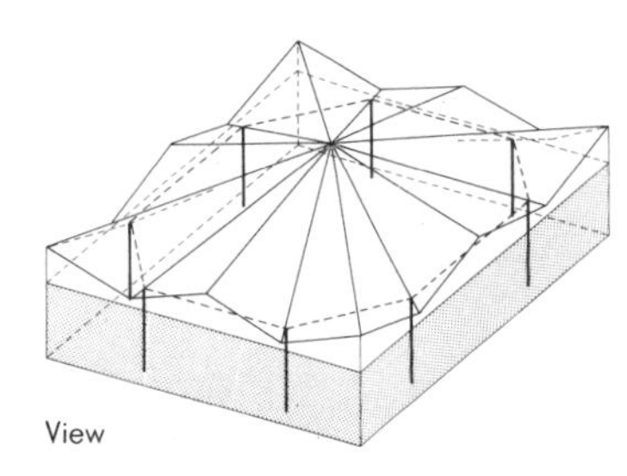

View

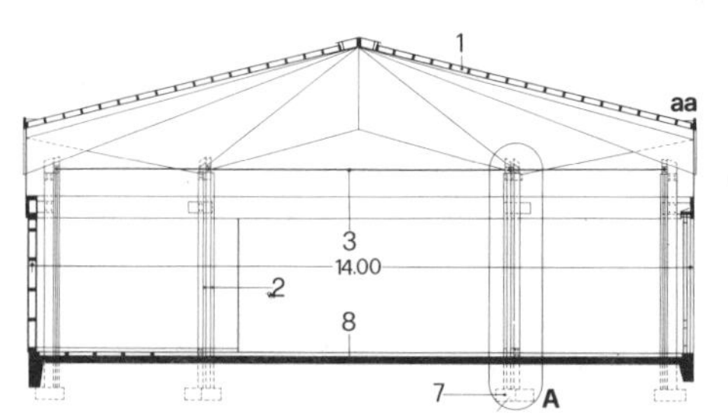

Section, scale 1:200

146 Church in Uitikon, Switzerland

Architect: D. Ercsi, Uitikon
Engineer: H. Gasser, Lungern

Church roof in shape of irregular pyramid, truncated by a skylight. Roof surfaces are irregular triangles or quadrangles. Folded surfaces consist of three layers. Lowest layer consists of purlins which run tangentially to center. Second layer, resting on purlins, consists of diagonal planking. Third layer consists of rafters which run radially to center. Purlins, rafters, and intermediate planking form a rigid plate to resist shear and a grid to resist bending.

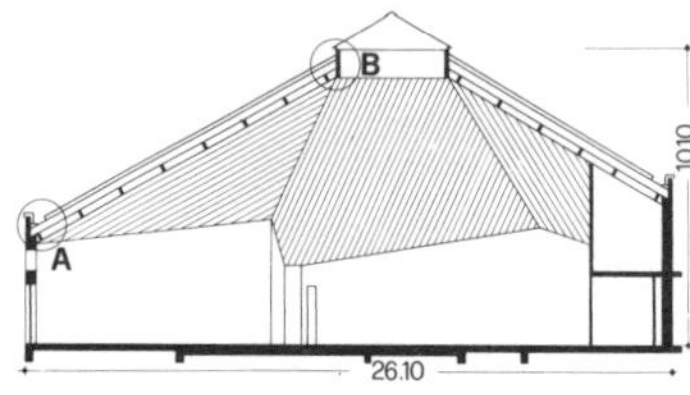

Cross section, scale 1:500

A Connection at gutter
B Connection of roof ridge to skylight

1 Purlins 8/19 to 22/25 cm
2 Diagonal planking 30 mm
3 Rafters 6/15 to 12/23 m
4 Skylight beams, laminated wood
5 Pyramidal skylight
6 Vented roof with double layer of asbestos-cement panels

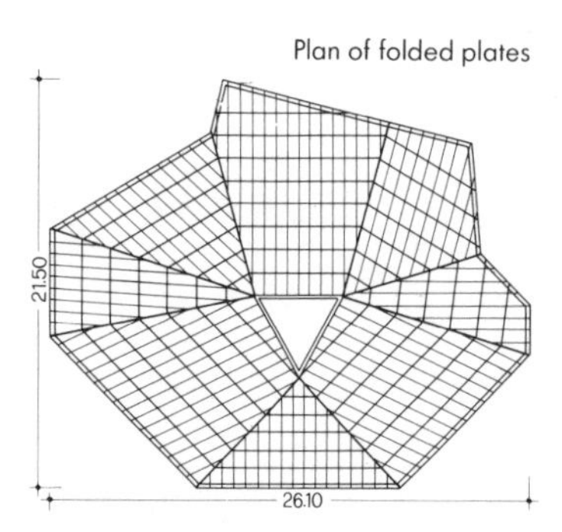

Plan of folded plates

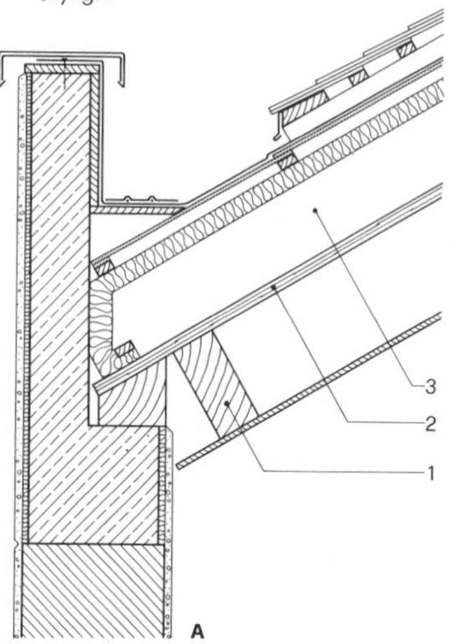

5
6
4
1
2
3
B

147 Music Pavilion in Montreal, Canada

Architect: Carmen Corneil, Toronto
Engineer: N. Seethaler, Toronto

Shell-shaped folded plates serve as a roof and acoustic reflector for open-air orchestra. Faceted surfaces are so arranged that both spectators and performers receive good reflected sound.

Folded plates consist of three elongated segments which rest on one end and are tied in back by steel tubes. Each segment is built from 5/7.5 and 5/10 cm lumber, sheathed with 12 mm plywood panels.

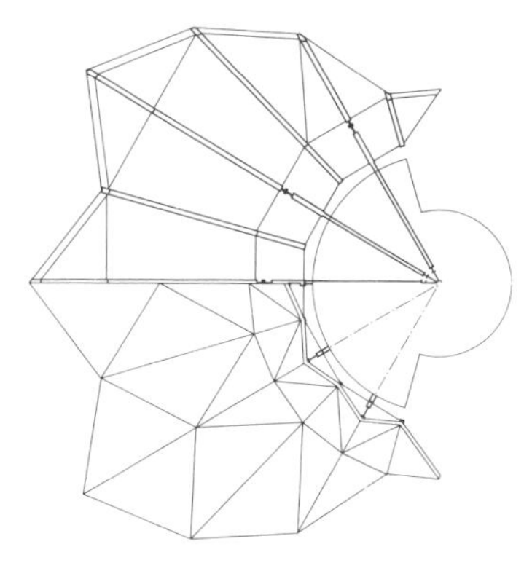

Plan of folded plates

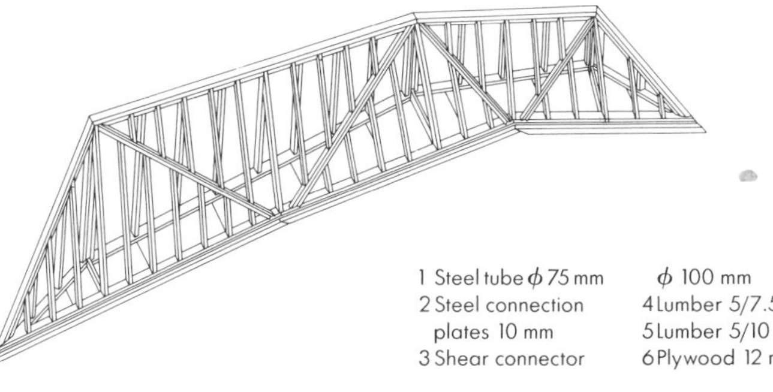

1 Steel tube ϕ 75 mm
ϕ 100 mm
2 Steel connection plates 10 mm
3 Shear connector
4 Lumber 5/7.5 cm
5 Lumber 5/10 cm
6 Plywood 12 mm

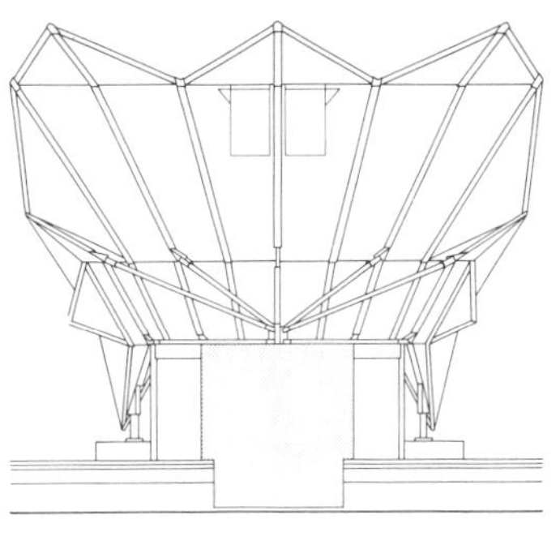

Rear view

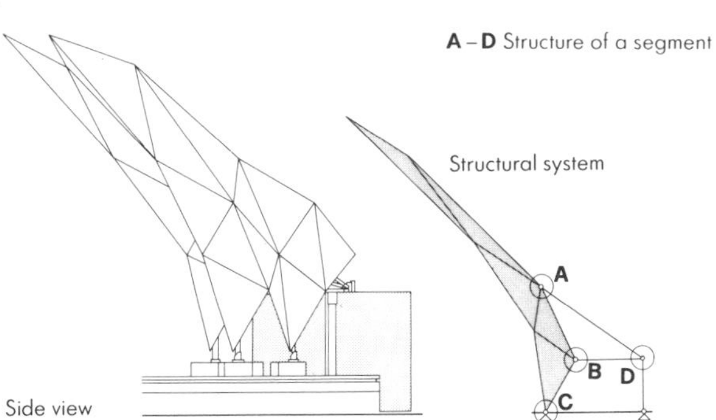

Side view

A – D Structure of a segment

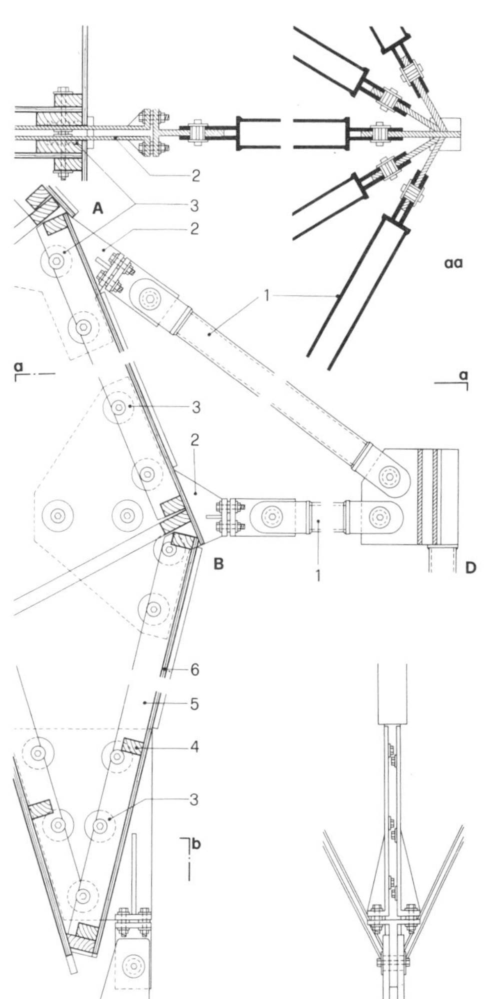

Construction of Panels

Plywood panel.

Crossed-plank panel consisting of at least three glued board layers. Grain of center layer offset at least 8 to 12° (Kämpf system).

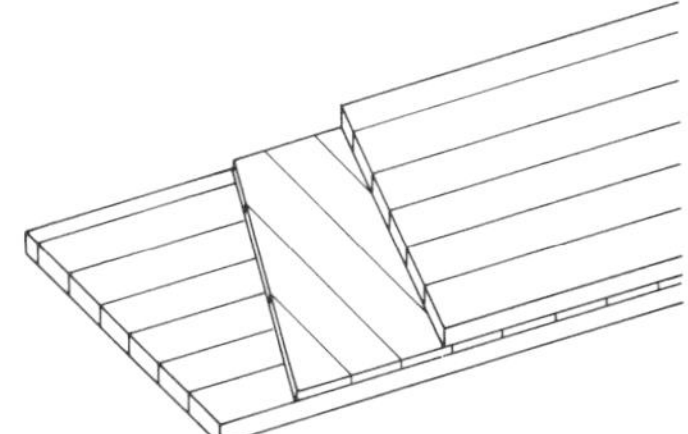

Crossed-plank panel of at least three board layers at 90° (Wolff system).

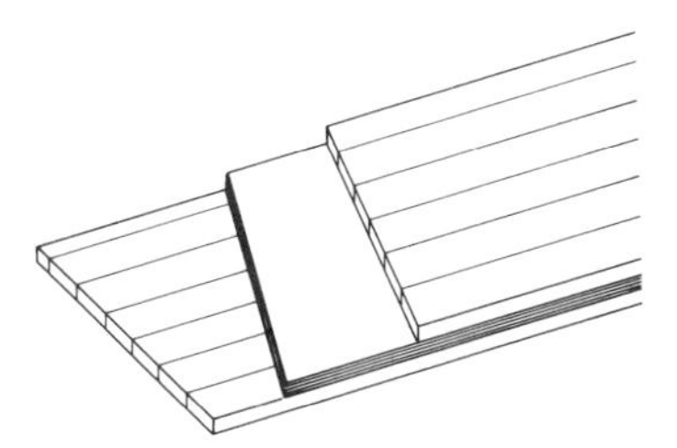

Panel consisting of glued boards and plywood.

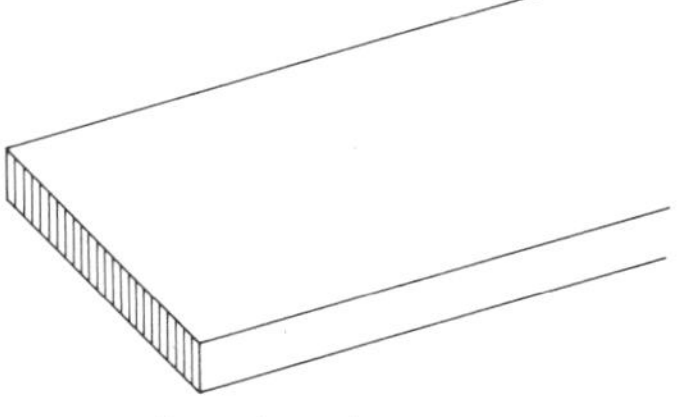

Laminated board panel.

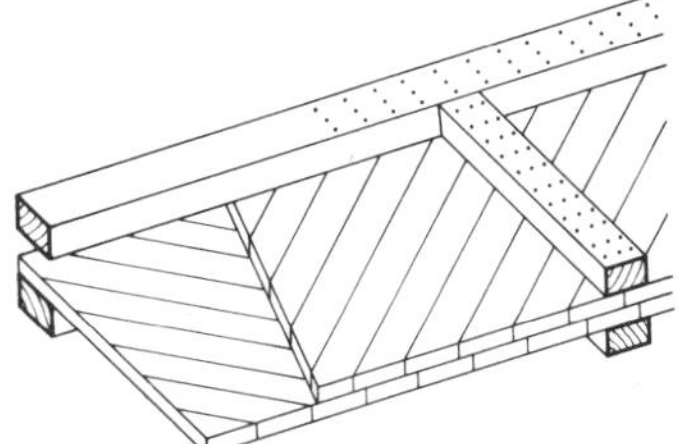

Beam with web made from diagonally placed boards.

Shells in the shape of barrel arches may have a circular, parabolic, or elliptic cross section. The shape of the shell governs the design. Long shells can be designed by beam analogy, but short shells must be designed by exact theories of anisotropic shells. In long shells the load is mainly resisted by the longitudinal bending stiffness of the shell. In shorter shells the load is resisted by bending stiffness in both the longitudinal and the transverse directions. The design, therefore, depends on the longitudinal and transverse bending stiffnesses. In addition, at the bearings, the shell must be amply stiffened against shear; in the transverse direction, the end of the shell must be stiffened by an arch, which may or may not be tied.

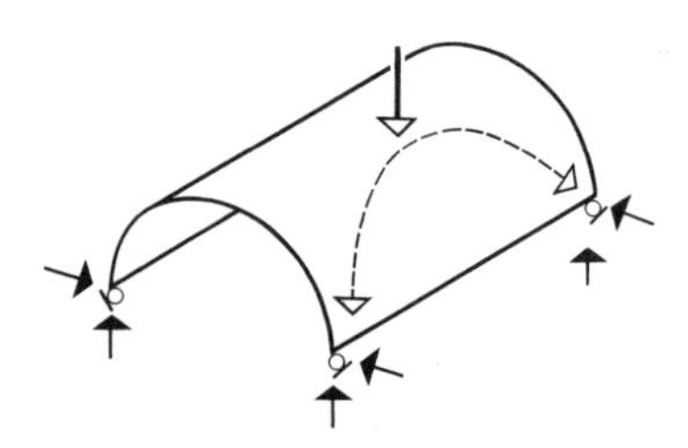

Bearing reactions and interior forces

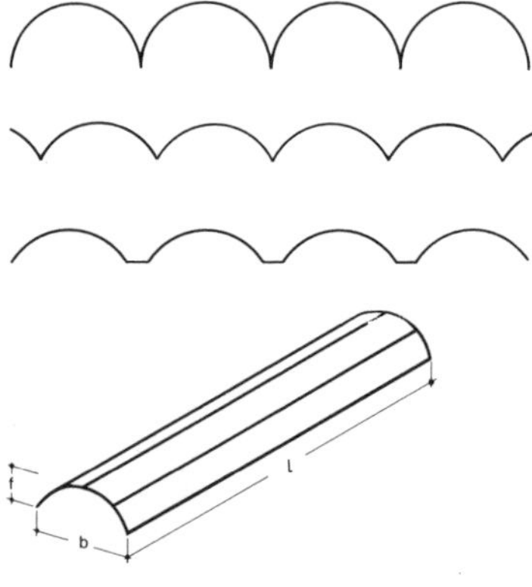

b ≤ l/5 long barrel vault shell

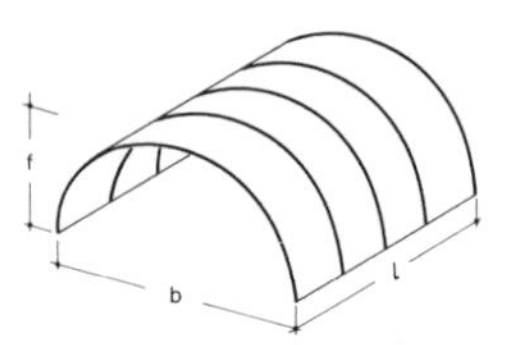

b > l/5 short barrel vault shell
l = 5 to 35 m
f = ≤ b/2

148 Barrel Vault Shell in Winnipeg, Canada

Dressing rooms at a lake beach were covered by 14 barrel vault shells with a length of 7.30 m. Shells have a rise of 0.53 m and a width of 2.77 m; they consist of longitudinal lumber ribs 5 × 5 cm and cross ribs 5 × 5 cm of laminated wood. Longitudinal edge rib is strengthened to 5 × 10 cm. At bearings over steel column there is a continuous arch of laminated wood, with a tie. Required stiffness is achieved by plywood sheathing on extrados and intrados.

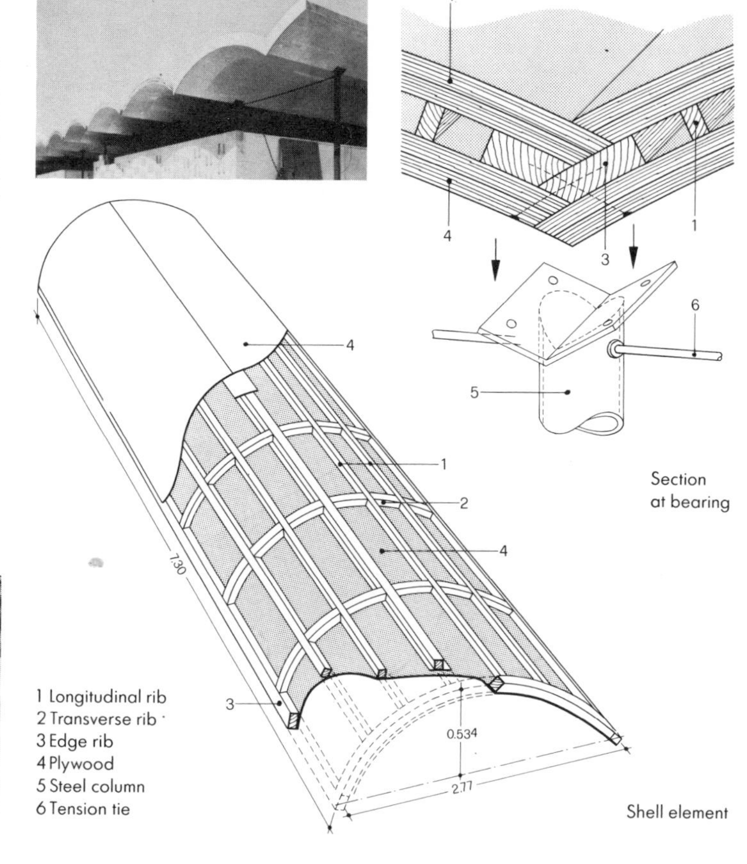

Section at bearing

1 Longitudinal rib
2 Transverse rib
3 Edge rib
4 Plywood
5 Steel column
6 Tension tie

Shell element

149 Railroad Yard Shed in Coventry, Great Britain

Architect: Railway Architects Department, London

Shed has an area 30.50 × 58.00 m. It is covered by five transverse cylindrical shells, each having 11.50 m width and 6.90 m radius. Edge support beams are box girders 30/84 cm, laminated wood and plywood, and cross ribs are 5/15 cm glued planks. The shell itself consists of four layers of 1.9 cm thick boards. The first and fourth layers are transverse, the second and third are placed at 60° to longitudinal axis and are nailed to resist shear. End panel consists of two layers of crossed and nailed tongue and groove boards, an end arch, and posts to resist wind loads.

1 Edge girder 30/84 cm, plywood box girder
2 Cross ribs, glued planks 5/15 cm
3 Longitudinal ribs 10/15 cm, laminated wood
4 4 layers tongue and groove boards 20 mm
5 Tongue and groove boards 20 mm
6 Posts 5/25 cm
7 Tension beam 10/25 cm, laminated wood
8 Shear connector ϕ 65 mm

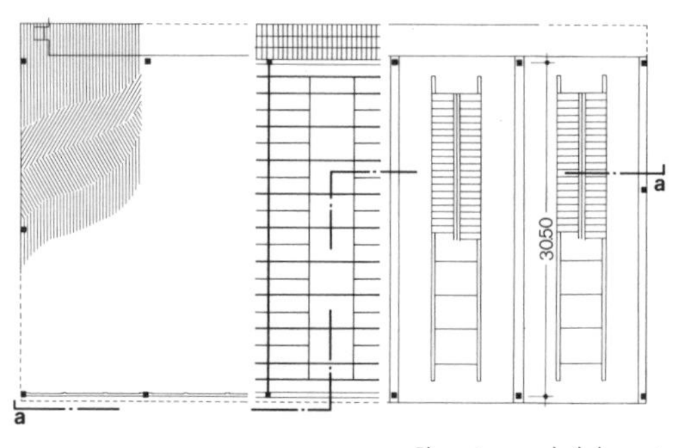

Plan view and rib layout

End view and longitudinal section

A, C Edge beam connection
B Skylight

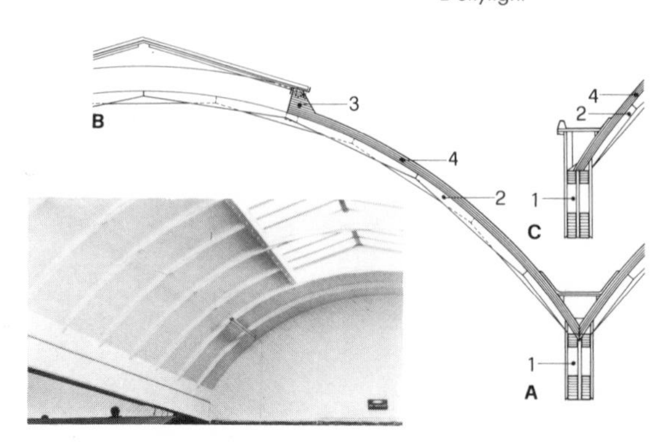

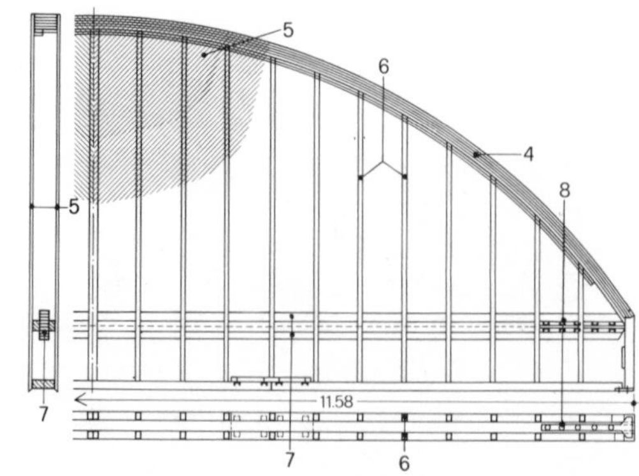

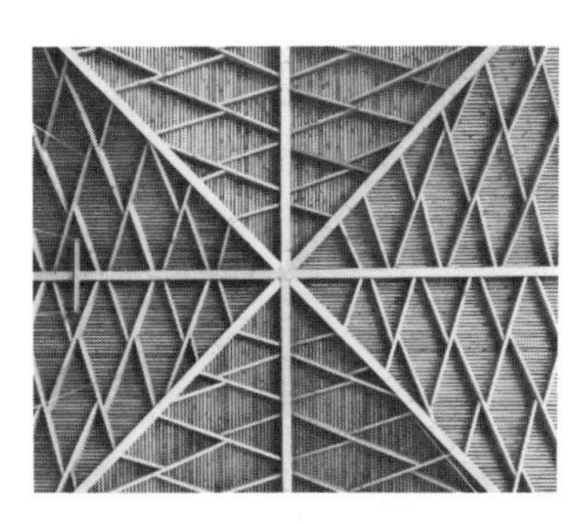

150 Ribbed Construction, Underside of Church Roof in Köln-Volkhofen, West Germany

Architect: J. Lehmbrock

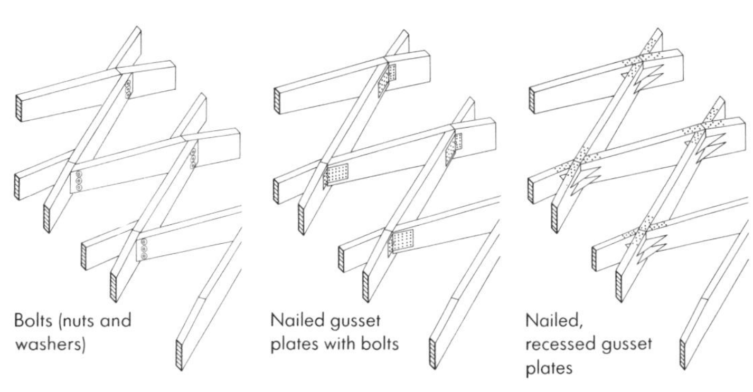

Lozenge shape arrangement of ribs as trusswork, with ribs curved one or two ways. Ribs are intermittently continuous.

151 Sports Arena in Bozeman, United States

Architect: O. Berg, F. F. Willson
Engineer: B. F. Hurlbut

University sports arena for 12,500 spectators. Roof is spherical, with radius of 75.00 m, resting on steel tension ring of 91.5 m diameter. There are 36 radial ribs 18/41 cm, spliced one-third points, and straight tangential beams, all of laminated wood. Flat steel diagonals were welded after assembly as a tension net.
Reference: *Engineering News Record* Jan. 1957

1 Laminated wood ribs, 17.8 × 41.2 cm at bearing
2 Steel compression ring on top
3 Laminated wood tangential beams
4 Steel diagonals
5 Rafters
6, 7 Tension ring of steel U shapes and flat bars
8 Steel plate
9 Shear connector for axial stresses
10 Dowel for shear stresses

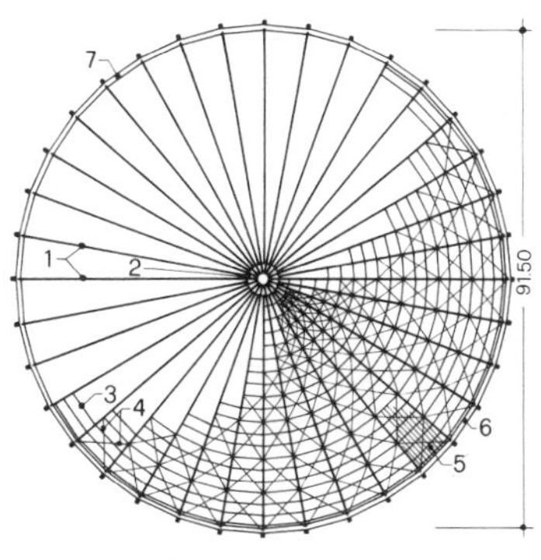

Plan layout of beams, scale 1:2000

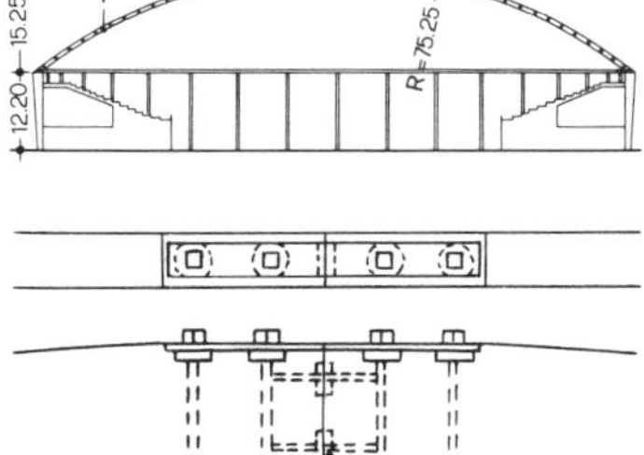

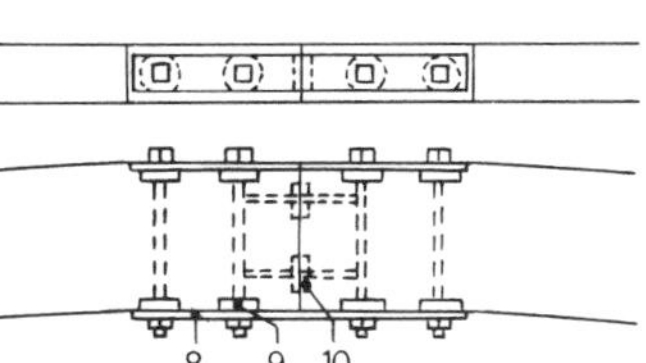

Rib field splice

152 Sports Arena in Salt Lake City, United States

Architect: Fowler, Salt Lake City
Engineer: Timber Construction Firm

Sports arena for 15,000 spectators. Spherical roof has radius of 105.00 m and rise of 37.00 m. Structure consists of triangular elements, roof sheathing is plywood. Spherical shell rests on steel tension ring, anchored in concrete pylons. In addition to dead load, wind, and snow, shell supports additional weight of an intermediate platform weighing 1800 kN and hanging from center of dome.

Ribbed Panels

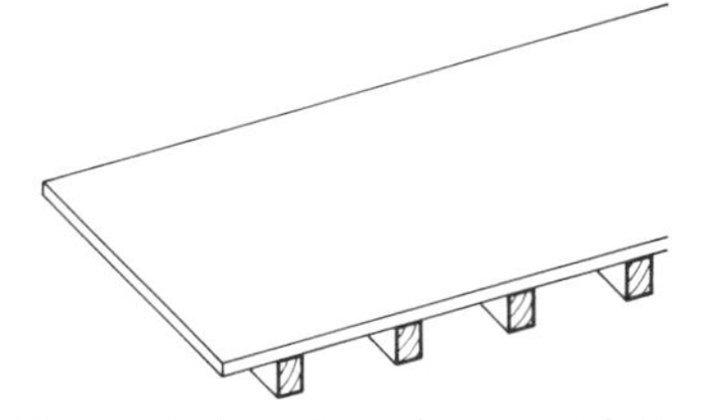

Ribs are lumber, plywood on one side is nailed or glued and nail-pressed.

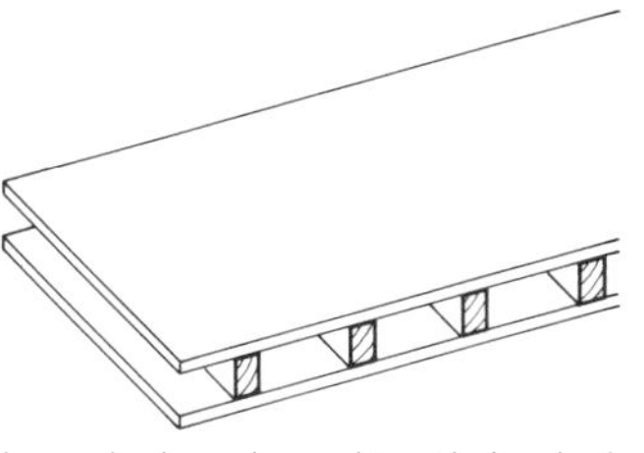

Ribs are lumber, plywood is nailed on both sides or glued and nail-pressed.

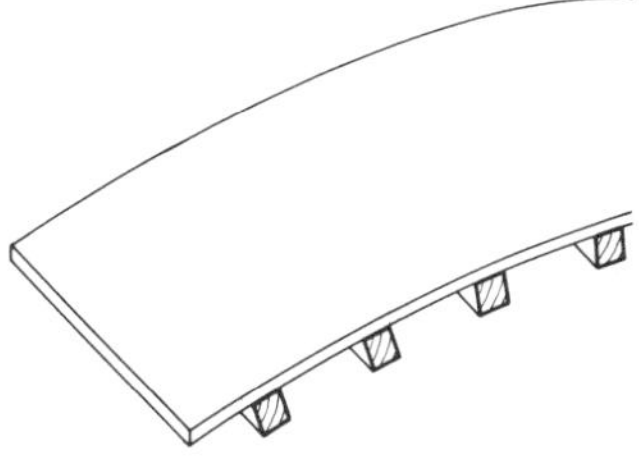

Rib grid of lumber, lapped, curved in one direction and sheathed on one side.

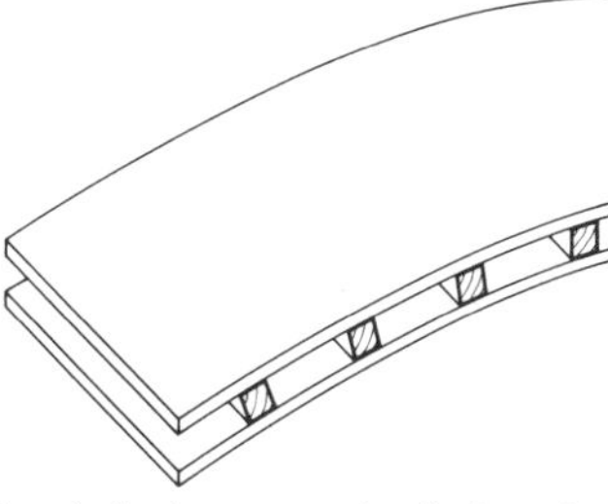

Rib grid of lumber as immediately above, but sheathed on both sides.

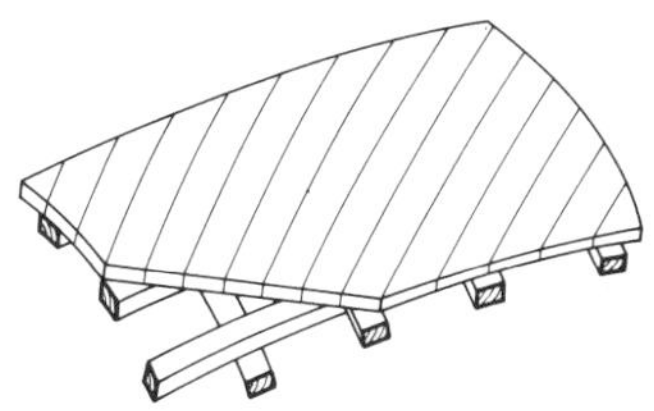

Ribs of lapped or overlapping lumber, curved two ways, with diagonal sheathing.

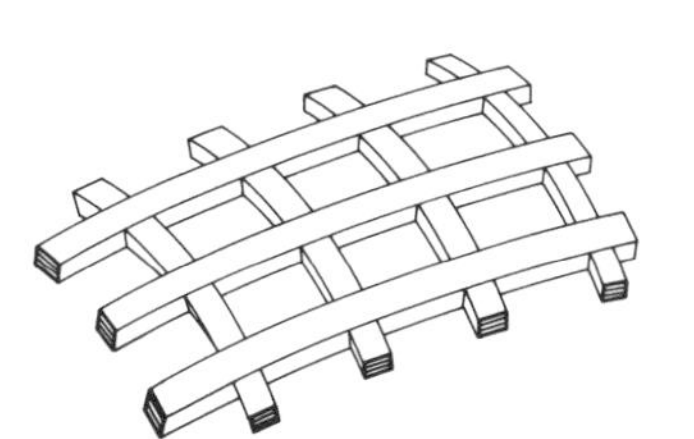

Grid of overlapping boards, curved in two directions.

In a geodesic dome the loads are resisted by radial and tangential compression and tension forces. Compression and tension stresses in members govern the design. A check must also be made of the buckling strength of members and of the cave-in resistance of the dome by verifying deformations and bending stiffness.

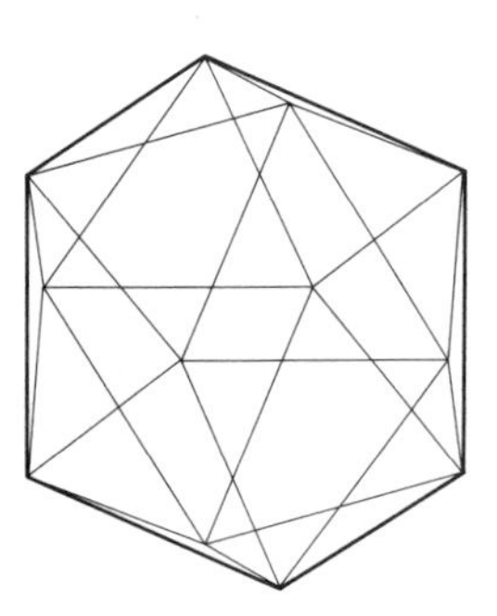

Icosahedron as a basic form of geodesic dome.

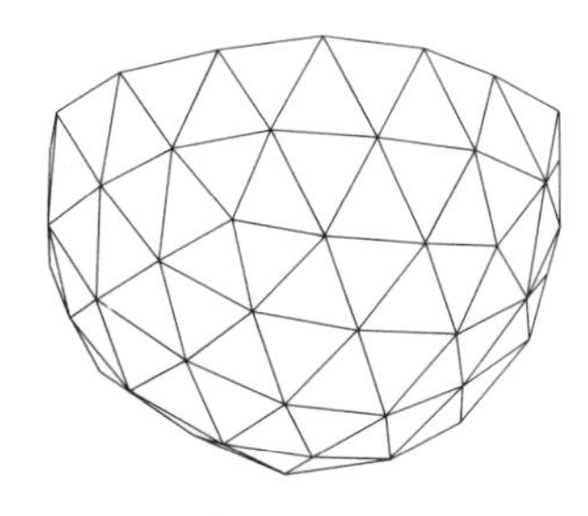

Icosahedron dome with triple frequency.

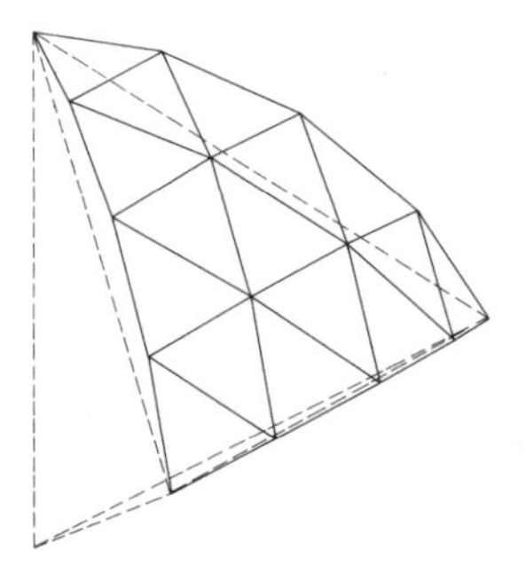

Icosahedron triangular segment, fourfold frequency. Network of parallel sides.

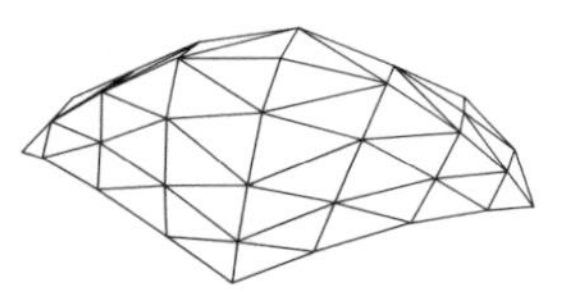

1/4 sphere with rectangular network and diagonals.

153 Geodesic Dome in Munich, West Germany

Architect: W. Ruhnau, Essen, and J. Weber, London
Engineer: J. Natterer and K. März, Munich

Geodesic dome with shape according to Fuller, on the basis of icosahedrons, built in connection with 1972 Olympic Games in Munich. Dome has a diameter of 7.00 m and is built with 7.5/6 cm lumber and plywood. Lumber is joined by 2 mm thick gusset plates and ϕ 12 mm bolts. Dome can be disassembled and reconstructed or designed with a larger diameter.

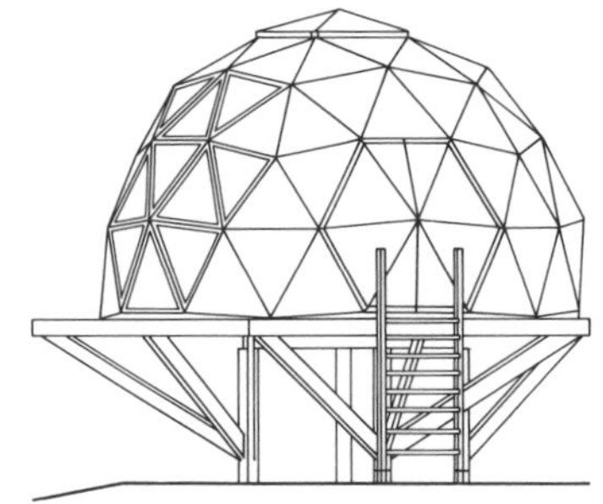

Elevation

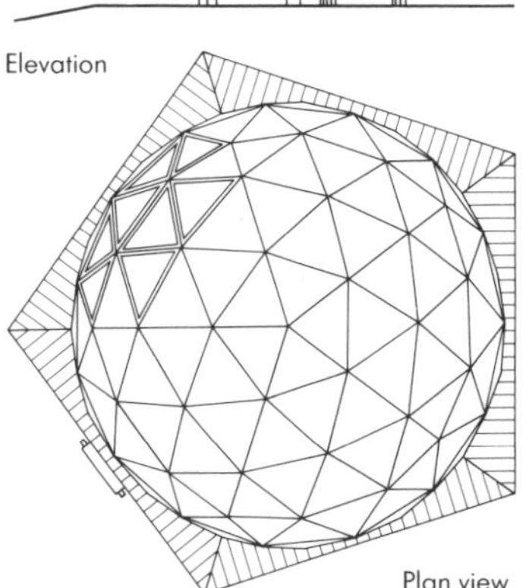

Plan view

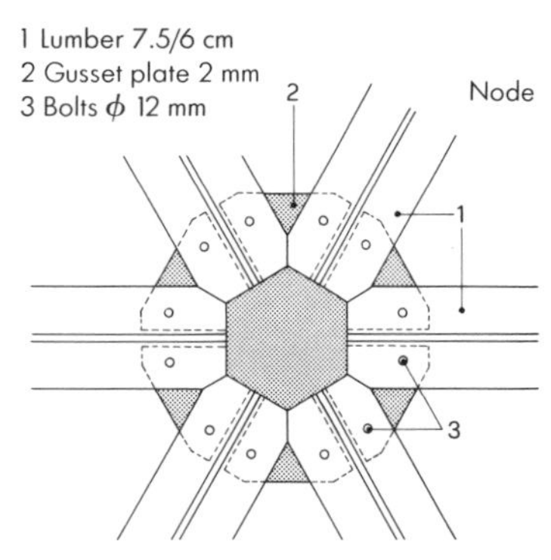

154 Geodesic Dome in Säckingen, West Germany

Architect: J. Köchlin, Braunschweig
Engineer: Fickert, Hannover

Series of overlapping geodesic domes for an exhibition pavilion. They are geometrically composed of triangles, squares, and pentagons. All side lengths are 2.00 m long. Individual surfaces consist of 30 mm thick wood-chip boards and are connected by hinges that resist shear. Anchorage to foundation is through steel angles. Joints between panels are sealed with plastic materials. A plastic waterproofing was applied to panels in shop.
Reference: *Bauen mit Holz* 11/1973

Plan

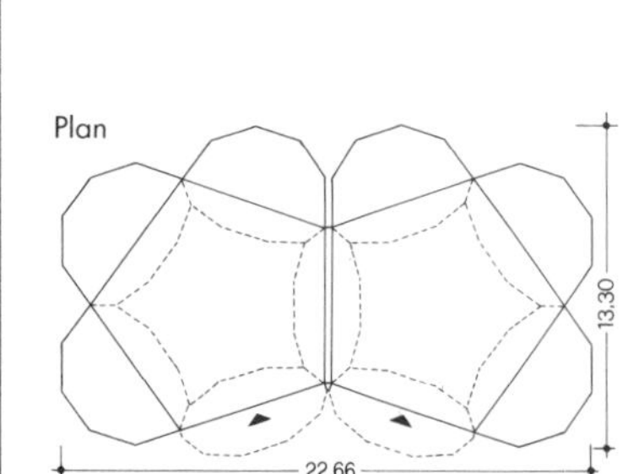

Plan view

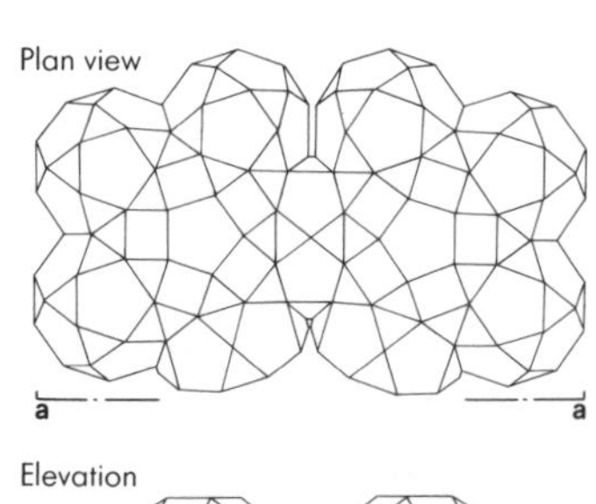

Elevation

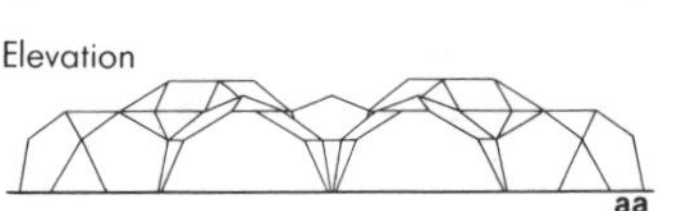

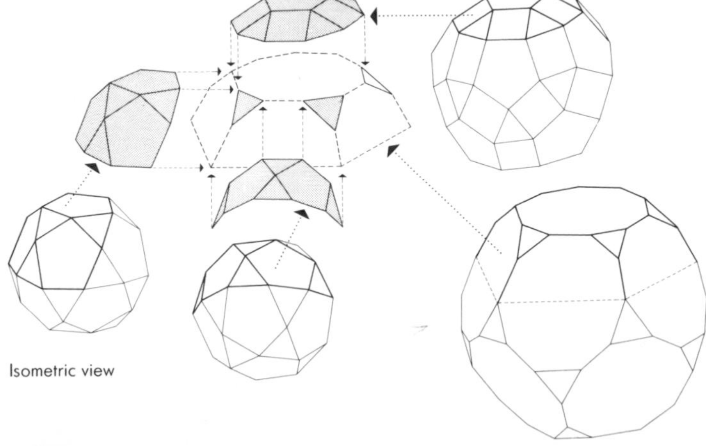

Isometric view

155 Multipurpose Hall in Mannheim, West Germany

Architect: C. Mutschler and Partner, Mannheim; F. Otto and Partner, Warmborn
Engineer: Ove Arup and Partner, London

Timber grid shell covering a 4700 m² surface. Spacially curved surfaces span up to 60.00 m and are composed of square timber elements on a 50 × 50 cm grid. Struts are 5 × 5 cm in two to four layers. Curvature of shell causes squares to become rhombs with angles 70 to 110°. Load is transferred at joints through friction between struts by using bolts and up to three lock-washers to increase pressure. The shape of the shell is such that a uniform vertical load causes only compression. Unsymmetrical snow and wind loads are absorbed through bending stiffness of multilayered grids and tension cables that run diagonally to grid.
Reference: *Baumeister* 8/1975, p. 702; *The Structural Engineer* 3/1975, p. 99; *Holzbau* 6/1975, p. 162

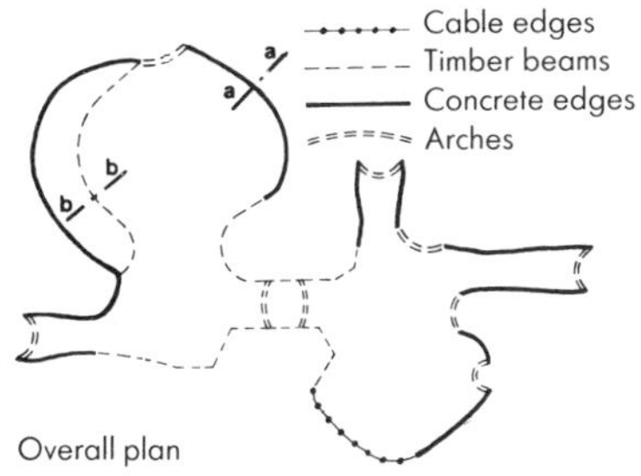

Overall plan

Partial plan of grid

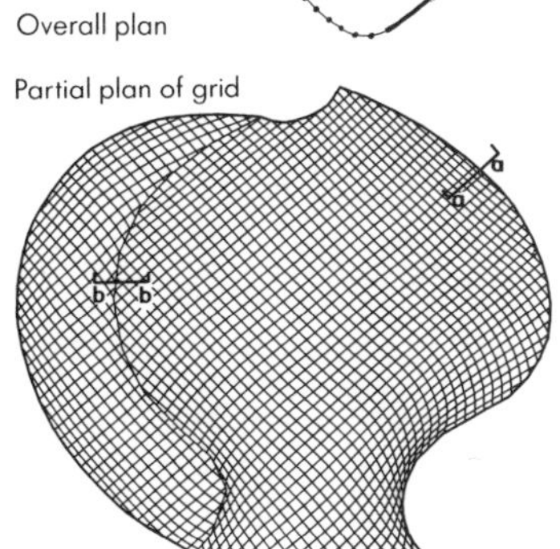

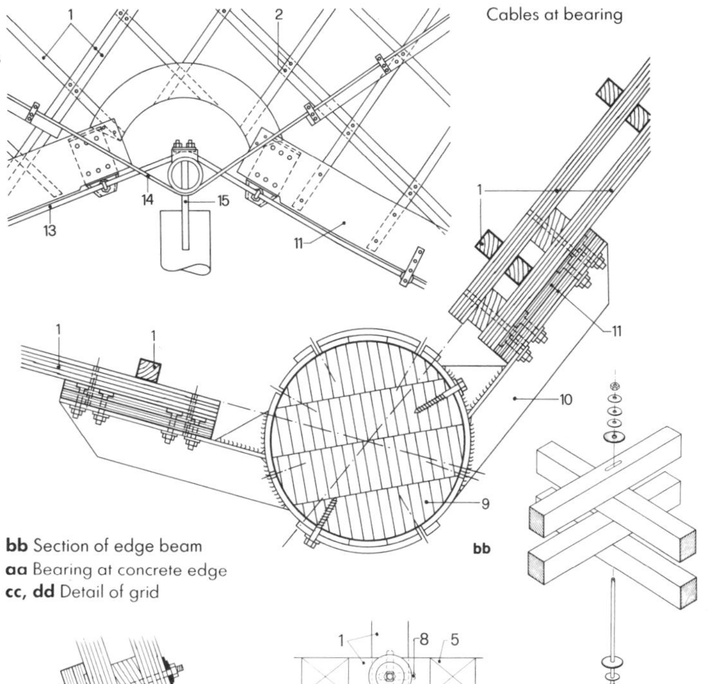

Cables at bearing

bb Section of edge beam
aa Bearing at concrete edge
cc, dd Detail of grid

1 Lumber 5/5 cm, finger-jointed
2 Bolts ϕ 8 mm
3 Base washer ϕ 55 mm
4 Lock washer ϕ 35 mm
5 Spacer
6 Nailing strip
7 Roofing
8 Slotted hole
9 Laminated wood ϕ 50 cm
10 Steel angle with collar screwed onto 9
11 Plywood edge board
12 Steel shape as bearing
13 Main edge cable 2 × ϕ 30 mm
14 Tension cable ϕ 15 mm
15 Web plate embedded in steel pipe column

aa

cc

dd

Joints in Grid Domes

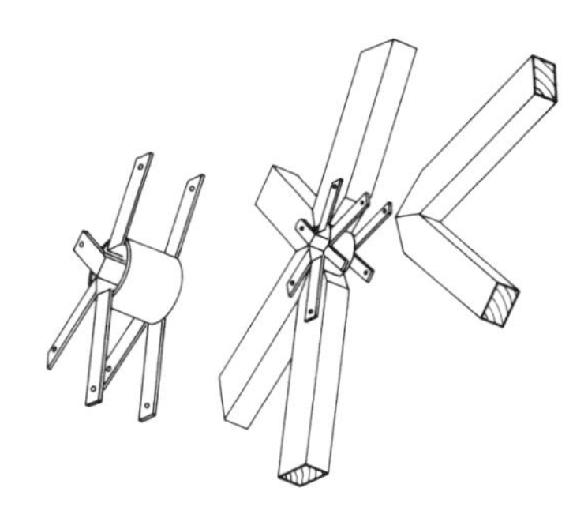

U-formed steel plates in steel ring. For transfer of compression forces nodes are filled in by casting or wedging. Lighter type of joint for smaller spans.

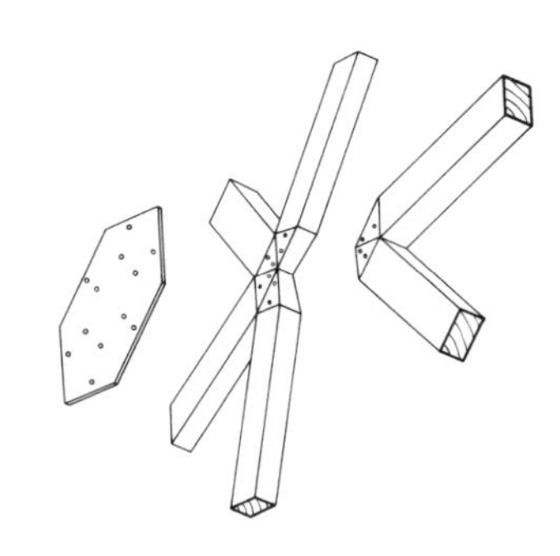

Nailed plywood or steel gusset plate.

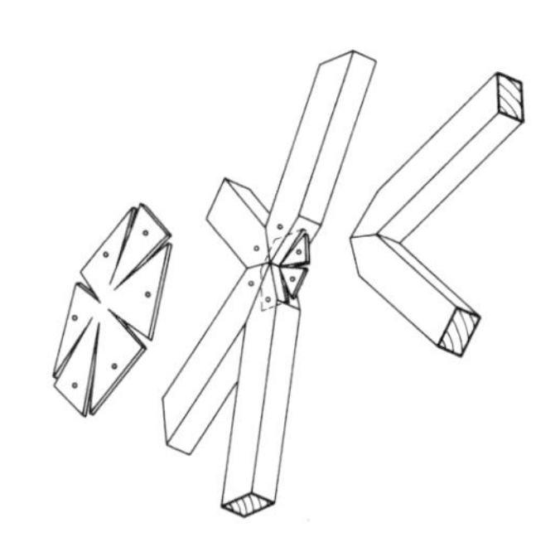

Cut steel plate bolted in slits.

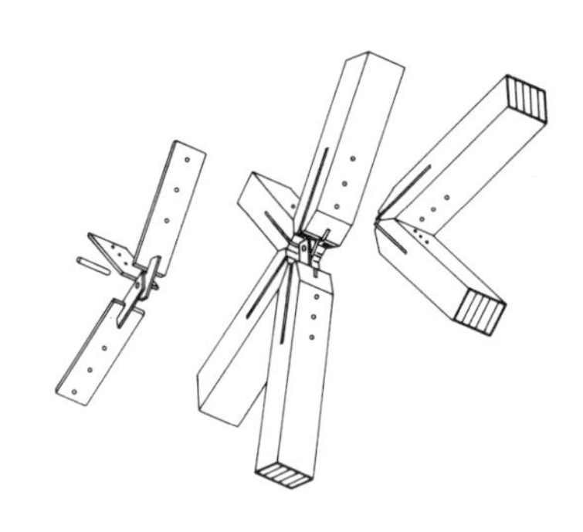

Steel plate gussets doweled into beams and pin jointed.

Conoid shells are forms generated by straight lines joining the points of two curves lying in two parallel surfaces. The generated curves may be parabolas, circles, ellipses, or even straight lines on one side. Conoid shells are especially suitable for roofs of halls with clerestory windows facing north.

The load is absorbed in two directions by axial forces which are taken by diagonally arranged board layers. The axial forces in the shell are resisted by edge members from where they are conveyed to the foundation. Curved edge members may be built as arches with ties or trusses, so that there are no horizontal loads on the bearings.

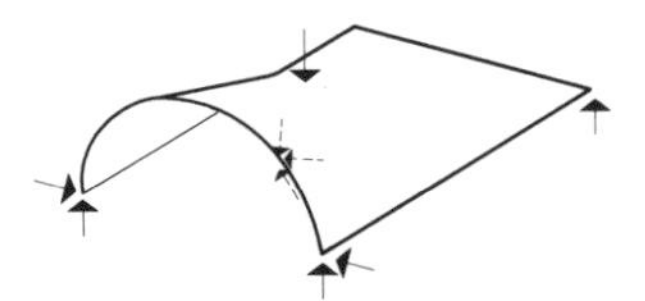

Bearing reactions and interior stresses

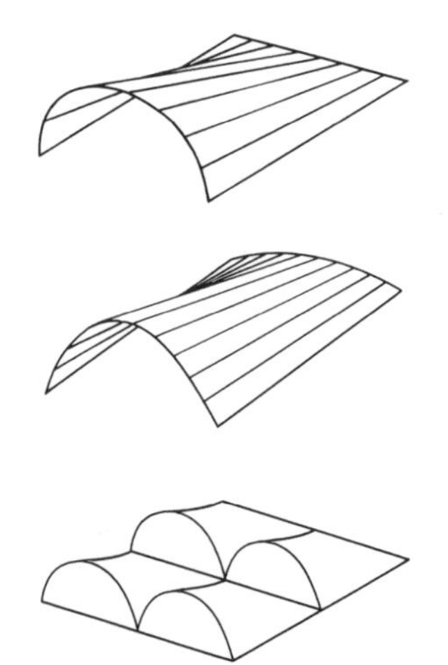

156 Institutional Building in Delft, The Netherlands

Architect: van den Broeck and Bakema, Rotterdam
Engineer: Aronsohn, Rotterdam

Roof of this flat building consists of square beam grid of reinforced concrete having beams spaced at 7.20 m and columns at 21.60 m. 54 open fields are covered with conoidal wood shells, each 6.20 × 6.20 m in plan and 2.50 m high. They consist of two layers of 2 cm thick boards at 45°, with longitudinal and transverse ribs, all nailed and glued together. Between ribs there is acoustical insulation. Planking under insulation has wide joints for better soundproofing.

Thermal insulation and waterproofing are sprayed on outside. Erection time for one shell was two days. Transport by ship was 20 shells at one time.

Reference: *Bouw* 14/1969, p. 550; *Bouwereld* 25/1967, p. 2945

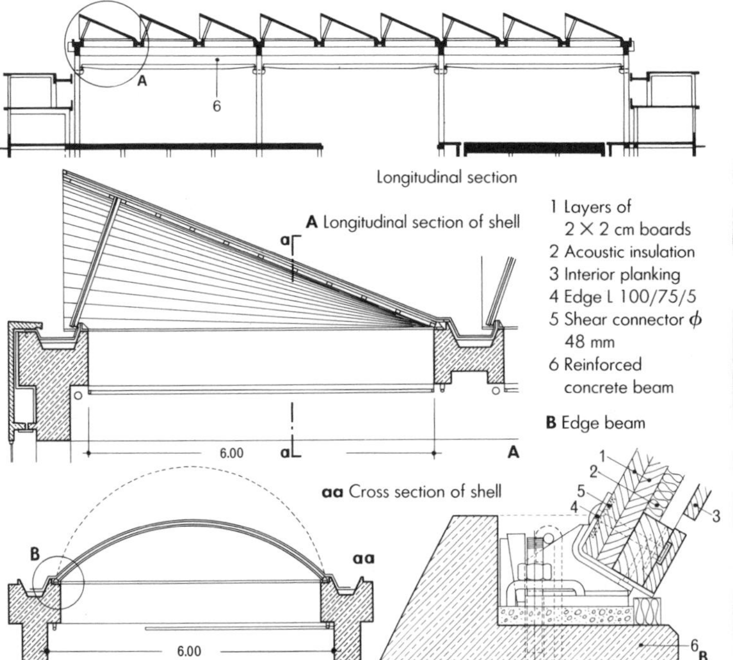

Longitudinal section

A Longitudinal section of shell

aa Cross section of shell

B Edge beam

1 Layers of 2 × 2 cm boards
2 Acoustic insulation
3 Interior planking
4 Edge L 100/75/5
5 Shear connector ϕ 48 mm
6 Reinforced concrete beam

157 Market Hall in Yeovil, Great Britain

Architect: Roydon Cooper, Yeovil
Engineer: L. Booth, Southampton

Two-bay market on trapezoidal plan. Each bay is covered by six wood shells of conoid shape. Width of shells is 5.95 to 6.85 m, spans are 12.80 to 17.75 m. Each shell is made from three layers of boards placed diagonally and nailed together for an overall thickness of 5.7 cm. Clerestory windows are sickle-shaped trusses with single-piece chords, double posts, and round steel bar diagonals.

Shells were assembled by placing structural frames on columns, setting three board layers on a scaffolding, and then nailing them in place.

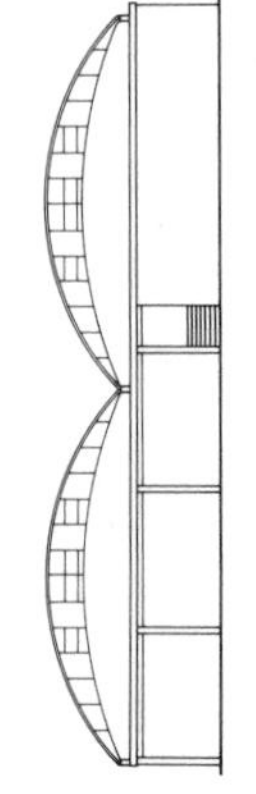

Elevation of gable

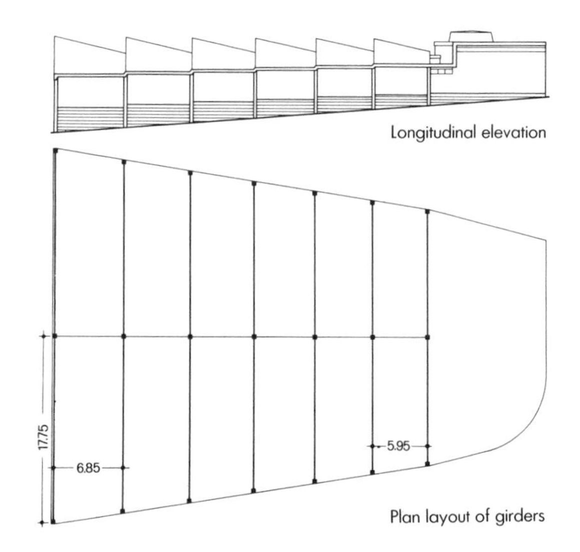

Longitudinal elevation

Plan layout of girders

158 Railroad Station in Manchester, Great Britain

Architect: Railway Architects Department, London
Engineer: Timber Construction Contractor

Railroad station with ticket office, waiting room, service rooms, and a platform on each longitudinal side. Station has a trapezoidal shape in plan and is roofed over by three conoidal shells which rest on laminated wood frames. Cantilevers over platform are circular cylindrical shells. Spans of conoid shells are 17.60 to 29.30 m, width is 10.20 m each, and height is 7.30 to 11.50 m. Shells consist of three layers of tongue and groove boards which are glued and nailed together.
Reference: *The Architect and Building News* Nov. 1959

Plan

Gable elevation

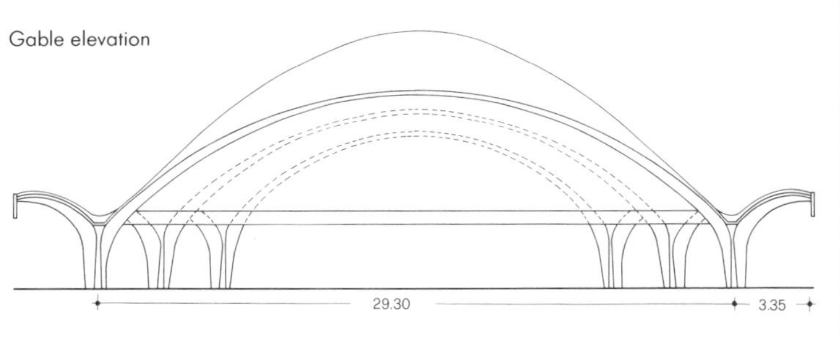

Longitudinal section

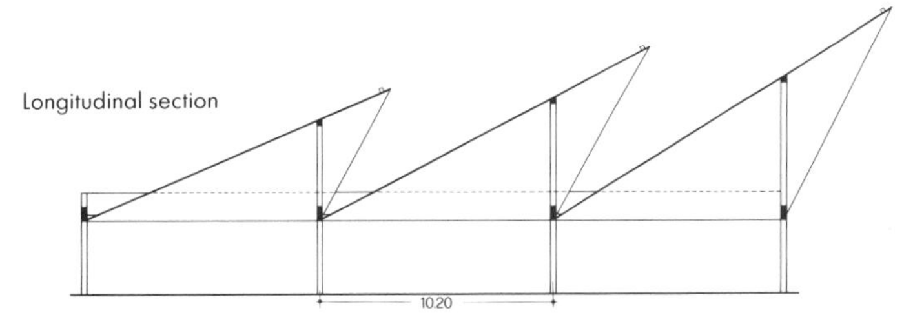

Bearing of Vaulted and Hyperbolic Paraboloid Shells

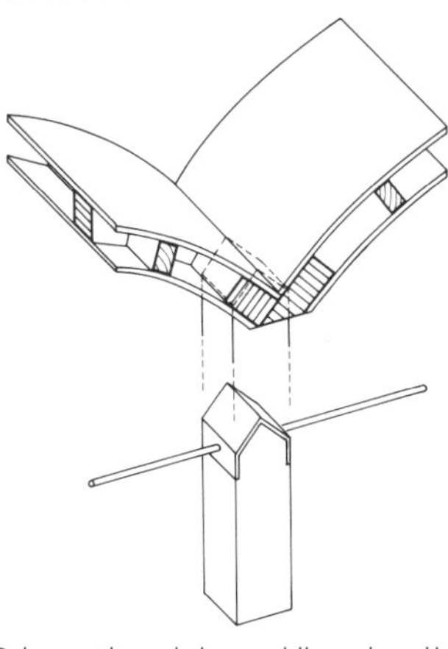

Column with steel plate saddle and steel bar tie. Longitudinal rib of the shell is notched out.

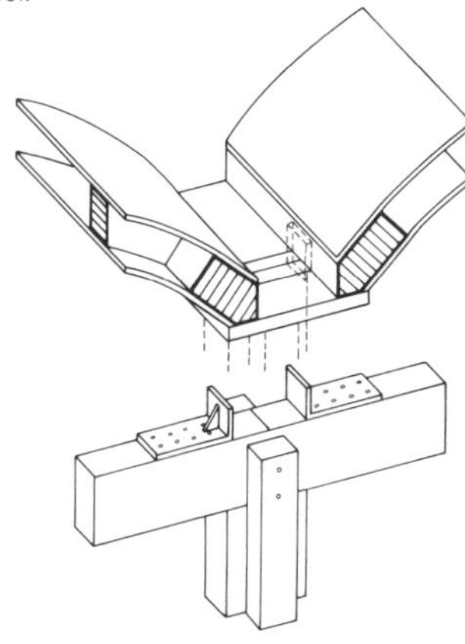

Cross-shaped column with wood tension tie. Steel angles to transfer horizontal forces.

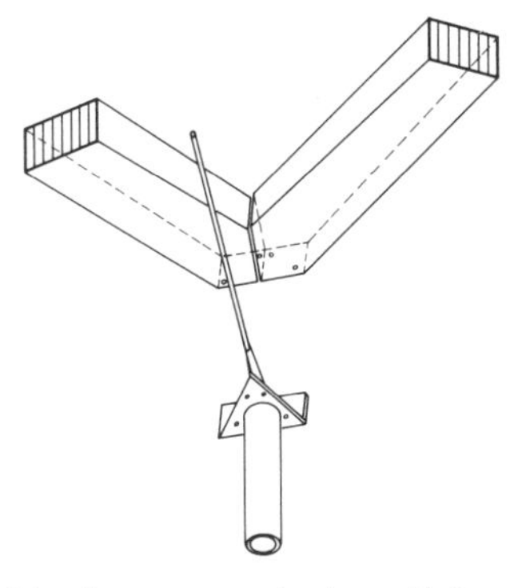

Edge beams on steel column. Horizontal forces are balanced by tie.

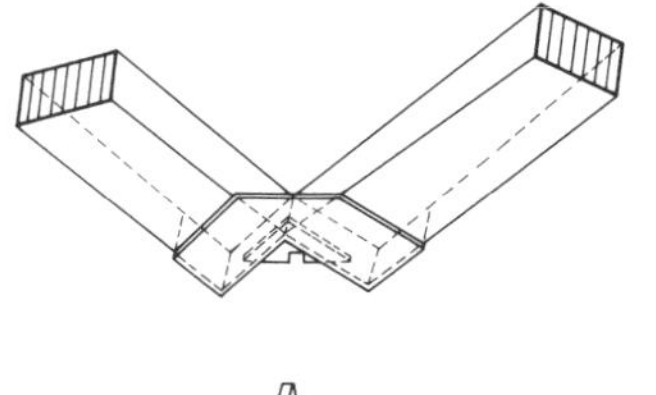

Edge beams on concrete base with a hinge joint.

A hypar (hyperbolic paraboloid) shell has a saddle-form shape generated by a series of straight intersecting lines. It is at the same time a translational surface of two parabolas, one concave, the other convex. The load is carried to edge members by tensile stresses between two high points and compressive stresses between two low points. The edge members convey these loads to bearings, mostly by axial compression. Horizontal components of bearing reactions must be absorbed by ties or by fixed bearings.

The design is governed by axial loads in boards or edge members, and by shear or bending stresses caused by unsymmetrical load near the edges of the shell.

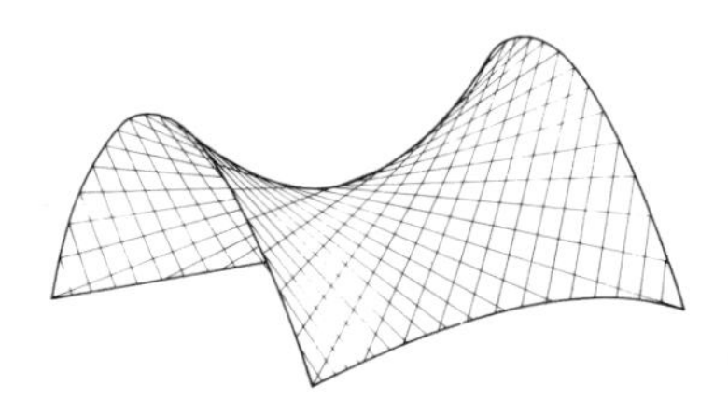

Hyperbolic paraboloid

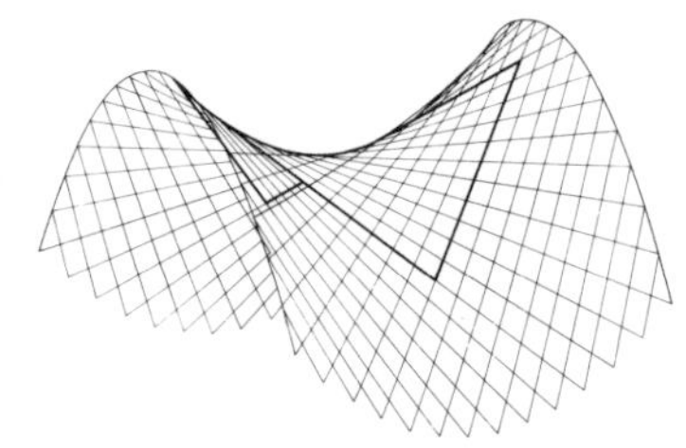

Hypar surface

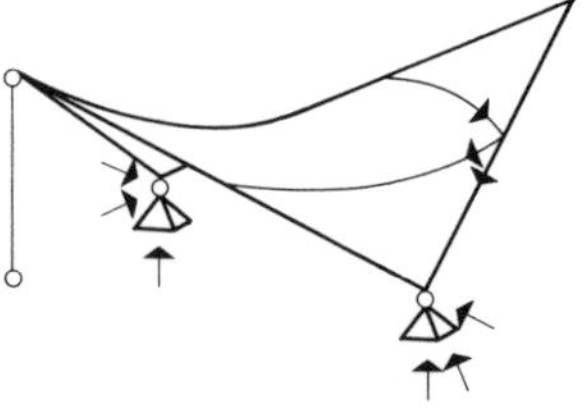

Bearing reactions and interior stresses

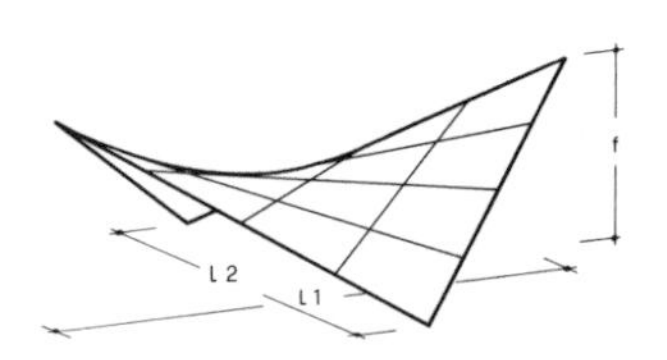

For $l_1 \approx l_2$, edge beam depth $h \approx b = l/60$ to $l/80$
$l = 14$ to 60 m (2 to 3 or 4 to 5 board layers)
Boards ±21 mm, finger-jointed continuously

159 Pavilion in Freiburg, West Germany

Architect: Hochbauamt Freiburg
Engineer: M. Scherberger, Freiburg

Roof of music pavilion in shape of a ribbed hyperbolic paraboloid. Plan projection of shell is a deltoid with 9.80 and 12.30 m sides. Both low points rest on reinforced-concrete foundations. One high point is 7.66 m high, the other is 1.95 m. The lower point is supported by a hinged steel tube column.

Shell is built from straight glued ribs as form generators on which are placed two layers of boards, one in direction of high point to high point, the other from low point to low point. These are the two main stress directions. Boards are glued between double edge beams and are secured by bolts with nuts and washers.

Construction and assembly of entire shell was done in shop. Shell was then transported and erected in one piece.

Reference: *Bauen mit Holz* 8/1969, p. 364

Longitudinal section

Plan layout of ribs

1 Edge beam 2 × 30/25 cm
2 Edge beam 25 + 29/70 cm
3 Ribs 10/25 cm
4 Two layers of 20 mm boards
5 Steel dowel ϕ 16 mm
6 Steel bolt ϕ 16 mm with nut and washer
7 Steel gussets with ϕ 16 mm wood screws
8 Shear connector ϕ 126 mm in edge beam
9 Nails N31/70

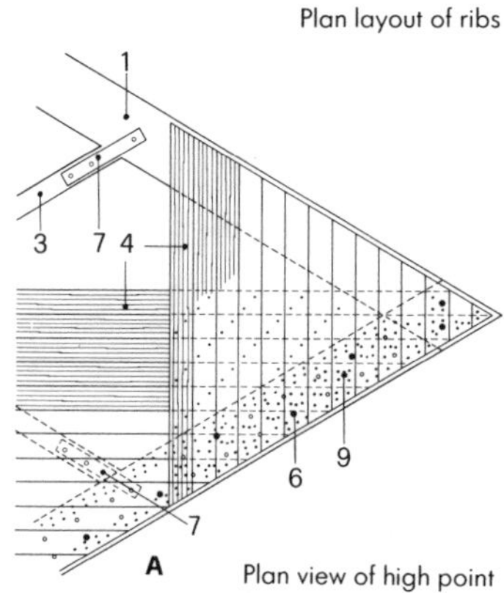

Plan view of high point

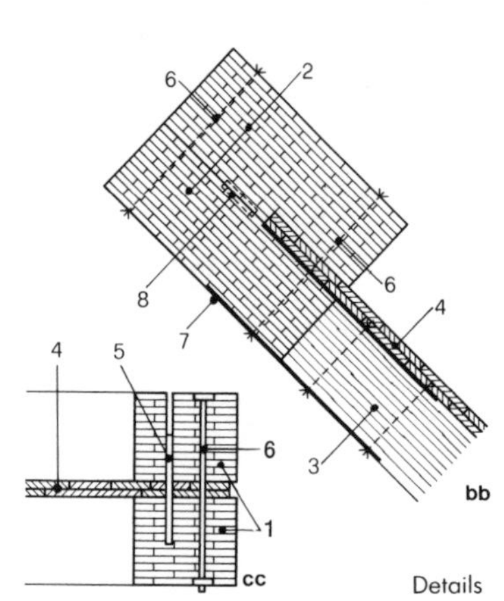

Details

160 Reception Hall in Honolulu, United States

Architect: J. Wimberly, H. Cook, G. Whisenand, Honolulu
Engineer: R. Bradshaw, Honolulu

Reception hall of a hotel. Roof has shape of a saddle cut out of the center of a hyperbolic paraboloid, plan is a rhomb. Edge beams between low points, which are on the ground, and high points are straight laminated wood, double, 15/25 and 10/25 cm. Edge beams are also supported by facade columns; shell is not cantilevered. Roof surface consists of two layers of 25 mm boards. Roofing is bituminous felt. For reasons of appearance, another layer of boards, nonbearing, was placed on felt and secured with spacer anchors.

Reference: Joedicke, *Schalenbau*, Stuttgart, 1962, p. 226

Plan and sections

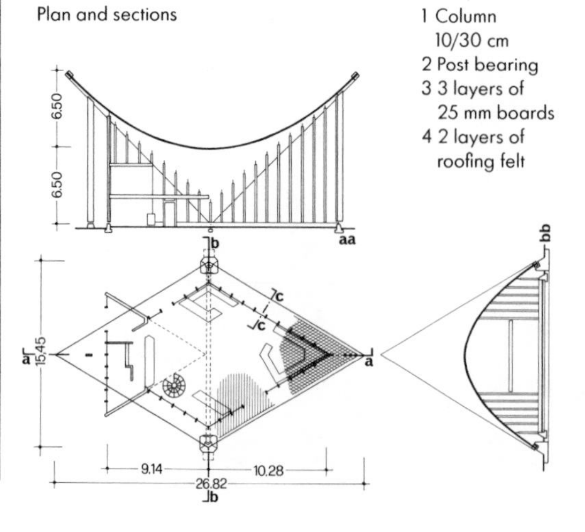

1 Column 10/30 cm
2 Post bearing
3 3 layers of 25 mm boards
4 2 layers of roofing felt
5 Edge beams 15 + 10/25 cm
6 Fascia board
7 Bolts ϕ 10 mm at 15 cm
8 Nails N31/70

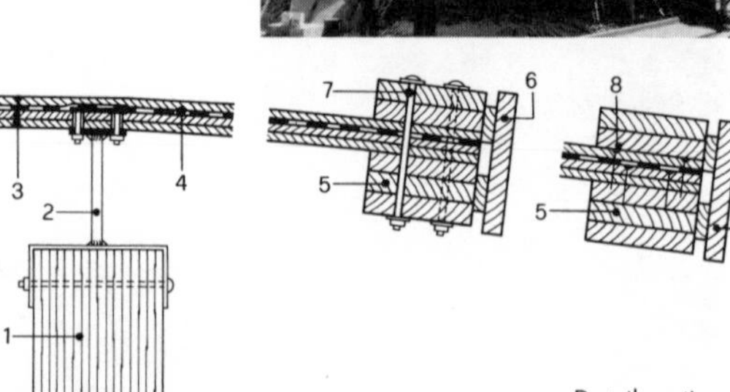

Detail sections

161 Sports Hall in Paris, France

Architect: J. Peccoux, Paris
Engineer: R. Lourdin, Paris

Roof consists of 12 wood shells of hyperbolic paraboloid shape, stepped to provide daylight. They are supported by a girder in the middle and by concrete columns on the outside walls.
Reference: *Technique & Architecture* 294/1973, p. 102

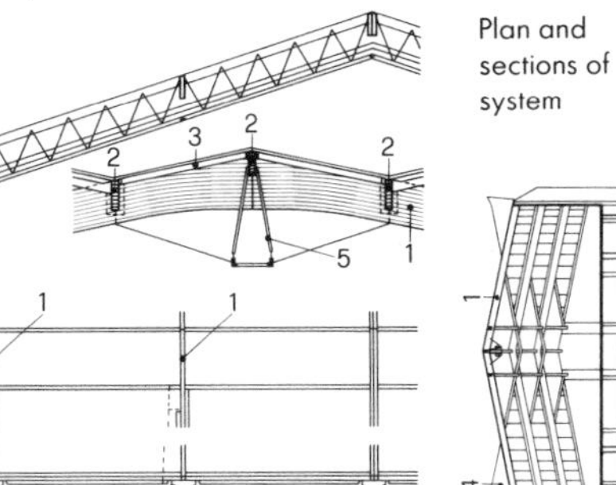

Detail section,
Ridge section
Plan layout

1 Main girder 22/160 cm
2 Secondary beam 21/80 cm
3 Longitudinal bracing
4 Shell element
5 Erection truss

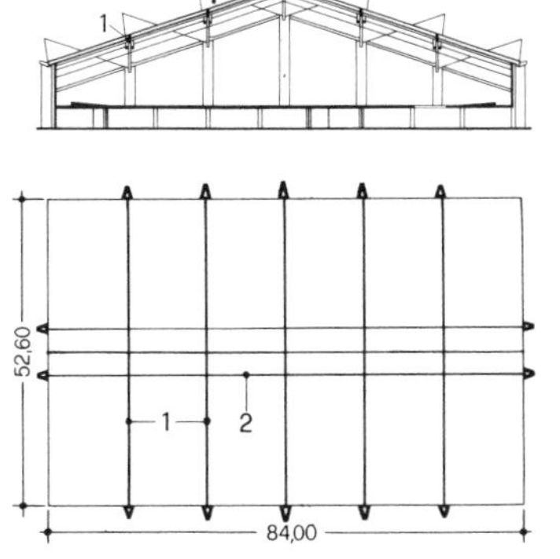

Plan and sections of system

162 School in Ipswich, Great Britain

Architect: Johns, Slater, Haward
Engineer: Timber Construction Contractor

Every classroom is covered with two shells in the shape of a hyperbolic paraboloid, square in plan with 7.60 m sides. Horizontal forces at low points of shell are balanced by tension ties. Edge beams are laminated wood. Shells consist of two layers of 2.5 cm boards parallel to upward and downward parabolas.
Reference: Joedicke, *Schalenbau*, Stuttgart, 1962, p. 245; *The Architect and Building News* Aug. 1959, p. 45

1 2 layers of 25 mm boards
2 Edge beam
3 Steel tension tie ϕ 20 mm
4 Bearing angle

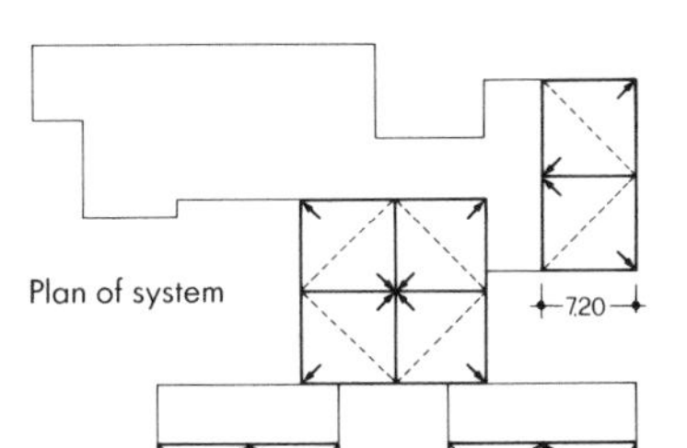

Plan of system

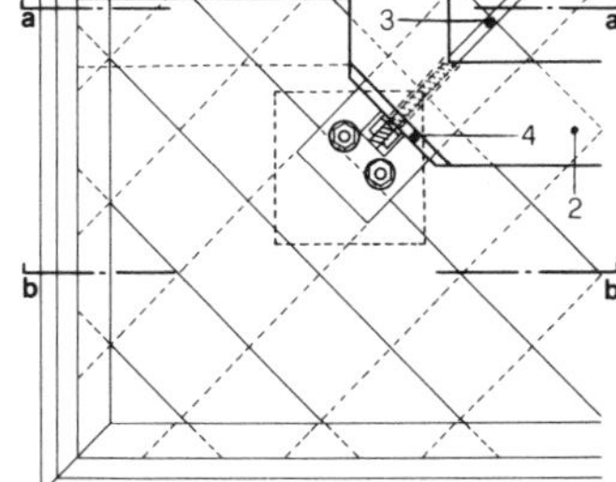

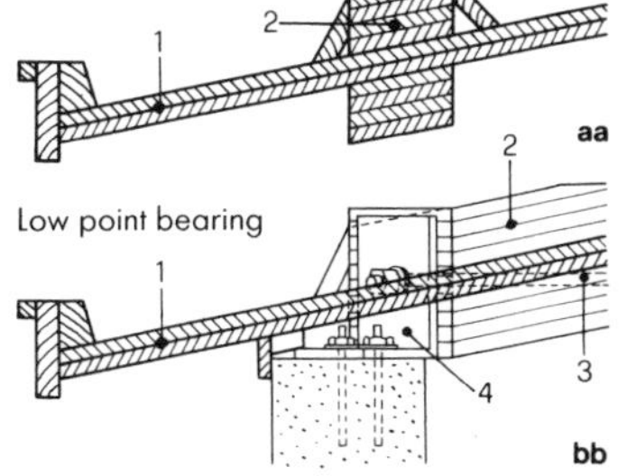

Low point bearing

163 Information Pavilion in Brussels, Belgium

Architect: L.-J. Baucher, J.-P. Blondel, O. Filippone, R. Sarger
Engineer: Oosterhoff, Tjebes, Barends

Hyperbolic paraboloid shell with parabolic edges. Plan is deltoid with sides 18.00 and 14.00 m.

Shell is made of three layers of 2 cm thick wood boards, nailed together to resist shear. In order to reduce deformations and increase its buckling stability, shell was prestressed in such a way that a uniform load generates mostly tensile stresses in the direction joining the two low points, a direction usually subject to compressive forces. Prestressing is induced by weight of foundations suspended from edge beams at two high point columns.
Reference: Joedicke, *Schalenbau*, Stuttgart, 1962, p. 211

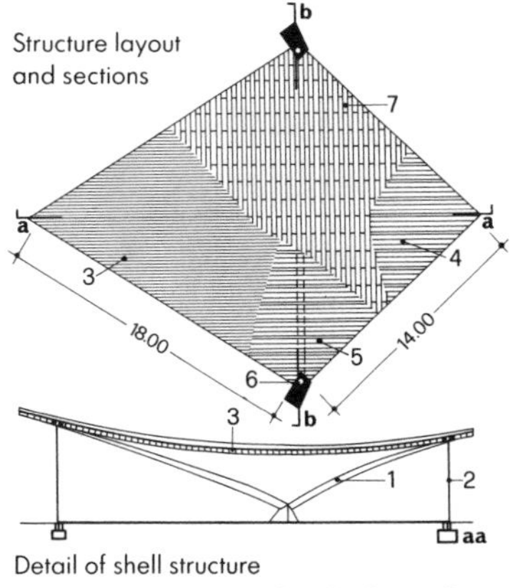

Structure layout and sections

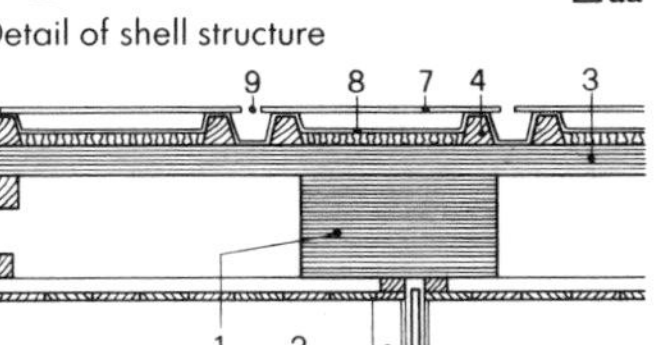

Detail of shell structure

1 Edge beam 20 to 25/45 cm
2 Tension columns
3 Shell, 3 layers 2 cm boards
4 Nailers for drainage
5 Perforations in 4
6 Drain
7 Intermittent decking
8 Roofing
9 Slot

Hypar Shells (Hyperbolic Paraboloids)

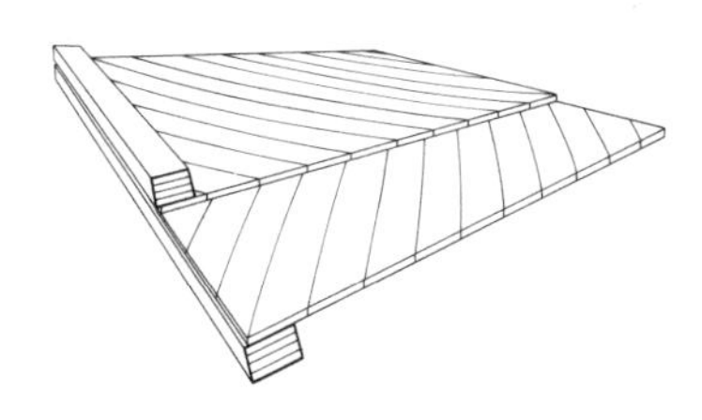

Two diagonally placed layers of boards, glued and press-nailed to double edge beam.

Three diagonally arranged layers of boards.

Edge beam and ribs of round timbers with diagonally placed layers of boards.

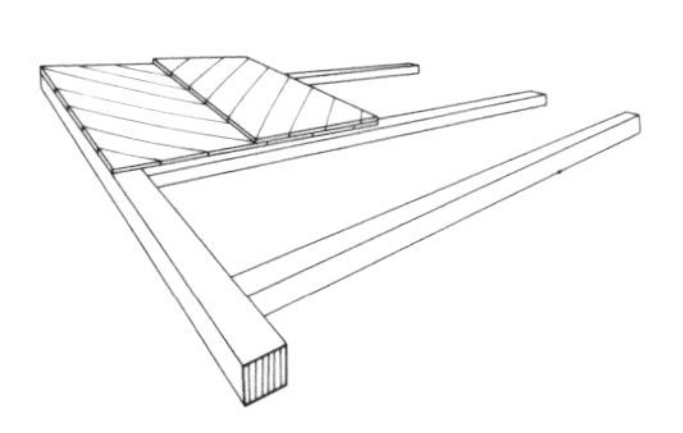

Laminated wood edge beams and ribs glued on curve.

When bending moments govern the design of a shell, the shell is called a ribbed shell and is designed to resist moments. Such a shell consists of two or three groups of ribs, and one or more layers of boards nailed to the ribs. The load is resisted not only through tension, compression, and shear within the board layers, but also through bending of ribs. It is thus possible to depart from the concept of pure membranes and provide free forms besides the domes, rotational forms, or saddle shapes.

The design of ribbed shells is governed by the span, the shape, and exterior loads (especially unsymmetrical loads and wind loads). The stability of ribbed shells in great spans can be enhanced by additional bracing.

The advantage of ribbed shells is that the ribs can be used as scaffolding for the installation of the shell.

164 Ribbed Shell in Munich, West Germany

Architect: G. Minke, Kassel
Engineer: J. Natterer, Munich

Ribbed shell as an exhibition pavilion at the Munich Fair. Shell consists of four joined saddle surfaces which are generated as tension membranes between spacially curved edge beams. Beams are laminated boards glued on a curve. Span length is 9.00 m and cantilevers are 4.50 and 9.00 m.

The free form and cantilevering of the shell required a structure that resists bending. It was constructed with a two-layered grid of ribs 3/6 cm and two layers of boards nailed to resist shear. Grid is doubled in transverse direction; Boards run from high point to high point and low point to low point.

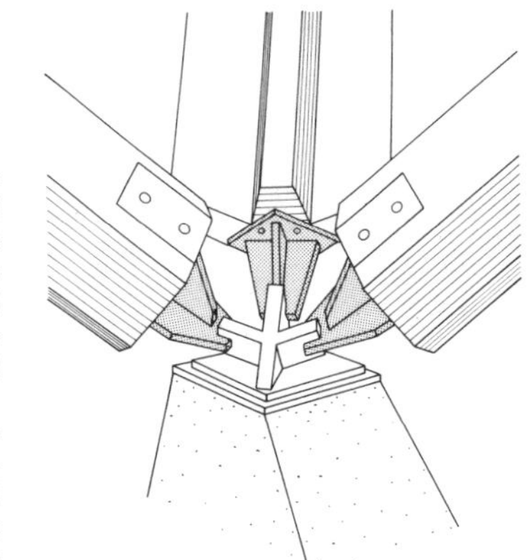

Connections at base bearing

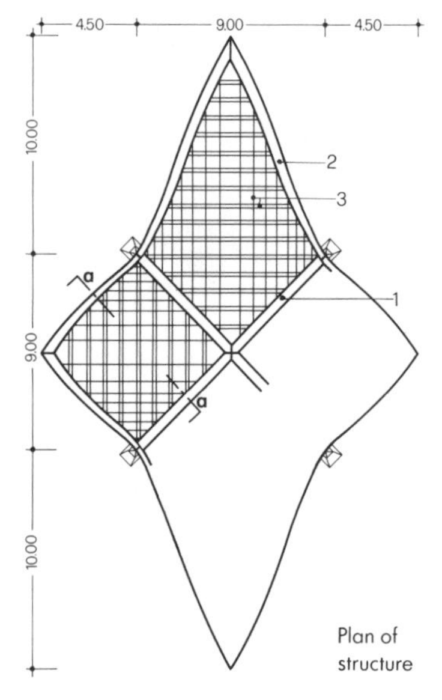

Plan of structure

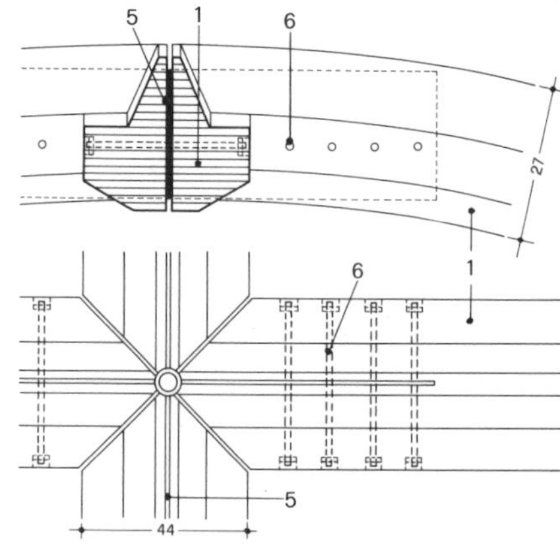

Crown point, section and plan view

1 Ridge beam 44/31 cm
2 Edge beam 22/35 cm
3 Ribs 3/6 cm
4 2 layers of 20 mm boards
5 Steel web 9 mm, welded to tube
6 Bolts ϕ 16 mm

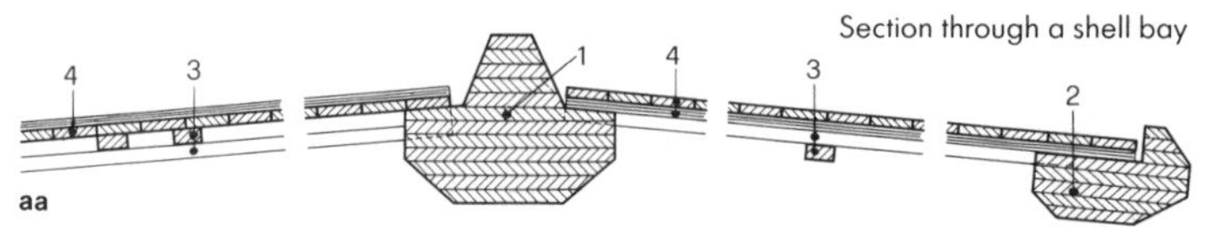

Section through a shell bay

165 Ribbed Shell in Rosenheim, West Germany

Architect: Oesswein, Rosenheim
Engineer: J. Natterer and K. März, Munich

Ribbed shell composed of three 18.00 m cantilevered hyperbolic paraboloids. Edge

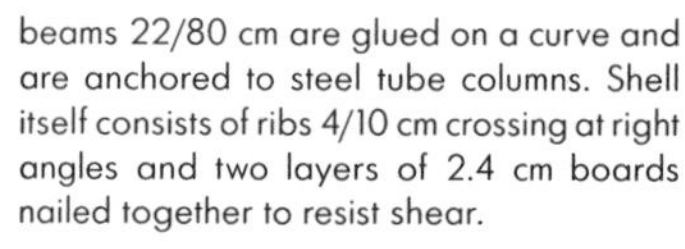
beams 22/80 cm are glued on a curve and are anchored to steel tube columns. Shell itself consists of ribs 4/10 cm crossing at right angles and two layers of 2.4 cm boards nailed together to resist shear.

1 Edge beam 22/80 cm
2 Radial beam 2 × 22/55 cm
3 Ribs 10/4 cm
4 2 layers of 24 mm boards
5 Edge layer of boards 40 mm

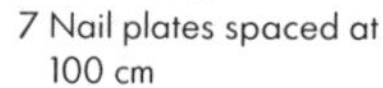
6 2 tension ties, ϕ 26 mm steel
7 Nail plates spaced at 100 cm

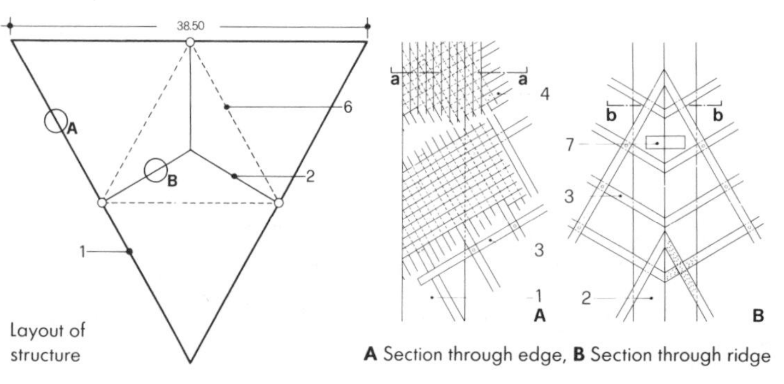

Layout of structure

A Section through edge, **B** Section through ridge

aa, bb Detail sections

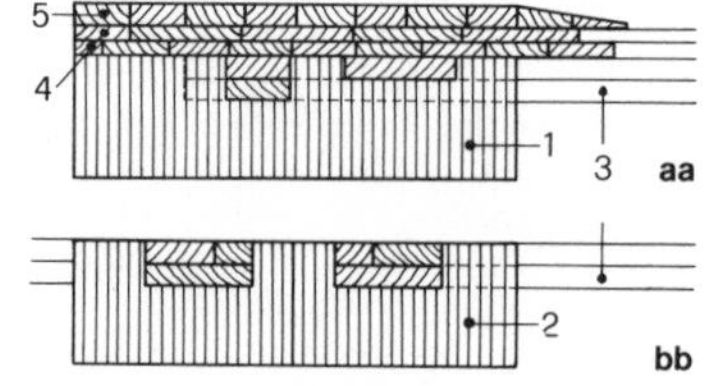

166 Suspended Shell in Dortmund, West Germany

Architect: Behnisch and Partner, Stuttgart
Engineer: G. Scholz, Munich
Consultant: J. Natterer, Munich

Pavilion for 1969 Garden Show in Dortmund. Suspension shell in form of a diamond. Between high and low points are double laminated wood edge beams, 18 cm high and 1.40 m wide each, curved and twisted on two axes. High points are supported by cross-shaped columns and one or two tension cables.

Concavely bent ribs 20 × 20 cm at 1.50 m, longest span 65.00 m, serve as main load-carrying elements between high points and edge beams. Edge beams lead tensile forces from suspended ribs to foundations and also serve to maintain shape of shell. Nailed on ribs are three layers of convexly curved layers of boards, placed at 45° and nailed to resist shear. To increase buckling stability, suspension shell is prestressed by tensioning the cables.
Reference: *Detail* 4/1969, illustrations

Plan and sections

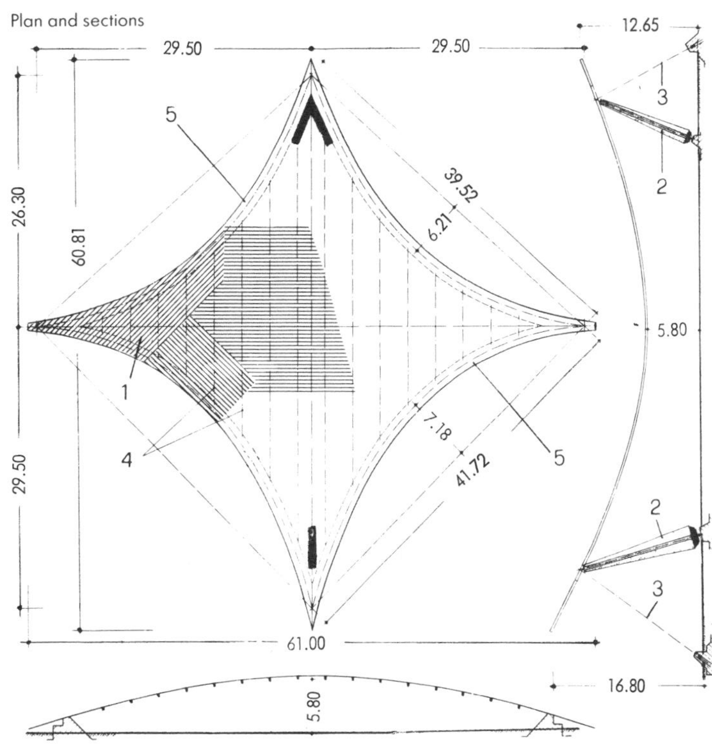

Detail of shell structure

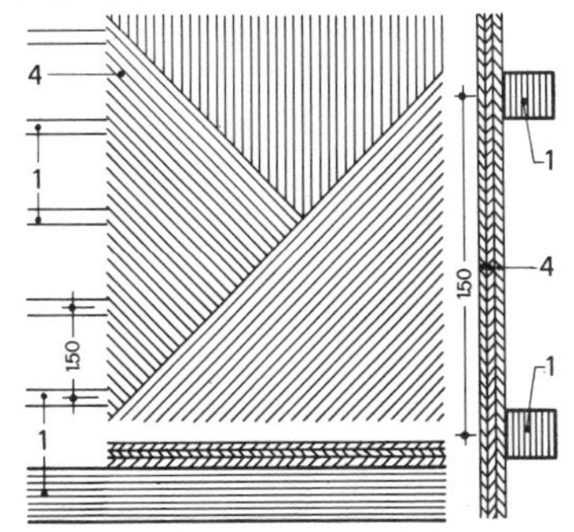

1 Suspension ribs 20/24 cm
2 Compression columns, cross-shaped with webs tapered in opposite direction 28/50 to 250 cm and 28/50 to 160 cm
3 Tension cable of 91 or 217 parallel single ϕ 7 mm bundled wires
4 Board layers 24 mm and 2 × 16 mm, crossed
5 Doubly curved and twisted edge beam 36/140 cm

Tensile Connections

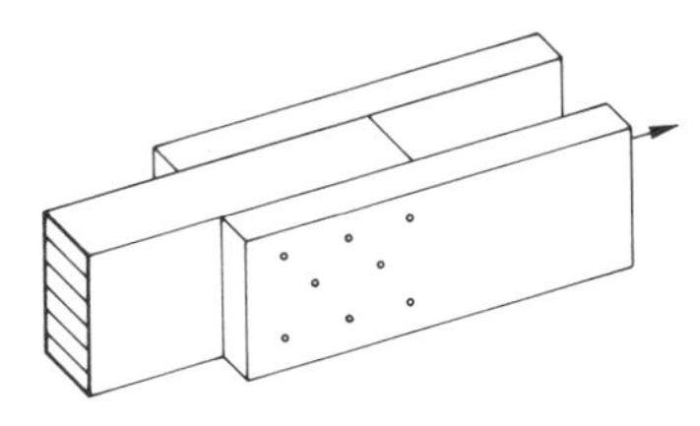

Two-sided lap connection with dowels or nails.

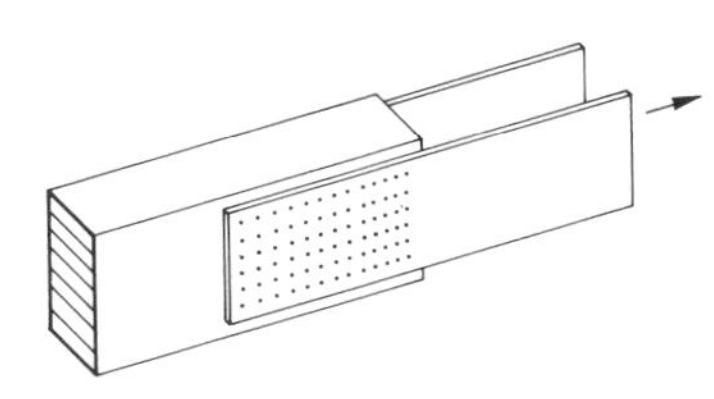

Steel gusset plates nailed sidewise.

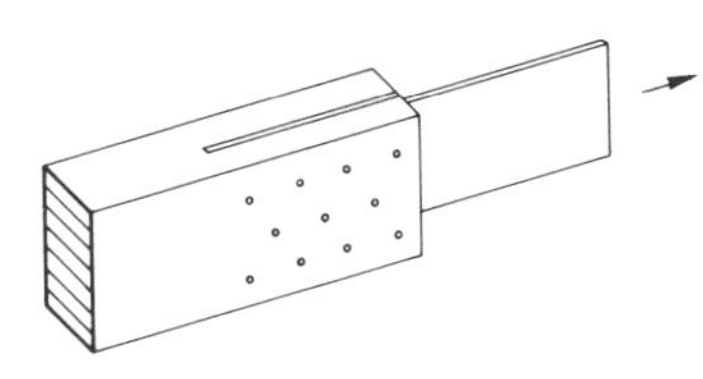

Steel plate doweled in beam slit.

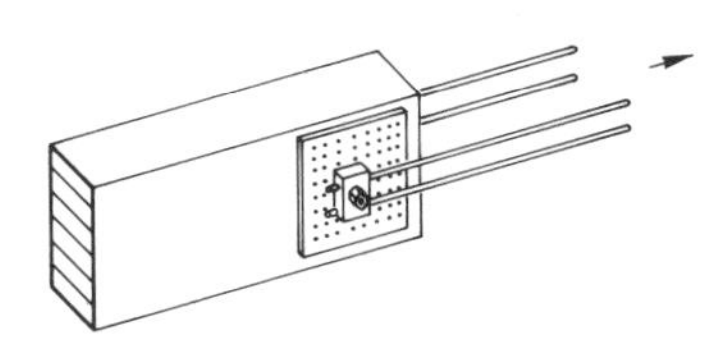

Beam with steel tie connection over nailing plates and linkage bolts.

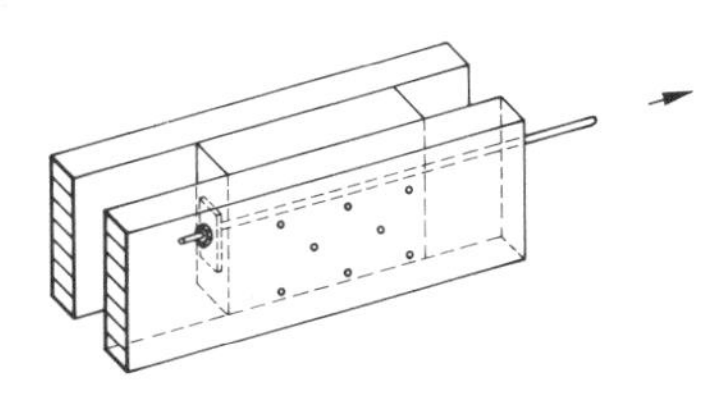

Twin beam and tension tie connected over doweled filler wood with bearing washer.

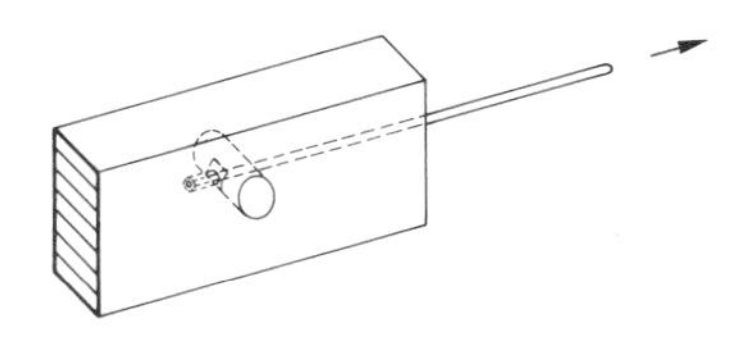

Tensile connection through tension bar threaded and screwed into round cross bar dowel.

Details of Structural Systems (Right-Hand Columns)

Building Functions (Illustration Numbers)

The photos on pages 84 to 171 were made available for publication in *Timber Design and Construction Sourcebook* by the architects and engineers, and by the timber construction contractors listed in the book. Some were obtained from *Detail*, a magazine for architecture, structural details, and finishes.

Timber Frame Construction

KARL-HEINZ GÖTZ

In collaboration with:
Gunter Henn
Johannes Goehl
Herman Rotermund

FUNDAMENTALS

Introduction

The development of timber frame construction progressed steadily over the course of many centuries, until it reached present levels. Today this includes the industrial fabrication of entire systems. No other type of construction underwent such an unbroken transition from handicraft to the newest techniques; in the following chapters this will be discussed at length. In this context, a classic timber frame house can be considered the precursor of a prefabricated building.

During the golden age of classic timber frame construction buildings were created with many technical peculiarities and unusual details, especially in Europe, but also in America and Japan. Beginning in

the eighteenth century, however, timber construction gradually fell victim to more massive masonry construction. This was due, among other things, to the growth of a middle class which formed new concepts of the value of buildings and preferred the "more solid" and "more durable" masonry construction. Thus, we read in a handbook on building construction written in 1885: "If stone, especially dressed stone, is suitable for monumental buildings, timber, on the contrary, is a no less worthy material for secondary and more transient buildings." In certain areas, this loss of value went so far that countless old timber buildings, often architecturally remarkable and unique, were made to look like masonry by being covered with stucco. This was not done for reasons of fire protection; but it led to the belief that such transformed buildings were actually more fireproof.

Building with timber persisted only where timber structures could be built economically and without much architectural pretense. This was especially true for industrial buildings, which started to spring up in the nineteenth century. Of these, some had remarkable characteristics and represented new building forms, which became influential in business and industry. Many appear to us today as very striking and worthy of preservation. Other examples of economically significant timber structures were built in certain rural areas on the then eastern fringes of Germany.

A more positive approach toward timber as a building material evolved slowly in the last few decades, particularly with regard to frame construction. In their quest, architects, engineers, and owners found in timber an opportunity to continue an old tradition and to develop new alternatives. Today economic motivations are less significant than they were for the previously described industrial and agricultural buildings. Instead, a new appreciation of the quality and the value of wood is gaining greater importance.

Architects became more aware of an essentially uninterrupted development of timber construction overseas, a development that contained outstanding architectural examples and many variants. This is true even today. A look at the United States and Japan shows many new trend-setting creations in the field of timber houses, not only from an architectural

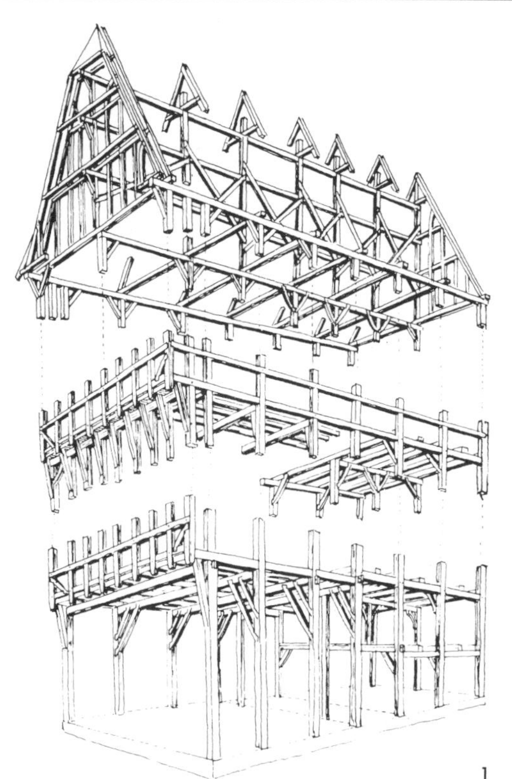

1

2

3

4

5

6

7

Fig. 1. Frame house in Alsfeld, Germany, second half of 14th century. Example of the golden age of European frame buildings.
Fig. 2. Frame structure finishes. Panels are treated creatively.
Fig. 3. Framing in the industrial area of the Siegerland, 19th century. Reduction of structure to its bare essentials.
Fig. 4. Imitation of traditional frame houses. Old construction and finishing methods are used together with new steel connections.
Fig. 5. Integrating the appearance of a classic frame building with new frame construction.
Fig. 6. Twin-beam construction coupled with new techniques (model).
Fig. 7. Modern timber construction in Japan follows the tradition of Japanese timber houses. Residence of architect Kenzo Tange, Tokyo.
Fig. 8. Residences in the United States; rib construction.
Figs. 9–11. Residences in Sea Ranch, California.
Fig. 12. Row houses in California; rib construction.

point of view, but also from the point of view of construction methodology. The renaissance of timber frame construction has not yet reached full course in Europe, but a trend in that direction is ever more noticeable.

The attitude of architects and skilled labor is important in creating, among developers, a favorable climate for the use of wood. However, many professionals feel much less secure in handling this type of construction than other types. This insecurity produced numerous unsightly and even incorrect results. Consequently in today's construction industry there are many instances in which modern trends are disregarded and old tested methods are followed; frame buildings represent the exception. A certain stimulus in such a direction is given by the current restoration work on cultural and landmark buildings. The pursuit of traditional frame architecture has been especially enhanced by the uncovering of timber in the facades of old landmark buildings, an event that aroused keen interest even in lay persons.

Timber frame buildings are not yet being developed to their full potential, in spite of their newly gained appreciation and new discoveries of old landmarks. Significant advancements have been achieved, however, particularly in the field of panel construction. A strong notion that a timber building is perhaps not as solid as a masonry structure still stands in the way. This attitude led to the introduction of stone or asbestos-cement siding intended to mask the appearance of timber.

In the meantime, many designers and contractors and their collaborators are becoming more and more familiar with the fundamentals of design and development of new timber construction techniques. They are pioneering new applications, sometimes in competition with other types of construction available today. Moreover, the knowledge of the effectiveness of timber preservatives speaks against the prejudice that timber is not durable. The confidence is growing that properly constructed timber buildings are equal in stability and durability to other types of construction and that they often result in considerable advantages.

8

9

10

11

12

Some of the advantages of timber follow:
1. Timber framed buildings are very adaptable to special situations.
2. Such buildings can be suited to many different uses and are generally not difficult to enlarge or to remodel.
3. From the architectural point of view, timber frame construction can often express its own peculiar structure and retain the natural appearance of wood.
4. From the structural point of view, good results can be achieved by careful design and optimum use of material in a way to realize the special potentials of timber construction.
5. Special advantages can be achieved by prefabricating widely used elements and components. A high degree of prefabrication makes precision assembly possible. Prefabrication is in itself a system that responds to the requirements and the potential of wood in an optimal and practical way. Experiences with other types of frame construction, such as steel and reinforced concrete, may sometimes seem to be applicable or useful, but are never to be adapted without extensive examination. Remember: wood is a material of its own.
6. Finally, there are advantages of simple transportation and easy installation, both due to the light weight of wood.

Depending on the circumstances, it is possible to build timber frame structures on the technological level of old carpentry techniques, but the architect has to plan accordingly. On an intermediate technological level there may be a combination of manual workmanship and industrial fabrication. In fully industrialized production, entire systems can be produced on assembly lines, provided appropriate erection techniques are applied. Essential to all these techniques, however, is the acknowledgment of the fact that wood is a special material; construction has to adapt to it. Properly constructed, buildings should have a long life without developing any problems. Designers and technicians who do not feel sufficiently secure in this field will do well to acquaint themselves as much as possible with wood and its techniques in order to prevent mistakes.

The most suitable finishes for a completed timber structure must be selected well in advance, during the planning of the building. Consideration must be given not only to the most desirable, but also to the most practical finishes. Very simple buildings from the structural and construction points of view are rarely feasible in moderate climates; they are more suitable to Mediterranean or subtropical regions. Methods that can be employed in one region are often not applicable in other regions. Technology and construction practice must relate to the climate. These considerations cannot be neglected, even in structures that will be erected with a certain amount of self-help.

Both single- and multistory buildings are feasible in timber "skeleton" framing construction. Such buildings are typically built with massive timbers whose cross sections and jointing must be designed according to the principles of statics. The normal length of timber members varies between 2.00 and 6.00 m.

Newly developed steel connections have improved the efficiency of traditional types of timber joints. Steel connections have advantages over other connections mainly because they do not require a reduction of timber cross sections. Thus the size of the members can be reduced correspondingly, or their span and load increased (see pages 46 to 54). In glue-laminated wood construction the "working" of members is reduced and loads can be increased.

Skeleton timber framing has developed more and more into a dominant category; other categories are receding. Among the latter are grid or rib construction, post-and-beam-type structures, and even the traditional timber frame structures. There is a certain similarity between skeleton and steel or reinforced-concrete framing. In the latter, there is a functional division between the carrying frame and other finishes; these systems are called "open."

In contrast to this concept of open framing stand "closed" structures, such as masonry buildings or prefabricated reinforced-concrete panel structures, in which the walls also have load-bearing functions. In the realm of timber buildings, the log type and the wood-panel construction are closed systems.

Each level of technology or workmanship in the skeleton type of timber construction may fully satisfy the purpose of a main frame and its finishes. Because of their general structural principle, skeletons are flexible in application and form; since the advent of new connection techniques, their scope has widened considerably. Architects, in particular, prefer them. The choice is made right from the instant of conception, sometimes due to professional preferences and at other times because of a desire to create works of significance. Even in this field, inventiveness and imagination lead to architectural creativity; engineering and knowledge of technology are not necessarily decisive, they serve to complement architectural creativity.

Unfortunately, many anonymous timber structures clutter the world with their inferior design and routine appearance. They are overshadowed, however, by excellent architectural examples, which lead the way thanks to their builders' imaginative creativity.

Framing Types

There are several basically different ways of constructing a timber frame building. They all differ in the arrangement of the load-carrying members and their connections. The structural system is determined by the way the horizontal, vertical, or diagonal members are brought together to a point, or node.

There are eight basic types of framing, differentiated by the arrangement of horizontal and vertical members. Either beams or columns are continuous, or all of them are; either beams or columns may be twin. The various framing types are as follows:

Traditional Framing	Single Columns and Girders			Multiple Columns and Girders		Rib Construction	
	Continuous Girders		Continuous Columns	Continuous Columns and Girders			
Traditional framing	Girder on column, single story	Girder on column, two stories	Tie beam	Split girder	Split column	Balloon	Platform

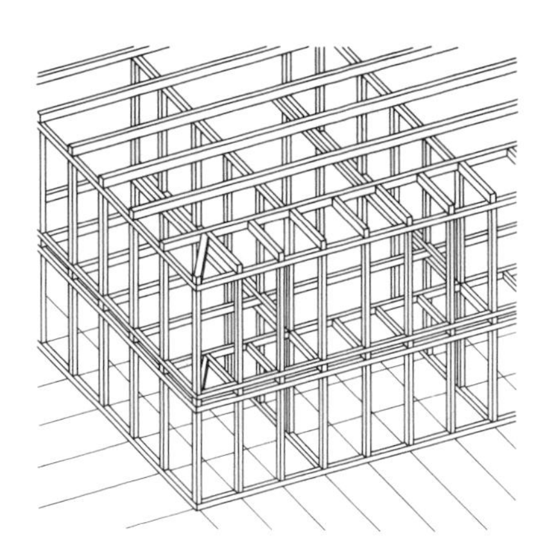

Traditional Building Frames (14th to 18th Centuries)

In this type of building, the frame consists of columns (pillars, posts, studs) and main beams (girders, headers, sleepers, or sills). Non-load-carrying partitions are anchored into a header. Columns are tenoned into mortises in sleepers or sills, but they may also be attached by lap connections. The entire building rests on a foundation sill; in multistory buildings the sill is repeated on every floor as a floor sill. The distance between columns is kept as short as necessary to carry the load and as required by appearance or construction detailing. A classic frame building is stiffened by diagonal struts notched into beams, or by top and bottom knee braces lap-jointed at both ends.

Loads in timber frames are generally transferred from timber to timber. The weakening of members caused by mortises or notches is compensated for by correspondingly larger cross sections. In order to avoid an accumulation of such weaknesses at one point, connections of load-carrying members are often placed eccentrically.

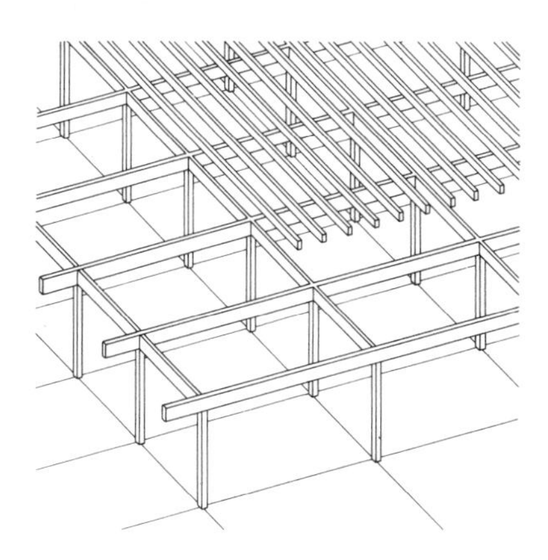

Post and Beam Construction, Single Story

Structures of this type consist of posts on which rest girders. All girders are parallel; secondary girders, beams, or planks are placed normal to them. Note that at bearings the post is loaded parallel to grain, but the beam is loaded normal to grain. Allowable stresses are determined accordingly, and required cross sections are derived from them. Since the allowable stress for grade II lumber is 2.0 N/mm^2 normal to grain and 8.5 N/mm^2 parallel to grain, the maximum column load is generally governed by the transverse compression on the girder.

If the bearing surface is not sufficient to transfer the load, bearing areas must be increased by means of steel plates or angles.

A special advantage of such a single-story structure is the potential for longer spans by an appropriate selection of girders (trusses, for example). Bearings, however, have to be designed accordingly.

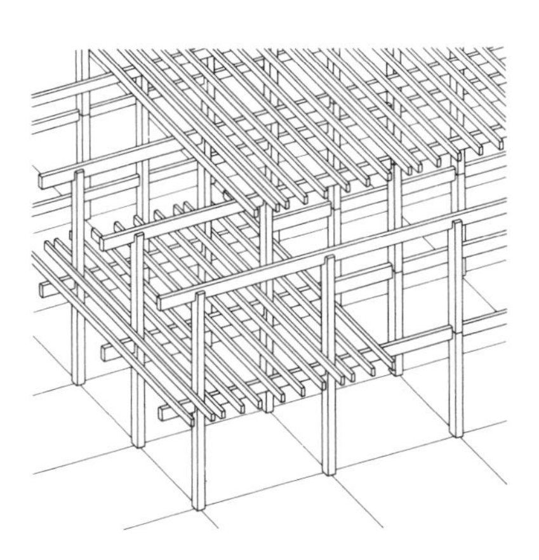

Post and Beam Construction, Two Stories

In this type of framing continuous girders rest on columns; columns are therefore interrupted by girders, but are set up again on the next floor. Connections between girders and columns can be made in various ways. Normally the load from the upper column is not transferred to the lower one through the girder, because transverse compression in the girder would be exceeded. It is necessary to use steel or timber gussets for this purpose. Floor beams or planks span between girders.

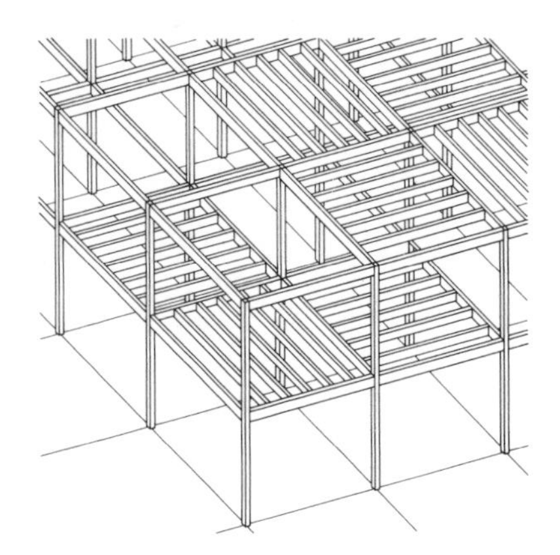

Tie-Beam Construction

The main girders are set as tie beams into continuous columns with identical details in all four directions. All interior and exterior connections occur on the same level. The beams in the adjacent floor panels span in alternate directions. In this way, the tie beams are loaded equally, but cantilevers are not feasible. The relatively high cost of connections may be offset by prefabrication only if there is a large number of them. In comparison with other types of framing, this system has the advantage of a uniform ceiling height. Tie-beam framing is therefore economical for industrial buildings having a large number of units.

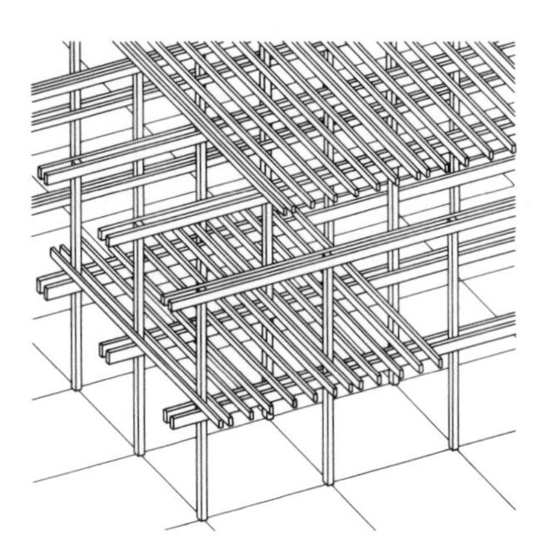

Twin-Girder Framing

Continuous twin girders span between continuous columns and are attached to their sides. Floor beams or planks, depending on the span, are supported by the twin girders. The advantage of this system is that both columns and girders are continuous.

A hallmark of this type of framing are the protruding ends of twin girders, necessary because of the required end length at dowel connections between girder and column. It is very necessary to secure these ends by preservatives, or by sealing them with sealers or metal covers.

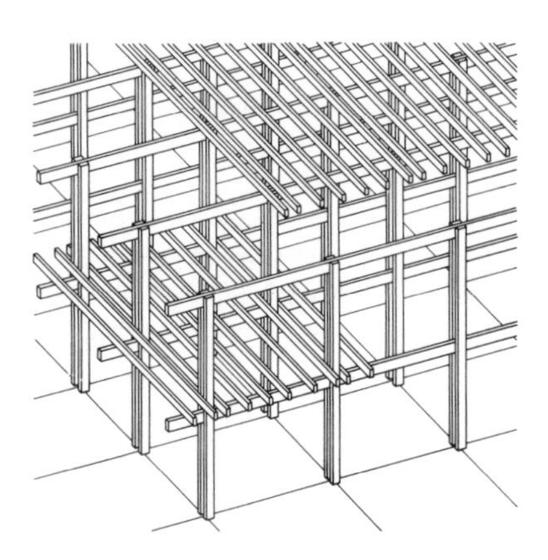

Split-Column Framing

Continuous girders are placed between split columns. Twin columns represent a reversal of twin-girder framing. Quadruple columns allow a two-way layout of girders. The application of the latter arrangement is limited because securing the building against fire requires either oversize columns to prevent their buckling or the insertion of fillers within the split columns. For this reason split columns are especially suitable for long spans; they have to be large to provide sufficient load capacity.

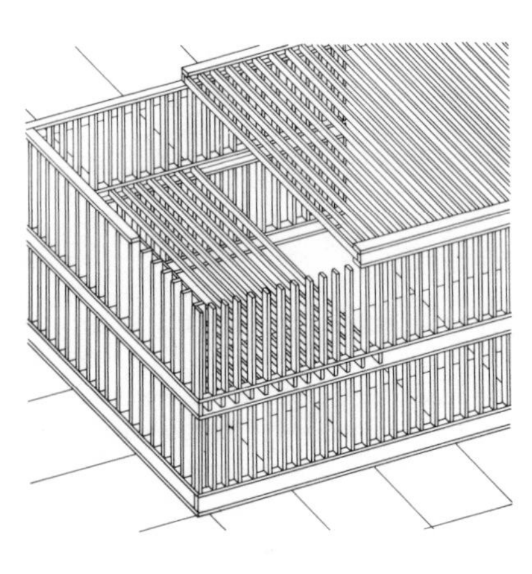

Rib Framing

This type of construction is mainly used in the United States under the names of balloon framing and platform framing.

The load-carrying members of a rib structure consist of standard 2 × 4 inch (5 × 10 cm) lumber studs. The trademark of this system is the narrow spacing of wall studs and floor joists (16 inches). Studs and joists are nailed together.

Studs carry sheathing on one or both sides. Sheathing takes some load and provides ample horizontal stiffening. Rib framing represents a transition from skeleton framing to panel construction.

In balloon construction the wall studs continue through all the floors. Upright planks are cut into the studs as sills at every floor; the joists resting on them are nailed sidewise to the studs.

In platform construction continuous floor sills are resting on top of wall studs; the joists of the next floor rest on sills. A new deck is laid on the joists to form a new platform.

Structural Connections

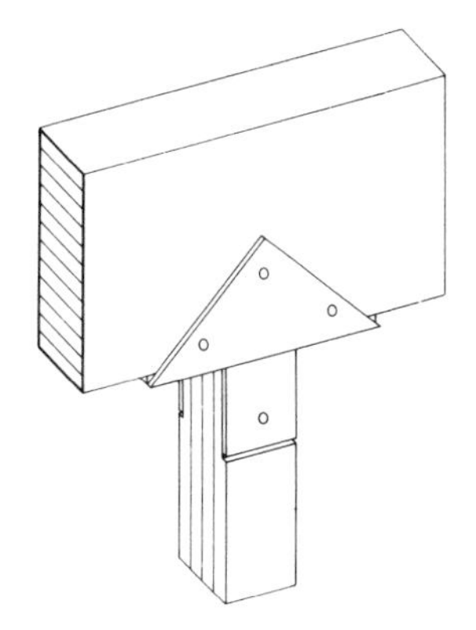

Girder on column with steel bearing

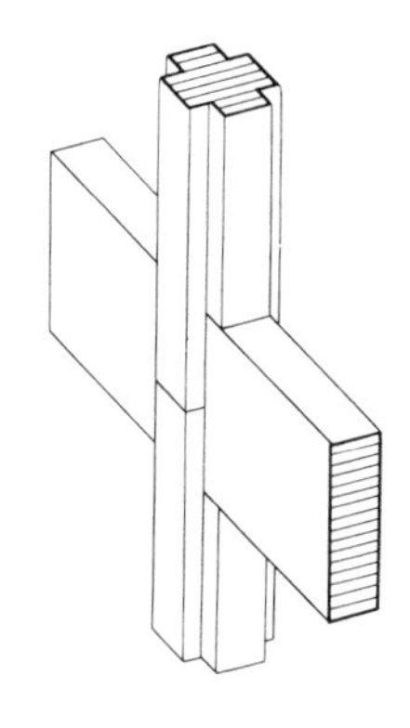

Column spliced, direct connection

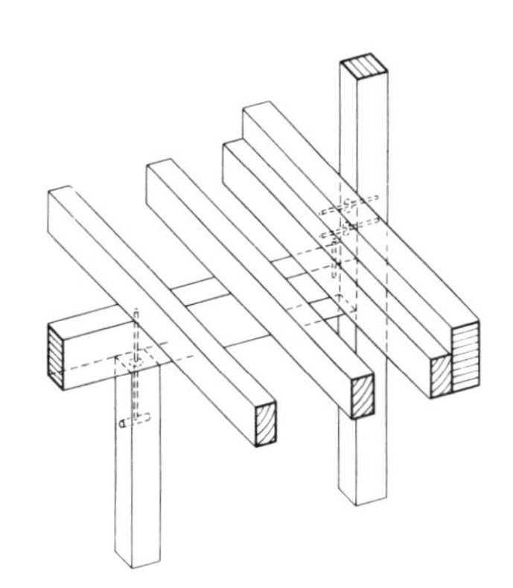

Lower- and upper-floor columns, separate, no continuity

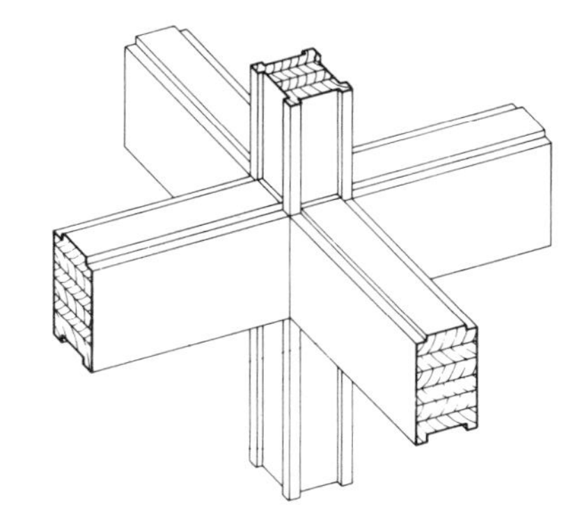

Girders connect to continuous column at 90°

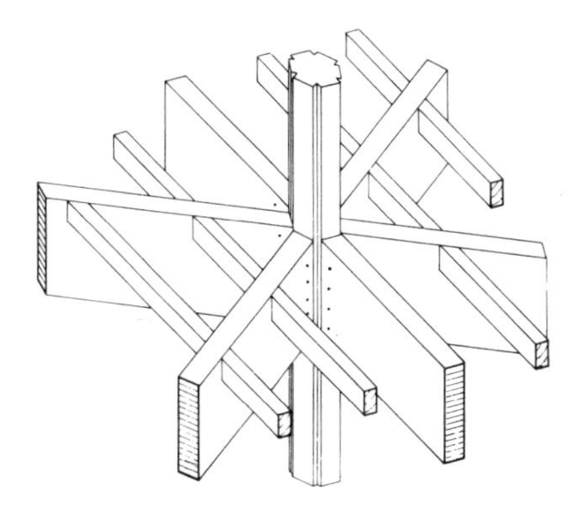

Girders connect to spliced column at 60°

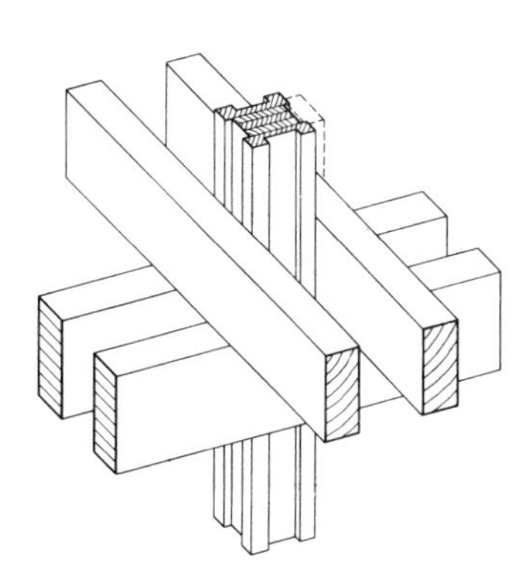

Twin main girders on continuous column

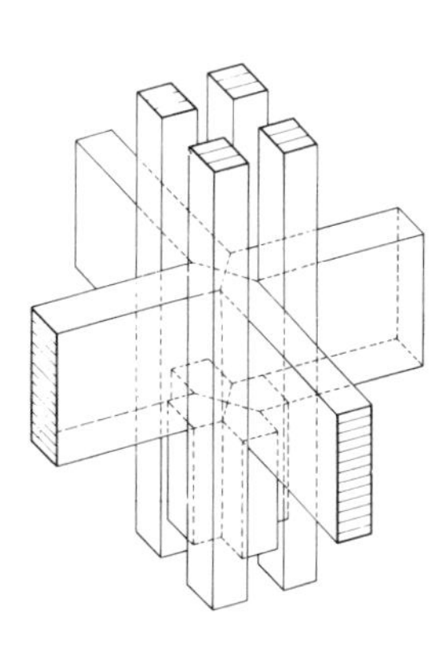

Main girder through split column

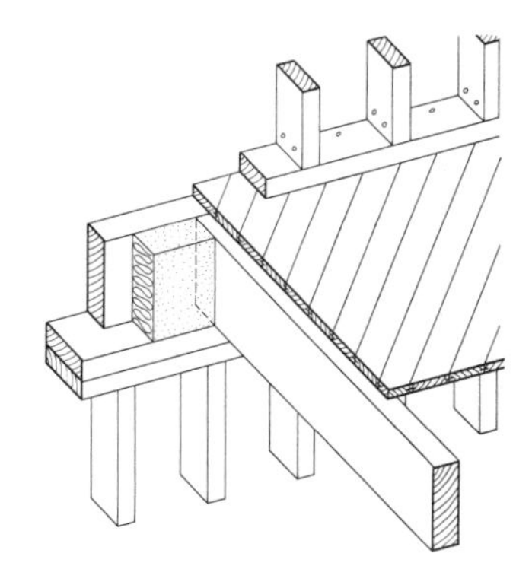

Floor girder on closely spaced studs

Frame Structures

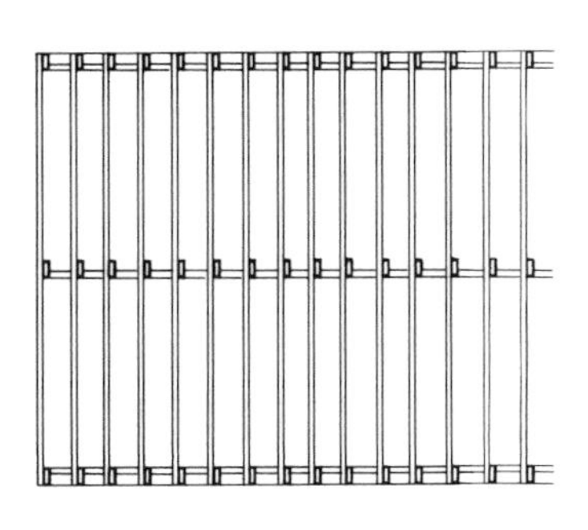

One-way structure with one-way floor beams

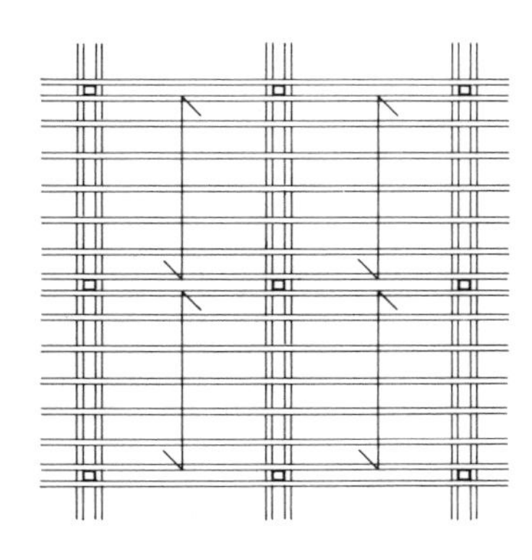

One-way structure

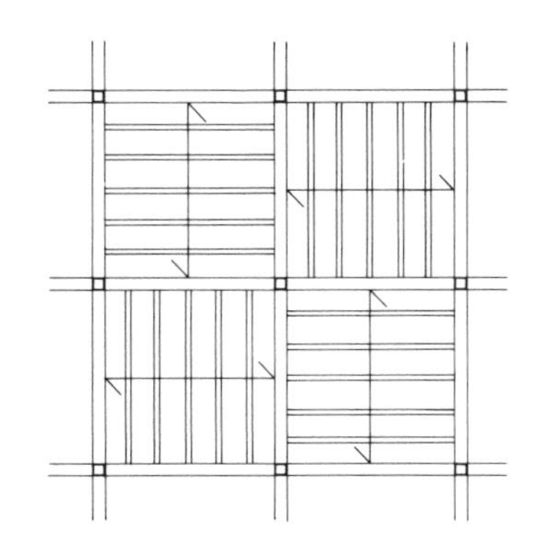

Two-way structure through change of floor beam direction

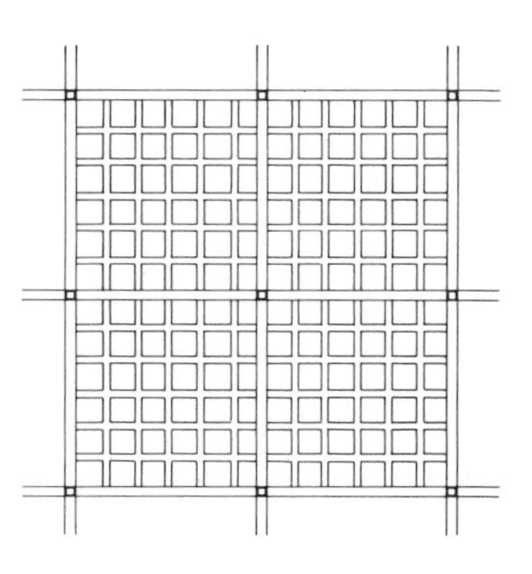

Two-way structure as a flat grid

Modular Arrangement

Both traditional and skeleton frame buildings consist of a structural frame and its finishing components. Single components can be prefabricated. In traditional frame buildings the spaces between the structural members were filled with clay or brick. Because of that, the spaces could be regular, but without need to adhere to a strict order. The finishing of modern skeleton structures is made with partially or completely prefabricated elements and requires a modular arrangement, which governs the plan. The Japanese residential house is a historically important example of this type of modular construction because it is built in both plan and elevation to fit tatami mats (91 × 182 cm).

The basic modular arrangement of a timber skeleton is determined by the layout of the columns.

A secondary modular arrangement is governed by functional requirements, such as partitions and door or window openings. Both levels of modular arrangement are so dependent upon each other that they are subject to the same dimensional units. The column distances in both the main and the secondary directions are thus derived through multiples of the secondary module or through additions of the basic modules.

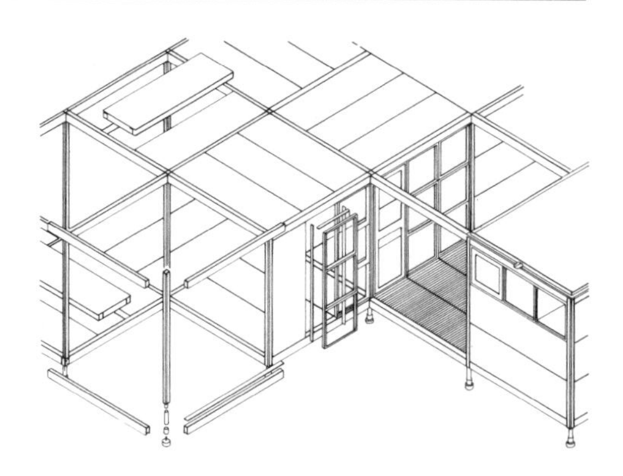

Modular dimensioning of a building

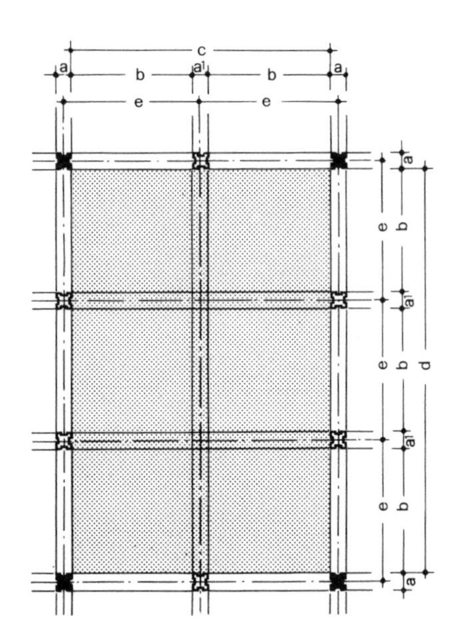

a Column 14/14 cm
a' Hollow column 14/14 cm
b Finishing element 111/14 cm
c Clearance between main girders
d Clearance for floor beams
e Centerline distance

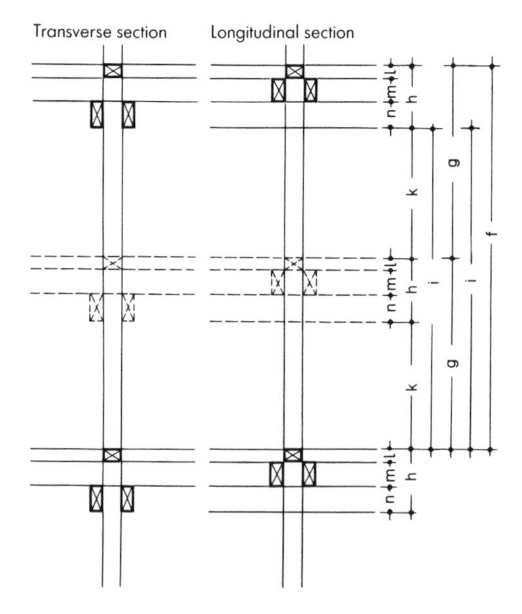

f Floor height 2.88 m
g Offset floor, half-height 1.44 m
h Band grid 0.475 m
i Finishing element 2.405 m
k Element 0.965 m
l Sill 0.965 m
m Floor beam ≃ plenum 0.18 m
n Main girder (split) ≃ plenum 0.20 m

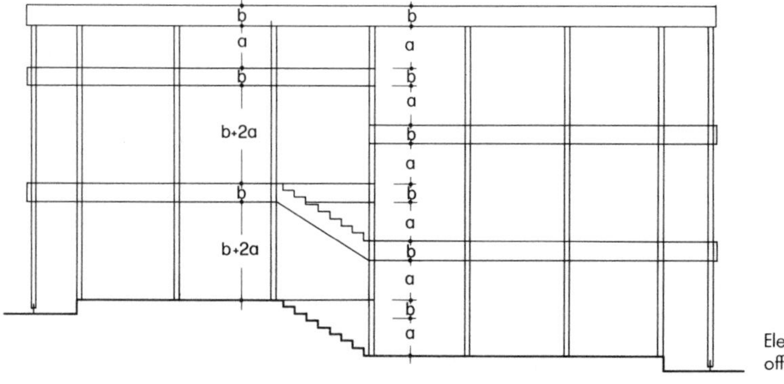

Elevation grid, offset half-story

The planning of a skeleton structure is done by means of a linear grid and a banded grid. The linear grid is laid out horizontally and vertically through the axes of the structural elements. The banded grid is used to differentiate between the depth or width of the structural elements and their clearances; it is superimposed over the linear grid.

In addition to the timber skeleton structures planned on a grid, there are many free-form structures, built by hand without prefabrication and according to need. The modular arrangement will be illustrated by an example.

The horizontal grid measures 1.25 × 1.25 m and the band grid 0.14 × 0.14 m.

The main and secondary spans are multiples of the grid in a ratio of 2 : 3, but could also be nondirectional with a ratio of 3 : 3. In order to achieve a uniform dimension of elements and equal connections, hollow columns are added to those required structurally. Hollow columns carry the utilities. In this way the geometrics of the structure are defined (2.5 × 3.75, 3.75 × 3.75, and 5.0 × 5.0 m). Also defined is the band grid for finishing work (axial dimensions 1.25 × 1.25 m, band size 0.14 × 0.14 m).

The height of the vertical module is given by a multiple of step risers (8 × 0.18 m = 1.44 m), corresponding to half a story; the full story is 16 × 0.18 m = 2.88 m. The vertical grid is overlapped by a vertical band grid. The vertical band is equal to the depth of the floor structure (0.475 m). The finishing elements consist therefore of two dimensioned units, 2.405 and 0.965 m, where 2 × 0.965 m plus the floor depth of 0.475 m corresponds to the basic height element of 2.405 m. The floor depth is obtained by the twin girder (0.20 m), the superimposed beams (0.18 m), and the sill (0.095 m).

Spans and Dimensioning

The spans of a frame building are primarily determined by room layout and structural design. The dimensioning of load-carrying members depends on vertical and horizontal loads, type of wood, choice of connections, fireproofing requirements, and finishes.

Optimum spans for floor beams of common lumber are around 3.60 m when they are spaced at about 60 to 80 cm. For shorter spans (about 2.40 m) a planking or wood-chip board floor may be placed directly on the main girders.

Main girders may span between 3 and 8 m, depending on the grade of lumber, and in one-story buildings even more. Even here the optimum span range is about 3.60 m, beyond which the required sizes will call for laminated wood. The 12/20 cm sections of stock lumber planking should not be exceeded for practical reasons. The column cross sections are determined mostly by the type of connections for framing and finishes; therefore, the structurally required size of single columns will often be exceeded even when they are designed for longer spans.

If a particular fire rating is desired, the dimensioning of frames may be governed by fire protection requirements (DIN 4102, "Fire Rating of Materials and Building Components"). Timber is fire-resistant, if unprotected, when it has a required minimum cross section, depending on locations, loading, and type of wood. For example, floor beams reach a fire rating of F30 (30 mins) if exposed on three sides when they have a cross section of 12/20 cm. Laminated wood beams reach that fire rating with a cross section of 11/20 cm for a three-sided exposure, and with 12/25 cm for a four-sided exposure. Columns reach it with a cross section of 15/15 cm. These minimum dimensions suggest the use of certain span lengths. For reasons of economy, designers should plan right from the beginning not to use spans that are shorter.

The choice of beam cross section is also governed by the structural requirements of partitions, finishes, bracing, or modular construction.

Minimum cross sections required by structural design may not always be the most economical when the entire building and its use are taken into consideration.

Foundations and Anchorages

A frame structure has to be anchored to a foundation. The question then arises: should this foundation consist of single or continuous footings, or even of a floating slab? Foundations will depend on local conditions, type of soil, intended use of building, and column spacing. There is a relationship between foundations and the building frame. The inaccuracy of foundation dimensions often causes problems when the prefabrication of frames cannot adapt to field conditions. The anchorage holes must therefore allow for adjustment in all directions, either before or during erection.

Adjustments may be made by means of either wedges, slotted holes in bearing plates, or vertically adjustable bolts. The elasticity of timber frameworks allows small dimensional adjustments as long as the finishes can absorb the resulting tolerances.

In any case the designer has to specify clearly the procedure for connecting the frame to the substructure. This is also necessary in order to delineate the responsibilities of each trade and eliminate problems with guarantees for completed work.

The design must differentiate between bearings working in compression only and those to which horizontal bracing is attached. In the latter case, the bearing has to resist not only horizontal, but possibly also uplift forces. Depending on load conditions, the columns are attached to footings by either steel anchors or expansion bolts.

If a column transmits only compressive forces, a nominal anchorage of its bearing is sufficient. On the other hand, if it is also subject to uplift and horizontal forces, there is a need to anchor the base of the column to the footing by means of a steel shoe. Uplift can occur especially when roofs are cantilevered and at corner columns.

Free-standing columns should be sufficiently protected against snow and standing water. Their shoes should be made from steel so that the wood can dry and no water can accumulate between wood and steel; the addition of a drip edge is desirable. Interior posts may rest directly on the foundation, insulated only by a layer of bituminous felt; they can be secured by gusset plates and bolts.

The construction of an exterior column base connection must correspond to the type of wall section. There are basically two types of connections: either the column is resting on the footing and the sill beam is laid between the columns, or the column is supported by the sill beam. In the latter case the column may be connected directly to the footing through a steel base passing through the sill (which is not the case in traditional building frames). The sill then becomes a spacer for the mounting of columns; it should be protected from humidity rising from the foundation by means of bituminous felt.

Column Shoes

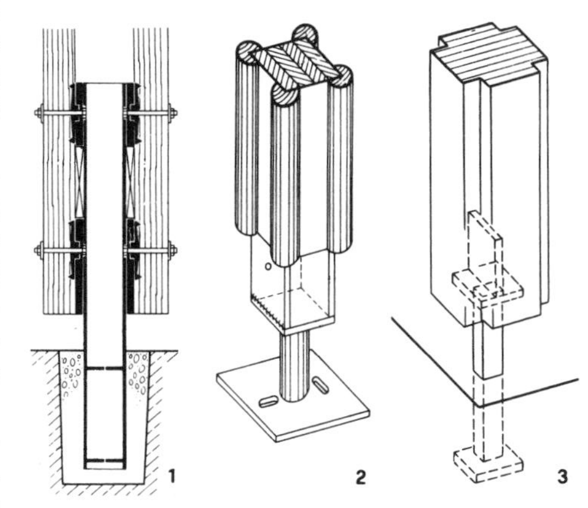

1 Anchorage for split column
2 Steel shoe with slotted holes for adjustment
3 Steel shoe without adjustment

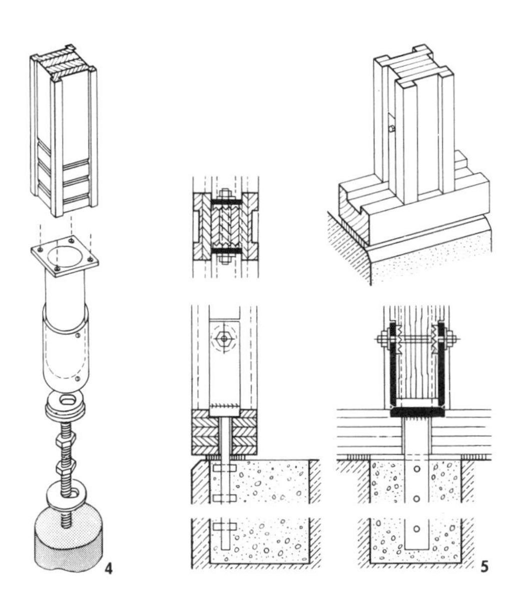

4 Height adjustment by means of jacking screw; horizontal adjustment through eccentric washers
5 Exterior and interior columns on a sill beam

Bracing

Horizontal wind loads on a building, that is, both positive and negative pressures, are absorbed by the bracing and transferred to the foundation. The wind loads act on the exposed surfaces, including roof and walls. The outer walls transfer the loads to the roof and floor surfaces, which must have horizontal bracing to transfer these loads to points of vertical anchorage. From these points the loads are further transferred by vertical bracing to the foundation. The bracing, therefore, consists of two types of trussing: horizontal trussing in the roof and floors and vertical trussing in certain column planes. Horizontal trussing typically consists of tie bars, flat steel bars, plywood panels, wood-chip boards, or diagonal sheathing. If floor beams and main girders lie in different planes, it is necessary to convey the loads from the stiffening plane through the appropriate steel connections or filler timbers to the plane of the main girders. Roofs and floors connected through these bracings form a structural plate. At least three vertical bracing trusses must be present in each floor; their plan axes must not intersect through one point. Vertical bracing may consist of steel crosses or timber diagonals placed between columns.

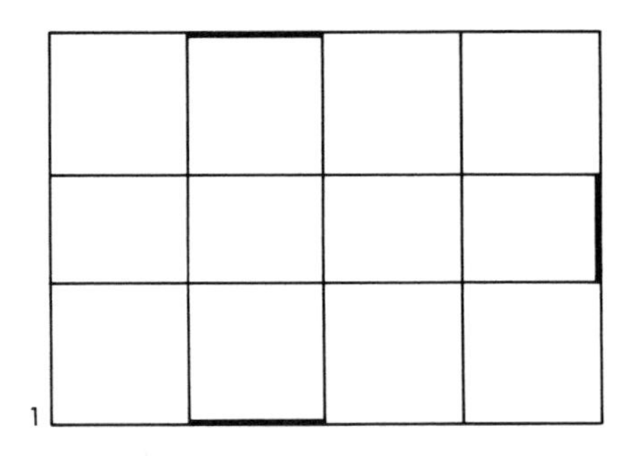

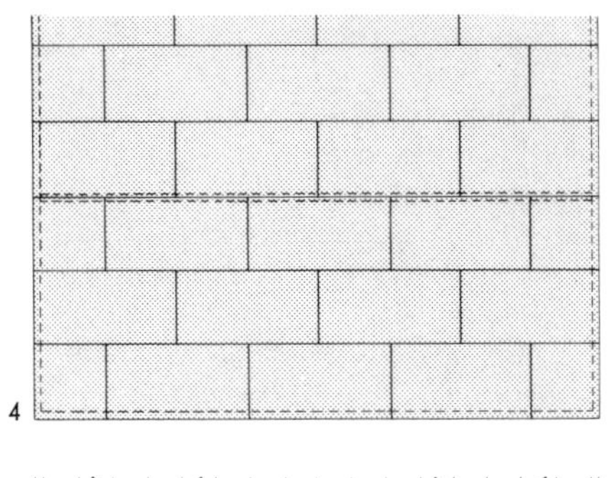

1 Arrangement of three vertical bracing trusses in plan
2 Vertical bracing as simple diagonal
3 Vertical bracing as half-bracing

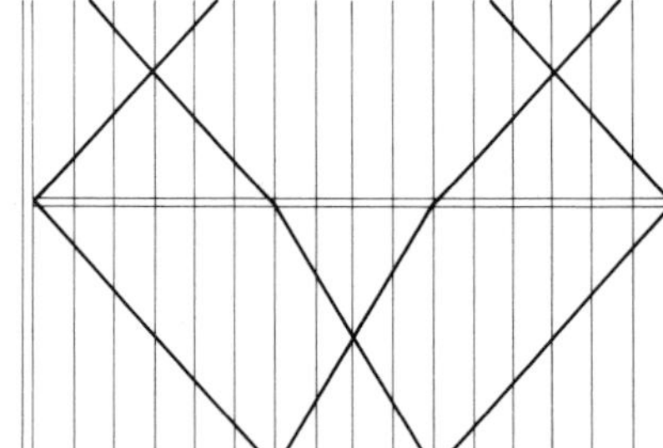

4 Horizontal stiffening plate of offset wood-chip boards or plywood panels, nailed or screwed
5 Horizontal bracing of flat steel bars
6 Horizontal panel stiffened with diagonal board sheathing

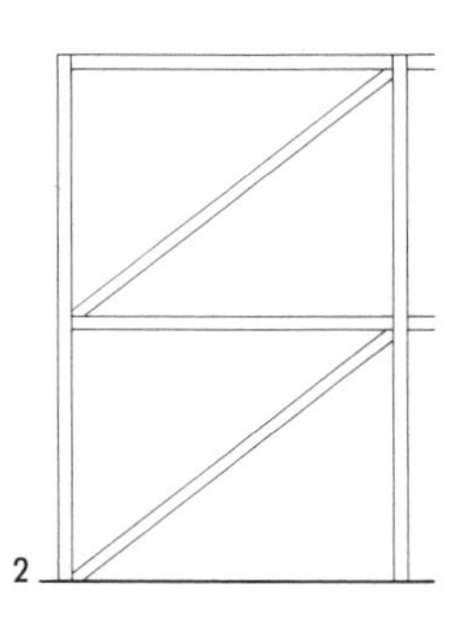

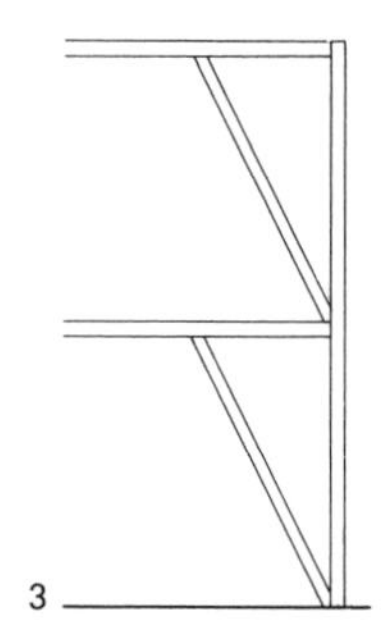

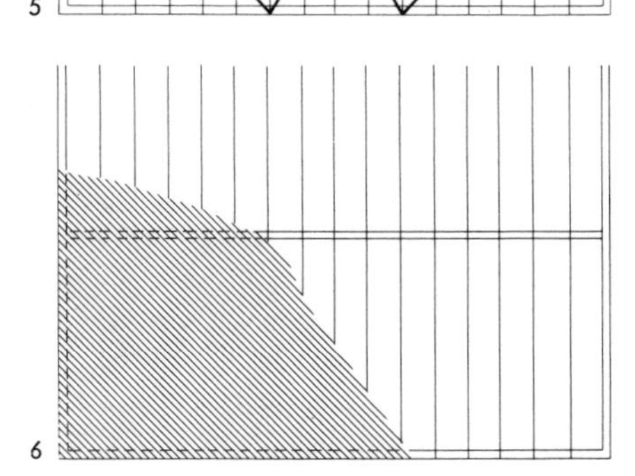

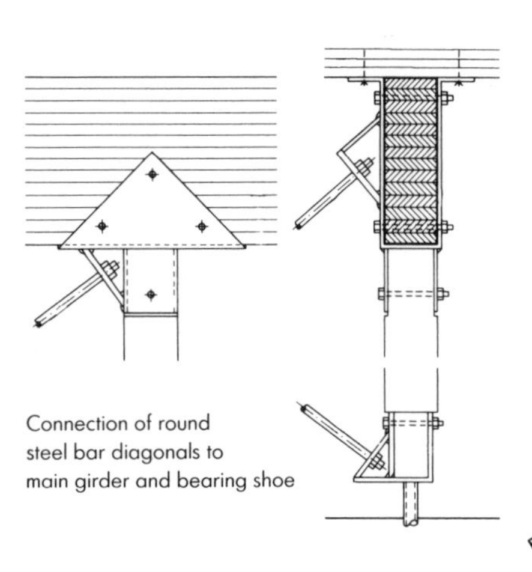

Connection of round steel bar diagonals to main girder and bearing shoe

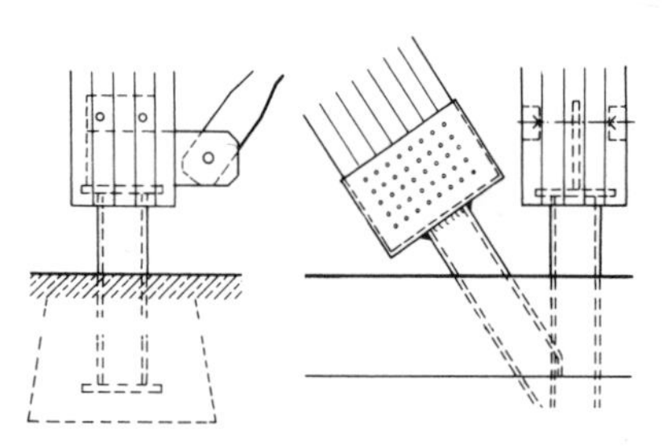

Connection of steel diagonal between timber and bearing shoe

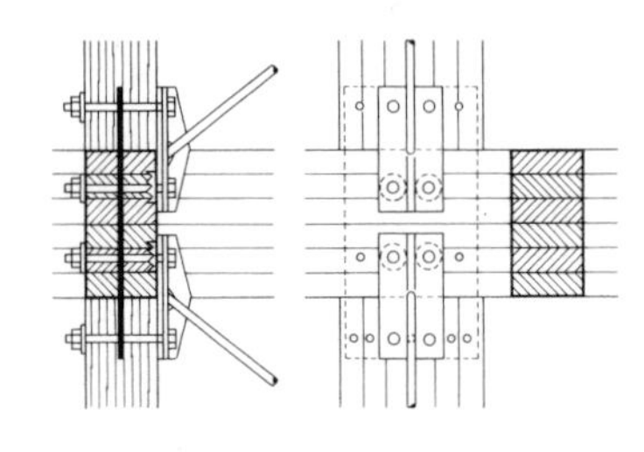

Connection of steel diagonals to main girder

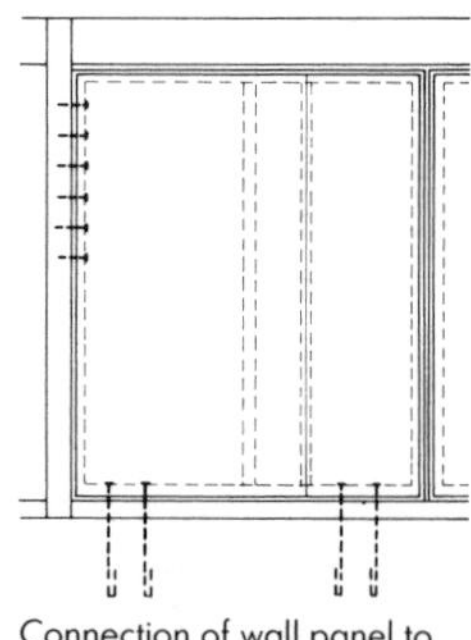

Connection of wall panel to column and foundation

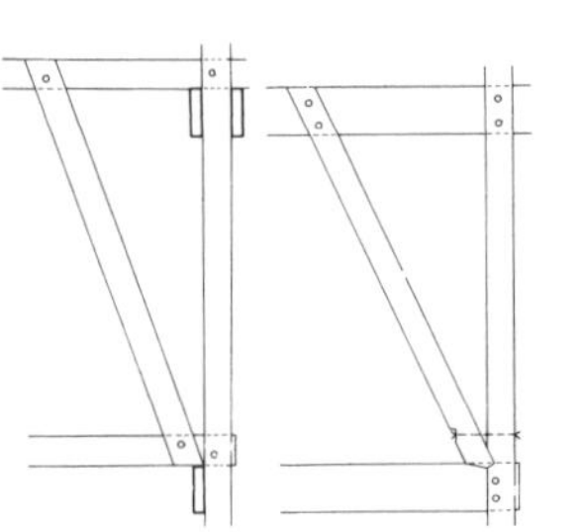

Half-bracing

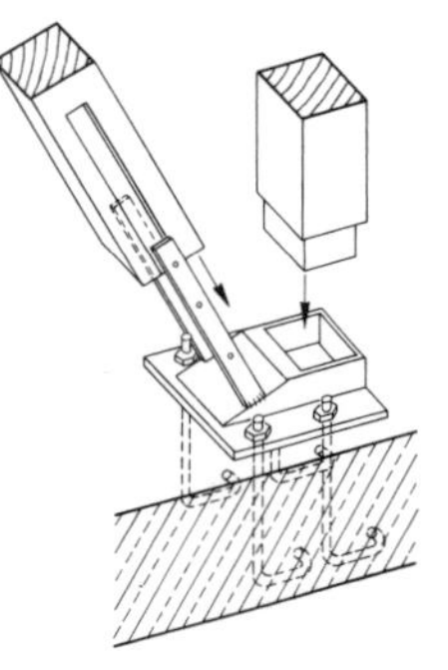

Anchorage of timber diagonal to bearing shoe

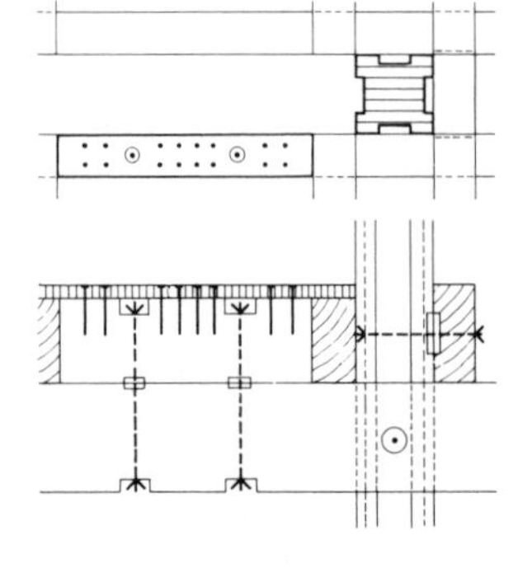

Connection of floor decking to main girder through filler timbers

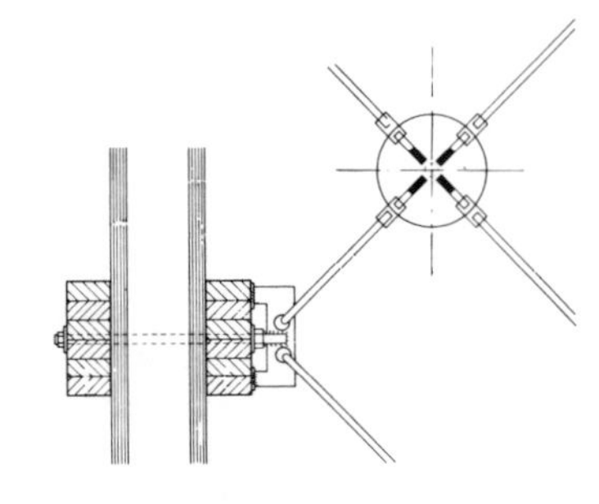

Connection of steel diagonal; intersection of diagonals with turnbuckle arrangement

Finishes

Components of a timber frame are subject to deformations and changes in length. These can be anticipated and should be taken into account in the design and in the choice of materials.

Timber is not subject to temperature deformations, such as occur in steel and reinforced concrete. On the other hand, variations in moisture content cause elongation change and deformations: wood "works." The moisture content varies with the environment; during construction it is different from that in a finished building. In exterior building members it typically amounts to 17%, in the interior it is about 8%.

Lumber nowadays rarely comes from aged stockpiles. It is therefore necessary to anticipate the distortion and splitting of wood in a finished building. These deformations are structurally unimportant, but they can affect the connections of finishing work, especially that which is prefabricated. It is therefore recommended to use glue-laminated wood where precise fit is necessary. Glue-laminated wood is dried prior to lamination in such a way that there is practically no difference in moisture content during and after construction. In addition, the wood lamination contains various wood layers so that their inner stresses counterbalance and the wood does not deform: the laminated wood "does not work," but it loses the liveliness of wood. Deformations are mostly due to the deflection of wood under load.

Timber structures do not create "cold bridges" as steel and reinforced-concrete structures do. This leads to an arrangement of facades which could not be possible with other materials because of difficulties of insulation. The finished facades of timber buildings can be located in the same plane as the columns and beams: between split columns or split beams, or connected to columns and beams. They can also be located behind the frame.

All Connections Concentrated in One Point

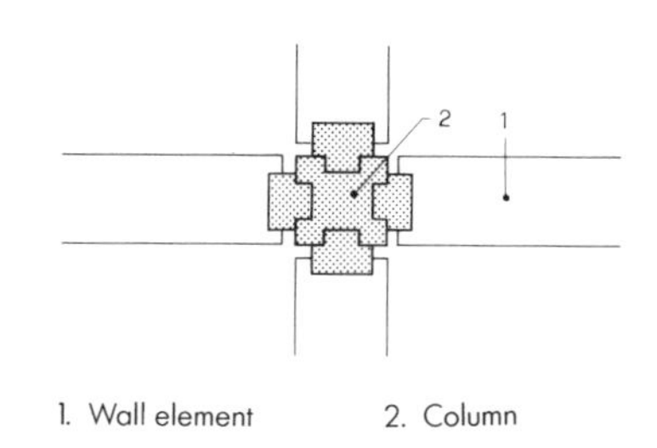

1. Wall element 2. Column

Connection with Vented Facade

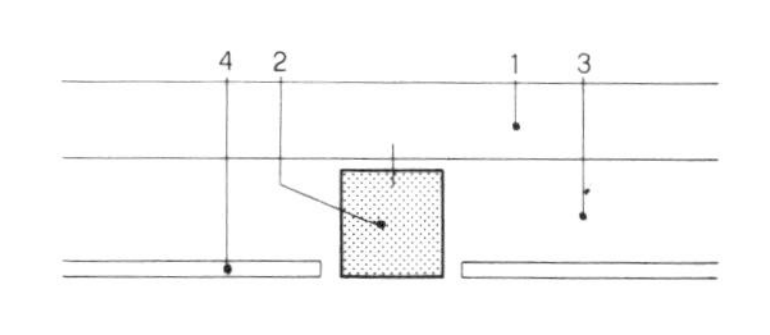

1 Wall element
2 Column
3 Vented interspace
4 Siding

Jointing

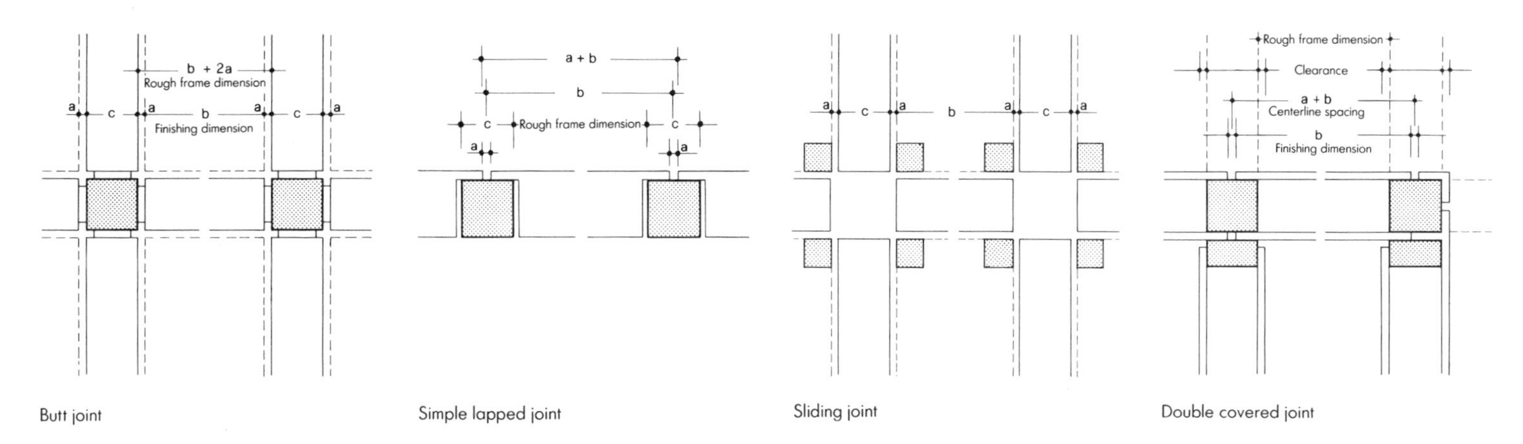

Butt joint Simple lapped joint Sliding joint Double covered joint

Finishing elements must be joined to the framing or to other finishing elements. These joints require first a dimensional tolerance to account for the inaccuracies of foundation and finishes (even when there is provision for adjustment) and, second, tolerances needed to facilitate installation.

These tolerances must be accounted for in the joints. Different arrangements are possible.

1. A butt joint is customary in a banded grid; the joint separates the framing from the finishing elements.
2. A simple lapped joint can be placed in front or behind the framing and serves as a joint between finishing elements, such as sheathing or design panels.
3. A sliding joint is covered by frame elements. Tolerances in the longitudinal direction are unimportant, those in depth are essential.
4. The double covered joint is placed in front of or behind the structure and serves as a joint between finishing elements, like a simple lapped joint.

The joints are also needed for mechanical protection of the wood.

On the exterior of a building all structural elements should be separated in such a way as to allow for sufficient ventilation; wood is then able to dry out after rain or snow. Joints should not be designed too tight, they should be at least 5 to 20 mm wide.

Joint details should allow for sealing all around; vertical and horizontal joints should be similar.

Connections between main structure and finishing

Layout and Arrangement of Interstitial Spaces

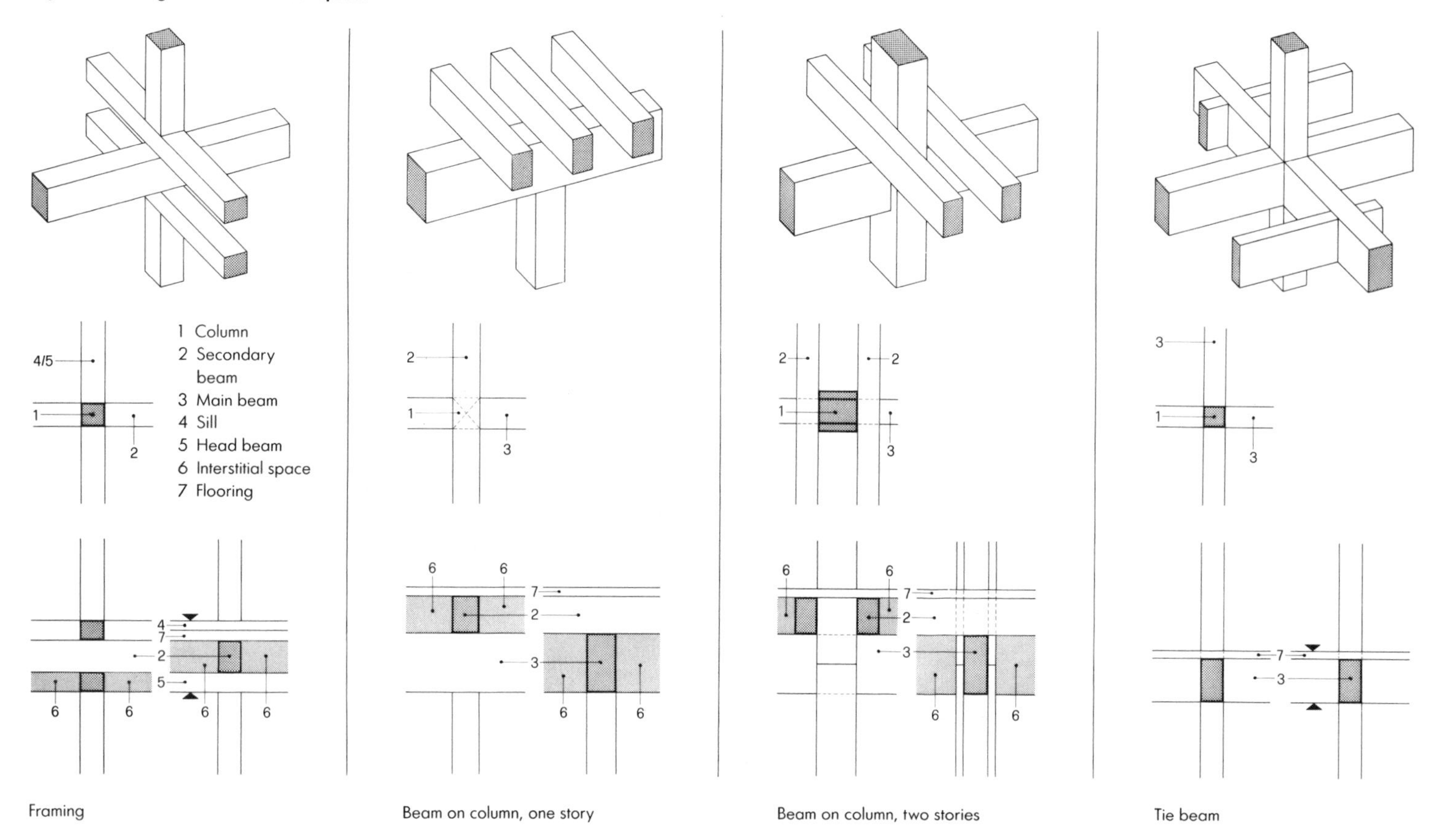

elements, or between two finishing elements, must be able to transfer dead and wind loads, and often also the bracing loads. At the same time they must be watertight, airtight, and easy to assemble. Customary joints have a drawback for prefabricated paneling because such joints cannot be made tight. However, good connections can be made if paneling is set and glued into precut grooves, or if it is set into the main structure before erection.

The air tightness of such connections is more difficult to achieve in prefabricated construction than in traditional frame structures. Putty, stucco, or moldings can serve the purpose well. Elastic joint materials should be used only where no other details can achieve a desirable result.

Protection against rain and snow is achieved by the so-called maze joints, in which the water can be shed vertically. Air tightness is achieved by additional compressed material, such as rubber or elastic compounds. Certain compressed joint materials, such as tubular or folded water seals, may serve both functions.

Finishing Elements

Wall elements in modular frame construction should preferably have the same width and height. In this case the design must provide for a pattern of outer and inner finishing elements. The result is the formation of interstitial spaces. Framing, finishing elements, and interstitial spaces can be shown in plan, elevation, and cross section. The following examples will illustrate how the individual components of a modular design converge (tolerance, construction, joints, assembly, and stiffening). The presentation shows a horizontally exploded view of each component. Below are the plan and the elevation. →

A review of the finishing elements illustrated on page 188 shows that a building system works with a limited number of components. A systematic investigation of all the factors that influence the design of nodal points indicates a wide-ranging flexibility in the choice of a system.

Layout and Arrangement of Interstitial Spaces

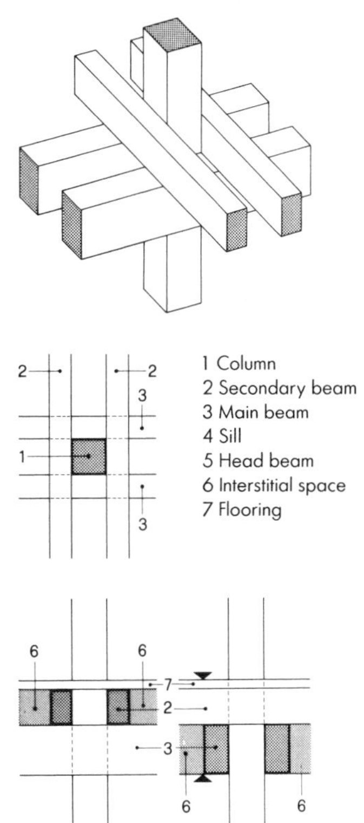

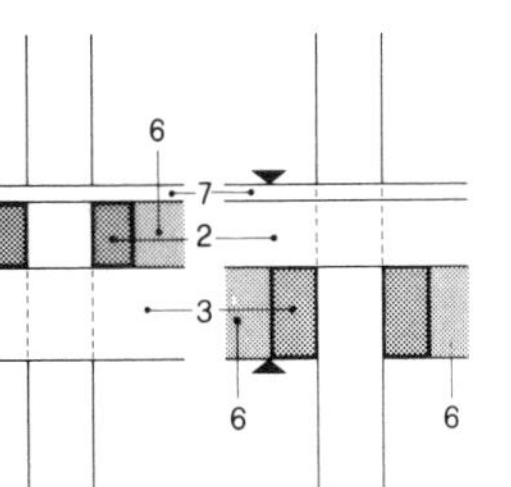

Split beam

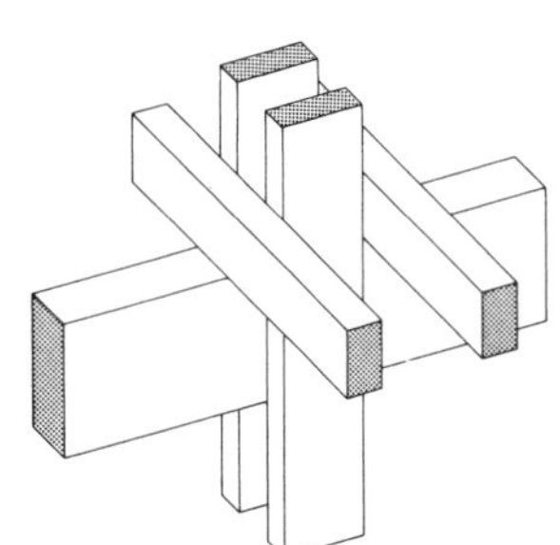

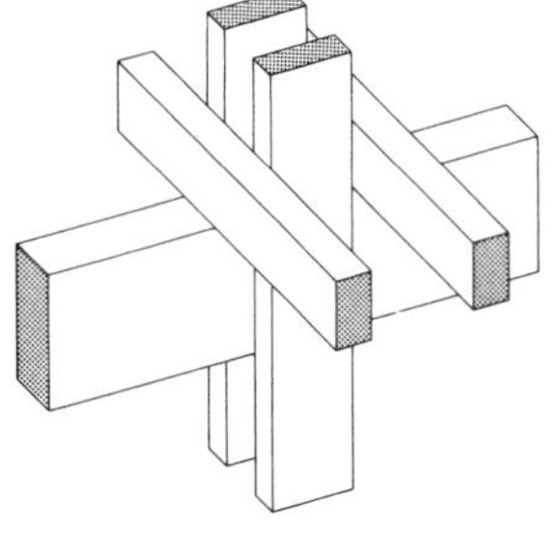

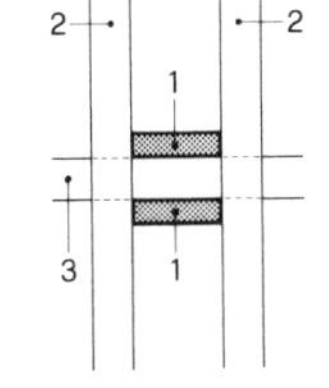

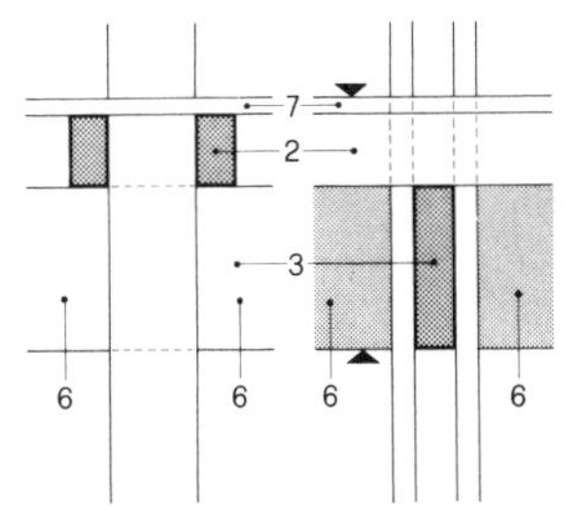

Split column

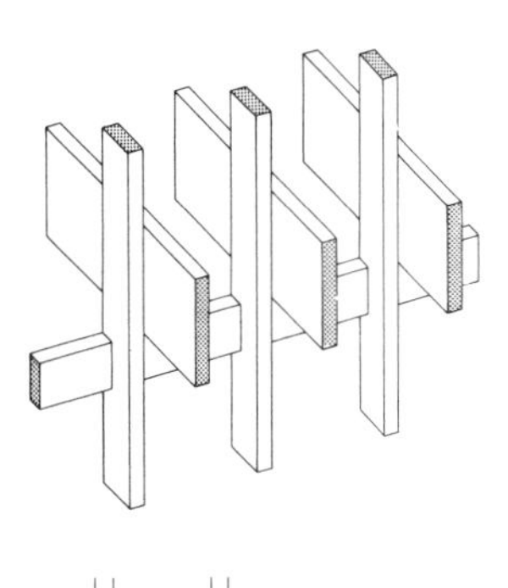

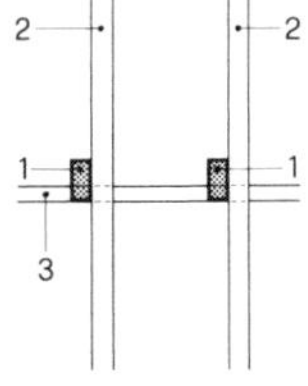

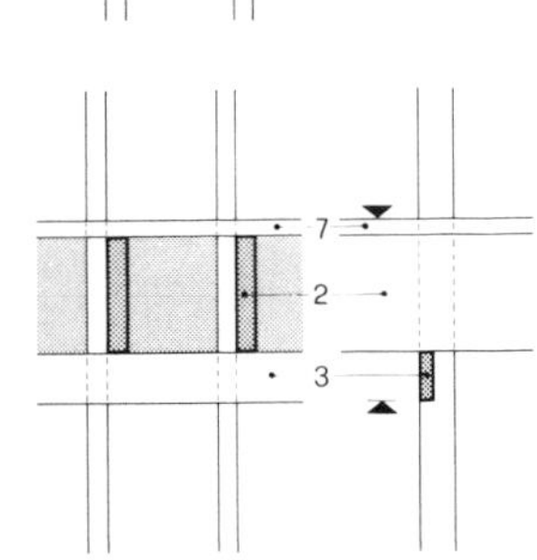

Rib construction, balloon type

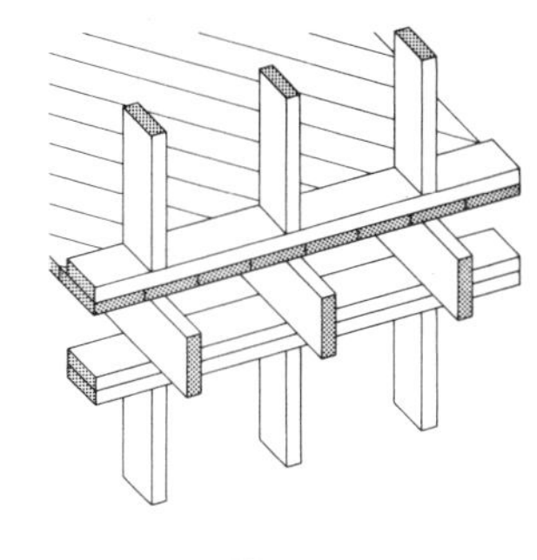

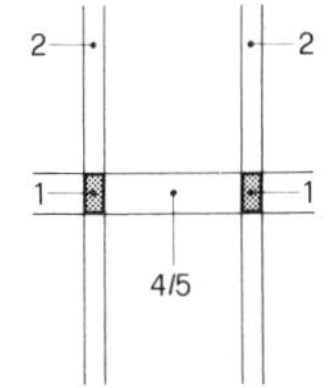

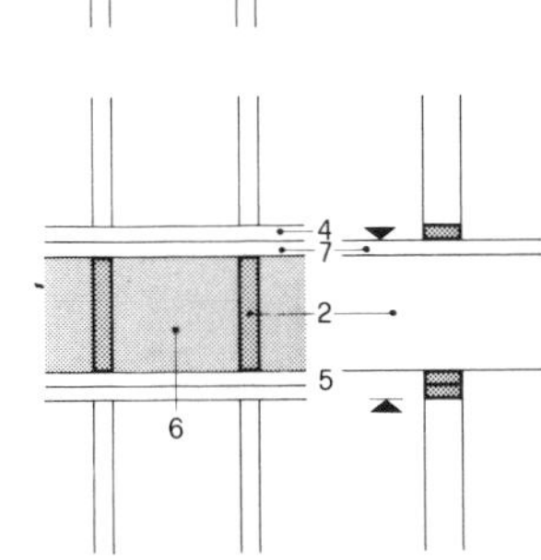

Rib construction, platform type

Finishing Elements Connected to a Column

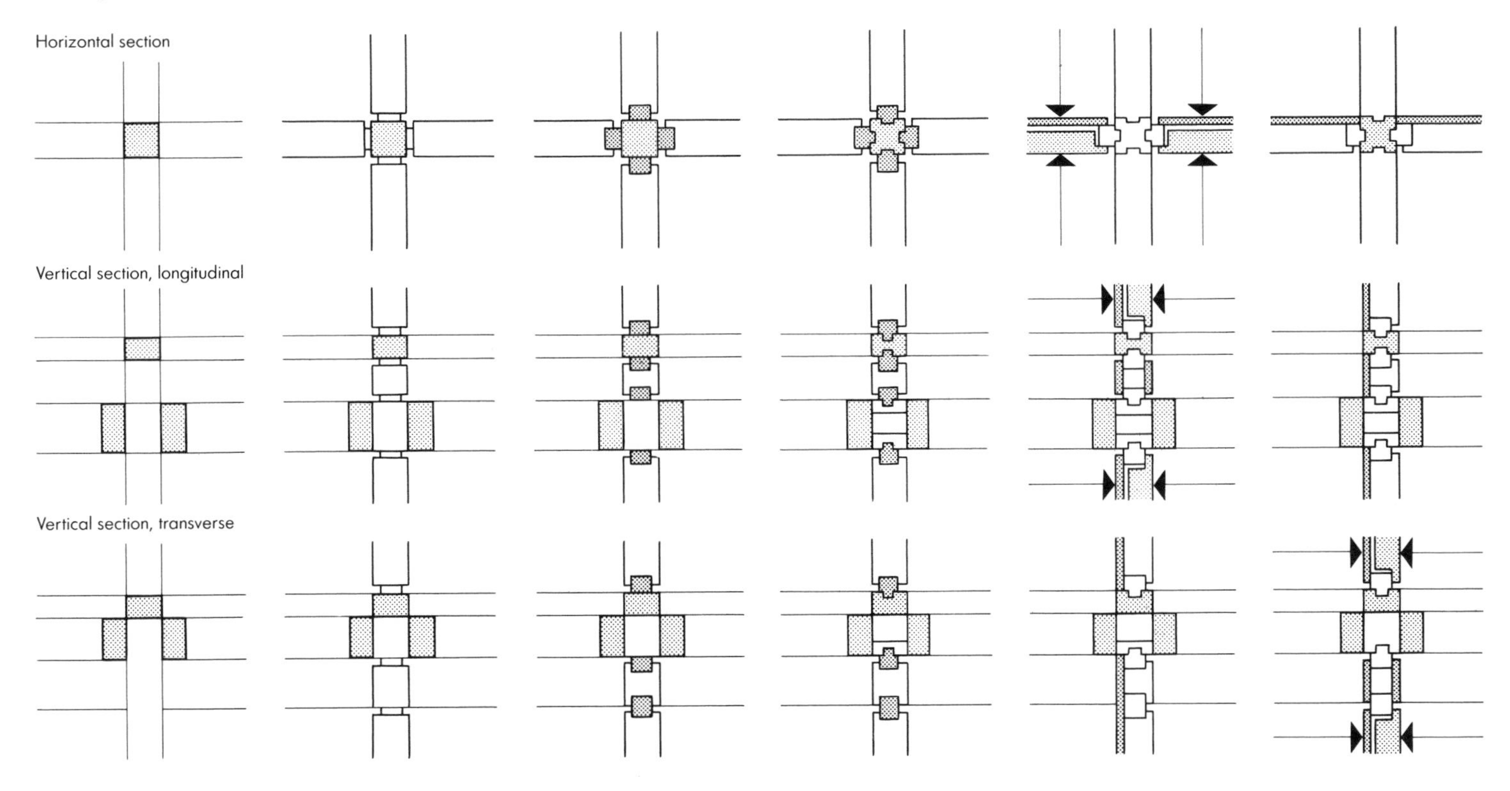

Simple layout of split-beam construction

Tolerances between elements

Connection timbers, connection of elements to frame

Connection timbers tenoned to column for air tightness

Separation of elements for assembly

Stiffening panel in plane of framing stud

Prefabrication

Timber construction requires the planning of prefabrication and assembly from the outset. The design must consider whether a building is to be erected entirely by hand, whether one or more buildings are to be built in a sequential and correspondingly mechanized way, or whether the construction warrants mass-producing an entirely self-contained building system.

A designer who chooses the latter method must have an intimate knowledge of the technology in this field. Detailing must be especially precise when a large number of parts are mass-produced; it must reflect the actual fabrication methods. In some cases, for example, it may be economically advantageous to conceive all structural members of the same size, even if some may be oversized. In order to decentralize production and optimize purchasing, various building components should be designed in such a way as to allow purchasing from several suppliers. The best conditions for transportation and installation are achieved when all building components can be moved by light cranes and installed by hand.

For individual construction it is sufficient that construction plans show appropriate detail; for mass production, on the other hand, the plans must provide information on details and assembly methods. This means that a complex design, extending from planning to erection, must be organized and coordinated from the very beginning.

An appropriate method is needed to translate planning ideas into production. One such method consists of an information system based on simple coding, but other completely self-contained methods are also available.

Industrial production must be cataloged for rational planning and efficiency of purchasing, production, storage, transportation, and installation. This is needed in order to focus the design not only on the main structural members, but also on all the components of the finishing system.

A practical application of an information system will be illustrated by means of an example. Three items of information are used for planning and purchasing: construction plans, a parts list, and an indexed inventory. For example, the drawings below show a sliding door as an element that is represented in drawings and tables in a threefold way. In practice this offers the following information:

1. The coded element is defined on plans by showing the carpenters its layout or the elevation it is to occupy in the finished building.
2. In a coded parts list the element is represented graphically in all its details.
3. In a coded inventory sheet the element is described by multiple codes dimensionally, functionally, and qualitatively. This inventory code carries a price list for fabrication, storage, transportation, and installation. Prices are divided into the costs of materials and labor so that a cost estimate can be developed for each item.

Exterior Wall Elements

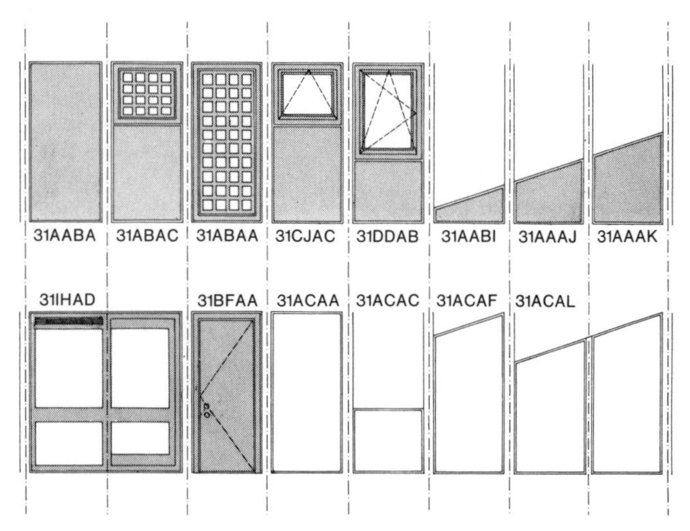

Interior Wall Elements

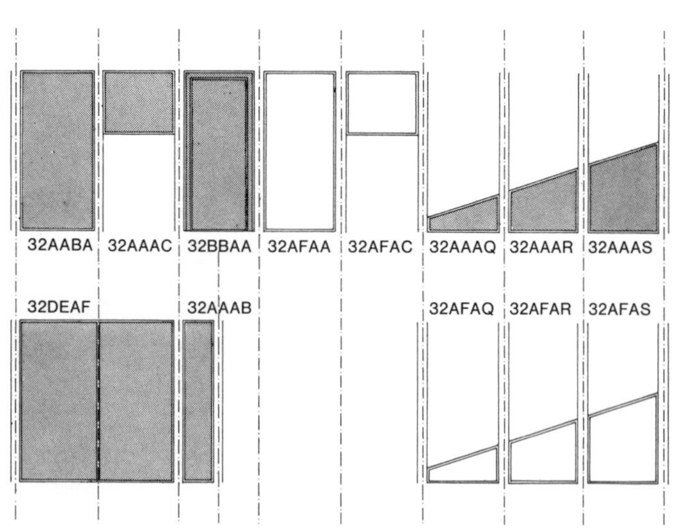

Parts List

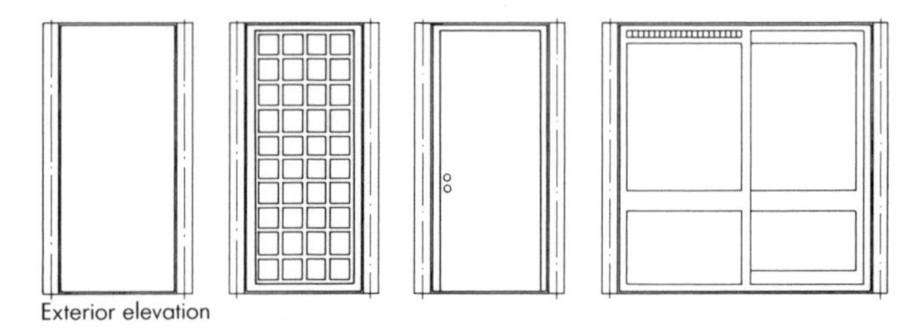

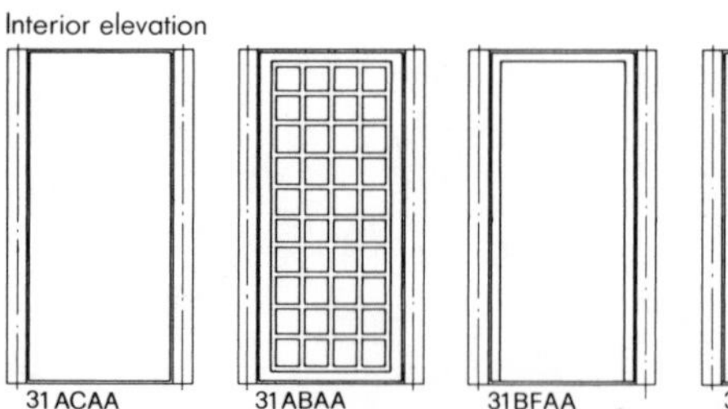

Layout

Coded Inventory Sheet

● NAME	● SYSTEM	● CONSTRUCTION	● INFO	● PHASE
CODE-DEFINITION ELEMENTS OF FACADE	0 0 0 0 0 0	3 1 0 0 0 0	4 8	D A
	● DOC. NO.	● DATE	● SCALE	● DWG.
	2 3 0 0 0 1	0 1 1 0 7 2		RO

Window elements	3 1
Frame element	A
Rotating element	B
Tilting element	C
Rotating/tilting element	D
Turning element	E
Sliding element	F
Sliding element	G
Lifting element	H
Lifting/sliding element	I
Closed wall element	A
Grid element	B
Fixed glazing	C
Rotating/tilting element	D
Rotating/tilting element	E
Door element	F
Door element	G
Lifting/sliding door	H
Lifting/sliding door	I
Tilting element	J

Review of Eight Types of Construction

In order to define more precisely the different principles of timber construction, it is useful to compare similar basic structures. An examination of these systems reveals the basic differences of structural frames and provides a systematic comparison of the underlying structural principles.

In the comparative review of construction types shown on pages 190 and 191, eight types of timber skeleton construction are presented schematically. Variants and mixed types of construction are not shown.

Presentation of Sixteen Examples

Shown are only those structures that are of importance because of their structural types. Our primary interest lies in their construction, disregarding aesthetic and spatial considerations. Therefore we excluded many timber buildings designed mostly on the basis of the latter criteria. The examples are arranged from the point of view of construction analysis so that they can be compared in their details, such as structural nodes, construction joints, ridge points, bracing, and finishing. The different points of view are compared in the following sections.

Type of Construction			Number	Example	Location	Country	Page
Single columns and beams	Continuous beams	Beam on column, one story	1	Nursery school	Stuttgart	W. Germany	192
			2	Nursery school	Erdweg	W. Germany	195
		Beam on column, two stories	3	Construction system		W. Germany	198
			4	Office building	Weingarten	W. Germany	201
			5	Building system		W. Germany	204
	Continuous columns	Tie beam	6	Building system		Finland	207
			7	School	Gurtweil	W. Germany	210
			8	Building system		Finland	212
Split columns and beams	Continuous beams and columns	Split beams	9	Framing system	Herrenalb	W. Germany	215
			10	Residence	Bad Honnef	W. Germany	218
			11	Office building	Konstanz	W. Germany	220
		Split columns	12	Community center	Freiburg	W. Germany	223
			13	Student cafeteria	Twente	The Netherlands	226
			14	Exhibition pavilion	Kommern	W. Germany	228
Rib construction		Platform	15	Two-family residence	Tokyo	Japan	230
			16	Apartment house	Vancouver	Canada	232

Review of Construction Types

	Framing	Single columns and beams		
		Continuous beam		Continuous columns
Structure Types Isometrics	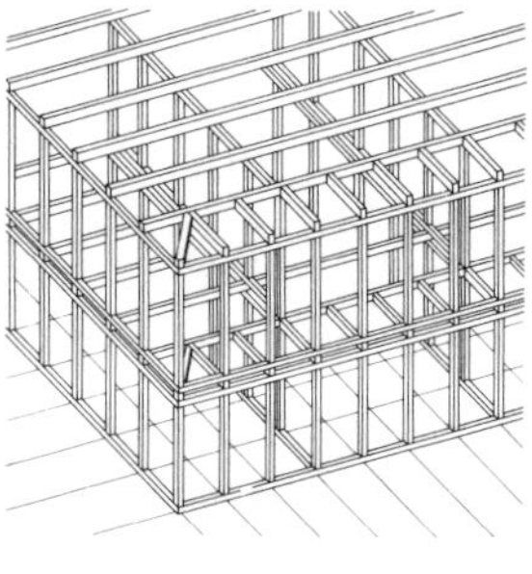	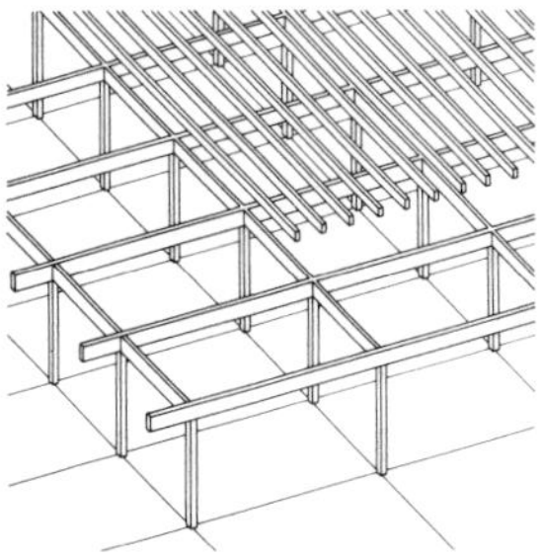	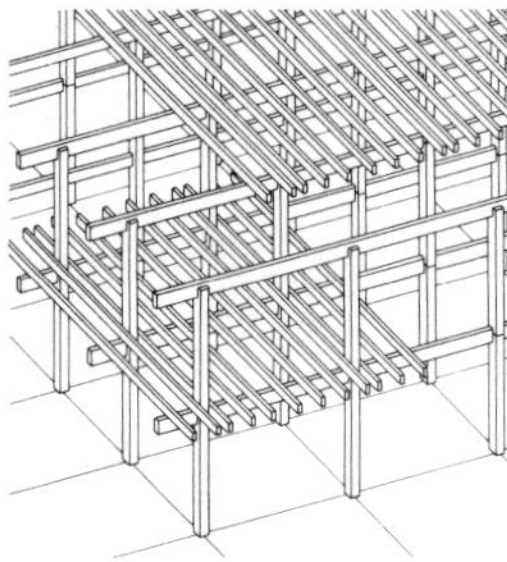	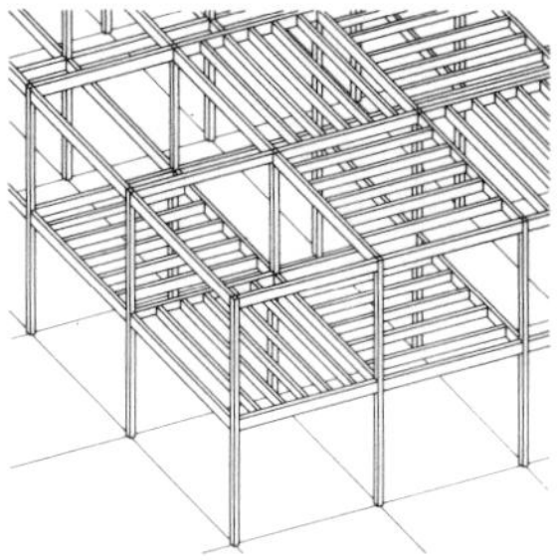
	Framing	Beam on column, one story	Beam on column, two stories	Tie beam
Cross section Plan	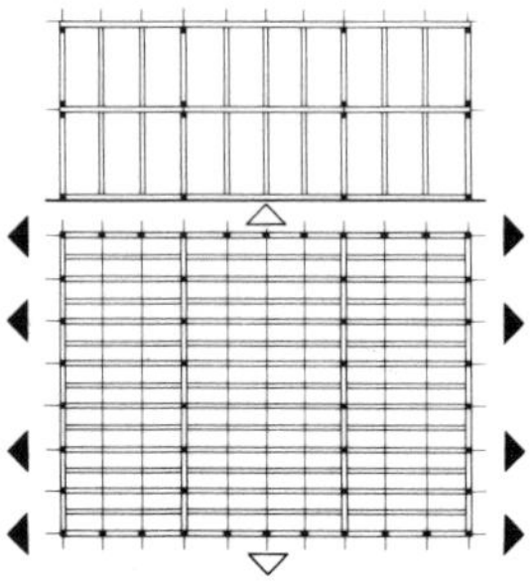	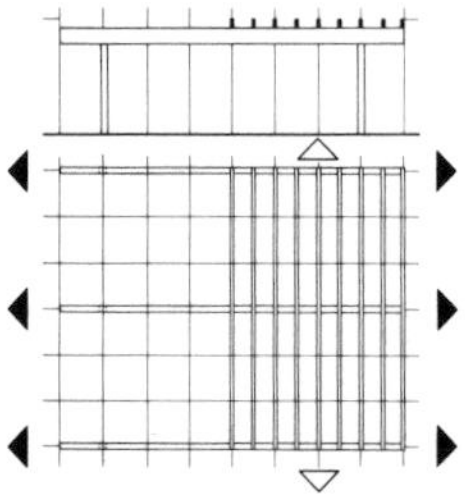	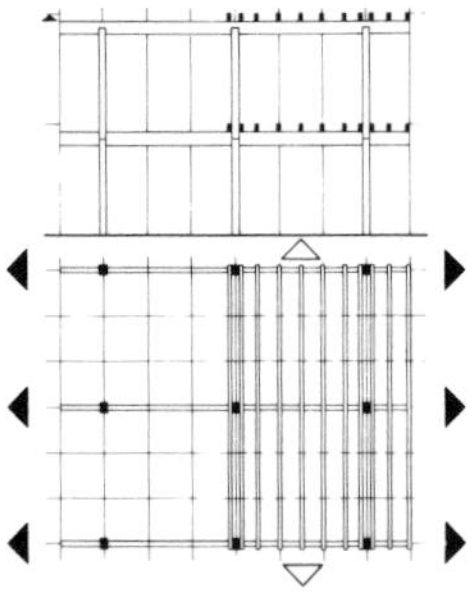	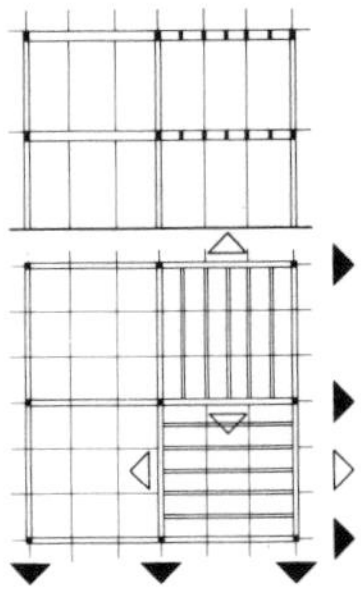
Nodes Isometrics		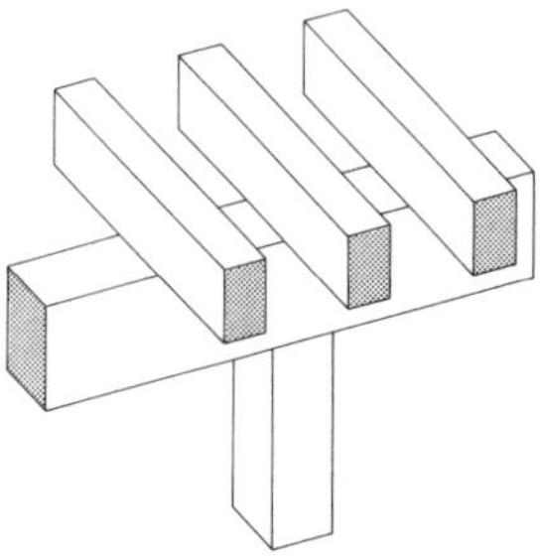	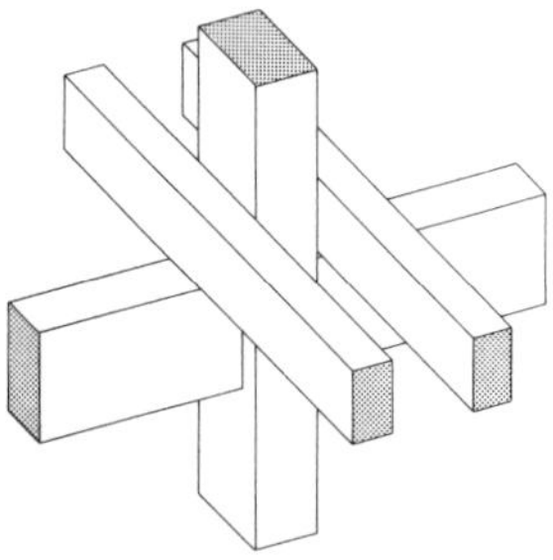	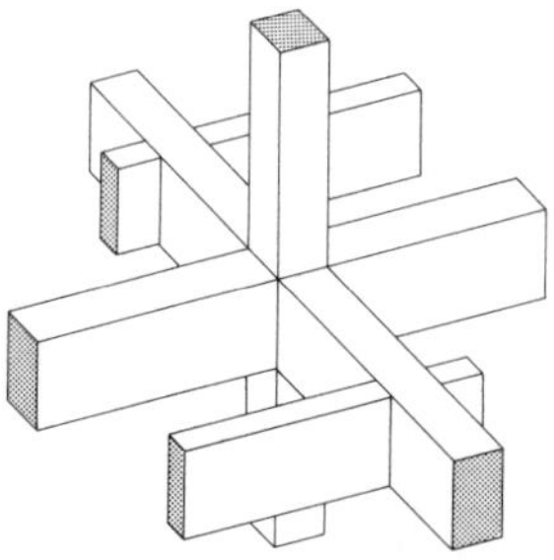
Cross section Plan				

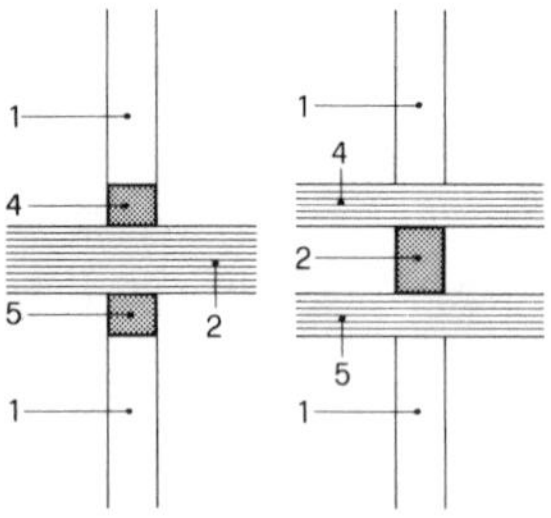

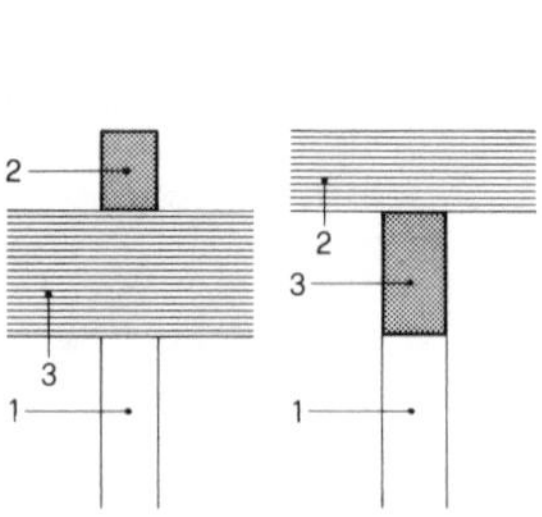

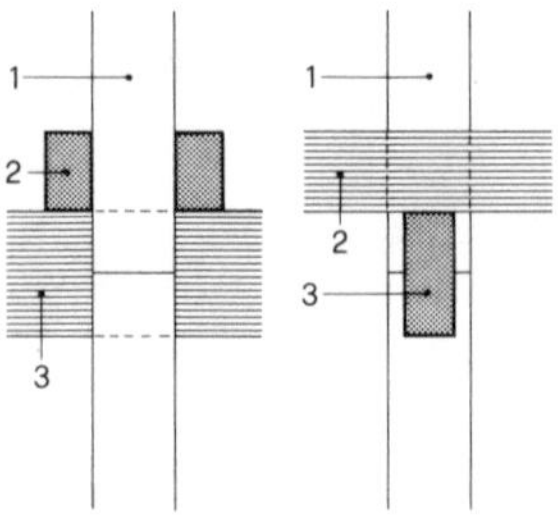

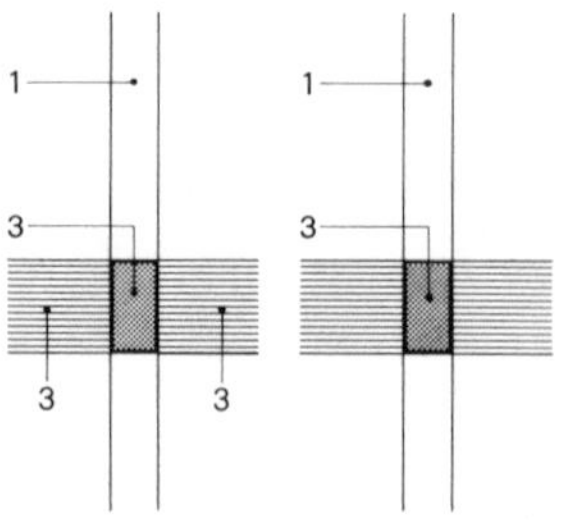

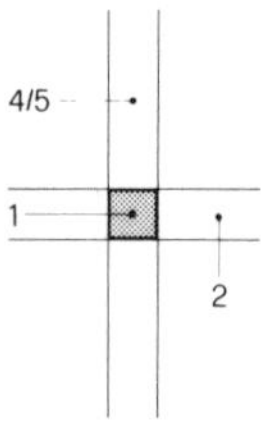

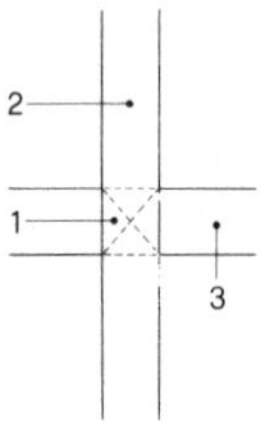

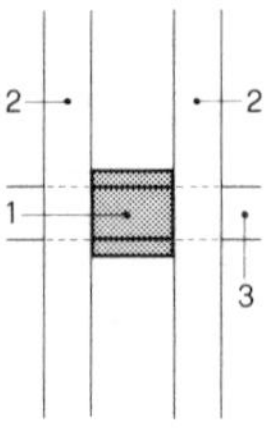

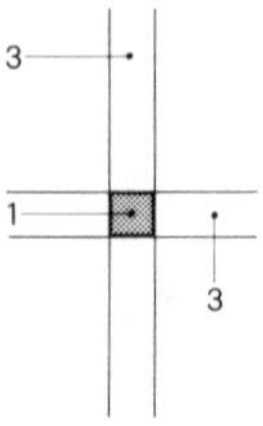

1 Columns
2 Floor beam
3 Main girder
4 Sill
5 Header

Split columns and beams		Ribs		
Continuous beams and columns				
				Structure Types
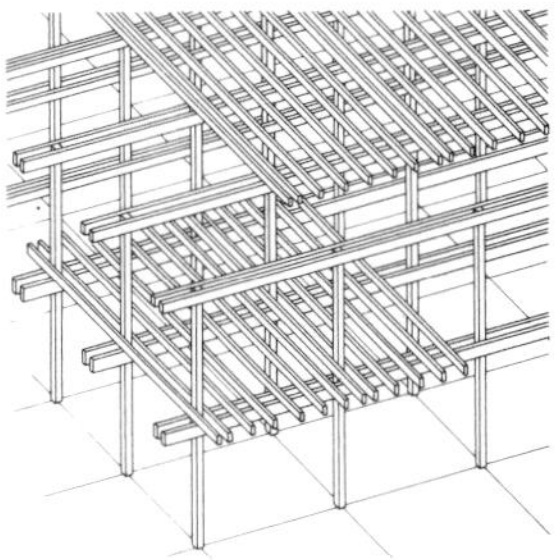	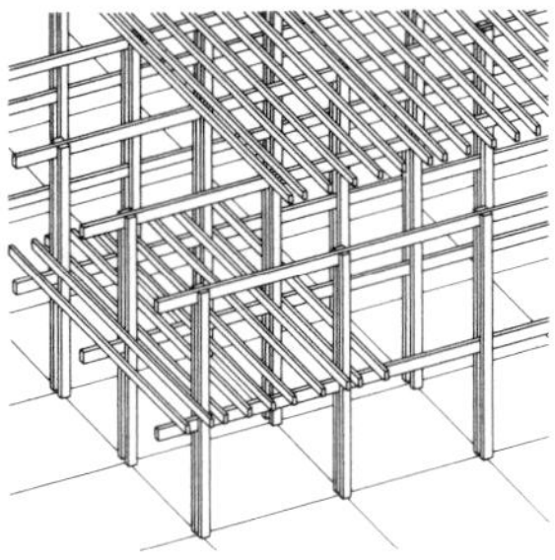	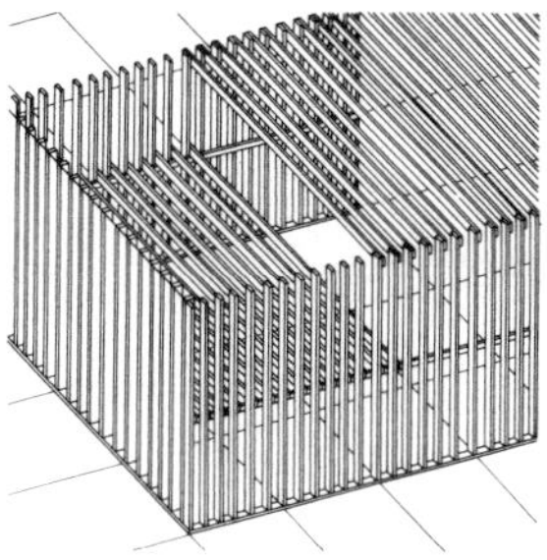	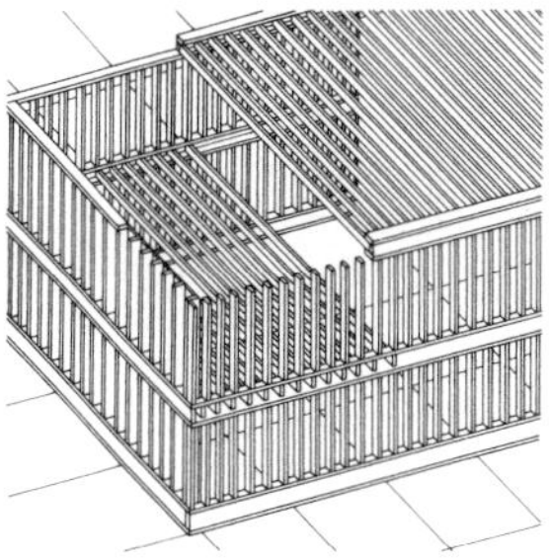	Isometrics
Split beam	Split column	Balloon	Platform	
				Cross section
				Plan
				Nodes
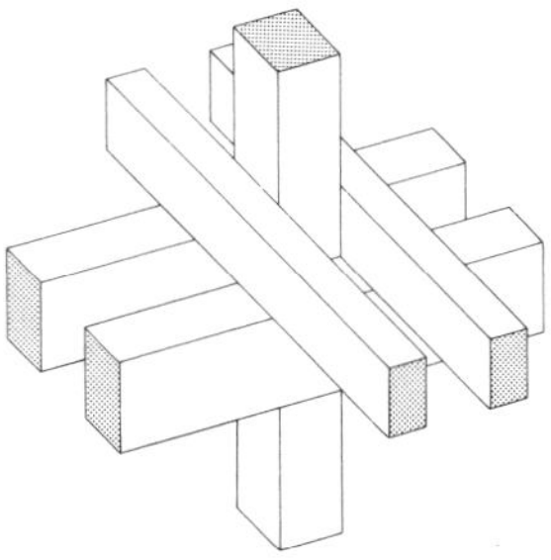	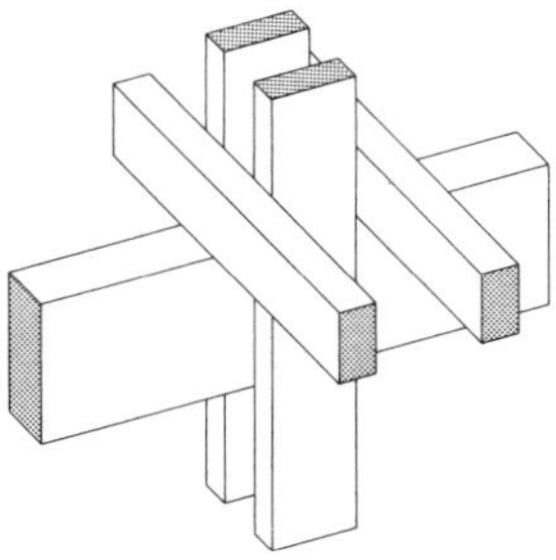	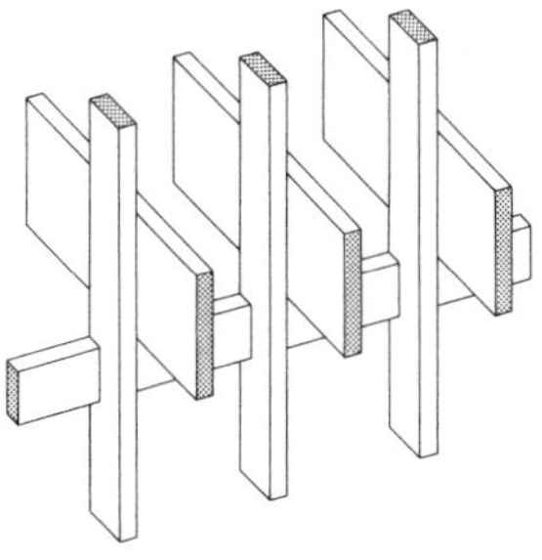	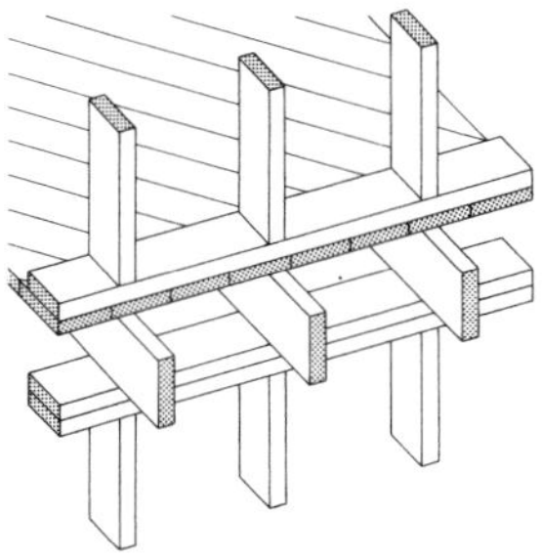	Isometrics
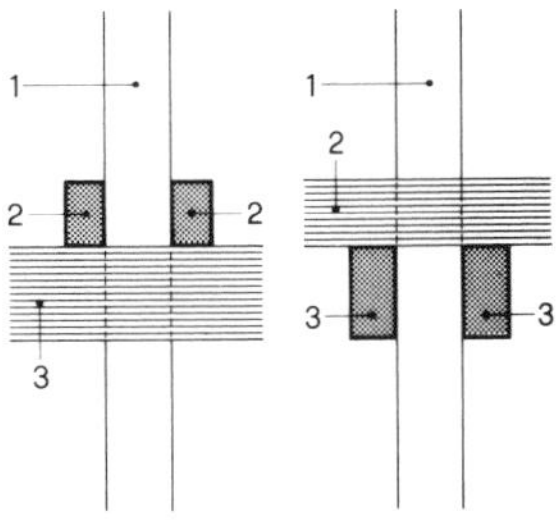	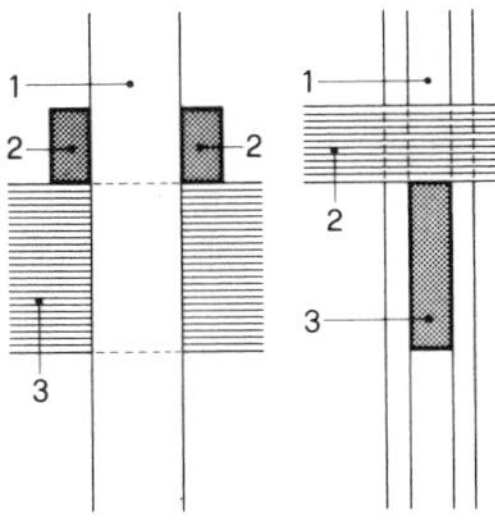	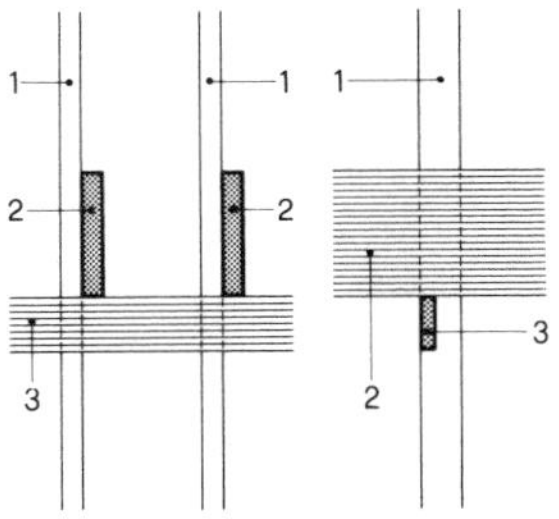	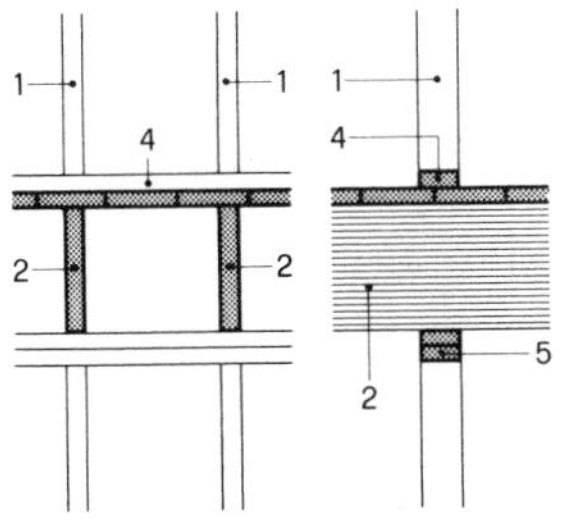	Cross section
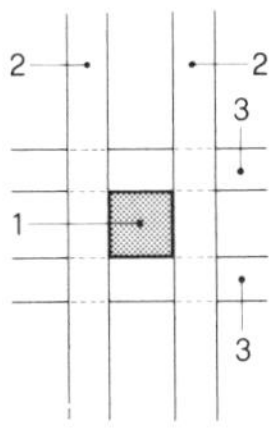	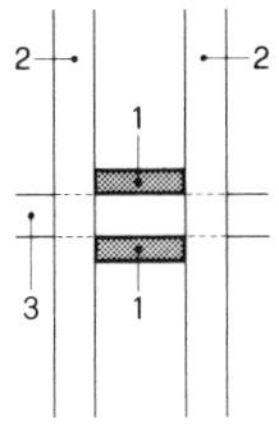	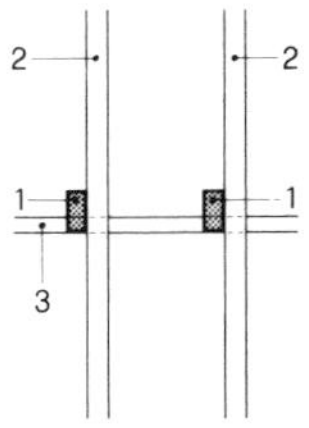	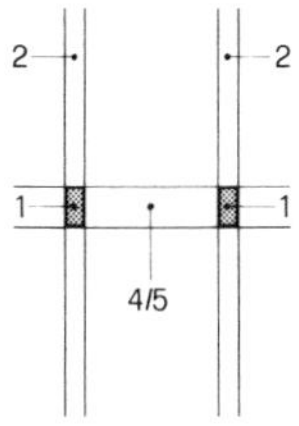	Plan

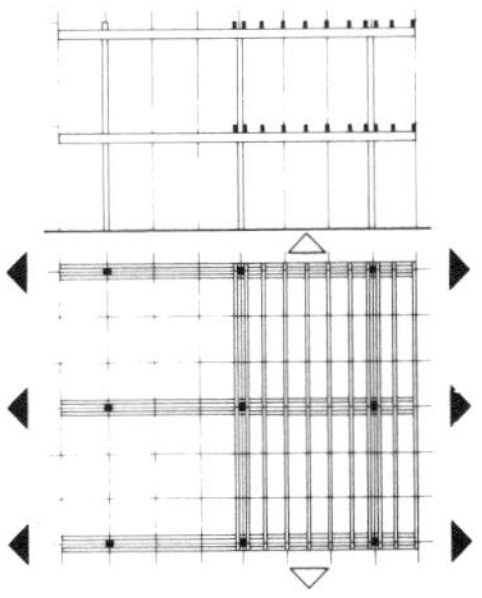

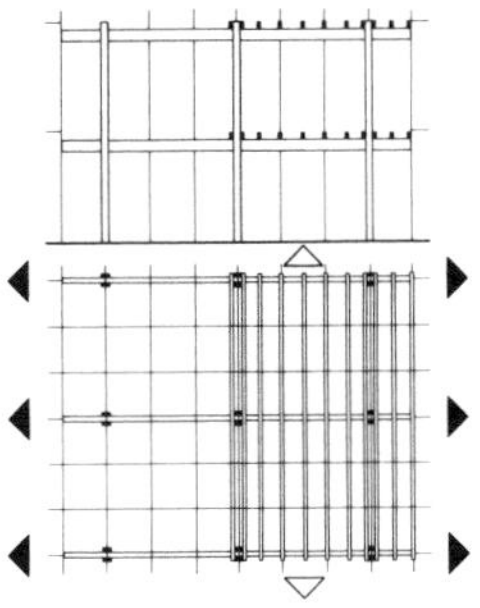

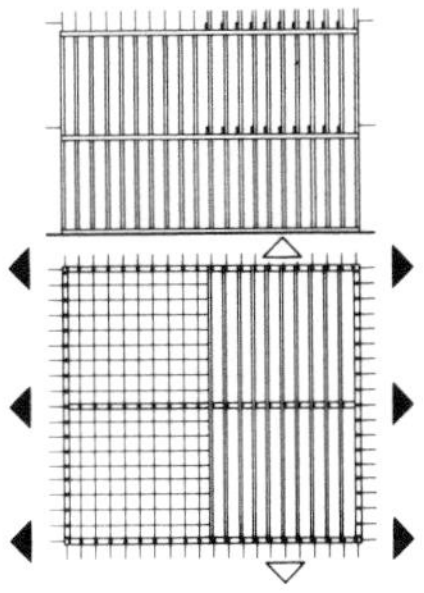

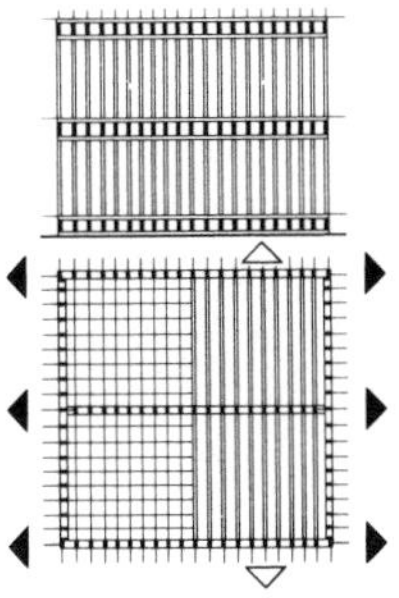

1 Column
2 Floor beam
3 Main girder
4 Sill
5 Header

1

Nursery School

Architect: Behnisch and Partner, Stuttgart, West Germany
Project engineer: Chr. Kandzia
Engineer: Umfahrer, Stuttgart

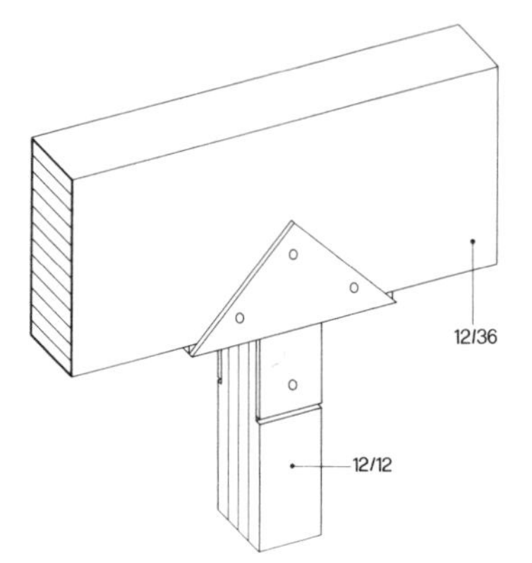

Structural node, bearing of girder on column

Design

One-story building with flat roof. The roof structure protrudes from thin roofing to form a pergola. The interior walls are set at various distances, often diagonally to the structural grid. They act as an improvised enclosure with no relationship to the structure. The functional and open environment of the school is visible everywhere.

Structure

The design of this nursery school is enhanced by simple construction, careful detailing, and a spatial form largely determined by woodwork. Timber framing consists of 12/12 cm columns, 12/36 cm main girders, all made from laminated wood; the rafters are 8/14 cm lumber. The main girders rest on columns with span lengths of 5.25 and 3.75 m. The rafters rest on girders; their span sometimes exceeds 3.75 m. The structural problem in this instance is the construction of the bearing of the girder on the column.

In order to secure the girder against overturning, the steel bearing has triangular sides, which are bolted to the girder.

The roof is stiffened horizontally by flat steel bars 4/40 mm, which rest on the roof decking. Wind loads are carried by a reinforced-concrete shear wall and by ϕ 14 mm diagonal steel bars placed in certain column planes. The diagonals at their intersection are connected to a ring, under which there is a hole for a drainage pipe.

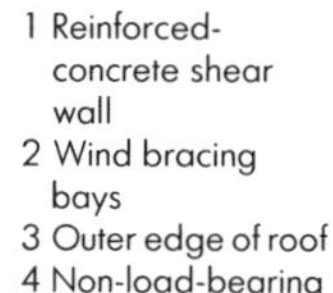

1 Reinforced-concrete shear wall
2 Wind bracing bays
3 Outer edge of roof
4 Non-load-bearing walls

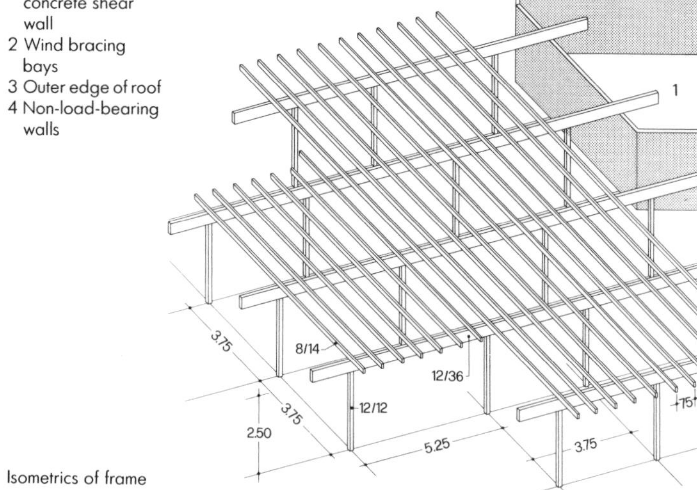

Isometrics of frame

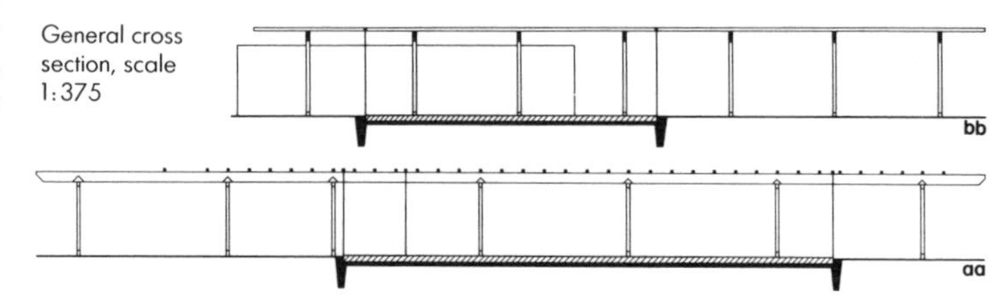

General cross section, scale 1:375

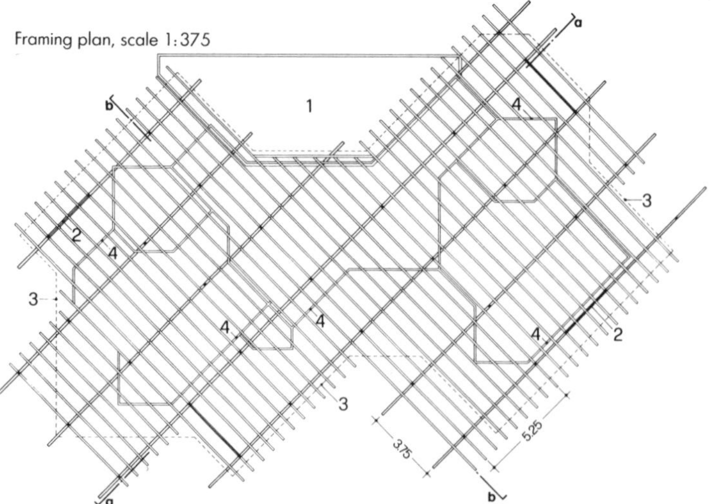

Framing plan, scale 1:375

Structure

Partial cross section

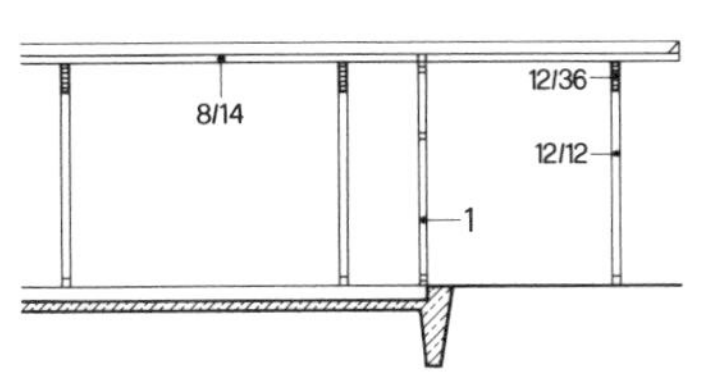

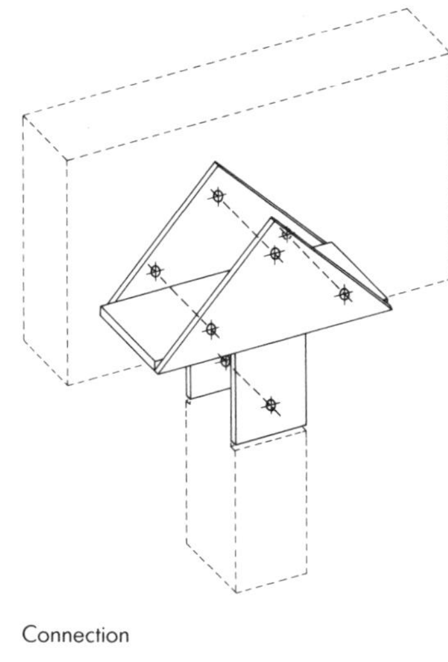

Connection

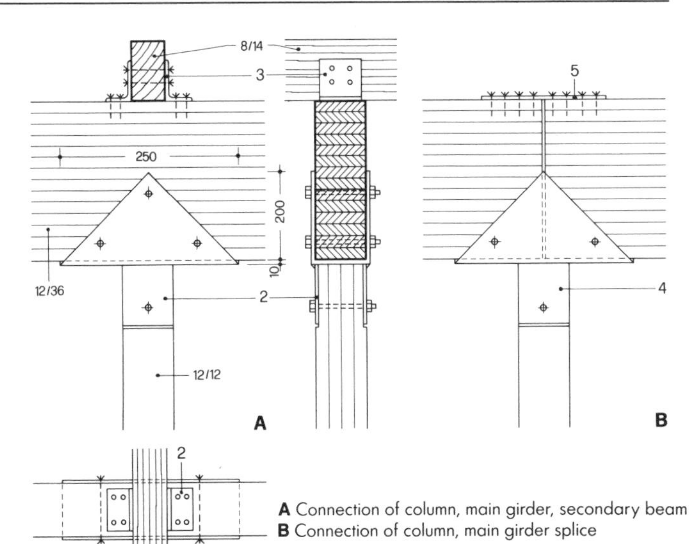

A Connection of column, main girder, secondary beam
B Connection of column, main girder splice

1 Non-load-bearing partition
2 Steel bearing plate, $t = 5$ mm, bolts M12
3 Steel angle 90 mm, nailed or bolted
4 Same as 2, with 2 × 2 shear connectors (GeKa 65)
5 Perforated steel plate 60 × 290 mm
6 Steel plate 100 × 100 × 10 mm
7 Steel connection, $t = 5$ mm, bolts M16
8 Steel tube ϕ 57 × 2.9 mm and bearing plate with slotted holes
9 Masonry plate with 2 M12 anchor bolts into concrete
10 Cylindrical sleeve with bituminous sealer
11 Round wood edge mouldings

Column bearing

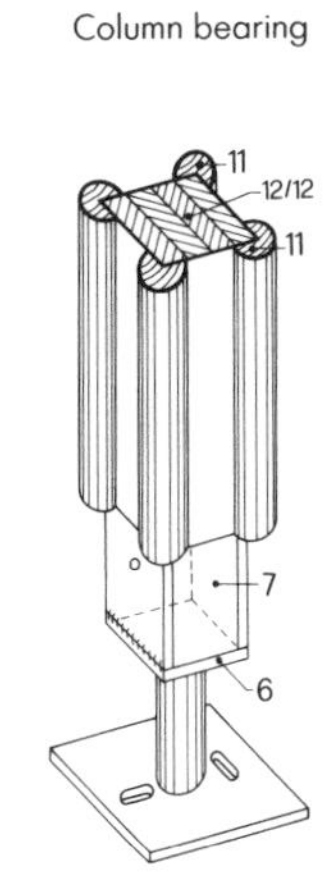

Interior column

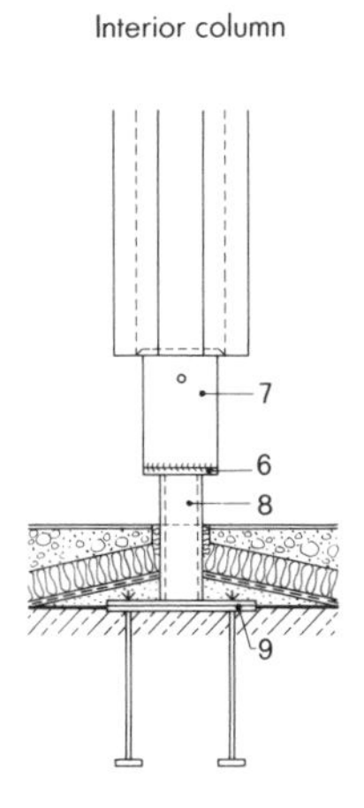

Exterior column

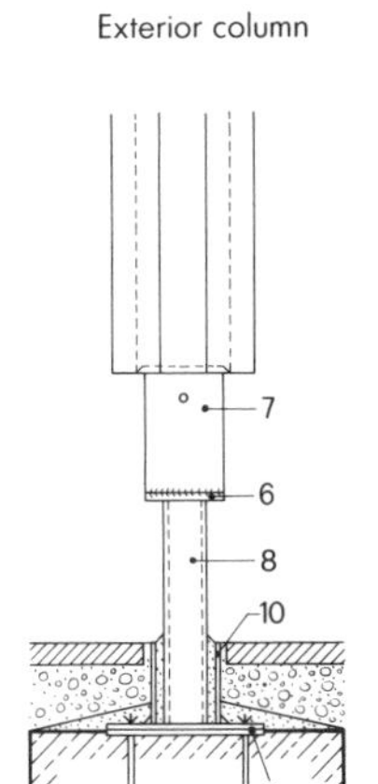

Bracing

1 Steel bar ϕ 24 mm
2 Steel ring ϕ 168.3 × 100 × 3 mm
3 Bearing shoe with welded angle
4 Bearing shoe to full depth of girder and angle connection
5 Column base with welded angle connection
6 Steel angle L 80 × 60 × 8 mm with shear connector (GeKa 50)
7 Steel plate 300 × 70 × 8 mm with shear connector (GeKa 50)
8 Same as 7 for girder or beam splices
9 Steel diagonals 40 × 4 mm bolted on 7

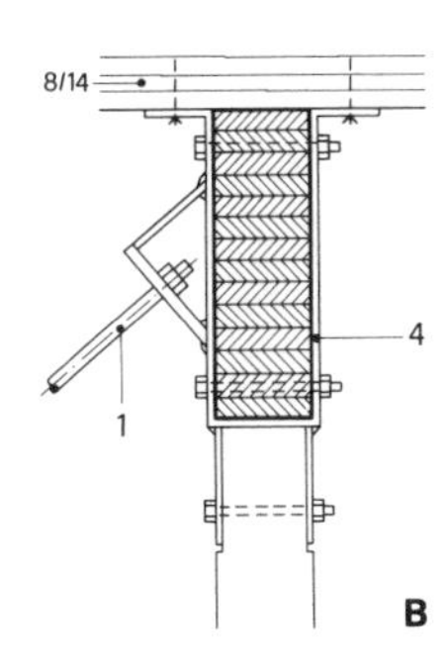

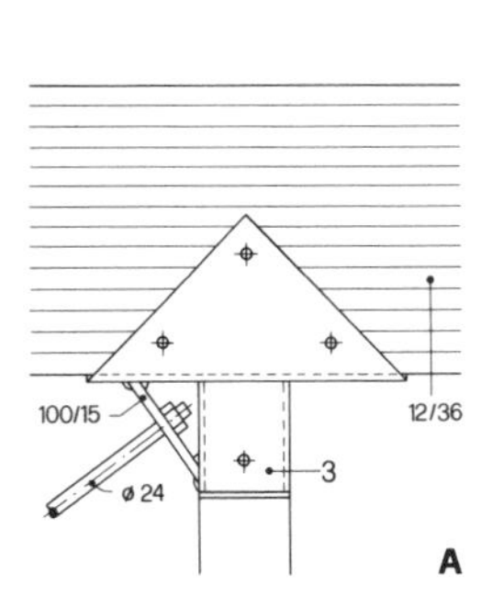

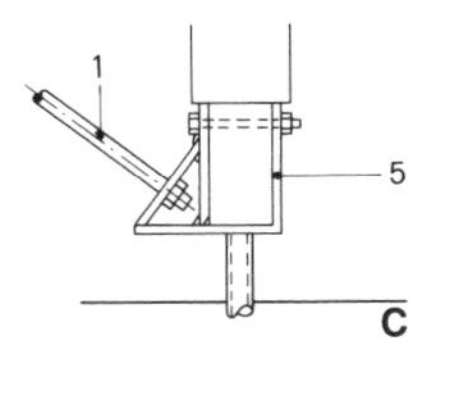

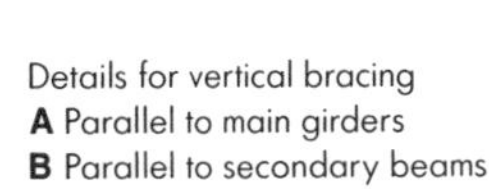

Details for vertical bracing
A Parallel to main girders
B Parallel to secondary beams
C Column base

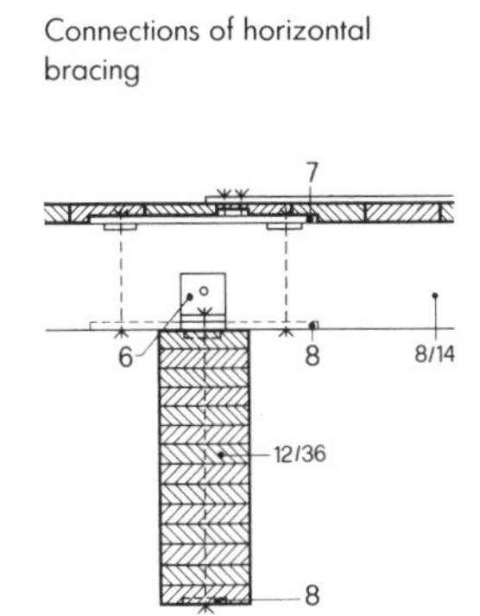

Connections of horizontal bracing

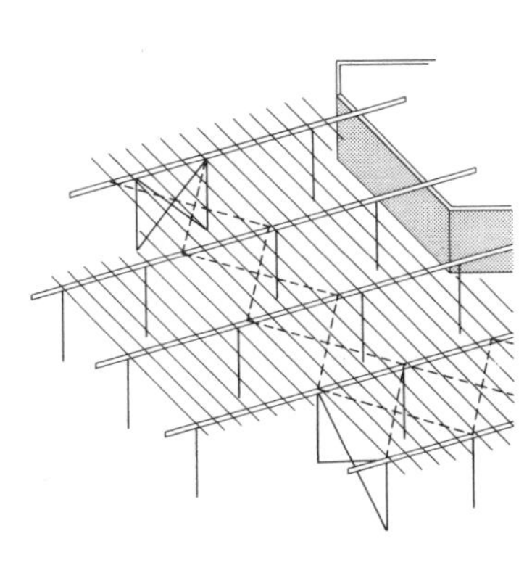

General view with layout of vertical and horizontal bracing

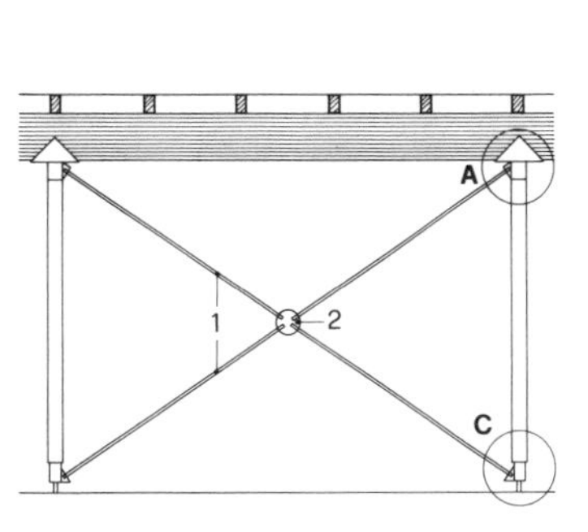

Finishes

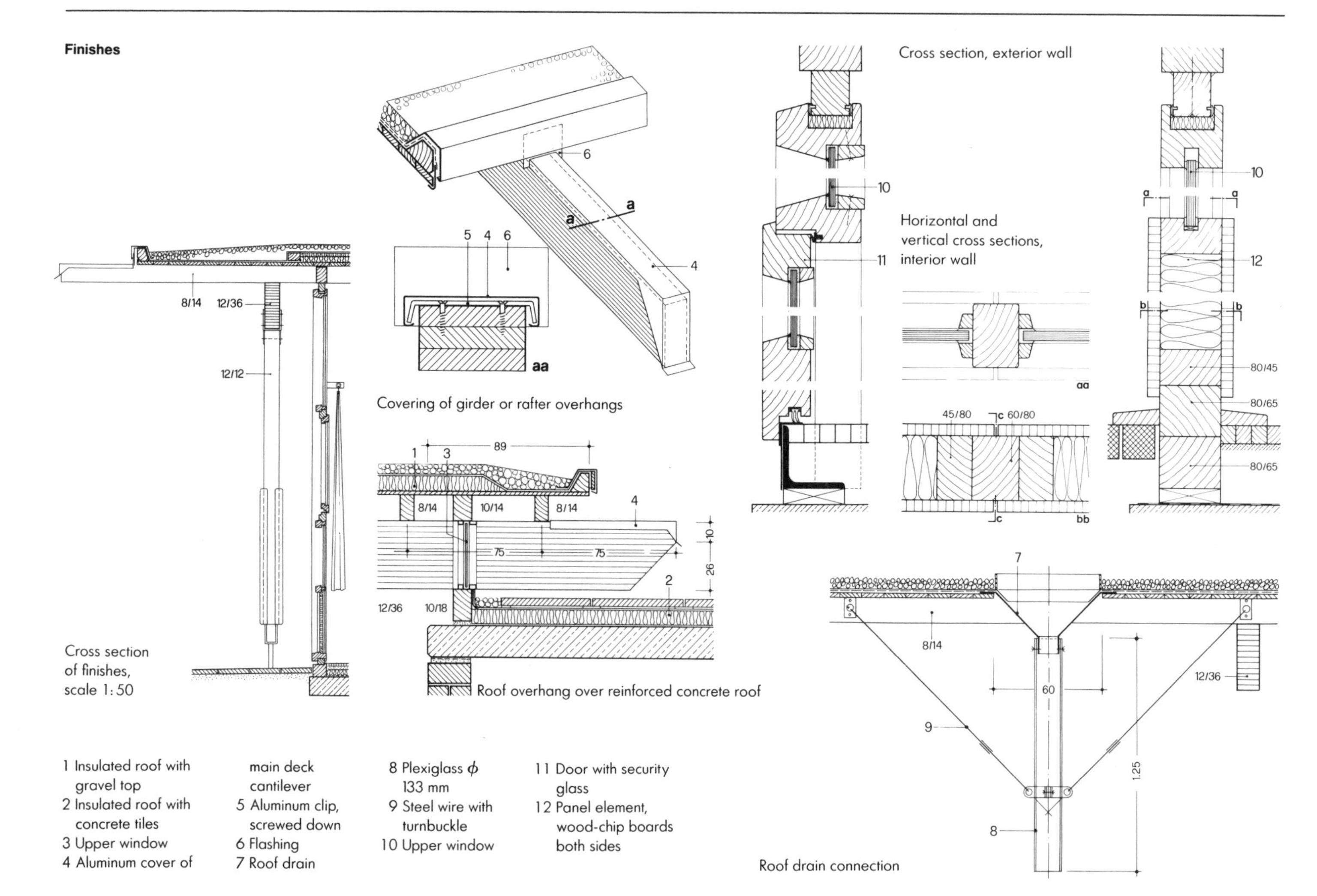

Layout

1 Roof canopy
2 Hall
3 Classroom
4 Group activity
5 Director
6 Toilets and washroom

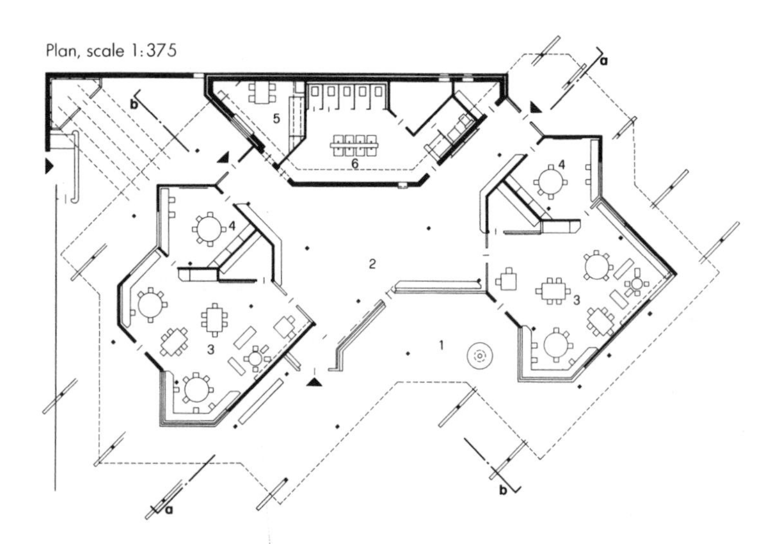

Plan, scale 1:375

2

Nursery School

Architect: O. Steidle and Partner, Munich, West Germany
Engineer: J. Natterer, Munich

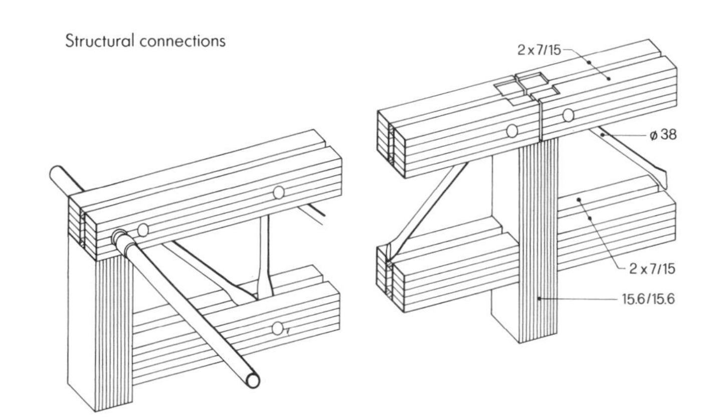

Structural connections

Design

The basic concept of this nursery school is one of a large roof under which the rooms are arranged freely without relation to the structure. This type of skeleton structure, having a flat roof on columns, permits plan arrangements other than the one shown here (two classrooms, a multipurpose room, and several side rooms). There could be rooms with movable partitions or continuous spaces without partitions.

Structure

The frames in cross section consist of 0.70-m-deep trusses spanning over two spans of 8.40 m each. The upper and lower truss chords consist of twin laminated beams, 2 × 7/15 cm. Diagonal and vertical struts are made from steel tubes ϕ 38 mm, whose ends are flattened in the direction of the truss. The flattened ends are connected between the split chords by means of one-sided shear connectors and bolts. These delicate trusses are simple to install. The steel tubes receive a foam coating, and the wood parts are so dimensioned that the structure has a fire rating of F30.

Columns are laminated wood 15.6/15.6 cm. The upper chords of the trusses rest on columns; they are affixed to the columns by means of steel plates and bolts. A double tongue and groove sheathing, 4.2 cm thick, spans the distance of 2.40 m between trusses. The insulation rests on sheathing.

Lateral bracing of the trusses is provided by sheathing layout. Wind loads and horizontal buckling loads from trusses are transferred to vertical bracing by means of a peripheral horizontal truss system (Gangnail system). Since this truss is as thick as the insulation, and no peripheral insulation is needed, the overall thickness of the roof remains uniform. Wind loads are conveyed to the foundation by means of crossed steel pipes within exterior column rows, as well as by wood struts in the central area of the building.

Finishes

Because of recess, there is no interference between facade and exterior columns. Only some interior walls are connected to columns through top wall headers. In order to allow for deflection of the main girders and sheathing, all wall and facade elements are connected by mouldings which permit vertical movement. The spaces between trusses are used for high windows.

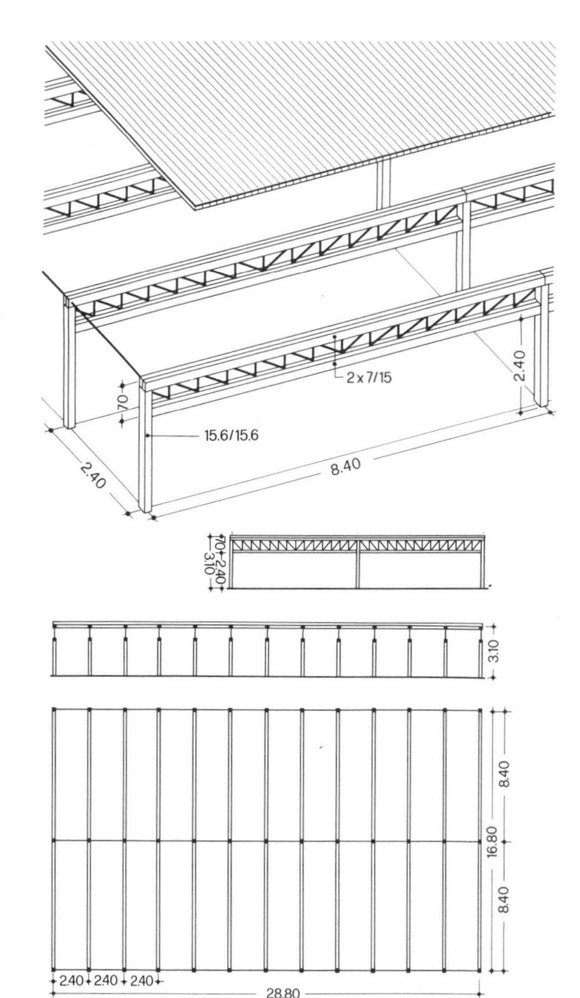

Framework, plan and cross section

Construction

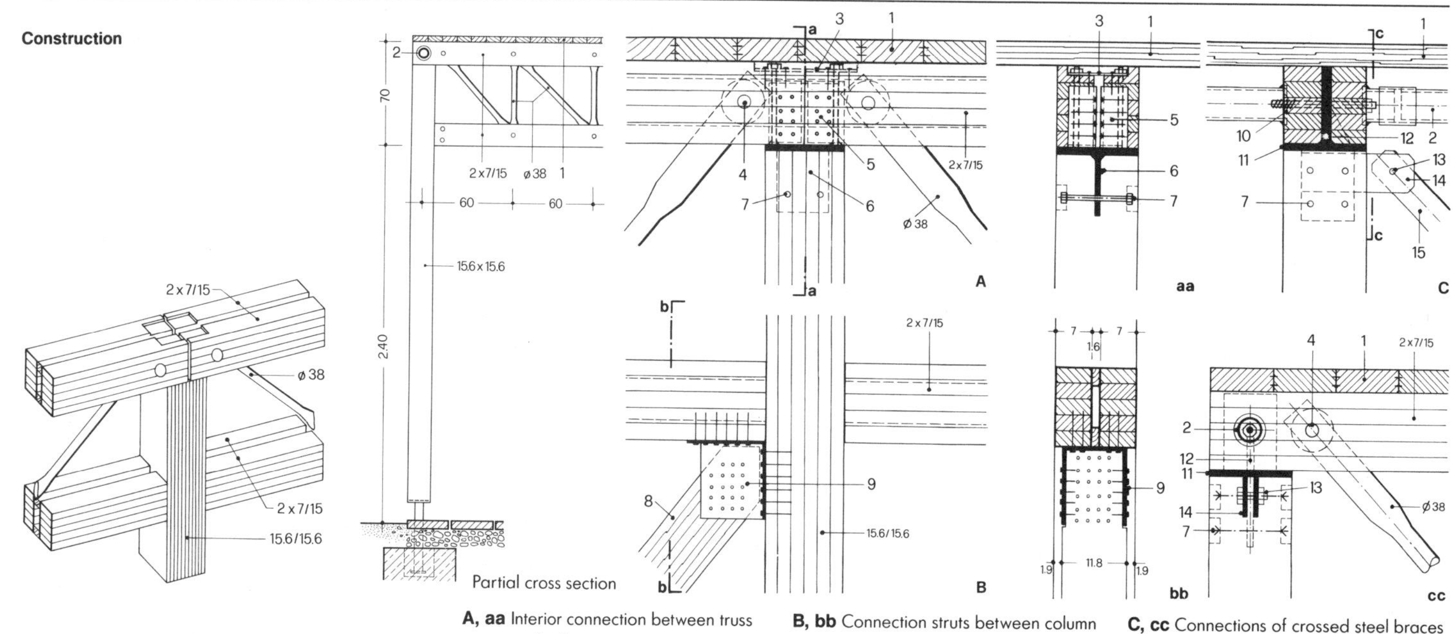

A, aa Interior connection between truss and column

B, bb Connection struts between column and sill

C, cc Connections of crossed steel braces

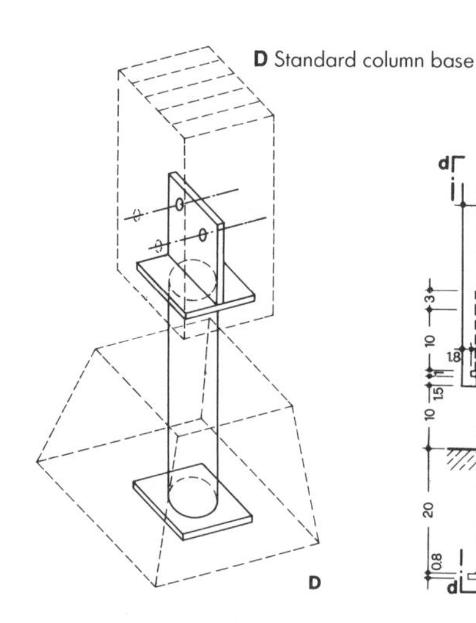

D Standard column base

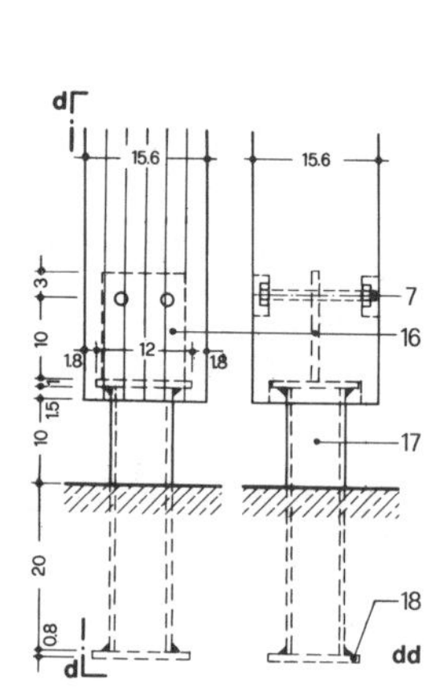

1 Tongue and groove sheathing 4.2 cm
2 Adjustable pipe sections between exterior columns
3 Nailed sheet metal as tension gusset
4 One-sided shear connector ϕ 80 mm
5 Steel angle, $t = 5$ mm
6 Welded steel angle, $t = 10$ mm
7 Bolts M12
8 Wood brace 12/12 to 12/20 cm
9 Steel plate connection, $t = 5$ mm, nailed
10 Anchor plate for pipe sections 2
11 Connection plate, $t = 5$ to 15 mm
12 Web plate
13 Bolt M16
14 2 flat steel gussets 80×5 mm
15 Crossed steel bracing
16 Steel plate column base, $t = 10$ mm
17 Steel tube ϕ 76 mm
18 Steel base plate

Bracing

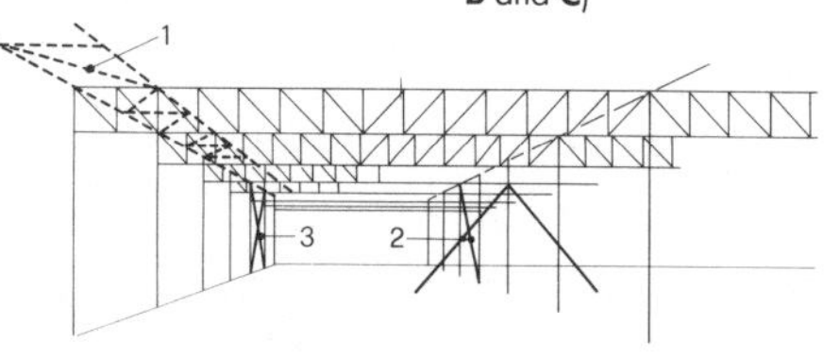

Connection of steel bracing and wood strut to column base (for upper connection see details **B** and **C**)

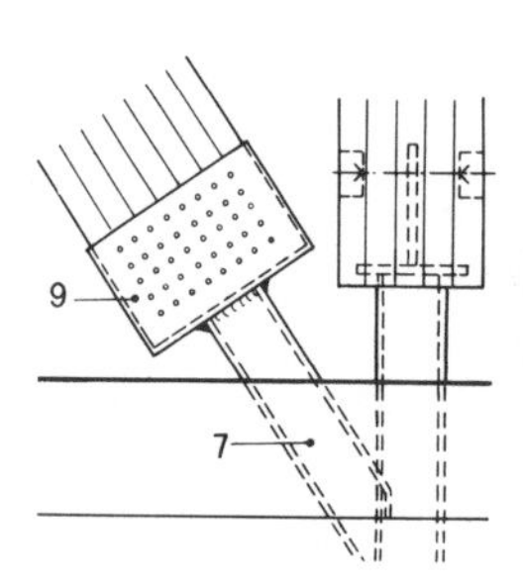

1 Horizontal truss (Gangnail system)
2 Vertical bracing with wood diagonals 11.8/20 cm
3 Diagonal bracing with steel pipes ϕ 38 mm
4 Steel column base
5 2 steel gusset plates 80×5 mm
6 Bolt M16
7 Steel tube ϕ 76 mm
8 Steel base plate
9 Steel shoe

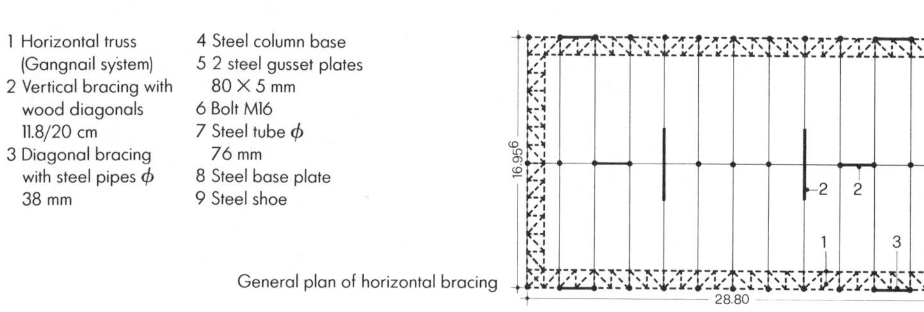

General plan of horizontal bracing

Finishes

Roof construction over exterior canopy

Roof over interior rooms

1 Tongue and groove sheathing 4.2 cm
2 Horizontal truss (Gangnail system)
3 Edging
4 Flashing
5 Roofing: gravel, roofing, leveling course, insulation, vapor barrier, slip sheet
6 Beam
7 Double glazing
8 Grate sill
9 Wall panel
10 Flashing
11 Suspended ceiling
12 Corner post
13 Glazed outer door
14 Width of truss
15 Vertical truss strut
16 Cover at truss
17 Connection of light partition
18 Interior door
19 Adjustment jamb

Horizontal section with corner at lower windows

Horizontal section across truss

Horizontal section at light partitions

Partition bath/shower

Vertical section of outer wall with glazed door, or upper window and wall

Layout

1 Entrance and vestibule
2 Multipurpose room
3 Classroom
4 Group activity room
5 Dressing room
6 Toilets and washroom
7 Director
8 Kitchen
9 Storage room
10 Garden tools and play equipment
11 Covered play area

Plan, scale 1:50

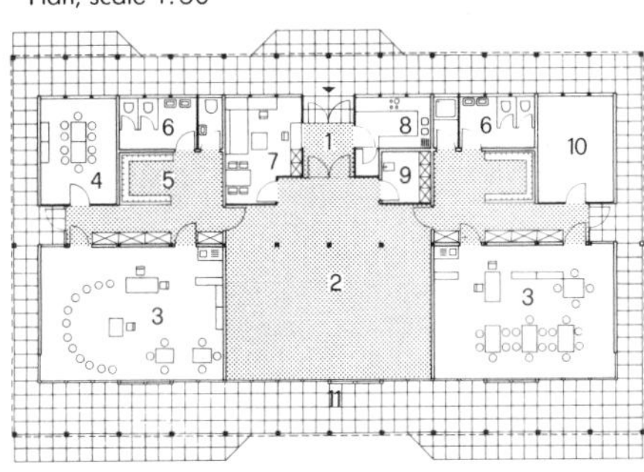

3

Construction System for a Two-Story Building

Developed by: J. Natterer, J. Goehl, G. Henn, Munich, West Germany

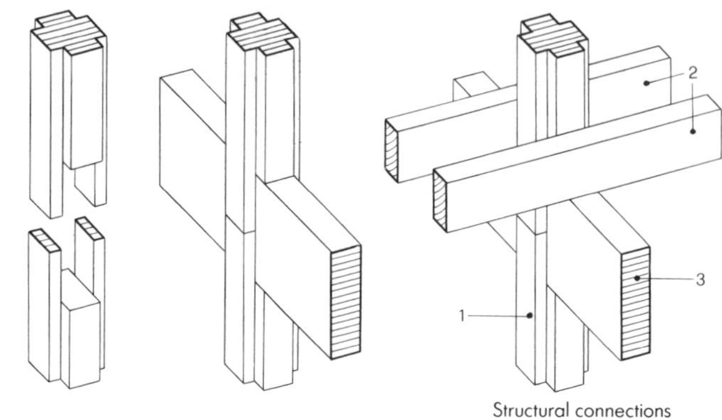

Structural connections
1 Column 12(20)/12(20) cm
2 Floor beam 12/22 cm
3 Main girder 12/32 cm

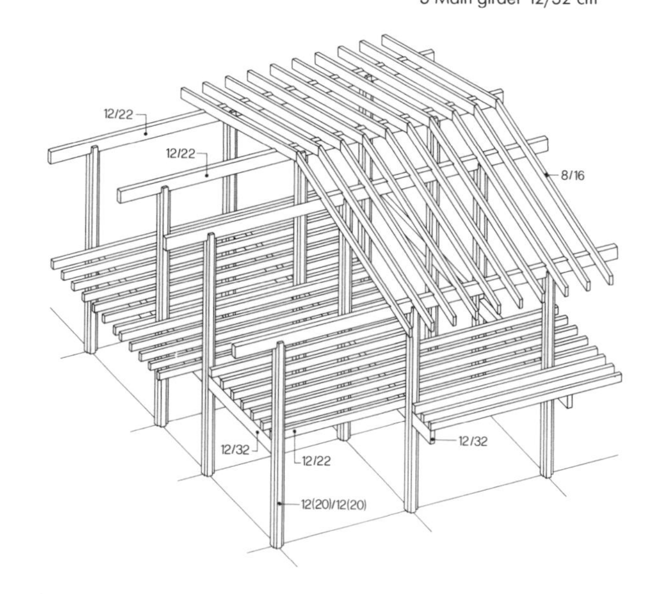

Design

This system provides for an economical frame that can be fabricated by any small timber construction enterprise without special equipment. It can be adapted to buildings of various uses, sizes, layouts, roof shapes, and finishes. This is not a prefabricated system, but an incentive to design and build a timber frame building.

Structure

The timber frame consists of single-piece cross sections. The columns are erected on the ground floor, the girders and floor beams are continuous. The girders span 3.60 and 2.40 m transversely, and the floor beams span 3.60 m longitudinally. The framing and connections consist essentially of a cross-shaped column and a nested girder. The columns are solid or laminated wood. They are made from 20/20 cm laminated wood with 4/4 cm corners and girder seat cutout, or they are made from 12/20 cm lumber with two side boards of 4 × 12 cm; the size depends on the structural requirements. The main beams are made from glue-laminated wood and are either 32 or 40 cm deep, depending on the load. Floor beams are solid wood 12/22 cm (or 8/22 cm if there is a fire-retardant layer underneath).

The transfer of forces occurs through direct timber contact. Steel angle connections are necessary at girder splices only, or if floor beams are in line with columns. Steel plates are only necessary if a bearing area must be enlarged underneath a girder in order not to exceed allowable wood stress normal to grain.

Horizontal stiffening is provided in floors or roofs by diagonal ties, diagonally placed planking, or offset chipboard panels. Wind forces are conveyed to the foundation by means of diagonal bracing.

Finishes

Finishing elements may be handmade or prefabricated, and may be added after some time. Wall, floor, and roof structures and their connections to the framing are developed so that no special installation expertise is needed.

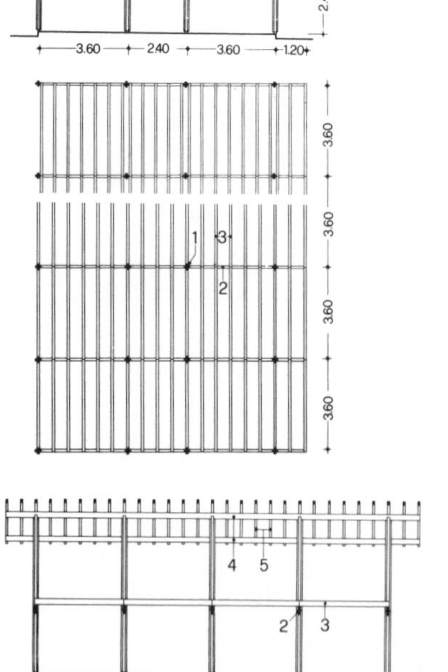

Plan and elevation of framework (for legend, see Structure, facing page)

Structure

1 Column 12(20)/12(20) cm
2 Main girder 12/32 cm
3 Floor beam 12/22 cm
4 Roof beams 12/22 cm
5 Rafters 8/16 cm
6 Column core 12/20 cm
7 Column side lashes 2 × 4/12 cm
8 Safety bolts
9 Bearing plate with stiffener
10 Bearing angle with stiffener, connected to column by bolt
11 Bearing plate with square tube and masonry plate; connected to column by web plate and bolts

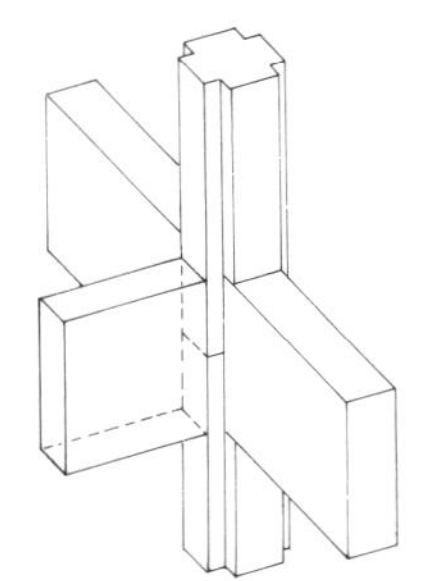

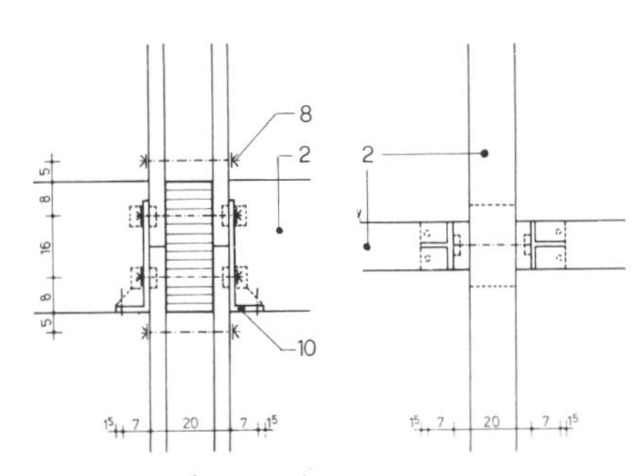

Intersection of main girders

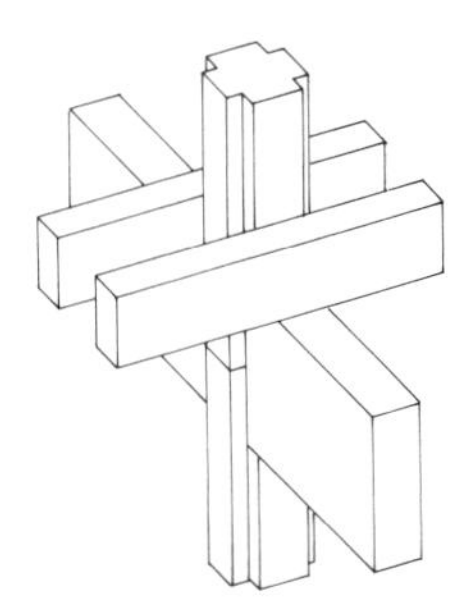

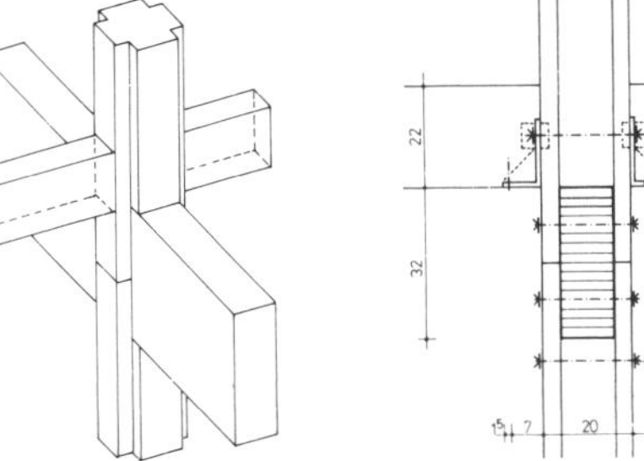

Bearing of main girder on column, floor beams

Axial connection of floor beam to column

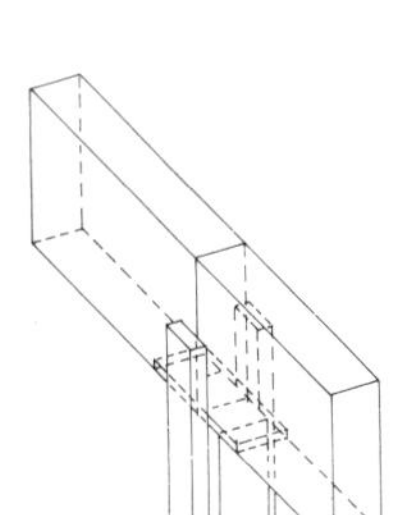

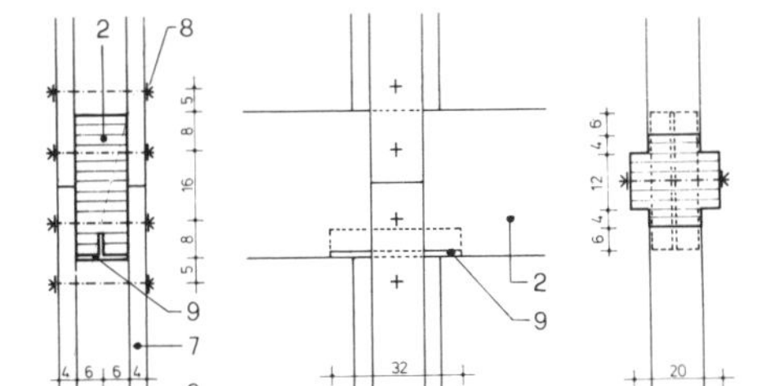

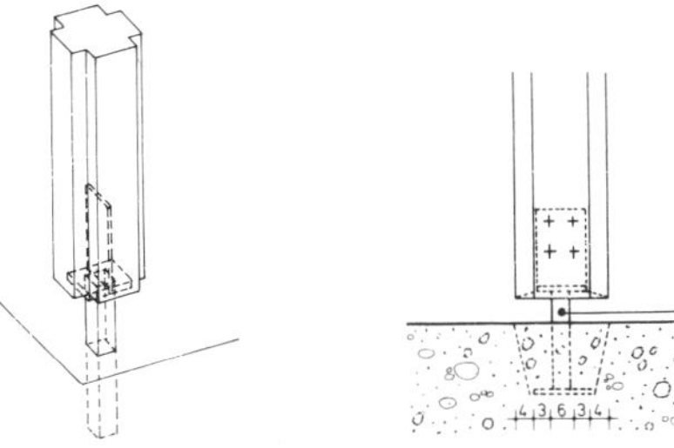

Bearing of main girder on column, with steel plate

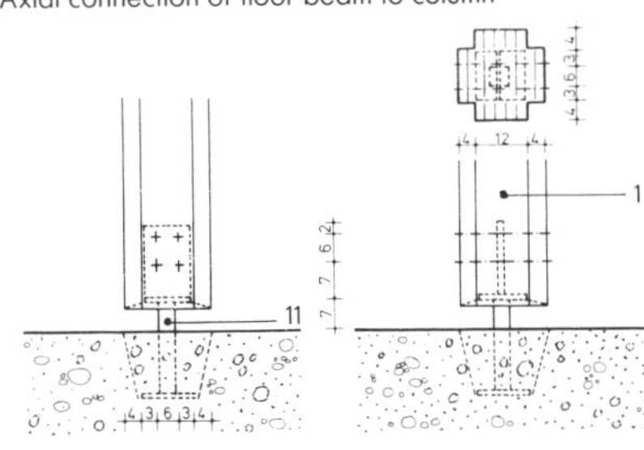

Column base

Bracing

1 Vertical trussing, wood struts, and diagonals
2 Horizontal trussing of floor, diagonal planking
3 Horizontal trussing in roof, steel ties

View of horizontal and vertical stiffening

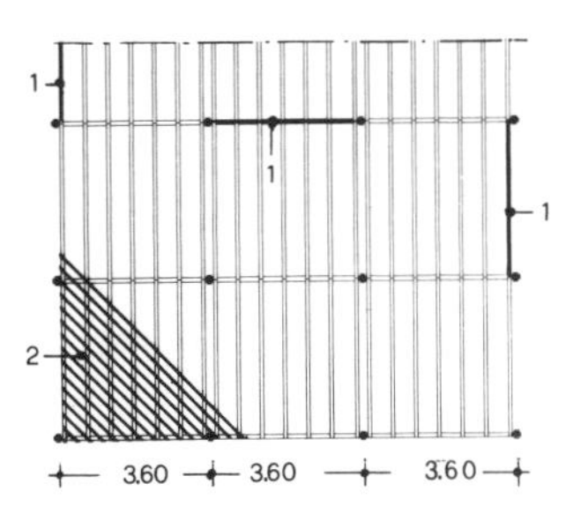

Finishes

Vertical cross section, exterior wall

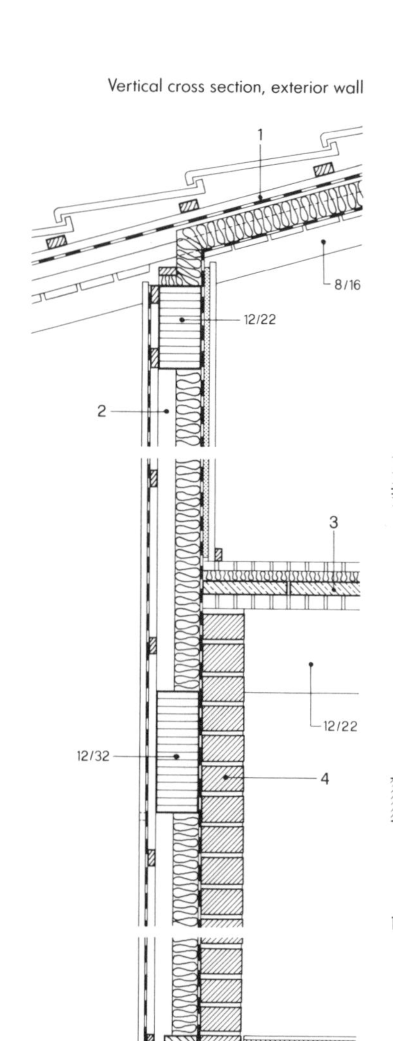

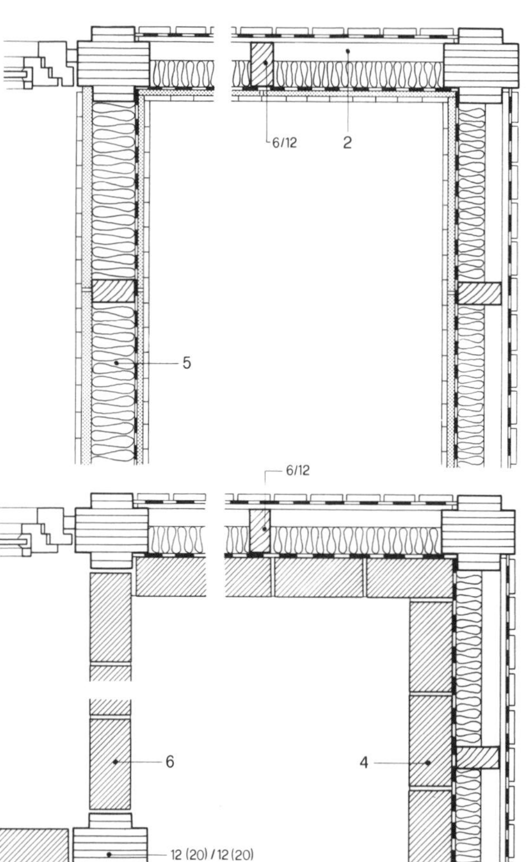

Horizontal section, ground floor and upper floor

1 Roof structure: tiles on nailing strips, cross slats, waterproofing, insulation, vapor barrier, sheathing
2 Exterior wall, upper floor: sheathing, waterproofing, ventilation, insulation, vapor barrier, gypsum board, lining
3 Floor: wood-chip boards, insulation, concrete planks, wood-chip boards
4 Exterior wall, lower floor: as in 2, but bricks on inside
5 Interior wall, upper floor: sheathing, gypsum board, insulation
6 Interior wall, ground floor: brick facing

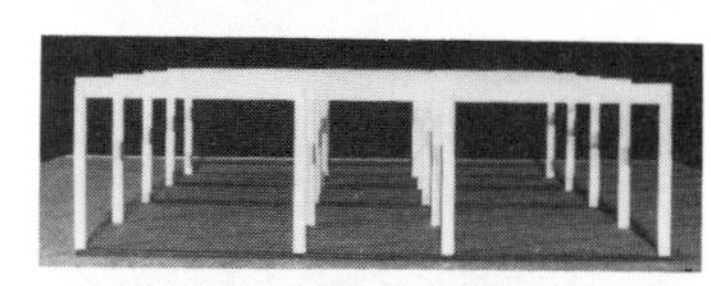

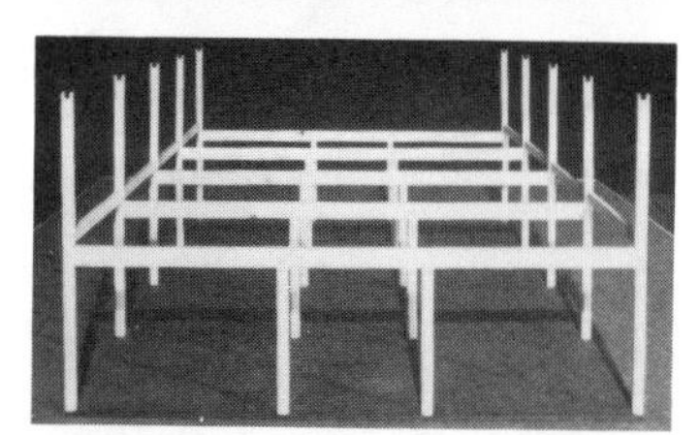

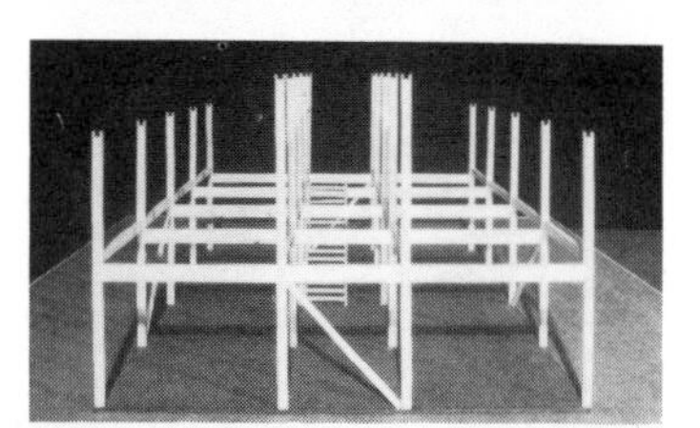

Erection sequence of framework

Layout

One-family residence, ground floor surface 212 m². Free plan with guest room or office, kitchen, dining area, and living room on lower floor. On upper floor two children's rooms, main bedroom, and bath.

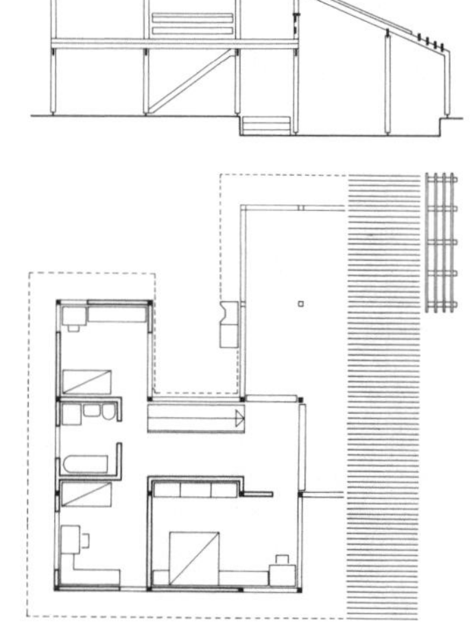

4

Office Building

Architect: E. Fahr, Munich, West Germany
Engineer: D. Steinmetz, Ettingen

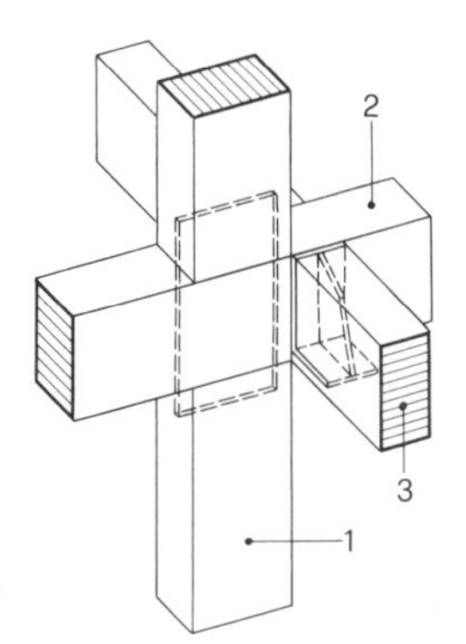

Connections
1 Column 15/30 cm
2 Continuous main girder 15/30 cm
3 Floor beam 15/30 cm

Design

Two-story office building of a woodworking firm, 500 m² floor area and 150 m² storage space under the roof. The design intent was to have the structure built as the firm's own project; the firm's own metal and concrete shop facilities were available. This explains the use of concrete gutters and concrete solar protection: the firm's own building capabilities were to be made visible. Siding on the solid walls consists of corrugated asbestos-cement panels and rounded shapes made by the firm.

Structure

The two-story frame consists of equal columns and floor beams 15/30 cm which lie in one plane. Transverse girders span over three spans (5.40, 3.60, and 5.40 m); they are cantilevered 1.20 m on each side. Since the girders are continuous, columns have to be spliced. These connections are arranged such that each column bears on a girder and is connected to the girder and lower column with an 8-mm-thick steel plate. Shear connectors between plate and column transfer the load through the plate directly from the upper to the lower column. Floor beam connections are steel angles. There is 6-cm planking on floor beams. The roof rests on floor beams and columns and is stiffened horizontally by means of diagonal framing. Floors are stiffened horizontally by screwed-on woodchip boards. Horizontal loads are transferred to foundations through diagonal steel ties in both longitudinal facades and through a massive timber shear wall at the centerline.

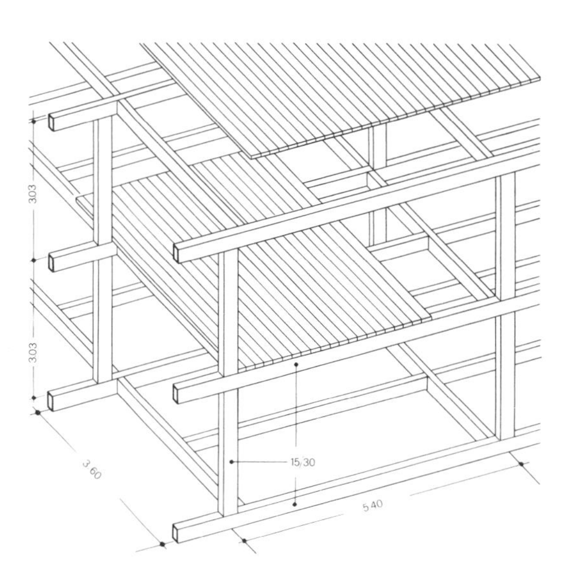

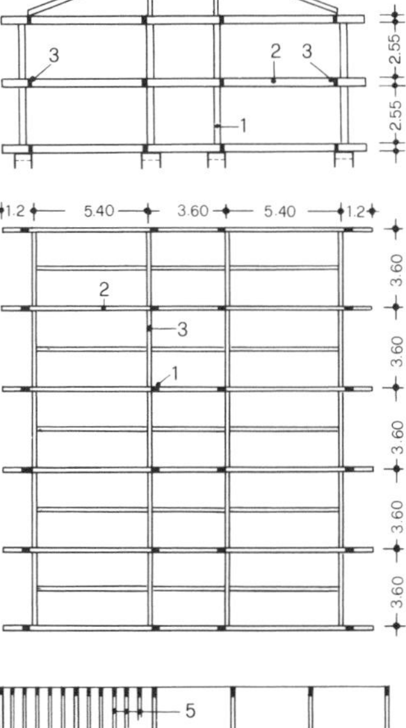

Framework, plan and section
1 Column 15/30 cm
2 Continuous main girder 15/30 cm
3 Floor beam 15/30 cm, bearing on 2
4 Ridge beam 15/30 cm
5 Rafters 8/10 to 8/19 cm

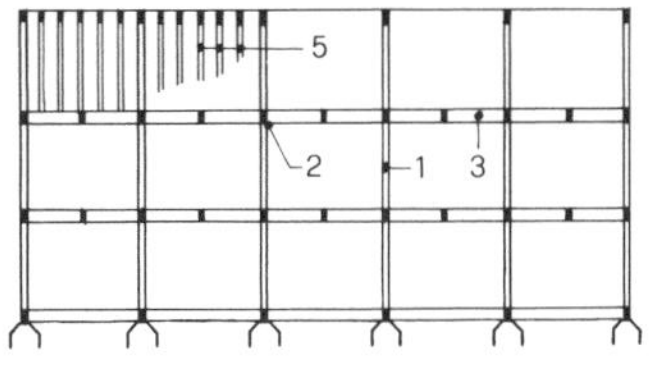

Structure

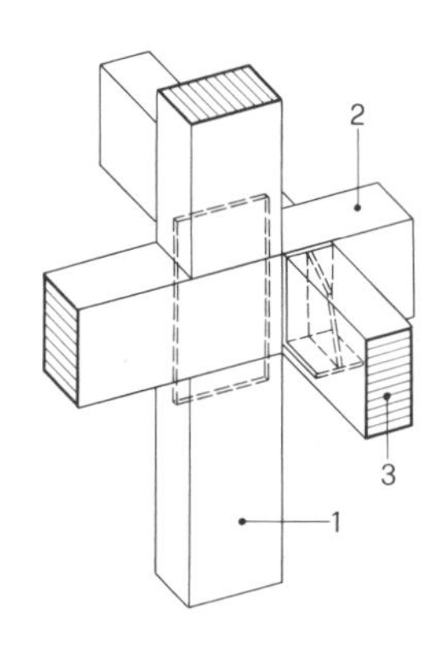

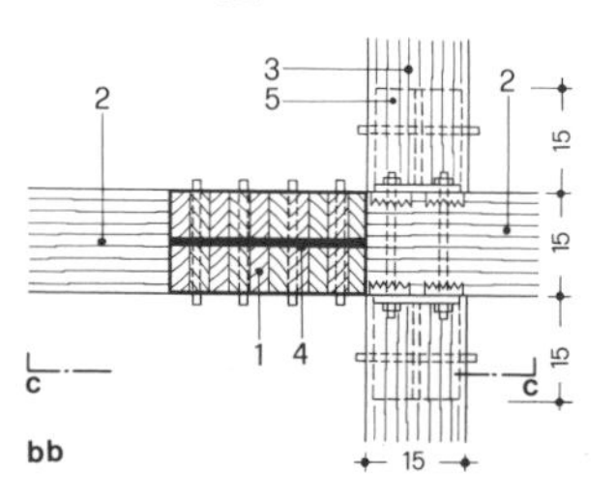

aa – cc Connection: main girder to column to inner floor beam

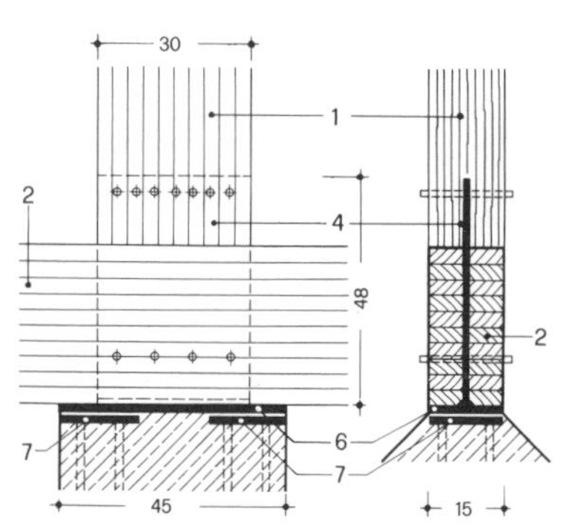

Connection to foundation

1 Column 15/30 cm
2 Main girder 15/30 cm, continuous
3 Floor beam 15/20 cm, bearing on 2
4 Steel plate 8 mm in girder and column slit, connected with bolts ϕ 12 mm
5 Bearing angle with stiffener, $t = 20$ mm, with 2 × ϕ 65 mm dowels secured with a ϕ 12 mm bolt
6 Steel plate 150 × 450 × 12 mm
7 Steel plate 150 × 150 × 12 mm with anchors ϕ 10 mm welded to 6 on site

Stiffening

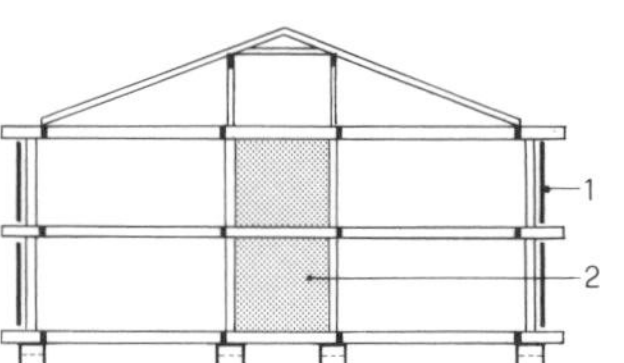
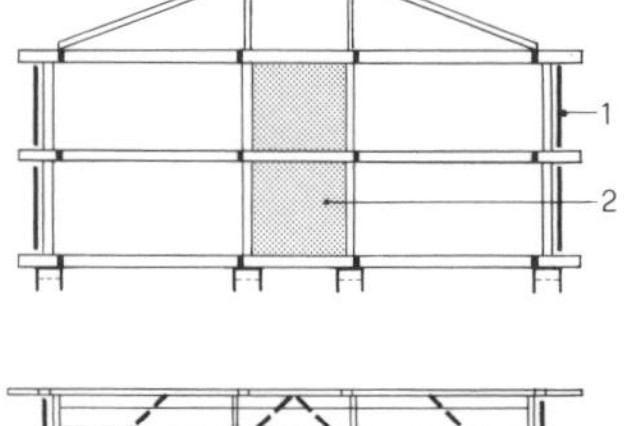

1 Diagonal steel tie ϕ 16 mm
2 Laminated wood panel, $d = 15$ cm, transversely bolted to column
3 Tongue and groove planks 6/14 cm nailed to girder with N42/110, and 10 mm wood-chip board with 10 cm N31/65 nails
4 Wind bracing 2.4/14 cm
5 Anchor plate for 1 with ϕ 50 mm bolts

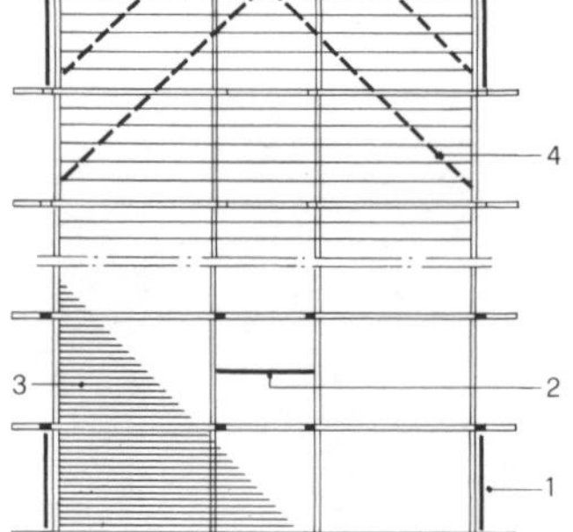

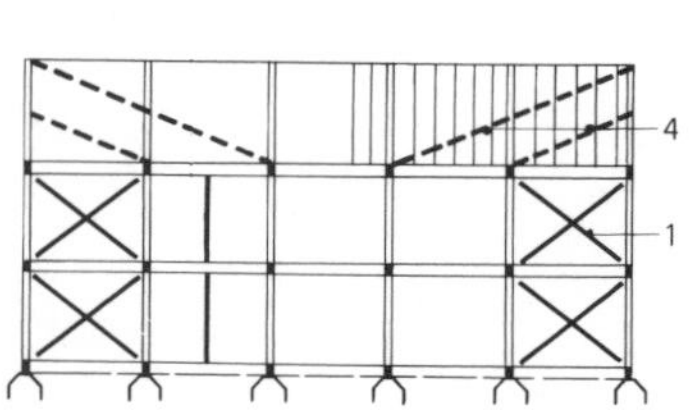

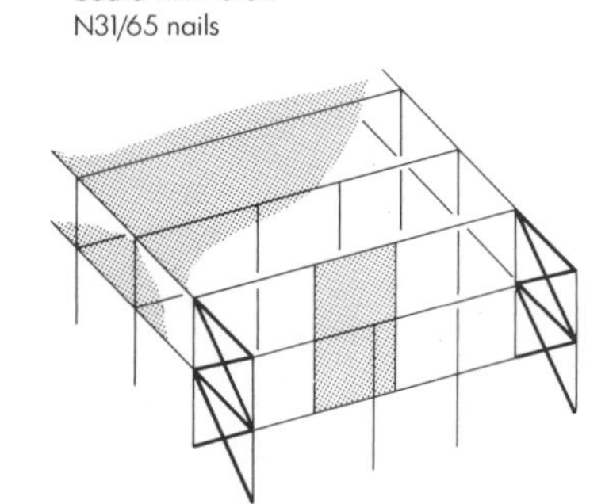

View of horizontal and vertical bracing

Connection of diagonal ties

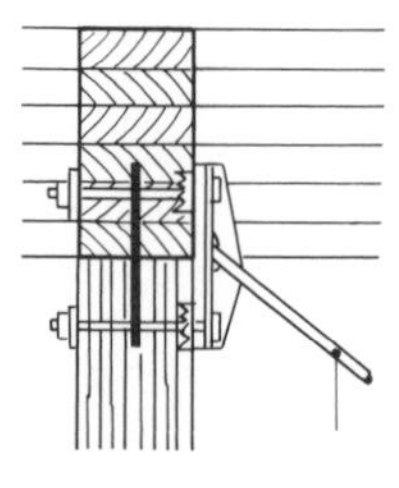

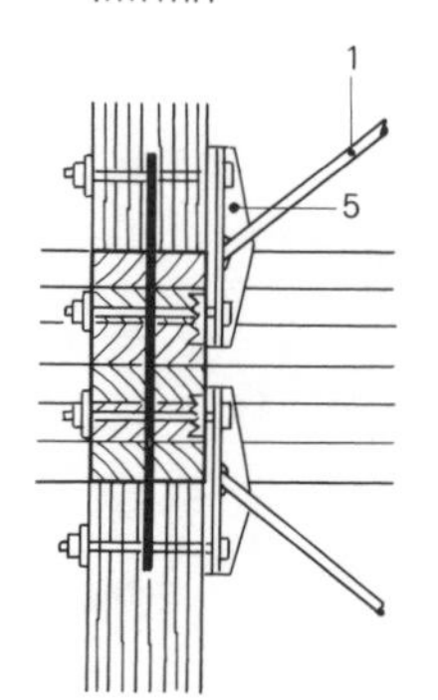

Finishes

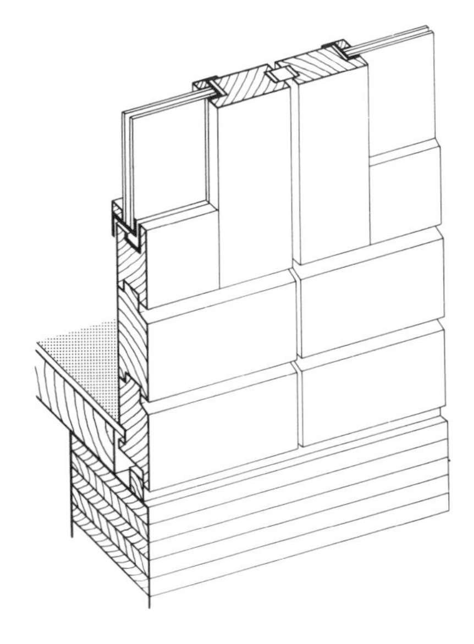

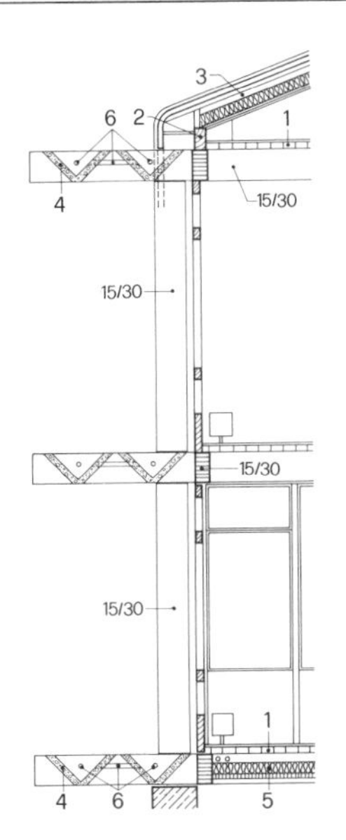

Partial section

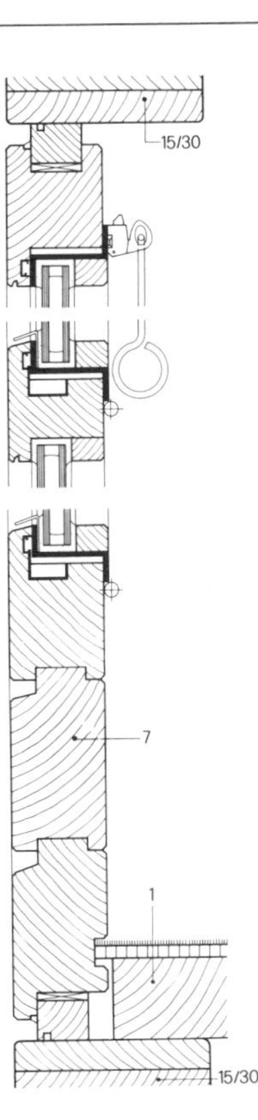

Vertical section, parapet and window

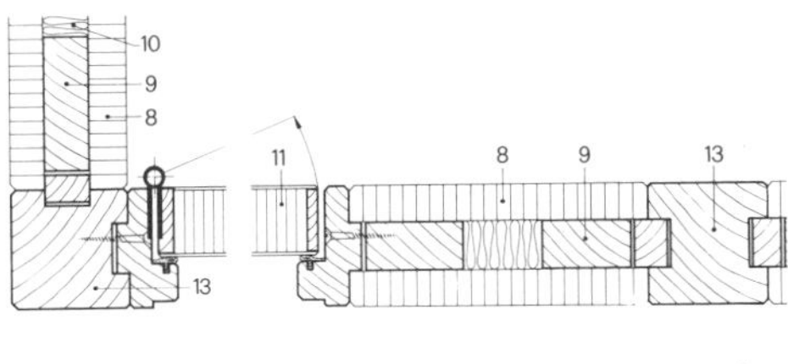

Horizontal section, wall and interior door

Vertical wall section, interior door section

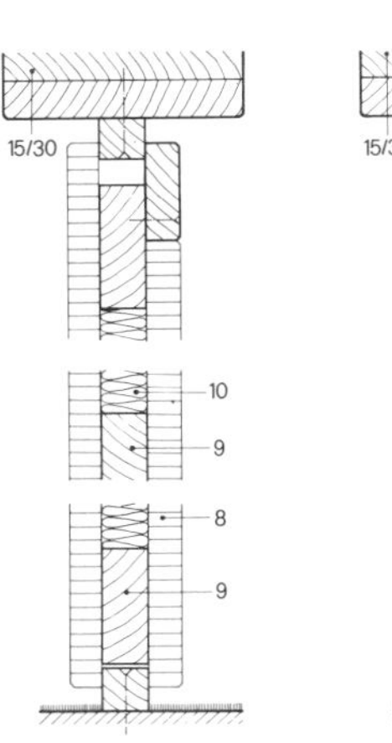

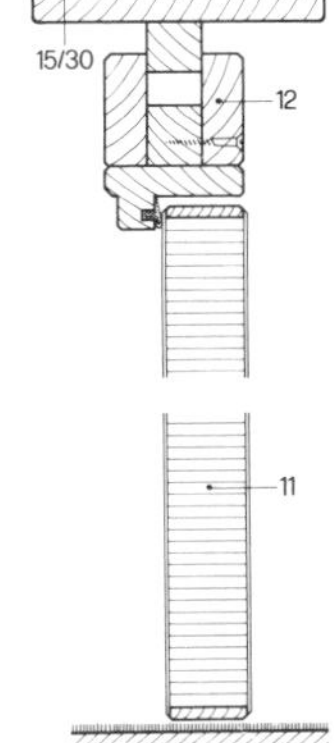

1 Tongue and groove planks with wood-chip board
2 Roof base beam
3 Roofing with corrugated asbestos-cement panels
4 Concrete beam as gutter
5 Insulation between beams
6 Connection pipes for drains
7 Tongue and groove parapet planking
8 Wood-chip boards 22 mm
9 Tie beam 28 mm
10 Fiberglass
11 Hollow door
12 Beech wood door header
13 Beech wood column

Layout

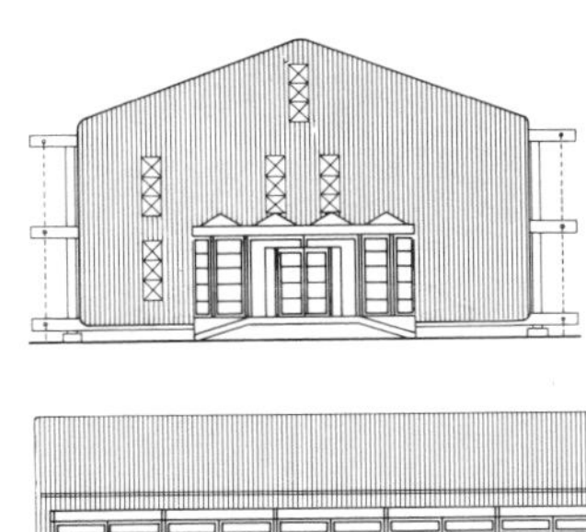

Elevations of gable wall and side wall; plan

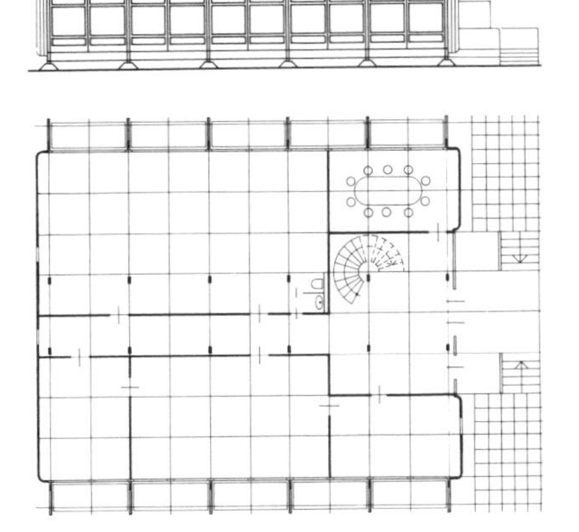

5

Two-Story Building System

Architect: G. Henn, Munich, West Germany
Engineer: J. Natterer, Munich

Structural joints

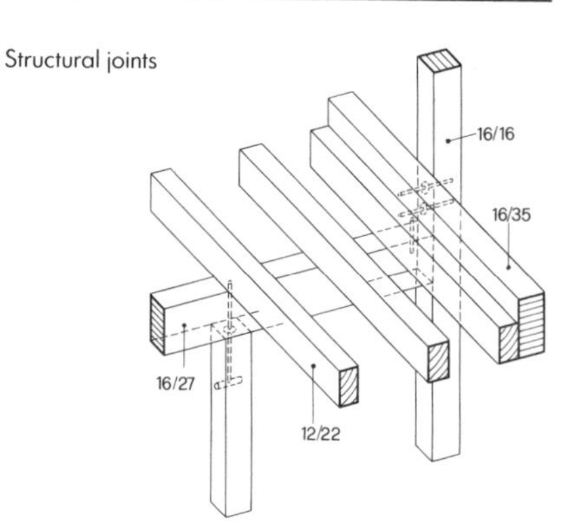

Design

The system does not require splices in beams or columns. Simply constructed, it contains continuous columns, with floor and peripheral beams supported by girders.

Structure

Connections usually required at the intersection of girders and columns are not necessary here. Interior columns supporting the roof are separate from those carrying the upper floor; roof loads are also carried by peripheral columns. The upper floor is carried by its own columns. This system represents, in a way, a house within a house (upper floor carried by its own columns within a roof envelope carried by exterior columns). This division of supports makes structural sense because all columns are thus subjected to an approximately equal load.

The roof forms a structural plate, stiffened in the cantilevered area by means of wood-chip boards screwed onto joists. Similarly, a plate is formed by the upper floor by means of diagonal planking or wood-chip board paneling. Horizontal wind forces are transferred to interior footings by diagonal trussing.

Finishes

The structural separation between roof and upper floor creates an upper floor that can be divided at will because it has few columns. The ground floor has double peripheral column rows, spaced at 1.2 m. This double row allows for an offset of the facade and the formation of a canopied space.

The outer wall has three layers: interior sheathing, vented space, and exterior sheathing. The interior sheathing with finishing is attached to the inside face of the columns and runs continuously without the need for joints at columns. In lieu of the customary light wall construction, it is possible to use a wall 11.5 cm thick in both the upper and lower stories. This provides good insulation in summer and winter.

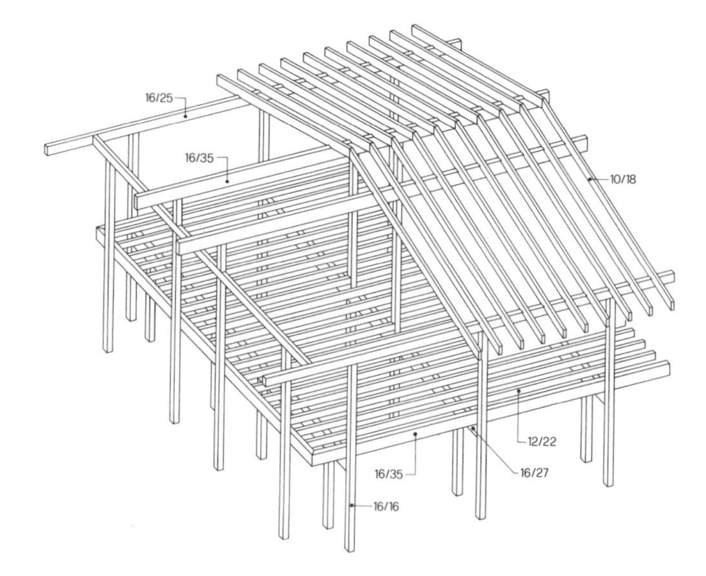

Plan and section of framework

1 Columns 16/16 cm
2 Main girder 16/27 cm
3 Peripheral girder 16/35 cm
4 Floor beam 12/22 cm
5 Interior roof beam 16/35 cm
6 Exterior roof beam 16/25 cm
7 Rafters 10/18 cm

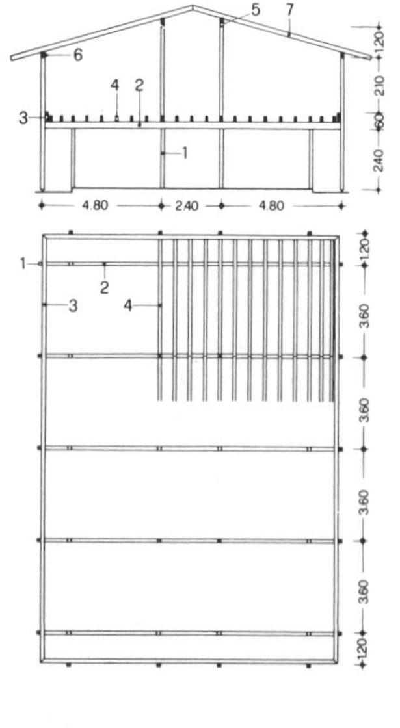

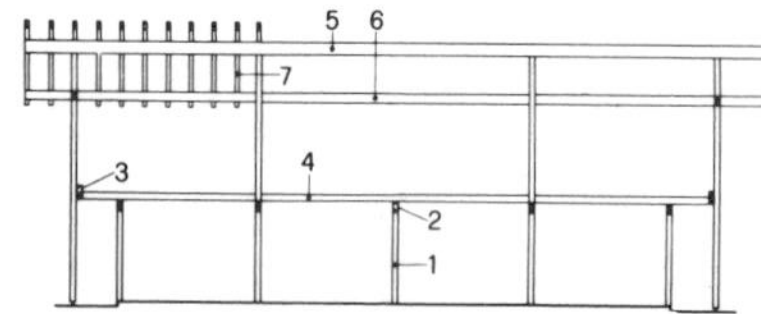

Structure

Erection sequence:
1 Ground floor with cantilevers all around
2 Exterior columns with perimeter girders and roof edge beams
3 Beam and rafter roof

1 Column 16/16 cm
2 Main girder 16/27 cm
3 Perimeter girder 16/35 cm
4 Floor beam 12/22 cm
5 Shear connectors with bolts
6 Steel dowels
7 Cross bar with interior bolt
8 Bolts attached to 7
9 Round steel bearing plate
10 Washers to adjust height
11 Nut on washer of 8
12 Steel shoe embedded in concrete
13 Hole in 12 for adjustments larger than diameter of 8

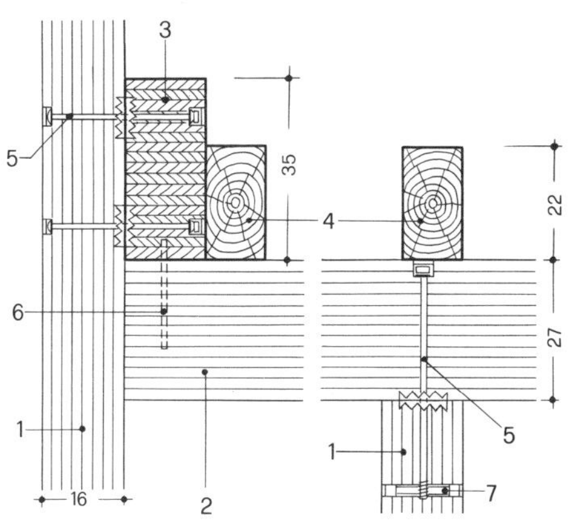

Connection of peripheral and main girders to column

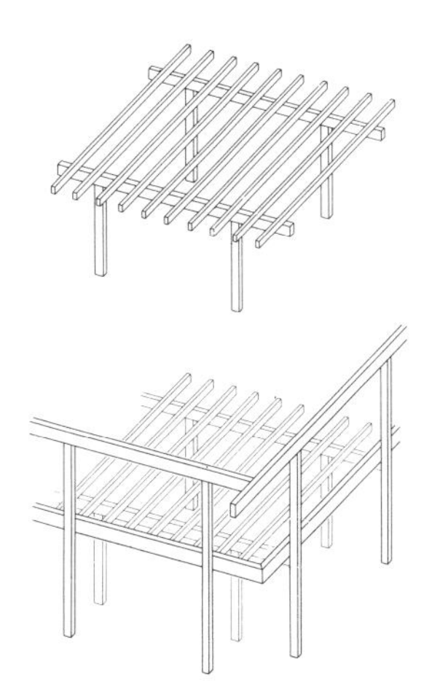

1

2

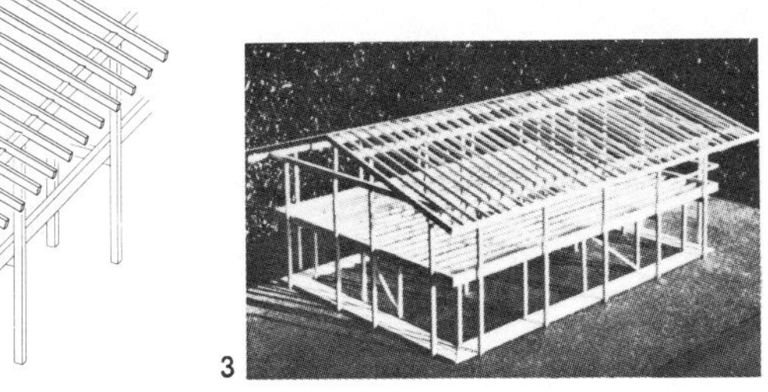
3

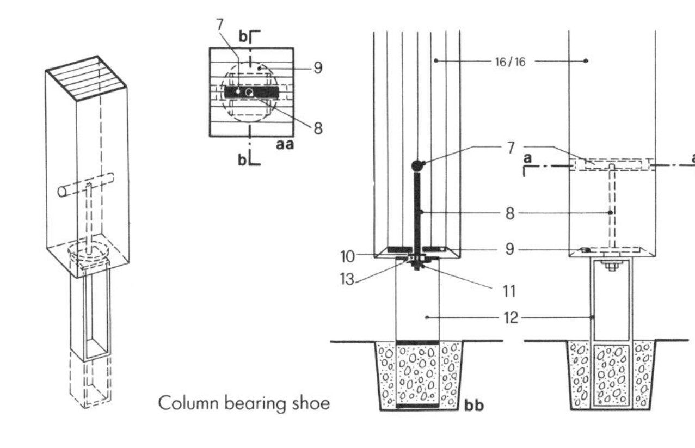

Column bearing shoe

Bracing

1 Vertical trussing: solid wood diagonals on ground floor, crossed bars on upper floor
2 Horizontal bracing deck, diagonal planking
3 Horizontal roof bracing, peripheral stiffening of cantilevered area

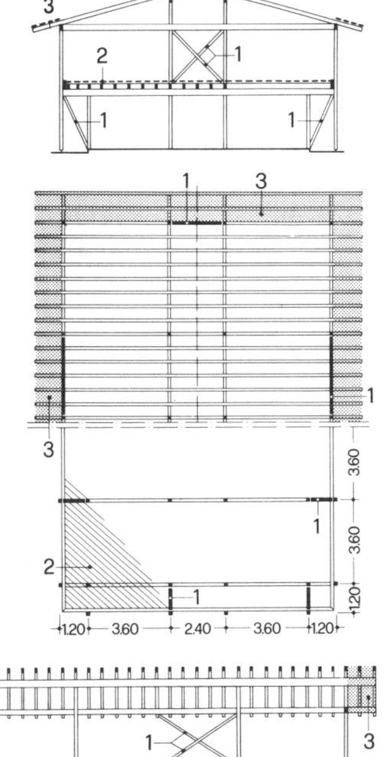

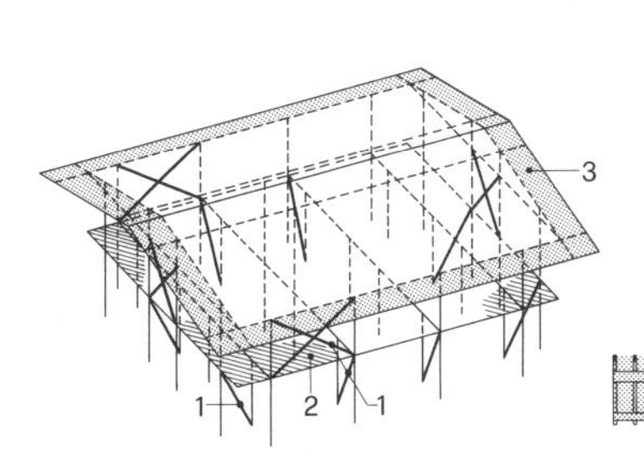

Views of horizontal and vertical bracing

Finishes

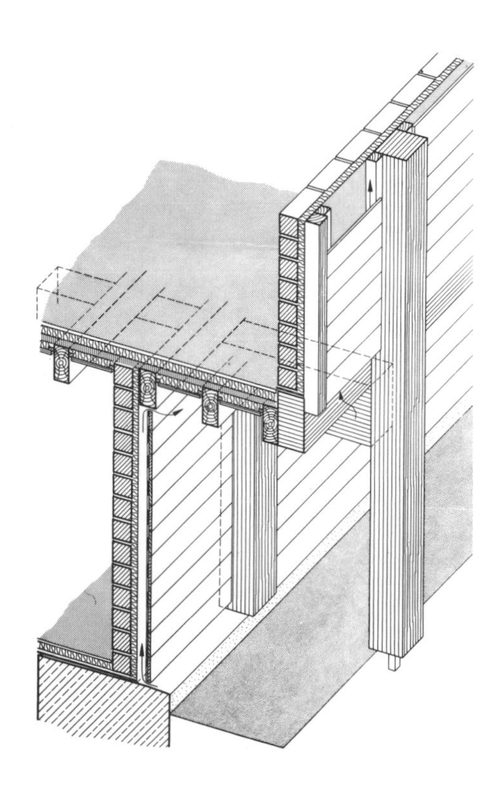

1 Rafters 10/16 cm
2 Insulation
3 Sheathing
4 Wall structure: sheathing, waterproofing, vented space, insulation, massive interior sheath such as masonry
5 Bituminous paper strips
6 Floor structure: wood-chip boards, insulation, concrete planking (or flagstones and sand), wood-chip boards, additional thermal or acoustical insulation
7 Timber window frame with double glazing
8 Facade columns 10/10 cm

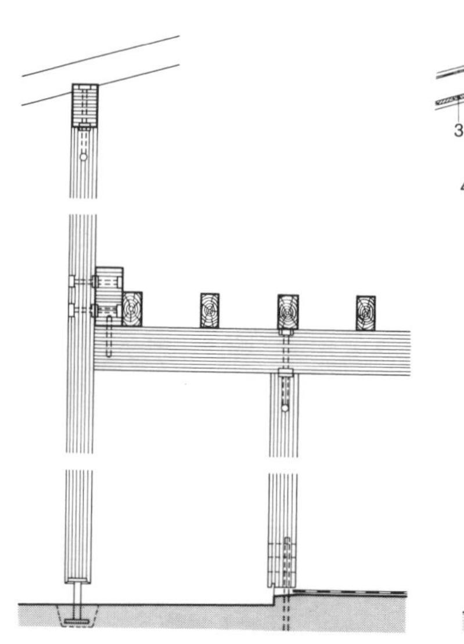

Vertical section, framework

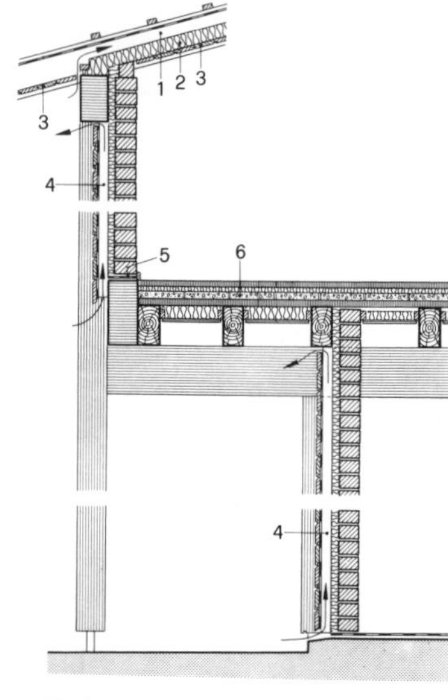

Finishes

A Centerline spacing 3.60/3.60 m
A1 Girder direction
A2, A3 Girder intersections for column-free rooms 7.20 × 7.20 m
B Centerline spacing 3.60/2.40/3.60 m
B1 Girder direction
B2–B4 Girder intersections for column-free rooms up to 7.20 × 9.60 m
C Centerline spacing 3.60/3.60/3.60 m
C1 Girder direction
C2–C4 Girder intersections for column-free rooms up to 7.20 × 10.80 m

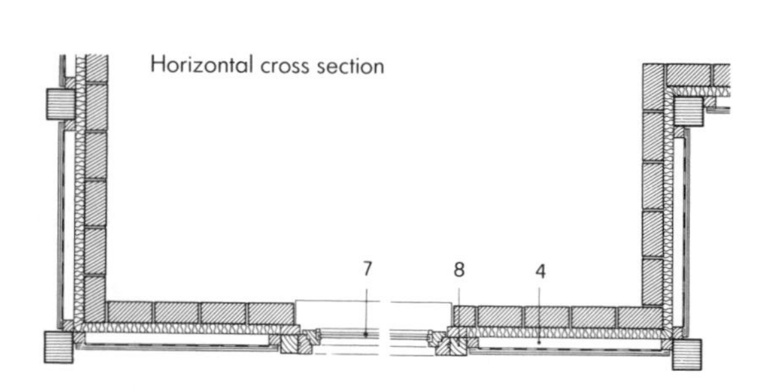

Horizontal cross section

Alternative designs for ground floor

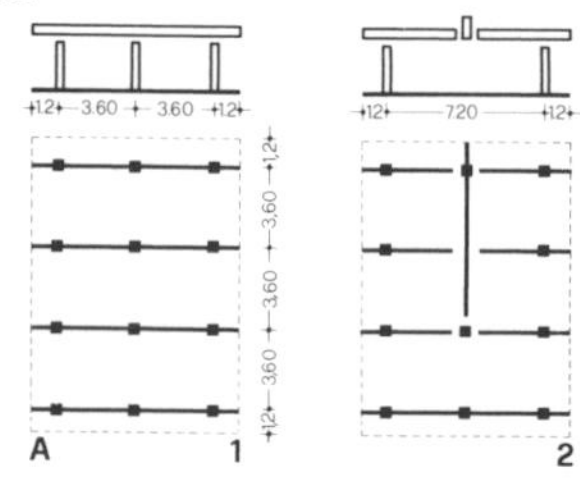

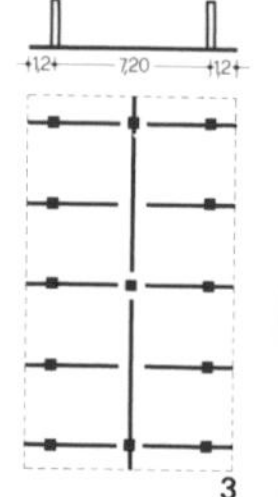

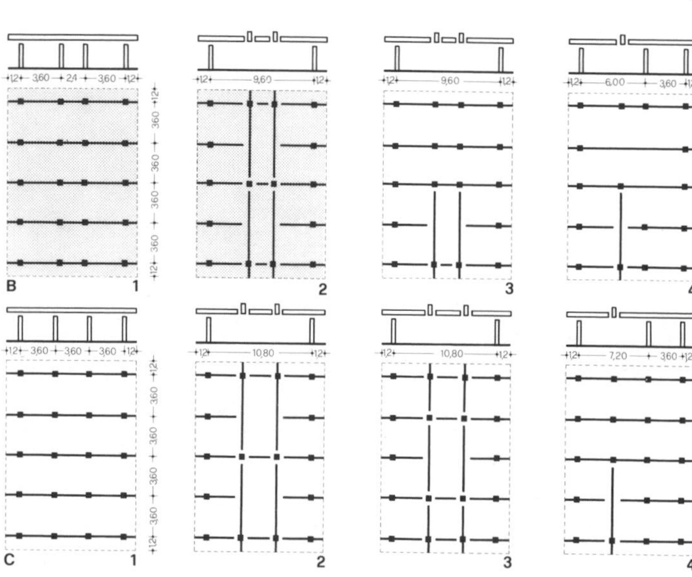

Building System from Finland

Architect: J. Vainio, Helsinki

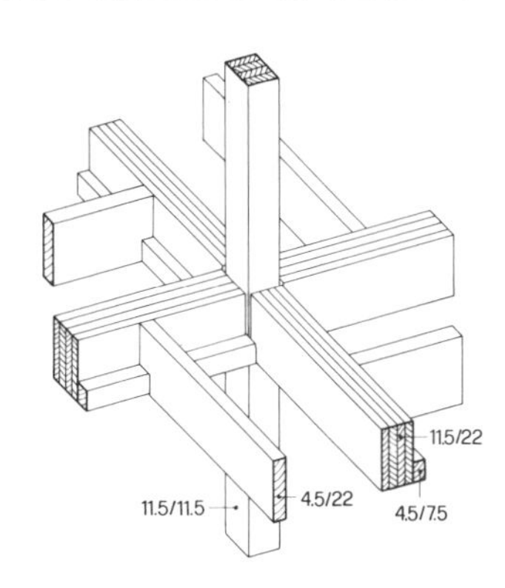

Structural node

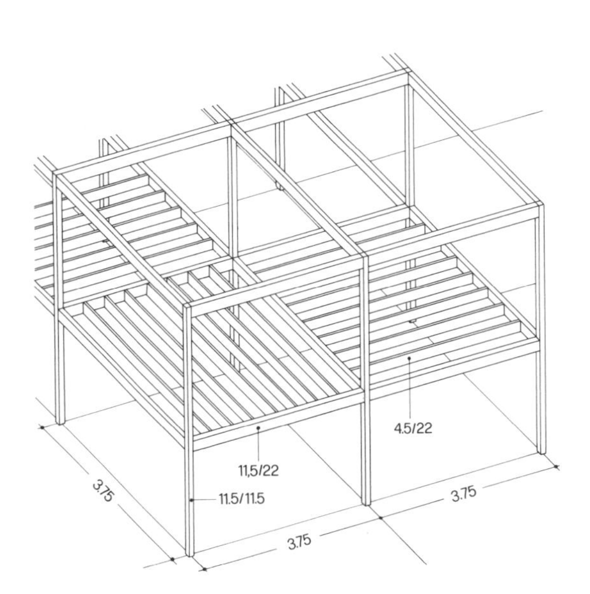

Design

Square column grid of 3.75 m for one- or two-story buildings located on flat or sloping land, with or without basement. The units can be adapted to both single- and multifamily houses as well as to dense settlements. They are also suited for expansion and remodeling. Two basic heights of 2.16 and 2.58 m allow for variations of height. The nonstructural exterior and interior walls permit flexible partitioning of facades and rooms. Roof terraces, free spaces, pergolas, covered passages, and storage rooms are feasible without special elements.

Structure

The two-story frame consists of continuous columns 11.5/11.5 cm on a square grid, and of main girders 11.5/22 cm which run in both directions as tie beams. The tie beams abut against column sides; they are connected by either bearing angles or connection plates. Floor beams consist of upright planks 4.5/22 cm connected to girders by ledger slats 4.5/7.5 cm. The direction of the floor beams changes in every panel so that the tie beams and the columns are loaded equally and the entire system is nondirectional.

Bracing of roof and floor planes occurs by means of screwed-on wood-chip boards. Horizontal forces are conveyed to the foundation by means of plywood shear walls.

Finishes

Finishing elements are 1.80 m wide. They are fabricated in 15 different configurations (full, partially or fully glazed, with doors, windows, opaque panels, etc.). Floors and roofs are not standardized. Between floor beams there is fiberglass insulation.

Framework, plan and section

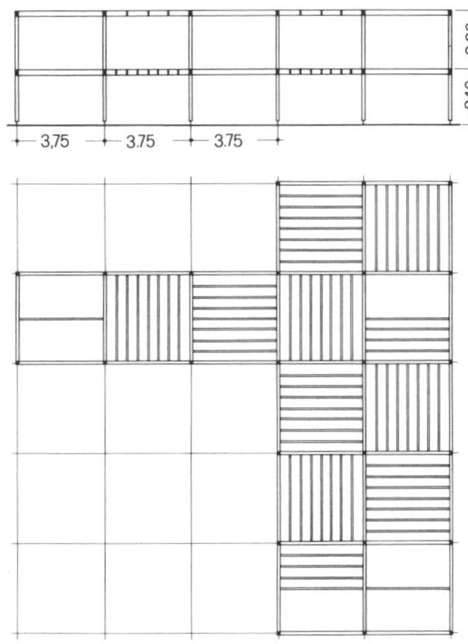

Construction

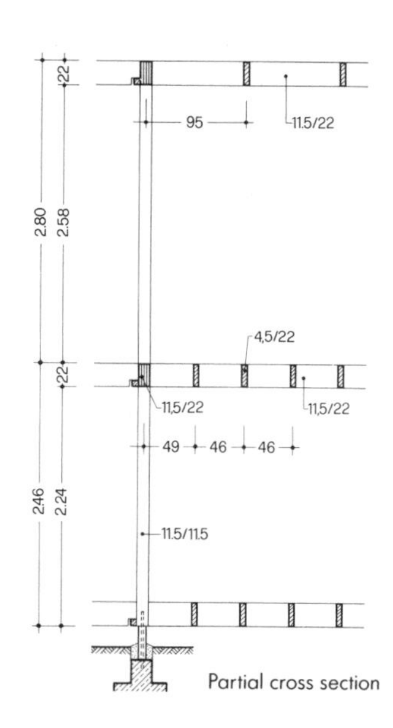

Partial cross section

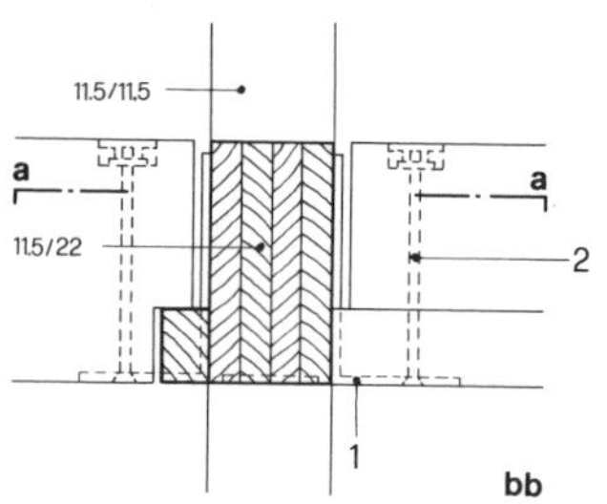

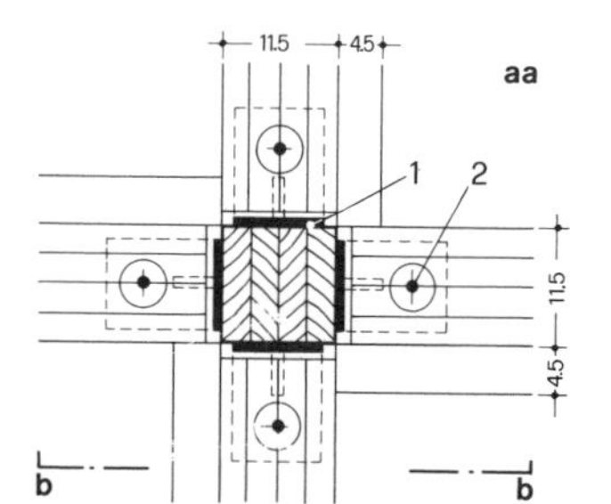

aa, bb Connection of main girder to column

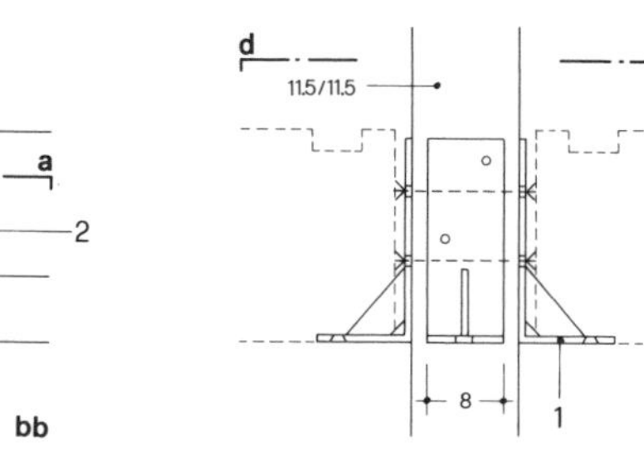

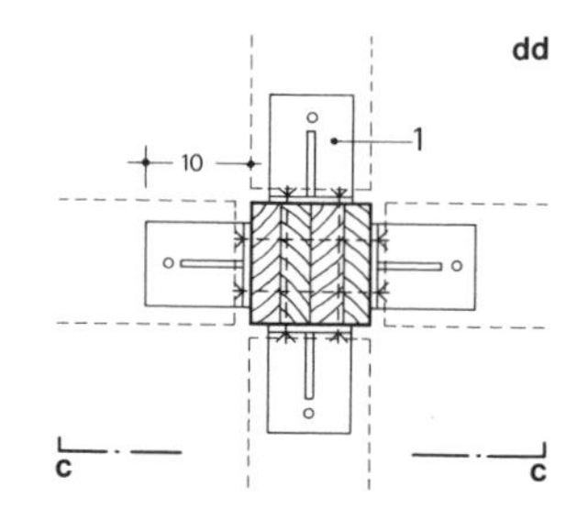

cc, dd Connecting hardware of main girder to column

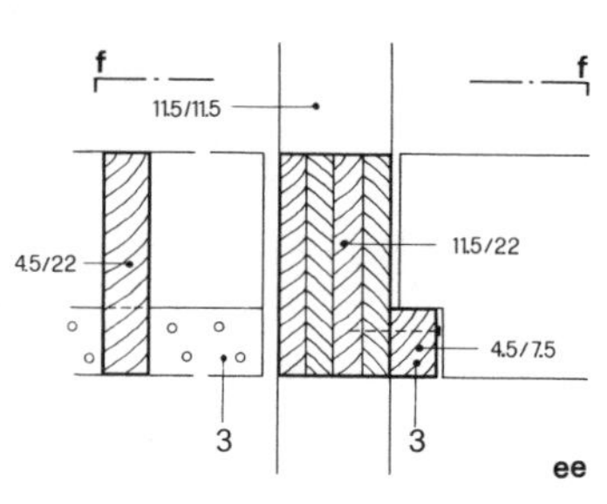

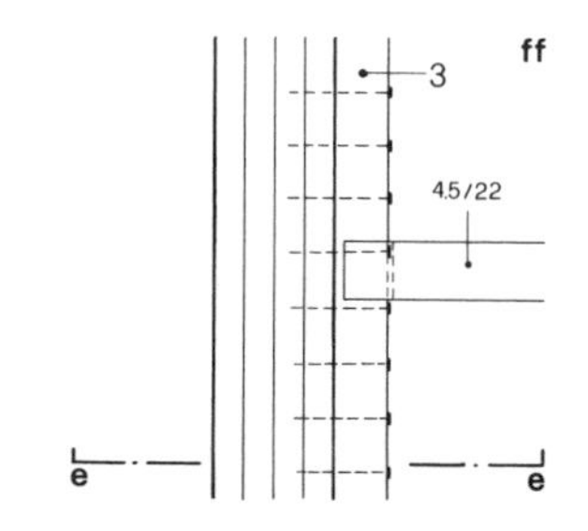

ee, ff Connection of floor beam to main girder

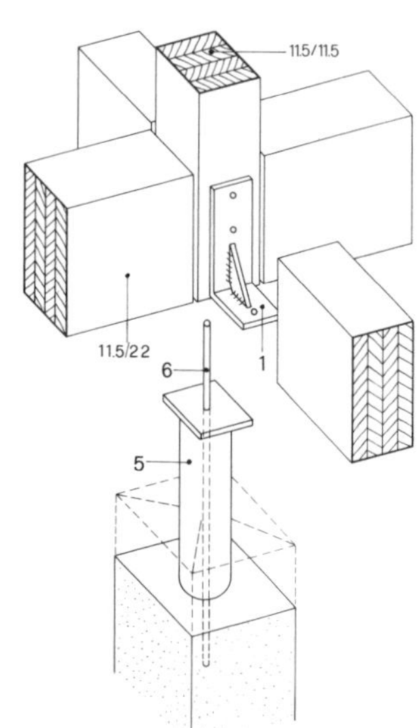

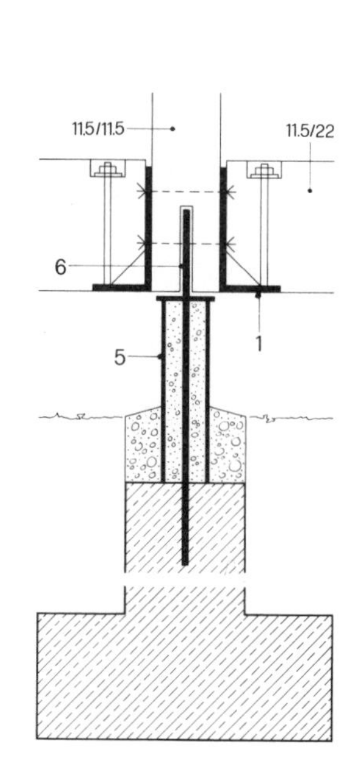

Column base; isometrics and section

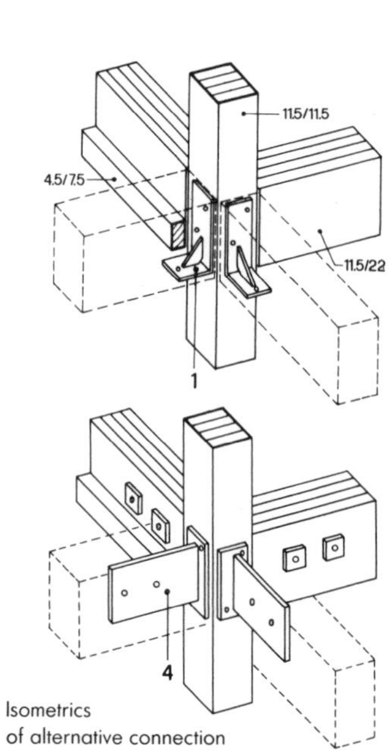

Isometrics of alternative connection

1 Steel angle with stiffener, screwed onto column
2 Security bolts, recessed
3 Bearing ledger 4.5/7.5 cm nailed to main girder
4 Anchor plate screwed onto column, girder held by bolts
5 Steel tube ϕ 80 mm with bearing plate
6 Round steel in column hole ϕ 15 mm

Bracing

Elevation

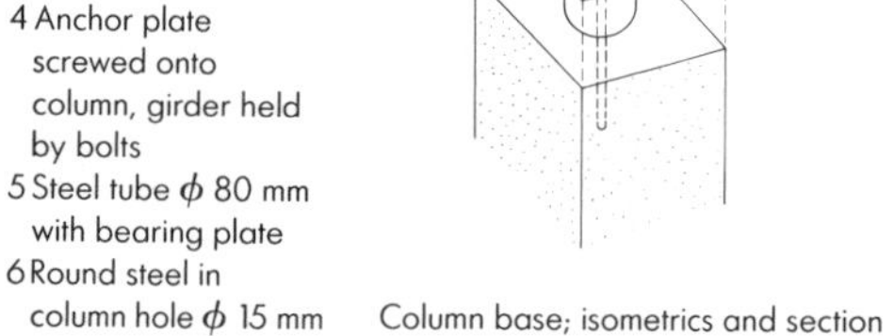

Plan

Elevation

Bracing wall panels shown in solid black lines

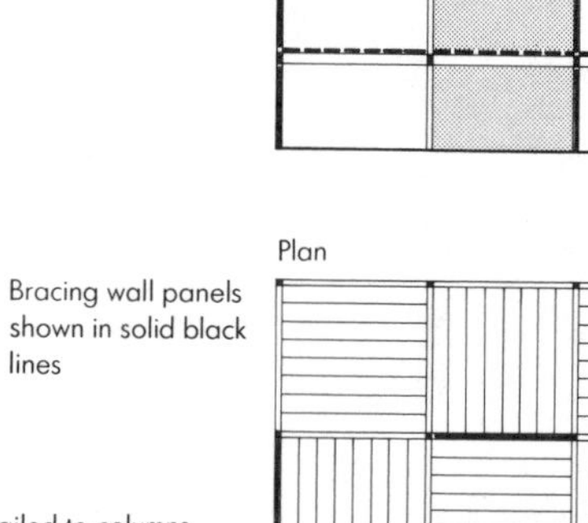

Elevation of bracing wall panel

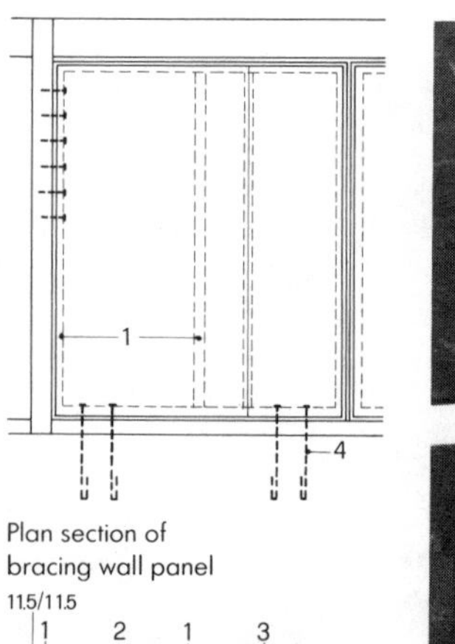

Plan section of bracing wall panel

1 Lumber frame 5/13 cm nailed to columns
2 Plywood panel 12 mm, attached to 1 to resist shear
3 Tongue and groove sheathing
4 Anchor bolts

Finishes, Layout

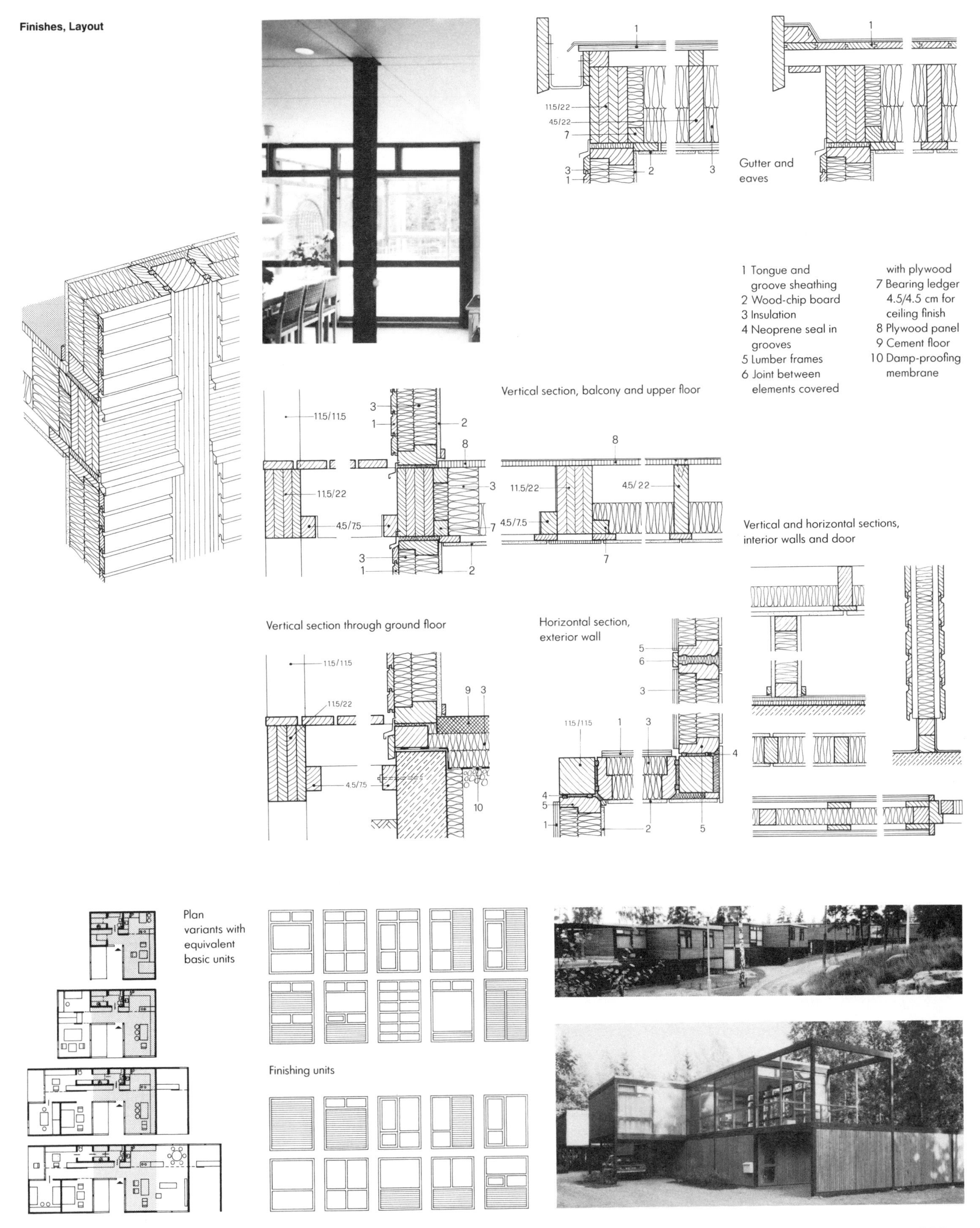

7

School

Architect: H. Schaudt, Konstanz, West Germany
Engineer: Ingenieurbüro für Holzbau, Karlsruhe

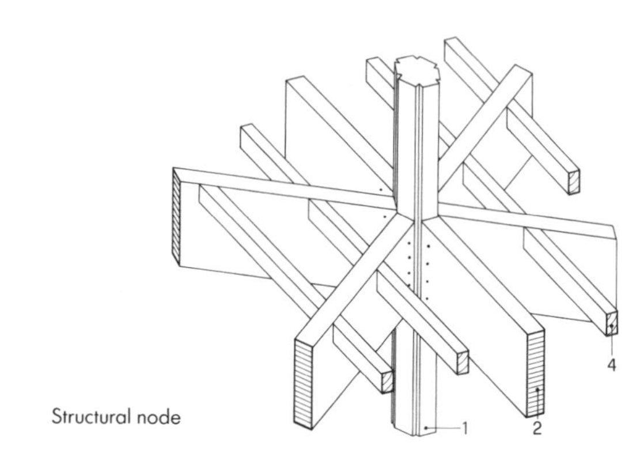

Structural node

Design

One- or two-story building with adjacent classrooms arranged as a hexagonal honeycomb. All classrooms are on the upper floor and can be illuminated and ventilated through the roof. Articulated facades reflect great variety of room arrangements, but exterior wall panels are rather uniform.

Structure

Hexagonal laminated wood columns (side width 12 cm) are grooved and connected to main girders, which are arranged on a triangular grid. The loads are transferred from the upper to the lower column by means of a steel tube with top and bottom bearing plates. Girders are also spliced and are attached to bearing plates by shear connectors and bolts. Secondary beams, also on a triangular grid, are attached to girders by steel shoes. On the upper floor, parallel floor beams are laid on them. The bracing is achieved by floor plates and crossed round steel bars in front of or behind facades.

Finishes

A basic frame element was used for all exterior and interior walls. Depending on the need, it is filled with glass, insulation, or acoustic filler. The flooring consists of floating woodchip boards with acoustical and thermal insulation.

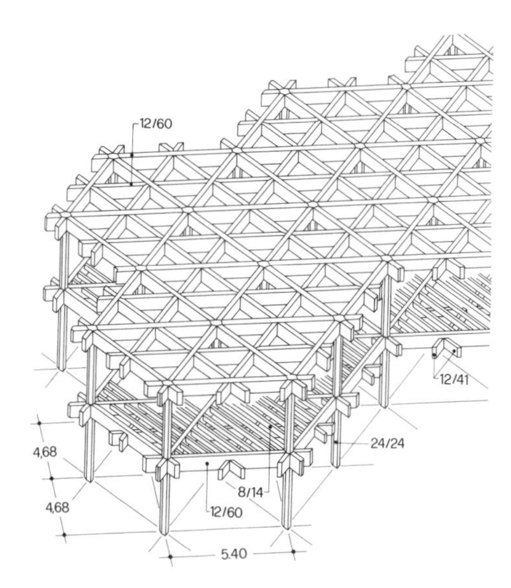

Diagrammatic view

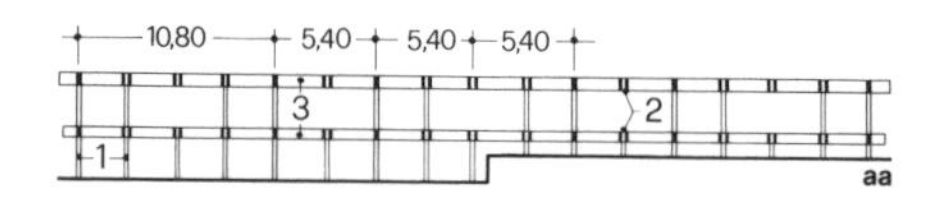

Framework, plan and section

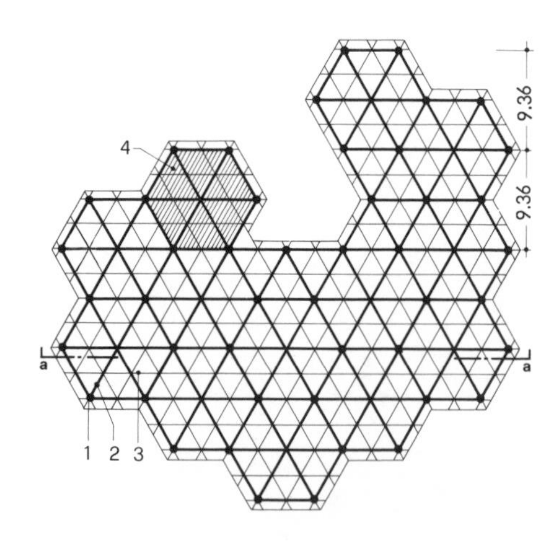

Structure

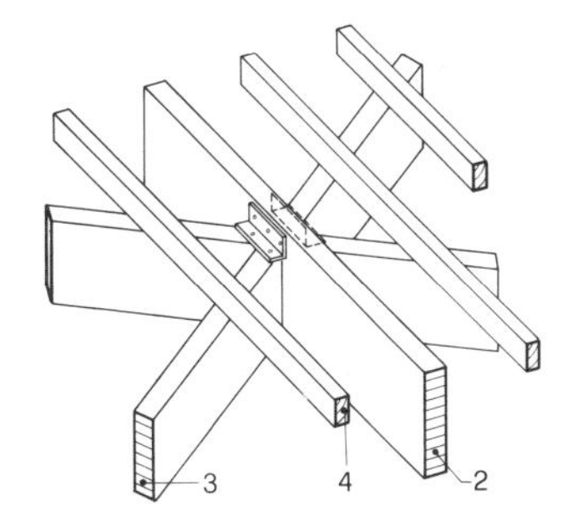

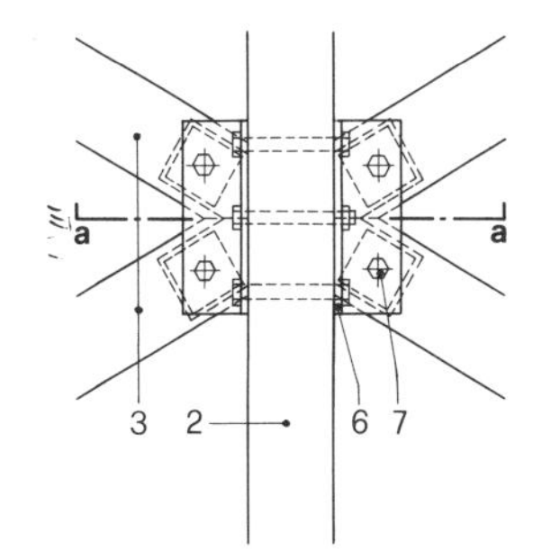

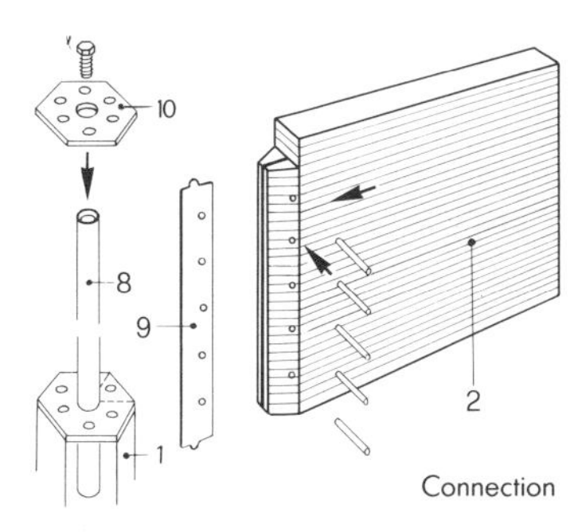

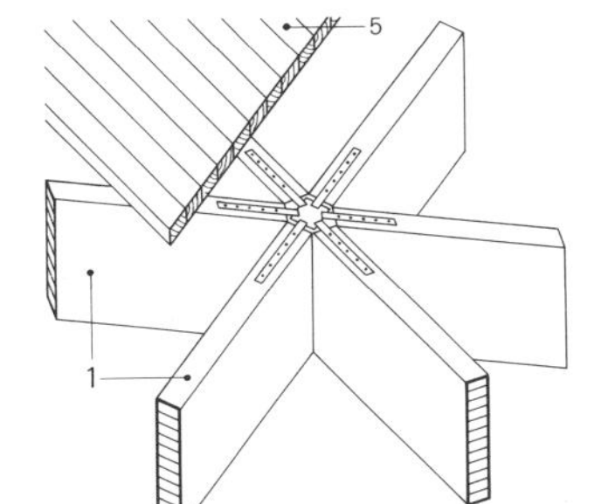

1 Column 24/24 cm, hexagonal
2 Main girder 12/55 cm on upper floor, 12/60 cm on roof
3 Secondary girder 12/41 cm on upper floor, 12/60 cm on roof
4 Floor beams 8/14 cm on upper floor
5 Tongue and groove planking 4.5 cm
6 Steel angle with dowels on 2
7 Bolts with counter plate
8 Steel tube ϕ 42.4 mm
9 Flat steel bar doweled in slit
10 Top bearing plate

Bracing

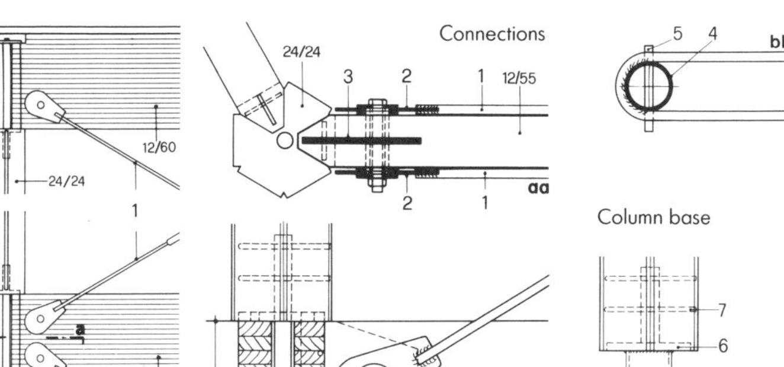

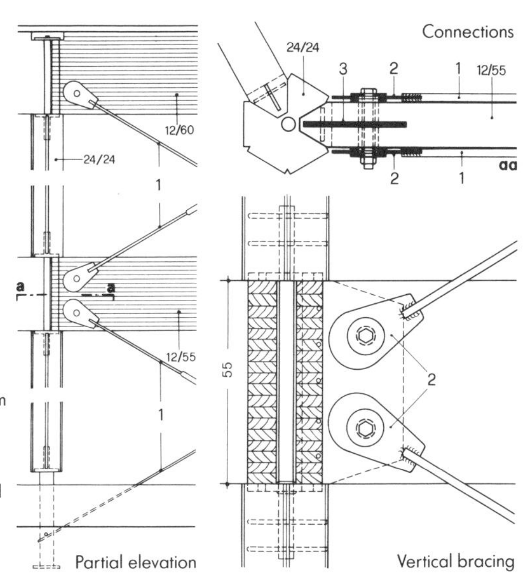

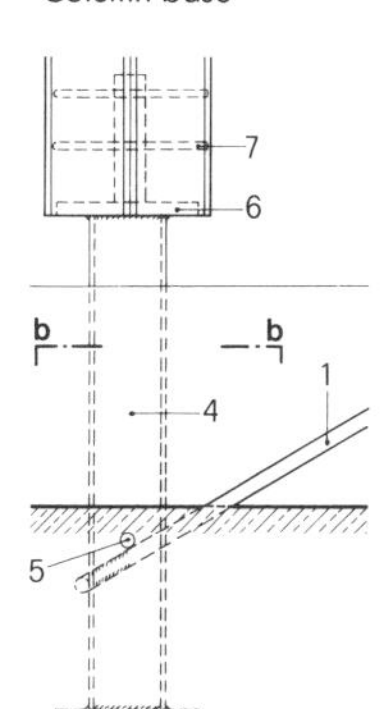

1 Steel diagonals 2 × ϕ 24 mm with turnbuckles
2 Connection plate with pins
3 Connecting plate, $t = 16$ mm, bolted in girder slit
4 Steel tube ϕ 108 mm with base plate
5 Steel anchor ϕ 24 mm
6 Base plate with steel tube
7 Steel dowels

Layout

For details see Example 136 on page 154.

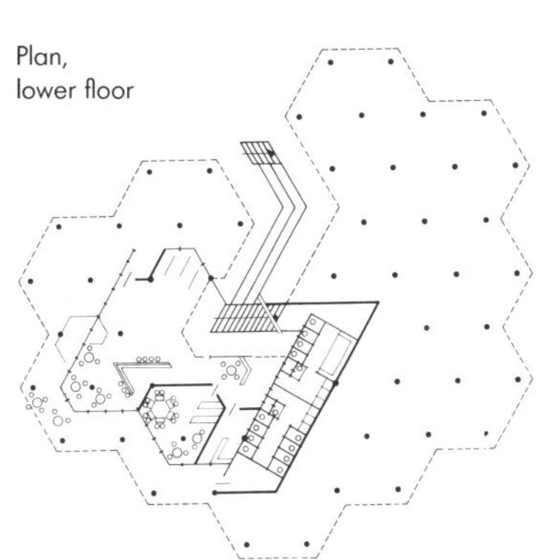

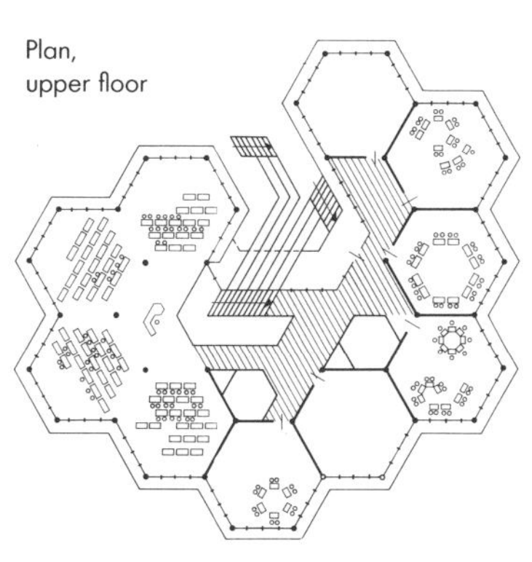

8

Prefabricated Modular Structure

Architect: Gullichsen, J. Pallasmaa, Helsinki, Finland

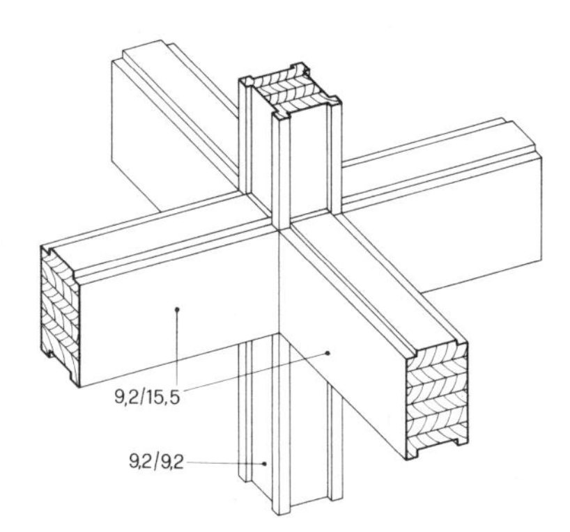

Structural node

Design

Prefabricated building system for one-story structures with flat roof. Columns, tie beams, and panels are laid out on a cubic grid of 2.25 m clear distance. The subpanel size for floors, roof, skylights, walls, windows, and doors is 75/225 cm. The assembly of cubes is arbitrary and can result in free sitting areas, pergolas, or covered passages.

Structure

The load-carrying framework consists of columns 9.2 × 9.2 cm and main girders 9.2 × 15.5 cm. Columns are spaced on a grid of 2.35 × 2.35 m; the main girders run in both directions between columns and are joined to columns on all four faces by means of aluminum extrusions (one fixed to the column, the other to the end of the girder). These extrusions are locked into each other and are secured by a key.

Column bases are aluminum tubes, adjustable according to grade. Roof, wall, and floor units span between the girders. Wall units provide horizontal bracing and carry wind forces to the foundation.

Finishes

The system is developed for extremely cold and snowy areas, but it is also useful in milder climates. The roof is of hot asphalt construction and is covered with a waterproofing membrane. The rain is drained through a leader. All horizontal and vertical units are sealed with rubber tubes or nesting extrusions. Single components weigh less than 50 kg each and are easy to handle because of their small size. The structure can be erected as a do-it-yourself project.

Plan and section of framework

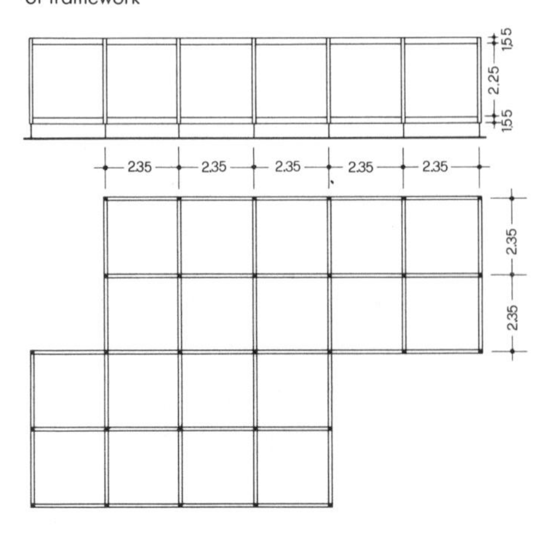

Structure

1 Aluminum connection hardware, screwed onto girder and column
2 Aluminum key wedged into groove
3 Tube with base plate, screwed into 1
4 Sleeve for 3, welded to 5
5 Adjusting plate
6 Base plate
7 Bolts ϕ 20 mm

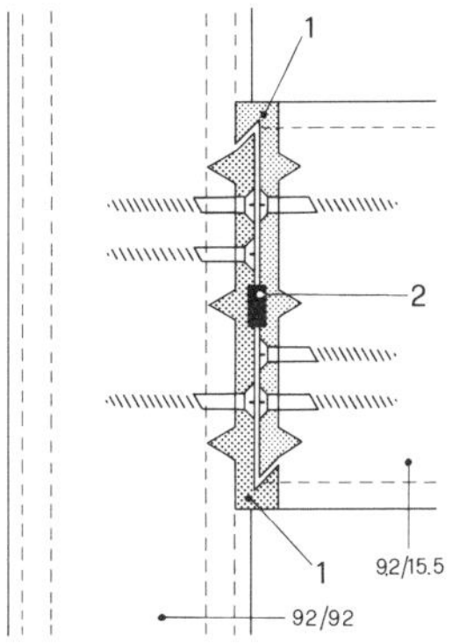

Detail of connecting hardware

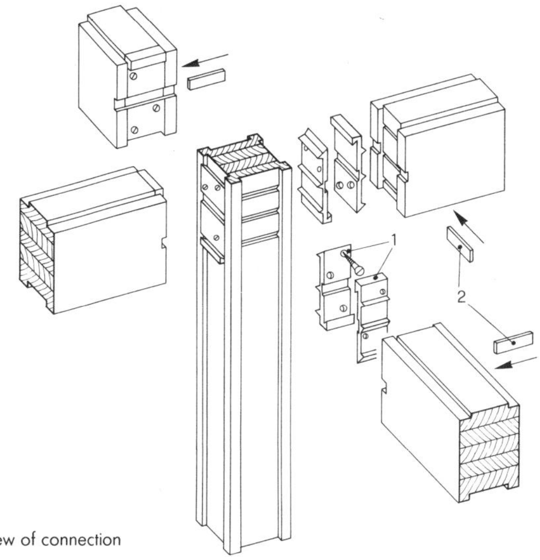

View of connection

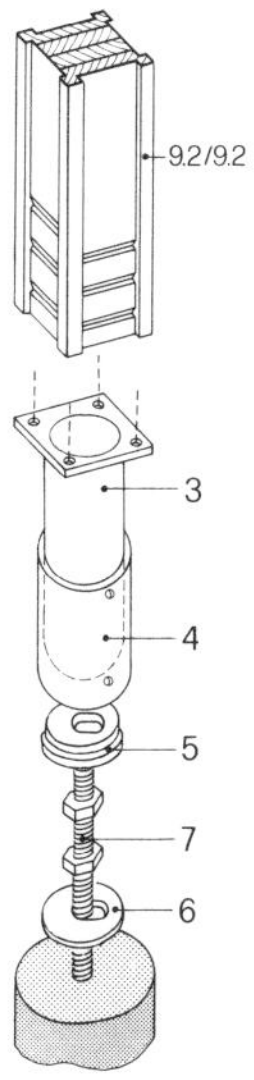

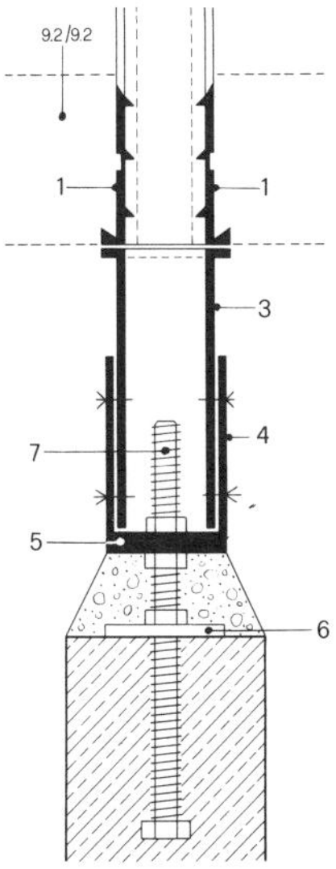

Connection of girder to column

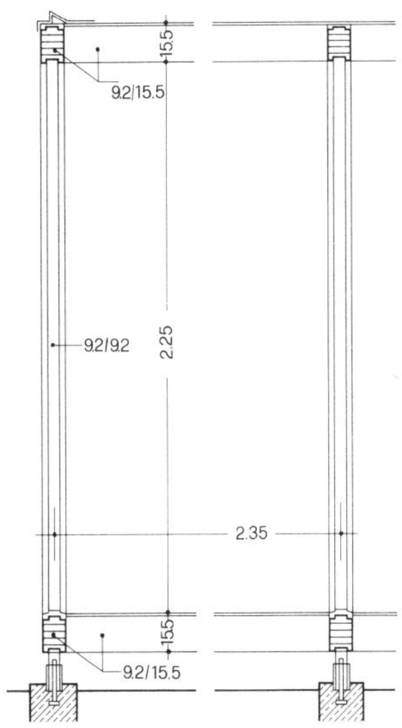

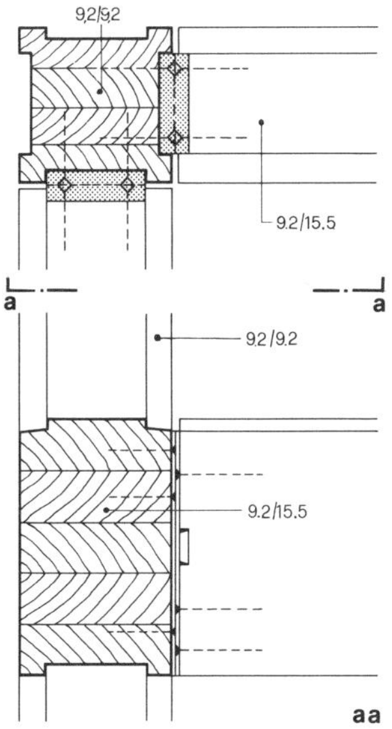

Partial section

Column base

Finishes

Eave

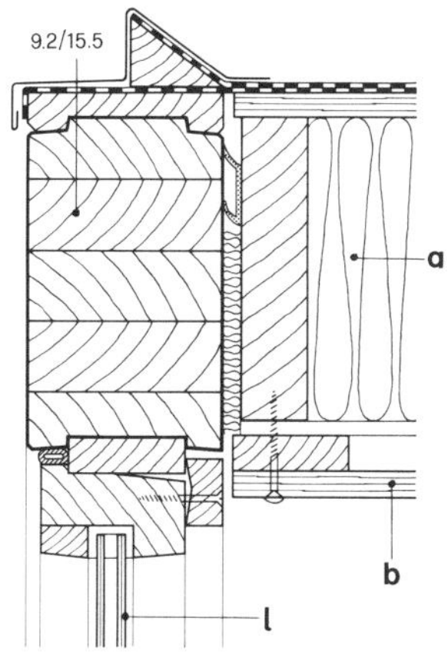

Horizontal cross section

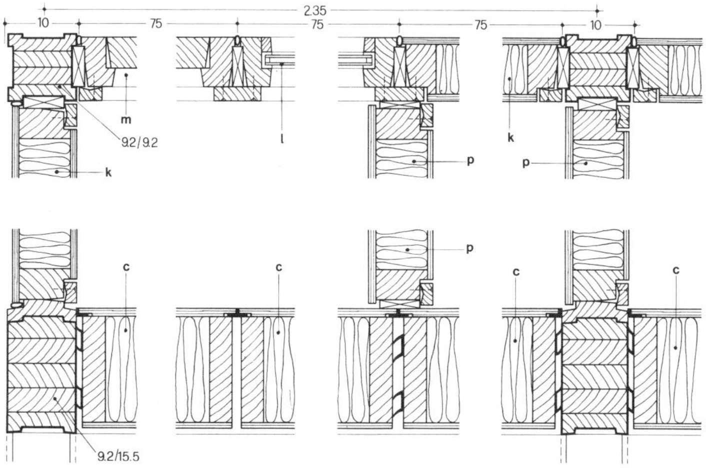

Details of finishes

a Roof unit
b Ceiling unit
c Floor unit
k Exterior wall unit
l Window unit
m Door
p Wall unit

Vertical cross section

For shape of finishing units, see overleaf

Finishes (Continued)

a Roof unit
b Ceiling unit
c Floor unit
d Girder
e Terrace roof unit
f Sunshade grid
g Terrace floor
h Skylight
i Column
k Exterior wall unit
l Window unit
m,n Doors
o Grillage
p Wall unit
q Wall finish unit

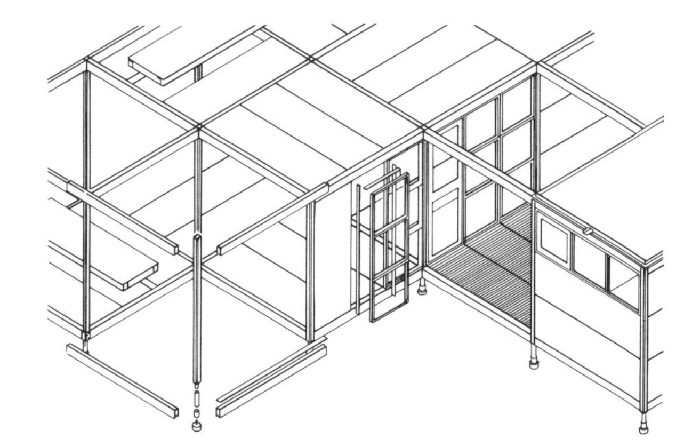

Finishing units

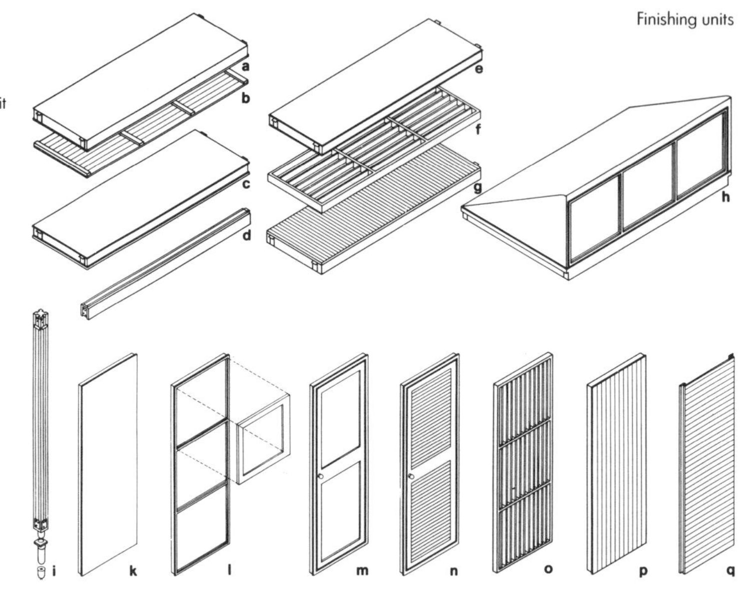

Layout

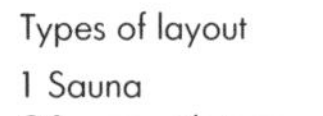

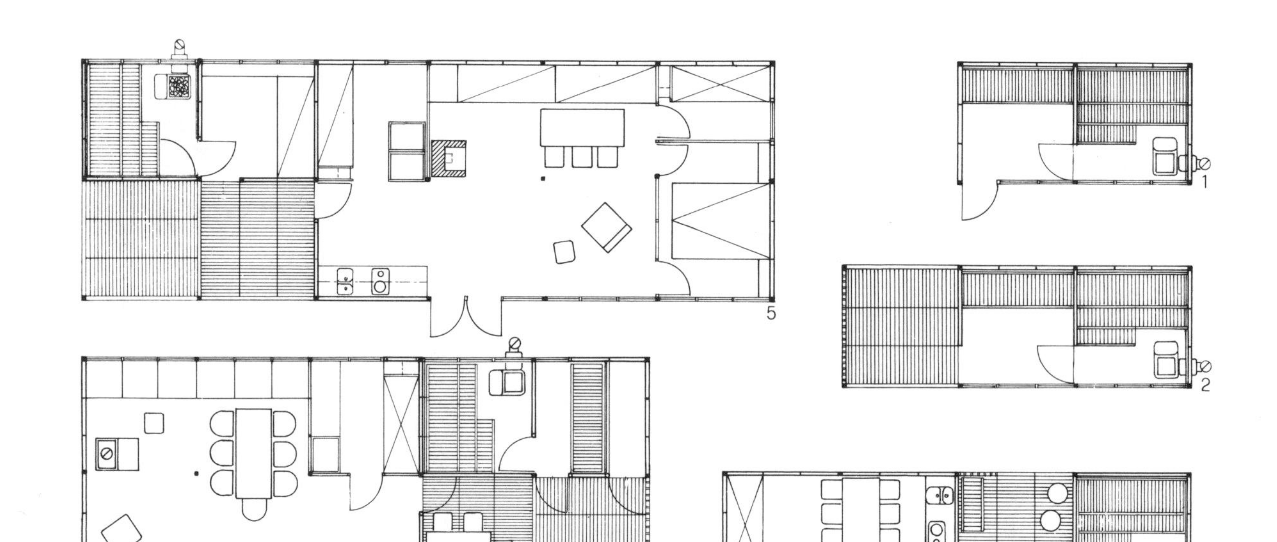

Types of layout
1 Sauna
2 Sauna with terrace
3 Sauna with terrace and living room
4 Small weekend house
5 Large weekend house

Herrenalb Framing System

Architect: K.-H. Goetz, Karlsruhe, West Germany
Engineer: Ingenieurbüro für Holzbau, Karlsruhe

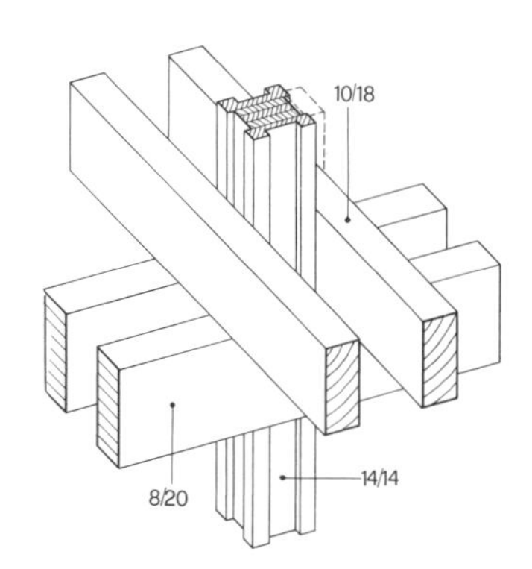

Structural node

Design

Industrial timber building system for residential and multiple housing. There is no standard building type, but the flexibility of the system allows for individual planning. The residential buildings represented here are built on a parcel of land sloping 10%. The total building floor area is 383 m² and total volume is 1601 m³.

Structure

The timber frame consists of continuous columns 14 × 14 cm and continuous split main girders 2 × 8/20 cm. The latter are placed on either side of the columns and are connected with shear connectors. The 10/18 cm floor beams span across them. The basic structural feature is the cross-shaped column node. A continuous groove is cut into each face of the square-shaped column and connecting timber is glued into it. The sill and floor beams also have a groove into which a similar connecting timber is glued, so that there is a continuous connecting timber available for attaching finishing elements.

Bracing of the roof is through diagonal struts, and bracing of floors is by means of screwed-on wood-chip boards. Horizontal wind loads are conveyed to the foundation by means of plywood panels in the facade.

Finishes

All finishing units are standard; they encompass 16 exterior and 14 interior alternatives. Many room units are also standardized (bathroom, kitchen, stairs, closets, ets.). Exterior units are attached to the frame from the outside and can be exchanged at a later time.

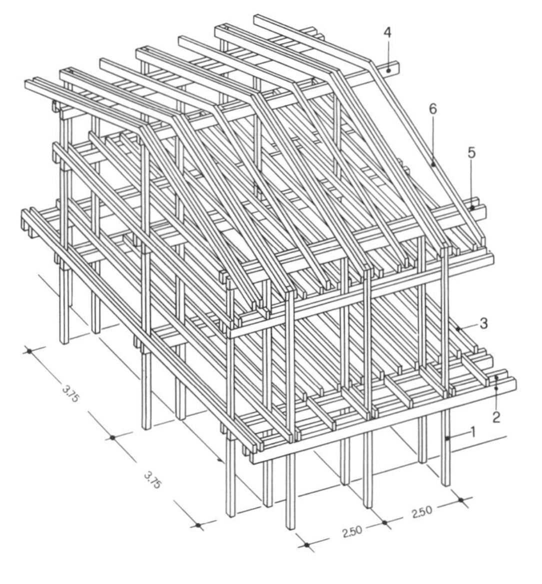

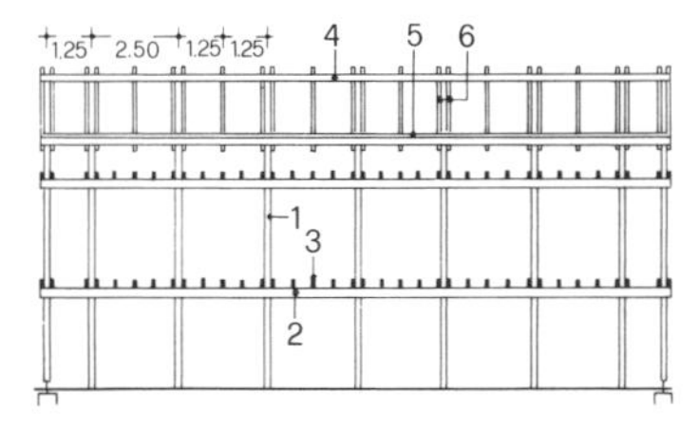

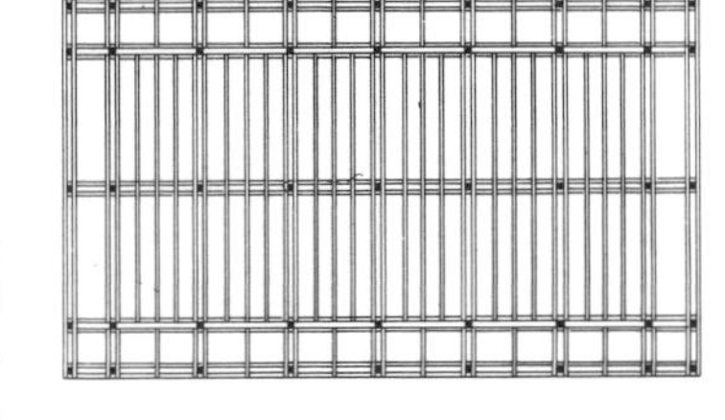

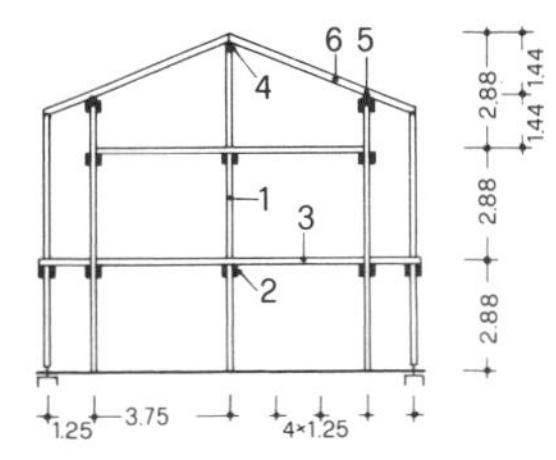

Plan and section of frame

1 Column 14/14 cm
2 Main girder 2 × 8/20 cm
3 Floor beam 10/18 cm
4 Ridge beam 14/25 cm
5 Eave roof beam 14/20 cm
6 Rafters 8/18 cm

Structure

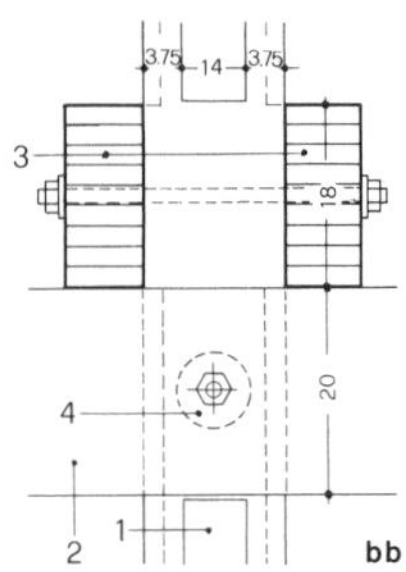

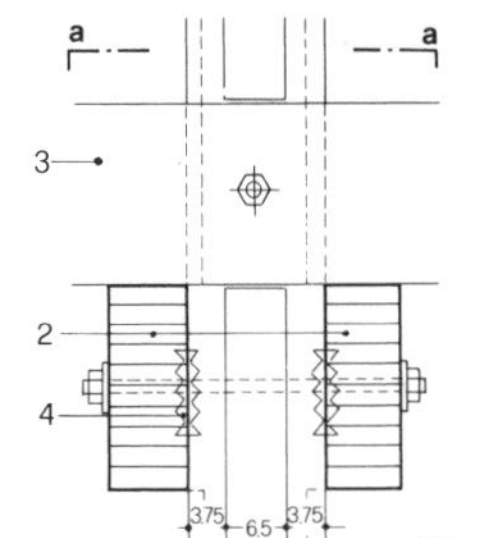

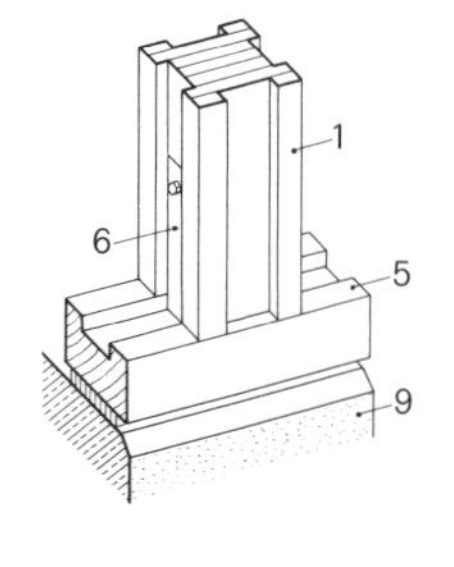

Exterior column base

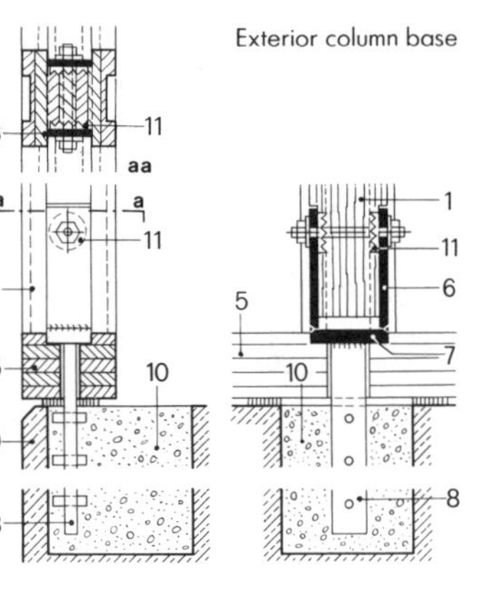

Partial cross section

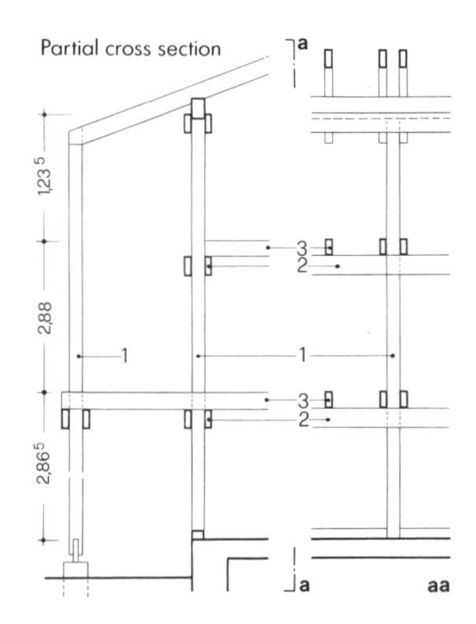

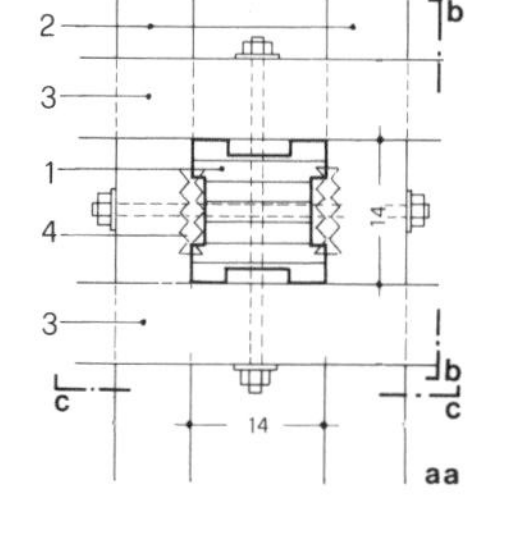

aa – cc, Girder to column connection

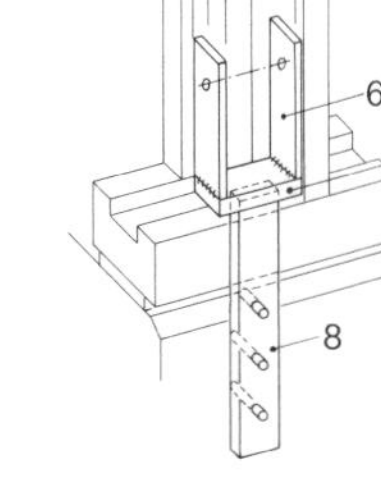

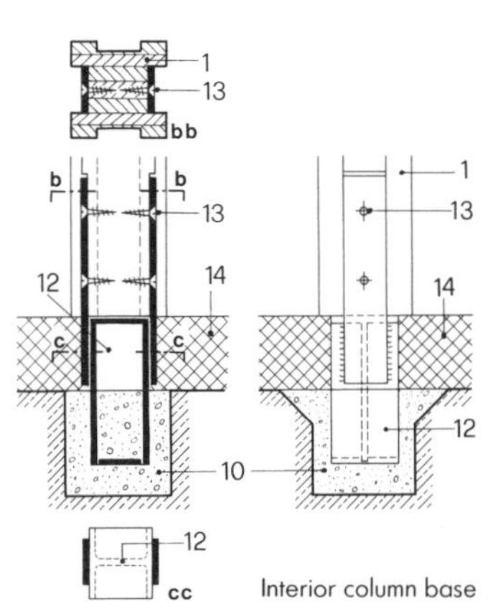

Interior column base

1 Column 14/14 cm
2 Main girder 2 × 8/20 cm
3 Floor beam 10/18 cm
4 Shear connector ϕ 95 mm
5 Sill beam
6 Steel gusset plate 65/10 mm
7 Column base with welded anchor
8 Flat steel anchor welded to 7 with ϕ 16 mm anchors
9 Concrete foundation
10 Cast-in-place concrete
11 Shear connector ϕ 65 mm
12 IPBL 100 with top and bottom bearing plates and welded gusset plates
13 Flathead screws 6/50 mm
14 Flooring

Bracing

Horizontal bracing: connection of floor plate to girder by means of filler

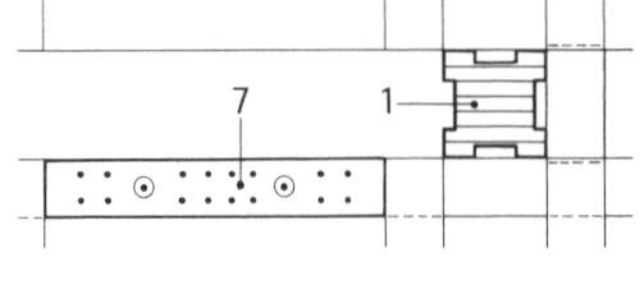

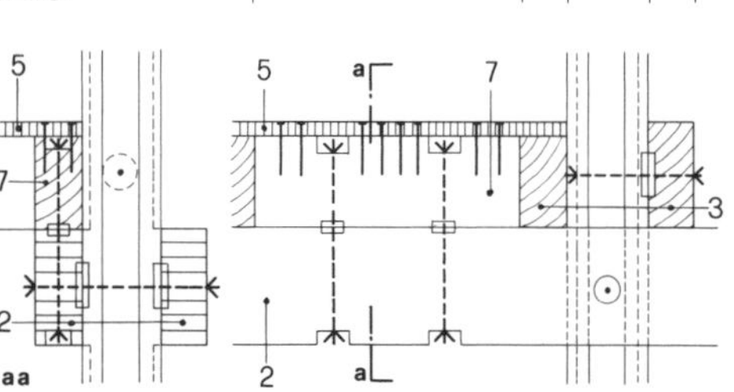

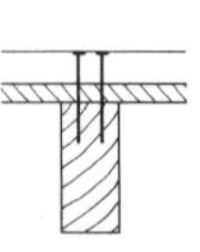

1 Column 14/14 cm
2 Main girder 2 × 8/20 cm
3 Floor beam 10/18 cm
4 Wind bracing 4/18 cm with nails N46/130 nailed to rafters
5 Wood-chip boards 22 mm, nailed to floor beam with N34/90 nails
6 Wall panel 12 mm plywood, nailed to column through connection timber
7 Filler 8/18 cm between floor beams with ϕ 50 mm shear connectors, fastened to girder to transmit horizontal loads

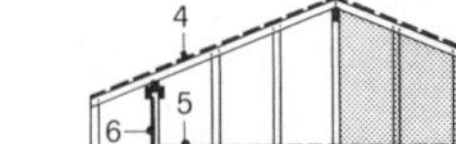

View of horizontal and vertical bracing

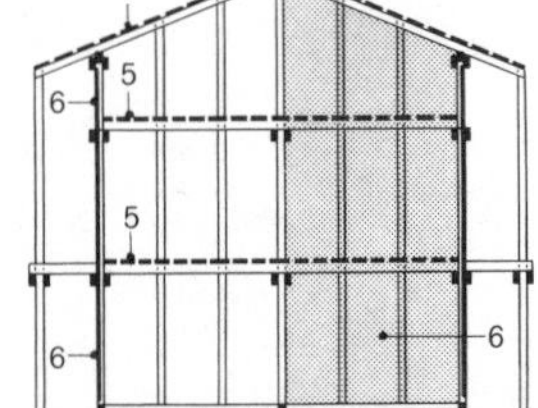

Vertical bracing: connection of wall to column

Connection of diagonal struts to rafters

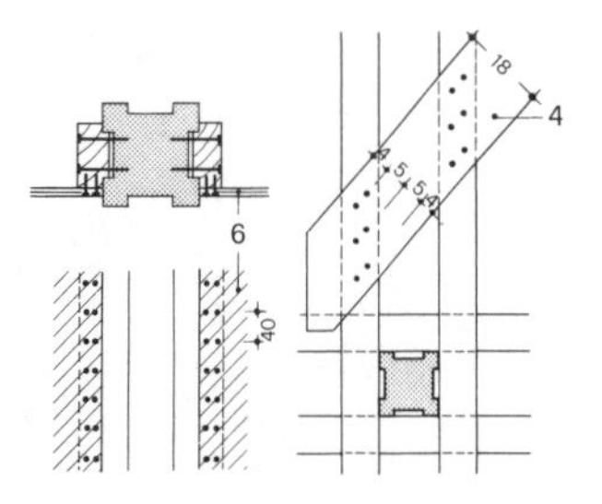

Finishes

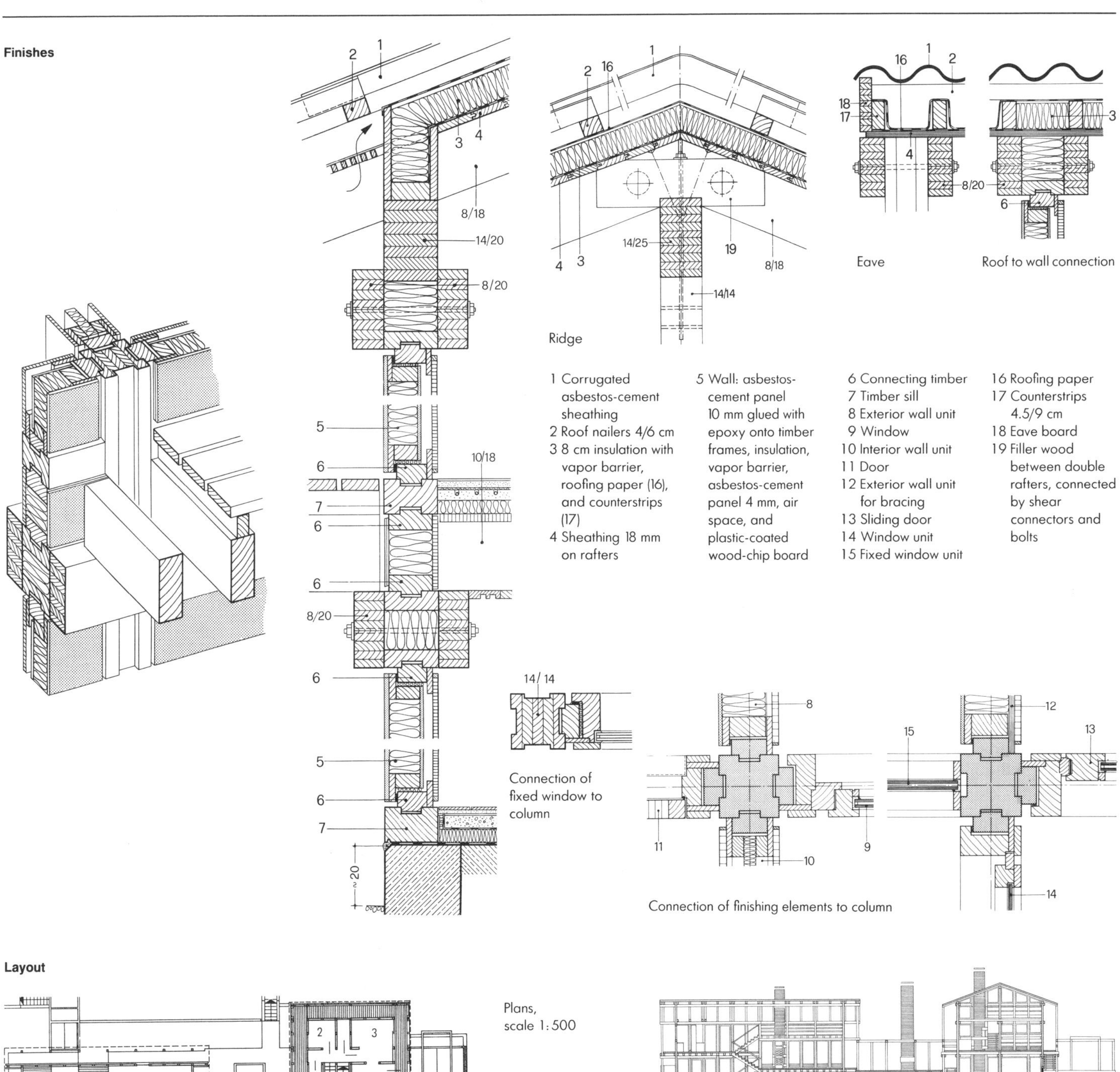

Ridge

Eave

Roof to wall connection

Connection of fixed window to column

Connection of finishing elements to column

1 Corrugated asbestos-cement sheathing
2 Roof nailers 4/6 cm
3 8 cm insulation with vapor barrier, roofing paper (16), and counterstrips (17)
4 Sheathing 18 mm on rafters
5 Wall: asbestos-cement panel 10 mm glued with epoxy onto timber frames, insulation, vapor barrier, asbestos-cement panel 4 mm, air space, and plastic-coated wood-chip board
6 Connecting timber
7 Timber sill
8 Exterior wall unit
9 Window
10 Interior wall unit
11 Door
12 Exterior wall unit for bracing
13 Sliding door
14 Window unit
15 Fixed window unit
16 Roofing paper
17 Counterstrips 4.5/9 cm
18 Eave board
19 Filler wood between double rafters, connected by shear connectors and bolts

Layout

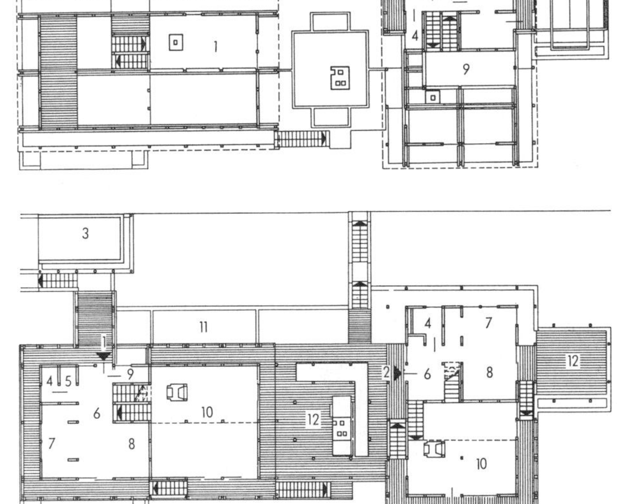

Plans, scale 1:500

Upper floor
1 Hall,
2 Bath
3 Bedroom
4 Room

Ground floor
1 Entrance, house 1
2 Entrance, house 2
3 Garage
4 Toilet
5 Closet
6 Entrance
7 Kitchen
8 Dining room
9 Walk-in closet
10 Living room
11 Reflecting pool
12 Sitting area

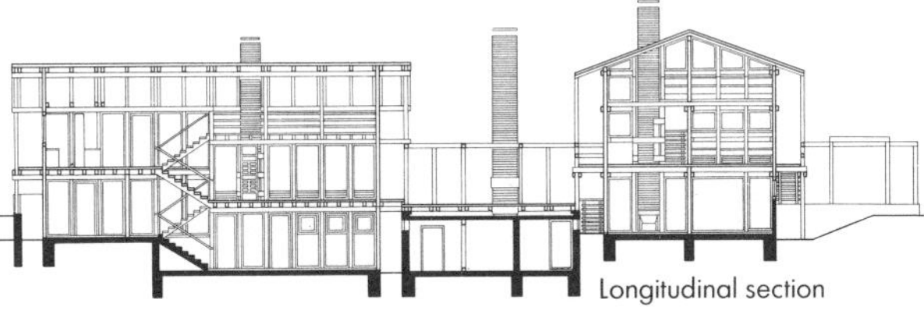

Longitudinal section

10

Residence

Architect: W. Döring, Düsseldorf, West Germany
Engineer: H. Genske, Düsseldorf

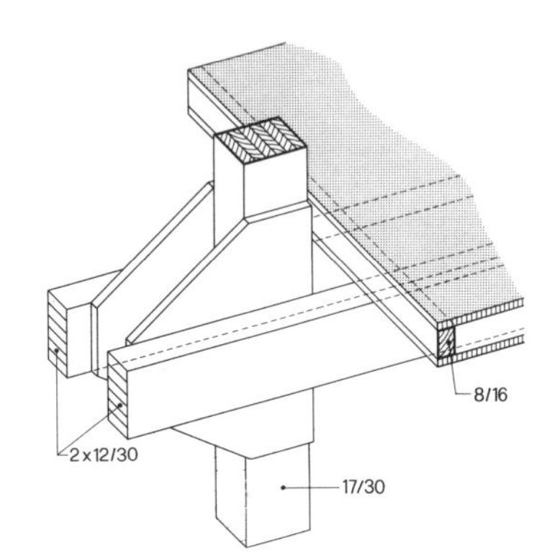

Structural connection

Design

Elongated single-family house with flat roof, 150 m² area. The living room takes half the space and reaches to the roof; the upper floor opens into it as a balcony. The building has no basement.

Structure

Transverse to the building there are eight frames spaced at 2.5 m. These frames consist of 17/30 cm columns protruding from the longitudinal facade, and twin main girders 2 × 12/30 cm spanning 6.61 m. Connection of girders to columns is achieved by weatherproof plywood gussets. The gussets are nailed to the columns in the shop. Girders are nailed to the gussets in the field. These gussets transfer both shear and moment to the columns so that the frames resist wind forces. In the longitudinal direction exterior round steel bar diagonals in the end panels brace the structure. Deck or roof panels rest on girders.

Finishes

Exterior walls rest freely behind the columns and are prefabricated, as are deck and roof panels. The size of the units is 2.50/5.00 m. Fixed windows fill the spaces between girders so that the wall heights are uniform.

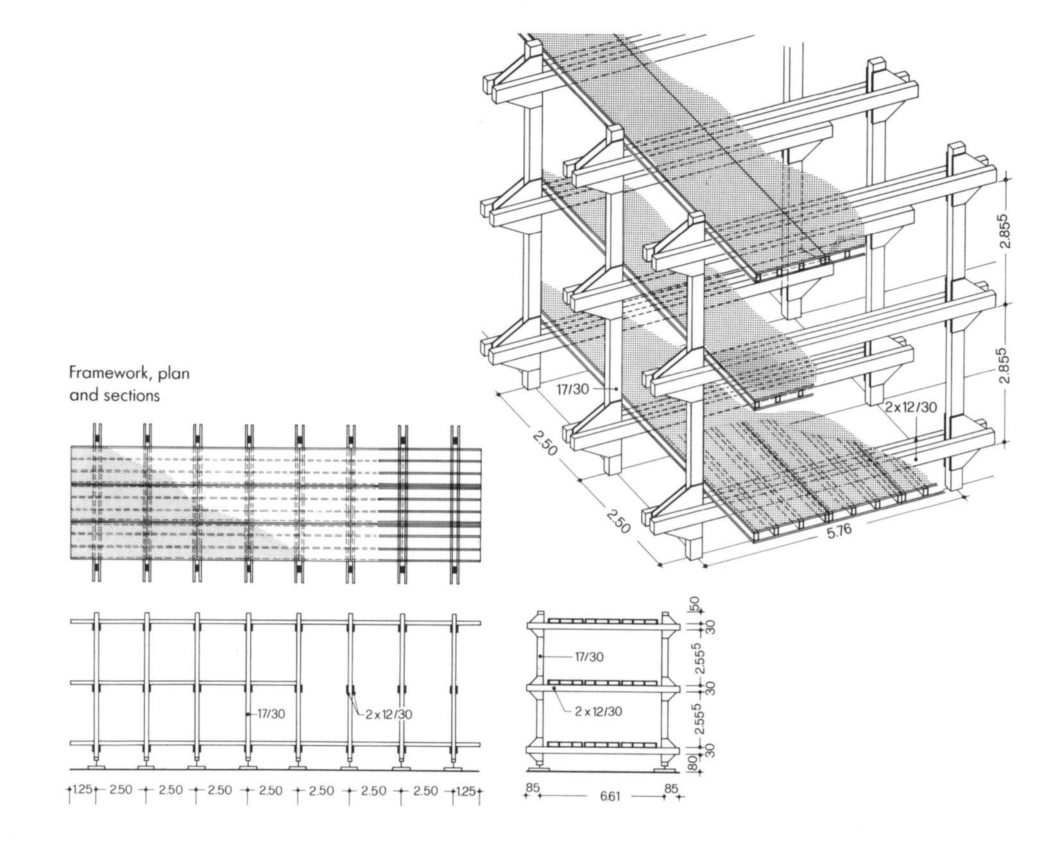

Framework, plan and sections

Structure

1 Bending-resistant gusset plate, 4 cm plywood
2 Nails 56 and 98 N34/90 (in shop)
3 Nails 2 × 49 N34/90 (in field)
4 Panel units with ribs 8/16 cm
5 Column base of U-shaped steel with round bar anchors and welded base plate
6 Cast-in-place concrete

aa – cc Column to girder connection

Column base

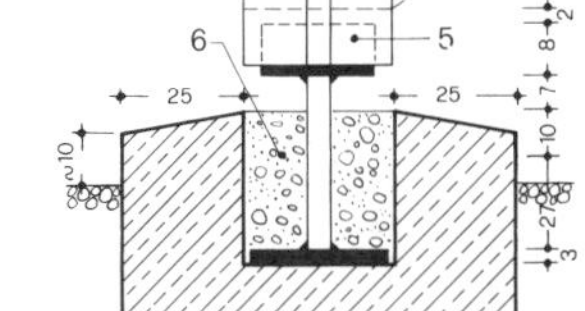

Bracing

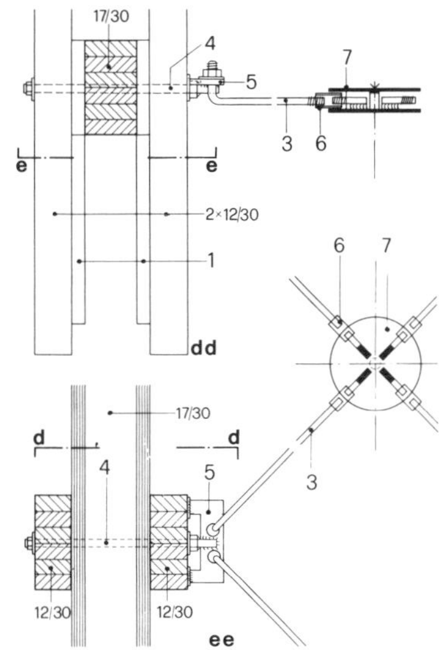

dd, ee Bracing connections

1 Gusset plate, 4 cm plywood
2 Panel units with ribs 8/16 cm
3 Diagonal bracing ϕ 16 mm steel bars in end panels
4 Tension bolts ϕ 20 mm
5 Steel plate welded on 4, with welded bearing plates
6 Turnbuckle
7 Plates with welded bolts

View of horizontal and vertical bracing

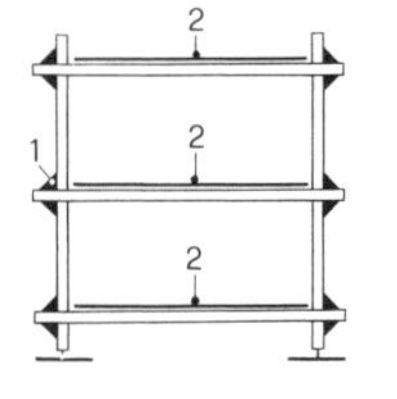

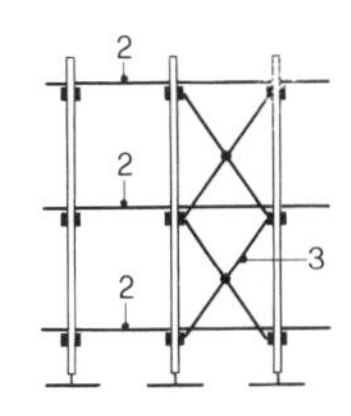

Layout

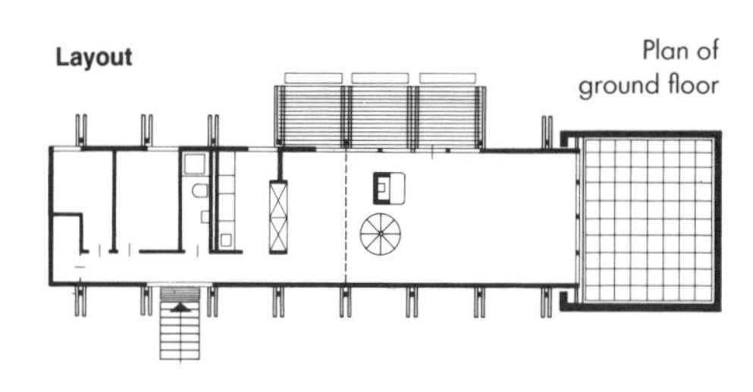

Plan of ground floor

Finishes

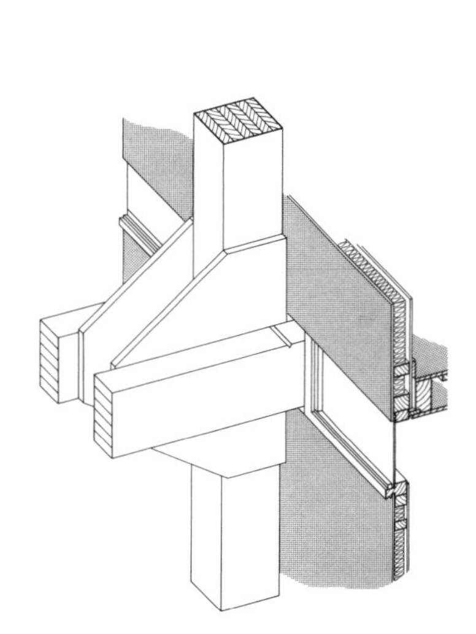

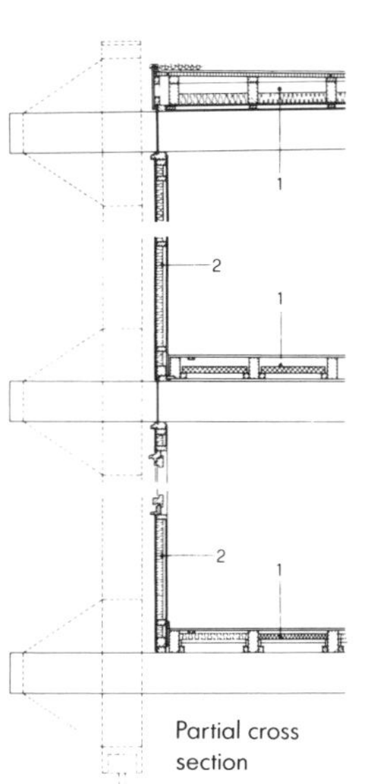

Partial cross section

1 Panel units with ribs and acoustic or thermal insulation
2 Exterior wall panels with 5/10 cm frames, 12 mm exterior, and 16 mm interior asbestos-cement panels, wood-chip boards, and insulation
3 Bolts for connecting walls at corners

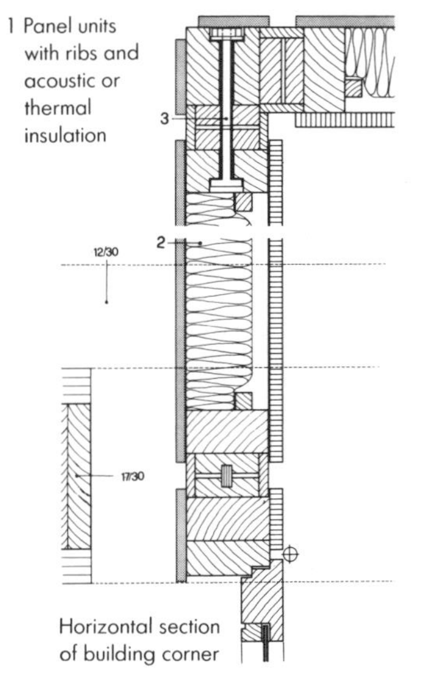

Horizontal section of building corner

11

Office Building

Design: University Building Office,
Konstanz, West Germany
Director: W. von Mann

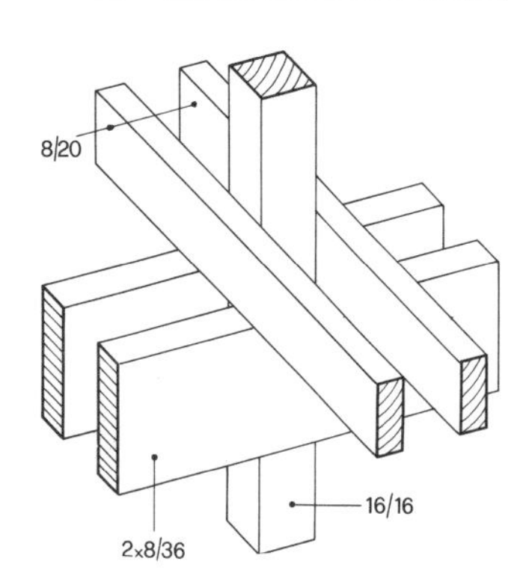

Structural node

Design

Three-story timber building with concrete basement. Split-level floors are arranged around the foyer, connected by steps. The articulated floor plan is also readable from the outside through variable heights of flat roofs and stepping of facades. The timber frame permits an extension of the ground floor over the areas without a basement.

Structure

The split-level structure requires a simple connection of girder to column, feasible at any level. Continuous 16/16 cm columns were chosen, together with continuous split girders 2 × 8/36 cm. Connections of girders to columns are made with shear connectors. Floor beams are 8/20 cm, spaced at 60 cm, placed as twin beams at columns. Roofs and floors are built as rigid panels with woodchip boards and tongue and groove planking. The wind load is transferred from these horizontal plates to the foundation by means of wood struts 16/16 cm, which are connected as half-diagonals between girders and floor beams. Struts are anchored to foundations with side straps.

Finishes

For acoustical insulation of floors, ceilings are supported on secondary beams attached to the floor beams. Above the workshop the space between floor beams is filled with light concrete. The movable partitions are fabricated from several layers to increase their acoustical insulation. Gravel roofing with interior drainage covers the building.

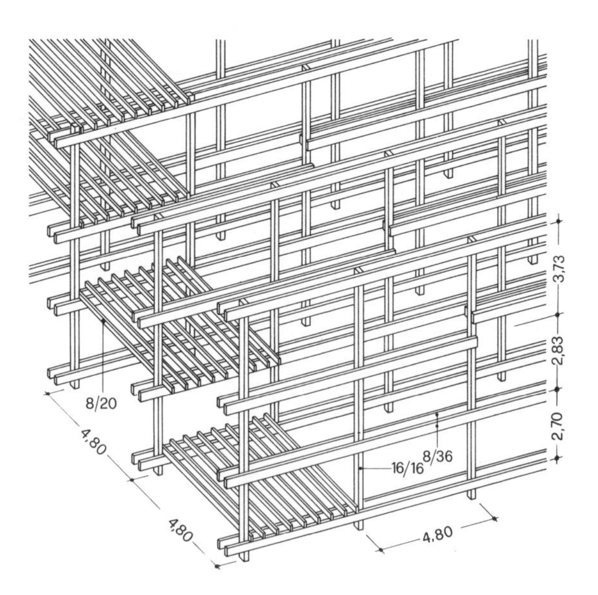

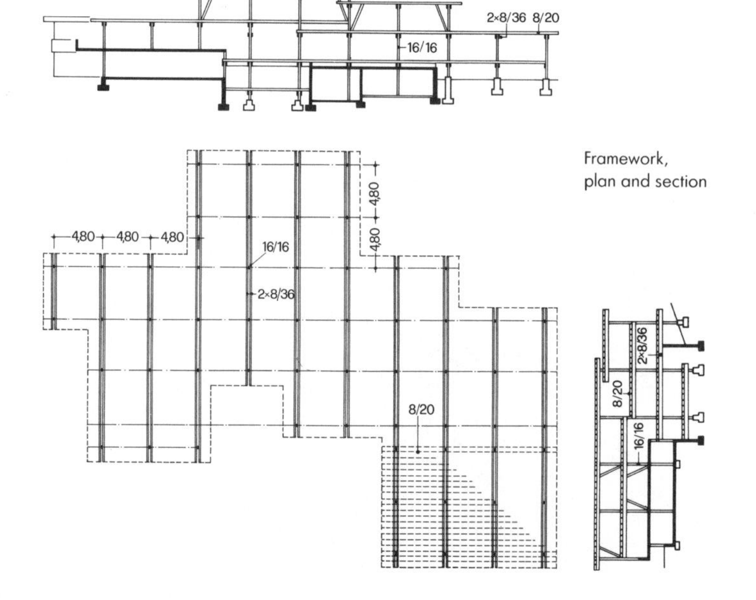

Framework, plan and section

Structure

Partial section

1 Shear connector 65 to 115 mm
2 Shear connection for floor beams, bolt M12
3 Bolts M12
4 Welded bar
6 Anchor bar ϕ 20 mm
7 Flat steel 50/6 mm
8 Bolts M16
9 Wood lashes 8/16 cm

Connections: columns – girders – floor beams

Bases

Exterior column   Interior column   Fixed interior column

Bracing

A Wind bracing, half-diagonal struts fixed between floor beams
B Same, fixed between girders
C Same, connected between girders as V frames
D Connection of wind strut to footing

1 Wind strut 16/16 cm
2 Flat steel 50 × 8 mm with 3 bolts M16
3 Strut 16/14 cm
4 Shear connector 50 to 80 mm
5 Filler wood 16/24 cm
6 Bolts M16

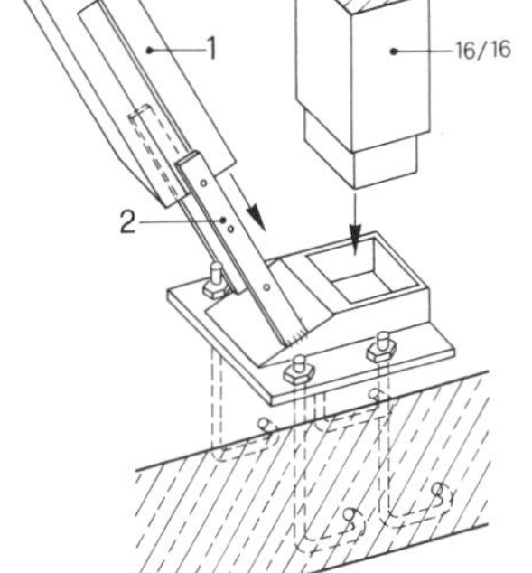

Split Beams

Finishes

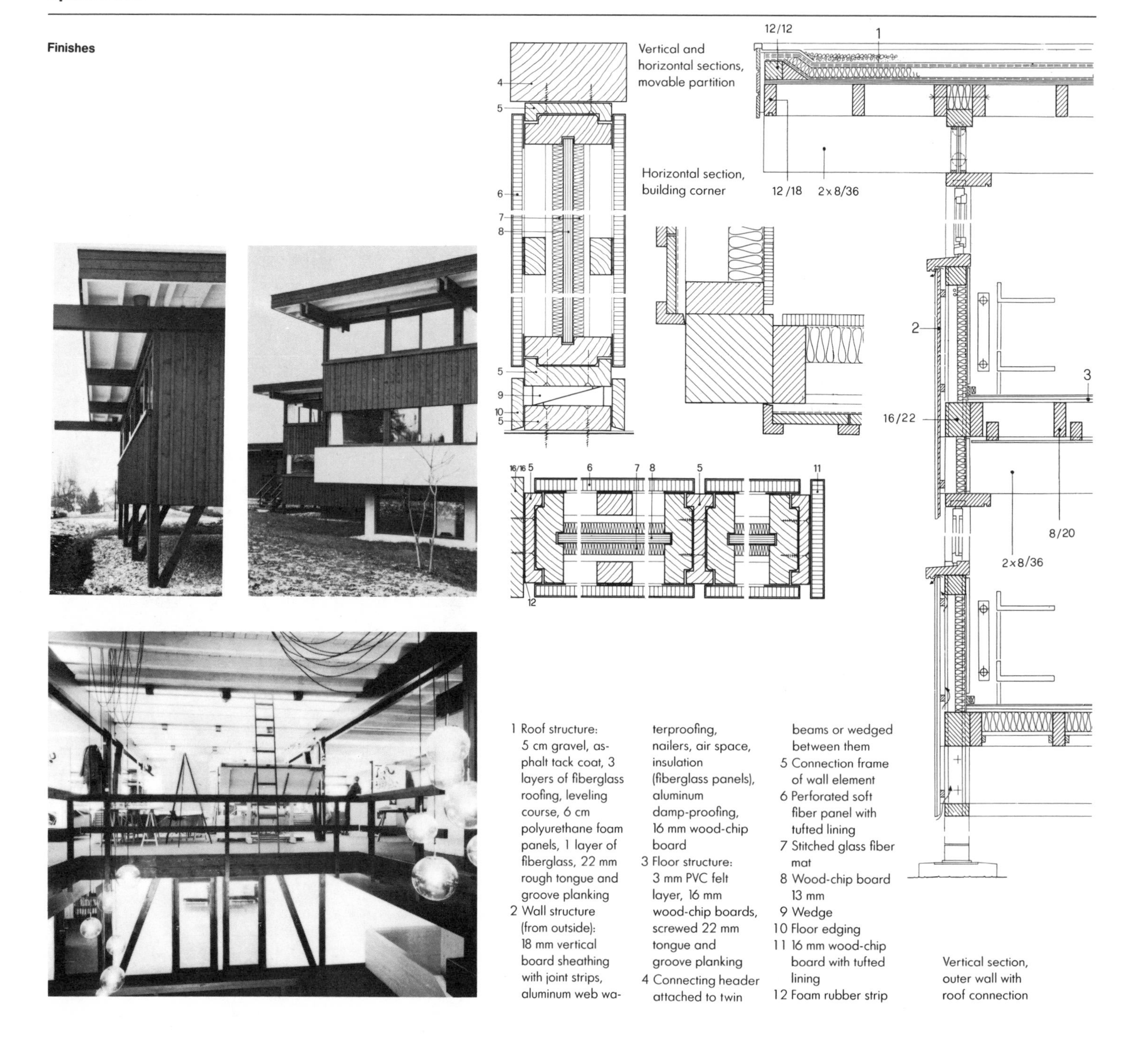

Vertical and horizontal sections, movable partition

Horizontal section, building corner

1 Roof structure: 5 cm gravel, asphalt tack coat, 3 layers of fiberglass roofing, leveling course, 6 cm polyurethane foam panels, 1 layer of fiberglass, 22 mm rough tongue and groove planking
2 Wall structure (from outside): 18 mm vertical board sheathing with joint strips, aluminum web waterproofing, nailers, air space, insulation (fiberglass panels), aluminum damp-proofing, 16 mm wood-chip board
3 Floor structure: 3 mm PVC felt layer, 16 mm wood-chip boards, screwed 22 mm tongue and groove planking
4 Connecting header attached to twin beams or wedged between them
5 Connection frame of wall element
6 Perforated soft fiber panel with tufted lining
7 Stitched glass fiber mat
8 Wood-chip board 13 mm
9 Wedge
10 Floor edging
11 16 mm wood-chip board with tufted lining
12 Foam rubber strip

Vertical section, outer wall with roof connection

Layout

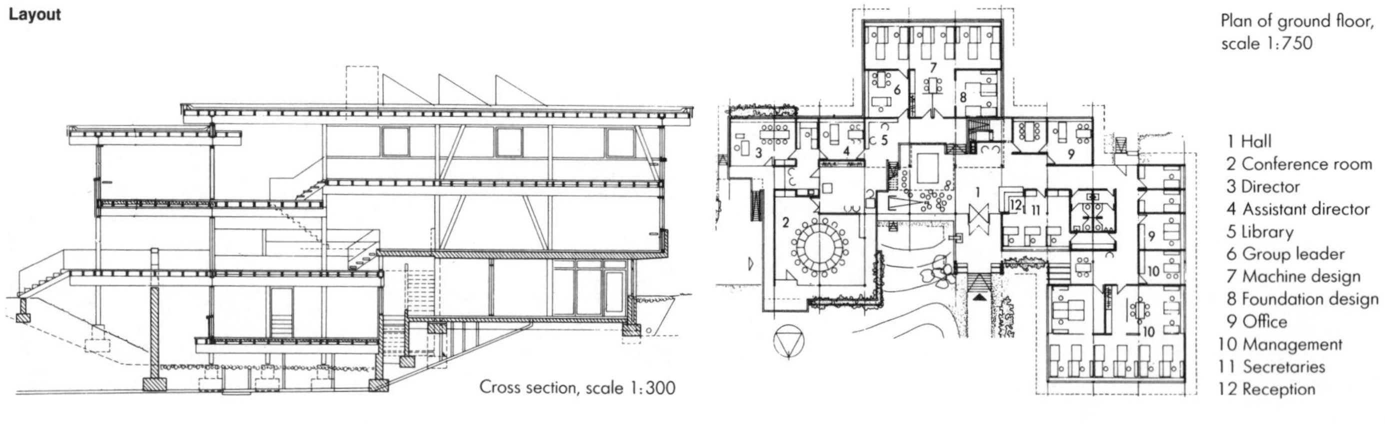

Cross section, scale 1:300

Plan of ground floor, scale 1:750

1 Hall
2 Conference room
3 Director
4 Assistant director
5 Library
6 Group leader
7 Machine design
8 Foundation design
9 Office
10 Management
11 Secretaries
12 Reception

Community Center

Architects: Group F70, L. Dorgerloh, M. Sass, Freiburg, West Germany
Engineer: M. Scherberger, Freiburg

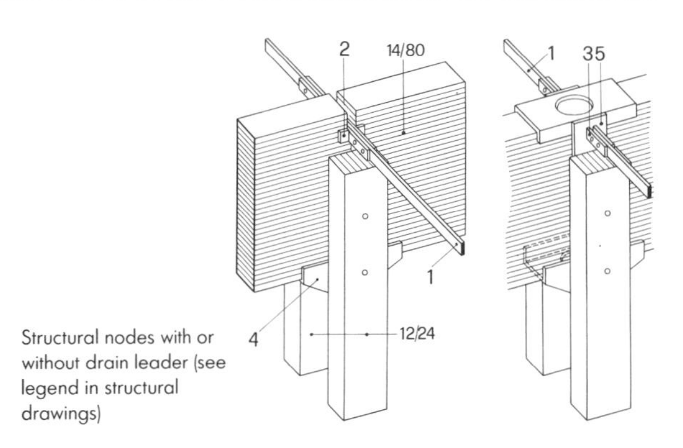

Structural nodes with or without drain leader (see legend in structural drawings)

Design

One-story building complex with adjacent gable roofs, assembly rooms, cafeteria, nursery, club rooms, and offices, 1390 m² usable space, 7067 m³ volume. The framework remains visible, finishes and partitions are offset in material and color.

Structure

The multiple gable roofs of this level structure are supported by rafters. The rafters work as three-hinged struts and deliver their inclined bearing forces to main girders. The main girders are spaced at 7.20 m and are supported by twin columns every 7.20 m. The uniform horizontal load is taken up at the columns. Longitudinal wind loads are taken by stiff roof surfaces and are transferred to columns. Steel ties at end columns take up the horizontal load. Split columns allow for simple fixity so that diagonal bracing is not needed in the transverse direction.

Finishes

The interior and exterior walls are mixed masonry and panel elements and are placed transversely adjacent to columns so that a clear structural articulation of the building is visible everywhere.

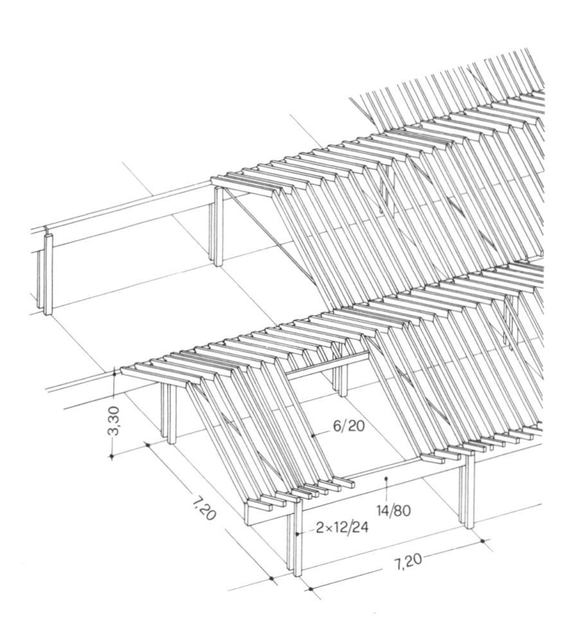

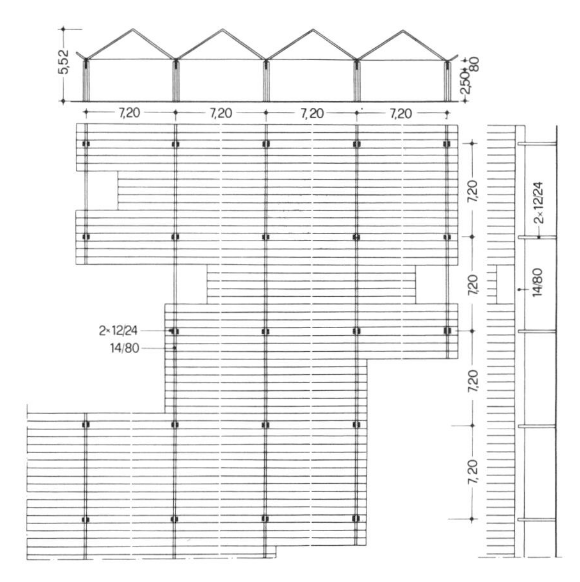

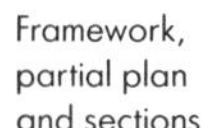

Framework, partial plan and sections

Structure

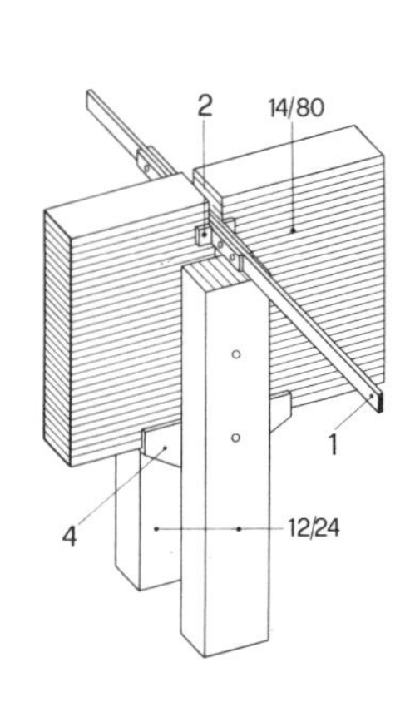

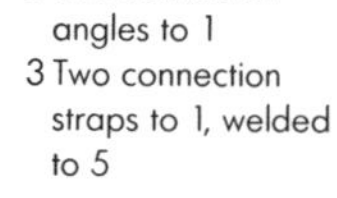

aa, bb Girder to column connection

1 Tension bar 14/60 mm
2 Two connection angles to 1
3 Two connection straps to 1, welded to 5

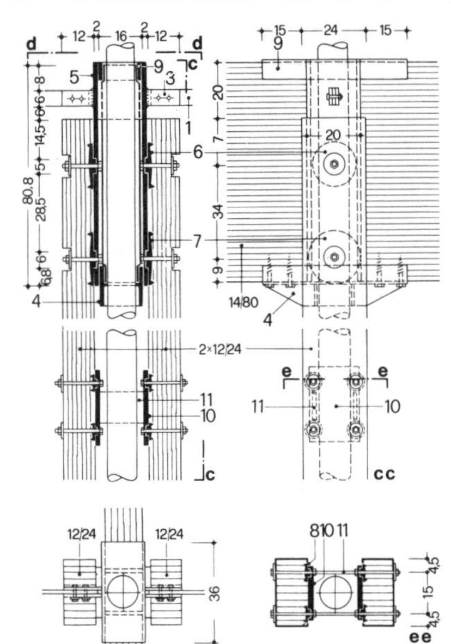

cc – ee Column top with drain leader between columns

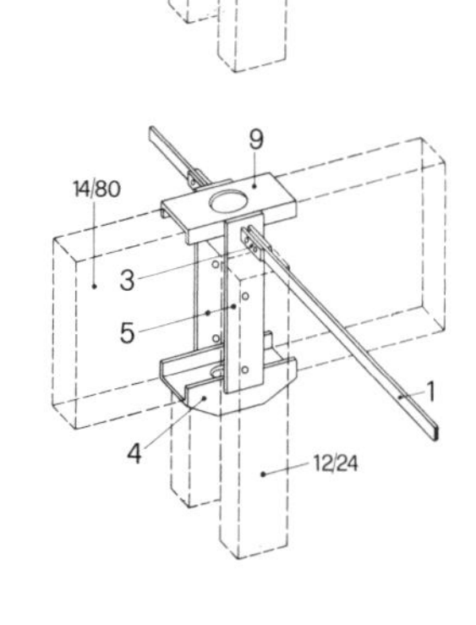

Connecting hardware, connection at node with drain leader

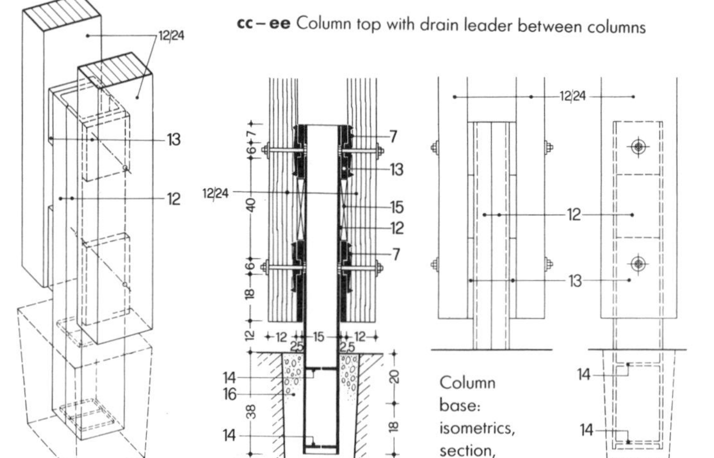

Column base: isometrics, section, elevations

4 Bearing shoe welded as I section, wood screws to girder
5 Side straps for 6 and 7, welded on 4
6 Shear connector ϕ 160 mm
7 Shear connector ϕ 190 mm
8 Shear connector ϕ 65 mm
9 Top plate with rain leader hole, welded to 5
10 Steel plates with shear connectors on column, connected with one spacer (or two, at leaders)
11 Steel plate as spacer
12 2 steel U channels 200, welded
13 Steel shape welded to 12 for connection of one-sided shear connector 7
14 Anchor plates
15 Wood filler 2.5/43 cm
16 Cast-in-place concrete

Bracing

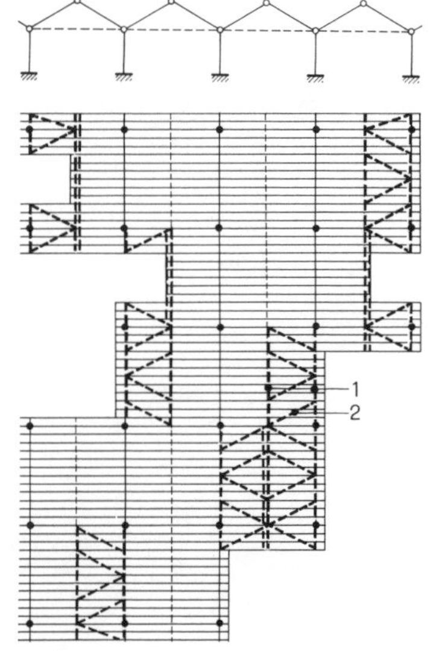

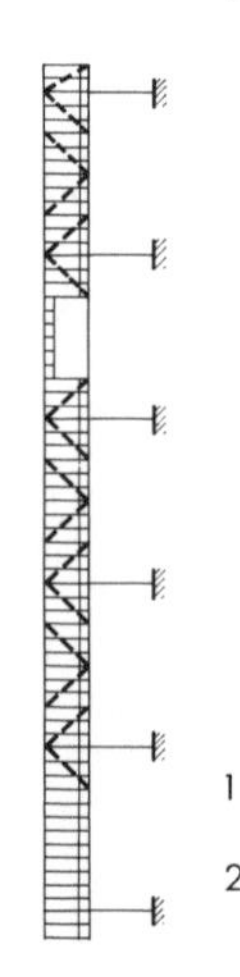

Partial plan and sections of bracing with diagonal struts, ties, and fixed columns

1 Longitudinal struts (ridge and valley) 8/25 cm
2 Diagonal wind struts 2.4/12 to 22 cm

Finishes

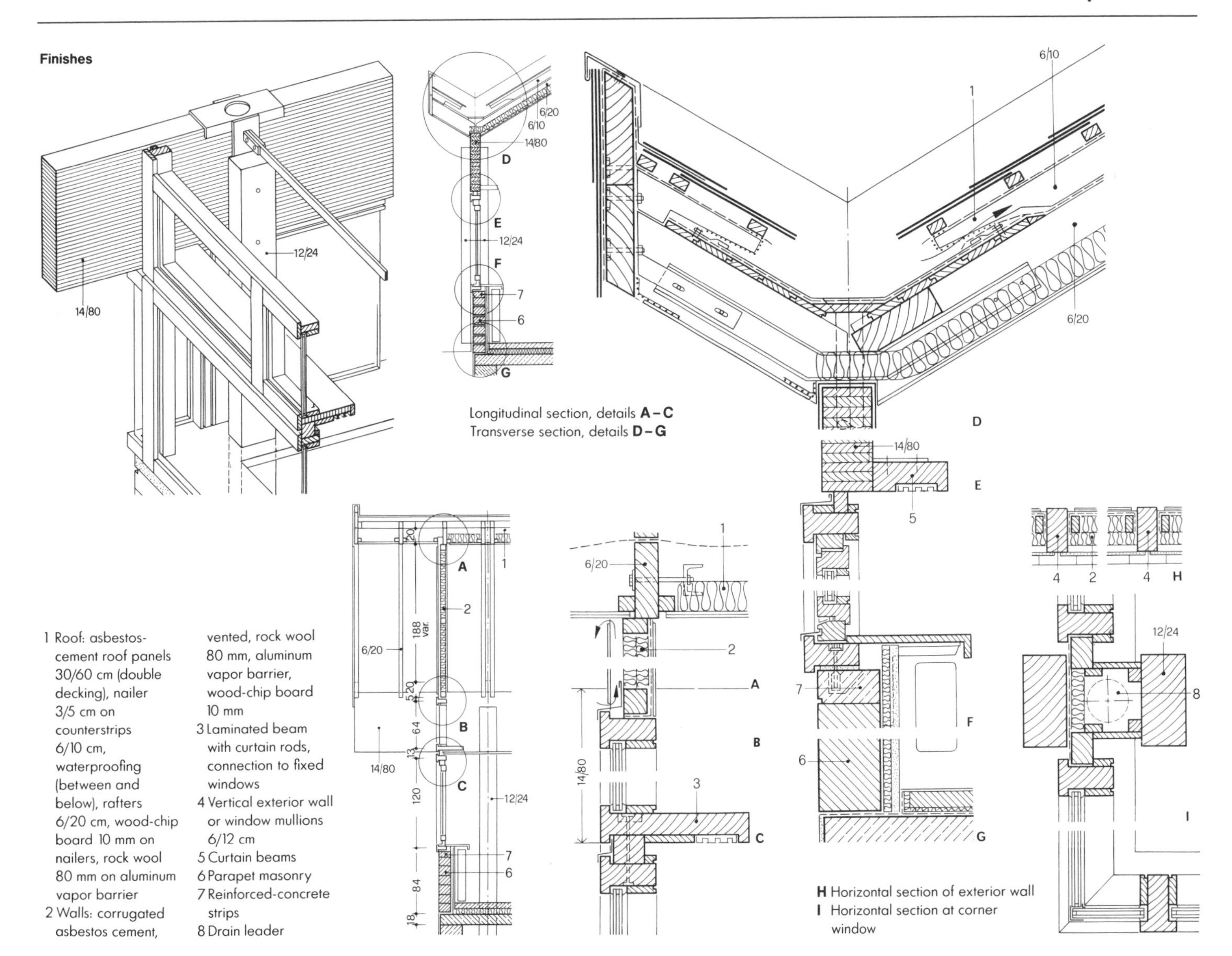

Longitudinal section, details **A – C**
Transverse section, details **D – G**

H Horizontal section of exterior wall
I Horizontal section at corner window

1 Roof: asbestos-cement roof panels 30/60 cm (double decking), nailer 3/5 cm on counterstrips 6/10 cm, waterproofing (between and below), rafters 6/20 cm, wood-chip board 10 mm on nailers, rock wool 80 mm on aluminum vapor barrier
2 Walls: corrugated asbestos cement, vented, rock wool 80 mm, aluminum vapor barrier, wood-chip board 10 mm
3 Laminated beam with curtain rods, connection to fixed windows
4 Vertical exterior wall or window mullions 6/12 cm
5 Curtain beams
6 Parapet masonry
7 Reinforced-concrete strips
8 Drain leader

Layout

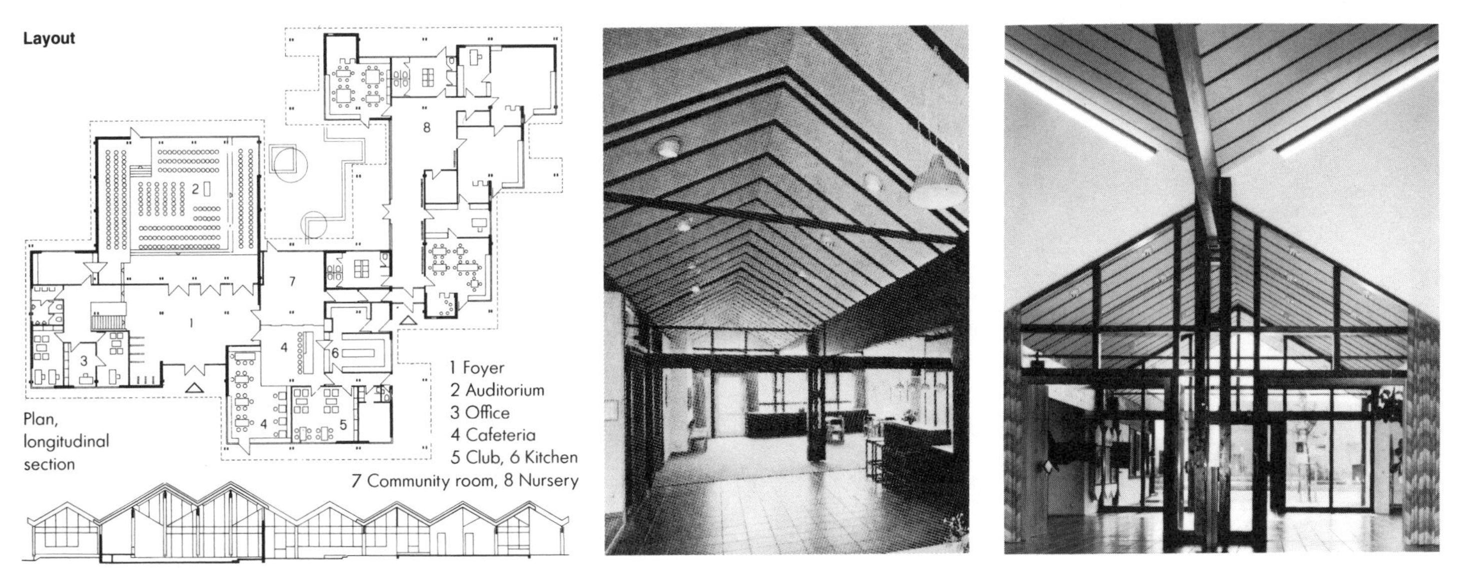

Plan, longitudinal section

1 Foyer
2 Auditorium
3 Office
4 Cafeteria
5 Club, 6 Kitchen
7 Community room, 8 Nursery

13

Student Cafeteria

Architect: J. van Stigt, Amsterdam, The Netherlands
Engineers: Oosterhoff, Tjebbes, and Barends, Arnheim

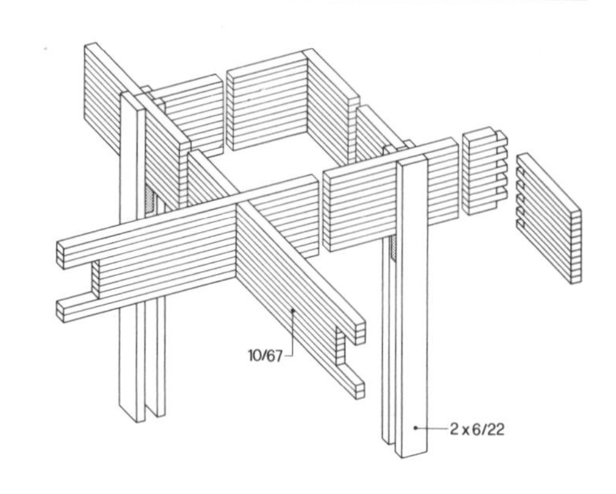

Design

One-story, strongly articulated building masses with a higher central core. Heating and washrooms in brick masonry. The cross-formed grid has equal projections in both directions; this allows column-free patios and entrances, and mullion-free corner windows.

Structure

Girders are placed between split columns and are anchored to them by means of shear connectors. The column grid is offset from the girder grid by a half-space, which makes girder intersections visible. Girders are interconnected by moment connections through finger joint splices with tension straps. Columns are attached to the foundation through a filler wood and a round bar. Horizontal bracing of rigid roof panels occurs through masonry walls.

Finishes

Parapets are laminated wood. Twin columns are joined by webs; utilities run through the hollow core. Fixed windows are set into grooves in girders, columns, and parapets.

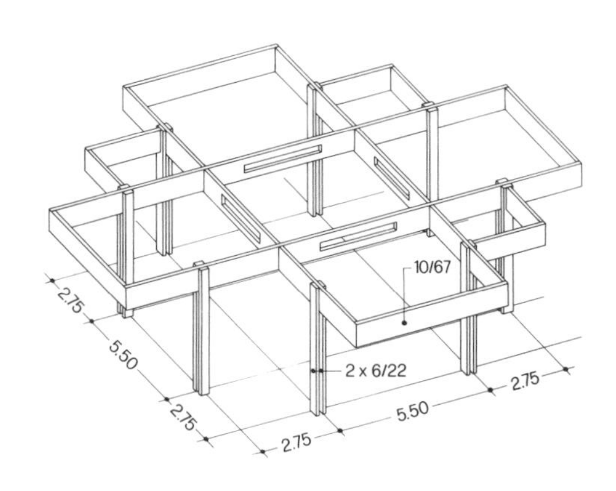

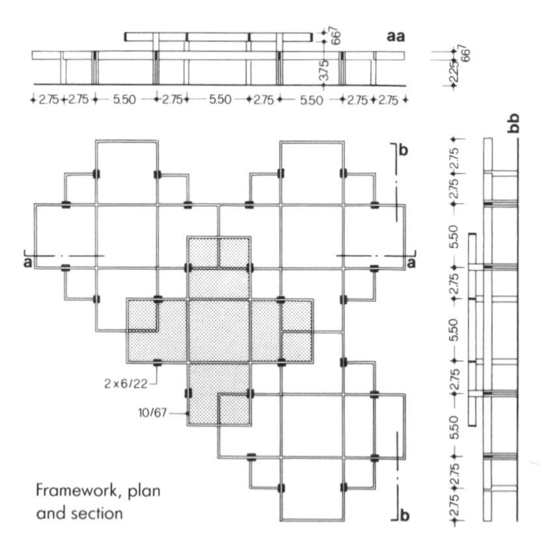

Framework, plan and section

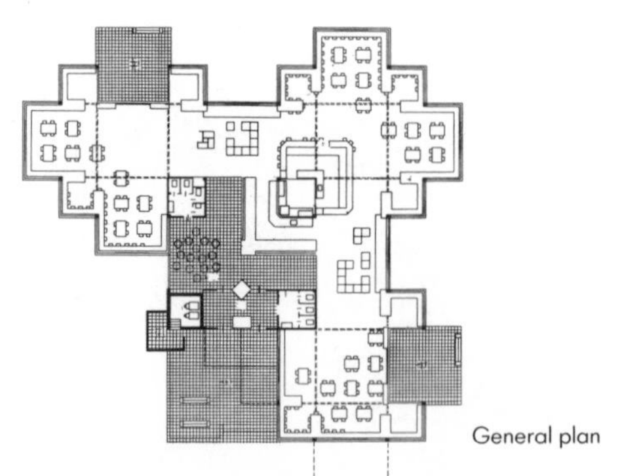

General plan

Structure

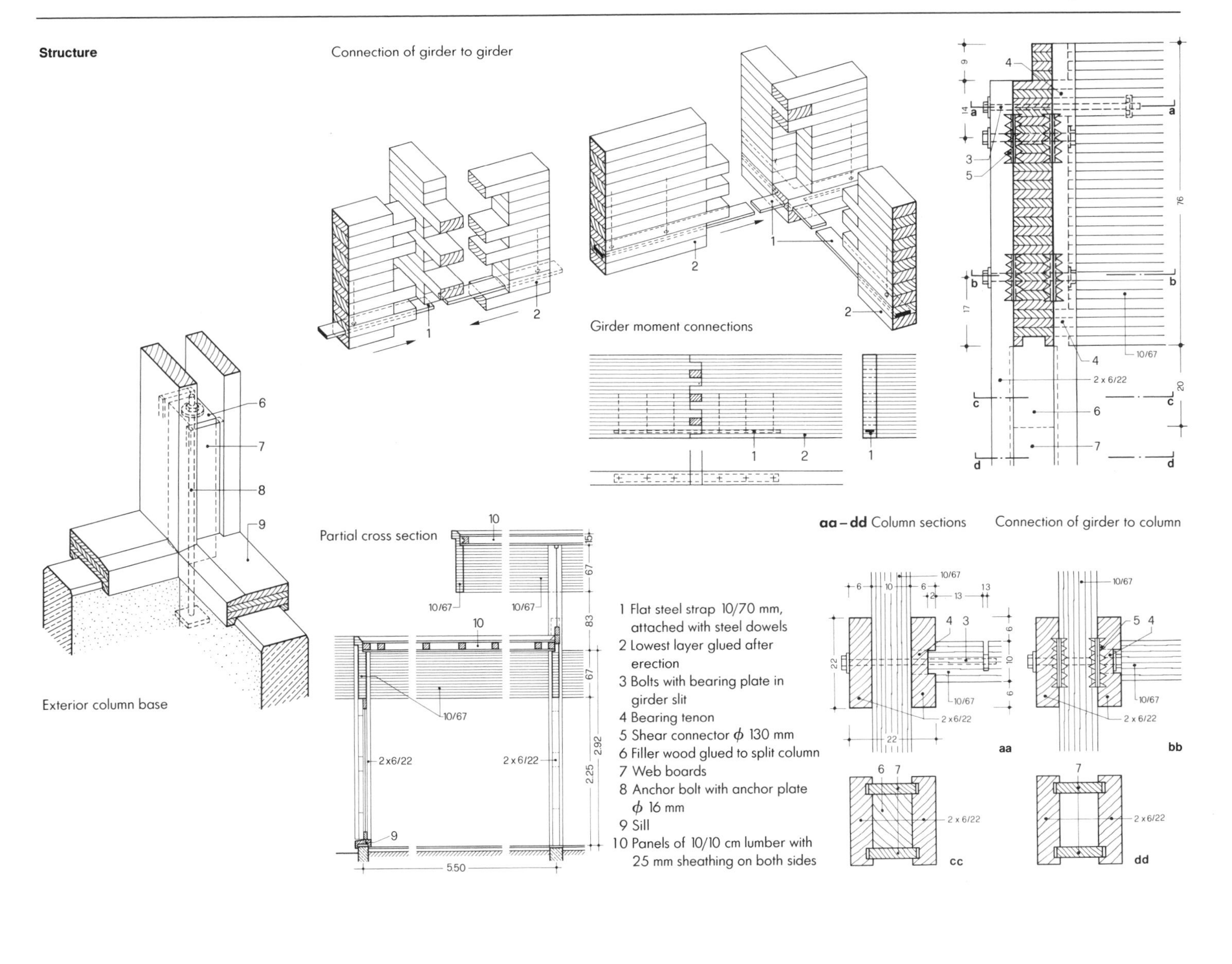

Connection of girder to girder

Girder moment connections

Exterior column base

Partial cross section

aa – dd Column sections

Connection of girder to column

1 Flat steel strap 10/70 mm, attached with steel dowels
2 Lowest layer glued after erection
3 Bolts with bearing plate in girder slit
4 Bearing tenon
5 Shear connector ϕ 130 mm
6 Filler wood glued to split column
7 Web boards
8 Anchor bolt with anchor plate ϕ 16 mm
9 Sill
10 Panels of 10/10 cm lumber with 25 mm sheathing on both sides

Finishes

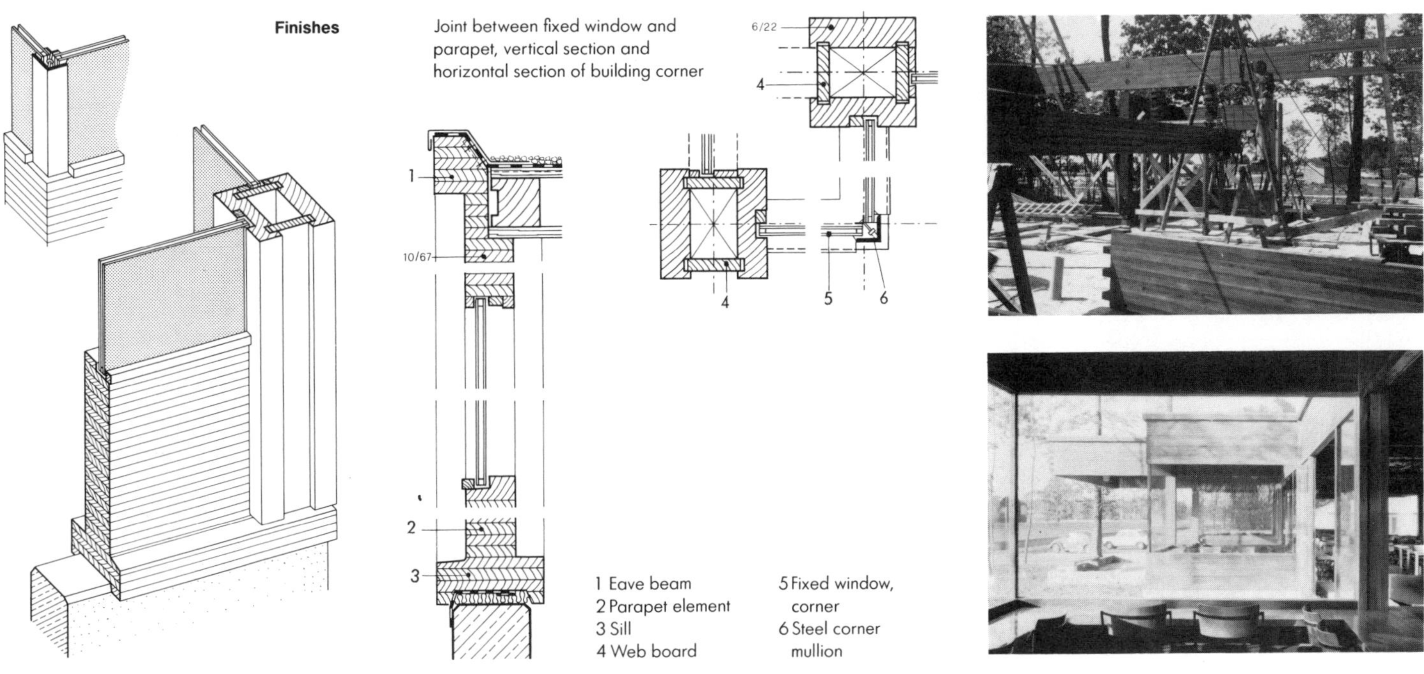

Joint between fixed window and parapet, vertical section and horizontal section of building corner

1 Eave beam
2 Parapet element
3 Sill
4 Web board
5 Fixed window, corner
6 Steel corner mullion

Exhibition Pavilion

Architects: W. von Lom and E. Kurt, Cologne, West Germany
Engineer: G. Tripler, Cologne

Structural node

1 Column 4 × 16/16 cm
2 Main girder 14/55 cm
3 Filler wood as bearing

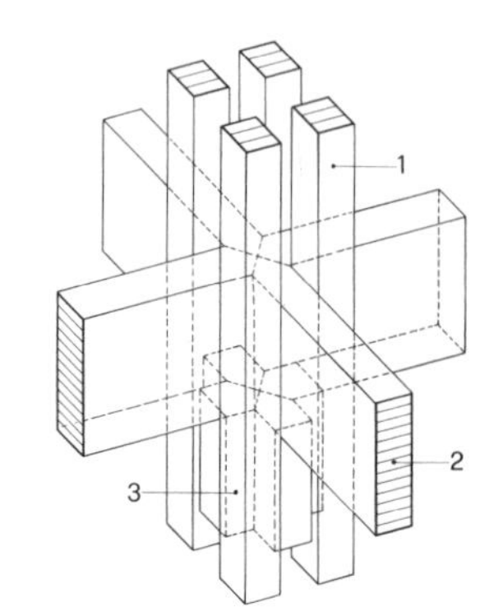

Design

Three buildings of an open-air museum have the same dimensions and grids. They are grouped around an exhibition court and are connected by passages. Balconies are variably arranged within the buildings and may later by easily expanded or modified by changes in layout.

Structure

The structure was chosen in such a way that the main girders can be changed later and balconies modified to suit new exhibits. The columns, placed on a square grid, were therefore split in four parts so that main girders can pass through columns in both directions. Girders are supported by filler wood. Floor beams 10/35 cm, spaced at 1.20 m, rest on main girders.

Horizontal bracing is achieved by fixing exterior columns so that the interior of the building can be changed. Exterior windows are not interrupted by bracing diagonals or full walls.

Finishes

Facades are mostly glazed over the full balcony height and are protected from the sun and the weather by cantilevered roofs. The structure underneath the insulated roof leaves a space which, together with a layer of acoustic insulation, provides good acoustics in the galleries.

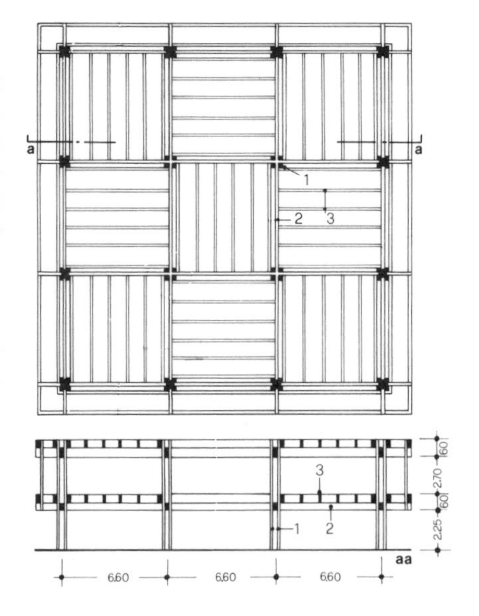

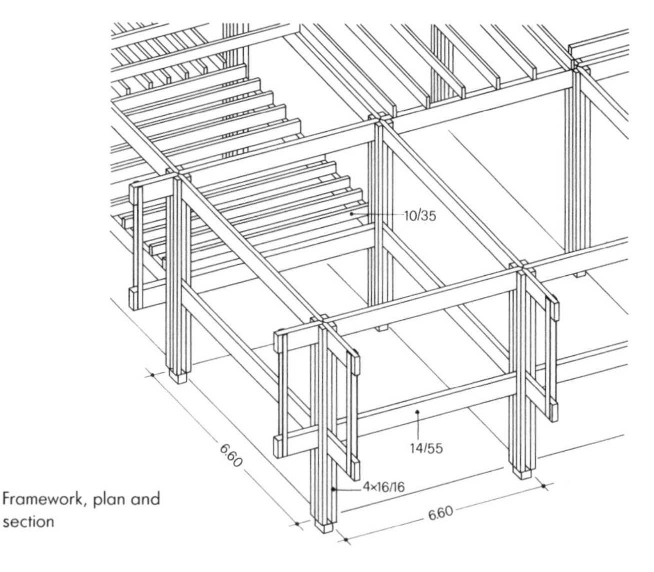

Framework, plan and section

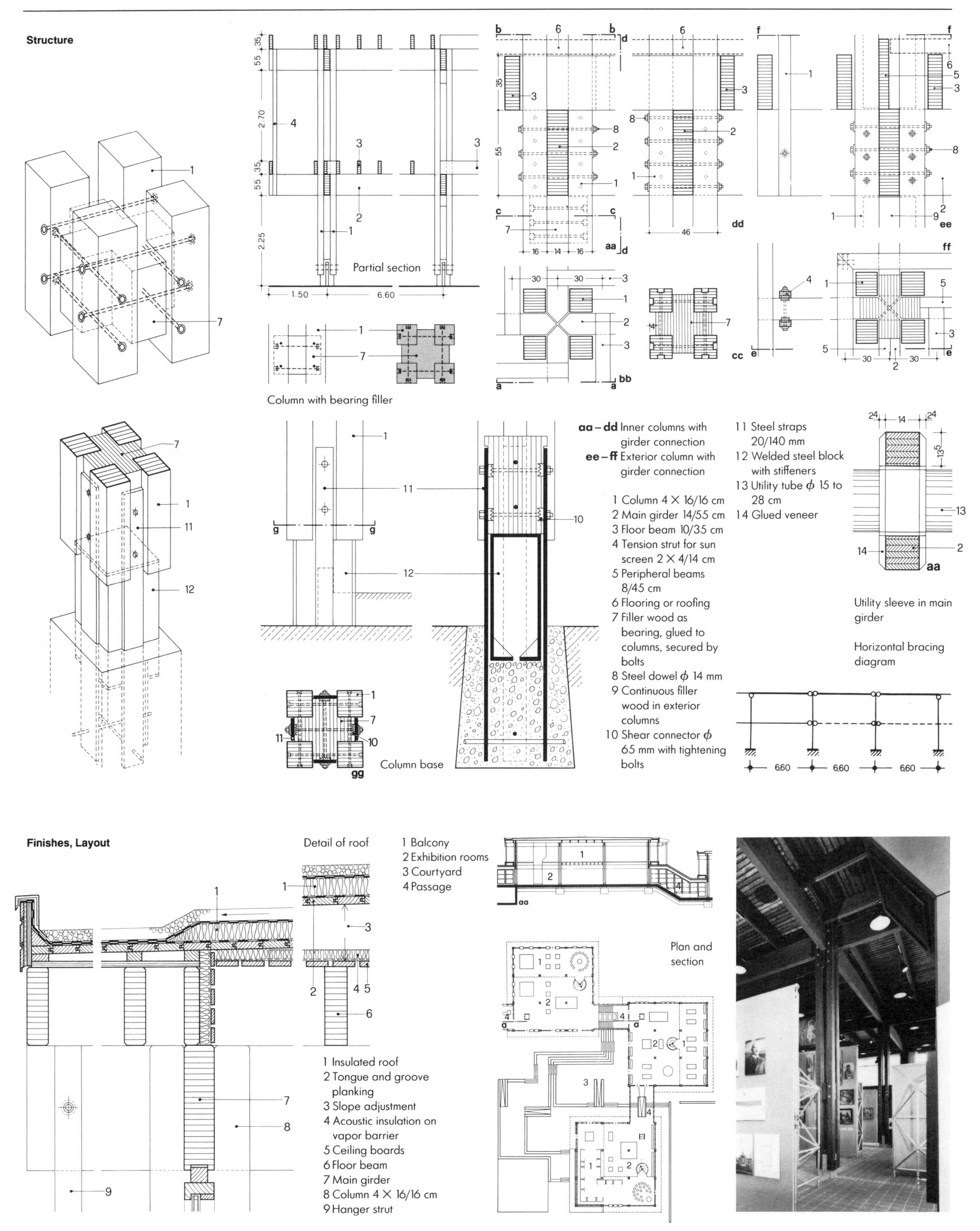
Structure
Partial section
Column with bearing filler
Column base
aa – dd Inner columns with girder connection
ee – ff Exterior column with girder connection
1 Column 4 × 16/16 cm
2 Main girder 14/55 cm
3 Floor beam 10/35 cm
4 Tension strut for sun screen 2 × 4/14 cm
5 Peripheral beams 8/45 cm
6 Flooring or roofing
7 Filler wood as bearing, glued to columns, secured by bolts
8 Steel dowel ϕ 14 mm
9 Continuous filler wood in exterior columns
10 Shear connector ϕ 65 mm with tightening bolts
11 Steel straps 20/140 mm
12 Welded steel block with stiffeners
13 Utility tube ϕ 15 to 28 cm
14 Glued veneer
Utility sleeve in main girder
Horizontal bracing diagram
Finishes, Layout
Detail of roof
1 Insulated roof
2 Tongue and groove planking
3 Slope adjustment
4 Acoustic insulation on vapor barrier
5 Ceiling boards
6 Floor beam
7 Main girder
8 Column 4 × 16/16 cm
9 Hanger strut
1 Balcony
2 Exhibition rooms
3 Courtyard
4 Passage
Plan and section

15

Two-Family House

Architects: Goto, Sohara, Kimura, Tokyo, Japan

A Connection of frame to roof
B Column – girder – peripheral girder connection
C Anchorage point

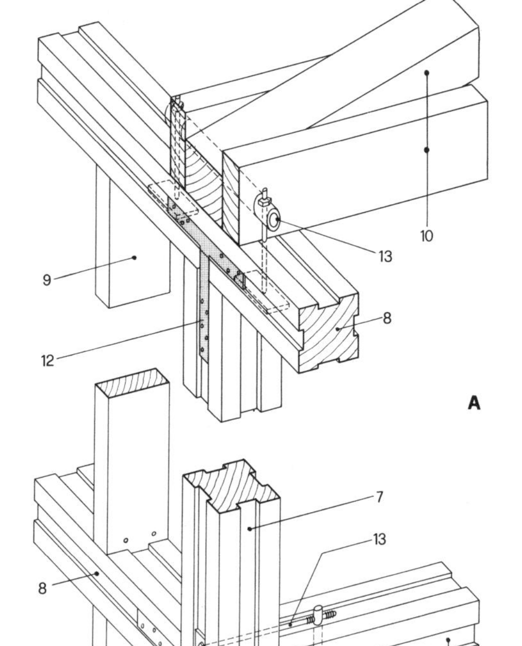

Design

Example of a simple Japanese structural system that requires small timber cross sections and simple connections. Wall panels are covered on all sides with plaster or gypsum board. Flat gable roofs provide a low attic over the entire living area.

Structure

The framework is a combination of tie-beam and rib construction. Continuous columns are spaced at 3.70 m. The main and peripheral girders run between the columns as tie beams which are connected to columns by means of nailed steel plates and tightening bolts. In the remaining panels there are vertical studs 3.8/10 cm spaced at 60 cm. These studs carry the vertical loads and at the same time serve as wall core for interior and exterior walls.

Horizontal bracing is provided by nailed plywood panels.

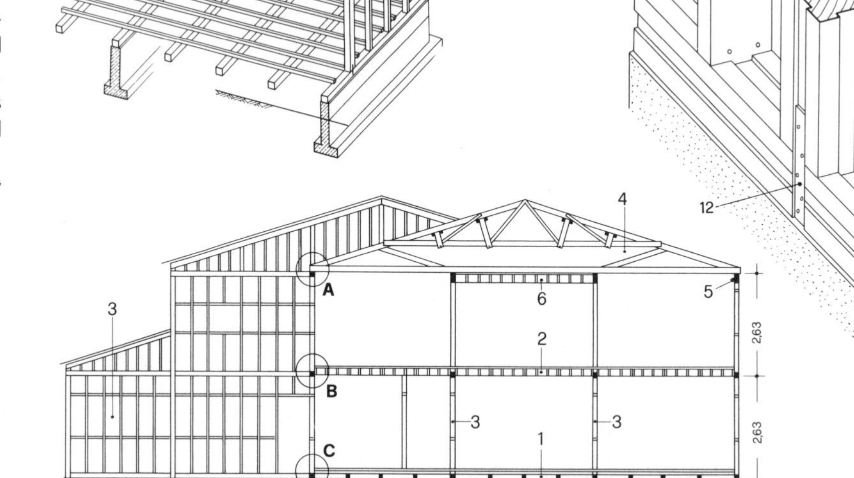

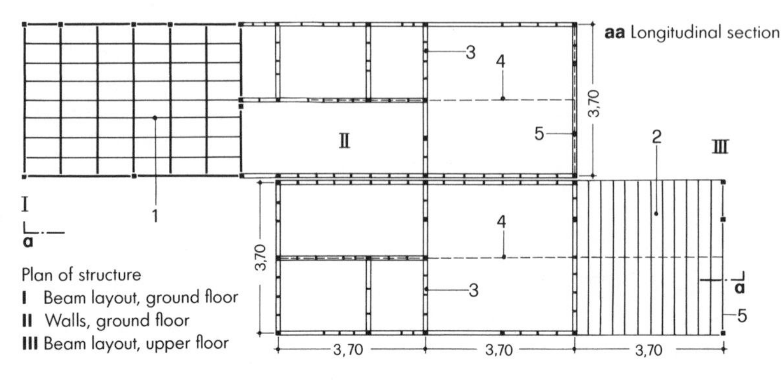

aa Longitudinal section

Plan of structure
I Beam layout, ground floor
II Walls, ground floor
III Beam layout, upper floor

1 Ground floor construction
2 Upper floor
3 Ground floor walls
4 Roof trusses
5 Cross beam for supporting 4
6 ttic floor
7 Continuous columns 10/10 cm
8 Main or peripheral girder 10/10 cm
9 Vertical wall stud 3.8/10 cm
10 Truss tie beam 2 × 3.5/12 cm, upper chord 9/9 cm
12 Nailed strap plates
13 Tightening bolts with compression washer screwed into transverse anchor

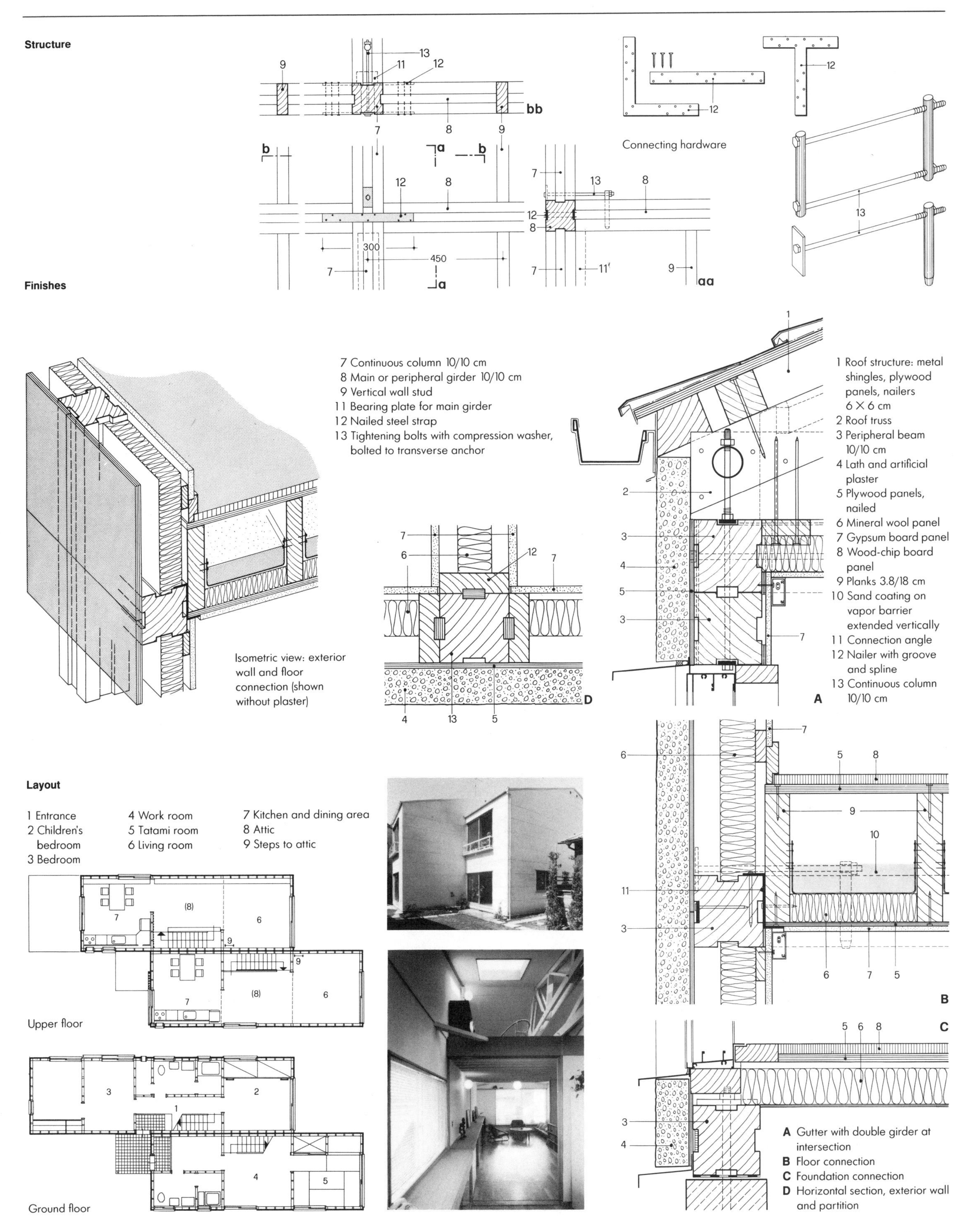
Structure
Finishes
Connecting hardware
7 Continuous column 10/10 cm
8 Main or peripheral girder 10/10 cm
9 Vertical wall stud
11 Bearing plate for main girder
12 Nailed steel strap
13 Tightening bolts with compression washer, bolted to transverse anchor
Isometric view: exterior wall and floor connection (shown without plaster)
1 Roof structure: metal shingles, plywood panels, nailers 6 × 6 cm
2 Roof truss
3 Peripheral beam 10/10 cm
4 Lath and artificial plaster
5 Plywood panels, nailed
6 Mineral wool panel
7 Gypsum board panel
8 Wood-chip board panel
9 Planks 3.8/18 cm
10 Sand coating on vapor barrier extended vertically
11 Connection angle
12 Nailer with groove and spline
13 Continuous column 10/10 cm
Layout
1 Entrance
2 Children's bedroom
3 Bedroom
4 Work room
5 Tatami room
6 Living room
7 Kitchen and dining area
8 Attic
9 Steps to attic
Upper floor
Ground floor
A Gutter with double girder at intersection
B Floor connection
C Foundation connection
D Horizontal section, exterior wall and partition

16

Multiple-Family Residence

Architect: D. Marshall,
Vancouver, Canada

Structural details

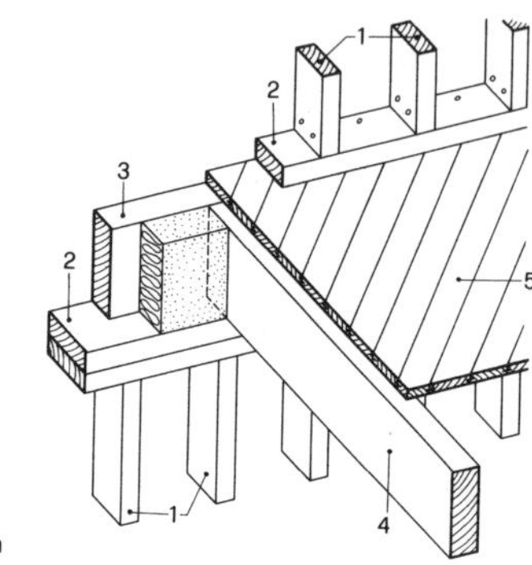

1 Studs 5/10 cm
2 Sill 2 × 5/10 cm
3 Edge beams 5/20 cm
4 Floor beams 5/20 cm
5 Diagonal planking 6 cm

Standard North American platform construction used for single and multi-family housing. Standard 2/4 inch (5/10 cm) lumber is used for load-carrying interior and exterior walls, and as sills, headers, and posts. Floor beams, cross beams, and lintels are 2/8 inches (5/20 cm). The spacing of studs and floor beams is 40 to 60 cm. Studs are sheathed on one or both sides. The resulting rib section can resist vertical and horizontal loads, so that additional bracing is not necessary. The narrow stud spacing and sheathing permits individual design, a free structure in plan, and an elevation that does not depend on any modular constraints.

The base may be either a continuous foundation or, as in this example, a specially treated lumber sill which rests on rolled gravel and is protected on the bottom and sides by vapor barriers.

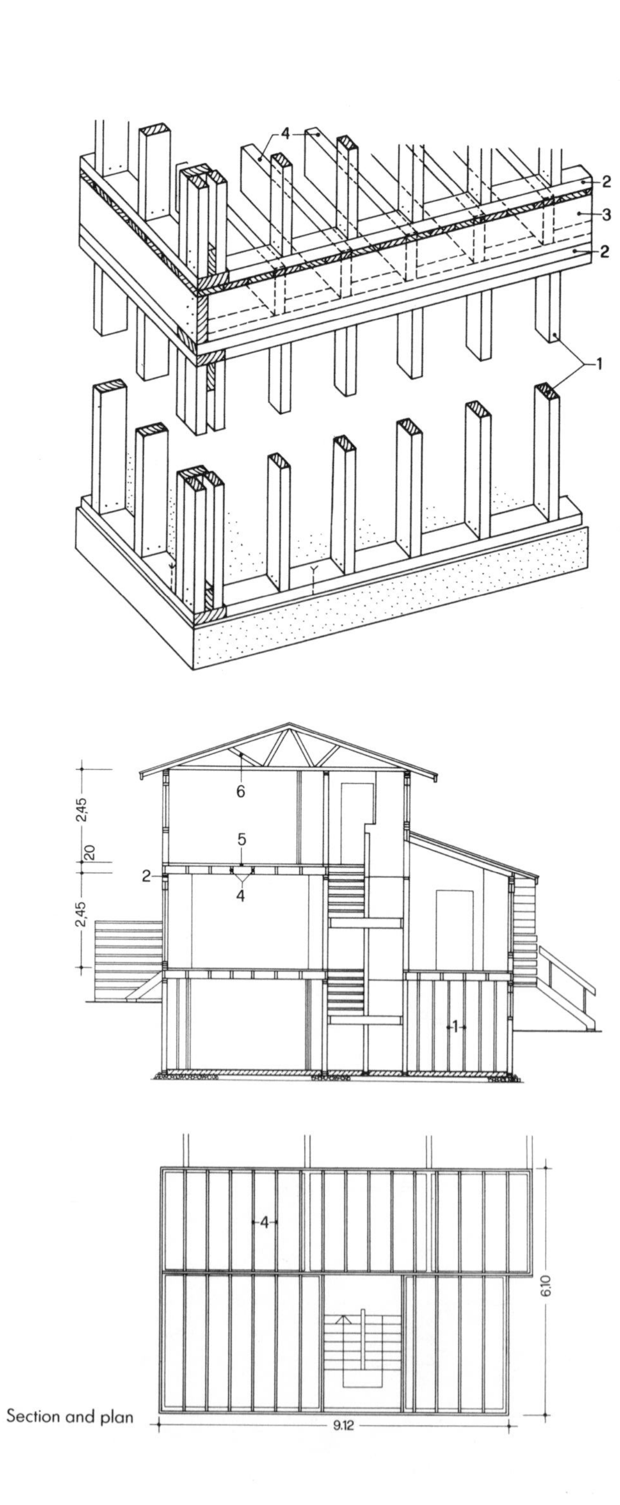

Section and plan

Structure

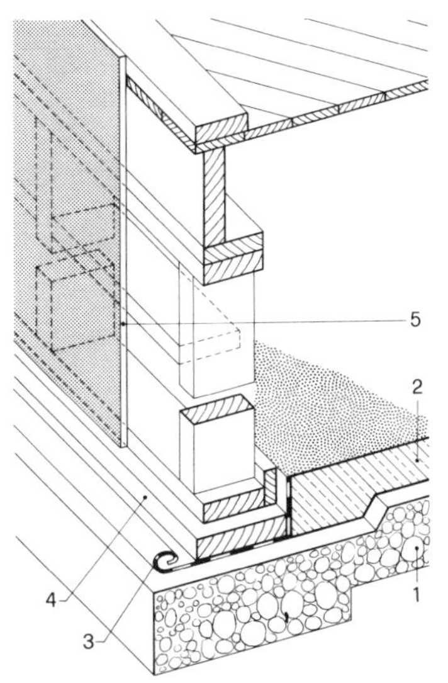

First and second floors, exterior wall

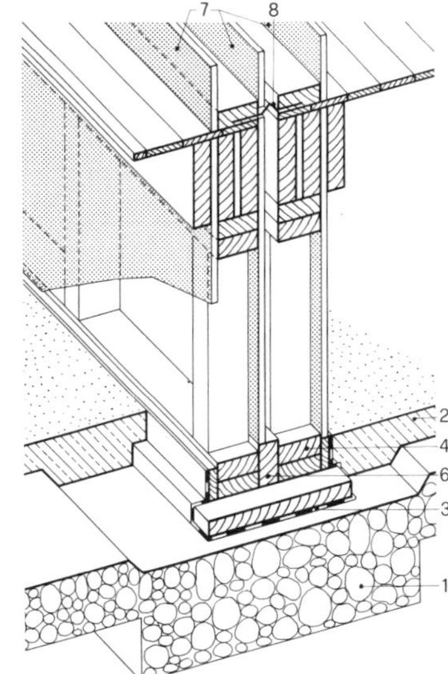

Partition walls

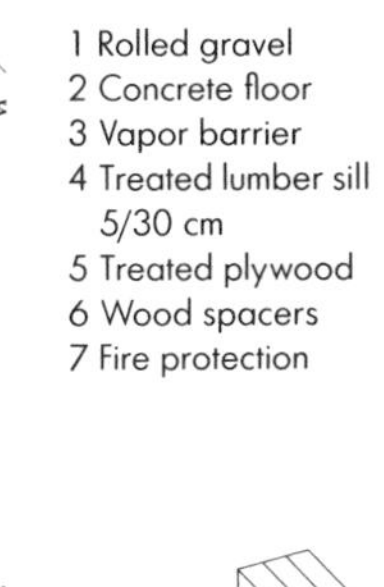

1 Rolled gravel
2 Concrete floor
3 Vapor barrier
4 Treated lumber sill 5/30 cm
5 Treated plywood
6 Wood spacers
7 Fire protection panels
8 Fire protection sheet metal
9 Nailed connection straps
10 Nailed wood splices

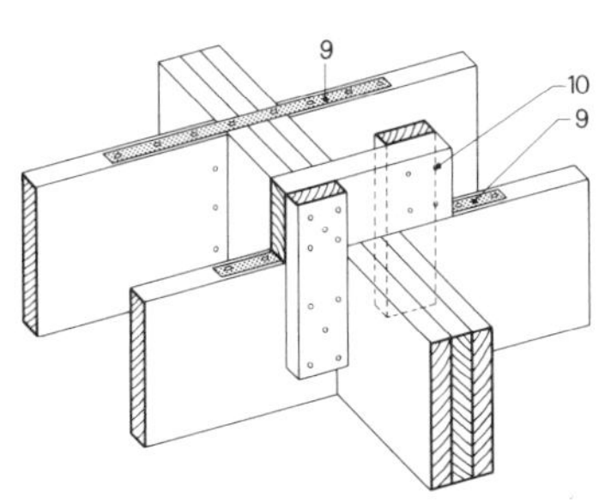

Connection at beam intersection

Finishes

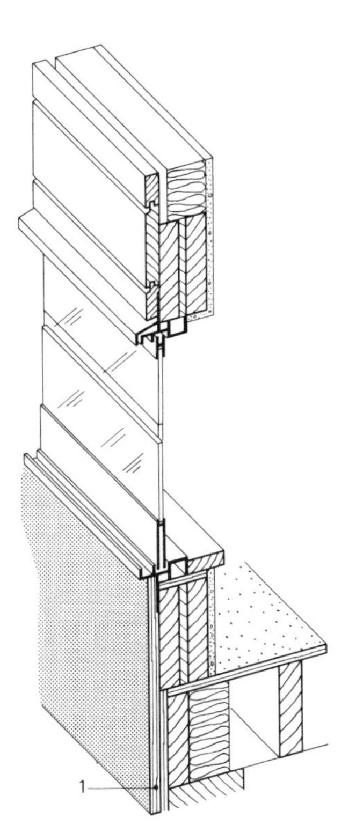

1 Treated plywood fascia
2 Plywood panels on diagonal sheathing
3 Sliding window
4 Gypsum board panel
5 Horizontal tongue and groove sheathing

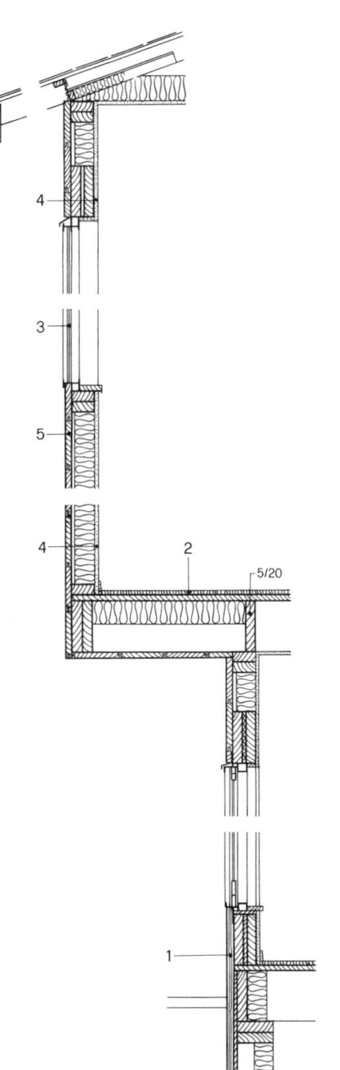

Exterior wall section

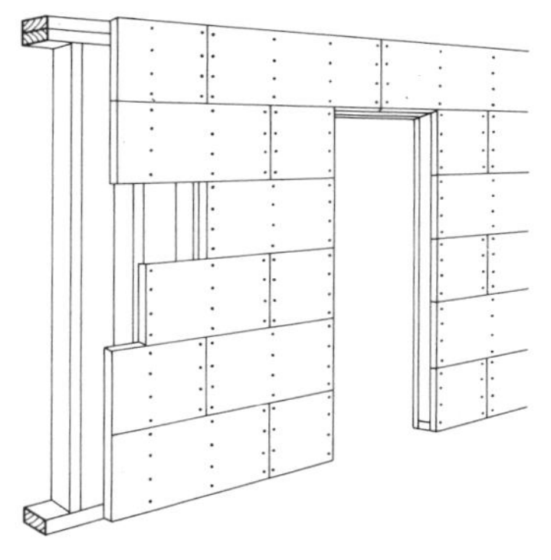

Sheathing of wall with plywood

Layout

General layout

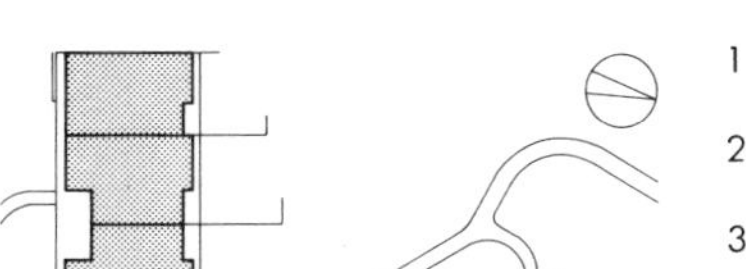

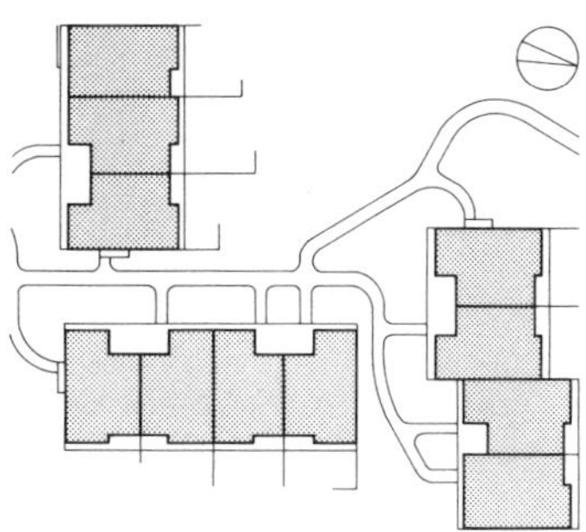

Credits: The following photographers gave permission to publish their photos in the *Timber Design and Construction Source Book:* Bauer, Waldshut (p. 210 bottom); H. Finke, Konstanz (p. 222 center); Glock, Karlsruhe (p. 210 top and center, p. 211 center, bottom); K. Halmburger, Murnau (p. 220 top and bottom, p. 222 top); G. Henn, Munich (p. 205 bottom); K. Kinold, Munich (p. 215 bottom, p. 216 bottom, p. 217); B. Krupp, Freiburg (p. 224, p. 225 bottom right); H.-J. Meier-Menzel, Murnau (p. 204 bottom, p. 206 center); P. J. van Puffelen, Lochem (p. 227 center); S. Rista, Helsinki (p. 214); H. Stahl, Cologne (p. 228 bottom right, p. 229); J. Versnel, Amsterdam (p. 226, p. 227 bottom); Wumige (p. 211 center top).

Wood-Panel Construction

DIETER HOOR

In collaboration with:
Wolfgang Haux

DEVELOPMENT AND POTENTIAL USES OF WOOD-PANEL CONSTRUCTION

Development of Wood-Panel Construction

Wood-panel construction, including the use of prefabricated load-bearing or non-load-bearing wood frames, was developed in the course of a search for optimum prefabrication of elements to be used in timber frame structures. Today's type of timber framing construction resembles steel and concrete framing with its advanced prefabrication of numerous structural elements, the application of newer, industrially prepared connections, the use of new connection methods, and the assembly of many individual elements on the construction site. The elements include columns, girders, walls, and facades, all of which fit together and must connect with one another. The speed of their assembly depends on weather conditions.

In an effort to increase efficiency, to industrialize construction techniques, and to reduce the dependence of the construction site on the weather, precision workshops sought at an early stage to assemble large units, including doors and windows, with the purpose of speeding assembly at the construction site. This is equally true for steel, reinforced concrete, and timber construction. Efficiency and industrialization resulted in prefabrication. Building elements are prefabricated in the workshop while foundations and basements are being prepared in the field. Nowadays this means that a structure is prefabricated to order, and not that an individual building is assembled rapidly by using prefabricated stock components.

In 1931, Walter Gropius developed a prefabricated system of large wall panels which was first used at the

Copper Houses for the Hirsch Copper and Brass Works AG in Finow, Germany. Standardized wall panels consisted of timber framing with aluminum foil lining, asbestos-cement panels on the inside, and corrugated copper sheets on the outside.

This system was modular: wall elements were of equal width and their joints went through the centerline. Panels were joined by "connectors," which were greatly improved several years later in the "General Panel Construction" system.

During the years of 1943 to 1945, the architects Walter Gropius and Konrad Wachsmann developed this system further for the General Panel Corporation in the United States under the name "Packaged House System." The basic idea was the same as that in the Hirsch Copper Houses.

The system consisted of load-bearing timber frame elements which are sheathed on the outside with vertical wood shingles. The system differed from the Hirsch Copper Houses by the small size of its wall elements, which was easier to adapt to individual building plans. The essential detail of wall-panel construction was the connector, a four-sided steel section that binds two wall elements together. This connector permitted the vertical and horizontal assembly of equal elements. Connector components were built into the edges of each panel at the factory and could be assembled in a maximum of four directions.

The Packaged House System was a trend setter in wood-panel construction and has changed little to this day. Improvements consisted mainly of newer sealers and joint materials and in the application of the system to different types of construction.

a

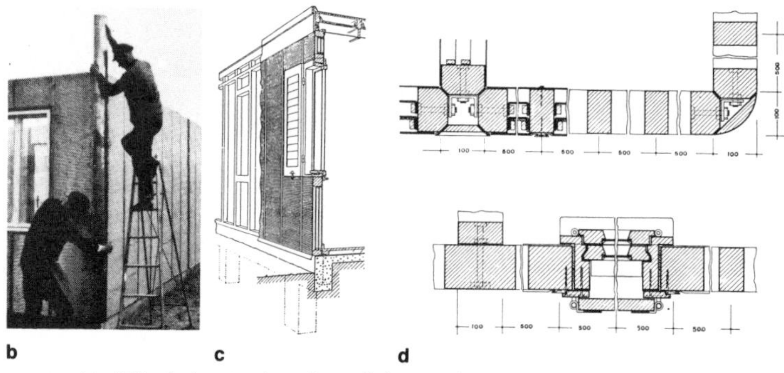
b c d

Fig. 1. Copper Houses in Finow. (a) Assembly of prefabricated walls. (b) House corner sealed with a copper strip. (c) Vertical section through a wall element. (d) Horizontal section and connection of wall elements.

a

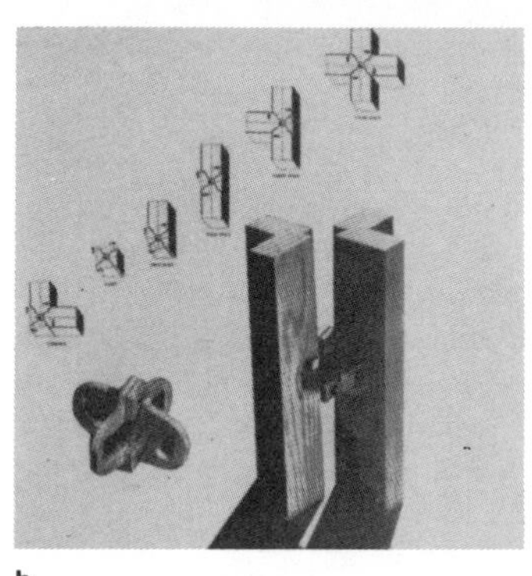
b

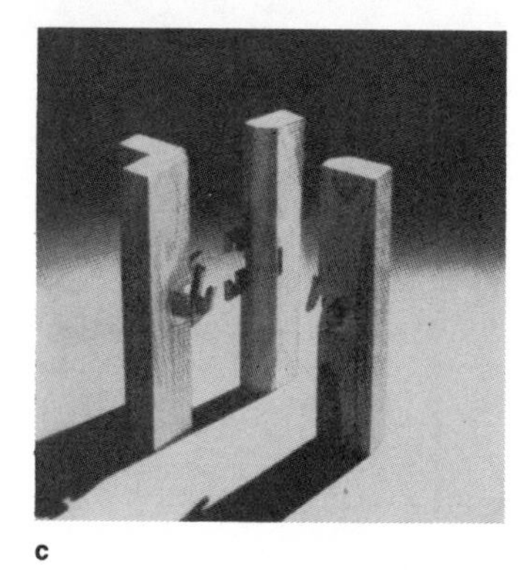
c

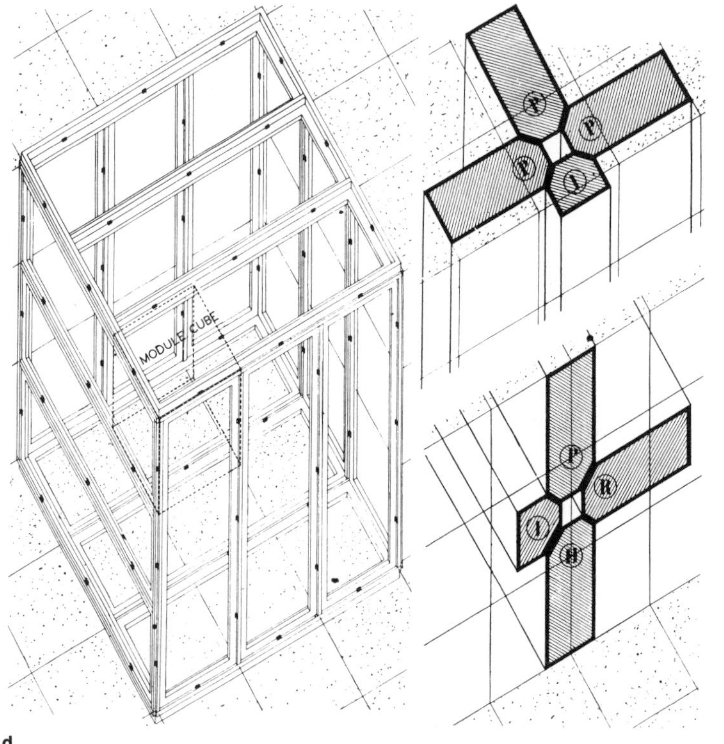

d

Fig. 2. "Packaged House System." (a) Rough construction before joining floor and roof panels. (b) Four-sided connection with metal connector. (c) Separated connectors. (d) Assembly and connection of wall, floor, and roof elements.

In addition to the widely applicable small frame elements, major prefabricated panels are now available, which can be assembled as walls of entire rooms. As in steel and reinforced-concrete structures, striving toward optimization is necessarily leading toward the production of room elements which can fit various floor plans. In addition to the economy of production and the advantages of prefabrication, important in the development of wood-panel construction were the properties of wood itself: high strength, high insulating values, easy workability, economy, and rich choice of surface treatments.

Mass Production versus Individual Requirements

Mass production and individual requirements seem to be a contradiction. Can the production of large elements satisfy individual needs at all? Prefabrication certainly helped reduce costs and construction time. Working against prefabrication is the individual user's desire to have a specific, functional, and well constructed building, including the adaptability to future needs. From the latter point of view, prefabrication may not be the best answer. However, even here individual requirements may be considered to a certain degree. It is therefore advisable to limit the standardization of elements to those types that can be combined easily to form different layouts.

On the other hand, individual requirements must consider the limitations of a prefabricated system. Frequently observed attempts to alter the basic characteristics of prefabrication, such as covering the joints of wall elements with sealers or plaster, do not respond to the technical demands of prefabrication and are not economical. Wood-panel elements are subject to standard woodworking procedures, which require allowance for tolerances and adjustments, and thus they should not be covered with additional rigid materials. Wood panels can be prefabricated with a high-quality finish. Panel field assembly time is relatively short and therefore rather independent of the weather. However, additional finishes are often added after assembly. This requires additional time and manual labor, both of which depend on the facilities of the local contractor.

Wood-panel construction must be accepted for what it is, namely, an efficient, economical, fast, and highly precise method of construction which uses a familiar material. The structure, the room elements, and the joints can provide a thoroughly satisfactory appearance when assembled properly.

3

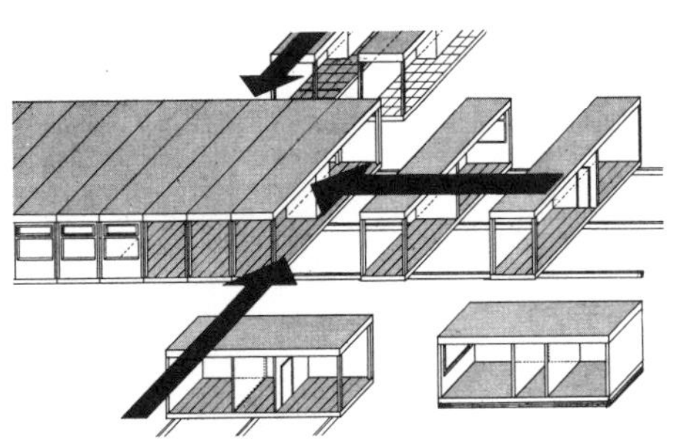
4

5

Fig. 3. Installation of large panel elements on locally built foundation.
Fig. 4. Room elements.
Fig. 5. Joints, as technically necessary features of prefabricated construction, govern facade surfaces and accentuate the modular type of construction.

6

7

Fig. 6. Residence using wood-panel construction.
Fig. 7. Nursery school using wood-panel construction.

Areas of Application

Wood-panel construction with load-bearing frame elements is especially suited for one-story buildings, such as schools, nursery schools, offices, and residences.

The need for more class rooms and nursery schools created a new task for timber construction: the development of portable buildings which can be quickly assembled or disassembled in order to be relocated elsewhere. A prefabricated system for permanent buildings grew out of that experience. Prefabricated residential housing, mostly one- and two-family residences, became popular at the same time. Depending on local building regulations and conditions, both one- and two-story houses can be built with prefabricated wood panels.

In general, it can be said that wood-panel construction is applicable wherever there is a need for lightweight, easily transportable, and economical buildings for temporary or permanent use. However, this type of construction can also be used for non-load-bearing interior and exterior wall elements in buildings constructed with other materials, such as masonry, steel, or reinforced concrete.

Wood-panel construction is limited by its low load capacity, when compared to other materials, and also by building regulations, primarily with regard to fire protection. For this reason, wood-panel housing is limited to two stories. For other applications, such as schools, there are specific regulations.

ELEMENTS OF WOOD-PANEL CONSTRUCTION

Prefabricated wood-panel elements can be distinguished according to their structural functions, dimensions, composition, or purpose. They can be load-bearing or non-load-bearing, vented or nonvented. They can also be distinguished by their application:

1. Load-carrying wood panels of small size, from 1.00 to 1.25 m in width, vented or nonvented, used for interior or exterior walls
2. Load-carrying wood panels of large size, up to 10.00 m length, vented or nonvented, used for interior or exterior walls, roofs, and floors
3. Large-size load-carrying wood panels of 2.40 to 8.40 m, coordinated with room-enclosing elements
4. Non-load-bearing small size wood panels with multiple layers, used for interior partitions
5. Non-load-bearing large size elements with multiple layers, used for interior partitions

Small Size Load-Bearing Panels

Load-bearing wood panels may be fabricated as interior or exterior wall elements of one-story buildings based on a modular dimension system. They are composed of structural frames of solid wood posts, sills, and headers. Such frames are sheathed on both sides, or in-filled with panes, and are filled with insulation. Doors and windows are set in the frames. Each frame element is anchored to the substructure by its own sill. The frames are joined together through their solid wood posts into strong and stable walls. Vertical loads are conveyed directly through the frames into the substructure. Horizontal loads are carried through sheathing, finishes, or additional bracing placed within the framing. The width of elements is governed by various factors:

1. The smaller the width of elements, the more they can be used as elements of various floor plans intended for different uses.
2. The location of vertical frame elements is governed by the location of roof loads. The roof beams should rest on vertical frame elements.
3. The thicknesses of panel sheathing elements, such as asbestos cement, gypsum board, or wood-particle boards, determine the thickness of the elements. Finishing and standard thicknesses of doors, windows, heating and lighting units, etc, also govern.
4. Economy of transportation and assembly plays a significant role in the determination of the width and the weight of elements. For example, small size elements can be stacked in their horizontal position and installed with a minimum of machinery.

Wood-panel elements today are generally covered with wood sheathing. The sheathing is nailed, glued, stapled, or, less frequently, screwed onto the headers, sills, posts, and tie beams, which form the frame and are called "ribs." The load-carrying members of the frames, together with their connections, are thus covered and protected from the weather. Joints are limited to vertical joints between the elements and perimeters of windows and doors. The appearance of sheathed wood panels is governed by the sheathing.

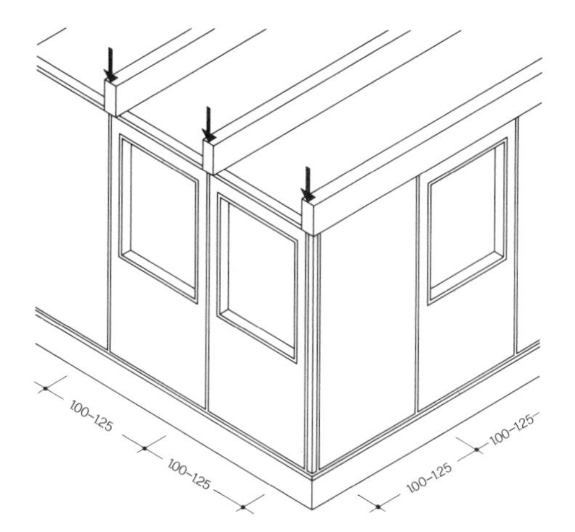

Fig. 8. Small panels with sheathing.

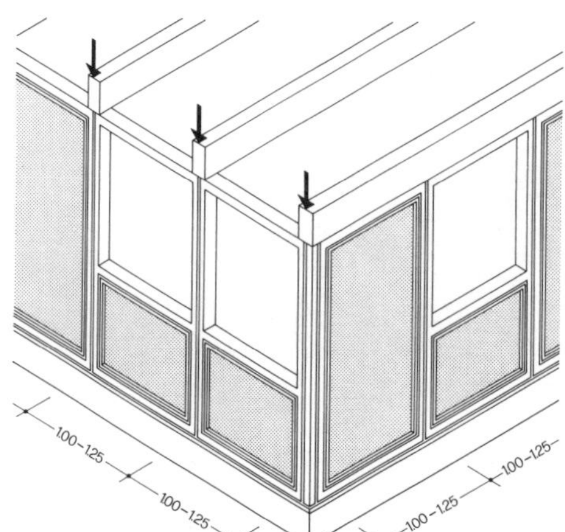

Fig. 9. Small panels with in-filled panes.

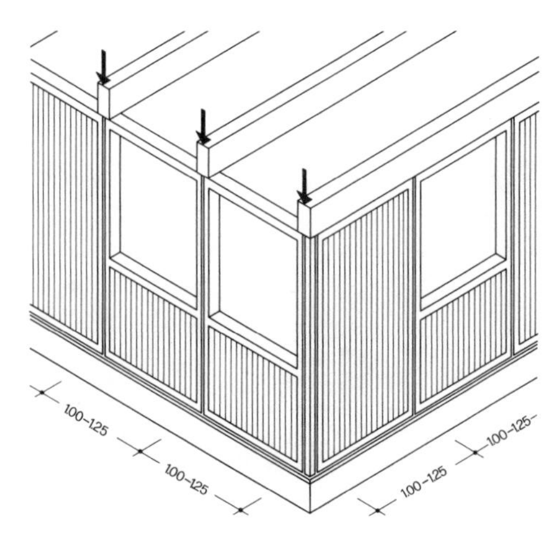

Fig. 10. Small panels with in-filled panes.

In lieu of being covered by sheathing, wood frames may be in-filled by panes. In this case all structural joints between the various solid wood members of the frame are exposed to humidity and temperature changes. The same applies to all the joints between the pane materials (such as finished boards, asbestos cement, or wood-product sheets) and the frames. This type of construction results in a great number of multiply stressed joints that present special detailing problems for both small and large wall panels. The appearance of in-fill panels is governed by wood framing.

Large Size Load-Bearing Panels

Large load-bearing panels of one-story size encompass within a larger panel the basic functions of small panels. They contain a longer sill, several posts, and a continuous header. Tie beams spanning between the posts serve to anchor sheathing, parapets, and windows. Large panels are attached to the substructure in the same way as small panels.

The spacing of posts inside the large panels is governed by the section modules, the required cross wall

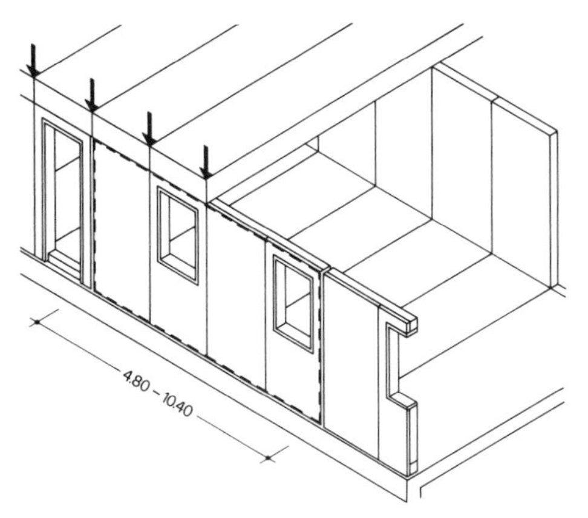

Fig. 11. Large panels with sheathing.

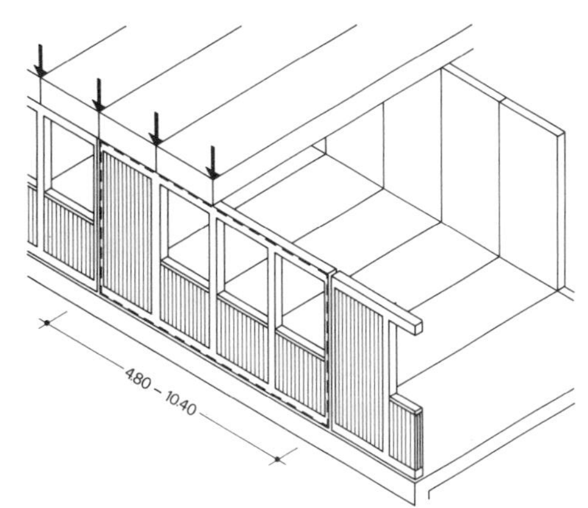

Fig. 12. Large panels with in-filled panes.

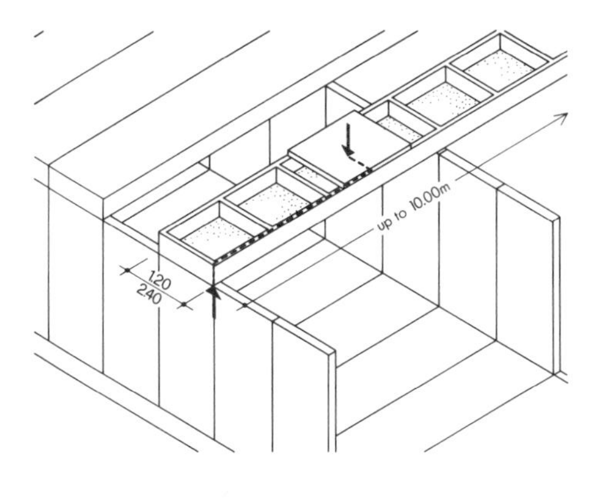

Fig. 13. Roof panels.

connections, the dimensions of the components, and the method of supporting the roof loads. The use of large elements reduces the number of vertical joints between elements; the labor connected with assembly and the sealing of joints is thus reduced. Large panels can be either in-filled by panes or sheathed. The overall length of a large panel is determined by the floor plan, transportation limitations, and the optimum lifting weight.

Large panels are generally considered for floor plans that are firmly established because they cannot be easily exchanged or combined to fit individual requirements.

Large panels are not only used for interior or exterior load-bearing elements, but also for prefabricated horizontal roof elements which rest on wall elements and carry the roof loads through their structural members to the ground.

Roof panels consist of wood frames and ribs, which are sheathed on both sides and are provided with insulation on the inside and with a first layer of waterproofing or protective coating on the outside. The depth of framing contains a vented space above the insulation. After assembly, roof panels are given two coats of waterproofing or a plastic coating, and the vertical exterior sides are fitted with louvers.

Prefabricated roof panels save up to 80% of field installation time. Thus the wall panels are protected from the weather much faster. Standard dimensions of large panels must be taken into consideration at the outset of the design process.

Room Units

In an effort to increase the prefabrication of structural components and finishes of buildings, room units were developed in timber construction, just as they were in steel, reinforced concrete, and plastic. They can reach a 90% degree of prefabrication.

Starting points for the development of such room units were motor homes, the American "mobile homes," as well as mountain refuges and construction sheds. After further improvements, they were adopted for the construction of school rooms, office buildings, apartments, and student dormitories. Room units consist of enclosed or partially open larger units, whose structures, floors, and walls are shop-fabricated and assembled on site. Several support systems are built into the elements. The elements are transported to the site and are attached to already prepared foundations.

Building with room units results in shorter construction times and reduced expenditures where compared with conventional, manual methods. This is due to their higher state of completion, their relatively simple transportation, their shorter installation time, and the possibility of replacing them at a later time. The design of a building with room units necessarily depends on the dimensions established by the industry, which are mostly determined by erection requirements, transport limitations, size of surfaces, and economical lifting weights.

The plans on page 242 show that combinations of equal size room units can result in high-quality interior and exterior floor plans. Room units can be arranged in both vertical and horizontal rows.

Fig. 14. Buildings composed of room units.

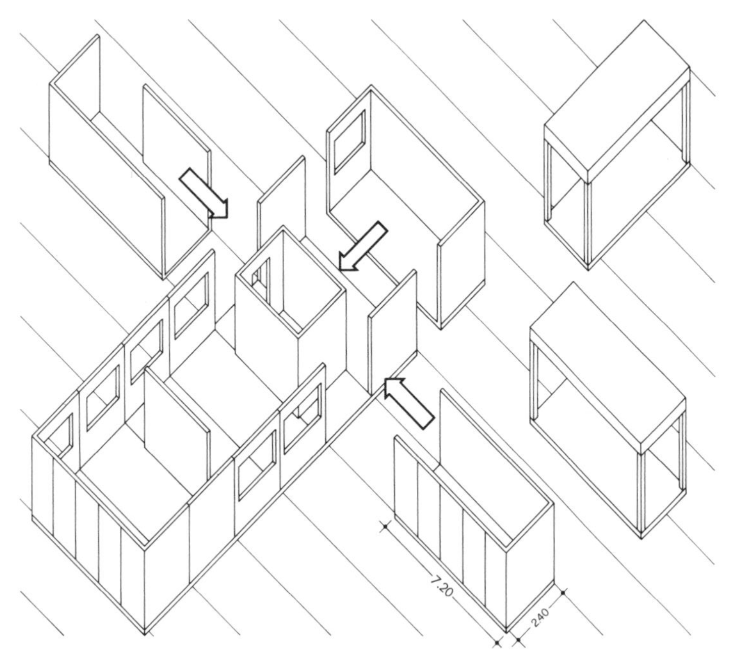

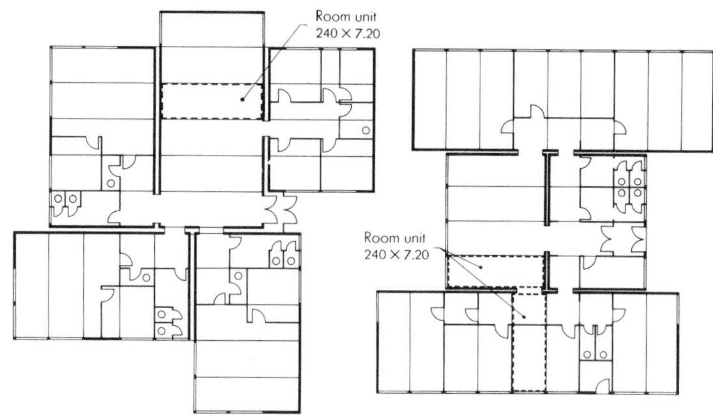

Fig. 16. Floor plan examples for room unit construction. Three short sides of units correspond to one long side.

Fig. 15. Building system with room units that were planned on a structural grid.

Small and Large Non-Load-Bearing Panels

Small and large multisheathed panels which have no load-bearing capacity can be used for permanent or movable interior partitions. They are fabricated in various ways, depending on the use of the building and the local building code, and differ mostly in their acoustical properties, surface treatments, installation, load capacity of connections, and fire resistance.

Depending on the particular requirements, partitions and their attachments have to connect to adjacent elements and to the structure itself.

Interior partitions are divided according to their mobility into:

a. Permanent partitions
b. Partitions of limited movability
c. Movable partitions

Depending on their acoustic properties, they are divided into:

a. Partitions sheathed on both sides with rigidly interconnected sheathing
b. Partitions sheathed on both sides with unconnected sheathing standing separately

The layout of partitions is governed by the building's basic modular dimensions. The connection of partitions to load-bearing panels of common modular dimensions requires that both have the same resistance to lateral forces.

Right-angle intersections of two elements create rectangular nodes or filler elements. The sides of these fillers serve as attachment points for the panels. Depending on the type of fillers, different degrees of workmanship and material are required, with the result that assembly or disassembly of wall elements may demand more or less time.

It is generally more economical to order load-bearing and non-load-bearing wall panels in equal wall thicknesses (for example, 10 cm) than to dimension them according to their actual loading requirements.

The frames of non-load-bearing partitions can be in-filled with panes or sheathed in the same way as the load-bearing partitions. Their appearance is goverend by either the "frames" or the "sheathing," similar to load-bearing partitions.

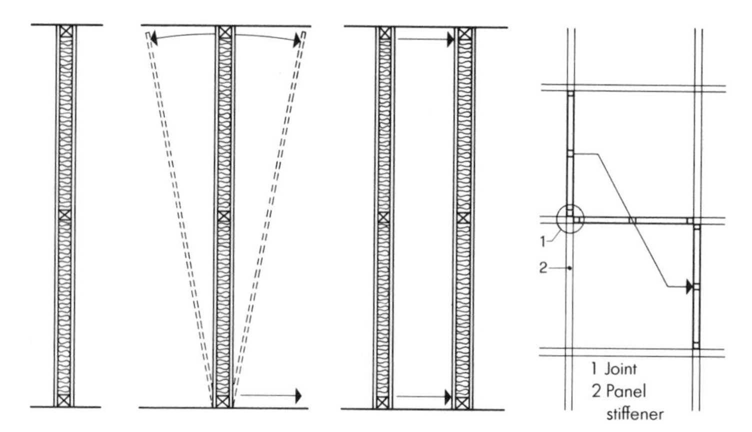

Fig. 17. A continuous modular grid allows interchangeability of partition units of equal size.

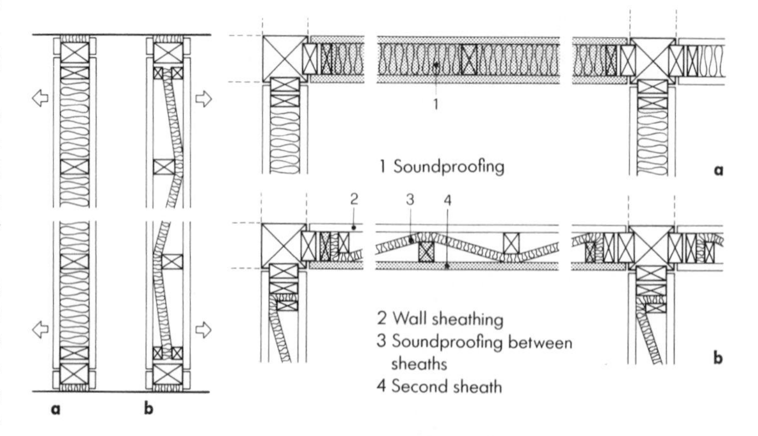

Fig. 18. Interior walls. (a) Interior wall sheathed on both sides with rigidly connected sheathing. (b) Same as (a), but separately supported sheathing.

STRUCTURAL PRINICIPLES OF WOOD-PANEL CONSTRUCTION

Load-Bearing Wood Panels, Exterior Walls

Structural Framework

Individual pieces of wood framing, such as studs or planking, sill, header, or breast beam, can be joined together in different ways:

a. Butt joints are toe-nailed together for further assembly. Actual load-bearing connection occurs through sheathing, such as wood-chip boards, which are screwed, nailed, or glued onto the frame. The frame is often stitched together with staples, sheathing is glued to it, and openings are cut in it after glue has set.

b. Vertical and horizontal elements of frames are joined by traditional methods, such as lap joints or mortise and tenons. These are rarely used because of the greater workmanship required.

c. Frame components are butted together and joined by means of nail plates, which are pressed into the wood simultaneously on both sides.

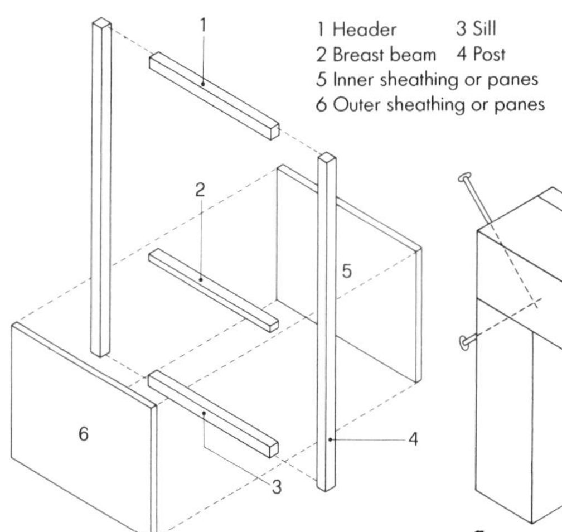

Fig. 19. Individual elements of wood panels.

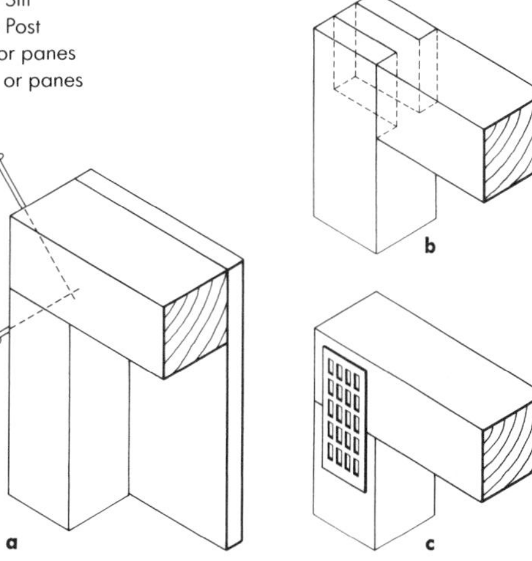

Fig. 20. Joints of wood frames. (a) Glued wood-chip boards and butt joints. (b) Mortise and tenons. (c) Nail plates and butt joints.

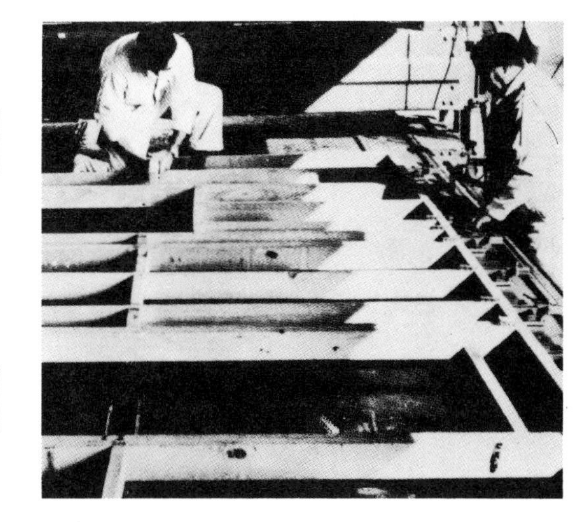

Fig. 21. Assembly of wood frames with nail plates.

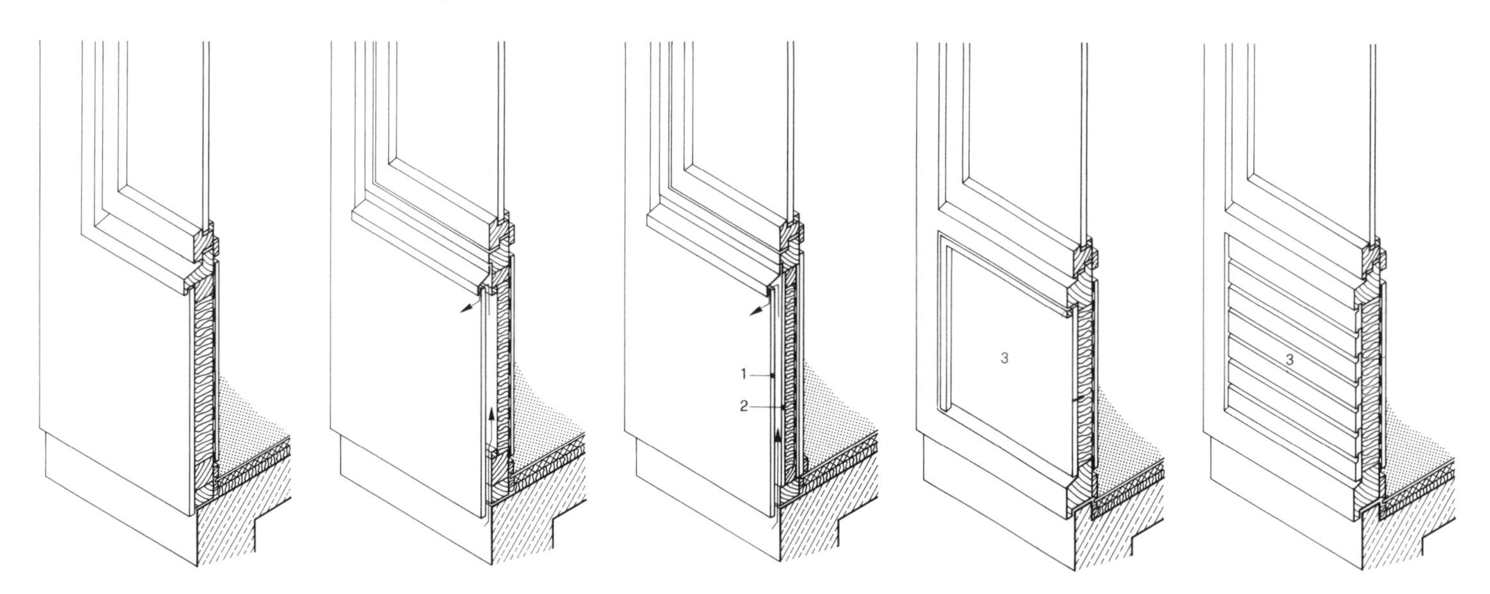

Fig. 22. Sheathing or in-fill panes of wood panels.

Panes or wood sheathing of vented or nonvented wood panels are glued, nailed, or screwed to the frames either directly or through wood spacers.

In-filled panes of wood panels can either be set into frame recesses and then screwed onto the frame, or be held in place by moldings and weather seals. Similarly, panes can be screwed onto nailers glued to the frames, or they can be set into grooves cut in the frames. Sheathing covers the framing and connections so that the framing is not visible, but in-filled panes leave the framing visible.

Wood-Panel Dimensions

The dimensions of a panel are determined by the practical and required dimensions of its components, its functional requirements, and its design proportions.

The dimensions of individual panels are governed by their primary purpose. Components subject to direct load and moment have to be designed for their strength, while walls and parapets intended to enclose rooms have their thicknesses determined by thermal and acoustic insulation requirements.

The dimensions of sheathing are determined by fabrication requirements. Sheathing materials are produced in certain widths and thicknesses, which have to be taken into account when designing the size of panels and their subdivisions. Panel sheathing is spliced vertically on posts and horizontally on breast beams.

Functional requirements, such as the need to provide flexibility of room arrangement, may lead to certain panel widths or panel subdivisions. Panel width and height should conform to the requirements of DIN 18000, "Dimensional Coordination of Buildings." Many accessories, such as lights and suspended ceilings, already conform to these requirements.

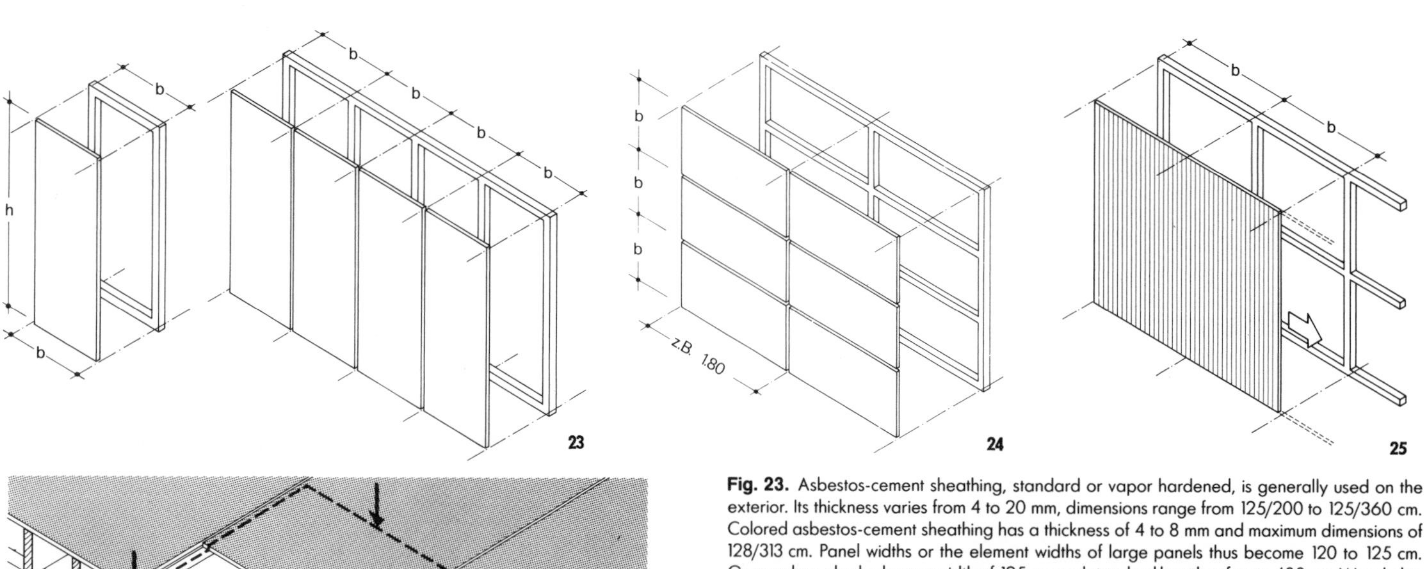

Fig. 23. Asbestos-cement sheathing, standard or vapor hardened, is generally used on the exterior. Its thickness varies from 4 to 20 mm, dimensions range from 125/200 to 125/360 cm. Colored asbestos-cement sheathing has a thickness of 4 to 8 mm and maximum dimensions of 128/313 cm. Panel widths or the element widths of large panels thus become 120 to 125 cm. Gypsum boards also have a width of 125 cm and standard lengths of up to 400 cm. Wood-chip boards for exterior or interior sheathing have dimensions to 250/1000 cm.

Fig. 24. Wood panels can be varied by placing the short sides of sheathing vertically instead of horizontally. The multiple of short sides then determines the height of the panel, for example, 3 × 125 cm = 375 cm. The panel width results from subdivisions of 125/360 cm sheathing, such as 180 cm.

Fig. 25. The application of small size sheathing or in-fill panes allows for variable dimensioning of panels, but it must be realized that the use of small size elements increases the jointing significantly. In order to increase the rigidity of a panel, wood sheathing can also be nailed to diagonal frame members. The number of necessary interior supports for sheathing and their locations are determined by deformations that may be caused by loads or moisture changes.

1 Roof panel span 4.80 to 7.20 m
2 Spacers
3 Wood-chip boards glued to framing
4 Insulation
5 Airspace
6 Asbestos cement or stucco
7 Butt joints
8 Header
9 Breast beam
10 Post
11 Sill
12 Wood-chip board

Fig. 26. Structural dimensioning. For 1- or 1½-story buildings, the spacing of posts is 1.25 and 1.20 m; for normal roof loads, post and header dimensions are about 10/10 cm. For practical and detailing purposes the sills are often made of the same size. The resulting hollow spaces are sufficient for ample insulation.

Nonvented Exterior Wall Panels

Ambient humidity tends to penetrate through openings, joints, and entire building components, generally outward, from a higher to a lower pressure, and from warm to cold surfaces. Condensation occurs within a building section at the point where the vapor pressure reaches saturation. As long as a wall section is permeable, vapor will diffuse easily. When the resistance to diffusion is low, no special measures are necessary; still, a computation is required.

However, if a wall section is impermeable on its outer face, the vapor cannot dissipate and condensation occurs on the inside. This can lead to permanent wetting of wood. When the panels are not vented, a vapor barrier can be placed on the warm, interior side of the panel. The barrier prevents vapor penetration into the panel as long as it is also vapor-tight along the panel edges (DIN 68800, part 2).

Wall Construction without Inner Airspace

The space between inner and outer sheathing is filled with insulation, which can be either blown in, stitched, or held in by moldings (Fig. 27). Insulation can also be glued to one sheath and pressed. Windows and doors can be cut into the panel (Fig. 28).

Wall Construction with Interior Airspace

The space between inner and outer sheathing is only partially filled with insulation. Thicker panels leave room for an airspace on the outer side, which enhances the insulating capacity of the panel (Fig. 29). If the airspace is left on the inside, insulation must be attached carefully along the edges so that the cooler outer air will not penetrate into the interior air space (Fig. 30). If the airspace between inner and outer sheathing is not vented, the outer sheath of the panel should consist of an insulating sandwich panel filled with a foam core, fitted into the frame recess, and anchored by a molding (Fig. 31).

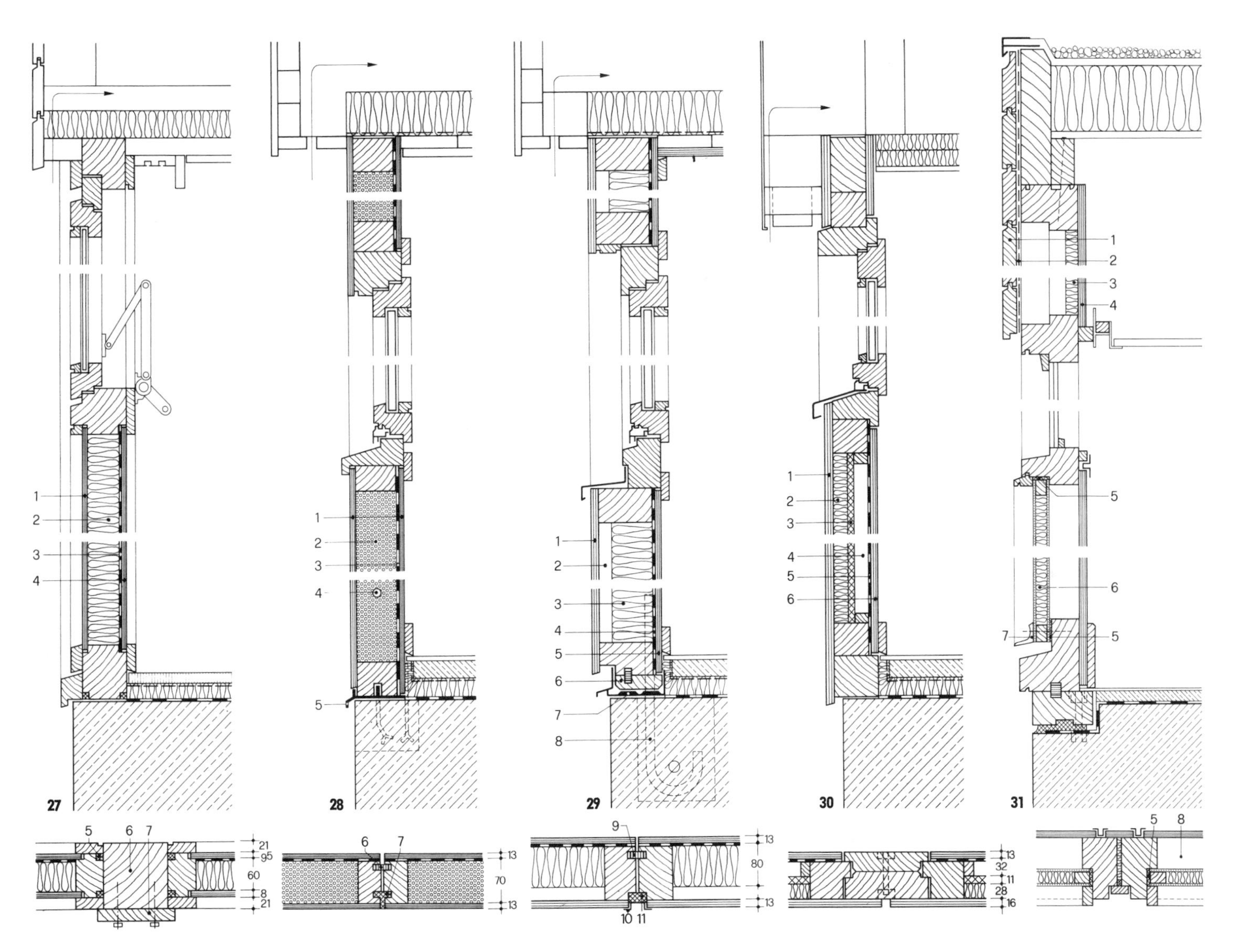

27

1 Asbestos-cement panel 8 mm
2 Mineral wool 60 mm
3 Vapor barrier
4 Decorative panel 9.5 mm
5 Sealer
6 Column 12/12 cm
7 Cover plank

28

1 Asbestos-cement panel
2 Stiff concrete foam 7.5 cm, with expanded aggregate ϕ 0.6 to 2.0 cm
3 Vapor barrier
4 Prestressed wire in PVC tube ϕ 2.1 cm
5 Steel T shape, galvanized
6 Spline
7 Joint extrusion

29

1 Wood-chip board 13 mm, with plastic lining
2 Sealed airspace
3 Mineral wool mat 80 mm
4 Vapor barrier
5 Wood-chip board 13 mm, with facing
6 Sill
7 Plastic base
8 Anchorage
9 Spline
10 Aluminum joint extrusion
11 Sealer

30

1 Wood-chip board 16 mm, sheathed
2 Glass fiber matting
3 Soft particle board
4 Sealed airspace
5 Vapor barrier
6 Wood-chip board 13 mm

31

1 Tongue and groove planking
2 Building paper
3 Insulation
4 Plywood 10 mm
5 Permanent plastic putty
6 Facade element 50 mm: colored asbestos-cement panel, insulation, asbestos-cement plate
7 Aluminum extrusion
8 Sealed airspace

Vented Exterior Wall Panels

In vented panel construction, the vapor can be conveyed, by means of porous insulation, through the panel to a vented space. The exterior waterproof cover is vented on its inner side so that the vapor is removed without condensation. The outer covering of the sealed airspace needs additional protection against radiated heat. This protection can be enhanced by white color (Figs. 32 to 34).

A combined vented and nonvented panel contains an additional exterior sheath. The wall element behind that sheath, in particular the insulation, must be protected against water penetrating from the exterior, contrary to what is illustrated in Fig. 35. The exterior sheath retains the radiant heat from the building itself (Fig. 36).

The layered buildup of both vented and nonvented panels increases their thermal insulation capacities. These capacities are reduced in the areas of framing, particularly at in-fill panes and generally at joints.

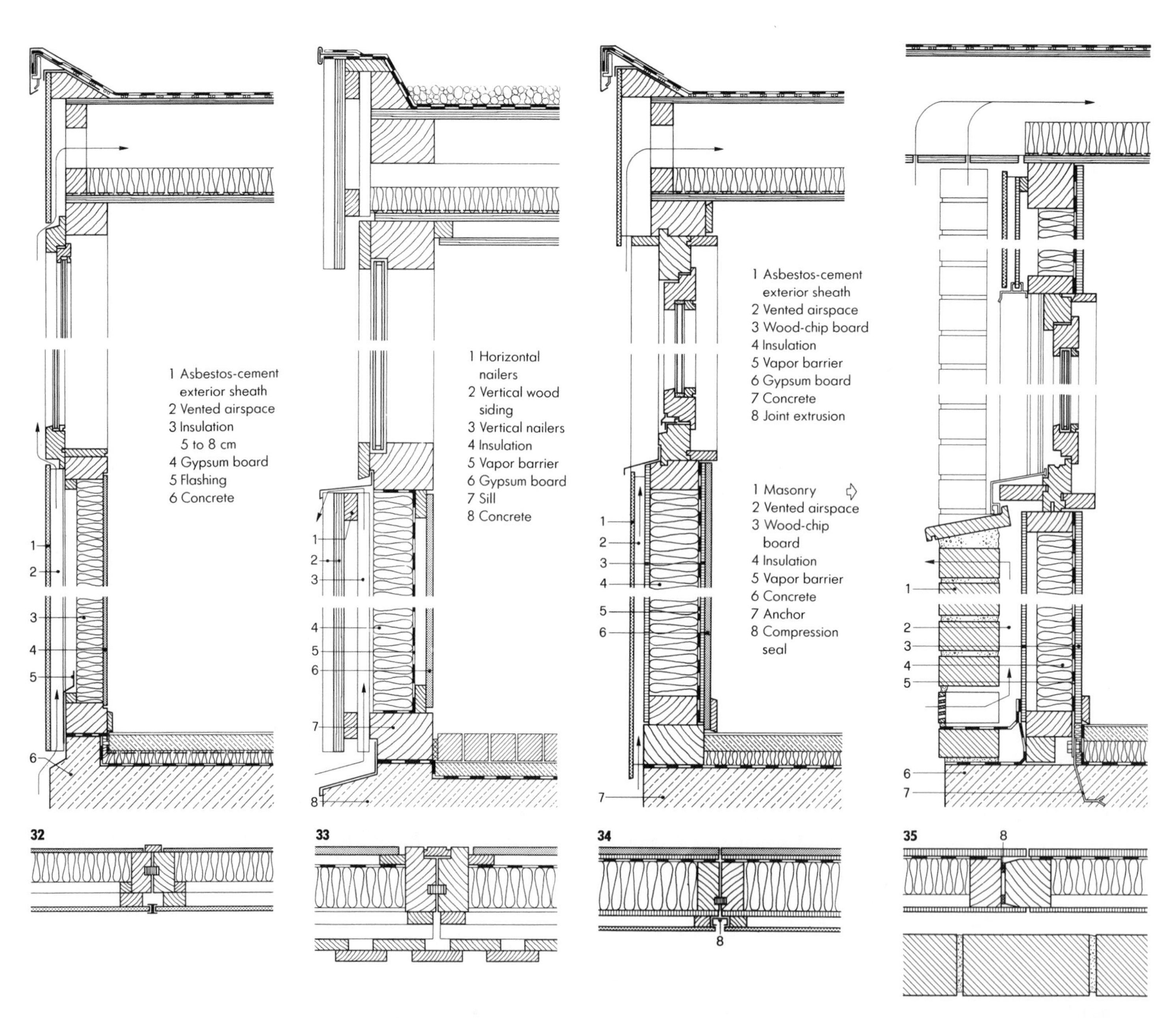

Figs. 32–34. Exterior sheaths vented in the rear are intended to provide equal physical properties over the entire structure, including framing. Exterior sheaths conceal the framing, which remains visible in nonvented paneling. Vented construction is meant to eliminate thermal bridging at framing. Additional insulation on the interior of the wall, between vapor barrier and inner sheathing, further eliminates such bridging. In vented wall construction preference should be given to nonvented panels with an additional exterior sheath. The additional material required, compared to single vented wall construction, is justified because a nonvented wall provides better fire protection. Flammable gases from the interior of the wall, from both framing and insulation, cannot escape through the vented space to catch fire. In comparison with open, vented construction, closed panels protect framing from insects and provide insulation from humidity. There is a requirement for all airspaces in closed panels to have sufficient air vents equal to 1/500 of the panel surface. These vents remove vapor that may have permeated through the vapor barrier and also the accumulated radiant heat. For a particular panel area, a larger vent is more effective than several smaller ones.

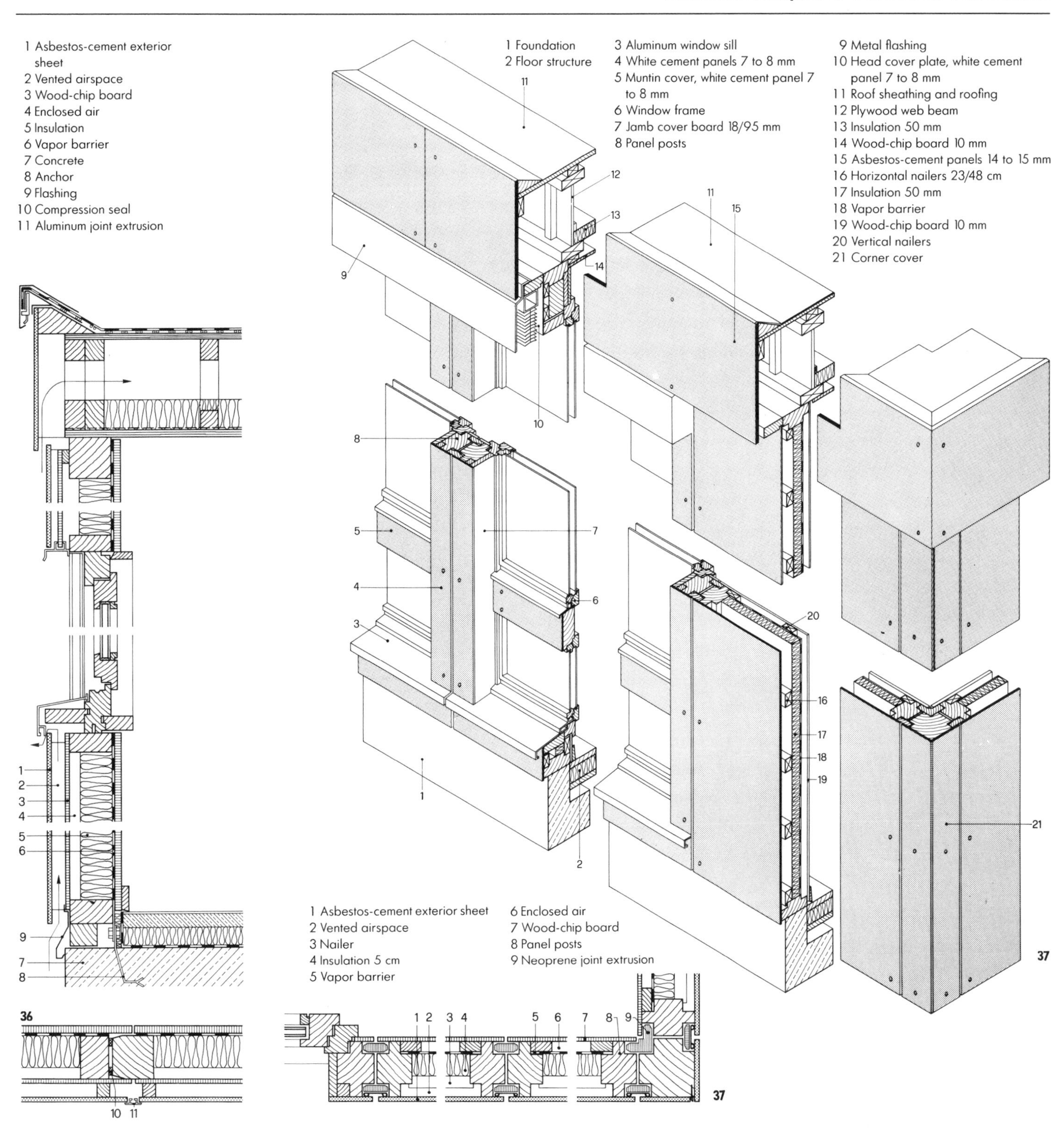

Fig. 35. Multilayered construction consisting of a prefabricated closed wall panel, exterior protective masonry siding, and an airspace of at least 4 cm width. Rain that may penetrate through the masonry runs out without wetting the wood. The airspace also eliminates humidity. A requirement for such mixed construction is good masonry. The mortar that may fall off the masonry on the inside may interrupt the airspace, making the wood wet. The panel has a vapor barrier on the inside.

Fig. 36. This alternative shows the masonry replaced by a prefabricated vented asbestos-cement plate which is stuccoed.

Fig. 37. In this prefabricated system the load-bearing vented wall panels have insulation that is exposed to air but is protected on the inside by a vapor barrier. Asbestos-cement sheets cover the entire wall panel, but the frame itself is covered without an airspace. Radiant heat is not contained in these parts as in the rest of the panel. The same type of panel may have various characteristics and degrees of thermal insulation.

Load-Bearing Wood Panels as Roof Panels

Wood-panel structures may have flat or inclined roofs. Roof beams are to be placed on frame posts and anchored to them. Wood sheathing or wood-chip boards close the panels on both sides. Vapor barrier, insulation, and roofing are then placed on the panels, depending on the type of construction. Complete roof elements have been developed, having widths ranging from 1.25 to 2.50 m and lengths of up to 10.00 m of free span. They can be distinguished by their relatively small thickness in comparison to their load capacity. Roof panels can be connected to the walls at their edges, but they can also be overhung to provide weather protection for the facades.

Roof panels are generally glued in a press so that a homogeneous, self-supporting, torsionally stiff box element is obtained. When the panels are installed, they are bound together in tension, shear, and compression to form a single plate. Roof panels generally consist of longitudinal ribs, sheathed on both sides. They are seldom stiffened through additional transverse ribs. Insulation is compressed between the ribs, or it may be glued to the ribs along its edges in order to comply with fire requirements. Plywood sheathing is glued on both sides of the ribs. Some manufacturers provide the panels with an exterior surface already coated with a hot layer of bituminous material. The undersides are sanded and primed. Because panel joints move due to moisture differentials, it is advisable to leave the joints visible. Edges may be covered with asbestos-cement plates or moldings.

Roof wood panels can achieve a fire rating of F30 or F60, depending on the type of insulation, attachment, and the design of the joints. Panels can be mass-produced with a fire-protective sheath of gypsum board on their undersides.

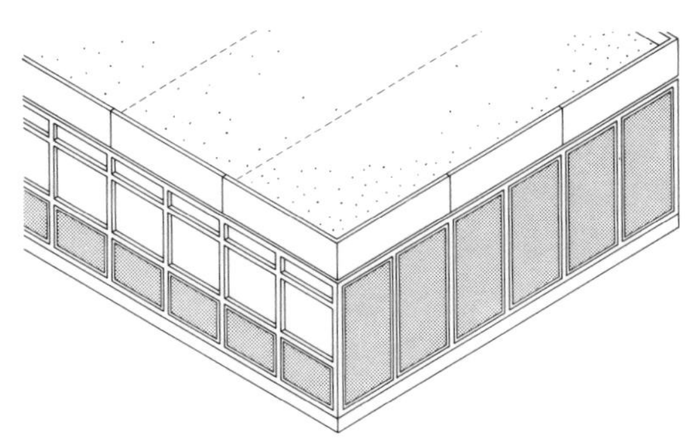

Figs. 38 – 39. Roof panels connect edgewise with walls.

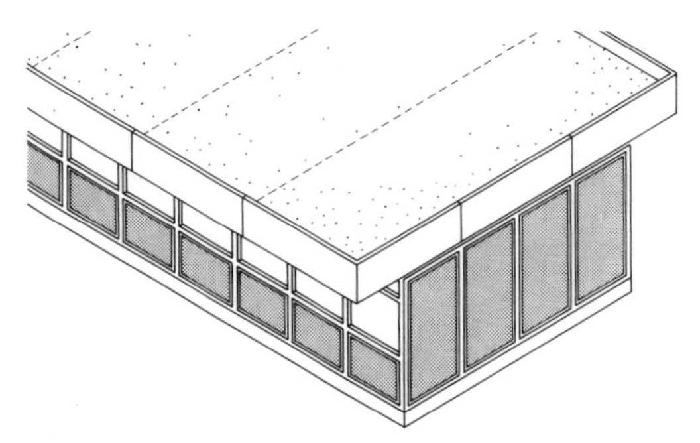

Figs. 40 – 41. Roof panels cantilevered over walls.

Fig. 44. Roof panel joints.

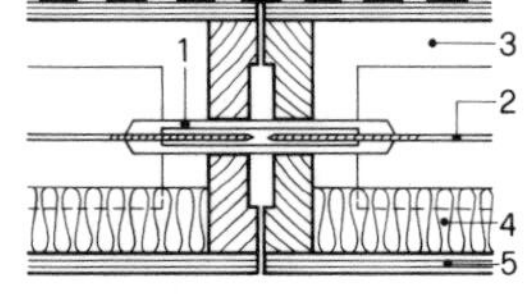

1 Bolt sleeve
2 Bolt M10
3 Transverse rib with ventilation
4 Insulation
5 Plywood

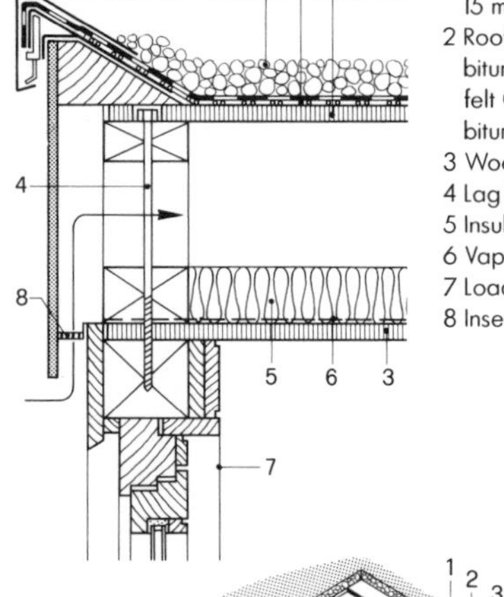

1 Gravel 30 mm (size 7 to 15 mm)
2 Roofing: 3-ply bituminous glass fiber felt G5, hot coated with bitumen
3 Wood-chip board 19 mm
4 Lag bolt
5 Insulation 60 mm
6 Vapor barrier
7 Load-carrying panel
8 Insect screen

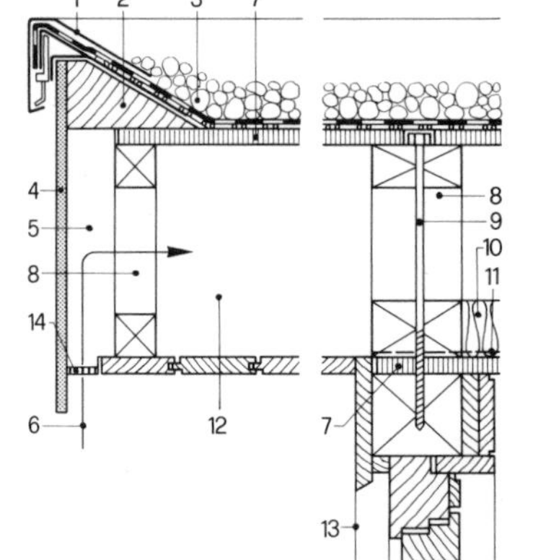

1 Prefabricated roof flashing
2 Wood filler
3 Roofing as in Fig. 39
4 Asbestos-cement panel
5 Nailer
6 Ventilation
7 Wood-chip board 19 mm
8 Cross stud
9 Anchorage through lag bolt
10 Insulation 60 mm
11 Vapor barrier
12 Cantilevered roof panel
13 Load-bearing panel
14 Insect screen

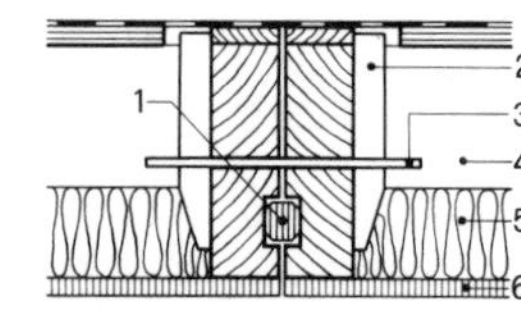

1 Joint spline
2 Steel wedge
3 Steel strap
4 Ventilated area
5 Insulation
6 Wood-chip board

1 Gravel 30 mm
2 3-ply bituminous glass fiber felt G5, hot coated with bitumen
3 Sheathing
4 Insulation 80 to 120 mm
5 Transverse rib
6 Flashing
7 Cover
8 Shear screws
9 Wood framing

Fig. 42. Roof panels with one central rib, width ±1.25 m.

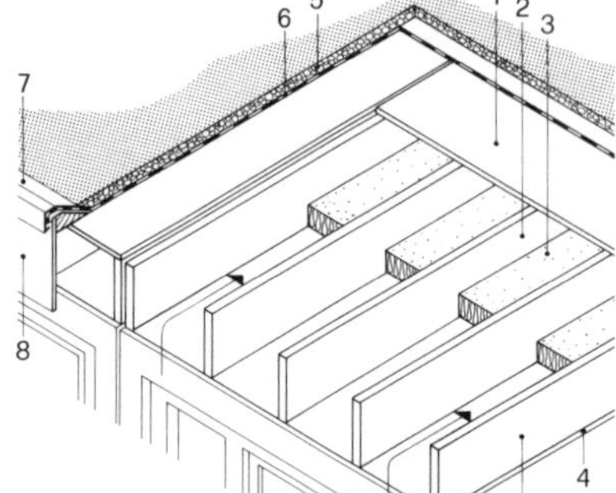

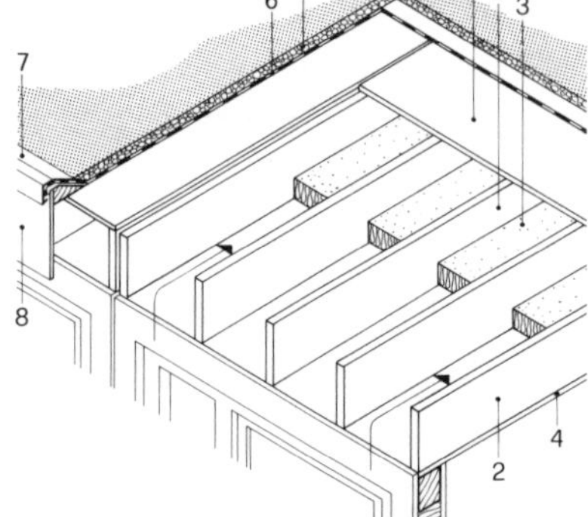

Fig. 43. Roof panels with multiple ribs, width ±1.25 m.

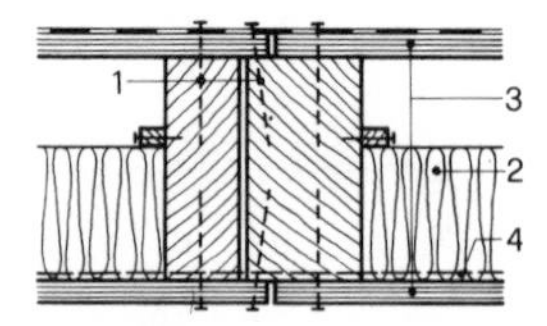

1 Nail 34/90
2 Insulation
3 Sheathing 25 mm
4 Polyethylene vapor barrier

1 Upper sheath
2 Longitudinal rib
3 Insulation 80 mm
4 Lower sheath
5 Gravel
6 Roofing
7 Flashing
8 Cover

Non-Load-Bearing Wood Panels, Interior Partitions

Concept

a. Fixed partitions are load-bearing or non-load-bearing walls which cannot be moved.
b. Potentially movable partitions are the non-load-bearing interior walls which can be moved only if the adjacent structure is not damaged and if their frame is reusable (sheathing may be destroyed).
c. Movable partitions are non-load-bearing wall systems which are built to be moved at a later date to another part of the building. The degree of prefabrication must be such that the individual elements can be installed without much finishing work.

Structure

Non-load-bearing partitions (fixed, potentially movable, and movable) are designed to carry only their own dead load, the load of their attachments, and horizontal loads. They are placed in the building structure such that unexpected loads cannot bear on them.

Grid System

Partitions, particularly movable partitions, may be placed on a linear or a strip grid. A linear grid calls for two different modular widths and a special corner piece. The strip grid uses only elements of equal width, which are then connected by posts, fillers, or connecting elements.

Soundproofing

The main task of partitions is to separate rooms acoustically, mainly by limiting the propagation of sound through the air. In single-layer walls, such as masonry, the sound is arrested by the mass of the material. In multiple-layer lightweight walls this is achieved by the material, the type of connection between layers, and the distance between studs.

The degree of soundproofing not only depends on partitions, but also on sound by-passes through the structure, and on connections between walls, or between walls and door frames or floors. These points must be considered when dealing with lightweight partitions because theoretical soundproofing values are significantly reduced by structural bypasses.

Wall Construction

The normal type of wall-panel construction consisting of studs sandwiched between sheets of wood-chip board or other materials does not provide sufficient acoustical protection.

Double-sheathed interior panels with connected lightweight sheets without insulation provide soundproofing values of about 30 dB.

The average value can be raised to 40 dB by using a wall thickness of about 100 mm, sheets weighing at least 10 kg/m^2, and hollow spaces filled with mineral wool.

A further improvement of the soundproofing value to 45 or 50 dB can be achieved by increasing the weights of sheets without greatly increasing the bending stiffness. For this purpose the sheets are covered with additional gypsum boards on their exterior or, less frequently, with lead sheets on their interior.

Double-sheeted interior panels whose sheets are separated from each other and which have the hollow space filled with acoustic insulation may reach a soundproofing value of 50 dB or more.

Surfacing

Various materials can be used to surface interior walls; they can be impact or blow-resistant, easy to maintain and repair, suitable for painting, or acoustically absorptive. These are the criteria that determine the cost of walls and their choice.

Wall surfacing materials generally used are:
a. Wood-chip boards or plywood panels suitable for painting, carpeting, or veneering
b. Gypsum boards

Installation

Non-load-bearing partitions are mounted in two ways:
a. When partitions are only partially prefabricated and only potentially movable, prefabricated frames are set up, attached, filled with insulation, and sheathed on both sides. Frames are attached to adjacent structures by braces or fasteners.
b. Movable partitions are prefabricated, including frames, insulation, and surfacing, and are installed in the finished building. They are fastened to the adjacent structures. The partitions are connected among themselves by means of connecting parts, which are bolted, clamped, or joined with splines.

Floor Connection

Fixed partitions are attached to the raw floor. The insulation base, which rests on the cement floor, is brought up at a partition. The propagation of sound to the next room is reduced by separating the wall from the floor by the insulation base.

If the partitions are very movable, they are installed on the finished flooring, whose underfloor construction remains continuous.

Fig. 45. (a) Linear grid.

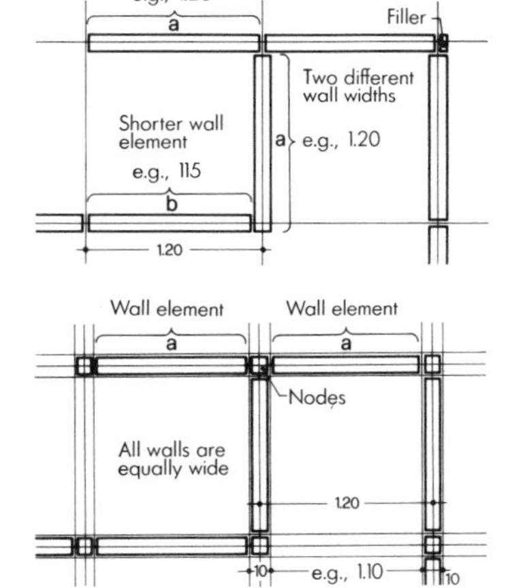

Fig. 45. (b) Banded grid.

1 Flooring
2 Subflooring
3 Height adjustment bolts
4 Framing
5 Movable partition
6 Floating cement floor
7 Bituminuous paper
8 Acoustic insulation
9 Fixed partition
10 Hardwood spline
11 Sill

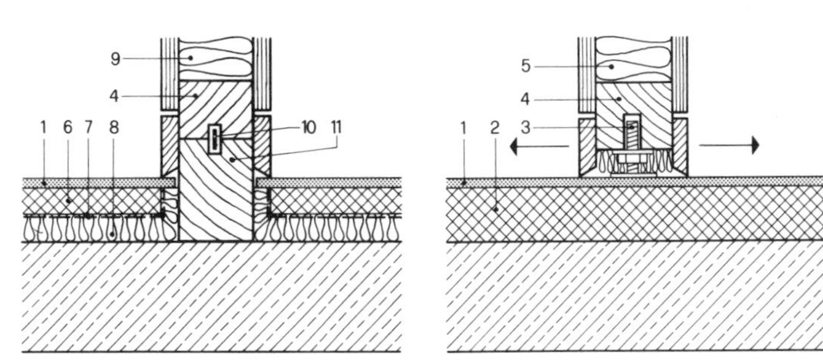

Fig. 46 (a) Fixed partition. (b) Movable partition.

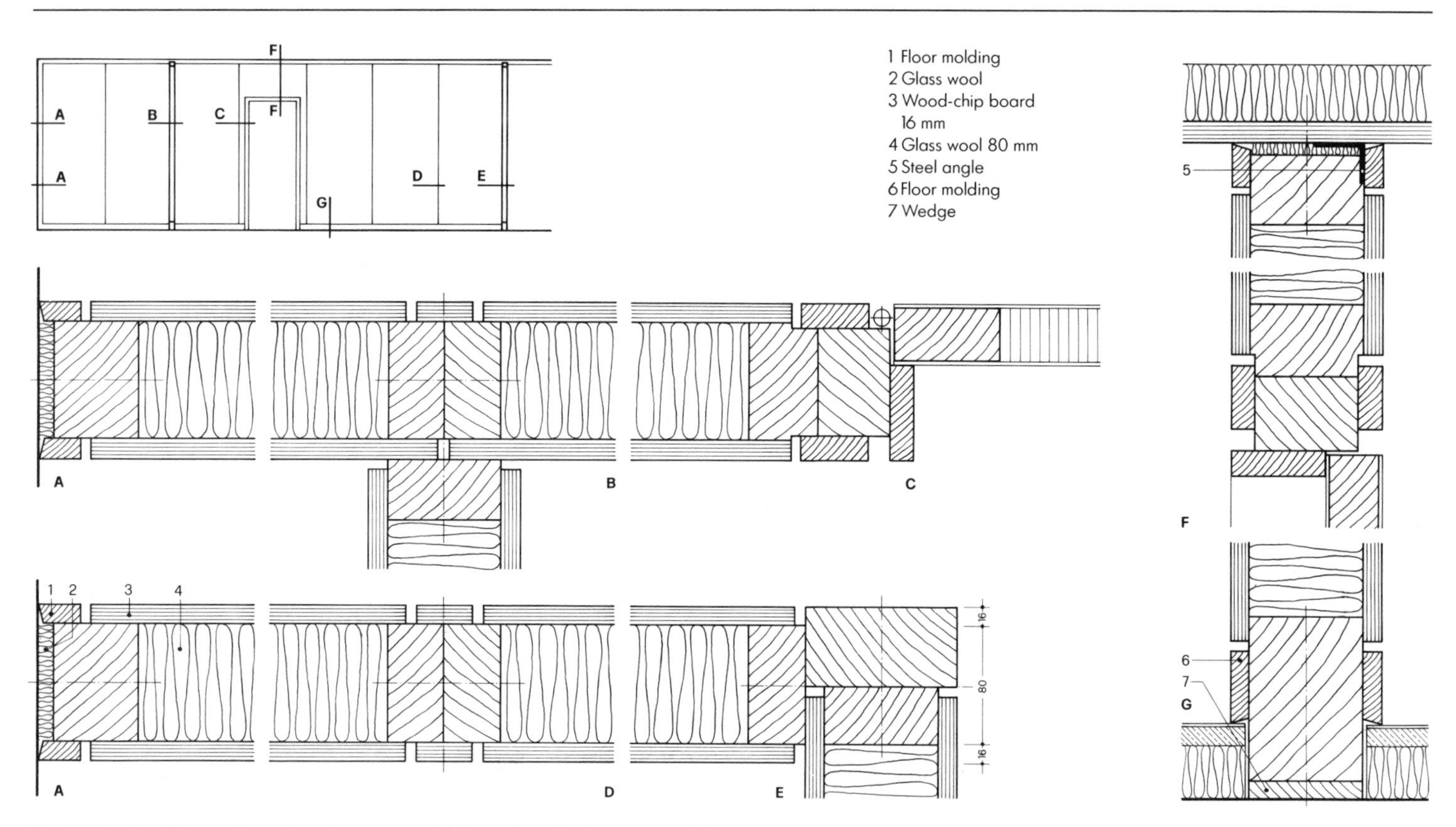

Fig. 47. Fixed prefabricated wood-panel partitions with full soundproofing between wood-chip boards. Boards are firmly attached together through framing and form a strong lightweight panel. Panels are erected between floor substructure and ceiling, and are bolted to them. Connection between panels is similarly done by bolting. Joints are concealed by moldings.

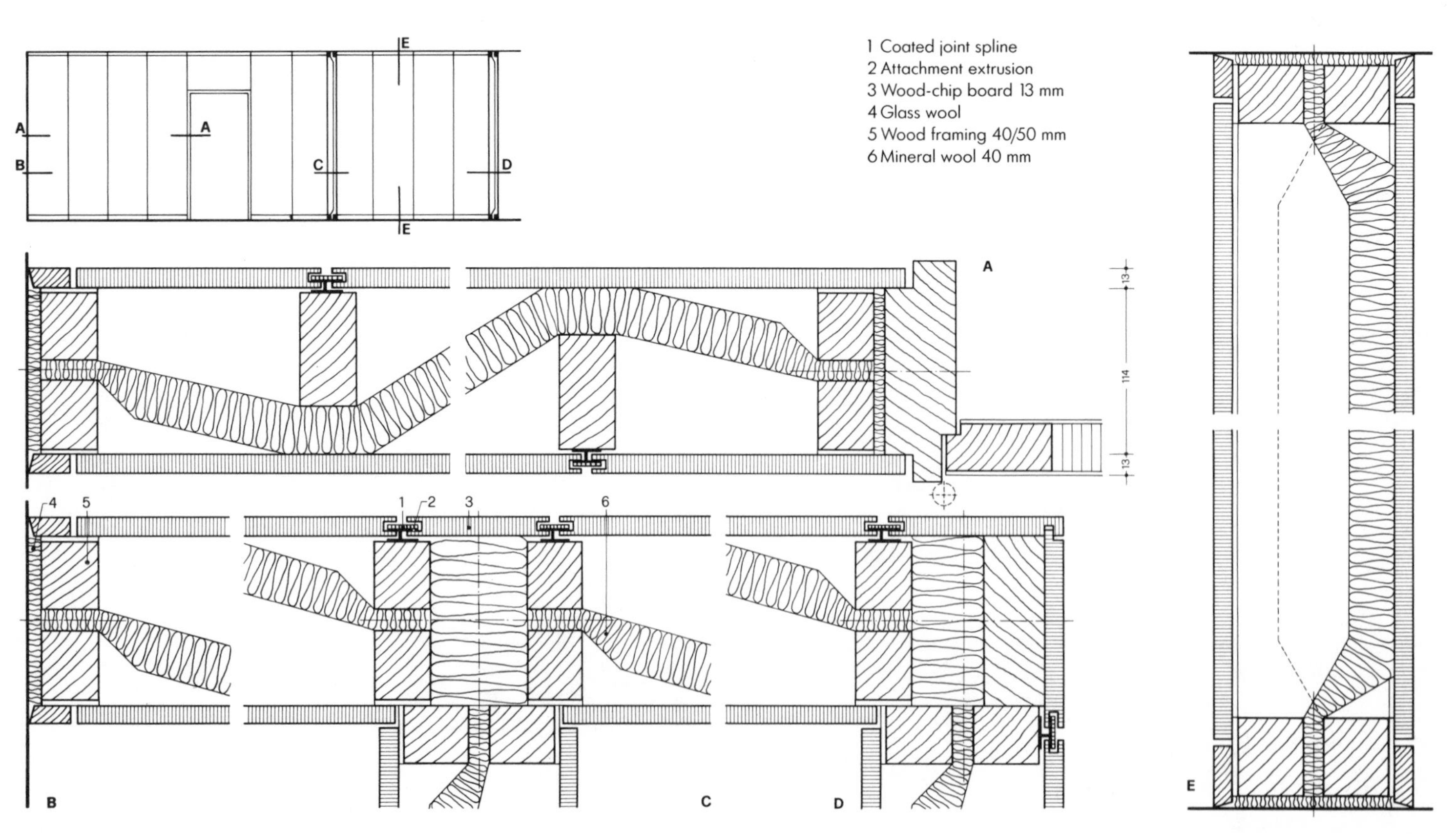

Fig. 48. Fixed partitions of wood-panel construction with separated ribs and boards. This type of partition provides better soundproofing but has to be assembled on site.

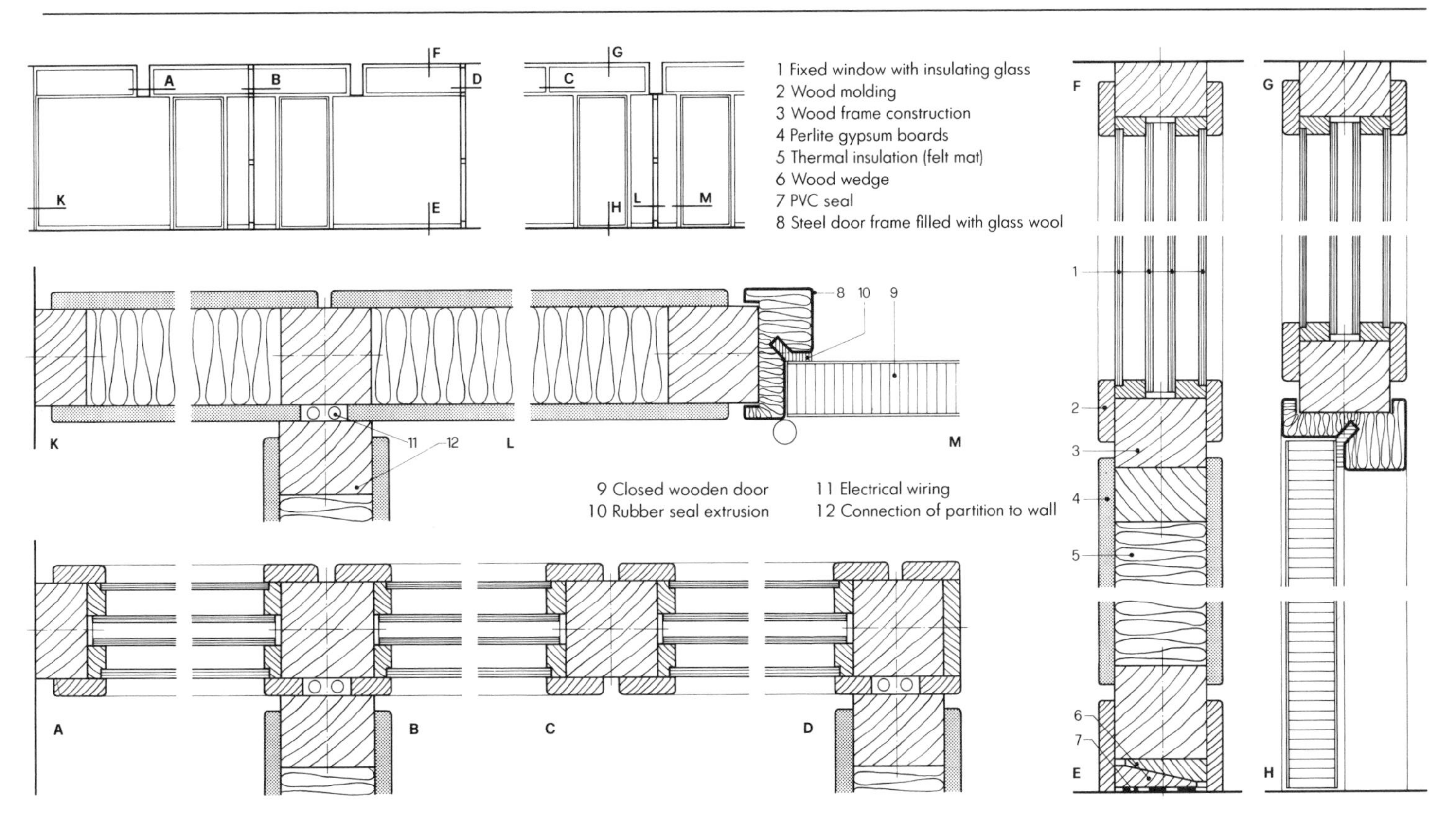

Fig. 49. Potentially movable partitions using wood rib panels with full soundproofing between perlite gypsum boards. Both panels are firmly attached together through framing. The wall can be moved, but not readily.

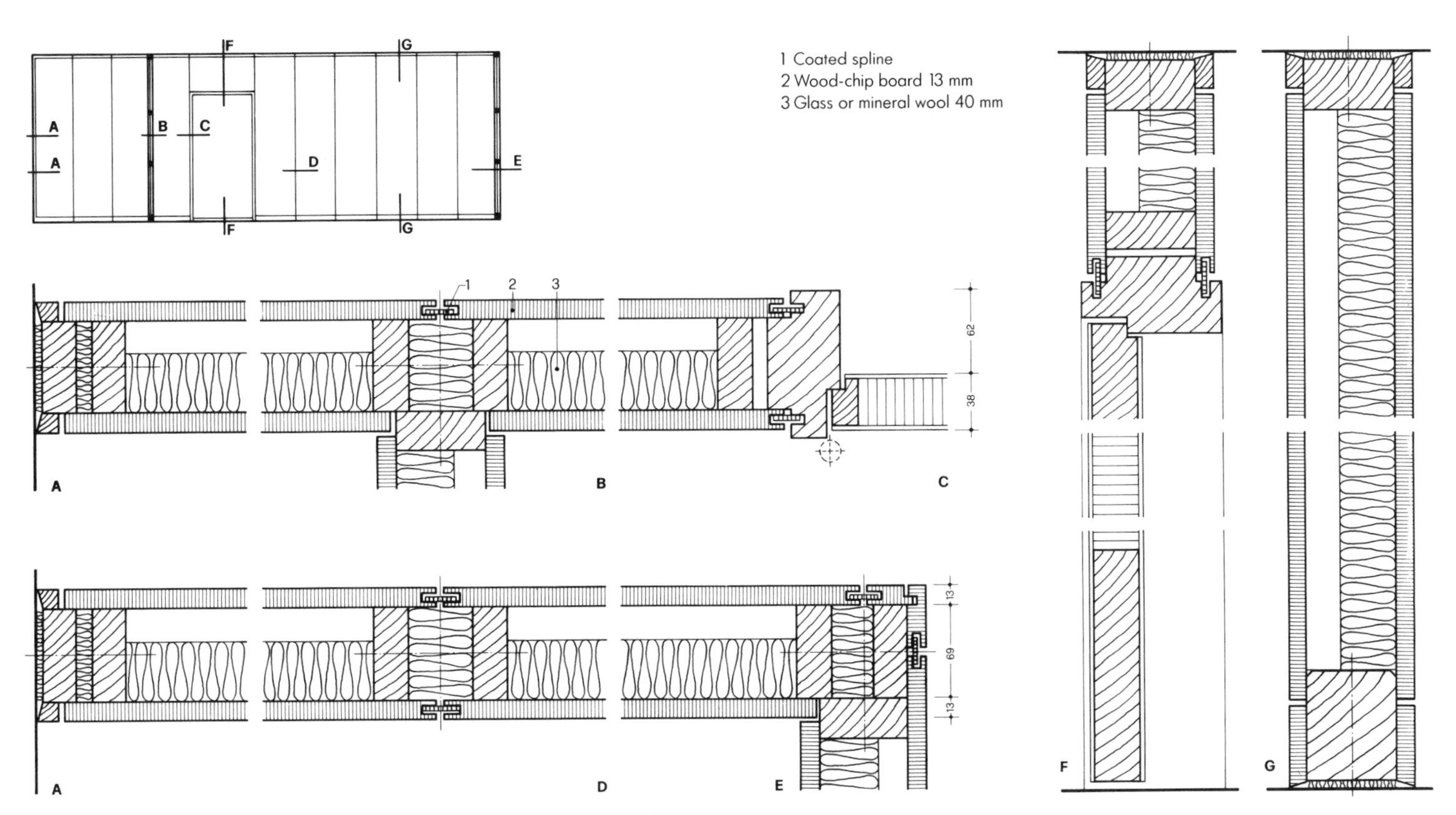

Fig. 50. Potentially movable prefabricated partition using wood framing with soundproofing between wood-chip boards. The interior void is only partially filled with soundproofing material. Panels are set on a floor guide sill and dropped until the guide moldings stop them. Panels are connected to each other by splines.

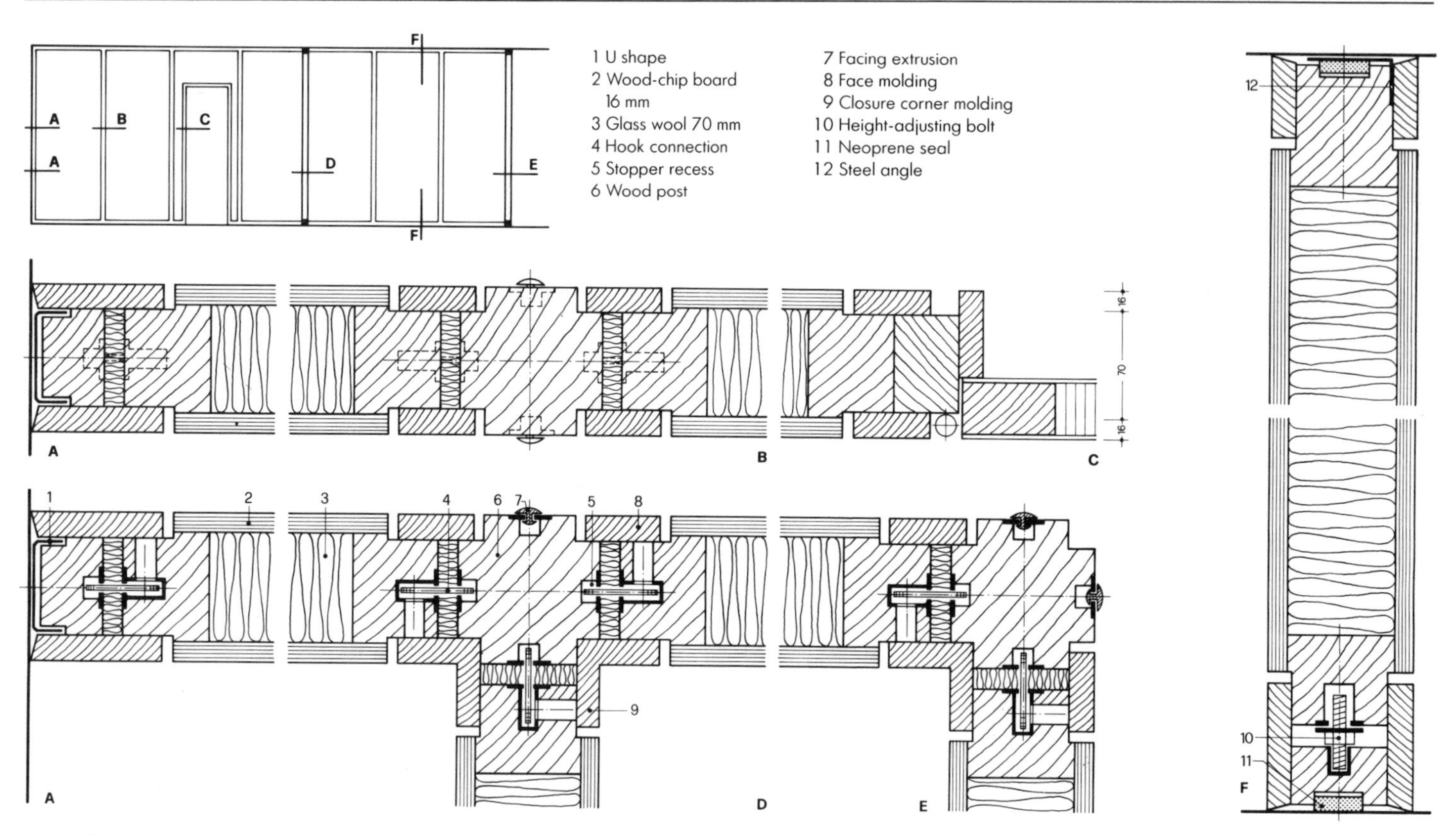

Fig. 51. Movable wood panel partitions with sheathing connected through framing, full soundproofing. Upper and lower connections are made in such a way that single panels can be removed and relocated without opening the panel itself.

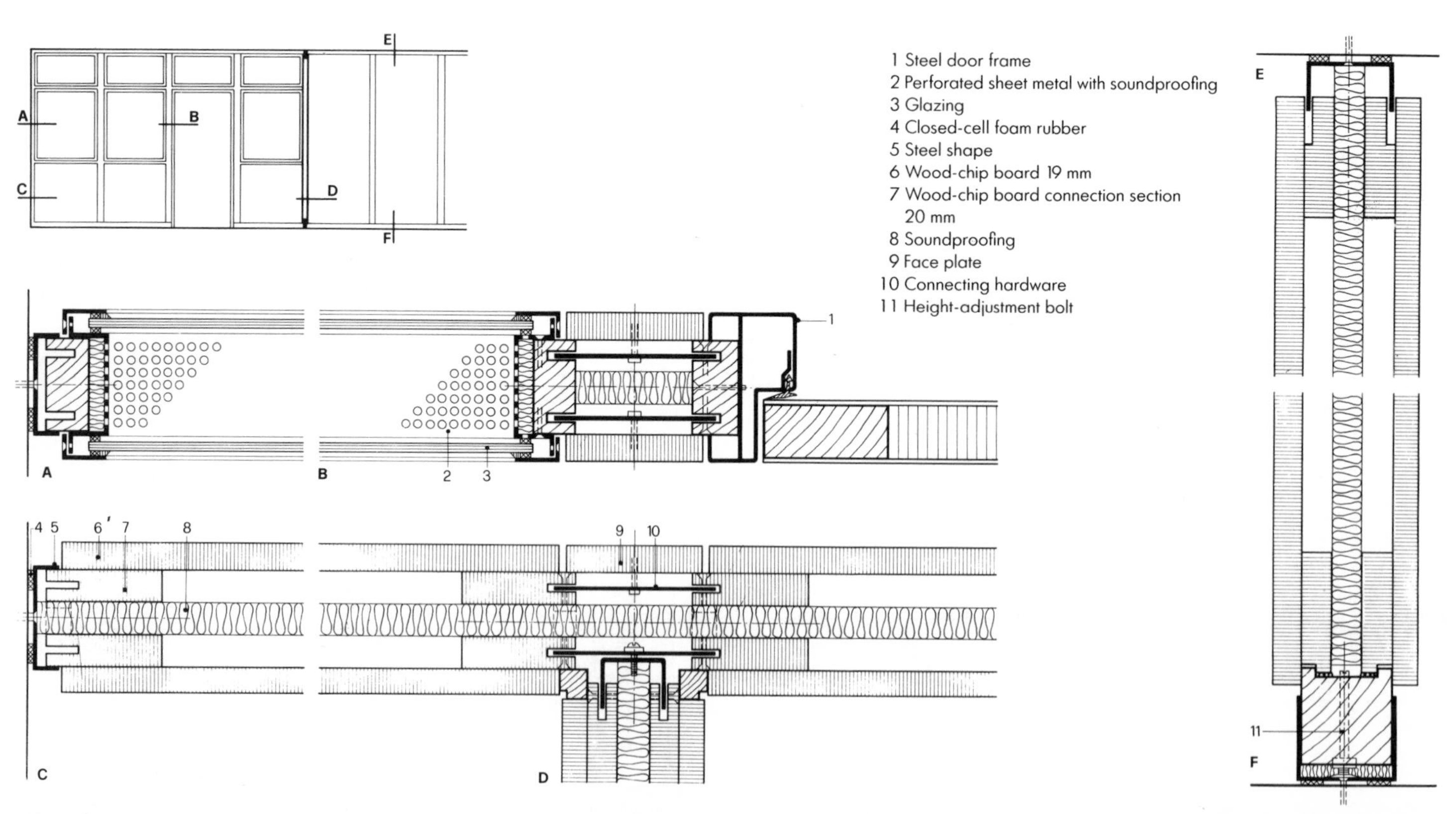

Fig. 52. Movable prefabricated panel with sheathing completely separated by soundproofing. The wall can be moved quickly by removing connection covers and loosening the connecting hardware.

Connections and Joints

In the industrial or shop fabrication of panels, joint assemblies acquire special significance and require careful workmanship.

Assembly of small or large wall units into a wall system results in vertical joints at which the panels have to be joined structurally and at the same time sealed against wind, moisture, and sound. The same applies to horizontal joints between walls, floors, and roofs.

Layout of Connections between Wall Units

In order to achieve flexibility in combinations and to provide for future extension or an exchange of components, it is best to develop the connections between wall elements as a four-faced system. The location of wall elements and their joints can then be established on a linear or banded grid.

Structural Connections

Structural connections between two or more panels are achieved by connecting their load-bearing posts. Connections between floors or roofs and panels occur through the anchorage of sills or headers. Connecting hardware consists of either lag bolts, threaded bolts, steel angles, or sheet-metal shapes.

Sealing of Joints

The tightness of seals between walls, floors, and roofs is of special importance for the durability of a building. Through joints should not open. Laps, grooves, or splines may close a joint. Sealers of various types are used to seal joints; these include bitumen-impregnated foam strips, permanently elastic seals, metal flashing shapes covering the joint, wood covering strips, and planks. Joints should always be easily accessible in order to control any movements due to the working of wood or sheathing.

Vertical joints of interior partitions need only be sealed against noise transfer; this can be achieved easily by inserting soundproofing strips.

Joints between Panel Elements and Floors or Roofs

In order to prevent damage from rain splash, DIN 68800, part 2, requires a vertical distance of about 30 cm between the finished grade and the wood construction. The construction in this splash zone is generally masonry, either a foundation or a basement wall.

Timber construction should be protected from rising humidity by a vapor barrier. The joints between timber panels and floor can be weatherproofed in many ways.

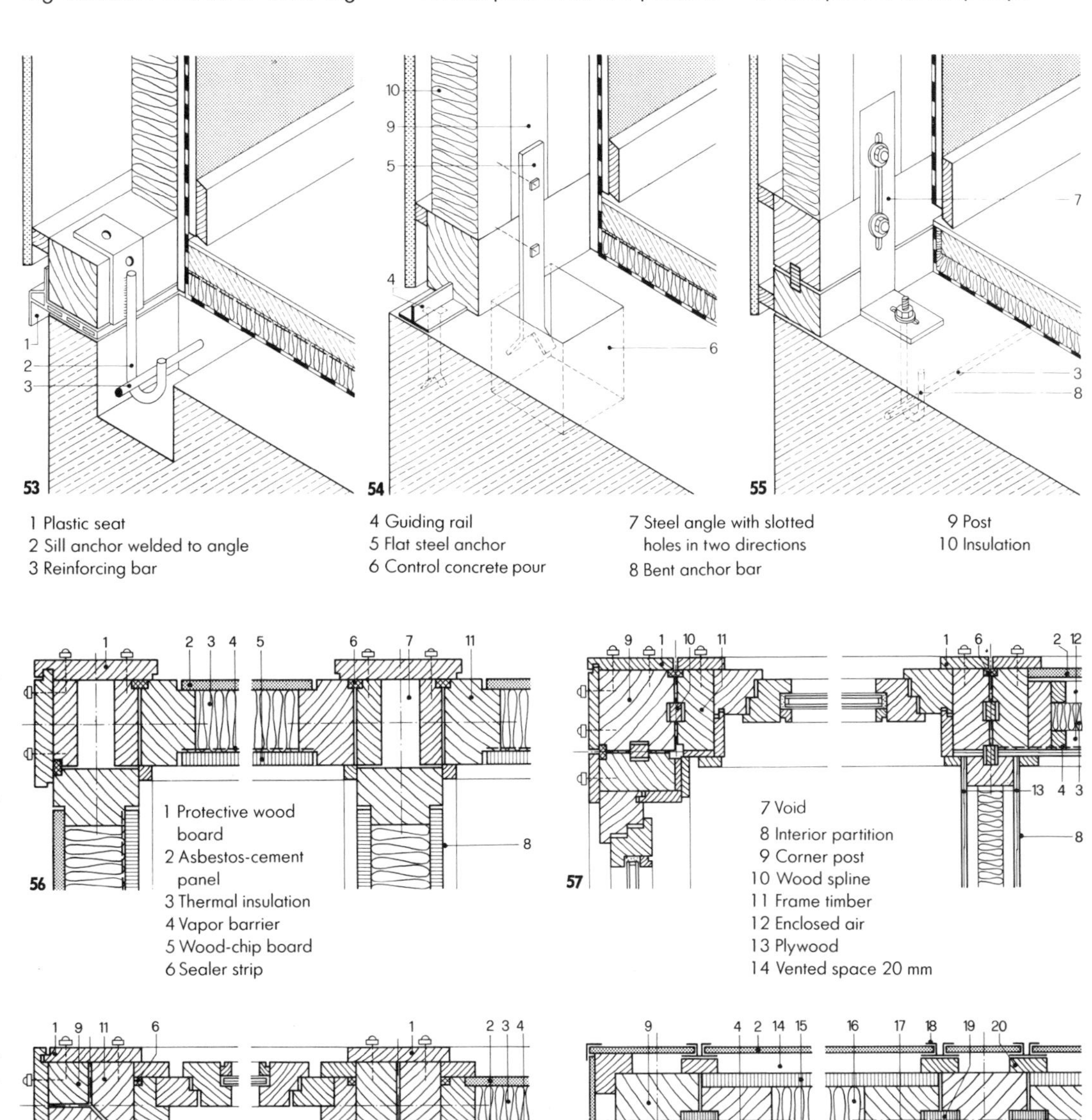

Figs. 53–55. Structural connections of wood panels to the substructure can be made with round or flat steel bars which are fastened to sills and are anchored to the substructure.

Fig. 56. Wood panels are joined in such a way that square spaces are left at intersections. Panels are connected by means of bolts. Joints are sealed with sealer strips, which are protected from temperature variations by means of wood board covers.

Fig. 57. Wood panels are erected in the field on grid lines. At the corners once again there is a square space, here filled with solid wood. Panels are connected with fitted splines, joints sealed with sealing strips.

Fig. 58. Wood panels are arranged to form a square connection point. The outer corner is divided diagonally. Face boards provide the seal.

Fig. 59. Wood panels are placed to form a square joint, which is built as an additional post. Panels and post are connected by fitted splines. A seal is provided on the outside by an aluminum extrusion. The joint between panel and post is covered by a molding which supports the exterior sheath.

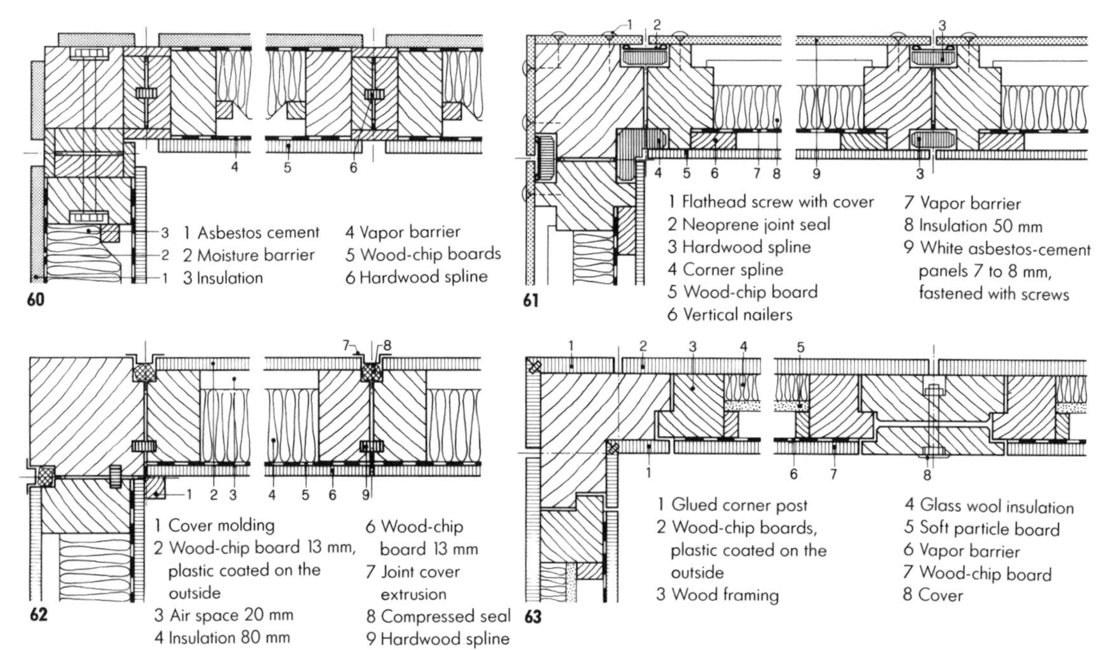

Fig. 60. Joints are closed with face boards, overhanging outer sheathing, and also splines.

Fig. 61. Joints are sealed with neoprene extrusions, which are compressed by overhanging sheathing.

Fig. 62. Sealing is achieved by aluminum extrusions which overhang the sheathing, and by a compressed seal under the extrusions.

Fig. 63. Seal between panels is achieved solely through the geometrical configuration of joint, panel edges, and boards.

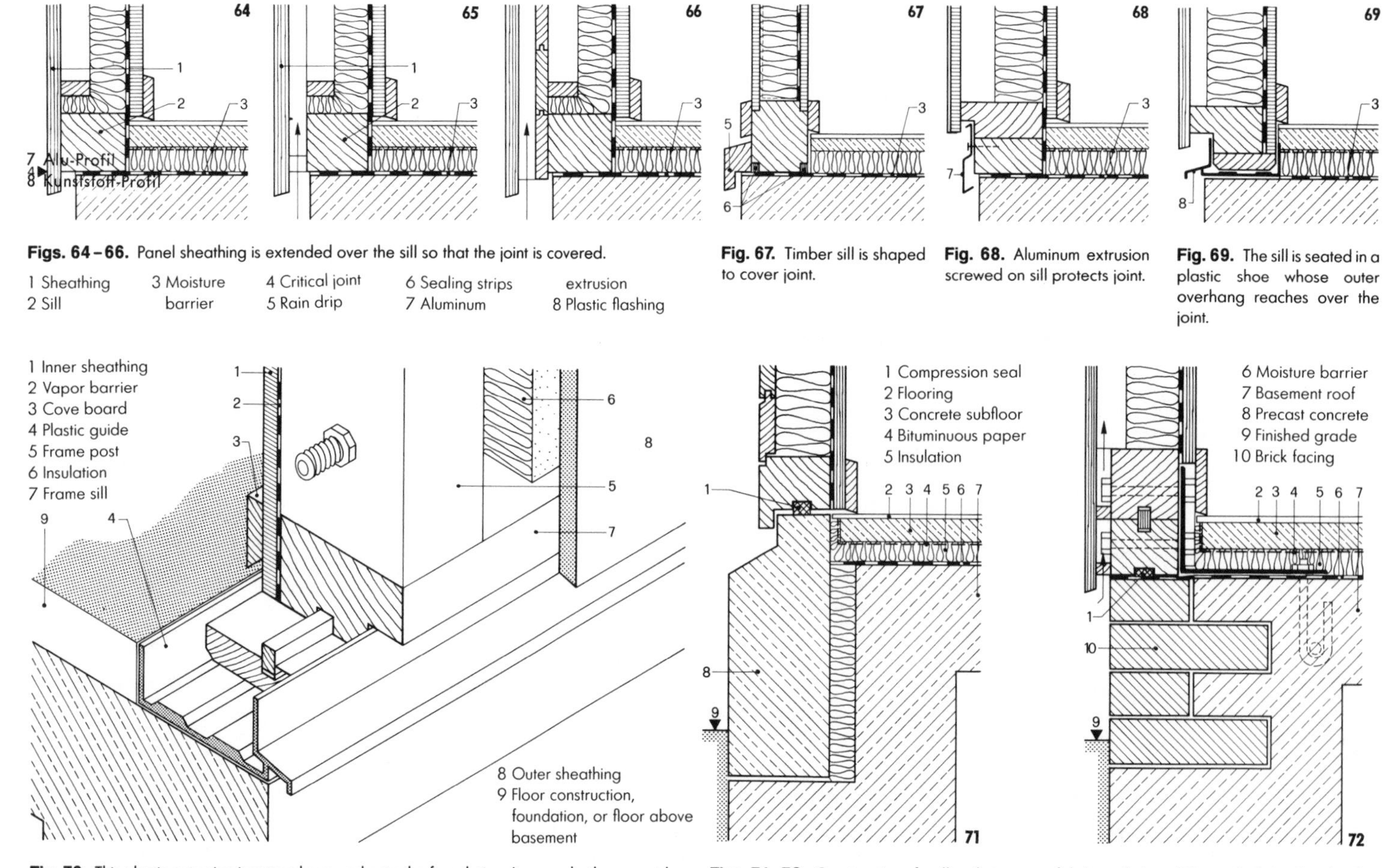

Figs. 64–66. Panel sheathing is extended over the sill so that the joint is covered.

Fig. 67. Timber sill is shaped to cover joint.

Fig. 68. Aluminum extrusion screwed on sill protects joint.

Fig. 69. The sill is seated in a plastic shoe whose outer overhang reaches over the joint.

Fig. 70. This plastic extrusion is set and screwed onto the foundation. It serves both as a guide for panels and as a joint cover with drip.

Figs. 71–72. Construction of wall socket as a prefabricated piece (71) or as built-in-place brick masonry (72). Socket raises wood construction above splash zone.

Foundations and Floor Construction

Wood framing may rest on various foundations. Criteria governing the choice are:

1. Can a basement be used and is it necessary? Could the rooms planned for the basement be located on the first floor?
2. What are the requirements for the ground floor? Must it be concrete, or can it be timber construction if building regulations permit it?
3. Soil conditions, ground water level.
4. Which foundation system is the best for maintenance?
5. Should the foundations also be movable if the building is?

Following are some basic types of construction that will govern the choice. Essentially, it must be kept in mind that foundations for timber structures require a greater degree of workmanship than foundations for concrete structures.

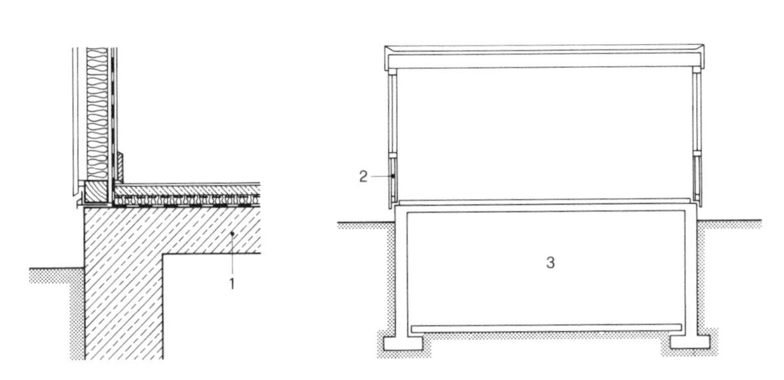

Fig. 73. Cast-in-place concrete basement. This is the substructure on which the timber structure is placed.

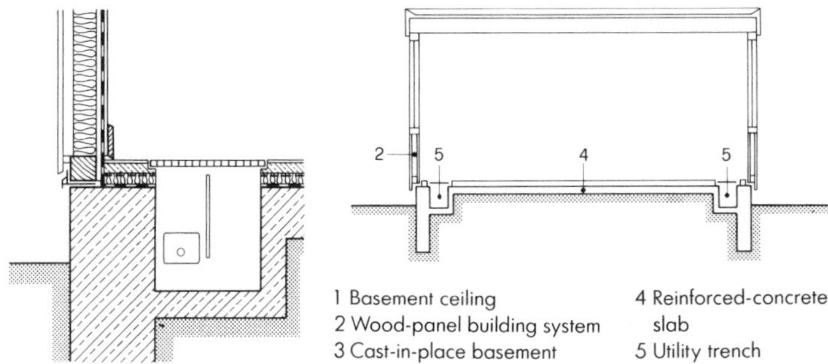

Fig. 74. Cast-in-place concrete platform. When a basement is not needed or when it is not feasible because of the subsoil conditions, a timber structure can be erected on a concrete platform. Utilities have to be located in trenches and led upward.

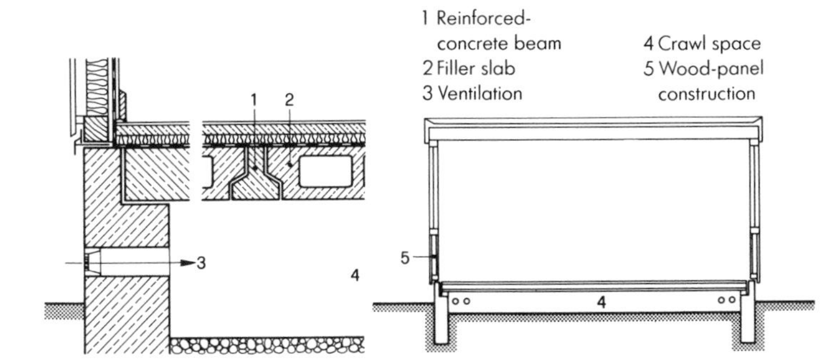

Fig. 75. Cast-in-place concrete foundations with precast slabs. Here only the foundations are cast in place, the slabs are placed on them. This creates a crawl space which shelters the utilities. The crawl space must be insulated and ventilated, but it has to remain accessible. The prefabrication of slabs reduces construction time and provides better dimensional accuracy of the substructure.

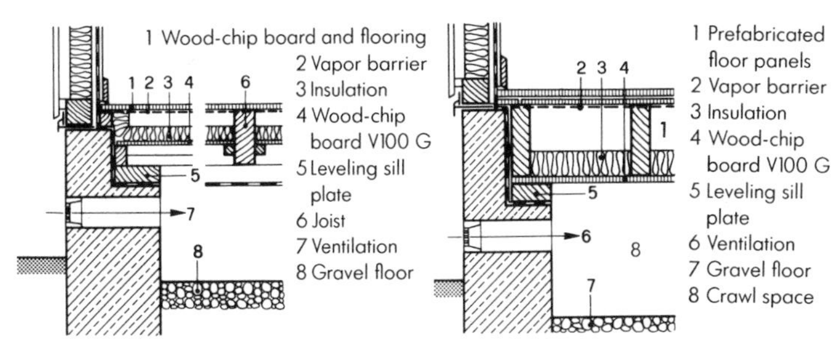

Fig. 76. Cast-in-place foundation with timber floor. Timber joists which carry a floor made from wood-product sheets are placed on a concrete foundation. Between the joists there are other sheets resting on ledger strips; they carry the insulation. Construction of the floors shown in Figs. 76, 77, and 78 must follow the guidelines of DIN 68800, part 2.

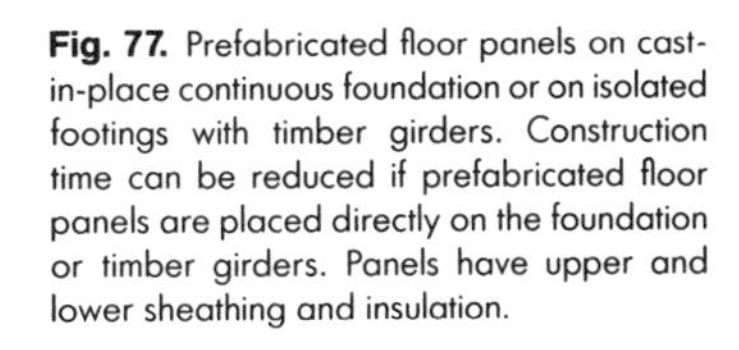

Fig. 77. Prefabricated floor panels on cast-in-place continuous foundation or on isolated footings with timber girders. Construction time can be reduced if prefabricated floor panels are placed directly on the foundation or timber girders. Panels have upper and lower sheathing and insulation.

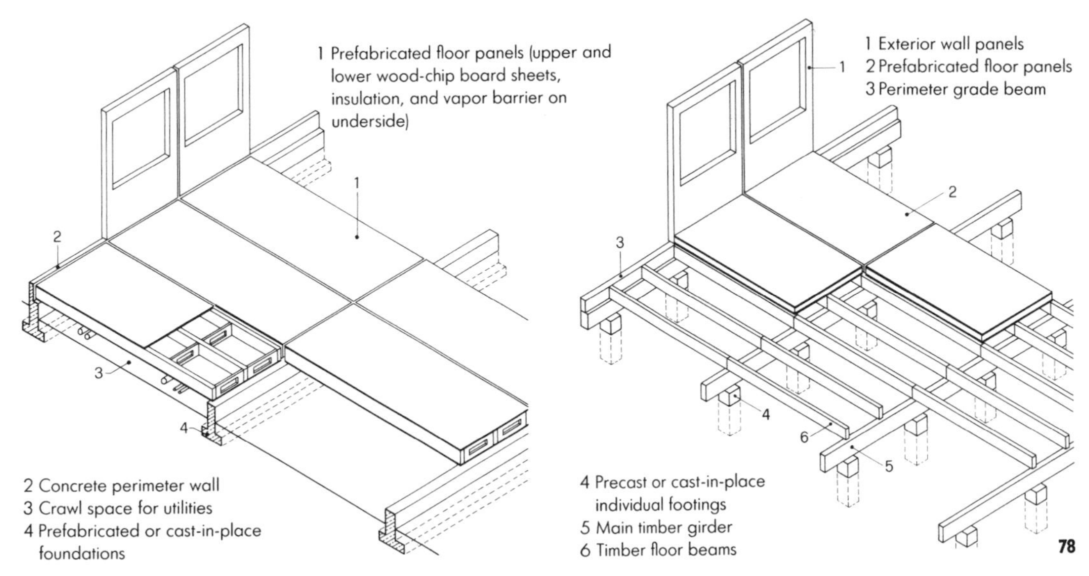

Fig. 78. Another alternative is a timber floor on a load-bearing grid. Wood-chip boards or exterior grade plywood serve as underflooring. Concrete work is limited to continuous perimeter footings and individual interior footings.

Stability of Wood-Panel Systems

The spatial stability of wood-panel systems must conform to DIN 1052, "Timber Structures," and to the "Regulations for Wood Panel Buildings" published as an addendum to DIN 1052. Single-story buildings are exempted under certain conditions.

The basic design of a wood-panel building requires that its building corners and interior walls contain closed wall elements having sufficient shear strength and stiffness. If panels are used as roof elements, proof has to be provided that they and their connections can act as stiff plates, resisting and transferring tension, compression, and shear.

Regulations do not require a proof of stability for one-story buildings, provided:

- Each exterior wall contains at least three bracing panels 1 m wide. The same is valid for interior walls, less than 12 m long and spaced at no more than 6 m.
- Each corner of an exterior wall contains a bracing panel. Walls longer than 12 m must have an additional bracing panel for every additional 4 m length.
- The strength of bracing panel connections to the floor is tested, even when such a proof is not required for panel bracing.
- Roofs are built with panels that have sufficient shear strength and stiffness to act as plates. Panels must be interconnected to resist shear.

Wood-panel roofs which are accessible only for cleaning and maintenance work must conform to regulations for roof panels made with wood-chip board or veneers.

Proof of stability is also not required for those wood panels that act as rigid plates with regard to shear and stiffness when the minimum thickness of their sheathing is stiff enough to resist buckling within the unsupported length of sheathing between ribs. If the actual conditions vary from the ones mentioned here, either because of the number of floors, or because of the number or construction of panels, the design has to prove that the panels can carry the wind loads to the foundations in addition to carrying the usual roof and floor loads. Even if proof of stability is not required for one-story buildings, it is necessary to prove the spatial stiffness required to resist wind loading.

Wood panels with wood-product materials glued on both sides can act as rigid plates. On the other hand, one-sided sheathing on timber beams has to be checked for strength of connections if it is to be used as a rigid plate. Wood-product sheets are by their nature stiffer than planking.

If for architectural reasons a building cannot contain any exterior closed-wall panels, horizontal loads must be conveyed, as in frame construction, by the roof acting as a rigid plate to interior shear walls. In this case, the design of the roof as a rigid plate and the transfer of horizontal loads to the foundation must be documented (Fig. 81).

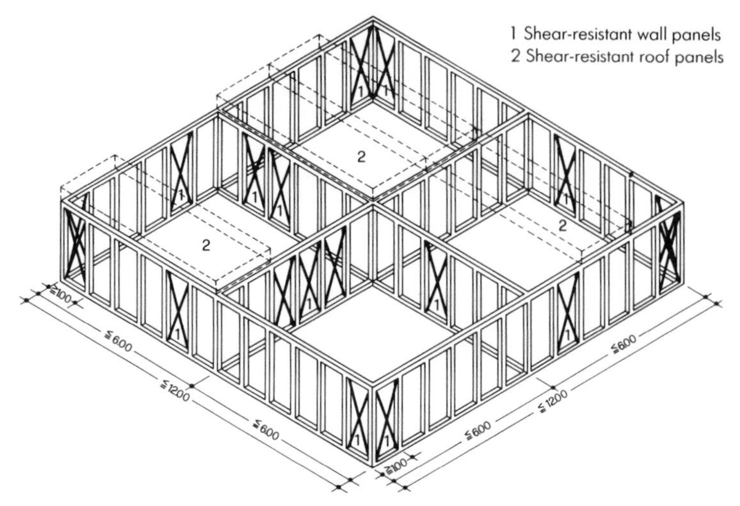

Fig. 79. Spatial stability of a wood-panel building is achieved without any special design when bracing panels are arranged as shown.

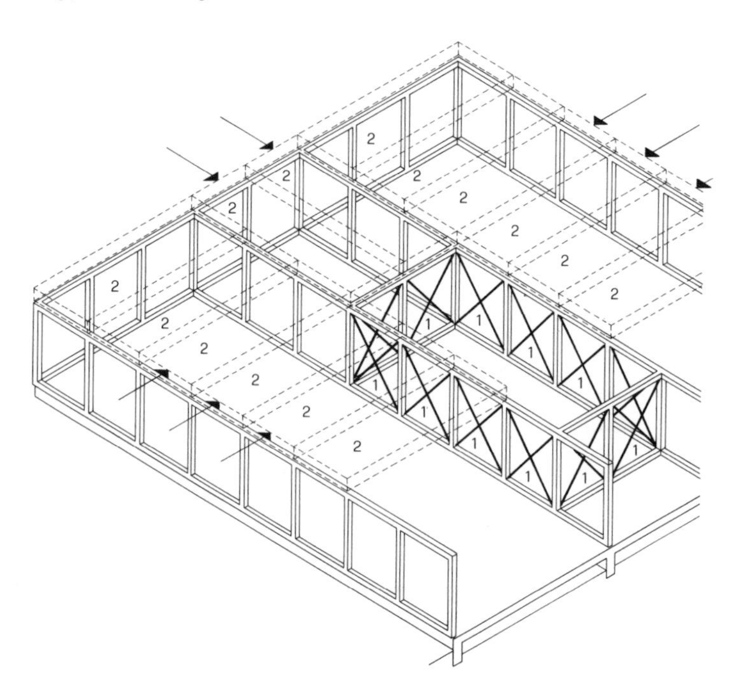

Fig. 80. Stability is achieved by a closed-ring arrangement of shear-resistant interior wall panels which are connected to roof panels.

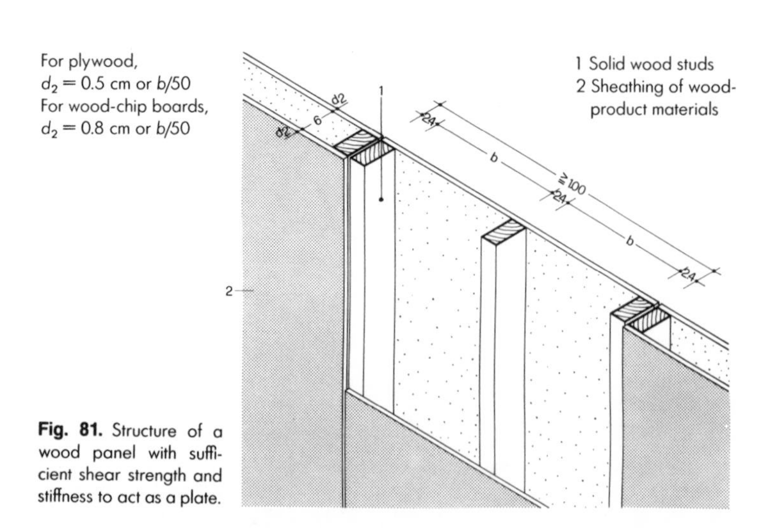

Fig. 81. Structure of a wood panel with sufficient shear strength and stiffness to act as a plate.

Electrical, Sanitary, and Heating Installations

Providing sanitary, heating, and electrical facilities in prefabricated buildings requires more careful planning and execution than in ordinary construction, because of the thin wall sections and prefinished wall surfaces typically used in prefabricated structures. This is in contrast to ordinary construction where heavier walls are constructed in place and utilities are installed under the plaster or in chases within rough construction, a method that permits changes if they become necessary. All this is not possible in prefabricated wood-panel buildings, whose wall thicknesses generally do not exceed 10 cm. Utilities are built into the panels, generally in the shop. The only work on the construction site is to splice the utilities, connect them to outside services, and attach the fixtures. After completion of construction, any changes are practically impossible.

Pipes and cables may be placed best as follows:

• In wall panels or their connections, as long as the diameter of the pipe permits it. Water pipes, however, should only be placed in interior walls because of the danger of freezing.
• In crawl spaces, in floor depressions, or inside the floor panel (Fig. 82).
• In specially built utility panels (Fig. 83).
• In attic crawl space (for double roof structures) or in the interspace between roof structure and suspended ceiling (Figs. 84 and 85).

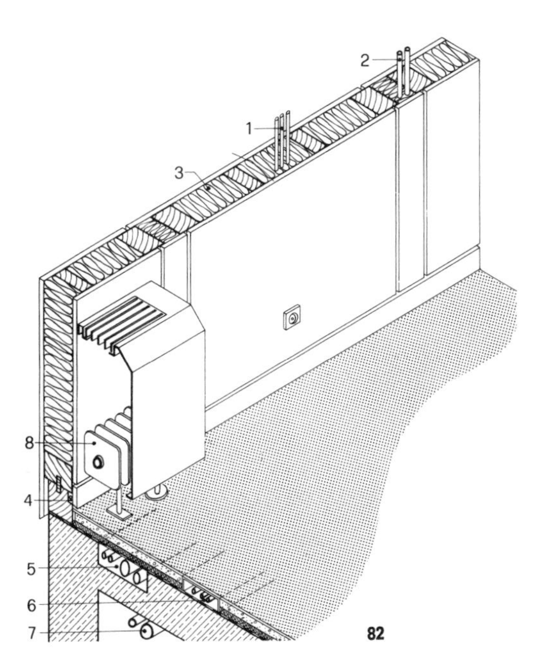

1 Ducts or pipes in wall
2 Ducts in panel connection
3 Enhanced insulation
4 Ducts or wiring under baseboard
5 Ducts in floor chase
6 Ducts and wiring in floor structure
7 Ducts in crawl space
8 Radiator with cover in front of wall panel

82

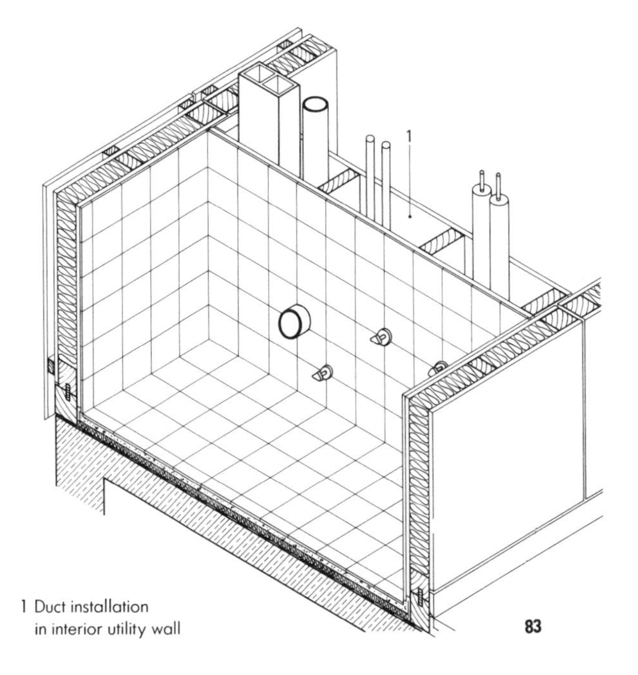

1 Duct installation in interior utility wall

83

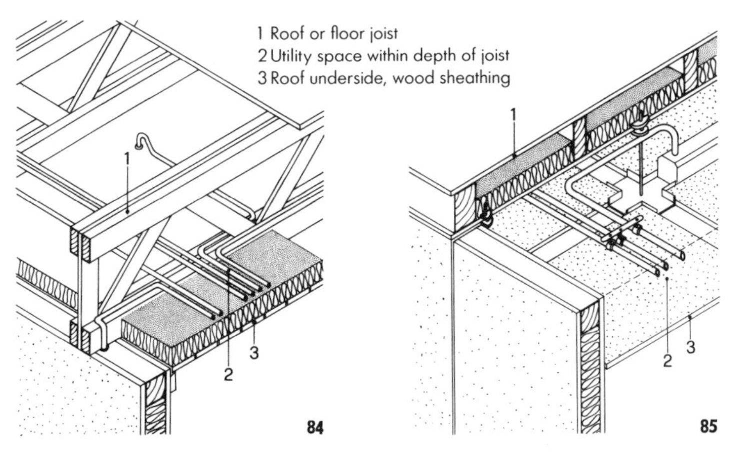

1 Roof or floor joist
2 Utility space within depth of joist
3 Roof underside, wood sheathing

84

1 Roof or floor panel
2 Utilities interspace
3 Suspended ceiling, mineral particle board

85

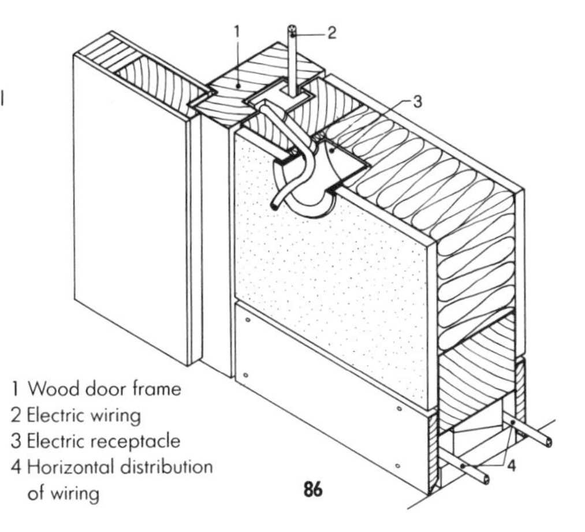

1 Wood door frame
2 Electric wiring
3 Electric receptacle
4 Horizontal distribution of wiring

86

Electrical Installations

Electric wiring is laid mostly in underfloor chases, baseboards, or roof interspaces. These feeder wires connect to vertical wiring, which is simply and expediently placed in door frames, in wall connections, in flat ducts attached to interior walls, or within the walls themselves. Distribution boxes or receptacles are attached to vertical wiring. Empty ducts are often left in the panels in order to facilitate later installations. When ordering distribution boxes, switches, or receptacles, it is necessary to consider the wall strength necessary to receive them.

Electrical installation in lightweight wood panels must conform to special requirements established by the code. Metal condulets are generally used instead of the coated wiring. Plastic housing for switches and receptacles must be made from material of low flammability.

Sanitary Installations

Installation of hot and cold water piping is possible even in relatively thin interior walls. This piping generally occurs in bathrooms and kitchens together with sewer pipes which are considerably larger and whose sections cannot fit within the 6-cm-wide clear inside space of 10-cm-thick walls.

Because of this, wood-panel buildings should have their sanitary facilities concentrated in one place and vertically stacked (but not in outer walls) (Figs. 87 and 88), or such systems should be placed together in special wall chase panels.

Wall chase panels can be built by attaching to the interior side of a wall panel all pipes, connections, and stubs, and placing between them additional studs serving as spacers. The voids between piping and studs are filled with sound insulation. A covering of wood-chip board with openings for protruding piping is then screwed onto the studs of the chase (Fig. 89).

It is necessary to remember that such installations cannot contain any plastic piping because of necessary fire protection. Only galvanized sewer pipes can be used.

In addition to such chase walls, the wood-panel building systems lend themselves to the preparation of self-supporting prefabricated utility units, utility walls, or complete sanitary facilities.

Figs. 87–88. Examples of arranging utility chases or walls.

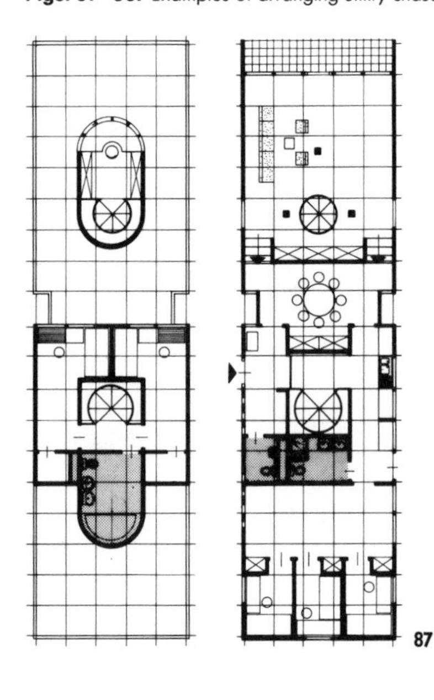

87

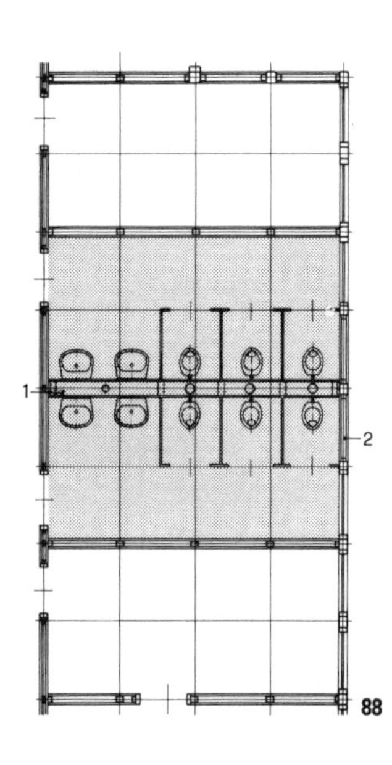

88

1 Utility wall with bundling of utilities
2 Exterior wall
3 Interior wall panel
4 Spacer studs
5 Waterproof wood-chip board
6 Glued-on tiles

89

Heating Installations

The heating system is distributed throughout the building and its course must be planned carefully. It differs from the electrical system which has flexible and thin wiring, and from the plumbing with its heavier but rather concentrated piping cluster.

The heating system's piping can be carried in the panel walls only at considerable cost. It is less expensive to place it in the crawl spaces, in floor chases, in floor structures, or in vertical wall chases.

The heat is conveyed through radiators, convectors, plates, or piping. Thin walls allow a recess only at the cost of reduced insulation. The radiators stand independently from walls and, therefore, occupy usable space. Plates or flat radiators occupy less space than regular radiators or convectors. Floor heating with its simple piping is preferred if no room is to be wasted.

A potential need for room layout changes may require the removal of interior walls. This can be done only if the layout of the heating units already corresponds to a modular plan, that is, the radiators must correspond in their lengths to the width of a panel (Fig. 98).

The location of the heating unit in a wood-panel building without a basement presents a special problem.

Building regulations call for walls and ceilings of furnace rooms to be fireproof. This excludes combustible materials. If the furnace room is at the ground floor, its walls must be at least 11.5-cm-thick concrete blocks, and its ceiling must consist of at least 10 cm of concrete, foam concrete, or similar material. There are some local exceptions to these requirements, allowing an F30 rating for floors or roofs over furnace rooms. In such cases timber beams are permitted.

The walls of a furnace room may be prefabricated in lightweight materials provided they are not combustible. These conditions can be fulfilled by using metal studs, continuous insulation, and gypsum board sheathing (see DIN 4102). The thickness of such a wall can be 10 cm, which corresponds to the normal thickness of a wood-panel wall. Thus both types of walls can fit into the same grid system.

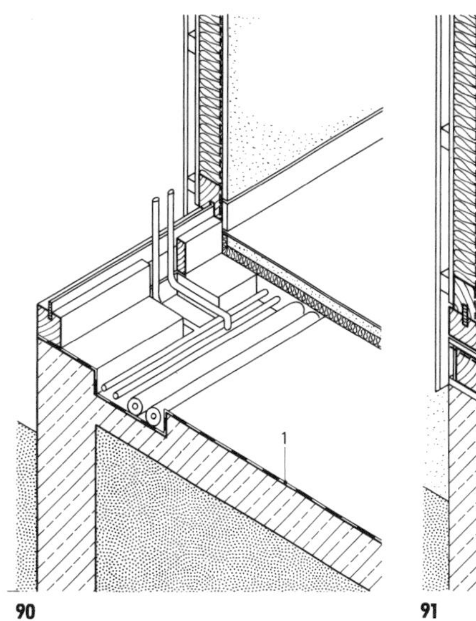

90

Possible heating installation.

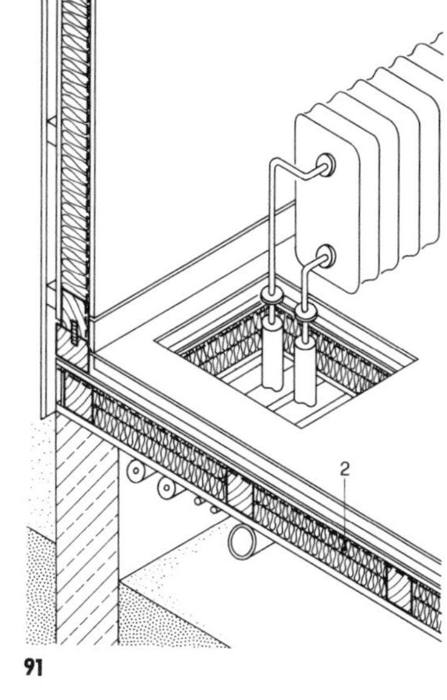

91

1 Vapor barrier
2 Prefabricated floor panels
3 Increased thermal insulation

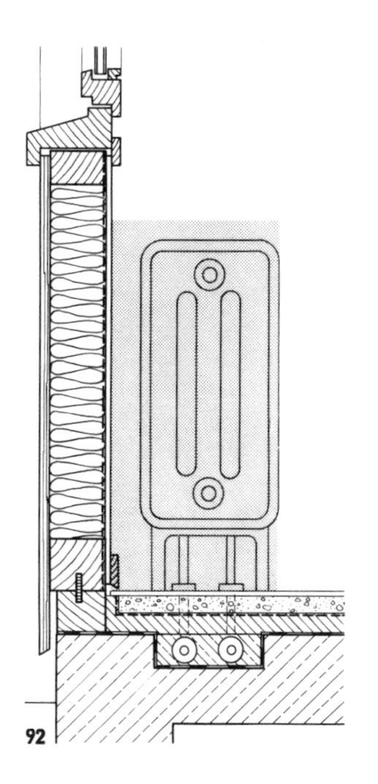

92

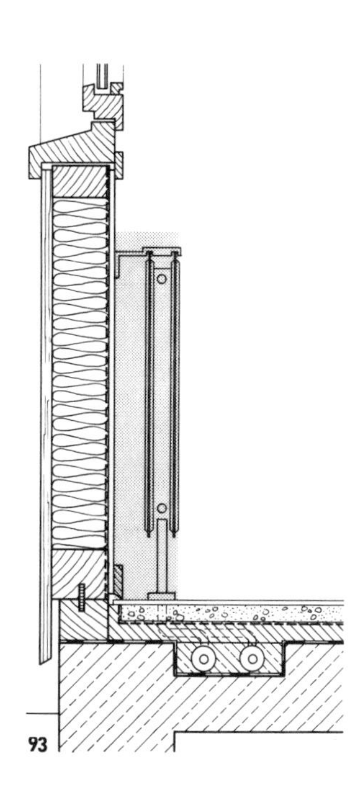

93

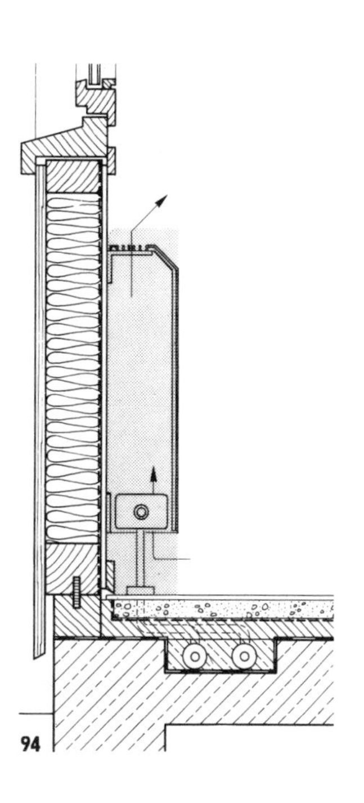

94

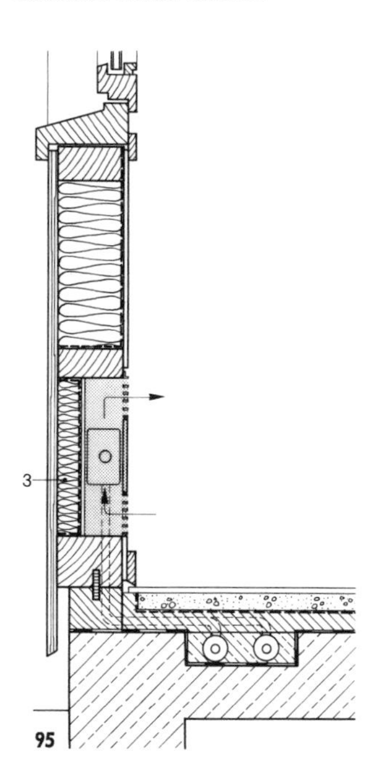

95

Examples of heating installation layouts.

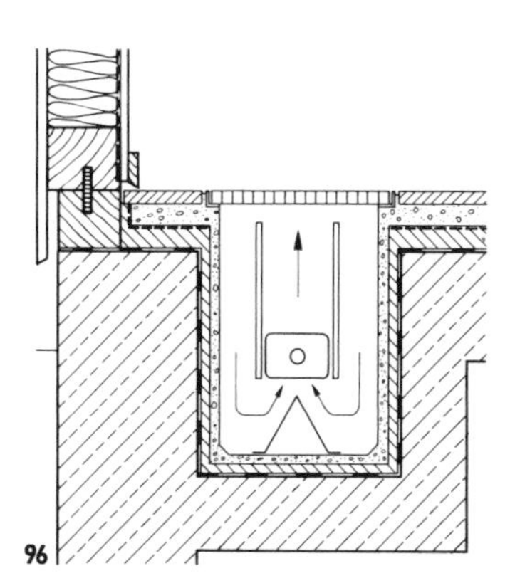

96

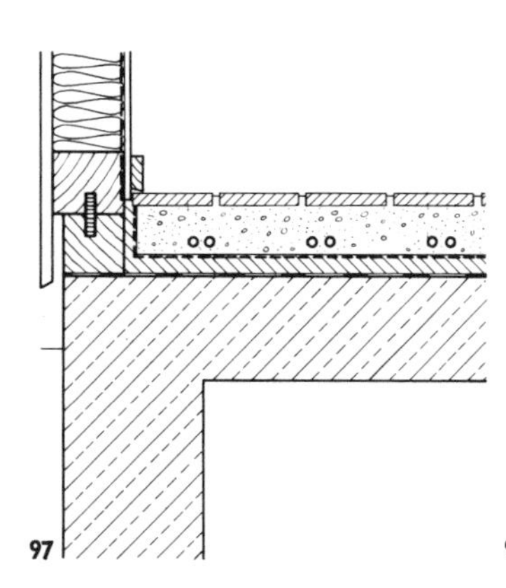

97

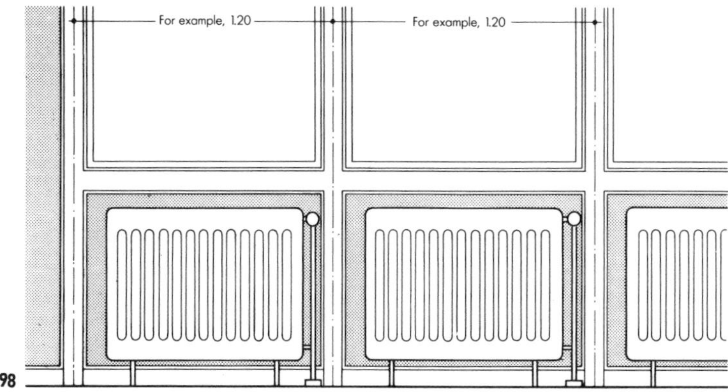

98

FIRE PROTECTION IN WOOD-PANEL BUILDINGS

General

The same building fire protection regulations govern wood-panel buildings as other structures. Local ordinances govern and may be complemented by special rules and guidelines, such as those for school buildings.

The requirements relate to the function of a building component (load-bearing or not), its location (interior or exterior), and its specific task (fire wall, staircase wall, fire escape). They also depend on the number of floors, the use of the building, and the expected fire hazard.

The fulfillment of fire protection requirements does not present any problems for buildings of up to two floors, because in this case walls and floors have to have a fire rating of F30 (fire-retardant), while the outer surfaces of exterior walls have to conform to material classification B1 (fire-resistant). Both conditions can be fulfilled by wood panels without any difficulty. Buildings taller than two stories must have their bearing columns made from noncombustible material, regardless of the required fire rating. This excludes wood-panel construction. Figure 99 illustrates the requirements for residential or office buildings in relation to the number of floors and the distance from property lines or other buildings.

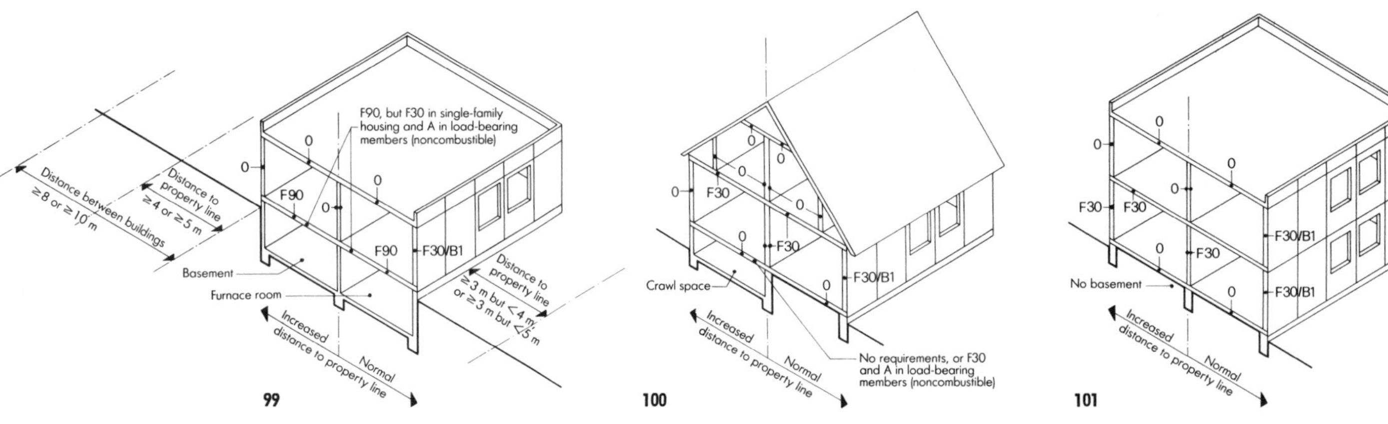

99

100

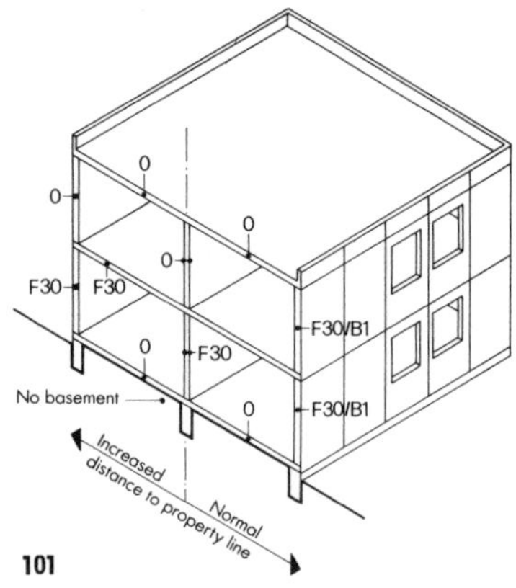

101

Load-Bearing Walls

Load-bearing and bracing walls for buildings of up to two floors must conform to fire rating class F30 (fire-retardant). In free-standing residential buildings, this is valid for up to two apartments; for other buildings of similar size this is valid only for floors above which there are other floors or occupied attic spaces.

Exterior Walls

There are no fire requirements for exterior walls when they are at least 5 m from the property line or 10 m from the nearest building. For lesser distances, but distances larger than 3 m, the exterior surfaces must conform to material class B1 (fire-resistant). Buildings at the property line or row buildings must have their exterior surfaces constructed of class A material (noncombustible) for a minimum distance of 1 m.

Party Walls

As a rule, party walls in row houses must have an F90 rating. They have to be built from stone masonry or concrete.

Stairway Walls

Stairway walls in two-story buildings must have an F30 fire rating (fire-retardant).

Floors

Second floors must have a fire rating of F30.

Roofs

The only requirement for roofs is to resist sparks and radiating heat. These conditions can be fulfilled readily by a double roofing paper on wood sheathing and an underlying thermal insulation.

Building codes generally do not specify the fire requirements for slightly inclined or flat roofs. Flat roofs are not governed by requirements for floors, while steep roofs are not governed by exterior wall requirements.

Fire Resistance of Wood and Wood Products

Wood or wood products can achieve a high fire rating although they are combustible. The reason for this apparent contradiction is a special characteristic of wood: charring builds an outer protective layer which reduces its flammability. The loading capacity of wood is thus reduced only after a considerable time. It is relatively easy to achieve a fire rating of 30 min and, therefore, a classification of F30 according to DIN 4102. This corresponds to a "fire-retardant" property. Wood or wood-product members can also achieve a fire rating of much more than 90 min. Still, they cannot be classified as "fireproof" by the code if they are load-bearing and combustible.

Walls

The fire resistance of wood or wood-product panels is basically determined by their structure, the type of joints, and the properties of sheathing and linings.

Wood framing of panels, normally 4/8, 8/8, or 8/10 cm in cross section, retains its load capacity for over 30 min as long as the panel lining on the fire side has a fire resistance of 22 min. The fire resistance of a panel wall can be increased by a nonflammable insulation as long as the insulation is well secured and cannot fall out if sheathing is burned out.

Figures 102 to 105 show examples of panel walls that have a fire resistance of 30 min. There are many more alternatives for the fabrication of panel walls which have a fire resistance of 30 to 60 min without special certification. They are illustrated in DIN 4102, part 4, "Fire Resistance of Materials and Structural Components; Assembly and Application of Classified Materials, Building Components and Special Members."

Vented exterior linings generally cannot achieve a definite fire rating. Exterior walls must, therefore, be built in such a way that they achieve the necessary rating without the vented linings (Fig. 105).

Joints between the panels must have splines or cover moldings arranged in such a way as to prevent the passage of fire. DIN 4102, part 4, describes the appropriate arrangement.

Floors

The requirement for a 30-min fire resistance of floors is fulfilled if the upper and lower panel sheaths have at least 19-mm thickness. These thicknesses can be reduced by using combinations of wood and other materials, such as gypsum boards conforming to DIN 4102 or other fireproof materials. For details of such combinations which do not require special certification see DIN 4102, part 4.

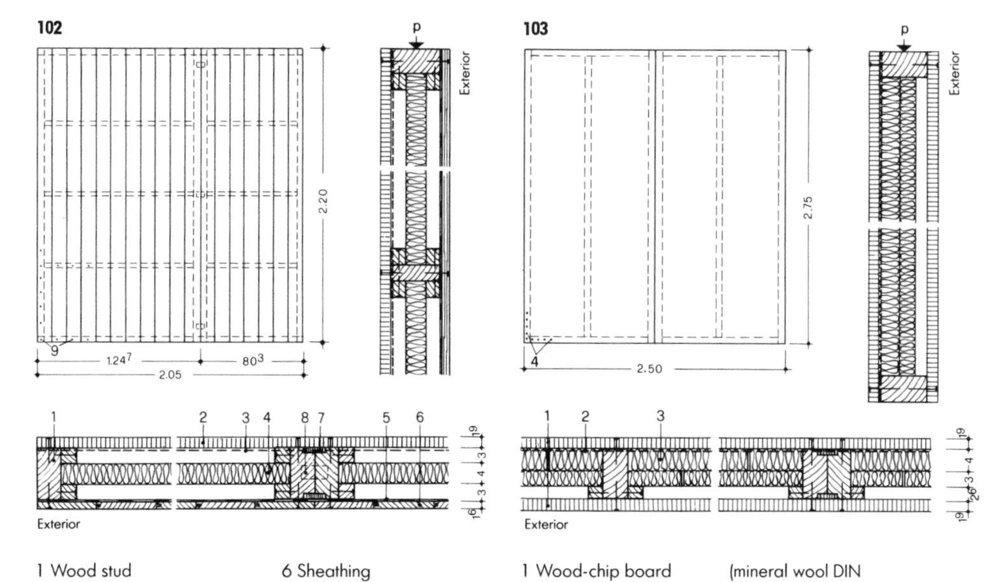

102
1 Wood stud
2 Wood-chip boards
3 Vapor barrier
4 Thermal insulation (Mineral wool DIN 18165)
5 Closure layer
6 Sheathing
7 Wood spline seal
8 Hardwood spline
9 Wire brads

103
1 Wood-chip board
2 Vapor barrier
3 Thermal insulation (mineral wool DIN 18165)
4 Wire brads

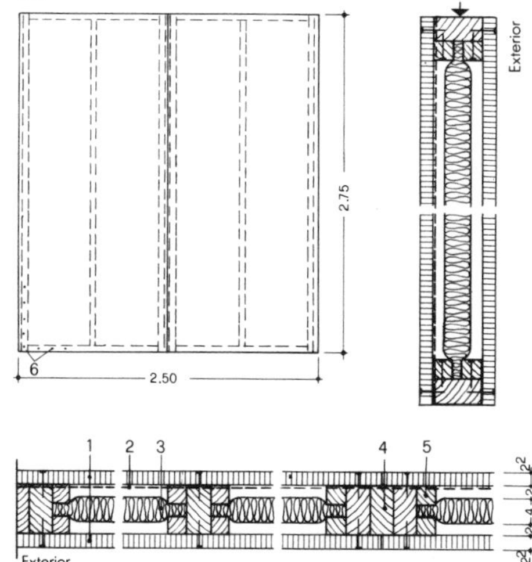

104
1 Wood-chip board
2 Vapor barrier
3 Thermal insulation (mineral wool DIN 18165)
4 Wood filler
5 Molding
6 Wire brads

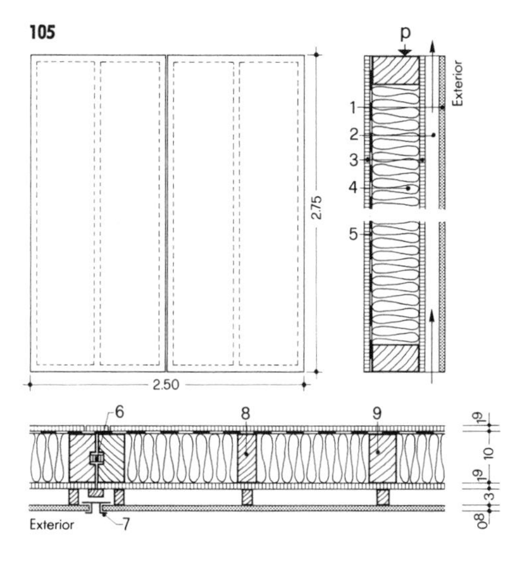

105 Vented load-bearing exterior wall (fire rating F30).
1 Asbestos-cement panel 8 mm
2 Vented space
3 Wood-chip board 19 mm
4 Thermal insulation class A
5 Vapor barrier
6 Panel joint with hardwood spline
7 Aluminum joint extrusion
8 Non-load-bearing stud (supports sheathing only)
9 Load-bearing stud

106 Roof panel (wood panel F30), Okal system.
1 Wood framing
2 Steel dowel
3 Steel plate
4 Glue
5 Wood-chip board 13 mm
6 Mineral wool 60 mm
7 Aluminum foil
8 Wood-chip board 15 mm
9 Double coat of spray paint

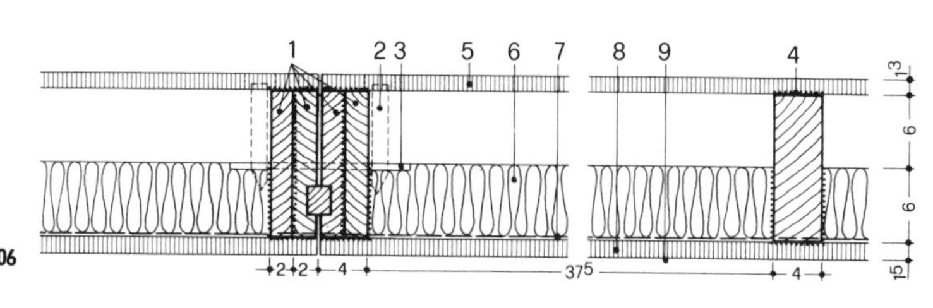

STRUCTURAL SYSTEMS IN WOOD-PANEL CONSTRUCTION

Load-Bearing Transverse and Longitudinal Walls

Construction of a wood-panel system requires three basic types of structural support:

1. Transverse load-bearing walls
2. Longitudinal load-bearing walls, sometimes in connection with the roof or floor structure and wall bracing
3. Combined transverse and longitudinal load-bearing walls, sometimes in connection with the roof or floor structure and wall bracing

Transverse Load-Bearing Walls

Roof or floor panels span longitudinally through the building, from transverse wall to transverse wall. The exterior and interior wall panels placed longitudinally between transverse walls have no other structural function than to brace the transverse walls. Therefore, they can be weaker, have more penetrations, and may be moved for remodeling. They cannot be made thinner because of the standard thickness of joints, but their wood framing can be more slender. However, from the point of view of standardized fabrication, it is advisable to have all panels dimensioned equally (Fig. 107).

Spacing between transverse load-bearing walls may vary in relation to the roof or floor construction. For prefabricated roof panels the economical spacing is about 7.20 m, for joists it is about 6.00 m. The room length between transverse walls is arbitrary.

Longitudinal Load-Bearing Walls

In this case the roof or floor panels span from longitudinal wall to longitudinal wall, transversely to the building. Longitudinal walls are braced by the transverse non-load-bearing walls. The openings in longitudinal walls are limited by the required dimensions of load-bearing frames. The distance between longitudinal walls is governed in the same manner as for transverse walls. Rooms of different widths can be arranged between longitudinal walls, following a basic grid layout. The length of the rooms is governed by the roof span or by the arrangement of transverse walls (Fig. 108).

Combined Transverse and Longitudinal Load-Bearing Walls

It is not always possible to obtain a building layout that clearly follows one or the other direction. Often it is necessary to use layouts that switch from transverse load-bearing walls to longitudinal load-bearing walls (see Figs. 109 and 110).

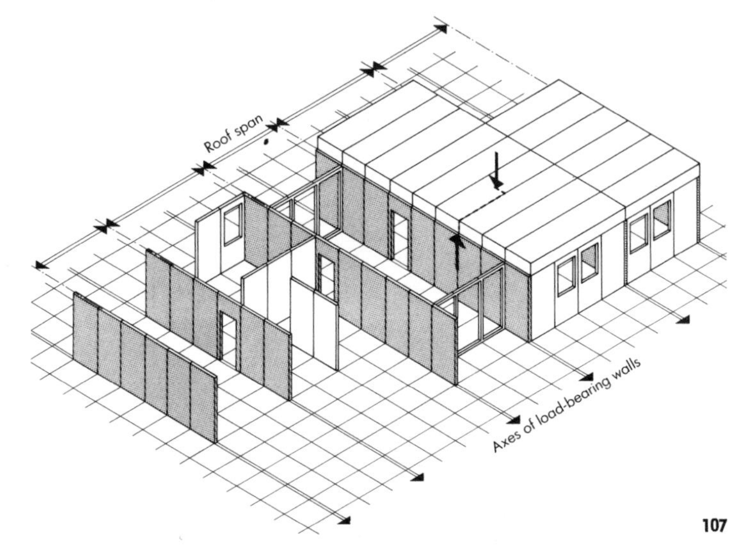

107

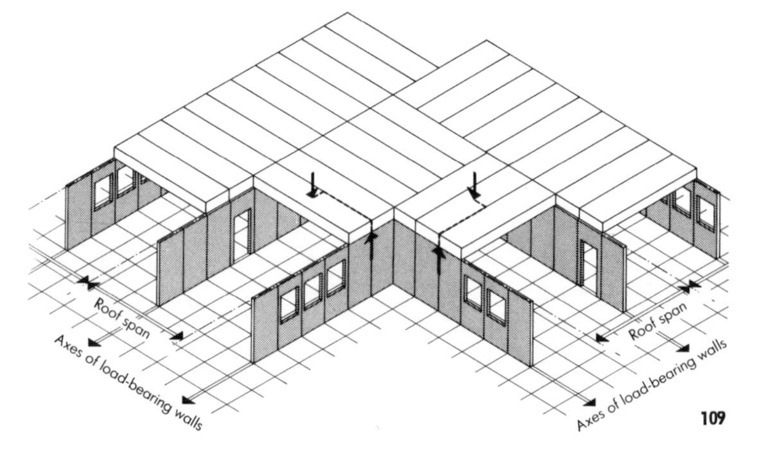

109

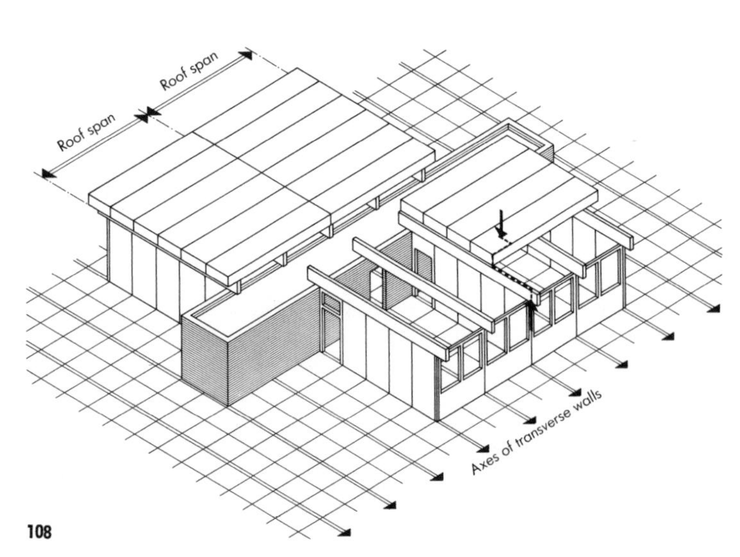

108

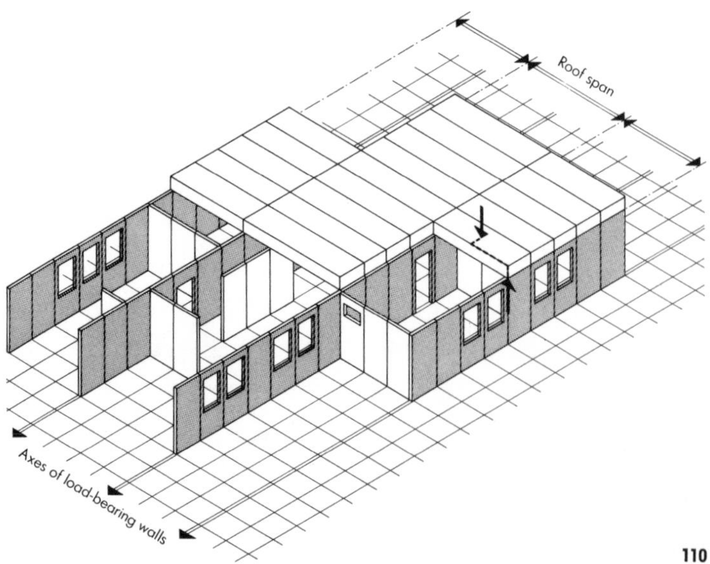

110

Room Units

Layouts with Room Units

The design of a building based on room units has many more restrictions than either an ordinary frame house or one with wood panels that can be planned on a grid of 1.20 or 1.25 m. The grid of a room unit design depends on the size of the rooms, but their width is governed by transport limitations. Widths of up to 2.50 m do not require police permits; widths between 2.50 and 3.00 m require police approval and must follow prescribed routes. Units over 3.00 m wide can be transported only with police escort. Thus, widths over 2.50 may be costly.

The lengths of rooms are governed mostly by structural requirements, finishing requirements, weight, and layout. The lengths for pure timber construction range from 4.80 to 7.50 m, and for a mixed construction of steel framing and timber walls from 8.40 to 10.00 m.

The heights of rooms are determined by building code requirements for various uses, and vary from 2.50 to 3.00 m.

The room lengths should be a multiple of their widths. For normal room widths of between 2.40 and 2.80 m, this multiple varies between 2 and 5. Under these restrictions the room unit system can be combined into large units and varied layouts.

Because of fire protection requirements, assembling room units into multistory buildings is simple only up to two stories.

Cost savings using room unit type construction may be as high as 30%.

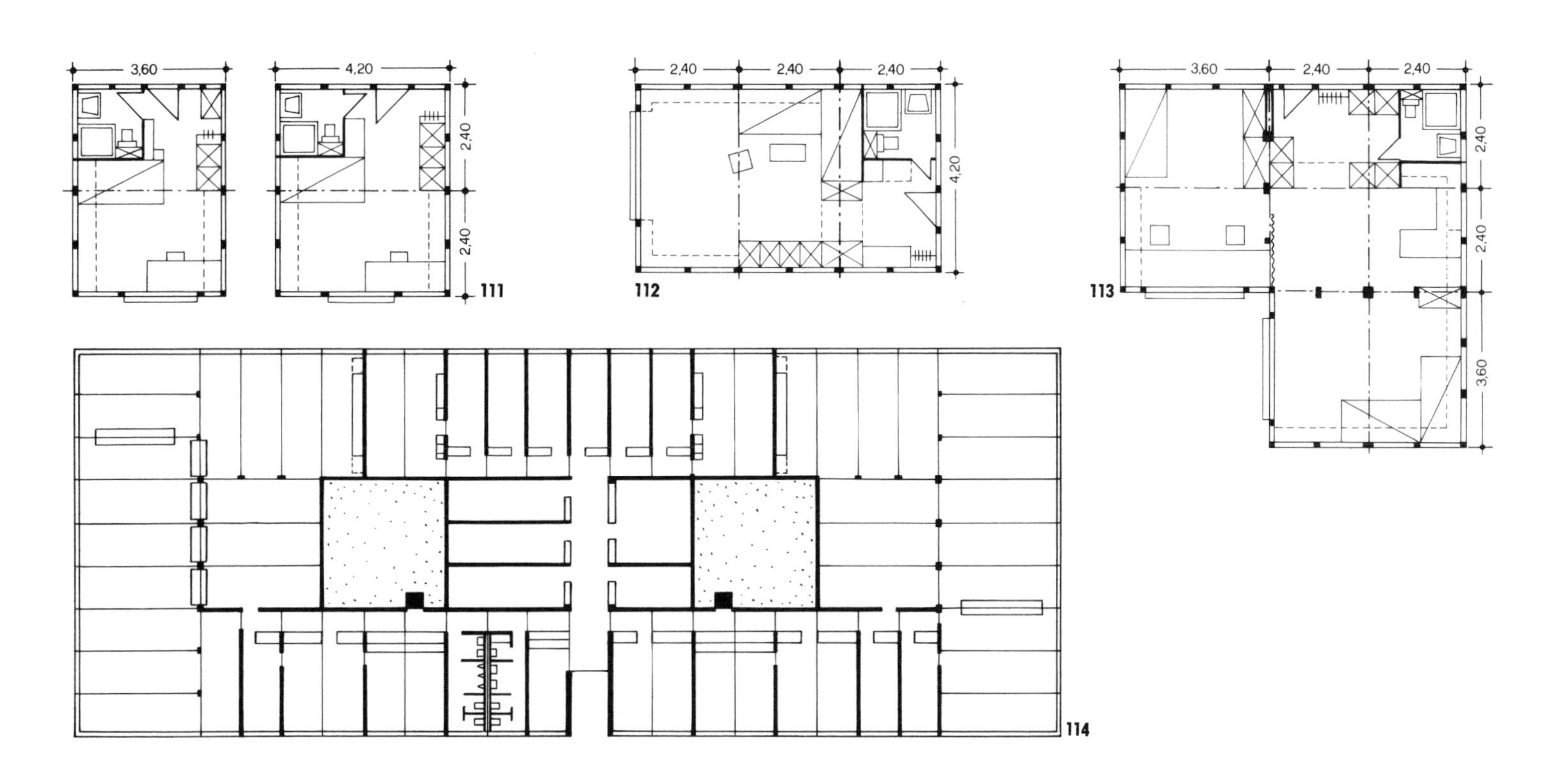

111

112

113

114

Structure of Room Units

Room units may be either pure timber structures with load-bearing elements of wood or wood products, or they may be of mixed construction. In the latter type, the structure of the units is either completely or partially a steel frame, and the remainder is wood.

Room units with a timber structure are frames that can be opened and extended on two or three sides, depending on the type or location of wind bracing. They consist of timber columns, beams, floors, roof panels, and wall panels.

The units that are open on two sides can be designed as hinged frames in which the wind loads are transferred to the foundation by two walls and the roof plate.

Units open on three sides are braced against the wind on one side by a wall and on the other sides by rigid frames. Rigid frames can be placed on either the long or the short sides.

Structural connections between components of room units, as well as between the units themselves, consist of steel angles, steel shoes, and bolts.

The sealing of vertical joints is generally achieved by covering moldings. Horizontal joints at roof level are sealed either through glued expansion extrusions or through sealer moldings. The construction of roofs, floors, and walls is similar to wood-panel construction.

Foundations for room units, if there is no basement, consist of individual reinforced-concrete footings within the area of the plan, and of continuous footings or grade beams between individual footings along the perimeter. Depending on the contractor, foundations can be either precast or cast in place.

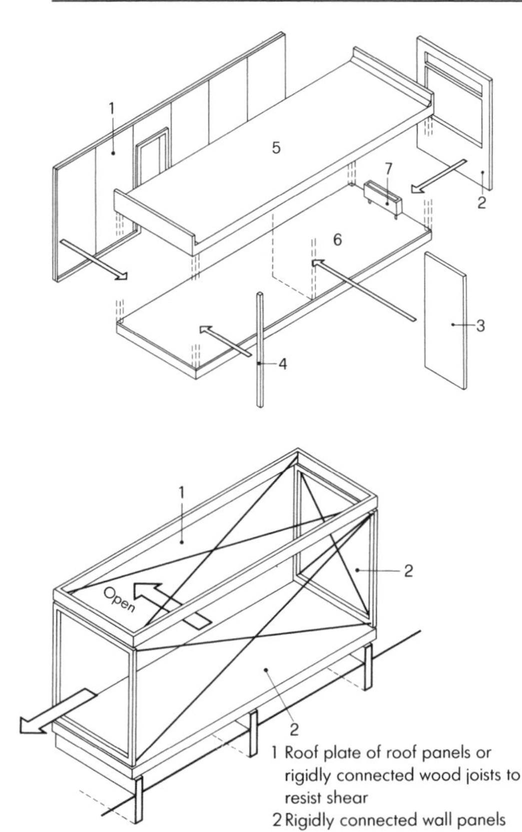

Fig. 115. Components of a timber room element with dimensions of 2.50 × 7.50 m. Connections between wood members are steel. Wind bracing, the main problem in room units, occurs mostly through roof plates and walls that are built as wood panels, or through rigid frames.

1 Walls
2 Exterior walls
3 Partitions
4 Columns
5 Complete roof
6 Complete floor plate
7 Heating

1 Roof plate of roof panels or rigidly connected wood joists to resist shear
2 Rigidly connected wall panels

Fig. 116. Bracing of a room unit through wall plates in two planes at right angles to each other.

1 Roof plate as in Fig. 116
2 Rigid connection
3 Shear-resisting wall panels as plates
4 Floor panel

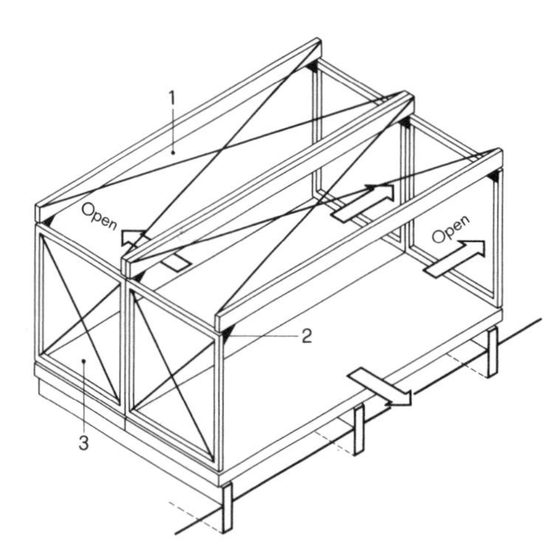

Fig. 117. Bracing of a room element in one direction (longitudinal direction of building) by means of wall panels, in the other direction through rigid frames.

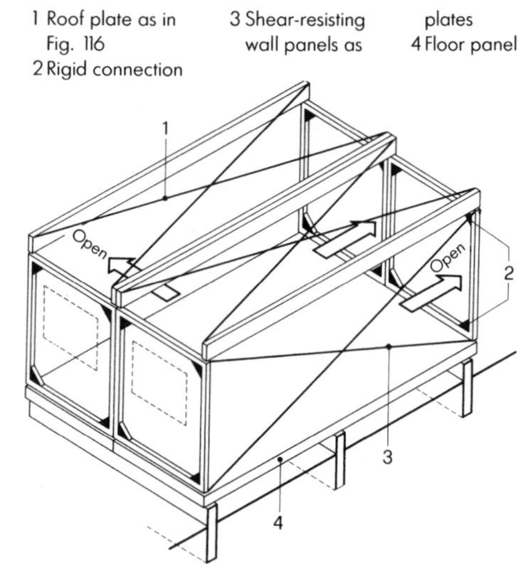

Fig. 118. Bracing of a room unit in one direction through wall panels (transverse to building), and through rigid frame in the other direction (longitudinally).

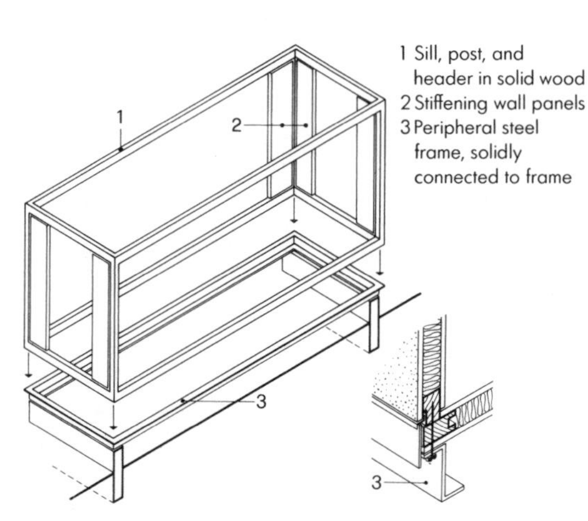

1 Sill, post, and header in solid wood
2 Stiffening wall panels
3 Peripheral steel frame, solidly connected to frame

Fig. 119. Timber construction with partial stiffening walls in the corners.

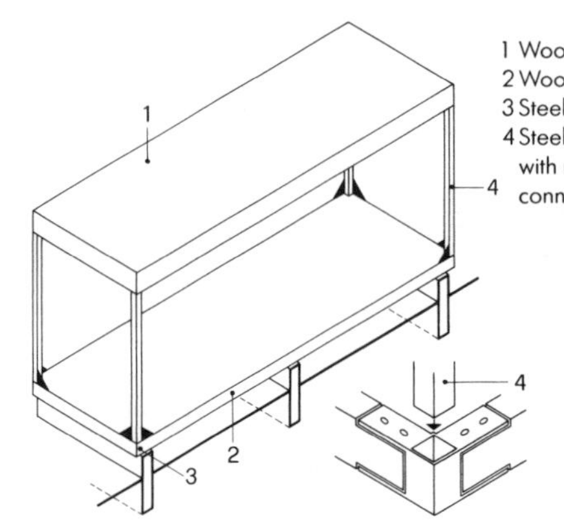

1 Wood roof panel
2 Wood floor panel
3 Steel sleeve
4 Steel support with moment connection

Fig. 120. Steel beams linked to wood panel.

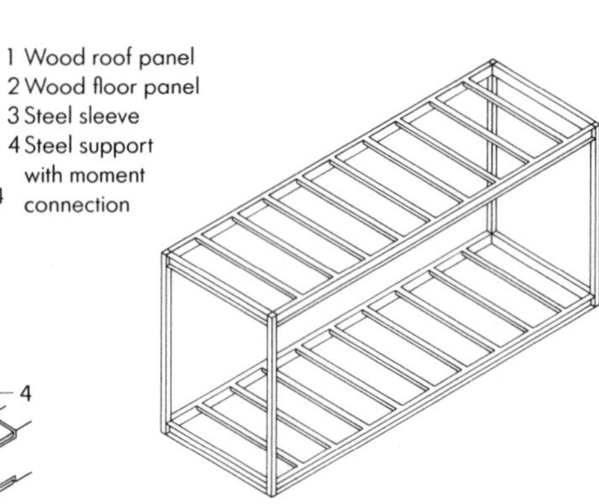

Fig. 121. Steel framing of a room unit. All room-enclosing elements, such as floor, roof, and walls, are of wood or wood products.

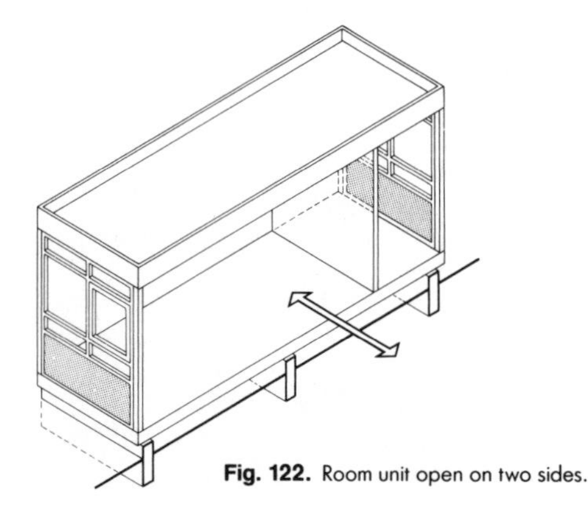

Fig. 122. Room unit open on two sides.

1 Beam
2 Column
3 Floor platform
4 Panels or sheathing

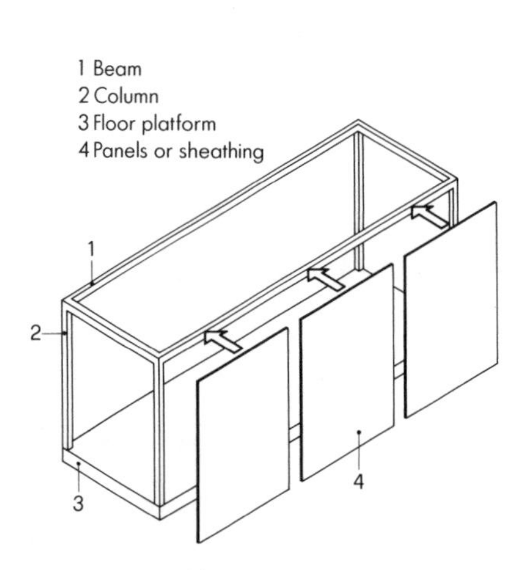

Fig. 123. Frame structure erected on a floor platform with attached panels on both sides and roof panel added.

1 Roof panel
2 Wall panel
3 Floor panel

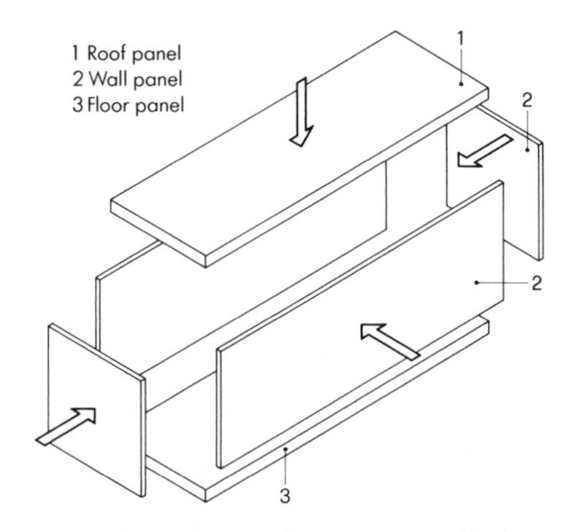

Fig. 124. Preparation of wall, roof, and floor platforms on separate assembly lines, after which the individual elements are joined on the main assembly line.

Finishing of Room Units

Two methods are available:

The first method consists of prefabricating all the room element panels and then assembling them. Prefabrication includes windows, doors, and electrical and plumbing installations. The panels are then put together on the assembly line, first the floor platform, then the wall and roof elements (Fig. 124).

In the second method, columns and beams are erected and their ends are secured by end connections. This frame is then completed by attaching panel elements to it. The room unit is assembled from the beginning as a unit and is gradually further completed on the assembly line (Fig. 123).

Transportation and Erection of Room Units

Complete room units are transported on flatbed trucks. They are lifted with a crane and placed on prepared continuous or individual footings.

The transportation of entire room units involves moving much empty space. Therefore, a system has been developed to hinge vertical panels into a horizontal position so that four room units can be transported at one time on a flatbed truck (see photos).

First the floor platforms are placed on the foundation. Roof panels with their hinged walls are then raised to the roof level and walls are let down. Columns are then nested in steel sleeves of the floor platforms, where they are secured with moment connections.

Drawings and illustrations on pages 237 to 265 are derived from the following building systems (figure numbers in parentheses): Cron (30, 63), Edcon (31), Frutiger (37, 61), Knödler (29, 69, 70), Nachbarschulte (4), Nusser (52), Okal (35, 36, 43), Polymur (28), Schleifenbaum (21), Sengler (111–113), Streif (119), Tarapin (14, 120, 125–132), Wideflex (42). The architects of buildings and drawings shown are W. Döring (6), P. Schneider-Esleben (49, 51), and K. Thut (5). *Literature:* Gideon "Walter Gropius" (p. 238), Schulze "High Buildings in Panel Construction" (pp. 256, 260), Kordina/Meyer-Ottens "Fire Prevention in Timber Structures" (p. 261).

Building components that enclose rooms must always satisfy structural, insulating, acoustical, and fire prevention criteria at the same time.

The examples of timber construction categories that follow satisfy the minimum requirements of codes and regulations; often they exceed these requirements. Given first are some technical values for thermal insulation, soundproofing, and fire protection of the structures shown. They are presented in tabular form.

Thermal values are computed; soundproofing values are generally obtained by testing.

The temperature amplitude relationship (TAV) can be used for evaluating the thermal protection of a building in summer.

The building components shown are designed such that during normal use there is no danger of dew point buildup of condensation inside the component or on its surface. If the component is modified, it is necessary to check that there is sufficient margin of safety for dew buildup.

Fire resistance ratings shown correspond to DIN 4102, part 4. Classifications of individual components in the corresponding fire resistance categories follow the code; they can be used without additional certification. Structures shown are mostly in category F30. In every case it must be proven that actual construction conforms to this category. If the use or the code do not require that the exterior walls have a fire resistance rating, simpler construction details may be available.

Roofs

Design and Execution*

The design of roofs follows DIN 1052, "Timber Structures, Design and Execution," and also DIN 1055, "Loads for Buildings." Roof sheathing of wood-chip boards is designed and built according to supplemental rules to DIN 1052.

Thermal Insulation

The requirements for the insulation of roofs have been newly arranged according to the legal ordinance of November 1977, issued for the purpose of saving energy. Also governing is the previously issued DIN 4108,"Insulation in Buildings," which indicates an improved thermal protection. The new edition of DIN 4108 includes the requirements of the ordinance of November 1977.

Soundproofing

The requirements for soundproofing of roofs are contained in the "Regulations for Protection against Exterior Noise," issued as a supplement to DIN 4109, "Soundproofing in Buildings." In order to fulfill the minimum requirements, the upper floor ceiling may be included in the values for roofs under certain layout conditions.

In the vicinity of airports the minimum requirements for roofs and exterior walls must conform to protection zones I and II.

Fire Protection

Generally, roofs are not subject to fire protection requirements. If in some cases some requirements must be satisfied, the guidelines of DIN 4102, "Fire Resistance of Building Materials and Components," govern.

Cold Roof, Rafters Covered

Alternative designs 1 to 5

1 Roof tiles
2 Nailers 30/50 mm
3 Underlying waterproofing
4 Rafters 6/16 cm
5 Mineral wool 100 mm, unit weight
≥30 kg/m³, material class A (noncombustible)
6 Vapor barrier
7 Nailers 24/60 mm
8 Underside finish

	Unit Weight (kg/m²)	Estimated Soundproof Value R_w' (dB)	Temperature Amplitude Relationship TAV	Thermal Resistance $1/\Lambda$ (m²·K/W)	Thermal Conductivity Coefficient k (W/m²·K)	Fire Resistance Class, DIN 4102	Notes
1	71	48 (~50[1])	0,26	2,75	0,34	– F 30 F 30	Roofing: Concrete tiles Underside finish: a. 13 mm chipboard V20 b. 15 mm gypsum board GKF c. 13 mm chipboard with additional 12.5 mm gypsum board GKF
2	82	48 (~50[1])	0,26	2,75	0,34	F 30*	Roofing: Concrete tiles *Underside and fire resistance as in 1a – c
3	64	44 (~46[1])	0,26	2,75	0,34	F 30*	Roofing: Clay tiles, hollow tiles *Underside and fire resistance as in 1a – c
4	73	47 (~49[1])	0,26	2,75	0,34	F 30*	Roofing: Clay tiles, corrugated tiles *Underside and fire resistance as in 1a – c
5	65	50 (~52[1])	0,26	2,75	0,34	F 30*	Roofing: Corrugated asbestos-cement panels *Underside and fire resistance as in 1a – c

[1] Improved because of additional gypsum board

* See also *Dachatlas*, Institut für Internationale Architectur-Dokumentation GmbH, Munich, 1975.

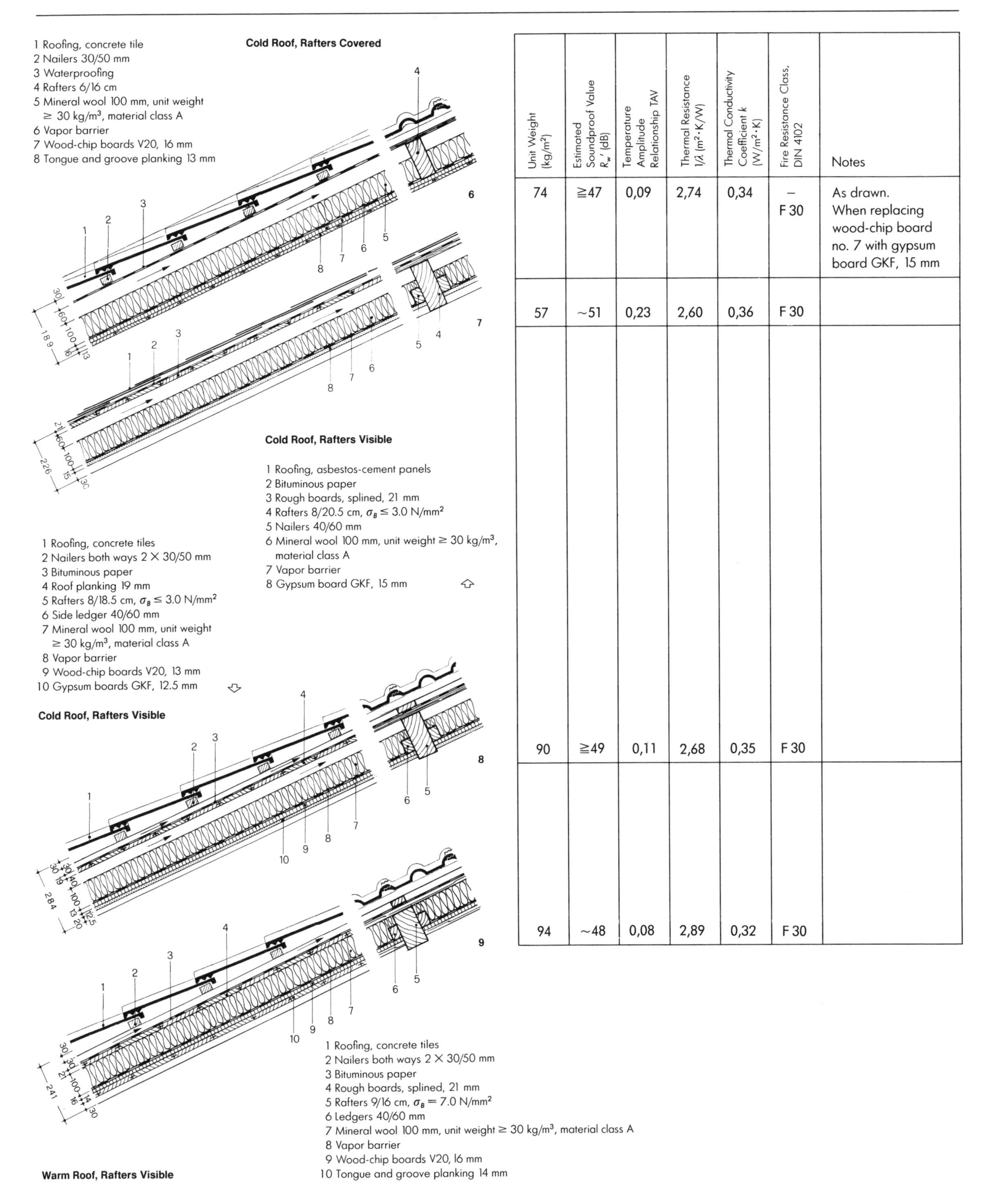

Cold Roof, Rafters Covered

1 Roofing, concrete tile
2 Nailers 30/50 mm
3 Waterproofing
4 Rafters 6/16 cm
5 Mineral wool 100 mm, unit weight ≥ 30 kg/m³, material class A
6 Vapor barrier
7 Wood-chip boards V20, 16 mm
8 Tongue and groove planking 13 mm

Cold Roof, Rafters Visible

1 Roofing, asbestos-cement panels
2 Bituminous paper
3 Rough boards, splined, 21 mm
4 Rafters 8/20.5 cm, $\sigma_B \leq 3.0$ N/mm²
5 Nailers 40/60 mm
6 Mineral wool 100 mm, unit weight ≥ 30 kg/m³, material class A
7 Vapor barrier
8 Gypsum board GKF, 15 mm

Cold Roof, Rafters Visible

1 Roofing, concrete tiles
2 Nailers both ways 2 × 30/50 mm
3 Bituminous paper
4 Roof planking 19 mm
5 Rafters 8/18.5 cm, $\sigma_B \leq 3.0$ N/mm²
6 Side ledger 40/60 mm
7 Mineral wool 100 mm, unit weight ≥ 30 kg/m³, material class A
8 Vapor barrier
9 Wood-chip boards V20, 13 mm
10 Gypsum boards GKF, 12.5 mm

Warm Roof, Rafters Visible

1 Roofing, concrete tiles
2 Nailers both ways 2 × 30/50 mm
3 Bituminous paper
4 Rough boards, splined, 21 mm
5 Rafters 9/16 cm, $\sigma_B = 7.0$ N/mm²
6 Ledgers 40/60 mm
7 Mineral wool 100 mm, unit weight ≥ 30 kg/m³, material class A
8 Vapor barrier
9 Wood-chip boards V20, 16 mm
10 Tongue and groove planking 14 mm

Unit Weight (kg/m²)	Estimated Soundproof Value R_w' (dB)	Temperature Amplitude Relationship TAV	Thermal Resistance $1/\Lambda$ (m²·K/W)	Thermal Conductivity Coefficient k (W/m²·K)	Fire Resistance Class, DIN 4102	Notes
74	≧47	0,09	2,74	0,34	– F 30	As drawn. When replacing wood-chip board no. 7 with gypsum board GKF, 15 mm
57	~51	0,23	2,60	0,36	F 30	
90	≧49	0,11	2,68	0,35	F 30	
94	~48	0,08	2,89	0,32	F 30	

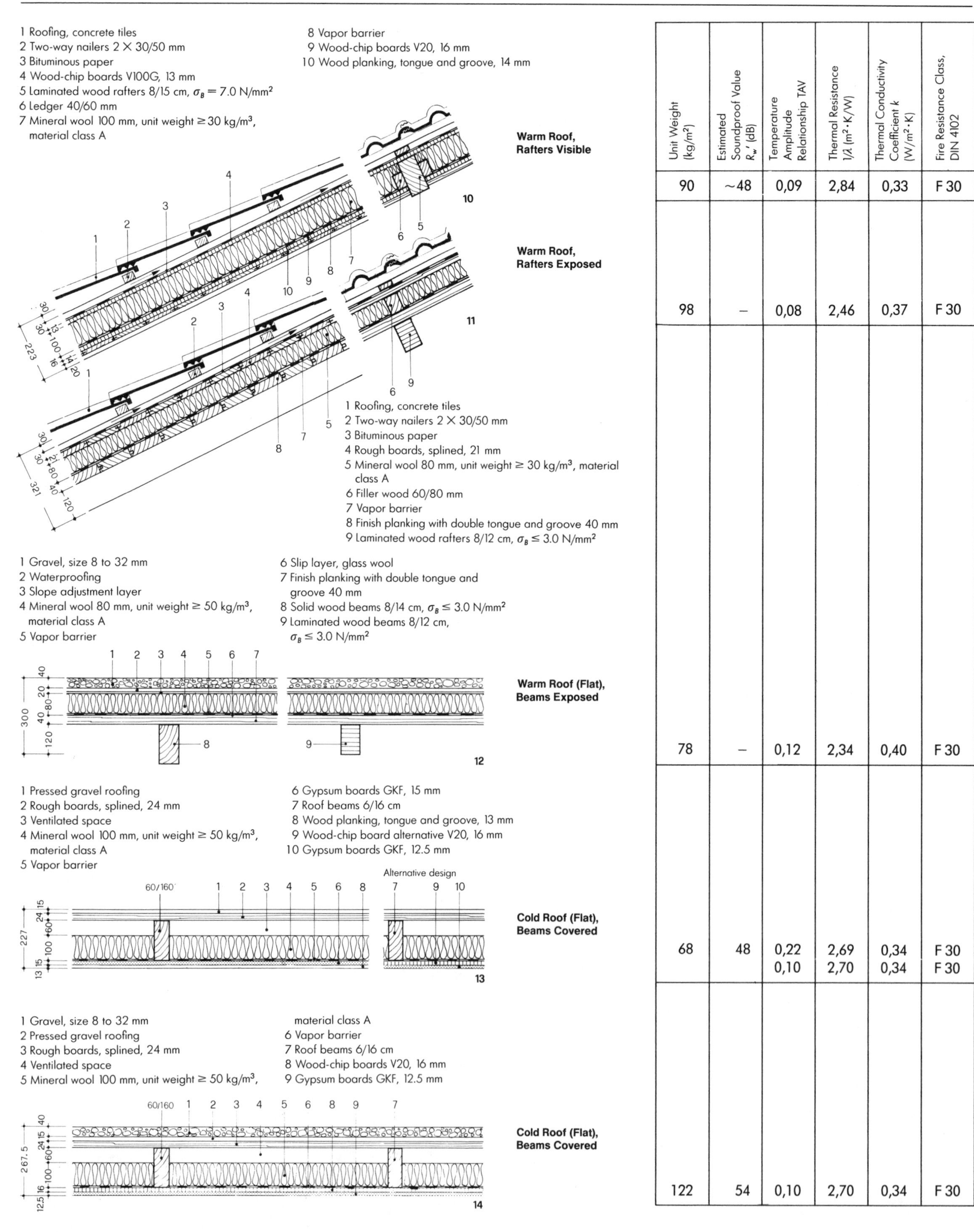

10 – Warm Roof, Rafters Visible

1 Roofing, concrete tiles
2 Two-way nailers 2 × 30/50 mm
3 Bituminous paper
4 Wood-chip boards V100G, 13 mm
5 Laminated wood rafters 8/15 cm, $\sigma_B = 7.0$ N/mm²
6 Ledger 40/60 mm
7 Mineral wool 100 mm, unit weight ≥ 30 kg/m³, material class A
8 Vapor barrier
9 Wood-chip boards V20, 16 mm
10 Wood planking, tongue and groove, 14 mm

11 – Warm Roof, Rafters Exposed

1 Roofing, concrete tiles
2 Two-way nailers 2 × 30/50 mm
3 Bituminous paper
4 Rough boards, splined, 21 mm
5 Mineral wool 80 mm, unit weight ≥ 30 kg/m³, material class A
6 Filler wood 60/80 mm
7 Vapor barrier
8 Finish planking with double tongue and groove 40 mm
9 Laminated wood rafters 8/12 cm, $\sigma_B \leq 3.0$ N/mm²

12 – Warm Roof (Flat), Beams Exposed

1 Gravel, size 8 to 32 mm
2 Waterproofing
3 Slope adjustment layer
4 Mineral wool 80 mm, unit weight ≥ 50 kg/m³, material class A
5 Vapor barrier
6 Slip layer, glass wool
7 Finish planking with double tongue and groove 40 mm
8 Solid wood beams 8/14 cm, $\sigma_B \leq 3.0$ N/mm²
9 Laminated wood beams 8/12 cm, $\sigma_B \leq 3.0$ N/mm²

13 – Cold Roof (Flat), Beams Covered

1 Pressed gravel roofing
2 Rough boards, splined, 24 mm
3 Ventilated space
4 Mineral wool 100 mm, unit weight ≥ 50 kg/m³, material class A
5 Vapor barrier
6 Gypsum boards GKF, 15 mm
7 Roof beams 6/16 cm
8 Wood planking, tongue and groove, 13 mm
9 Wood-chip board alternative V20, 16 mm
10 Gypsum boards GKF, 12.5 mm

14 – Cold Roof (Flat), Beams Covered

1 Gravel, size 8 to 32 mm
2 Pressed gravel roofing
3 Rough boards, splined, 24 mm
4 Ventilated space
5 Mineral wool 100 mm, unit weight ≥ 50 kg/m³, material class A
6 Vapor barrier
7 Roof beams 6/16 cm
8 Wood-chip boards V20, 16 mm
9 Gypsum boards GKF, 12.5 mm

Construction	Unit Weight (kg/m²)	Estimated Soundproof Value R_w' (dB)	Temperature Amplitude Relationship TAV	Thermal Resistance $1/\Lambda$ (m²·K/W)	Thermal Conductivity Coefficient k (W/m²·K)	Fire Resistance Class, DIN 4102
10 Warm Roof, Rafters Visible	90	~48	0,09	2,84	0,33	F 30
11 Warm Roof, Rafters Exposed	98	–	0,08	2,46	0,37	F 30
12 Warm Roof (Flat), Beams Exposed	78	–	0,12	2,34	0,40	F 30
13 Cold Roof (Flat), Beams Covered	68	48	0,22 0,10	2,69 2,70	0,34 0,34	F 30 F 30
14 Cold Roof (Flat), Beams Covered	122	54	0,10	2,70	0,34	F 30

Exterior Walls

Design and Execution

The design of exterior walls of wood and wood products follows DIN 1052, "Timber Structures, Design and Execution." Loads are given in DIN 1055, "Loads for Buildings," and in the appropriate parts of DIN 4103, "Light Partitions."

Thermal Insulation

The minimum requirements for thermal insulation of exterior walls are given in DIN 4108, "Insulation of Buildings," and the ordinance of November 1977 regarding energy saving, which is incorporated in the new edition of the code.

Soundproofing

The requirements for soundproofing of exterior walls are contained in the "Regulations for Protection against Exterior Noise," issued as a supplement to DIN 4109, "Soundproofing in Buildings." There are all together six noise level categories with appropriate minimum soundproofing requirements, depending on the location of the building and the level of outside noise.

In the vicinity of airports the minimum soundproofing requirements for walls and roof must conform by law to protection zones I and II.

Fire Protection

Fire protection guidelines for walls are contained in local regulations. Basic requirements are shown in DIN 4102, "Fire Resistance of Building Materials and Components."

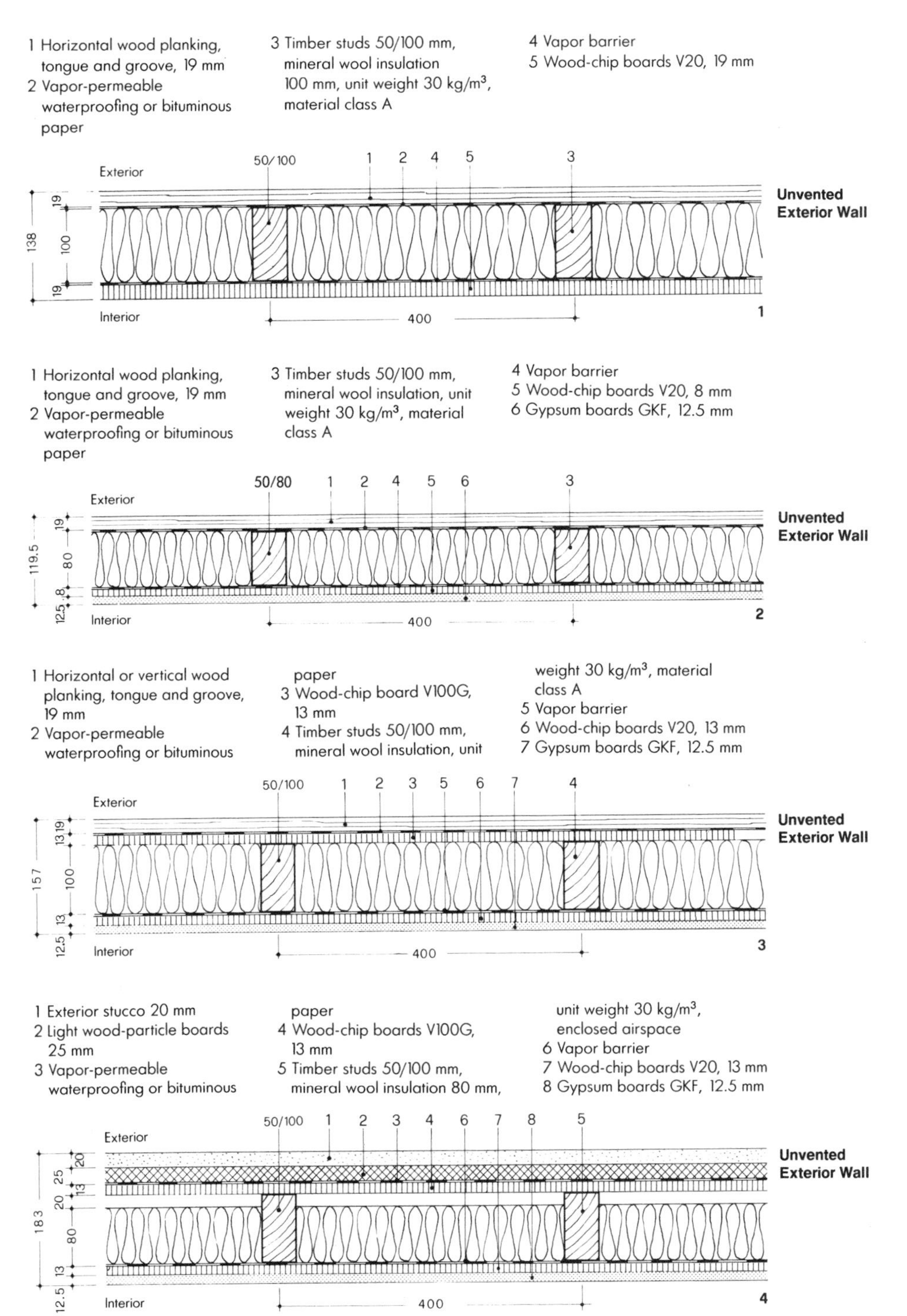

Wall	Unit Weight (kg/m²)	Estimated Soundproof Value R'_w (dB)	Temperature Amplitude Relationship TAV	Thermal Resistance $1/\Lambda$ (m²·K/W)	Thermal Conductivity Coefficient k (W/m²·K)	Fire Resistance Class, DIN 4102*[1]
1	31	38	0,17	2,80	0,46	F 30
2	33	42	0,23	2,44	0,38	F 30
3	46	44	0,14	2,92	0,33	F 30
4	80	50	0,15	2,69	0,35	F 30

*[1] Stud compression stress $\sigma_{D\,max} \leq 2.5$ N/mm² without buckling

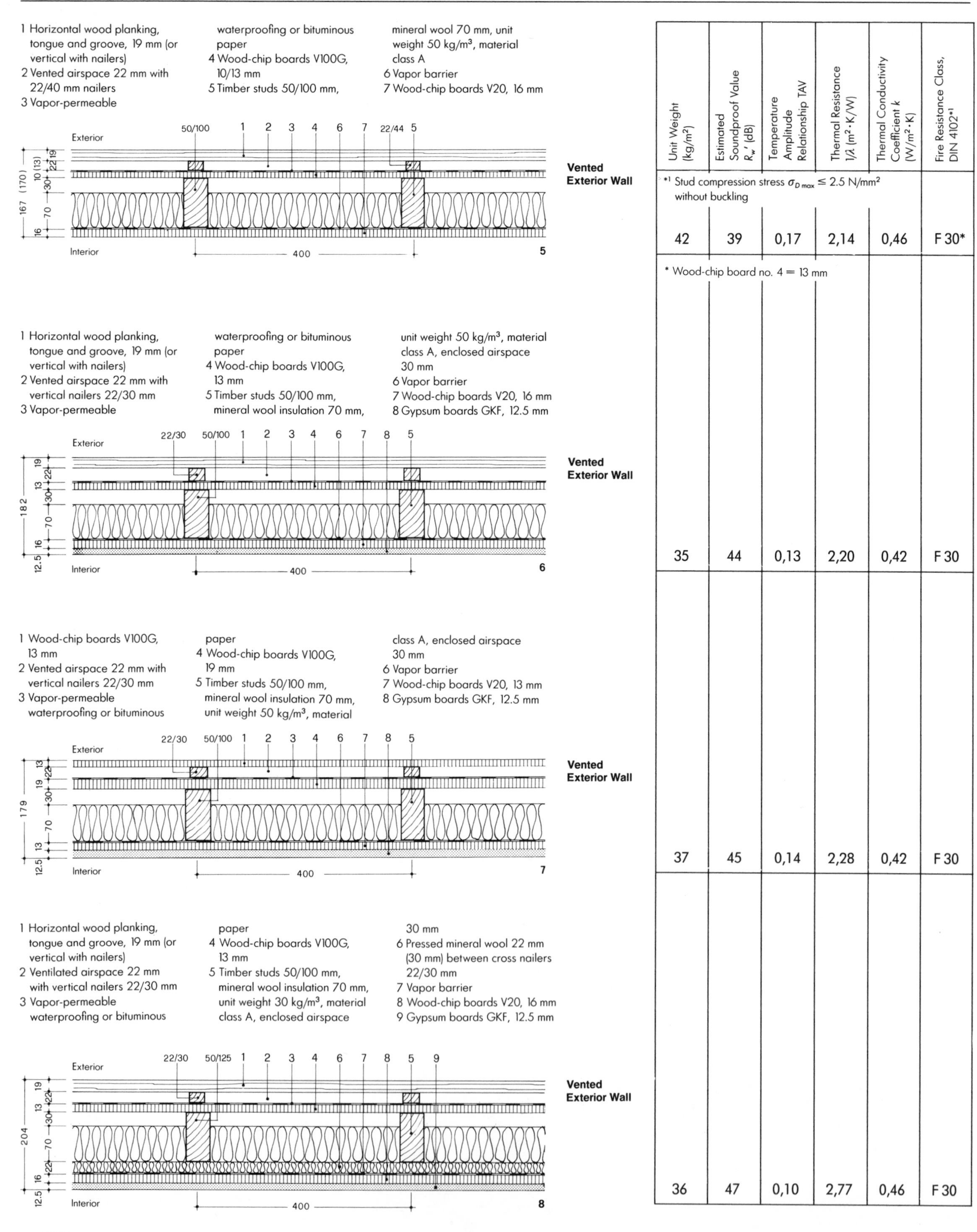

5 — Vented Exterior Wall

1 Horizontal wood planking, tongue and groove, 19 mm (or vertical with nailers)
2 Vented airspace 22 mm with 22/40 mm nailers
3 Vapor-permeable waterproofing or bituminous paper
4 Wood-chip boards V100G, 10/13 mm
5 Timber studs 50/100 mm, mineral wool 70 mm, unit weight 50 kg/m³, material class A
6 Vapor barrier
7 Wood-chip boards V20, 16 mm

6 — Vented Exterior Wall

1 Horizontal wood planking, tongue and groove, 19 mm (or vertical with nailers)
2 Vented airspace 22 mm with vertical nailers 22/30 mm
3 Vapor-permeable waterproofing or bituminous paper
4 Wood-chip boards V100G, 13 mm
5 Timber studs 50/100 mm, mineral wool insulation 70 mm, unit weight 50 kg/m³, material class A, enclosed airspace 30 mm
6 Vapor barrier
7 Wood-chip boards V20, 16 mm
8 Gypsum boards GKF, 12.5 mm

7 — Vented Exterior Wall

1 Wood-chip boards V100G, 13 mm
2 Vented airspace 22 mm with vertical nailers 22/30 mm
3 Vapor-permeable waterproofing or bituminous paper
4 Wood-chip boards V100G, 19 mm
5 Timber studs 50/100 mm, mineral wool insulation 70 mm, unit weight 50 kg/m³, material class A, enclosed airspace 30 mm
6 Vapor barrier
7 Wood-chip boards V20, 13 mm
8 Gypsum boards GKF, 12.5 mm

8 — Vented Exterior Wall

1 Horizontal wood planking, tongue and groove, 19 mm (or vertical with nailers)
2 Ventilated airspace 22 mm with vertical nailers 22/30 mm
3 Vapor-permeable waterproofing or bituminous paper
4 Wood-chip boards V100G, 13 mm
5 Timber studs 50/100 mm, mineral wool insulation 70 mm, unit weight 30 kg/m³, material class A, enclosed airspace 30 mm
6 Pressed mineral wool 22 mm (30 mm) between cross nailers 22/30 mm
7 Vapor barrier
8 Wood-chip boards V20, 16 mm
9 Gypsum boards GKF, 12.5 mm

No.	Unit Weight (kg/m²)	Estimated Soundproof Value R_w' (dB)	Temperature Amplitude Relationship TAV	Thermal Resistance $1/\Lambda$ (m²·K/W)	Thermal Conductivity Coefficient k (W/m²·K)	Fire Resistance Class, DIN 4102*¹
5	42	39	0,17	2,14	0,46	F 30*
6	35	44	0,13	2,20	0,42	F 30
7	37	45	0,14	2,28	0,42	F 30
8	36	47	0,10	2,77	0,46	F 30

*¹ Stud compression stress $\sigma_{D\,max} \leq 2.5$ N/mm² without buckling

* Wood-chip board no. 4 = 13 mm

Timber Beam Floors

Design and Execution

The structural design is based on DIN 1052, "Timber Structures, Design and Execution." Loads are given in DIN 1055, "Loads in Buildings."

Sometimes the dimensioning of floor beams is governed by the minimum cross section requirements for fire protection instead of structural requirements (see tables).

Thermal Insulation

The requirements for thermal insulation are given in DIN 4108, "Insulation for Buildings."

Floors which are also exterior, such as over open carports, must in addition comply with the 1977 ordinance regarding energy saving and DIN 4108 (see section on exterior walls).

Soundproofing

Minimum requirements and recommendations for soundproofing of residential floors and floors in buildings that need adequate soundproofing, such as offices and schools, are contained in DIN 4109, "Soundproofing in Buildings."

If the timber decks are at the same time facing the exterior, the "Regulations for Protection against Outside Noise" give the categories of minimum soundproofing requirements in relation to the levels of area noise.

In the vicinity of airports the minimum soundproofing requirements for timber floors are governed by protection zones I and II in accordance with the law for protection against aircraft noise.

Fire Protection

Fire protection of timber floors should be designed and executed according to DIN 4102, "Fire Resistance of Building Materials and Components." Given for the first time in part 4 of this code are the relationships between cross-sectional dimensions, degrees of stress, and fire resistance.

Table 1a. Minimum Dimensions of Bare Wood Beams

Fire Resistance Class	F 30				F 60			
Exposure to Fire	Three-Sided		Four-Sided		Three-Sided		Four-Sided	
Bending stress σ_B, N/mm²	min b (mm)	min h (mm)	min b (mm)	min h (mm)	min b (mm)	min h (mm)	min b (mm)	min h (mm)
13	150	260	160	300	300	520	320	600
10	120	200	130	240	240	400	260	480
7	90	160	100	200	200	320	220	400
3	80	140	90	180	180	240	200	320

Interpolate for intermediate values of bending stresses.

Table 1b. Minimum Dimensions of Bare Laminated Wood Girders or Beams

Fire Resistance Class	F 30				F 60			
Fire Exposure	Three-Sided		Four-Sided		Three-Sided		Four-Sided	
Bending stress σ_B, N/mm²	min b (mm)	min h (mm)	min b (mm)	min h (mm)	min b (mm)	min h (mm)	min b (mm)	min h (mm)
14	140	260	150	310	280	520	300	620
11	110	200	120	250	220	400	240	500
7	80	150	90	190	160	300	180	380
3	80	120	80	160	140	220	160	300

Interpolate for intermediate values of bending stresses.

1 Concrete layer 50 mm
2 Roofing paper
3 Soundproofing panels 30/25 mm
4 Wood-chip boards 40 mm
5 Mineral wool 50 mm
6 Timber ledgers 24/48 mm
7 Gypsum board GKF, 12.5 mm
8 Timber beams 12/20 cm
9 Alternative: laminated wood beams 11/20 cm

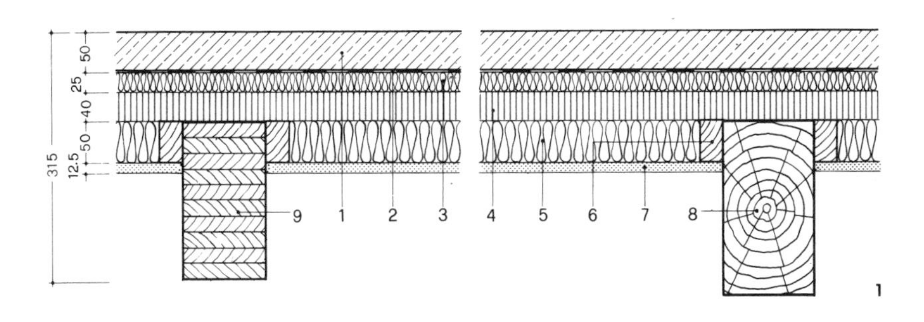

* For design and construction see DIN 4102, part 4. For fully exposed beams Tables 1a and b give the minimum cross sections.

Degree of Air Noise Protection LSM (dB)	Degree of Footstep Noise Protection TSM (dB)	Unit Weight (kg/m²)	Thermal Resistance $1/\Lambda$ (m² · K/W)	Fire Resistance Class, DIN 4102*	Notes
+ 8	+ 13*	180	2,25	F 30	* With carpet

1 Wood-chip boards, tongue and groove, 25 mm
2 Soundproofing boards 30/25 mm
3 Lightweight concrete blocks 60 mm
4 Cold bitumen
5 Wood planking 28 mm
6 Wood beams 12/20 cm, spaced at 60 cm
7 Alternative: laminated wood beams 11/20 cm

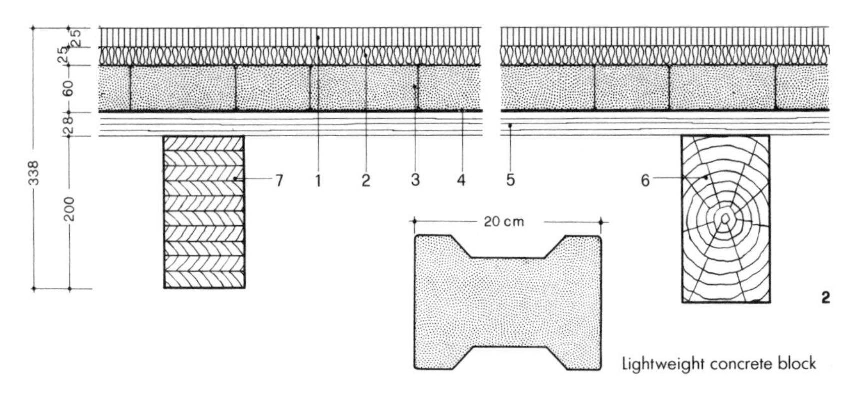

1 Wood-chip boards 25 mm
2 Mineral wool 40 mm
3 Wood nailers
4 Sand 30 mm
5 Soundproofing strips
6 Wood-chip boards 40 mm
7 Wood beams 12/20 cm, spaced at 60 cm
8 Alternative: laminated wood beams 11/20 cm

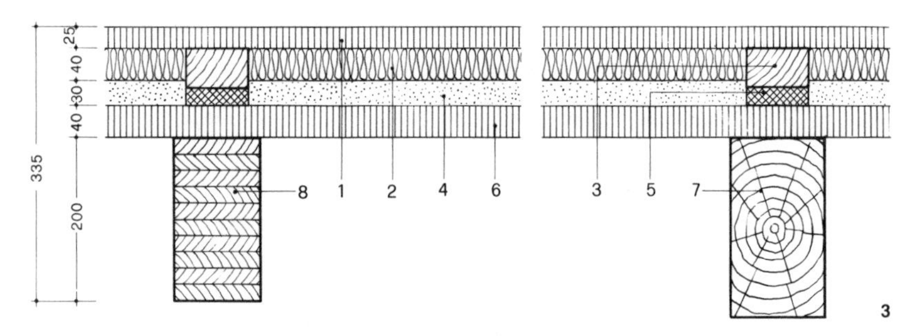

1 Wood-chip boards 25 mm
2 Mineral wool panels 30/25 mm
3 Concrete blocks 50 mm, 30 × 30 cm
4 Vapor barrier in cold bitumen bed
5 Tongue and groove planking 35 mm
6 Wood beams 12/20 cm, spaced at 60 cm
7 Alternative: laminated wood beams 11/20 cm

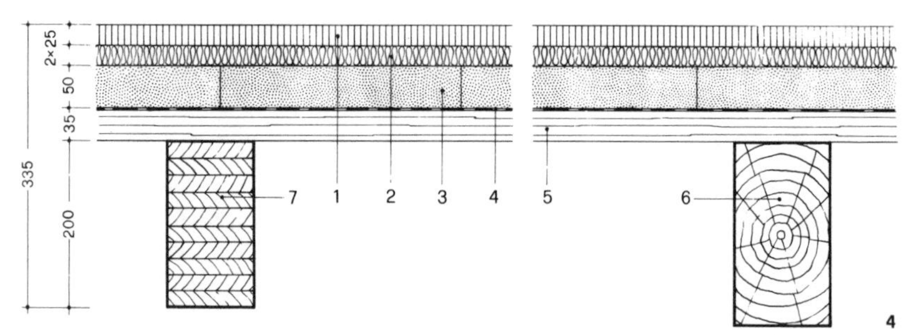

1 Wood-chip boards, tongue and groove, 25 mm
2 Soundproofing panels 30/25 mm
3 Concrete blocks 40 mm, 30 × 30 cm
4 Bitumen
5 Wood-chip boards 38 mm
6 Mineral wool 60 mm
7 Wood ledgers 30/50 mm
8 Gypsum boards GKF, 12.5 mm
9 Finish planking 13 mm
10 Wood beams 12/20 cm, spaced at 60 cm
11 Alternative: laminated wood beams 11/20 cm

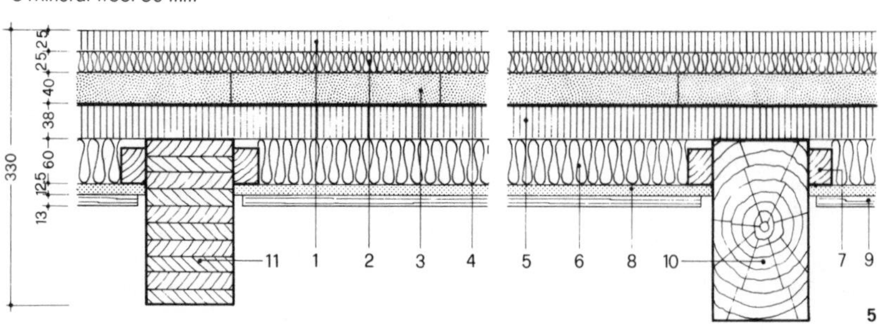

Degree of Air Noise Protection LSM (dB)	Degree of Footstep Noise Protection TSM (dB)	Unit Weight (kg/m²)	Thermal Resistance 1/λ (m²·K/W)	Fire Resistance Class, DIN 4102*	Notes
+ 13	+ 17	195	1,28	F 30*	* Wood planking ≥ 50 mm
+ 6	+ 13*1	120	1,76	F 30*2	*1 With carpet *2 Wood-chip board joints covered with moldings
+ 8	+ 13*1	175	1,33	F 30*2	*1 With carpet *2 Wood planking ≥ 50 mm
+ 15	+ 13	200	2,65	F 30	

* For design and construction see DIN 4102, part 4. For exposed beams see minimum cross sections in Tables 1a and b.

1 Wood-chip boards 25 mm
2 Soundproofing panels 25 mm
3 Concrete blocks 40 mm
4 Wood-chip boards 40 mm
5 Mineral wool 60 mm
6 Finish planking 13 mm
7 Wood beams 12/20 cm
8 Alternative: laminated wood beams 11/20 cm

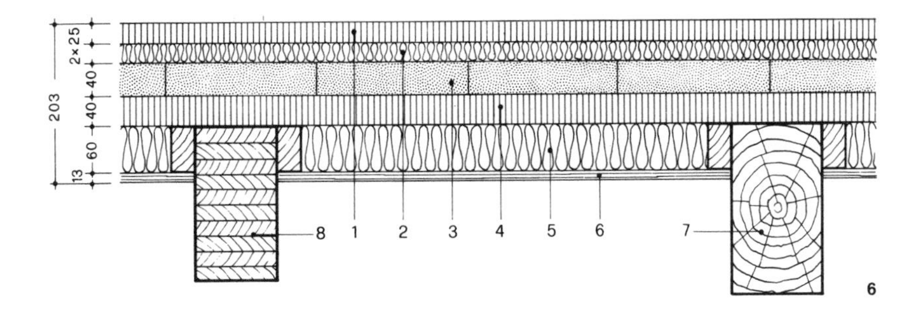

6

1 Clay tiles 19 mm
2 Floor heating 30 mm
3 Soundproofing panels 30 mm
4 Wood-chip boards 16 mm
5 Mineral wool 50 mm
6 Wood beams 8/18 cm
7 Metal extrusion ceiling support 20 mm
8 Gypsum board GKF, 12.5 mm

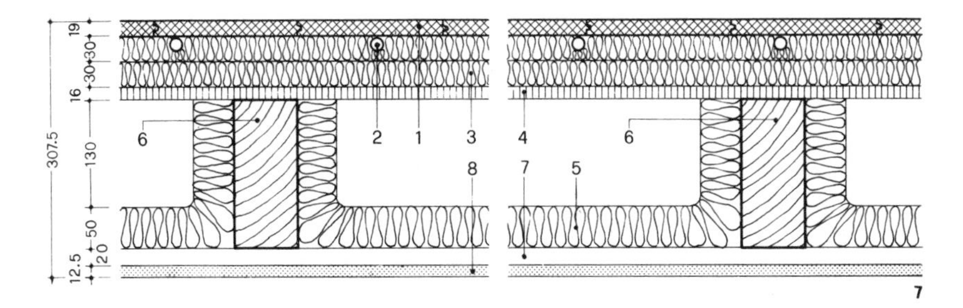

7

Alternatives of suspended ceiling

Metal channel

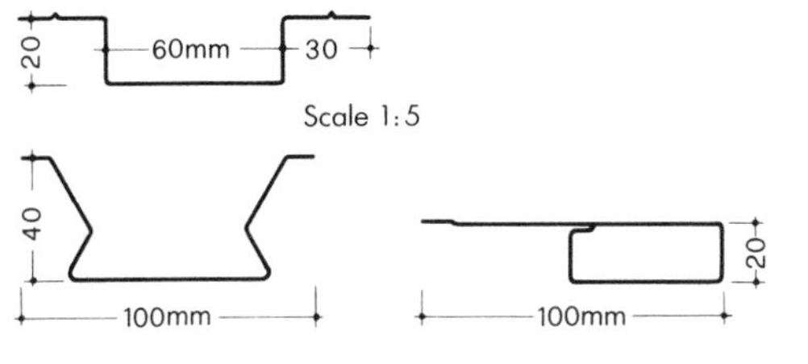

Metal extrusion

100mm

20

Metal tube

Scale 1:2

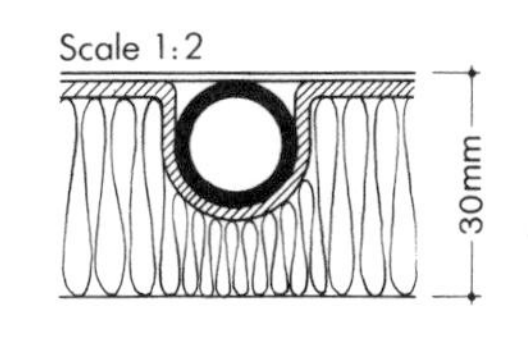

Detail of floor heating

1 Wood-chip boards 22 mm
2 Mineral wool panels 15/10 mm
3 Wood nailers 40/60 mm
4 Felt mat strips
5 Sand fill 30 mm
6 Wood-chip boards 16 mm
7 Wood beams 8/18 cm
8 Mineral wool 50 mm
9 Metal extrusion
10 Cross nailers 24/48 mm
11 Gypsum boards GKF, 2 × 12.5 mm

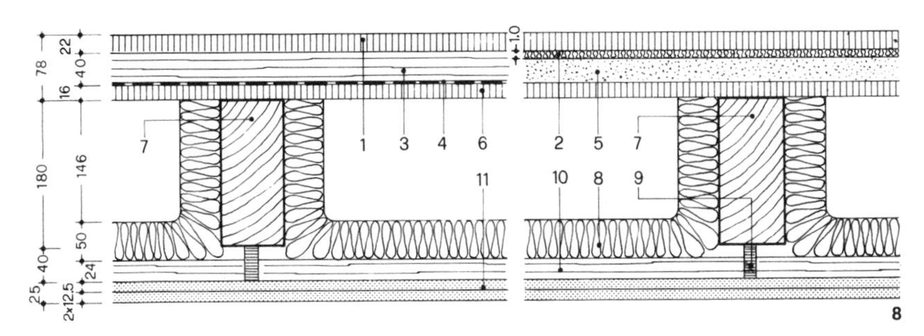

8

Degree of Air Noise Protection LSM (dB)	Degree of Footstep Noise Protection TSM (dB)	Unit Weight (kg/m²)	Thermal Resistance 1/λ (m²·K/W)	Fire Resistance Class, DIN 4102*	Notes
+ 11	+ 12*1	163	2,59	F 30	*1 A PVC or carpet flooring is needed to achieve minimum requirements.
+ 14	+ 14	115	3,25	F 30	
+ 16	+ 28	140	2,27	F 30	

* For design and construction see DIN 4102, part 4. For exposed beams see minimum cross sections in Tables 1a and b.

1 Concrete floor 50 mm
2 Mineral fiber panels 30/25 mm
3 Wood-chip boards 16 mm
4 Wood beams 8/18 cm
5 Mineral wool 50 mm
6 Metal extrusion 20 mm
7 Gypsum boards GKF, 2 × 12.5 mm

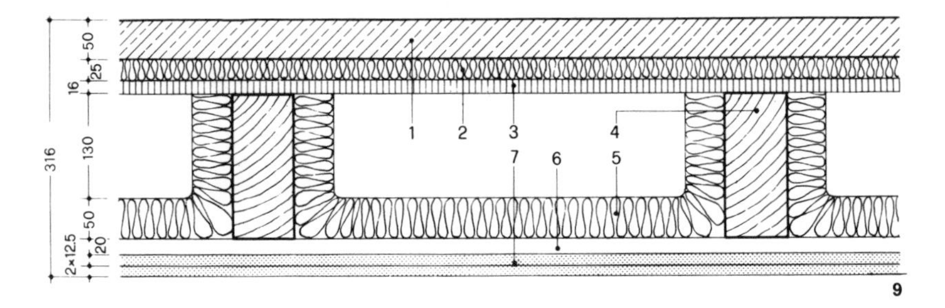
9

1 Hardwood floor 10 mm
2 Wood-chip boards 25 mm
3 Mineral fiber panels 30 mm
4 Concrete blocks 40 mm, 30 × 30 cm
5 Felt
6 Wood-chip boards 38 mm
7 Laminated wood beam
8 Alternative: wood beams (or 7 + 8 according to structural design)
9 Mineral wool 60 mm
10 Metal extrusion
11 Cross nailers 24/48 mm
12 Gypsum board GKF, 12.5 mm

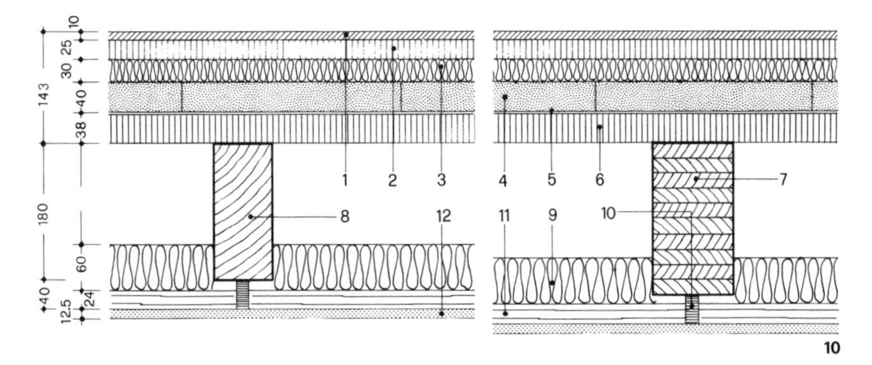
10

1 Wood-chip boards V20, 25 mm
2 Wood beams 8/18 cm
3 Mineral wool 50 mm
4 Metal extrusion 20 mm
5 Gypsum board GKF, 2 × 12.5 mm

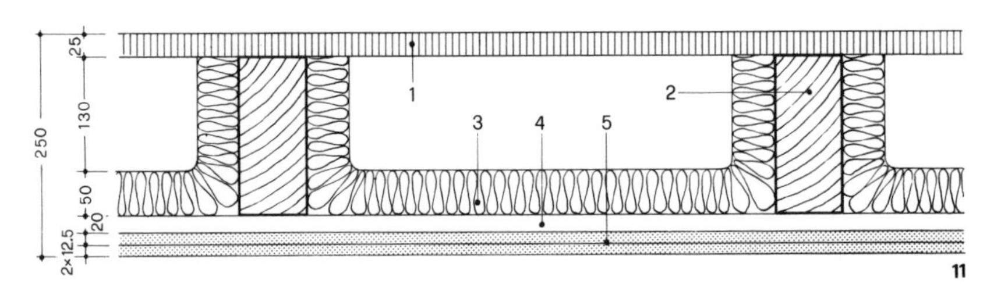
11

1 Tile flooring 40 mm
2 Soft particle boards 10 mm
3 Wood-chip boards 16 cm
4 Wood beams 18 cm
5 Mineral wool 50 mm
6 Metal extrusion 20 mm
7 Gypsum board GKF, 12.5 mm

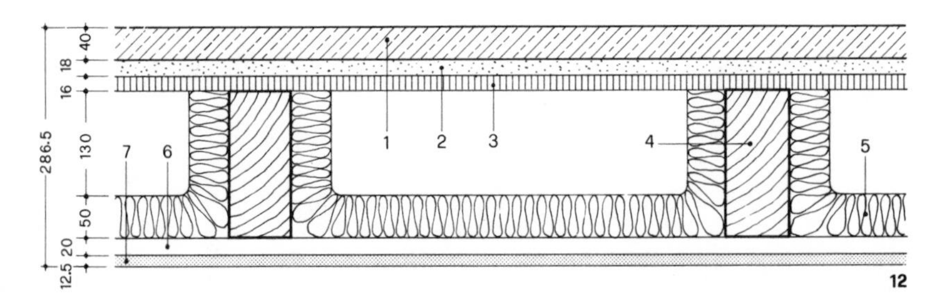
12

Degree of Air Noise Protection LSM (dB)	Degree of Footstep Noise Protection TSM (dB)	Unit Weight (kg/m²)	Thermal Resistance 1/Λ (m²·K/W)	Fire Resistance Class, DIN 4102*	Notes
+ 15	+ 21	175	2,39	F 30	
+ 8	+ 26*1	200	3,00	F 30	*1 With finished hardwood flooring
+ 9	+ 8*1	75	1,85	F 30*2	*1 With carpeting +22 dB, with felt pad +13 dB *2 Fire from underside
+ 12	+ 10*1	81	1,90	F 30	*1 With carpeting +21 dB, with felt pad +13 dB

* For design and construction see DIN 4102, part 4. For exposed beams see maximum cross sections in Tables 1a and b.

Interior Partitions

Design and Execution

The design of load-bearing and non-load-bearing partitions of wood and wood products follows DIN 1052, "Timber Structures, Design and Execution," as well as DIN 4103, "Light Partitions."

Thermal Insulation

Interior partitions generally do not have to comply with any thermal insulating requirements. The only exceptions are partitions between apartments, separate workrooms, and stairs. In such cases the minimum requirements are those of DIN 4108, "Thermal Insulation in Buildings."

Soundproofing

Minimum requirements for soundproofing, and also the recommendation for improved soundproofing are given in DIN 4109, "Soundproofing in Buildings." They depend on the use of the building and the type of partitions.

Fireproofing

Fire protection requirements for interior partitions, if they are given, are contained in various local codes. The basic design and execution are detailed in DIN 4102, "Fire Resistance of Building Materials and Components."

1 Gypsum boards GKF, 12.5 mm, joints on centerline of studs
2 Mineral wool 40 mm, unit weight 40 kg/m³, material class A
3 Enclosed airspace 40 mm
4 Wood studs 80/60 mm
5 Gypsum boards GKF, 12.5 mm, joints on centerline of studs

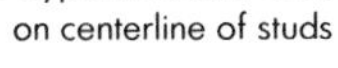

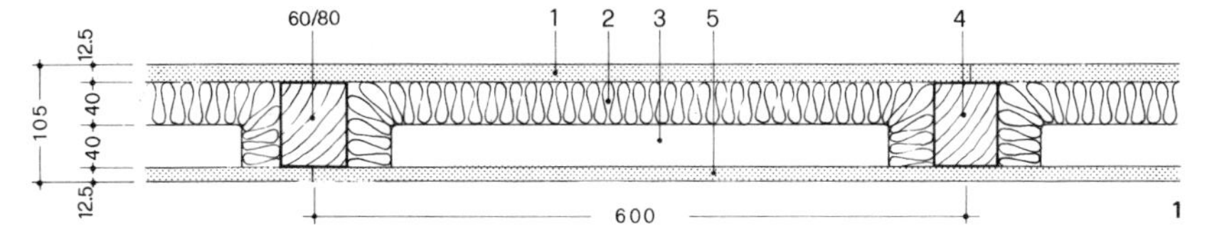

Interior Partition, Load-Bearing or Non-Load-Bearing, Room Enclosure

1 Finish planking 19 mm, tongue and groove, horizontal
2 Mineral wool 100 mm
3 Wood studs 100/50 mm
4 Wood-chip boards V20, 13 mm

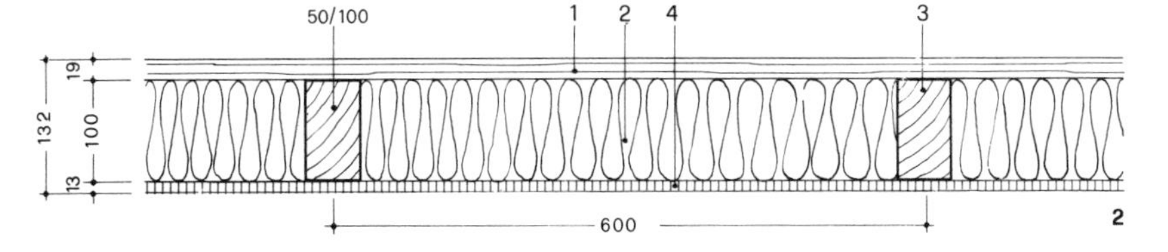

Interior Partition, Load-Bearing or Non-Load-Bearing, Room Enclosure

1 Gypsum boards GKF, 15 mm, joints on centerline of studs
2 Mineral wool 80 mm, unit weight ≥30 kg/m³, material class A
3 Wood studs 80/60 mm
4 Gypsum boards GKF, 15 mm, joints on centerline of studs

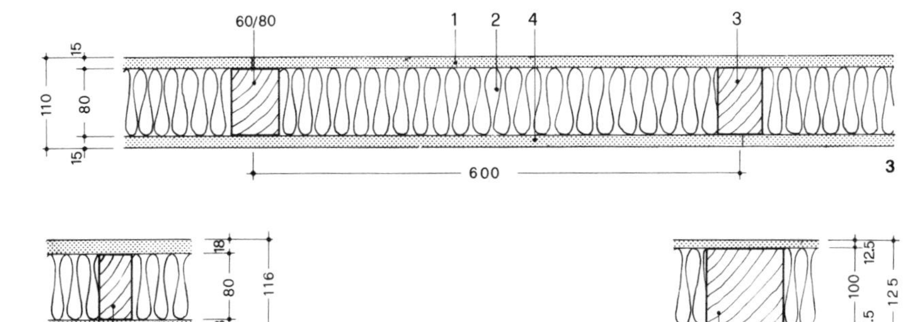

Interior Partition, Load-Bearing or Non-Load-Bearing, Not for Room Enclosure

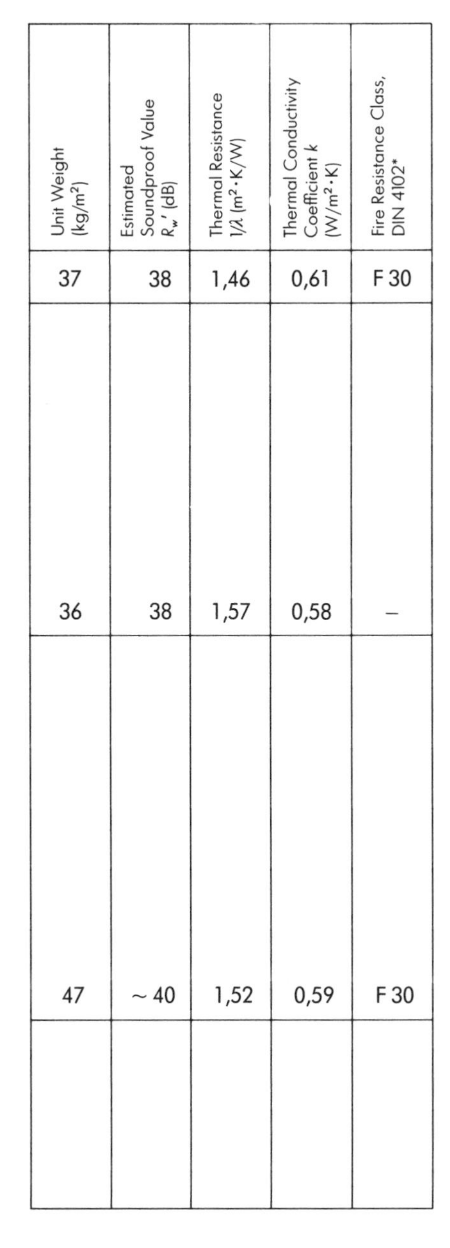

Unit Weight (kg/m²)	Estimated Soundproof Value R_w' (dB)	Thermal Resistance $1/\lambda$ (m²·K/W)	Thermal Conductivity Coefficient k (W/m²·K)	Fire Resistance Class, DIN 4102*
37	38	1,46	0,61	F 30
36	38	1,57	0,58	–
47	~ 40	1,52	0,59	F 30

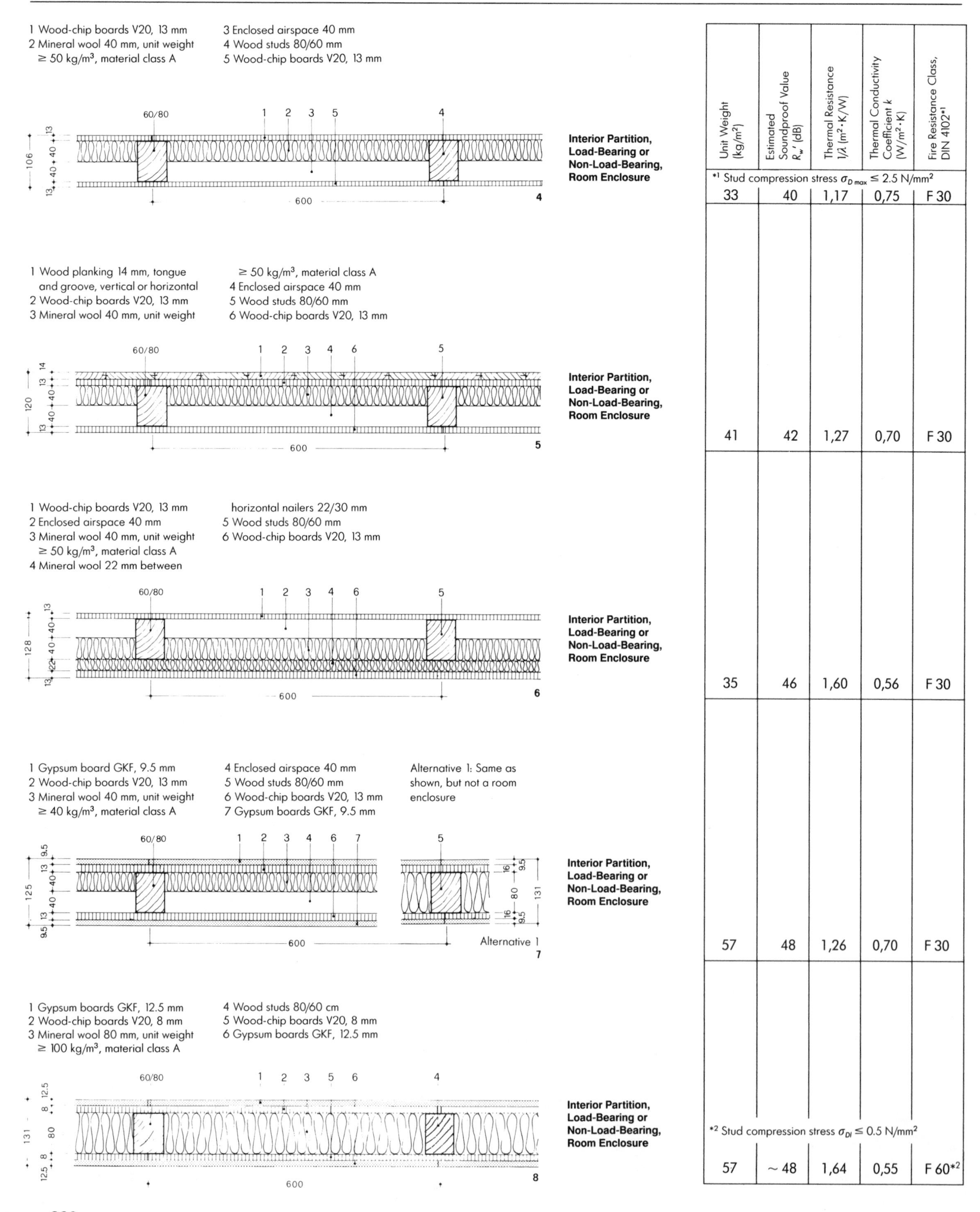

1 Wood-chip boards V20, 13 mm
2 Mineral wool 40 mm, unit weight ≥ 50 kg/m³, material class A
3 Enclosed airspace 40 mm
4 Wood studs 80/60 mm
5 Wood-chip boards V20, 13 mm

Interior Partition, Load-Bearing or Non-Load-Bearing, Room Enclosure

4

1 Wood planking 14 mm, tongue and groove, vertical or horizontal
2 Wood-chip boards V20, 13 mm
3 Mineral wool 40 mm, unit weight ≥ 50 kg/m³, material class A
4 Enclosed airspace 40 mm
5 Wood studs 80/60 mm
6 Wood-chip boards V20, 13 mm

Interior Partition, Load-Bearing or Non-Load-Bearing, Room Enclosure

5

1 Wood-chip boards V20, 13 mm
2 Enclosed airspace 40 mm
3 Mineral wool 40 mm, unit weight ≥ 50 kg/m³, material class A
4 Mineral wool 22 mm between horizontal nailers 22/30 mm
5 Wood studs 80/60 mm
6 Wood-chip boards V20, 13 mm

Interior Partition, Load-Bearing or Non-Load-Bearing, Room Enclosure

6

1 Gypsum board GKF, 9.5 mm
2 Wood-chip boards V20, 13 mm
3 Mineral wool 40 mm, unit weight ≥ 40 kg/m³, material class A
4 Enclosed airspace 40 mm
5 Wood studs 80/60 mm
6 Wood-chip boards V20, 13 mm
7 Gypsum boards GKF, 9.5 mm

Alternative 1: Same as shown, but not a room enclosure

Interior Partition, Load-Bearing or Non-Load-Bearing, Room Enclosure

Alternative 1

7

1 Gypsum boards GKF, 12.5 mm
2 Wood-chip boards V20, 8 mm
3 Mineral wool 80 mm, unit weight ≥ 100 kg/m³, material class A
4 Wood studs 80/60 cm
5 Wood-chip boards V20, 8 mm
6 Gypsum boards GKF, 12.5 mm

Interior Partition, Load-Bearing or Non-Load-Bearing, Room Enclosure

8

Fig.	Unit Weight (kg/m²)	Estimated Soundproof Value R_w' (dB)	Thermal Resistance $1/\lambda$ (m²·K/W)	Thermal Conductivity Coefficient k (W/m²·K)	Fire Resistance Class, DIN 4102*1
4	33	40	1,17	0,75	F 30
5	41	42	1,27	0,70	F 30
6	35	46	1,60	0,56	F 30
7	57	48	1,26	0,70	F 30
8	57	~ 48	1,64	0,55	F 60*2

*1 Stud compression stress $\sigma_{D\,max} \leq 2.5$ N/mm²

*2 Stud compression stress $\sigma_{Dl} \leq 0.5$ N/mm²

1 Wood-chip boards V20, 13 mm
2 Porous wood-particle boards 14 mm
3 Mineral wool 60 mm, unit weight ≥ 50 kg/m³, material class A
4 Enclosed airspace 20 mm
5 Wood studs 80/60 mm
6 Porous wood-particle boards 14 mm
7 Wood-chip boards V20, 13 mm

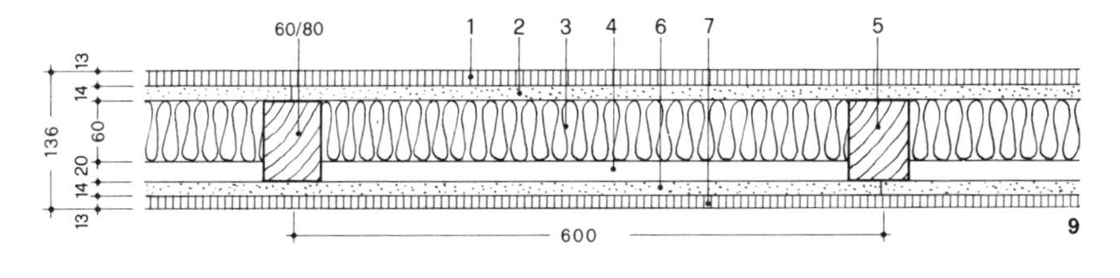

Interior Partition, Load-Bearing or Non-Load-Bearing, Room Enclosure

1 Gypsum boards GKF, 12.5 mm
2 Enclosed airspace 30 to 80 mm
3 Mineral wool 40 mm, unit weight ≥ 50 kg/m³, material class A
4 Enclosed air space 30 to 80 mm
5 Wood studs 80/60 mm, offset
6 Gypsum boards GKF, 12.5 mm

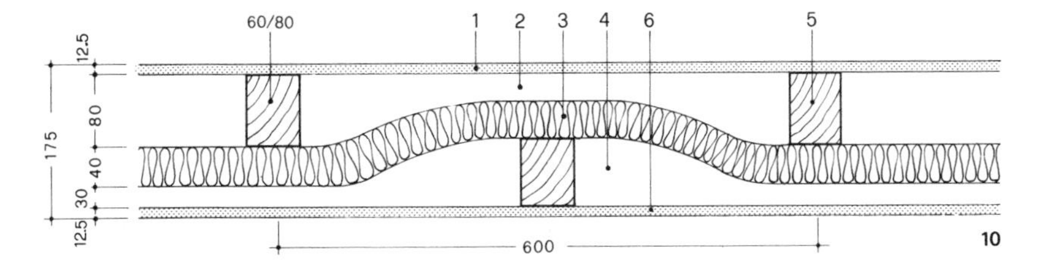

Interior Partition, Load-Bearing or Non-Load-Bearing, Room Enclosure

1 Wood-chip boards V20, 13 mm
2 Mineral wool 60 mm, unit weight ≥ 50 kg/m³, material class A
3 Enclosed airspace 20 mm
4 Separation joint 5 mm
5 Wood studs 80/60 mm, offset
6 Enclosed airspace 20 mm
7 Mineral wool 60 mm, same as 2
8 Wood-chip boards V20, 13 mm

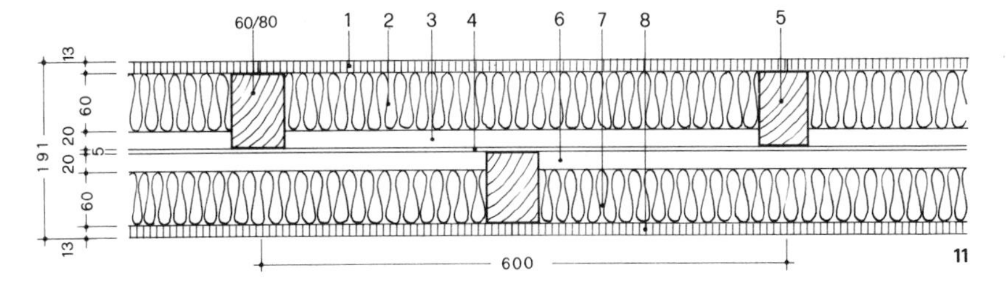

Interior Partition, Load-Bearing or Non-Load-Bearing, Room Enclosure

1 Wood-chip boards V20, 13 mm
2 Enclosed airspace 30 mm
3 Mineral wool 60 mm, unit weight ≥ 50 kg/m³, material class A
4 Mineral wool 27 mm between horizontal metal extrusions
5 Wood studs 90/60 mm
6 Gypsum boards GKF, 2 × 12.5 mm

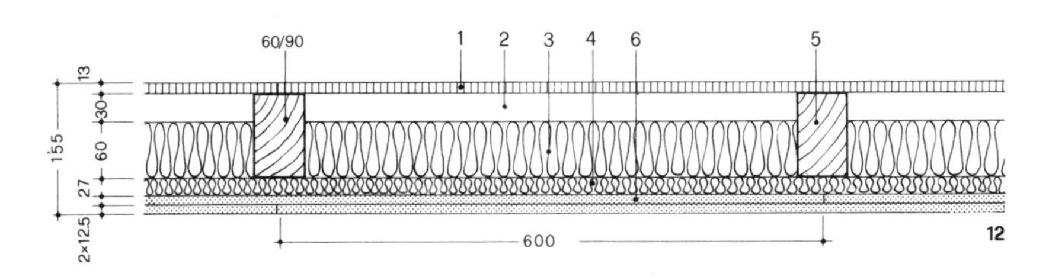

Interior Partition, Load-Bearing or Non-Load-Bearing, Room Enclosure

Unit Weight (kg/m²)	Estimated Soundproof Value R_w' (dB)	Thermal Resistance $1/\lambda$ (m²·K/W)	Thermal Conductivity Coefficient k (W/m²·K)	Fire Resistance Class, DIN 4102*¹
44	50	2,09	0,44	F 30
40	50	1,50	0,60	F 30
44	51	2,87	0,33	F 30
55	53*²	1,87	0,49	F 30

*¹ Stud compression stress $\sigma_{D\,max} \leq 2.5$ N/mm²

*² When only one GKF is used, R_w' reduces to 51 dB

Log Construction

Log buildings can be used for residential housing, especially weekend houses. In addition, they are frequently used for agricultural buildings. The criteria given for exterior walls are valid in this case, but Table I and the illustrations in this chapter give the appropriate data.

The following examples illustrate the basic designs for the use of log-type construction in agricultural buildings.

Design

Log-type buildings are designed according to DIN 1052, "Timber Structures, Design and Execution," and DIN 1055, "Loads for Buildings."

Thermal Insulation

Winter Protection

Thermal insulation has great importance in barns because of their high air humidity and the barn environment. Minimum requirements for thermal resistivity and protection of building components against surface condensation are given in DIN 18910, "Environment in Closed Barns." They depend on the weight of the walls.

It has to be noted that even exposed masonry walls should be thermally insulated in order to preferably achieve the same thermal insulation value as the timber walls above them. This will prevent future damage and result in a dry wall surface.

Insulation requirements depend on the interior climate of the stable, or ventilation, and on the temperature variations. Because of their complexity, it is more appropriate to use DIN 18910, edition 1974, as the design basis for general purposes.

Table 1. Thermal Values for Log Walls

Thickness (m)	Unit Weight (kg/m²)	Temperature Amplitude Relationship TAV	Thermal Resistance $1/\lambda$ (m² · K/W)	Thermal Conductivity Coefficient k (W/m² · K)
0,10	60	0,34	0,71	1,13
0,11	66	0,28	0,79	1,05
0,12	72	0,23	0,86	0,98
0,13	78	0,19	0,93	0,91
0,14	84	0,16	1,01	0,86
0,15	90	0,13	1,07	0,80
0,16	96	0,11	1,14	0,77
0,17	102	0,09	1,22	0,72
0,18	108	0,08	1,29	0,69

Summer Protection

In order to achieve an optimum climate for animals housed in the stalls of a stable, it is necessary to reduce temperature variations to a minimum, in addition to providing necessary ventilation. Basically, the interior temperature in the summer should not exceed the outside temperature. The appropriate design values related to use are also given in DIN 18910.

Figure Number	Unit Weight (kg/m²)	Temperature Amplitude Relationship TAV	Thermal Resistance $1/\lambda$ (m² · K/W)	Thermal Conductivity Coefficient k (W/m² · K)
1	90	0,13	1,07	0,80
2	84	0,16	1,01	0,86
3	72	0,23	0,86	0,98
4	69	0,25	0,83	1,01
5	69	0,25	0,83	1,01
6	90	0,13	1,07	0,80

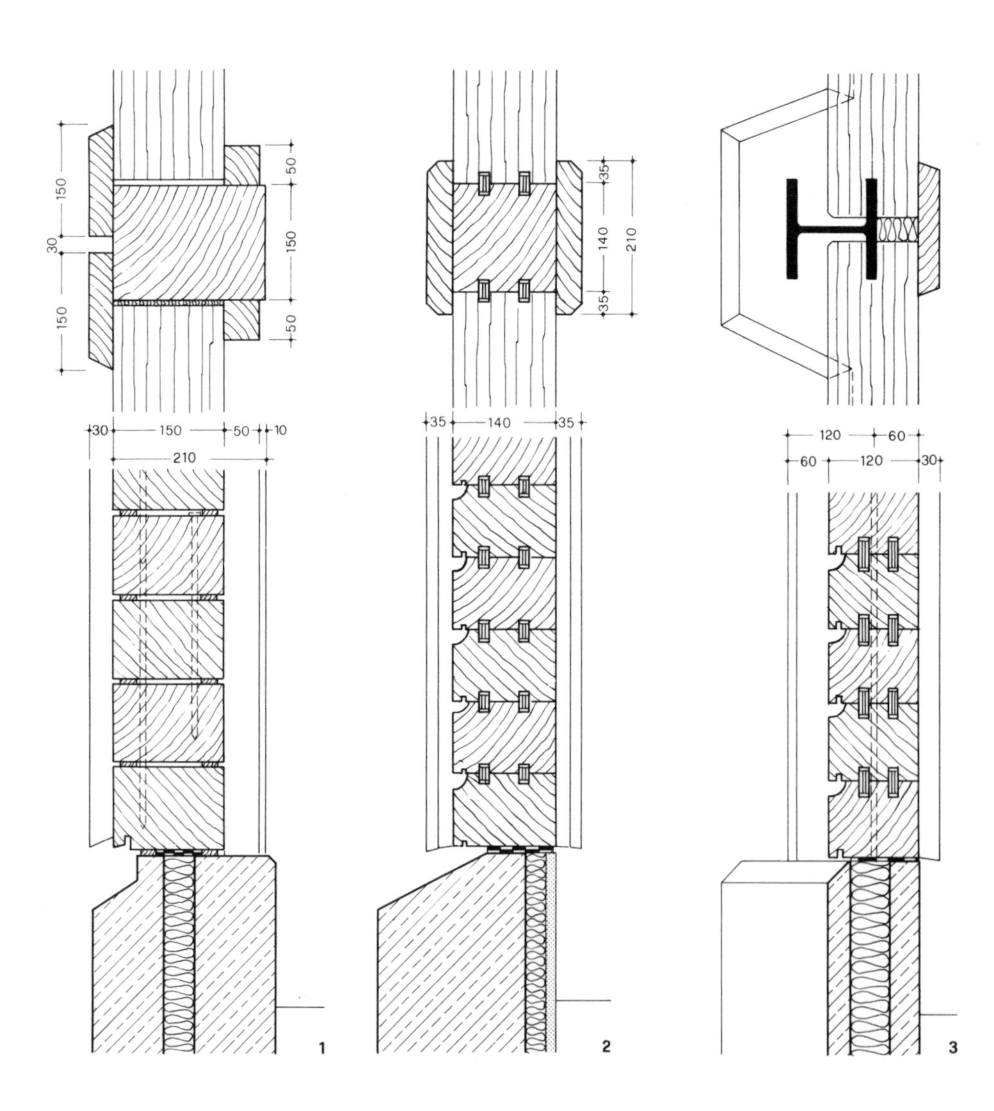

Log construction, non-load-bearing wall, so-called "do-it-yourself" construction. Sealing of joints through elastic bituminous foam-adhesive strips. Nail length = 2.5 × height of logs.

Log construction, non-load-bearing wall. Load-carrying posts within wall.

Log construction, non-load-bearing wall. Steel posts in cold transfer zone.

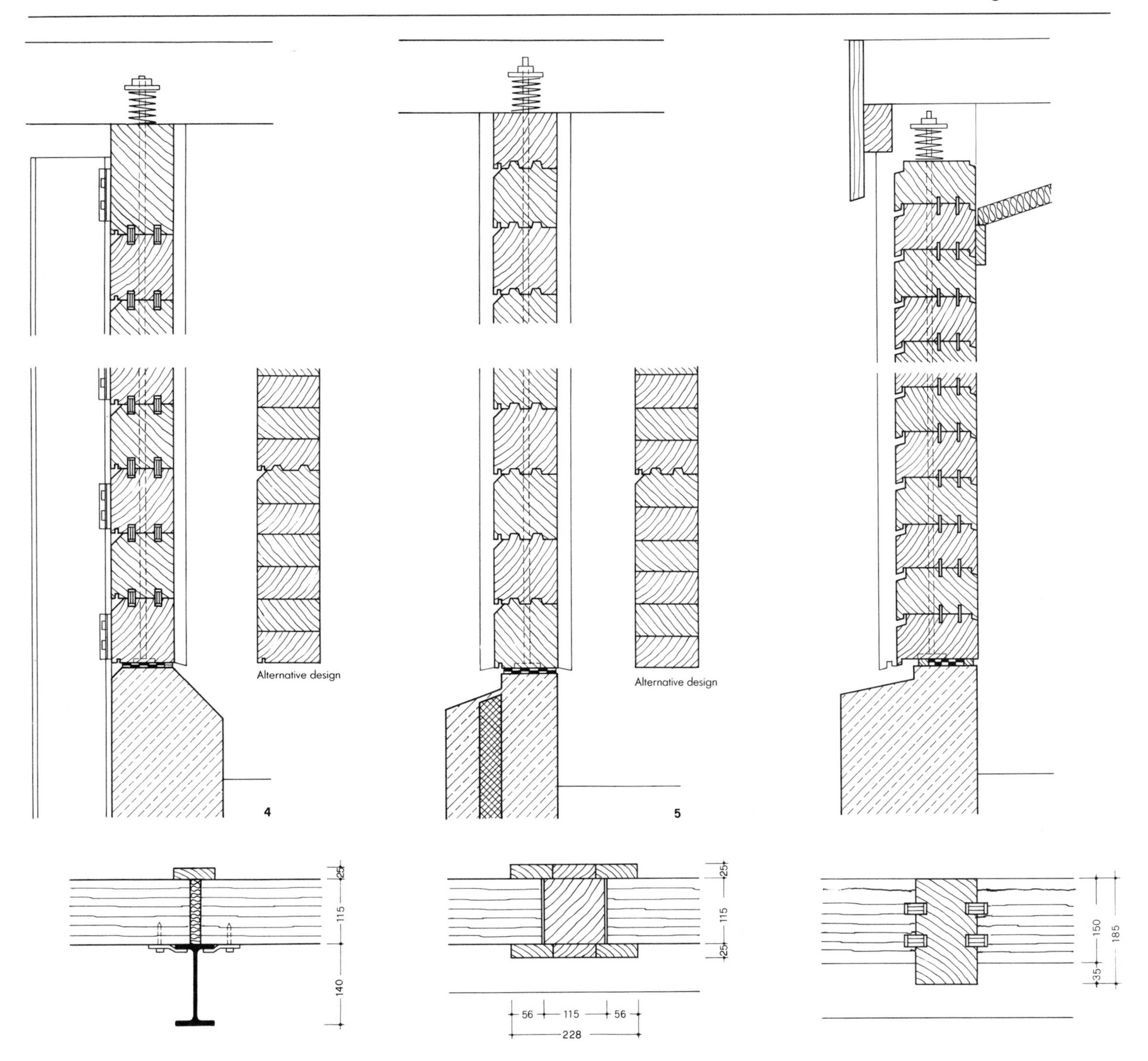

Log construction. Bracing by means of steel columns placed outside of wall section. Joints sealed by spring pressure.

Log construction, load-bearing wall. Alternative to Fig. 4, with wood column and double tongue and groove logs. Gluing is also possible. Joint sealed by spring pressure.

Log construction, non-load-bearing. Alternative with nested log sections. Joints sealed by spring pressure.

This section of the book (pages 269 to 283) stems from research conducted within the framework of development of timber construction by the German Society for Timber Research (Deutsche Gesellschaft für Holzforschung) and the Timber Worker's Association (Arbeitsgemeinschaft Holz e. V.). From reports contained in the architectural journal *Detail*, 1978.

UNIT CONVERSION TABLES

Length cm	Length in
0.48	0 3/16
1	0 13/32
1.27	0.5
2	0 25/32
2.54	1
3	1 3/16
4	1 9/16
5	1 31/32
5.08	2
6	2 3/8
7	2 3/4
7.62	3
8	3 5/32
9	3 17/32
10	3 15/16
10.16	4
12.70	5
15.24	6
17.78	7
20	7 7/8
20.32	8
22.86	9
25.40	10
27.94	11
30	11 13/16
30.48	12
40	15 3/4
50	19 11/16
60	23 5/8
60.96	24
70	27 9/16
80	31 1/2
90	35 7/16
91.44	36
100	39 3/8

Length m	Length ft
0.305	1
0.5	1.640
0.610	2
0.914	3
1	3.281
1.219	4
1.524	5
1.829	6
2	6.562
2.134	7
2.438	8
2.743	9
3	9.842
3.048	10
4	13.123
5	16.404
6	19.685
6.096	20
7	22.966
8	26.247
9	29.527
9.144	30
10	32.808
12.192	40
15.240	50
18.288	60
20	65.617
21.336	70
24.384	80
27.432	90
30	98.425
30.480	100
40	131.233
50	164.042
60	196.850
60.960	200
70	229.658
80	262.466
90	295.275
91.440	300
100	328.083

Length mm	Length in
0.3968	1/64
0.7937	2/64
1	0 3/64
1.1906	3/64
1.5875	4/64
1.9843	5/64
2	0 5/64
2.3812	6/64
2.7781	7/64
3	0 8/64
3.1750	8/64
3.5718	9/64
3.9687	10/64
4	0 10/64
4.3656	11/64
4.7625	12/64
5	0 13/64
5.1593	13/64
5.5562	14/64
5.9531	15/64
6	0 15/64
6.3500	16/64
6.7469	17/64
7	0 18/64
7.1437	18/64
7.5406	19/64
7.9375	20/64
8	0 20/64
8.3344	21/64
8.7312	22/64
9	0 23/64
9.1281	23/64
9.5250	24/64
9.9219	25/64
10	0 25/64
10.318	26/64
10.715	27/64
11.112	28/64
11.509	29/64
11.906	30/64
12.303	31/64
12.700	32/64

Length mm	Length in
15	0 38/64
20	0 50/64
25	0 63/64
30	1 12/64
35	1 24/64
40	1 37/64
45	1 49/64
50	1 62/64
55	2 11/64
60	2 23/64
65	2 36/64
70	2 48/64
75	2 61/64
80	3 10/64
85	3 22/64
90	3 35/64
95	3 47/64
100	3 60/64
110	4 21/64
120	4 46/64
130	5 8/64
140	5 33/64
150	5 58/64
160	6 19/64
170	6 44/64
180	7 6/64
190	7 31/64
200	7 56/64
210	8 17/64
220	8 42/64
230	9 4/64
240	9 29/64
250	9 54/64
260	10 15/64
270	10 40/64
280	11 2/64
290	11 27/64
300	11 52/64

Force

kg	N	lb
0.102	1	0.225
0.204	2	0.450
0.306	3	0.674
0.408	4	0.899
0.454	4.448	1
0.510	5	1.124
0.612	6	1.349
0.714	7	1.574
0.816	8	1.798
0.907	8.896	2
0.918	9	2.023
1	9.807	2.205
1.020	10	2.248
1.361	13.34	3
1.814	17.79	4
2	19.61	4.409
2.039	20	4.496
2.268	22.24	5
2.722	26.69	6
3	29.42	6.614
3.059	30	6.744
3.175	31.14	7
3.629	35.59	8
4	39.23	8.818
4.079	40	8.992
4.082	40.03	9
4.536	44.48	10
5	49.03	11.02
5.099	50	11.24
6	58.84	13.23
6.118	60	13.49
7	68.65	15.43
7.138	70	15.74
8	78.45	17.64
8.158	80	17.98
9	88.26	19.84
9.072	88.96	20
9.177	90	20.23
10	98.07	22.05
10.20	100	22.48
13.61	133.4	30
18.14	177.9	40
20	196.1	44.09
20.39	200	44.96
22.68	222.4	50
27.22	266.9	60
30	294.2	66.14
30.59	300	67.44
31.75	311.4	70
36.29	355.9	80
40	392.3	88.18
40.79	400	89.92
40.82	400.3	90
45.36	444.8	100
50	490.3	110.2
50.99	500	112.4
60	558.4	132.3
61.18	600	134.9
70	686.5	154.3
71.38	700	157.4
80	784.5	176.4
81.58	800	179.8
90	882.6	198.4
90.72	889.6	200
91.77	900	202.3
100	980.7	220.5

Uniform load

kg/m²	lb/ft²
1	0.205
2	0.410
3	0.614
4	0.819
4.882	1
5	1.024
6	1.229
7	1.434
8	1.639
9	1.843
9.765	2
10	2.048
14.65	3
19.53	4
20	4.096
24.41	5
29.29	6
30	6.144
34.18	7
39.06	8
40	8.193
43.94	9
48.82	10
50	10.24
60	12.29
70	14.34
80	16.39
90	18.43
97.65	20
100	20.48
146.5	30
195.3	40
200	40.96
244.1	50
292.9	60
300	61.44
341.8	70
390.6	80
400	81.93
439.4	90
488.2	100

Stress

kN/m²	lb/in²
1	0.145
2	0.290
3	0.435
4	0.580
5	0.725
6	0.870
6.89	1
7	1.015
8	1.160
9	1.305
10	1.450
13.8	2
20	2.901
20.7	3
27.6	4
30	4.351
34.5	5
40	5.802
41.4	6
48.3	7
50	7.252
55.2	8
60	8.702
62.1	9
68.9	10
70	10.15
80	11.60
90	13.05
100	14.50
138	20
200	29.01
207	30
276	40
300	43.51
345	50
400	58.02
414	60
483	70
500	72.52
552	80
600	87.02
621	90
689	100

Force

1.00000 lb = 0.45359 kg = 4.44822 N
2.20462 lb = 1.00000 kg = 9.80665 N
0.22481 lb = 0.10197 kg = 1.00000 N

Linear Load

1.00000 lb/ft = 1.48816 kg/m = 14.59391 N/m
0.67197 lb/ft = 1.00000 kg/m = 9.80665 N/m
0.06852 lb/ft = 0.10197 kg/m = 1.00000 N/m

Uniform Load

1 lb/in^2 = 144 lb/ft^2 = 703.070 kg/m^2 = 6894.762 N/m^2
0.006944 lb/in^2 = 1 lb/ft^2 = 4.882431 kg/m^2 = 47.88029 N/m^2
0.001422 lb/in^2 = 0.204815 lb/ft^2 = 1 kg/m^2 = 9.80665 N/m^2
0.000145 lb/in^2 = 0.020885 lb/ft^2 = 0.101971 kg/m^2 = 1 N/m^2
(1 pascal = 1 N/m)

Weight

1 lb/ft^3 = 16.01846 kg/m^3 = 157.0874 N/m^3
0.062427 lb/ft^3 = 1 kg/m^3 = 9.80665 N/m^3
0.006365 lb/ft^3 = 0.101971 kg/m^3 = 1 N/m^3

Moment

1 ft·lb = 0.138254 kg·m = 1.355818 N·m
7.233011 ft·lb = 1 kg·m = 9.80665 N·m
0.737561 ft·lb = 0.101971 kg·m = 1 N·m

Stress

1 lb/in^2 = 0.070306 kg/cm^2 = 0.689475 N/cm^2
14.22333 lb/in^2 = 1 kg/cm^2 = 9.80665 N/cm^2
1.450376 lb/in^2 = 0.101971 kg/cm^2 = 1 N/cm^2

INDEX*

* Number refer to pages or reference numbers of architectural examples.

ABOUT THE AUTHORS

KARL-HEINZ GÖTZ, Architect
Past Professor, Architectural Department, School of Arts, University of Berlin, West Germany
Chair for Industrialized Building Methods
Dean of Architecture, 1977–1978
Principal, Consulting Architects, offices in Karlsruhe and Berlin
Numerous publications in the fields of building system development, timber construction, housing, office buildings, and urban development
Born 1932 in Karlsruhe, died 1979 in Berlin

DIETER HOOR, Architect
Professor, School of Architecture, Hamburg, West Germany
Principal, Consulting Office, Steimhorst, West Germany (apartment buildings, sports arenas, industrial plants, retirement communities, interior decorating, reconstruction)
Principal, Consulting Office, Hamburg, West Germany (residential buildings, schools, nursery schools, reconstruction)
Diploma in Architecture, University of Karlsruhe, 1958
Studied at Ecole des Beaux Arts in Paris, 1959
Born 1931 in Düsseldorf

KARL MÖHLER, Dr. Eng.
Past Professor, Timber Construction, University of Karlsruhe, West Germany
Past Director, Research Laboratory for Steel, Timber, and Concrete at the University of Karlsruhe
Diploma in Engineering, University of Karlsruhe, 1938
Consulting Engineer for bridges and buildings, 1948
Born 1912 in Karlsruhe

JULIUS NATTERER, Engineer
Professor and Chair, Institute for Wood Construction, Swiss Federal Institute of Technology, Lausanne, Switzerland
Principal, Planning Group of Natterer and Dittrich, Munich, West Germany
Principal, Wood Consultants, Etoy, Switzerland
Professor Natterer is a leading figure in Europe in the field of engineered timber structures. Concepts and construction technology developed by Professor Natterer are at the forefront of the state of the art for major timber structures and space enclosures. Together, his two firms form the largest wood engineering enterprise in Europe. He is credited with the design of over 400 unique wood structures, including those pictured in this book. About 20 projects have received national and international awards and prizes for architecture and engineering. He chairs the Institute for Wood Construction at the Swiss Federal Institute of Technology and directs much of its innovative research and the development of actual structures.
Diploma in Engineering, University of Munich, 1965
Published works on research in the use of timber and glass in buildings.
Born 1938 in Munich

PETER F. MARTECCHINI, Dr. Eng.
Professional Engineer, Land Surveyor
Partner and Chief Engineer, Clarke and Rapuano Inc.,
Consulting Engineers and Landscape Architects, New York, N.Y.
Mr. Martecchini had a long and distinguished career as the designer of numerous award-winning structures. His particular interest in timber design led him to translate this remarkable study for the benefit of all those who are interested in working with timber.